D1105360

WILLIAM ARNON HENRY (1850–1932)

Professor William Arnon Henry, the author of the early editions of *Feeds and Feeding*, was one of the most eminent agricultural scientists of his period. He gained an international reputation as an investigator, a teacher, and a writer in the field of livestock feeding, and was also recognized as one of the great leaders in the development of the American system of agricultural colleges and experiment stations.

FEEDS AND FEEDING

A HANDBOOK FOR THE STUDENT AND STOCKMAN

F. B. MORRISON

PROFESSOR OF ANIMAL HUSBANDRY AND ANIMAL NUTRITION,
AND HEAD OF THE ANIMAL HUSBANDRY DEPARTMENT,
CORNELL UNIVERSITY

First to Ninth Editions by the late W. A. Henry, formerly Dean of the College of Agriculture and Director of the Agricultural Experiment Station, University of Wisconsin. Tenth to Fourteenth Editions by W. A. Henry, assisted by F. B. Morrison. Fifteenth to Nineteenth Editions revised and rewritten by F. B. Morrison.

TWENTIETH EDITION, *Unabridged*

ITHACA, NEW YORK
THE MORRISON PUBLISHING COMPANY
1936

6 3 6

M

Copyright, 1936

BY

THE MORRISON PUBLISHING COMPANY

All rights reserved

First edition published 1898; second edition 1900; third edition 1901; fourth edition 1902; fifth edition 1903; sixth edition 1904; seventh edition 1906; eighth edition 1907; ninth edition 1908. Tenth edition, rewritten and reset, published 1910; eleventh edition 1911; twelfth edition 1912; thirteenth edition 1913; fourteenth edition 1915. Fifteenth edition, rewritten and reset, published 1915; sixteenth edition 1916; seventeenth edition, August 1918; reprinted December, 1918; February, 1919; June, 1919; October, 1919; January, 1920; August, 1920; September, 1921; December, 1921. Eighteenth edition, rewritten and reset, published September, 1922. Illustrated edition published February, 1923; reprinted November, 1923; January, 1927; September, 1928. Nineteenth edition, published August, 1929; reprinted, September, 1930; April, 1934; December, 1934; September, 1935. Twentieth edition, rewritten and reset, published May, 1936; reprinted with minor changes, October, 1936.

Translated into Portuguese by F. M. Draenert, Sao Paulo, Brazil, 1907.

Translated into Russian under direction of Paul Dubrovsky, editor of "Agriculture and Forestry," and published by the Department of Agriculture, for the use of agricultural schools and other institutions of the Department, Petrograd, 1912.

Printed in the United States of America.

HAMMOND PRESS
W. B. CONKEY COMPANY
CHICAGO

PREFACE

The first edition of *Feeds and Feeding*, written by Dean W. A. Henry, and published in February, 1898, was received with immediate and widespread favor by practical stockmen and by professors and students of animal husbandry. In the United States and also in several other countries *Feeds and Feeding* was soon used more widely as a text book and as a reference book than any other book on livestock feeding.

During the years that have passed since 1898, nineteen editions of *Feeds and Feeding* have been issued, several printings having been made of each of the later editions. In 1910 the book was entirely rewritten by Dean Henry with the help of the author of the present edition. In 1915 and in 1923 complete revisions of the book were again brought forth. It was necessary for the present author to assume the responsibility for these revisions, since ill health had kept Dean Henry from active work for some time. He died in November, 1932, at the age of 82 years.

In the preparation of this entirely rewritten edition, the twentieth of the book, the author has spent much time during the past few years in compiling and analyzing the results of the many experiments on livestock feeding conducted in this and other countries. He has been aided greatly in this task by many investigators who have furnished him with information and with reports of experiments in advance of regular publication.

In order to present adequately the results, it has been necessary to make a considerable increase in the number of pages in the book. To save space and also to differentiate between the information of major importance and that of only local or minor interest, some parts of the text are set in a smaller type than that of the main portion. To aid students and others in their study of the book, review questions are now included at the end of each chapter.

It is the purpose of this volume to present in as simple and concise a manner as is possible the most important facts concerning the feeding, care, and management of the various classes of larger farm animals. Also, full information is given concerning the composition, use, and value of the many different feeding stuffs, especially those of importance in the United States.

Part I presents briefly the fundamental principles of animal nutrition and emphasizes the bearing of these principles upon the practical feeding of livestock. Particular attention is given to the recent discoveries in nutrition, including the functions and importance of vitamins and minerals, as well as the necessity of proper quality of protein in the rations of livestock.

The various feeding standards for farm animals are then discussed, and the method of using the Morrison feeding standards is explained in detail. Some of the economic principles which should be considered in the feeding of livestock are briefly discussed in Chapter X, "Economy in Feeding Livestock."

Part II gives comprehensive information concerning the composition, properties, and use of all common feeding stuffs used in this country. On account of the importance of hay, pasture, and other roughages in livestock feeding, the order of presentation has been changed in this volume, and the roughages are now considered first, before the grains and other concentrates. In Chapter XX the manurial value of feeding stuffs is discussed, and the vital relation of livestock to the economical maintenance of soil fertility is made clear.

Part III presents in condensed form the most important findings of the experiment stations of this and other countries on the feeding and care of horses, dairy cattle, beef cattle, sheep, and swine. The values of the many different feeds for each class of livestock are shown by the results of actual feeding trials. Instead of giving merely the results of single typical trials, in most cases the data for all the similar trials on a given subject have been carefully compiled and averaged together. The feeder is thus given more trustworthy information concerning the relative value of the different feeds than has been previously available. In addition to this information, practical suggestions are given on the care and management of each kind of stock.

Neither time nor expense has been spared on the compilation of data for the exhaustive Appendix Tables, which show the average composition and the content of digestible nutrients and mineral and fertilizing constituents in all important American feeding stuffs. The compilation of the data first presented in the Appendix Tables of the fifteenth edition of the book, published in 1915, required time equivalent to one person working full time throughout three years, in addition to the supervision of the author. Approximately the same amount of time has been required for the compilation and averaging of the recent analyses of feeding stuffs, which are presented for the first time in the Appendix Tables of this edition.

The sincere thanks of the author are extended to the many friends who by suggestions and reports of experiments and experiences have furnished invaluable assistance in this and previous revisions—only by such help so generously given has the making of this book been possible. The author is indebted to his colleagues in the Animal Husbandry Department of Cornell University for their many helpful suggestions. He wishes in particular to acknowledge the aid of Professor L. A. Maynard, Professor E. S. Savage, Professor K. L. Turk, Professor J. P. Willman, Dr. G. W. Salisbury, Mr. J. I. Miller, and Mr. H. M. Briggs. Acknowledgment is especially due my wife, Mrs. Elsie B. Morrison, for invaluable aid throughout the entire preparation of the book, and to my sons, Roger B. Morrison and Spencer H. Morrison, for assistance in the compilation of data.

F. B. MORRISON.

March, 1936.
Ithaca, New York.

CONTENTS

Part I.—Fundamentals of Animal Nutrition

Part II.—Feeding Stuffs

Part III.—Feeding Farm Animals

APPENDIX

v

CONTENTS

INDEX AND CROSS REFERENCES

When seeking information on any subject presented in this book, the reader should first consult the copious index, the figures of which refer to the *page* on which the topic is presented. Additional information bearing on the subject given at other places may be found by following up the cross references set in black-face figures in parentheses, occurring in the body of the text. These figures refer to the numbered *black-face* sideheads, and *not to the pages*.

FEEDS AND FEEDING

PART I

FUNDAMENTALS OF ANIMAL NUTRITION

CHAPTER I

THE VARIOUS FOOD NUTRIENTS

I. THE COMPOUNDS OF WHICH PLANTS AND ANIMALS ARE COMPOSED

In no field of agriculture has more progress been made in recent years than in livestock feeding and nutrition. This rapid advance has come about chiefly as a result of the numerous discoveries made by the many skilled investigators in the American experiment stations and other research institutions in this and other countries.

These new developments have been so outstanding that they have overturned many of the beliefs and theories of the past. Often rations that were considered ideal only a few years ago can now be radically improved, by applying the results of these recent investigations. Thus, it is now known that the kind or quality of protein in a ration may be fully as important as the amount of this nutrient. Likewise, a lack of any of the essential minerals or vitamins may be more injurious than a scanty supply of feed.

Many of these discoveries are so recent that the results have not as yet been summarized in publications that reach the majority of farmers. Consequently, they are not acquainted with this newer knowledge in stockfeeding, or they do not understand definitely how these results can be applied to their own conditions.

In the preparation of this volume especial attention has therefore been given to the recent experiments which show how the efficiency of livestock production can be increased. Throughout the book the primary object has been to explain clearly the ways in which farm animals can be fed more economically, so that they will return more profit to their owners.

In order to master the science of livestock feeding and animal nutrition, it is necessary, first of all, to have in mind the most important facts concerning the chemical compounds that make up plants and animals. Knowledge of the chemical composition of farm animals is necessary to understand their food requirements, and information about the substances in plants is required because they furnish most of the food consumed by livestock.

1

1. Water; organic compounds; mineral matter.—All living plant or animal tissue is composed of the following: (1) Water; (2) organic compounds; and (3) mineral matter, or ash. The water can be driven off as water vapor by heating the material at the temperature of boiling water until it will lose no more weight. By then burning the dry matter that is left, the organic matter will be destroyed and pass off in gaseous form, and there will remain only the *mineral matter,* or ash.

The *organic compounds* are all made up of carbon, united with hydrogen and oxygen, and in some cases with nitrogen and other chemical elements. These compounds are grouped in three general divisions: (1) The carbohydrates; (2) the fats and fat-like substances; and (3) the nitrogenous compounds.

The division of the dry matter of plant and animal tissue into organic compounds and mineral matter is a convenient general method of grouping, but not an exact separation. For example, sulfur is classed as mineral matter, but a large part of it occurs in the proteins, which are organic compounds. When plant or animal substances are burned under ordinary conditions, some of the sulfur will remain in the ash, but a part will pass off in gaseous form, along with the carbon and hydrogen. On the other hand, some of the carbon in the true organic compounds may be converted into carbonates when such materials are burned, and then will remain in the ash.

2. Water.—Water is not only the largest single constituent of all living matter, both plant and animal, but also performs exceedingly important functions. The most active parts of plants and animals contain 70 per cent or more of water. For example, green, growing plants usually have 70 to 80 per cent of water, and in animals the muscles and such internal organs as the liver and kidneys contain 75 per cent or more. The gray matter of the brain is even more watery, having over 80 per cent.

The seeds of plants at maturity, though apparently dry, generally contain considerable water, having 25 per cent or more before they are thoroughly cured. Even the dentine of the teeth contains about 10 per cent of water.

Water performs the following important functions in plants and animals:

1. It carries the nutrients from one part of the living structure to another by holding them in solution or in watery suspension. Plants can absorb mineral nutrients from the soil only as they are dissolved in water.

2. Water enables living plants and animals to hold their shape. This is accomplished by the watery solution inside the cells filling them so full that they are distended and firm.

3. Water has the property of reacting with many types of chemical compounds, and the intricate life processes could not take place without it. For example, the digestion of food by animals consists primarily of the breaking apart of complex substances into much simpler ones, water being added to these simpler compounds in their formation.

4. Water is important in the control of the temperature of animals and plants on account of two different properties. First, much heat is absorbed when water evaporates. As we shall see in Chapter V, the

evaporation of water is one of the most important means by which animals keep their body temperatures constant. Second, water in the liquid state has a much greater capacity than most substances for absorbing heat. Therefore a certain amount of heat produces less increase in the temperatures of plants and animals than it would if their tissues were less watery.

While we might well consider water the most vital of all nutrients for animals, it is given but little space in this volume. This is because under usual conditions livestock can readily be provided with an abundance.

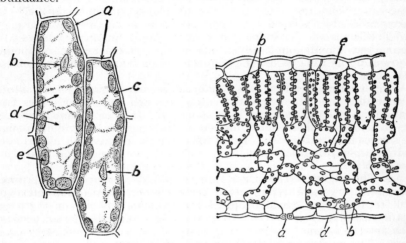

Left—PLANT CELLS, MAGNIFIED 350 TIMES

A, Cell wall; b, nucleus, or life center of cell; c, strands of protoplasm; d, spaces filled with cell sap; e, chlorophyll bodies. (After Strassburger.)

Right—SECTION OF LEAF, MAGNIFIED 400 TIMES

A, Stoma, or opening on under side of leaf through which air enters; b, chlorophyll bodies in leaf cells; d, lower epidermal cells of leaf; e, upper epidermal cells of leaf. (After Strassburger.)

3. The carbohydrates.—The carbohydrates comprise about three-fourths of all the dry matter in plants, on the average. They form the woody framework and also are the chief reserve food stored in such plant parts as seed, roots, and tubers. It is pointed out later that the amount of carbohydrates in the bodies of animals at any one time is very small. However, this small amount is continually replenished, and carbohydrates usually serve as the chief fuel to maintain the body temperature and to furnish the energy needed for all body processes.

The term *carbohydrates* means that these compounds are composed of the three elements, carbon, hydrogen, and oxygen, and that the latter two are present in the same proportion existing in water, the chemical formula for which is H_2O. (This means that every molecule of water contains two atoms of hydrogen and one of oxygen.)

The carbohydrates consist of two groups: the *sugars*, which are relatively simple in composition, and the group of much more complex compounds called *polysaccharides*. Some of the carbohydrates are easily digested by animals and therefore have a high value as feeds. On the other hand, the very complex carbohydrates which form the woody fiber of plants are digested with difficulty, and, moreover, there is a large loss of energy in the process. Therefore these carbohydrates have a low value for stock.

Through the action of sunlight on the green-colored chlorophyll in the leaves and other green parts, plants are able to build simple carbohydrates from carbon dioxide and water. Carbon dioxide from the air is taken into the leaves through the openings, called stoma, on their lower surfaces. In the leaves it is united with water taken up from the soil by the roots. In some mysterious manner the chlorophyll builds the carbon, hydrogen, and some of the oxygen furnished by the carbon dioxide and water into some simple organic compound, the rest of the oxygen being given off to the air through the stoma as free oxygen gas.

The energy necessary for the formation of the energy-rich organic compound from the energy-poor carbon dioxide and water comes from sunlight, which is absorbed by the leaves. It is not known whether the first organic compound formed in this action is a simple sugar or some other substance. From the sugars, plants can form much more complex organic compounds, including polysaccharides, fats, and proteins.

4. The sugars.—The sugars are all soluble in water, have a sweet taste, form crystals, and also have certain other definite characteristics, such as rotating a beam of polarized light to the left or the right, as the case may be. It is of interest to note that this latter property provides the means by which the chemist at a beet-sugar factory determines how much sugar can be made per ton from any given lot of sugar beets.

5. The simple sugars.—Only two classes of simple sugars are of importance. These are: (1) The *hexoses*, or 6-carbon sugars, so-called because each molecule contains 6 carbon atoms; and (2) the *pentoses*, or 5-carbon sugars. All of the hexoses have the general chemical formula, $C_6H_{12}O_6$, but the molecules of the various hexoses differ in the arrangement and grouping of the atoms. The pentoses have the general formula, $C_5H_{10}O_5$.

Only three of the several hexoses that have been found in plants are of any importance. These are *glucose, fructose,* and *galactose. Glucose,* also known as dextrose, is found in the free state, for example, in ripe fruits, sweet corn, and honey. It is of especial importance in animal nutrition, for it is the sugar in blood. Glucose is only three-fourths as sweet as cane sugar.

Fructose, or levulose, occurs along with glucose in ripe fruits and honey. It is the sweetest of the sugars, being considerably sweeter than cane sugar.

Galactose does not occur free in nature, except perhaps in traces in certain plants, but it forms a part of various compounds. The most important of these is milk sugar, or lactose, in which galactose is combined with glucose.

The *pentoses* do not compare in importance with the hexoses. They occur free in nature only in traces, but form part of certain of the more complex carbohydrates that are discussed later.

6. The compound sugars.—The compound sugars consist of combinations of two or more molecules of the simple sugars. The most common of these sugars is *sucrose,* or cane sugar, which is made of one molecule of glucose and one of fructose. The sugar beet and the sugar cane store their reserve food chiefly in the form of sucrose, and therefore are our chief sources of cane sugar.

Maltose is another important compound sugar, which is composed of two molecules of glucose. In germinating seeds maltose is formed in large amounts from starch, and it is also produced in the digestion of starch by animals. It is only about one-third as sweet as cane sugar.

Lactose, or milk sugar, is a compound sugar composed of one molecule of galactose and one of glucose. It is not found in plants but is the sugar in the milk of all mammals. Lactose is only about one-sixth as sweet as cane sugar.

There are also compound sugars made up of three molecules of the simple sugars, but these occur only in very small amounts and in a few plants. They are therefore unimportant in stock feeding and need no further discussion.

7. The more complex carbohydrates.—The term *polysaccharides* is used for the group of carbohydrates that are more complex than the sugars. This term means that each molecule is formed by the combination of several molecules of the sugars (saccharides). In this process of combination, water is eliminated. The polysaccharides differ decidedly in physical properties from the sugars, for they are almost tasteless and can only rarely be crystallized. Some are insoluble in water and the others do not form true solutions, but only sticky, gelatinous solutions.

These carbohydrates are so complex in nature and have such properties that chemists have been unable to determine their exact chemical formulas. It is known, however, that those composed of the hexoses, or 6-carbon sugars, all have the general approximate formula, $(C_6H_{10}O_5)_x$. This means that the molecules are composed of an unknown number of $C_6H_{10}O_5$ groups. For example, the starch molecule may contain many thousands of atoms.

The *pentosans,* which are formed from the pentoses, or 5-carbon sugars, have the general formula, $(C_5H_8O_4)_x$. Some of the polysaccharides are composed of both hexose sugars and of pentose sugars, or they contain still other substances related to the sugars.

The process by which these complex carbohydrates are formed by the combination of molecules of simple sugars can be reversed. When a solution of one of these compounds is acted upon by the proper enzyme, or when it is acidified and heated, the complex molecules are broken down, or hydrolyzed, into the sugars, water being added to the molecules in the process. This is what occurs when starch is digested by animals, or when corn sugar or corn syrup is manufactured from corn starch.

The polysaccharides formed from the hexose sugars will be discussed first, on account of their much greater importance. Of chief interest in this group are starch, glycogen, dextrins, and cellulose.

8. Starch, dextrins, and similar compounds.—*Starch,* which is composed of many molecules of glucose, is one of the most important carbohydrates in plants and therefore one of the chief nutrients in the feed of farm animals. Most plants store their reserve food principally

STARCH GRAINS

A, From corn grain; b, from wheat; c, from oats; d, from potato. (Magnified 330 times.)

as starch, which is deposited in the form of starch grains. These have a characteristic size and shape in each kind of plant, and therefore by examining the starch grains in plant products under a microscope, the source can be determined. This is often a useful method of detecting adulteration in human foods or stock feeds.

While plants are growing, they commonly store starch in the special parts that later nourish the new plants that develop. Thus, nearly all seeds are rich in starch, especially the cereal grains. For example, corn, wheat, rye, and the grain sorghums all have 60 per cent or more of starch. Starch is also stored in large amounts in certain fruits, such as apples, and in such underground parts as potato tubers and parsnip roots.

Starch is insoluble in water and therefore must be changed to sugar by an enzyme before it can be carried from one part of a plant to another. Thus, in a germinating seed the stored starch is gradually converted into sugar, which is transported to nourish the various parts of the growing plantlet. Since starch is readily digested by animals, it has a high food value, being equal to the sugars.

Upon heating an acidified starch solution, the starch molecules first break down into *dextrins,* which are simpler in structure than starch, but more complex than the sugars. Dextrin is familiar to us as the adhesive on postage stamps, envelopes, etc. If the treatment is continued, maltose (malt sugar) will be formed, and eventually glucose.

A few plants, such as artichokes and dahlias, store reserve food in the form of *inulin,* instead of starch. This is similar to starch, except that it is formed from fructose, instead of glucose.

No starch is found in the bodies of animals, but reserve food is stored to some extent in the form of *glycogen,* or animal starch. As is pointed out in the next chapter, this is stored chiefly in the liver, but also in the muscles and certain other tissues. Like starch, glycogen is formed by the combination of molecules of glucose.

9. Cellulose.—Cellulose and related compounds are the chief components of the cell walls of plants. Cellulose is still more complex than starch and is very insoluble and resistant. It is made in plants by the combination of many molecules of glucose, and by heating cellulose with acid it can be broken down into this sugar. The thickness of the cell walls, and consequently the percentage of cellulose, vary greatly in different parts of plants, the walls being thick and resistant in the woody stems, and thin and delicate in the softer portions, such as the fruits and leaves. Especially in the woody parts of plants, the cell walls do not consist merely of pure cellulose, but of cellulose combined with other carbohydrates, these combinations being even tougher and more resistant.

In analyzing plants the chemist includes cellulose and these other resistant compounds under the term *crude fiber,* also called merely *fiber.*

It is pointed out in later chapters that cellulose is digested by animals much less completely than starch or the sugars, and also that much energy is wasted in utilizing the portion that can be digested. Cellulose therefore has a relatively low feeding value. For such animals as man and the pig its value is especially low, for their digestive tracts are not suited to its utilization.

10. Pentosans; other carbohydrates.—The *pentosans* are similar to starch and cellulose, except that they are formed from the pentoses, or 5-carbon sugars. They are widely distributed in plants, being found in the largest amounts in the more woody portions and in the outer coats of seeds. For example, while corn grain contains only 7 per cent or less of pentosans, average legume hay contains about 12 per cent of pentosans, non-legume hay as high as 20 per cent, wheat bran 20 per cent, and such feeds as cottonseed hulls even more.[1]

It is pointed out in the next chapter that the pentosans are digested in the same manner as is cellulose, and that they have a similar value for livestock.

The *hemicelluloses* include a group of compounds, somewhat less resistant than cellulose, which are composed of pentose sugars and also hexose sugars. They not only form part of the cell walls of plants, but also are sometimes stored as reserve food. For example, some of the root crops contain a considerable amount of hemicelluloses.

Other classes of carbohydrates found in small amounts in certain plant structures are the gums, mucilages, and pectins. These are all very complex carbohydrates. Gum arabic and agar-agar are familiar examples of these classes. The setting, or jellying, of fruit jellies is due to the pectin which they contain.

It is pointed out later in this chapter that in the usual chemical analysis of feeding stuffs, the more soluble parts of the celluloses and pentosans, including the hemicelluloses, are grouped with the sugars and starch under the term *nitrogen-free extract.* Organic acids, such as the acetic acid and the lactic acid of silage, are also included in this group.

11. Fats and oils.—The fats, oils, and related substances are of much importance, both in plants and animals. Fats and oils are alike in composition and properties, except that fats are solid at ordinary temperatures, while oils are liquid. In discussions of livestock feeding both classes are usually included under the term "fat."

All fats and fat-like substances are soluble in ether and certain other solvents. Therefore in analyzing feeding stuffs, the sample of feed is extracted with ether, and all the substances thus dissolved are included under the classification of *fat,* or *ether extract.* (Chemists often use the terms *lipids,* or *lipoids,* for the entire group of fats and other substances soluble in ether.)

Fats, like carbohydrates, are made up of carbon, hydrogen, and oxygen. However, the proportion of oxygen is much less and of carbon and hydrogen much greater than in carbohydrates, as is shown by the following formulas for three common fats:

Stearin $C_{57}H_{110}O_6$ Palmitin $C_{51}H_{98}O_6$ Olein $C_{57}H_{104}O_6$

Due to the larger proportion of carbon and hydrogen, fats furnish about 2.25 times as much heat or energy per pound on oxidation as do the carbohydrates. They therefore have a correspondingly higher value per pound as food for animals.

From the chemical standpoint, a molecule of fat is formed by the combination of three molecules of certain fatty acids with one molecule of glycerol (glycerine). The reverse occurs in the digestion of fats by animals, or when fat turns rancid. It then breaks down into free fatty acids and glycerol, water being taken up in the process.

The various fats differ in their melting points and other properties, depending on the particular fatty acids they contain. It is beyond the scope of this volume to discuss the various fatty acids in fats. These range in complexity all the way from butyric acid, a liquid at ordinary temperatures, which is present in considerable amounts in butter fat, to stearic acid, a solid at usual temperatures, which is one of the chief constituents of beef fat. Even more complex fatty acids occur in certain fats.

Some fatty acids are "unsaturated," which means that they have the capacity to absorb oxygen or certain other chemical elements. Also, unsaturated fatty acids differ in degree of unsaturation. The value of linseed oil for paint and varnish is due to its large content of highly unsaturated fatty acids. Because of this, a film of linseed oil soon absorbs oxygen, on exposure to the air, and turns into a tough, resistant coating.

As is pointed out in Chapter V, it has recently been discovered that certain unsaturated fatty acids are apparently necessary for animal life.

12. Other substances included in the fat group.—In the grains and other seeds nearly all the ether extract, or so-called fat, consists of true fat, but in hay, grass, and other forages a considerable part is made up of other substances. While about 86 per cent, on the average, of the ether extract in seeds and their by-products consists of true fat, in the case of forages the true fat may form less than one-half of the ether extract.[2] Certain of the non-fat substances included in this group are of vital importance to animals, though only very small amounts are present in feeds. On the other hand, other substances in the group may have no food value whatsoever.

The *sterols* are complex alcohols which are found in traces in plants and animals. One of the sterols, *ergosterol*, is of vital importance in stock feeding. As we shall see in Chapter VI, it is the substance from which vitamin D, the anti-rachitic vitamin, is chiefly formed through the action of certain rays of light.

Small amounts of another sterol, called *cholesterol*, are widely distributed in living tissues. It is found especially in the brain, other nervous tissues, and blood. One of its important functions is apparently to aid in transporting fat from one part of the body to another, combinations of cholesterol and the fatty acids being formed in the process.

The *carotenes* and related pigments, or coloring substances, are also of outstanding interest, though contained in only very small amounts in plants or animals. It is pointed out in Chapter VI that the carotenes are the substances that animals transform into vitamin A, which is essential for their life. The different carotenes and closely-related compounds which can be changed into vitamin A are all commonly included under the general term carotene (sometimes spelled carotin).

Carotene is the yellow-coloring substance in carrots, sweet potatoes, squash, and butter fat. One of the very important facts in animal nutrition is that carotene is also supplied by the green-colored parts of plants, where its yellow color is hidden by the green chlorophyll. Certain yellow substances in this group, such as xanthophyll, do not serve as a source of vitamin A.

Chlorophyll is the green-colored substance in all green plant parts. It has the remarkable property of synthesizing or building carbohydrates from carbon dioxide and water, the energy required for the process coming from the sunlight. Though chlorophyll is essential for the growth of all green plants, it is not necessary, so far as is known, for animal life. Indeed, recent Georgia experiments indicate that it apparently has no food value to animals.[3]

The *phospholipids* (also called phosphatides) are fat-like substances that contain in their molecules not only fatty acids and glycerol, but also phosphoric acid and nitrogenous groups. Though present in only small amounts in most plant and animal tissues, they apparently are of great importance in all life processes, for they are a vital part of the living protoplasm. It is believed by some that fats are transported from one part of the animal body to another in the form of these combinations. One of the most important of this group is lecithin, which is present especially in egg yolk, blood, and liver. Other phospholipids are found in brain tissue.

The *waxes* occur widely distributed in plants, but usually in only small amounts. They are generally found in thin films on plant surfaces, as on stems and on the surface of fruits, to which they give the characteristic "bloom." Apparently their function in plants is to protect the surface from the weather. The waxes are composed, like the fats, of fatty acids, but these are combined with compounds other than glycerol. Lanolin, or wool fat, is really a wax and not a true fat. Likewise, beeswax is mainly a wax.

Other substances, of which only traces occur in plants, are included in the "fat" group. For instance, one class of such substances is the *essential oils,* which largely give plants their characteristic odors and tastes. These do not serve as nutrients to animals, but aid in making food palatable.

13. The nitrogenous compounds.—It has been pointed out that the various compounds grouped under the carbohydrates and fats generally are composed only of carbon, hydrogen, and oxygen. The substances in another great and important group—the nitrogenous compounds—contain nitrogen in addition, and also usually sulfur and sometimes phosphorus. Of the compounds in this group, the proteins will be discussed first, on account of their outstanding significance in plants and animals.

14. The proteins.—The proteins are essential to all life, for the active protoplasm in living cells and also the nucleus, which controls the activity of each cell, are chiefly protein. In plants the greater part of the protein is usually concentrated in the reproductive parts and in the actively growing portions, such as the leaves.

In animals not only the protoplasm, but also the cell walls are composed mostly of protein. Therefore protein forms by far the greater part of the muscles, the internal organs, the cartilages and connective tissues, and also such outer tissues as skin, hair, wool, feathers, nails, and horns. Protein is one of the chief constituents of the nervous system, and it even forms an important part of the bony skeleton, giving it tenacity and elasticity.

The proteins are among the most complex of all plant or animal compounds, each molecule probably containing many thousands of atoms. On account of this great complexity, chemists have been able to study the structure of these substances only by breaking the molecules apart into much simpler compounds. This is usually done by digesting or boiling the protein for several hours with strong acid. A somewhat similar but more efficient process occurs in the digestion of food protein in the digestive tract of animals.

15. Structure of the proteins.—Many different proteins have been separated by chemists from plant and animal products, and their composition studied. These investigations have shown that each protein is composed of a considerable number of different amino acids, which are combined with each other to form the complex protein molecules. The amino acids may therefore be called the ''building-stones'' from which the proteins are made. The simpler of these amino acids are similar to the fatty acids in structure, except that they contain the nitrogenous amino group, NH_2. Other amino acids are much more complex in nature.

At least 22 different amino acids have already been found in the mixture formed when proteins are digested by the drastic acid treatment. Possibly still others exist in the protein molecules, for in the acid digestion a certain portion of the nitrogenous matter is destroyed or converted into substances that defy chemical study. Just as the letters of the alphabet may be combined into innumerable words, so the possibility for the combination of the amino acids into different proteins is almost limitless.

16. Formation of proteins in plants and animals.—Plants are able to build the complex protein molecules from simple inorganic nitrogenous salts, such as the nitrates, which are taken from the soil through the roots. To form the proteins, the nitrogen is united with carbon, hydrogen and oxygen from the sugars or other simple carbohydrates, and generally with small amounts of sulfur. Certain of the important proteins also contain phosphorus.

As is well known to all interested in agriculture, legume plants are able to utilize indirectly the nitrogen gas in the air to build proteins. This is brought about through the fixation of the free nitrogen by the legume bacteria in the nodules on the legume roots. These bacteria build the nitrogen into organic nitrogenous compounds which are later used by the host plants.

In strong contrast to plants, animals can form the proteins in their body tissues only from the amino acids which result from the digestion of protein in their food. To make a molecule of any particular body protein, several different amino acids are necessary, and these must be in certain definite proportions for each kind of protein.

It is of great importance that animals have but limited capacity to change the amino acids of which they may have an excess into others that are needed. They can readily make some of the simpler amino acids from the amino acids of which there may be a surplus, or from other substances. However, as is pointed out in detail in Chapter VI they are

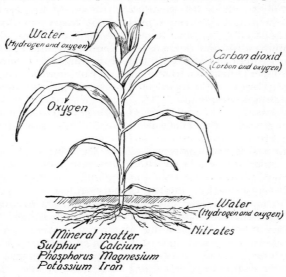

WHERE PLANTS SECURE THEIR FOOD

Plants obtain carbon dioxide from the air, and water, mineral matter, and nitrates from the soil. Legumes are able to use indirectly the nitrogen of the air. Plants give off water and free oxygen gas to the air through their leaves.

not able to form certain of the amino acids from any other source. These particular amino acids are therefore necessary for their life and must be supplied in adequate amounts by the food. For this reason these vital amino acids are called the *essential* or *indispensable amino acids,* to distinguish them from those that can be made from other amino acids.

17. Quality of proteins.—Certain proteins entirely lack one or more of the essential amino acids. Therefore, as is pointed out at greater length in Chapter VI, if a purified protein of this kind is fed continuously to an animal as the only protein food, disaster will follow, due to the poor *quality* of the protein and not to a deficiency in the total amount.

None of the ordinary feeds for livestock is completely deficient in any of the essential amino acids. For example, although zein, the chief protein in corn grain, lacks two of the essential amino acids, the other proteins in the grain partially make up this deficiency. However, the entire mixture of proteins furnished by corn contains insufficient amounts of these necessary protein building-stones to meet the body requirements completely. Therefore corn grain does not produce good results in stock feeding, unless this lack is corrected by including in the ration other feeds that will make good the deficiency in quality of protein.

Rations or feeding stuffs that furnish insufficient amounts of any of the essential amino acids are said to have *protein of poor quality*. Those which provide the proper proportions of the various necessary amino acids are said to supply *protein of good quality*.

18. Crude protein; true protein; amids.—In addition to the proteins, plants contain other nitrogenous substances of simpler composition. While the nature of these compounds varies widely in different plant substances and feeding stuffs, in most feeds the greater part is made up of amino acids and their derivatives. These are similar to the products formed when protein is digested by animals, and they therefore can be used for the same purposes in the body. For example, in corn silage nearly one-half the protein has been pre-digested, as it were, into such simpler nitrogenous compounds.

Plants also contain smaller amounts of other nitrogenous compounds, especially those that the chemist calls *amids*. These are found in largest quantities in green plant tissues. In the amids, the nitrogenous group is attached in a different manner than in the case of the amino acids. Experiments indicate that, as a result, farm animals probably cannot use the amids directly as a substitute for protein, though they do serve as sources of heat and energy, like the carbohydrates.

Formerly, many scientists differentiated sharply between true proteins and all the simpler nitrogenous compounds, believing that none of the latter could replace the proteins in animal feeding. We now know that there may be just as great a difference in nutritive value between two pure proteins, as there may be between a protein and the mixture of these simpler compounds occurring in common feeds. Therefore, in the computation of rations for livestock all the nitrogenous substances in feeds are now generally classed together.

The term *crude protein* has been commonly used to designate all the nitrogenous substances in feeding stuffs. The simpler nitrogenous compounds have been called *amids*, or *non-protein nitrogenous compounds*. (The use of the term amids for this group has been unfortunate, for it includes not only the true amids, but also considerably larger amounts of the amino acids and their derivatives.)

For the sake of simplicity and also because the separation of nitrogenous compounds into proteins and amids now has no real significance, the term *protein* is generally used in this volume to denote all nitrogenous compounds. When it is desired to refer to the substances which are actually proteins from the chemical standpoint, the term *true protein* is employed.

19. Mineral matter.—Though present in most plants in relatively small amounts, mineral nutrients are essential for their growth. It has long been known that phosphorus, potassium, sulfur, calcium, iron, and magnesium are necessary, and recent investigations have shown that certain other minerals are also needed, of which only traces occur in plants. Minute amounts of manganese and copper are required, at least by many plants, and perhaps also traces of boron, zinc, and other minerals.

The mineral substances used by plants in their growth are taken from the soil through the roots in the form of solutions of the mineral salts. With the exception of nitrogen, phosphorus, potassium, and calcium, there is no general lack of minerals in soils. In rare instances, the addition of other minerals may cause marked improvement in plant growth. For example, sulfur is deficient in a few soils, and a lack of manganese or of copper has occasionally produced injurious effects on crops.

In plants the necessary minerals occur largely as parts of the organic compounds. For example, most proteins contain sulfur, and many have phosphorus as a component. Phosphorus is also a part of the phospholipids, which are constituents of all protoplasm. Magnesium is an essential part of the chlorophyll.

The higher animals contain much larger amounts of minerals than do plants, for their bony skeletons are composed chiefly of calcium and phosphorus. Iron is a vital part of the hemoglobin of the blood, and other minerals have important functions. On account of the importance of minerals for farm animals, this subject is discussed in detail in Chapter VI.

The amounts of the various important mineral elements in typical feeds are shown in Appendix Table IV. Because calcium and phosphorus are of especial significance in the selection of feeds for livestock, the amounts of these minerals in the various feeding stuffs are given in Appendix Table I, as far as the information is available.

20. Vitamins.—The discoveries made during recent years concerning the importance of vitamins for animals are among the most outstanding in the science of nutrition. The functions of the different vitamins and their occurrence in the various classes of feeds are discussed in Chapter VI. In Appendix Table V data are given concerning the relative amounts of the different vitamins in typical feeding stuffs.

II. The Composition of Feeding Stuffs

21. Chemical composition of feeds.—In order to combine the various feeds that may be available into rations which will meet the nutritive requirements of livestock, it is necessary, first of all, to have definite knowledge concerning their chemical composition. As we shall learn later, there must also be considered the other special characteristics of the feeds, in addition to the amounts of the various nutrients they contain.

In the usual chemical analyses of feeding stuffs and plant materials, all the compounds are grouped, for simplicity and also for ease of analysis, into a few general classes. The following determinations are commonly made: Water; mineral matter, or ash; protein; fiber; and fat. As is stated later, nitrogen-free extract is found by difference and not by direct determination.

22. Appendix Table I.—To make available as complete and authoritative information as is possible on the composition of American feeding stuffs, extensive compilations have been made for this volume of the analyses that have been reported by the American experiment stations, the United States Department of Agriculture, and the state feed-control services. The average composition of each feed, as found in these compilations, is given in Appendix Table I.

Where the composition of milling and other by-products has been changed in recent years because of modifications or improvements in manufacturing processes, care has been taken to include in these new averages, only the recent analyses of such by-products. When the composition of any feed is decidedly affected by any particular factor, separate averages are given, where possible, for the different qualities of that feed. For example, in many instances separate averages are given for hay cut at various stages of maturity, since this greatly affects the composition. The various factors that influence the composition of feeding stuffs are discussed at some length in Chapter IV.

Since a thorough understanding of the composition of feeds is necessary in the study of livestock feeding, let us consider briefly the significance of the figures given in Appendix Table I for the various groups of constituents.

The first four columns of figures in the table give for each feed the data that are most commonly used in computing rations for livestock. These are: (1) The percentage of dry matter; (2) the percentage of digestible protein; (3) the percentage of total digestible nutrients; and (4) the nutritive ratio. The meaning and significance of these terms are explained in Chapter III. In the fifth to ninth columns of figures are given the total percentages of each class of nutrients in the feed, including both the digestible and the indigestible parts.

23. Dry matter; water.—It will be noted that the first column of figures in Appendix Table I gives the average percentage of dry matter in each feed. This is found by determining the percentage of water and substracting the water content from 100 per cent.

The chemist determines the amount of water by drying a finely-ground sample of the feed for some hours in an oven at a definite temperature and under standardized conditions, until no more water is given off. The difference between the first and last weights is taken as the amount of water in the sample. Traces of volatile substances, such as those which give various plants their characteristic odors, are also driven off by this heating, but the weight of such compounds is generally insignificant.

From an inspection of Appendix Table I it is evident that even such "dry" feeds as the cereal grains usually contain only 91 per cent or less of dry matter and therefore 9 per cent or more of water. The water content of corn grain differs so much that separate averages are given for the various grades of corn. It will be noted that while well-dried corn contains 88.5 per cent dry matter, corn of Federal grade No. 5 contains only 78.5 per cent dry matter, on the average, and obviously has a correspondingly lower feeding value.

Milling or other by-products which are heated or dried in the manufacturing process, such as corn gluten feed, linseed meal, and cottonseed meal, generally contain slightly less water than the grains. After curing in the mow or stack, hay contains only 15 per cent water or less, while fresh green grass and other green forage usually have 70 to 80 per cent water. Roots are especially watery, mangels and turnips containing more than 90 per cent of water, on the average.

24. Protein.—As has been explained previously in this chapter, in the regular chemical analysis of feeds all the nitrogenous compounds are included together in the one group called *crude protein,* or merely *protein.* Contained in this group are not only the true proteins in the feed, but also all the simpler nitrogenous substances which are classed under the term amids. For simplicity, this entire group of nitrogenous substances is called *protein* in this volume. When it is desired to differentiate between the entire group and the amount of actual proteins, the term *true protein* is used for the latter.

The process of determining the percentage of protein in a feed is too complicated for presentation here. It is sufficient to say that the nitrogen content is found, and the result multiplied by 6.25 to give the protein, since about 16 per cent of proteins is nitrogen, on the average ($100 \div 16 = 6.25$).

The percentage of nitrogen in the proteins of various substances differs to an appreciable extent, and therefore other factors are sometimes used to convert the percentages of nitrogen into the percentages of protein. For example, the factor 5.83 is more exact than the factor 6.25 in the case of the grains from wheat, rye, barley and oats, and in the case of milk the factor 6.38 is often used.[4] However, in the computations of rations for livestock, the general factor 6.25 is commonly employed for all feeds.

In comparing the composition of various feeds, especial attention should be given to the protein content, due to the great importance of this group of nutrients in stock feeding. For this reason, in the detailed discussions of the many different feeding stuffs given in Part II, emphasis is placed on the amounts of protein they furnish.

As may be seen from an inspection of Appendix Table I, the percentage of protein differs widely, ranging from 2.8 per cent in cane molasses and 3.9 per cent in cottonseed hulls to 40 per cent or more in corn gluten meal, cottonseed meal, soybean oil meal and peanut oil meal.

In determining whether a given feed is actually rich or poor in protein or other nutrients, attention must be paid to the water content. For example, fresh, green young rye plants, 5 inches high, contain 6.5 per cent protein. However, at this stage they have over 80 per cent water. If dried to a hay basis, the rye would have more than 30 per cent protein, and is therefore actually rich in protein, in comparison with the amounts of other nutrients.

25. Fat.—All the substances soluble in ether are included under the term *fat.* This group therefore contains not only the true fats, but also the various other fat-like substances that have been discussed previously. As has been pointed out, the ether extract of seeds is nearly all true fat, while a large part of that in the roughages consists of other substances, such as waxes and chlorophyll. The percentage of fat in a feed is found by extracting a finely-ground sample with ether continuously for some hours in a suitable apparatus, and then evaporating the ether from the solution and weighing the fatty residue.

Appendix Table I shows that oats and corn are the highest in fat among the cereal grains, oats containing 4.7 per cent fat and corn 4.0 per cent. Certain seeds, such as cottonseed, flaxseed, and soybeans, are so rich in fat that much oil can be secured from them. These seeds therefore serve as important sources of oil for various purposes, and the oil meals that remain, which contain much less fat, are important stock feeds. Most roughages are relatively low in fat.

26. Fiber.—The fiber content of a feed is of much importance in livestock feeding, because feeds that are high in fiber are less digestible and therefore less nutritious than those that are lower in fiber. As has been pointed out previously in this chapter, this group of substances includes those celluloses and other carbohydrates which are so resistant and insoluble that they are not dissolved by weak acids and alkalies.

The fiber content of a feeding stuff is determined by boiling a sample successively in weak acid and in weak alkali, and washing out the dissolved material. The residue, which contains the fiber and some of the mineral matter, is dried and weighed. Then the residue is burned to an ash, and the ash, or mineral matter, weighed. The difference in weight is the amount of fiber.

Corn contains but 2.3 per cent of fiber and wheat 3.0 per cent or less, while oats contain 10.6 per cent, because of the woody hulls. Roughages contain much more fiber than the concentrates, and the straws are especially high in it. Mangels contain but 0.8 per cent fiber; were they dried to the same water content as oats, they would contain only 7.8 per cent fiber, which is less than oats.

27. Mineral matter, or ash.—The percentage of mineral matter is determined by burning a sample of the feed until the ash is free from carbon. It will be seen that the percentage of mineral matter in feeds differs widely, though most feeds contain a relatively small amount. Corn grain has only 1.4 per cent of mineral matter and wheat 2.0 per cent, while oats have 3.6 per cent, because of the hulls, which carry considerable minerals.

The hays and straws are higher in mineral matter than such grains as corn or wheat, due to the accumulation of minerals in the leaves during growth, to soil washed upon the growing plants by rain, and to dust settling on the roughage before it is housed. Owing to their high water content, the percentage of minerals in fresh grass, silage, and mangels is low.

On account of the especial importance of calcium and phosphorus in stock feeding, the percentages of these minerals in various feeds are given in Appendix Table I, so far as data are available. The percentages of most of the important minerals in typical feeds are shown in Appendix Table IV.

28. Nitrogen-free extract.—The nitrogen-free extract includes the more soluble and therefore more valuable carbohydrates, such as starch, the sugars, the hemicelluloses, and the more soluble part of the celluloses and pentosans. It also contains certain other substances, such as organic acids, which are present in only very small amounts, except in products like silage and certain fruits.

The percentage of nitrogen-free extract is found by difference and not by actual analysis. The percentages of water, ash, protein, fiber, and fat are merely added together and the sum subtracted from 100 per cent.

Appendix Table I shows that the cereal grains are particularly high in nitrogen-free extract. For example, corn, wheat, rye, and the grain sorghums have about 70 per cent. In the cereals nearly all of the nitrogen-free extract is starch. The hays and other roughages are much lower in nitrogen-free extract, and considerable of it consists of hemicelluloses and the more soluble portion of the celluloses and pentosans. The nitrogen-free extract of roughages is therefore less nutritious than the nitrogen-free extract of the seeds and other concentrates.

In the table headings in the Appendix Tables of this book, nitrogen-free extract is abbreviated to "N-free extract" to save space.

29. Guarantees of composition.—It is pointed out in Chapter IV that under the laws regulating the sale of commercial feeds, in most states the manufacturer must guarantee the minimum percentages of protein and of fat and the maximum percentage of fiber. In other words, the feed must not contain *less than* these percentages of protein and of fat and it must not contain *more than* the guaranteed percentage of fiber. Commonly it is required that these guarantees be plainly stated on tags attached to each sack of commercial feed. Usually, ground grains and certain other feeds are excepted from these regulations.

The average composition given in Appendix Table I will enable the purchaser to determine whether the particular lot of feed comes up to the usual grade. Since the feeding stuff laws are generally enforced strictly, the feed in the sack will commonly have as much protein and fat as is guaranteed, and often slightly more. Likewise it will usually contain no more fiber than guaranteed.

30. Carbohydrates.—The term *carbohydrates* includes both the fiber and the nitrogen-free extract in feeds.

In a few instances the percentages of fiber and of nitrogen-free extract are stated on the tags attached to sacks of commercial feeds, or in the advertising literature, and then the percentage of carbohydrates is also shown, with nothing to indicate that this is a duplication. This should not be done, as it may be misleading to purchasers.

31. Concentrates and roughages.—These terms are convenient to separate feeds into two general classes upon the basis of their fiber content and the amount of total digestible nutrients they furnish.

Concentrates are feeds that are low in fiber and high in total digestible nutrients. Examples of this class of feeds are the various grains and the high-grade by-products, such as hominy feed, wheat bran, cottonseed meal, linseed meal, corn gluten feed, etc. Attention should be called to the fact that concentrates may be either *low in protein* or *rich in protein*. This is often misunderstood and the term used only for protein-rich feeds of concentrated nature.

Roughages are feeds that are high in fiber and therefore low in total digestible nutrients. Such feeds as hay, corn fodder, straw, and silage belong to this class. Some of the low-grade milling by-products, such as oat hulls, ground corn cobs, and cottonseed hulls are roughages, rather than concentrates, for they are largely fiber and furnish but little nutriment.

Roots are watery and bulky, and contain only a small amount of nutrients per pound, yet based on the composition of their dry matter they are more like concentrates than roughages, as they are low in fiber. They are really watery, or diluted, concentrates, though for convenience they are included under green roughages in Appendix Table I.

III. The Composition of Animals

32. Animals and plants compared.—To fix in mind the fundamental differences between the nutrition and composition of plants and animals, let us review certain points that have already been mentioned in this chapter. One of the major differences in composition is that in animals the walls of the body cells are made chiefly of protein, while in plants they are composed of cellulose and other carbohydrates. Furthermore, in plants the reserve food is stored, for the most part, as starch, another carbohydrate. In animals, on the other hand, nearly all the reserve is stored in the form of fat.

Perhaps the most important difference in the nutrition of plants and animals is in their sources of energy. Plants can use energy supplied by the sun in building inorganic matter taken from earth and air into organic compounds. In this process the energy from the sun becomes latent, or hidden. Animals cannot secure directly from the sun the energy necessary for their life, but must live on the organic, energy-rich compounds built by plants. After the changes that occur in digestion, these organic compounds are built into body tissues or are broken down within the body to produce heat and energy. Plants are thus sun-power machines for furnishing food to support animal life.

33. Composition of animals.—Many years ago Lawes and Gilbert, the famous early English agricultural scientists, analyzed the entire bodies of several farm animals—a task involving much labor.[5] More recently similar studies have been made at certain of the American experiment stations, especially at the Missouri, Illinois, and Minnesota Stations.[6] The table on the next page, which gives some of the results of these investigations, shows that the composition of the bodies of livestock differs greatly, according to their age and degree of fatness.

The table shows that 71.8 per cent of the body of a 100-lb. calf is water and that the proportion of water steadily grows less as the animal matures and fattens, the body of an exceedingly fat 1,870-lb. steer containing only 39.8 per cent water. The percentage of protein remains fairly constant during growth but decreases as the animal fattens. On the other hand, the percentage of fat increases gradually during growth, and more rapidly while fattening. Over one-third of the carcass of the very fat 1,500-lb. steer is fat, and over 44 per cent in the case of the exceedingly fat animal. The percentage of mineral matter shows the least change, but decreases as the animal fattens, since the fatty tissue contains but little mineral matter.

Similar changes occur in the bodies of sheep and swine, as the animals mature and fatten. In general, swine at the same stage of fattening contain somewhat less water and protein and considerably more fat than cattle. The very fat pig, for example, contains 42.6 per cent fat and only 11.6 per cent protein. Due to their small skeletons, the bodies of swine contain less mineral matter than those of cattle and sheep.

Indian Corn—The King of the Cereals

On millions of farms the success of animal husbandry depends largely on corn. Corn grain is an excellent example of a concentrate, for it is very low in fiber and furnishes a large amount of digestible matter.

Legume Hay—Unexcelled as a Dry Roughage

Fortunate indeed is the farmer who has provided bounteous crops of choice legume hay for his stock. Clover or alfalfa hay is a roughage, for it is relatively high in crude fiber, but it is a roughage of the highest value, because it is rich in crude protein, calcium, vitamin A, and vitamin D.

MARKETING CROPS THROUGH LIVESTOCK SAVES FERTILITY

Fattening cattle, sheep, or swine store in their bodies only a small part of the nitrogen, calcium, and phosphorus in their feed, and the remainder is voided in the manure. When the manure is handled in the manner advised in Chapter XX, the loss of fertility is reduced to a minimum. (From U. S. Department of Agriculture.)

A HEAVY LOSS OF FERTILITY OCCURS WHEN HAY IS SOLD

Few farmers realize that each ton of hay or grain sold from the farm removes $4 to $6 worth of plant food. (See Chapter XX.) (From U. S. Department of Agriculture.)

*Composition of the bodies of farm animals**

	Water	Protein	Fat	Mineral matter
	Per cent	Per cent	Per cent	Per cent
Calf, wt. 100 lbs.	71.8	19.9	4.0	4.3
Calf, wt. 300 lbs.	65.7	18.8	11.2	4.3
Growing steer, wt. 700 lbs..................	60.3	18.6	16.6	4.5
Partly fat steer, wt. 1,000 lbs...............	52.0	17.1	26.9	4.0
Fat steer, wt. 1,200 lbs....................	48.0	16.0	32.3	3.7
Very fat steer, wt. 1,500 lbs................	43.5	15.7	37.6	3.2
Exceedingly fat steer, wt. 1,870 lbs..........	39.8	12.4	44.6	3.0
Thin 4-yr. old steer........................	57.2	20.0	17.2	5.1
Dairy cow	56.8	17.2	20.6	5.0
Fat dairy cow.............................	50.2	15.6	29.2	4.2
Mature horse	61.9	18.2	14.1	4.7
Fat lamb	50.9	17.4	24.9	4.2
Sheep, before fattening.....................	61.0	15.7	19.9	3.4
Half-fat sheep	55.2	15.4	25.9	3.5
Fat sheep	46.2	13.0	37.9	3.0
Very fat sheep.............................	37.1	11.5	48.3	3.1
Growing pig, wt. 100 lbs....................	66.8	14.9	16.2	3.1
Fairly fat pig, wt. 200 lbs..................	54.0	14.5	28.5	2.7
Very fat pig, wt. 300 lbs...................	42.5	11.6	42.6	2.1
Young brood sow...........................	48.3	15.8	33.6	2.4
Chick, wt. 0.07 lb.........................	76.0	17.3	4.7	2.1
Pullet, wt. 0.5 lb..........................	71.2	20.8	3.5	3.6
Pullet, wt. 1.0 lb..........................	71.1	22.6	2.6	3.7
Pullet, wt. 2.0 lbs.........................	65.7	22.8	6.6	3.6
Pullet, wt. 4.0 lbs.........................	55.8	19.2	20.0	3.1

*Not including contents of digestive tract.

The changes in composition are due chiefly to the accumulation of fat in the body. Indeed, it has been found that after an animal is only partly grown, the percentages of water, protein, and mineral matter, on a fat-free basis, change but little.[7]

The amounts of the principal mineral constituents in the bodies of farm animals are shown in Appendix Table IV. Because they form the chief minerals in the bones, calcium and phosphorus greatly exceed in amount the other mineral components of the body. Calcium, the largest mineral constituent of the bones, ranges in amount from about 0.45 per cent in the body of the fat pig to 1.5 per cent in unfattened cattle. The content of phosphorus is somewhat more than one-half that of calcium, and the amounts of other minerals are relatively small. For example, although iron performs exceedingly important functions, there is only about 0.01 to 0.03 per cent of iron in the body of animals. In other words, the body of a 1,000-lb. cow contains only 0.1 to 0.3 lb. of iron.

34. Nutrients and rations.—In discussing stock feeding it is necessary to understand clearly what is meant by each of the following terms:

The term *nutrient* is applied to any food constituent or group of food constituents of the same general chemical composition, that aid in the support of animal life. Crude protein, the carbohydrates, and fat constitute the generally recognized classes of nutrients, although air, water, mineral matter, and vitamins might likewise be so termed.

The term *digestible nutrient* means that portion of each nutrient which may be digested and taken into the body.

A *ration* is the feed allowed for a given animal during a day of 24 hours, whether it is fed at one time or in portions at different times.

A *balanced ration* is one which furnishes the several nutrients—protein, carbohydrates, and fat—in such proportion and amount as will properly nourish a given animal for 24 hours.

QUESTIONS

1. What 4 functions does water perform in plants and animals?
2. State the relative amounts of carbohydrates in plants and in animals.
3. Name the 3 most important hexoses, or 6-carbon simple sugars, and state where each occurs. Which of these is important in the animal body?
4. Name 3 important compound sugars and state where each occurs.
5. What are polysaccharides? State 5 important classes of plant substances included in this group.
6. What is the general formula for all polysaccharides composed of 6-carbon sugars? Of the pentosans?
7. What compound similar to starch is found in the animal body?
8. What is the function of cellulose in plants? Why does it have a relatively low feeding value for stock?
9. State the relative amounts of pentosans in various types of feeds.
10. State two other names given to the fats and fat-like substances.
11. Why do fats have a higher energy value per pound than carbohydrates?
12. Of what is a molecule of pure fat composed?
13. What is meant by the term, "unsaturated fat"? Name one common oil that is highly unsaturated and state its importance.
14. Name 6 other groups of substances that are not fats, but which are included in the general group of fats.
15. Of what importance in stock feeding are (1) ergosterol, (2) carotene?
16. Discuss the importance of proteins in the animal body.
17. Of what units are proteins composed? What is meant by the term *essential amino acid?*
18. Explain what is meant by *proteins of good quality* and *proteins of poor quality.*
19. Distinguish between crude protein and true protein.
20. Of what two minerals are the skeletons of animals chiefly composed?
21. In the usual chemical analysis of feeds, what six groups of substances are usually determined?
22. Name 4 common feeding stuffs that contain over 30 per cent total protein. Name 4 dry feeds that contain less than 10 per cent protein. (See Appendix Table I.)
23. Name 3 seeds that are so rich in fat that they are common sources of oil.
24. Name 4 feeds that contain over 40 per cent fiber. Name 4 common dry feeds that contain less than 4 per cent fiber.
25. Name 4 feeds that are rich in calcium; 4 that are rich in phosphorus; 4 that are poor in calcium; 4 that are poor in phosphorus.
26. How will the amounts of protein, fat, and fiber actually present in a commercial feed generally compare with the guarantee for protein, fat, and fiber?
27. Define *concentrates* and *roughages* and give examples of each. Does the amount of protein in a feed determine its classification as a concentrate or a roughage?
28. Compare and contrast the composition and the source of energy of animals and plants.
29. Discuss the changes in the chemical composition of animals as they grow and as they fatten.

30. Approximately what percentages of water, protein, fat, and mineral matter are there in the body of a fat steer?
31. Define *nutrient; digestible nutrient; ration; balanced ration.*

REFERENCES

1. Fraps, Tex. Buls. 175, 196, 290, 418.
2. Fraps and Rather, Tex. Bul. 150; Rather, Tex. Bul. 169.
3. Edwards and Holley, Ga. Bul. 173.
4. Jones, U. S. Dept. Agr. Cir. 183.
5. Lawes and Gilbert, Philosophical Transactions, England, 1859.
6. P. F. Trowbridge, Moulton, and Haigh, Mo. Res. Buls. 28, 43; P. F. Trowbridge, Mo. Res. Bul. 38; Moulton, P. F. Trowbridge, and Haigh, Mo. Res. Buls. 55, 61; Ritchie, Moulton, P. F. Trowbridge, and Haigh, Mo. Res. Bul. 59; Hogan, Weaver, Edinger, and E. A. Trowbridge, Mo. Res. Bul. 73; Hogan and Nierman, Mo. Res. Bul. 107; Griswold, P. F. Trowbridge, Hogan and Haigh, Mo. Res. Bul. 114; Haecker, Minn. Bul. 193; Mitchell and Hamilton, Ill. Rpt. 1927; Mitchell, Kammlade, and Hamilton, Ill. Bul. 314; Swanson, Jour. Agr. Res. 21. 1921, p. 279; Jordan, Me. Rpt. 1895; Washburn and Jones, Vt. Bul. 195.
7. Moulton, Jour. Biol. Chem. 57, 1923, pp. 79-97; Moulton, Trowbridge, and Haigh, Mo. Res. Bul. 55.

CHAPTER II

THE DIGESTION, ABSORPTION, AND USE OF FOOD

I. DIGESTION AND ABSORPTION

35. Digestion required before food can be utilized.—Most of the foods consumed by animals are too insoluble and composed of too complex substances to be absorbed unchanged from the digestive tract. In general, before food can be assimilated and used it must undergo extensive changes. In this process it is broken down into relatively simple chemical compounds. These are soluble and can pass through the mucous membrane that lines the digestive tract and thus reach the blood circulation. Water, glucose, soluble mineral matter (such as common salt), and a few other substances require no modifications before they can be assimilated.

All the changes which food undergoes within the digestive tract to prepare it for absorption and use in the body are known as *digestion.*

These changes which occur during digestion are both mechanical and chemical. First of all, the food must be broken into small particles by mechanical means, so that a large surface will be exposed to the action of the digestive juices. This is especially important in the case of seeds, which are protected by hard seed coats or hulls. The mechanical breaking apart of the food is accomplished by mastication, or chewing. Also, particularly in the case of ruminants, motions of the stomach aid in mixing and softening the food and even in breaking it apart.

The chemical changes by which the complex food compounds are broken down into much simpler substances are produced chiefly by enzymes. In the case of herbivora (herbage-eating animals) bacteria and possibly other micro-organisms are also important agents in digestion. In all animals the hydrochloric acid aids digestion in the stomach, and the bile in the small intestine.

36. Enzymes.—As most of the changes which food undergoes in digestion are effected through enzymes, their general nature should be clearly understood.

Enzymes are remarkable organic compounds which **bring** about changes in other organic compounds without themselves being changed or broken down.

To illustrate the action of enzymes, let us take ptyalin, the enzyme contained in the saliva of man and certain animals, which changes the starch of the food, which is insoluble, into sugar, which is soluble. If starch is mixed with saliva and the whole kept at body temperature, the starch gradually dissolves, being changed to maltose, or malt sugar. Through the action of the ptyalin, the complex starch molecule has been cleaved, or split, into the simpler molecules of sugar. If starch is mixed merely with water, instead of saliva, this change will not occur.

The ptyalin is not itself used up to any appreciable extent in this process, for, if more starch is added and the resulting sugar removed, the process may be repeated many times. The great activity of the digestive enzymes is shown by the fact that a given weight of the amylase of the pancreatic juice is able to digest 4,000,000 times its own weight of starch.[1]

Heating the enzyme above a certain temperature destroys it. At the freezing temperature its action ceases, though the enzyme is not destroyed, for on warming it becomes active again. Ptyalin acts best in a neutral solution or in one which is only very slightly alkaline or acid. It is destroyed by the presence of much acid or alkali, while some other enzymes act only in acid solutions. Each of the enzymes of digestion is capable of acting on only one of the groups of nutrients; for example, on proteins, on starch, or on fats.

The digestion of food by enzyme action consists of the splitting or cleaving of complex molecules of protein, starch, etc., into simpler compounds, which are soluble and can be absorbed into the body. During these processes, water is taken up chemically and enters into the molecules of the compounds undergoing digestion. There is but little loss of energy in this enzyme action on food, while in the breaking down of food compounds by bacterial fermentation, much energy is lost.

37. The alimentary canal.—The alimentary canal is a long, tortuous tube passing through the animal from mouth to rectum, enlarged in places for the storage of food or waste. It includes the mouth, esophagus (or gullet), stomach, small intestine, and large intestine. Within its linings are glands which secrete the various fluids of digestion, and into it, from other organs located near by, pour still other digestive fluids. Within its walls are nerves controlling its action, arteries which nourish it with fresh blood, and veins and lymphatics which absorb and carry from it the products of digestion.

Ruminants (animals which chew the cud), including cattle, sheep, and goats, have much more complicated digestive tracts than other animals. The horse and the pig have a simple stomach, containing only a single compartment. A ruminant has a compound stomach, which consists of four distinct compartments. Of these, the first and by far the largest is the paunch, or rumen; the second is the honeycomb, or reticulum; the third, the manyplies, or omasum; and the fourth, the abomasum, or so-called "true stomach." Enzymes are secreted only in the fourth compartment, where gastric juice is produced, the same as in the stomach of animals that have a simple stomach.

The four-fold stomach of a full-grown cow may hold over 250 quarts, while the single stomach of a horse holds only 12 to 19 quarts and that of a pig about 8.5 quarts. Cattle and sheep owe their ability to utilize large amounts of roughage to the great capacity of their stomachs, and to the digestion of the fiber of feeds which takes place therein.

The small intestine is the long, folded, tortuous tube into which the stomach empties. It is about 130 ft. long in mature cattle, 70 ft. in horses, 80 ft. in sheep, and 60 ft. in swine. Its average capacity is about as follows: cattle, 70 quarts; horse, 50 to 65 quarts; sheep and swine, 10 quarts. The large intestine, into which the small intestine empties, is larger in diameter but much shorter.

In the horse, that part of the large intestine next to the small intestine, called the blind gut, or caecum, is greatly enlarged, and also the colon, or second part of the large intestine, is much larger than in cattle.

Due to this, the large intestine of the horse holds from 120 to 140 quarts. Were it not for this, the horse would be unable to consume and digest large amounts of roughage.

In cattle, the large intestine has a capacity of about 40 quarts, and in sheep, 6 quarts. The pig, which has neither the compound stomach of the ruminants nor the large caecum of the horse, is not well fitted to use large amounts of roughage. His large intestine, however, holds nearly twice as much as that of the sheep, which aids him somewhat in disposing of coarse feed.

38. The circulation of blood.—In order to understand the manner in which nutrients are absorbed from the digestive tract and transported to various parts of the body, it is necessary to have in mind certain facts concerning the circulation of blood and lymph.

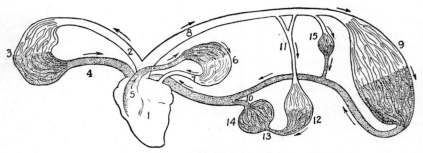

DIAGRAM OF THE CIRCULATION OF THE BLOOD

1, The heart; 2, artery carrying blood to the head and fore limbs; 3, circulation through the upper portion of the body; 4, vein carrying blood from upper part of body back to the heart; 5, artery carrying venous blood to lungs; 6, circulation through lungs; 7, vein carrying arterial blood back to heart; 8, artery carrying blood to lower portion of body; 9, circulation through rear extremities; 10, vein carrying blood to heart from rear extremities; 11, artery carrying blood to intestines; 12, circulation through intestinal capillaries; 13, portal vein carrying blood to liver; 14, circulation through liver; 15, circulation through kidneys. (From Smith, "Manual of Veterinary Physiology.")

The arteries and veins of the blood system permeate every portion of the body, the former carrying blood away from the heart, and the latter carrying it to the heart. At the extremities of the small arteries are still more minute blood vessels, called *capillaries,* which connect them with the veins.

If one extends his arms in front of him with his finger tips touching, his body will represent the heart, while one arm will represent an artery carrying blood from the heart, and the other a vein conveying blood to the heart. The touching fingers will correspond to the capillaries connecting the arteries with the veins, and the space all about the fingers will represent the surrounding body tissues.

In general, neither the veins nor the arteries allow any substance within them to escape through their walls proper. It is through the capillaries that the nutrients carried by the blood find their way into the body tissues for their nourishment, and through the capillaries and the lymph vessels that are mentioned later, the waste of the body drains back into the blood circulation.

39. The lymph.—The innumerable cells of which the various parts of the body are composed are bathed by the *lymph,* which fills the spaces between the cells. The lymph is a nearly colorless fluid that comes from the blood plasma, or the watery part of the blood. This passes through the walls of the capillaries and thus surrounds the body cells. It serves as the medium through which the nutrients and the oxygen from the arterial blood pass to the cells, and by which the carbon dioxide and other waste products are transferred to the blood in the veins.

Some of the lymph passes back directly to the blood capillaries, and the rest is drained away by the system of lymph vessels. These vessels resemble the veins, but they are thinner and more transparent. The small lymph vessels unite to form larger ones, and after passing through lymph glands, the lymph enters the venous blood stream near the heart. One purpose of this separate lymphatic system is probably to guard the body against infection, for when bacteria gain entrance to the body tissues they are commonly carried by the lymph to the lymph glands. Here they may be killed and digested, thus overcoming the infection.

40. The villi of the small intestine.—The digested nutrients are absorbed into the circulation chiefly through the mucous membrane which lines the small intestine. In order to provide a larger surface so that the nutrients may be more completely absorbed, this mucous membrane has innumerable cone-like projections, called *villi.* These villi, which give the mucous membrane a velvety appearance, project toward the center of the intestinal tube and thus come into intimate contact with the fluid contents.

Within each villus is a lacteal, or drainage tube of the lymphatic system, and a network of capillaries of the blood system. The veins from the intestine unite and form the portal vein, which carries the absorbed nutrients to the liver and then on to the heart.

41. Mastication.—In the mouth the food is crushed and ground by the teeth and at the same time moistened by the somewhat slimy saliva, so that it can readily be swallowed. Moist and slippery masses are formed which pass easily through the gullet and into the stomach. Exceedingly large amounts of saliva are secreted by the larger farm animals, especially when eating dry feed. For example, a cow may secrete as much as 125 lbs. in 24 hours.

The sensation of taste depends largely on the saliva, as this dissolves small amounts of the food, which affect the nerves of the tongue that are concerned with this sensation.

The chewing of food involves considerable muscular exertion, due to the great number of motions of the jaws that are required. For example, it is estimated that in the case of a dairy cow there are about 41,000 jaw movements a day in chewing.[2]

42. Rumination.—Ruminants chew their food, while eating, only enough to moisten it, if dry, and form it into masses of suitable size to be swallowed. These masses, or boluses, pass into the forward part of the paunch through the slit, called the esophageal groove, which opens into the paunch and the honeycomb.

The boluses of hay and other coarse dry forage are not saturated with saliva when swallowed, so they are light and do not sink into the fluid contents of the paunch at first. They are carried to the rear of the paunch by regular movements of the muscular walls, gradually absorbing fluid, until they sink and mix with the other contents. In the lower part of the paunch there is a movement of the heavier food masses toward the front, where the paunch opens into the honeycomb. The movements of the paunch and the honeycomb gradually accomplish a very thorough mixing and softening of their contents.

When a ruminant has satisfied its appetite, it seeks a quiet place, if possible, and proceeds to ruminate, or "chew its cud." In New Hampshire tests, dairy cows fed in the stable spent an average of about 6 hours a day in eating and 8 hours in rumination.[2]

In the process of rumination a mass of solid food, along with liquid, is carried from the honeycomb and rumen into the esophagus.[3] The mass is then forced up the esophagus to the mouth, the liquid portion is quickly swallowed, and the solid part is thoroughly chewed, after which it is again swallowed. It passes first into the paunch and then into the honeycomb, from which it enters the third and fourth compartments of the stomach through the connecting opening.

It was formerly believed that finely ground concentrates and water might follow along the esophagus, past the esophageal groove, directly into the third and fourth compartments. However, this has been disproved in recent North Dakota and Illinois investigations.[4] By means of skillful operations, openings or fistulas were made into the paunch, which healed, forming permanent entrances through which the movements of the stomachs could be studied.

It was found that even water and ground concentrates passed through the esophageal groove into the honeycomb or the paunch. Only in the case of young calves consuming milk did the slit-like esophageal groove close firmly enough to prevent the milk from entering the paunch or the honeycomb, and instead let it flow directly into the third and fourth compartments of the stomach.

In the case of cattle, if kernels of whole grain escape mastication when first eaten, they are brought up for rumination only if entangled in coarse forage. Consequently, such kernels may pass through the entire digestive tract in an unbroken condition. As is pointed out in later chapters, there may therefore be considerable saving of feed through grinding grain for dairy cows and also for fattening cattle. On the other hand, sheep chew their grain very thoroughly, and hence it does not pay to grind most kinds of grain for them.

43. Digestion and absorption of carbohydrates.—To fix in mind the most important facts concerning the digestion and absorption of food, a very condensed summary is first given for each class of nutrients. For those who desire further information, there are later presented in smaller type more detailed statements concerning the functions of the various organs and the changes which take place in the different parts of the digestive tract.

Carbohydrate digestion begins in the mouth with those animals whose saliva contains ptyalin, the starch-digesting enzyme. The pig, however, is the only one of the larger farm animals whose saliva has any appreci-

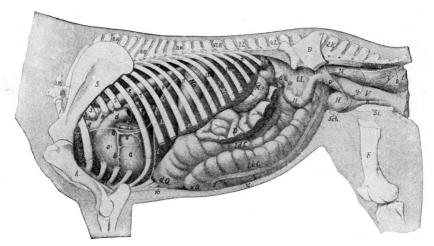

Internal Organs of Mare; Left View

The organs of greater interest are as follows: L, Left lobe of liver; Ma, stomach, the posterior part of which is indicated by dotted line, x; Mi, spleen; l N, left kidney, concealed part of which is indicated by dotted line, n; M, small colon; D, small intestine, parts of which have been removed; l.d.c., l.v.c., v.d., and v.q., parts of colon; O, left ovary; U, horn of uterus; M, rectum; V, vagina; H, bladder; a, a′, b, b′, b″, c, d, and e, heart and arteries entering it. (From Sisson, "Anatomy of the Domestic Animals.")

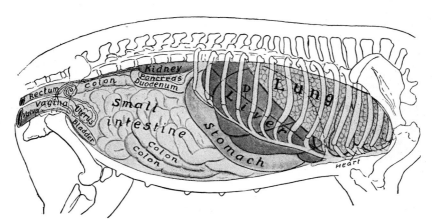

Diagram of Digestive System of Pig; Right Side

The pancreas and duodenum are not in contact with the flank, as would be inferred from this figure, but are situated nearer the center of the body, and if viewed from the right side, would be covered by the small intestine. (From Sisson, "Anatomy of the Domestic Animals.")

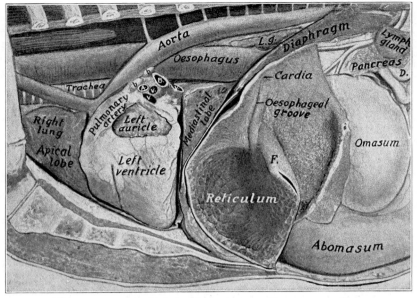

THORACIC AND FRONT ABDOMINAL ORGANS OF OX

Most of the rumen has been removed, and the left wall of the reticulum cut away. A, Left pulmonary artery; B, left bronchus; V, V, V, pulmonary veins; L g, lymph gland; D, end of duodenum; F, fold between rumen and reticulum. (From Sisson, "Anatomy of the Domestic Animals.")

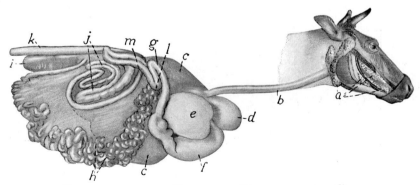

DIAGRAM OF THE DIGESTIVE TRACT OF THE COW

A, Salivary glands; b, gullet; c, paunch, or first stomach (only a small part of the paunch is here visible, the rear portion being hidden by the intestines); d, honeycomb, or second stomach; e, manyplies, or third stomach; f, fourth, or true stomach; g, duodenum, or first part of small intestine; h, mesenteric part of small intestine; i, caecum; j, colon; k, rectum; l, point of entrance of bile duct into duodenum; m, point of entrance of pancreatic duct into duodenum. The intestines are spread out somewhat in this diagram.

able starch-digesting power, and this is relatively weak. For example, the saliva of man is over 100 times as rich in ptyalin as that of the pig.

Ptyalin changes starch into malt sugar, as has been previously explained in this chapter. Even in the case of man or the pig, the amount of digestion in the mouth itself is small, due to the short time the food is there. It is therefore fortunate that the action continues in the first part of the stomach. Salivary digestion ceases when the food becomes acid in the rear portion. Simple, glucose-like sugars may be absorbed directly from the stomach in small amounts, but nearly all the carbohydrates are carried on into the small intestine.

In the small intestine the starch which has escaped being acted upon by the saliva is changed into malt sugar by amylase, an enzyme in the pancreatic juice. The compound cane, malt, and milk sugars are then split into simple glucose-like sugars by the action of the invertases, which are enzymes in the intestinal juice. The simple sugars are absorbed through the walls of the small intestine, and, entering the capillaries, pass into the veins and thence, by way of the portal vein, to the liver.

Thus, when a human eats bread, or an animal consumes hay or corn, the starch in the food must all be changed to glucose before it can enter the body proper. Similarly, the compound sugars in the food are converted almost completely into simple sugars, though insignificant amounts of the compound sugars may possibly be absorbed unchanged from the digestive organs. If any unchanged compound sugar is absorbed into the blood from the intestines, it is largely excreted in the urine, without being used in the body.

44. Formation of glycogen.—The amount of glucose in the blood of the general circulation is kept nearly constant, being about 0.1 per cent, or one part in a thousand, in the larger farm animals. However, the blood in the portal vein, which carries the blood from the intestines to the liver, may contain twice the normal content of glucose after a meal rich in carbohydrates. Also, it may contain smaller amounts of the other simple sugars.

In the liver the sugars are largely withdrawn from the blood and temporarily stored in this organ in the form of *glycogen*. This is a carbohydrate that is closely related to starch and is therefore often called animal starch. Normally, from 3 to 7 per cent of the weight of the liver is glycogen.

As the glucose is removed from the blood for the nourishment of the body tissues, the glycogen is gradually changed back to glucose, which is then doled out to the blood to keep its glucose content constant. The liver also has the ability to change the other simple sugars into glucose, and this is the only sugar that occurs in appreciable amounts in the general blood circulation.

Glycogen is also formed to some extent by the other tissues of the body, especially by the muscles. When the muscles are at rest, a reserve of energy is built up in the form of glycogen. This is used in the production of muscular work, as is described in Chapter VIII.

45. Digestion of cellulose and pentosans.—No enzymes produced by the digestive tract are able to digest cellulose and pentosans, which form the cell walls of plant structures and make up a large part of all roughages. However, these substances are attacked by bacteria in the first three compartments of the stomachs of ruminants, in the cæcum and colon of the horse, and to a lesser extent in the large intestine of other animals. These bacteria break down the cellulose and pentosans into organic acids (chiefly acetic acid and butyric acid) and possibly into simple sugars, such as glucose. In this process gases (principally carbon dioxide and methane) are formed and heat is produced. The organic acids serve as food to the animal, the same as sugars, but the gases are of no value. The heat produced is an entire waste, unless the animal needs this heat to maintain its normal body temperature.

The ability of livestock to use the fiber and pentosans in their feeds depends chiefly on this bacterial digestion. This action is therefore of great importance in the nutrition of cattle and sheep, and is the fundamental reason why they can live chiefly on roughage. Not only are the cell walls thus utilized for food, but also this digestion sets free the nutrients contained inside the cells, so they can be more easily acted on by the digestive juices in the true stomach and in the intestines.

Not only do the bacteria digest cellulose and pentosans, but also they may attack starch and sugar. This action is detrimental, for these nutrients would be digested more efficiently later on in the small intestine, while in the bacterial digestion an appreciable part of their feeding value is lost through the heat and gases produced in the fermentations. When fresh, easily-fermented forage, such as green alfalfa or clover, is eaten, the bacterial action may be so great that gas is produced faster than it can be carried away, and "bloat" results.

The fact that practically no ptyalin is present in the saliva of cattle and sheep is advantageous to them. If their saliva converted starch into sugar, much sugar would be formed in the paunch. This would then be attacked by bacteria, with a resultant loss of nutrients.

In addition to the digestion in the paunch caused by bacteria, more or less is undoubtedly produced by the enzymes contained in some foods, such as the cereal grains, for the moisture and warmth of the paunch are favorable to enzyme action in general. Also certain protozoa (microorganisms larger in size than bacteria) thrive in the food mass in the paunch and apparently aid in the digestive processes.

46. Digestion and absorption of protein.—The proteins of the food are first attacked in the stomach by pepsin, an enzyme of the gastric juice, which splits them into proteoses and peptones. These are soluble and simpler in composition than the proteins, but are still very complex in structure. The proteoses and peptones, together with any protein that escapes action by pepsin, pass into the small intestine. There trypsin, an enzyme in the pancreatic juice, not only cleaves the undigested protein into proteoses and peptones, but also digests them further, splitting them into amino acids, which are much simpler than the proteoses and peptones.

Erepsin, an enzyme in the intestinal juice, also acts on the proteoses and peptones and breaks them down into amino acids. Thus, through the action of trypsin and erepsin all the protein which can be digested is cleaved into amino acids. In this digestion of complex proteins into the much simpler amino acids, a large amount of water is taken up chemically and enters into combination with the digestion products.

The amino acids are soluble in the juices of the small intestine and are readily absorbed by the villi of the intestinal walls. They then pass into the blood and are carried into the general circulation. From the blood, each of the parts of the body—muscles, internal organs, etc.—absorbs a certain amount to be used for repair or in growth. The amino acids are the nitrogenous units that are used in the repair and formation of body tissues.

The digestion of the amids in general resembles that of the true proteins. In the previous chapter it has been pointed out that the amids include those nitrogenous substances which are more simple in composition than the true proteins. In many instances, such as in corn silage, the amids in feeds are similar in nature to some of the intermediate products of protein digestion in the animal body.

In the case of suckling animals or others consuming milk, rennin, an enzyme that is produced by the glands in the stomach, is of importance. This curdles milk, changing it from a liquid to a solid condition, so that it cannot pass too rapidly through the stomach and thus escape complete digestion.

47. Digestion and absorption of fats.—The fats of foods undergo no appreciable digestion until they reach the small intestine. Here, through the aid of the bile salts produced by the liver, the fat is emulsified, or broken up into very small droplets. The lipase of the pancreatic juice then splits the fats into fatty acids and glycerin. The fatty acids thus produced unite to some extent with the alkalies in the digestive fluids to form soaps. These soaps and the glycerin are absorbed by the villi of the intestines. Some of the fatty acids may also be dissolved by the action of the bile and be absorbed in this form.

The soaps or the fatty acids then react with the glycerin in the intestinal wall to form fats again. The fats largely enter the lacteals in the villi of the intestinal wall, forming with the lymph a milky-appearing fluid called *chyle*. This is carried by the lymphatics and poured into a vein near the heart, thus entering the blood circulation.

48. Mineral nutrients; vitamins; water.—That part of the *mineral matter* in feeds which is not already soluble is dissolved to a greater or less extent by the hydrochloric acid of the gastric juice. Further freeing of the mineral nutrients occurs as the organic nutrients are digested by the several enzymes. Minerals are absorbed chiefly from the small intestine. Sulfur and phosphorus, which occur in feeds largely as a part of proteins, are digested in the changes which these nutrients undergo.

Little is known about the manner in which the *vitamins* are digested and absorbed, on account of the very small quantities of these essential substances that occur in feeds.

Water requires no digestion and is absorbed along the digestive tract, from the stomach to the large intestine, but chiefly in the small intestine.

49. Disposal of undigested food.—As the intestinal contents pass through the latter part of the large intestine, some of the water is absorbed, and a more or less solid residue accumulates in the rectum. This is voided as the feces. With farm animals these are chiefly undigested food that has never really been within the body proper. This undigested food is mostly cellulose, or crude fiber, which has escaped bacterial action. Also a portion of the other nutrients usually escapes digestion. This may be due to insufficient chewing of such food as seeds, or because some nutrients are protected from the digestive juices through being enclosed in resistant cell walls of cellulose.

In addition to undigested food the feces also contain such excretory products as residues from the bile and other digestive fluids, waste mineral matter, worn-out cells from the intestinal lining, mucus, and bacteria. They may also contain such foreign matter as dirt consumed along with the food. In the case of humans and of such animals as dogs and cats, the greater part of the feces consists of excretory products, rather than undigested food.

50. Digestion in the mouth.—For those desiring detailed information on the steps in digestion that occur in each part of the digestive tract, the following summaries are presented.

The food is prepared for swallowing in the mouth. Also carbohydrate digestion begins here in the case of the animals whose saliva contains ptyalin, the enzyme that breaks starch down into maltose, or malt sugar. As has been pointed out previously, the pig is the only one of the larger farm animals whose saliva has any appreciable starch-digesting power, and this is small in comparison with that of man. Insignificant amounts of other enzymes than ptyalin may be secreted in the mouth.

51. Digestion in the stomach.—With such animals as the horse and pig, which have simple stomachs, the food passes directly from the mouth through the esophagus to the stomach. Here it remains in a more or less compact mass in the first part of the stomach for a time.

The glands in the walls of the middle and rear parts of the stomach secrete the digestive fluid called *gastric juice*. This contains the enzyme *pepsin* and may also contain *rennin*, a second enzyme. In addition, it has from less than 0.1 per cent up to about 0.5 per cent of hydrochloric acid, depending on the species of animal.

The gastric juice can penetrate the mass of food in the first part of the stomach only slowly. Therefore, in the case of the pig and other animals whose saliva contains ptyalin, the digestion of starch continues in this part of the stomach for a time. When the gastric juice makes its way into the mass of food, the action of the ptyalin is stopped, due to the acidity. The action of the pepsin of the gastric juice now proceeds.

Pepsin, which acts only in weak acid solutions, converts the very complex proteins into soluble and more simple, though still complex, products known as proteoses and peptones.

Rennin, another enzyme of the gastric juice, changes milk into a solid curd. Were it not for this, milk would pass too quickly into the small intestine, before its proteins had been acted upon by pepsin. Rennin may not be present in the gastric juice of mature animals that are not being fed milk or milk by-products. Traces of other enzymes, including a fat-digesting enzyme, are secreted by the stomach in the case of certain animals.

As the gastric juice penetrates the mass of food, it slowly softens, digests, and liquefies the outside portions. Contractions of the stomach walls start at the middle portion and pass in waves, following one another, toward the rear end. These squeeze off some of the softened parts of the mass, thoroughly mix it with the gastric juice, and carry it toward the rear.

At first, when a wave of contraction reaches the end of the stomach, the pylorus, the ring of muscles which keeps the stomach shut off from the small intestine, does not open. Therefore, the wave of contraction is reflected back toward the first part of the stomach, mixing the contents more thoroughly. When digestion has progressed sufficiently, every time a wave of contraction reaches the pylorus, the latter relaxes and allows a small quantity of the semi-fluid contents to spurt through into the small intestine. After this the pylorus closes, and the process is many times repeated, growing more vigorous as the acidity of the partly-digested food increases.

If too large a mass of solid food is carried along to the pylorus, it closes and does not let it pass. By these processes the contents of the stomach are gradually converted into a semi-liquid and liquid mixture, and forced out into the small intestine. In the case of herbivora, the stomach does not completely empty itself between meals.

In addition to making the stomach contents acid so that pepsin can act, the hydrochloric acid has another exceedingly important function in killing most of the bacteria present in the food. On account of the acidity of the contents of the latter part of the stomach, not only is bacterial action checked, but hosts of bacteria are actually killed. This aids in preventing undesirable putrefactions and fermentations which would otherwise occur.

52. Stomach digestion of ruminants.—Though the first three compartments of the stomachs of ruminants secrete no enzymes, but only water, they are highly important in digestion. The nutrients of plants are enclosed within the cellulose cell walls, and where these are hard and thick, as in hay and straw, the digestive fluids can not easily reach and attack the nutrients locked within. As we have seen, when ruminants swallow solid food, it passes chiefly into the paunch. Here it is softened by the moisture and slowly but thoroughly mixed and kneaded by muscular contractions. All this prepares the food for easy digestion further on.

A considerable amount of actual digestion also occurs in these compartments, especially in the paunch, through the action of certain bacteria. These attack the cellulose and pentosans of the feed and break them down into organic acids, chiefly acetic acid and butyric acid, and possibly into glucose and other sugars. In this bacterial action gases are produced, chiefly carbon dioxide and methane, and considerable heat is generated. The acids serve as food, the same as do the sugars, but the gases are useless and are excreted. The heat may serve a useful purpose under certain conditions, in keeping the body warm.

This digestive action is highly important, for a large part of hay and other roughages consists of cellulose and pentosans, and Nature has provided no enzymes of the digestive tract which are able to digest these compounds. The ability of the animal to use them as food therefore depends on the fermentations caused by these bacteria. In this action the cell walls of the plant materials are broken down, setting free the nutrients contained within, so they can be more easily acted on by the digestive juices in the true stomach and in the intestines.

53. The small intestine.—When received into the small intestine, the partially-digested food is a semi-liquid mass. As yet, the fats have not been digested appreciably, and the digestion of the proteins and carbohydrates is far from complete. Here the work of digestion proceeds even more vigorously than in the stomach, all classes of nutrients being attacked. The small intestine receives near its upper part digestive fluids from two outside organs, the liver and the pancreas, and another digestive juice is secreted by the wall of the intestine itself.

The partly-digested food entering from the stomach is gradually changed from an acid to an alkaline or neutral character by action of the pancreatic juice, the intestinal juice, and the bile, which are alkaline. The action of pepsin continues until the contents become sufficiently alkaline to check it.

The contents of the intestine are mixed and gradually moved along by various contractions of the walls.

54. The pancreatic juice.—The *pancreatic juice* is produced by the pancreas, or sweetbread, a slender gland lying just beyond the stomach and connected with the small intestine by a duct or by two ducts in certain animals, as the horse. Its chief enzymes are trypsin, amylase, and lipase.

Trypsin, like pepsin, changes protein into proteoses and peptones, but is also able to split some of these partially-digested substances into amino acids. The digestion of protein brought about by trypsin in the small intestine is thus much more complete than that occurring in the stomach through the action of pepsin. It is interesting that trypsin is secreted by the pancreas in an inactive form, which will not digest protein until it is activated by a substance contained in the intestinal juice.

Amylase changes starch into malt sugar.

Lipase splits fats into fatty acids and glycerin. The action of lipase is greatly increased by certain compounds in the bile, which aid in emulsifying the fat, or breaking it up into very small droplets, and also in dissolving the products of fat digestion. The fatty acids unite with the alkalies of the digestive fluids in the intestine to form soaps, and they are largely absorbed from the intestine in this form. Some of the fatty acids may be dissolved by the action of the bile, and the fatty acids and glycerin absorbed as such.

Ordinarily, when digestion is not going on in the small intestine, there is no secretion by the pancreas. However, the secretion of this digestive fluid begins promptly after the partially-digested food enters the small intestine from the stomach. It has been found that this is due to a substance called "secretin," which is produced or liberated in the lining of the small intestine when the acid, partially-digested food mixture comes in contact with it. The secretin is absorbed into the blood and is carried to the pancreas, and at once the pancreatic juice is poured forth just when needed. Secretin is one of the hormones, or chemical messengers, of the body, which aid in controlling its activities in a marvelous manner.

55. The liver.—The liver, which is the largest gland in the body, has several important functions in addition to the secretion of bile. As has previously been explained, it regulates the glucose content of the blood through the formation of glycogen and its change back into glucose, as needed by the body. It splits off nitrogen in the form of ammonia from waste amino acids and converts it into urea and other excretory products. It protects the body against various poisonous substances, formed in the digestive tract through putrefaction, by changing them into non-poisonous compounds. In addition, the liver is an important agent in the destruction of worn-out red blood cells and in the use of fat for fuel in the body.

Bile is a greenish or golden-colored fluid, extremely bitter in taste, and usually alkaline. In cattle, sheep, and swine the bile, as secreted, is stored in the gall bladder, whence it is poured through a duct into the intestine. The horse has no gall bladder, the bile passing directly into the intestine as it is secreted.

Bile contains no significant amounts of enzymes, but is nevertheless exceedingly important in the digestion of fat, as has been pointed out before. After performing its functions, the bile is not wholly excreted in the feces, but is in part taken up by the circulation and utilized again.

In addition to its action on fats, bile stimulates the action of the pancreatic and intestinal juices. It aids in the passage of food through the intestine by increasing the muscular contractions of the walls, and it also checks putrefaction. Furthermore, waste products which would be harmful if retained in the body, are excreted in the bile.

56. The intestinal secretion.—The intestinal secretion, which is produced by the small glands in the lining of the small intestine, contains several enzymes, the most important of which are erepsin and the invertases.

Erepsin, an enzyme of great digestive power, attacks the proteoses and peptones which have escaped the action of trypsin and breaks them up into amino acids. It can not act on protein that has not already been split into proteoses and peptones.

The *invertases* (sucrase, maltase, and lactase) change cane sugar, malt sugar, and milk sugar into the simple glucose-like sugars.

Through various contractions and movements of the small intestine, the contents are thoroughly mixed with the digestive juices, and the digestion is therefore very complete. Most of the digested nutrients are absorbed from the small intestine before reaching the large intestine. For example, in humans it is estimated that at least three-fourths of the food nutrients and a similar proportion of the water are absorbed before reaching the large intestine.

Movements of the villi aid greatly in the process of absorption. By means of muscular fibers in the walls of each villus, it is able to expand and contract, thus taking up nutrients like a sponge. The villi also have a lashing movement, which aids in mixing the intestinal contents.

57. The large intestine.—From the small intestine the undigested matter passes into the large intestine. Little, if any, digestive fluid is produced here, but a small amount of digestion may go on, owing to the digestive enzymes which are carried in from the small intestine and to the action of bacteria. The absorption of digested nutrients is completed in the large intestine.

As stated previously, most of the bacteria in the food are killed in the stomach by the acid of the gastric juice. Therefore, under normal conditions there is little bacterial action in the true stomach and in the small intestine. In the large intestine, where the contents remain longer, the bacteria which are still alive multiply tremendously in number, especially certain forms which thrive in the absence of air. Normally, this bacterial action is not harmful, unless the animal becomes constipated and the food residues remain unduly long in the large intestine. Substances which are injurious may then be formed, chiefly through putrefaction of proteins.

Some action by bacteria on the cellulose and pentosans of the food occurs in the large intestine, similar to that which takes place in the paunch of ruminants.

58. Special provision for the horse.—The horse, though eating much roughage like the cow, has a small stomach and no paunch for specially preparing such food for digestion. In partial compensation, the cæcum and colon of the large intestine are greatly enlarged, as has been previously pointed out.

The incompletely-digested matter from the small intestine, together with the enzymes mixed with it, pass into the cæcum and colon. Here the enzyme action continues, and the cellulose and pentosans of the feed are also attacked and digested by bacteria, as in the paunch of ruminants. Due to this, the horse is able to digest such feeds as hay and straw fairly well, though less completely than do cattle and sheep. The cæcum of other farm animals is relatively small and unimportant in digestion.

II. Use of Nutrients in the Body

59. Metabolism, or use of nutrients.—Chemists and physiologists have, through painstaking research, been able to gain much information on the various steps in the digestion of food. When the nutrients leave the digestive tract and enter the body, the difficulties of learning what becomes of them are much greater. Though many of the changes that occur in the body have been revealed, only a little of a definite nature is yet known concerning other processes.

All the changes which take place in the food nutrients after they are absorbed from the digestive tract, are included under the term *metabolism*. These changes include not only the building-up processes in which the absorbed nutrients are used in the formation or repair of body tissues, but also the breaking-down processes in which nutrients are oxidized for the production of heat and work.

60. Distribution of absorbed nutrients.—We have seen that the sugars, the amino acids, and the soluble mineral nutrients, resulting from the digestion of the food, are absorbed by the capillaries in the mucous membrane lining the intestines, and thus enter the blood stream. These nutrients are first carried in the portal vein to the liver and then to the heart, from whence they are transported to all parts of the body. Most of the digested fat passes first into the lymphatics and then into the blood, though some may go at once into the capillaries in the villi of the small intestine.

The blood, containing the absorbed nutrients, finally reaches the capillaries which permeate all the body tissues. The capillaries are so constructed that the nutrients in the blood can go through their walls into the lymph that surrounds the body cells. The nutrients then pass into the cells, thus providing nourishment and energy for the various life processes.

61. Functions of the various nutrients.—The nutrients thus brought to all the tissues of the body may be used for several purposes. First come the maintenance needs for the preservation of life. These are discussed in detail in Chapter V. To maintain the body, the daily breakdown of the protein tissues must be replaced by the amino acids resulting from the digestion of the protein of the food. Also, some of the nutrients must be oxidized to provide heat for maintaining the body temperature and to furnish energy for the various necessary movements of the body.

In case more nutrients are supplied than are needed for mere maintenance, the excess nutrients can be transformed into new body tissue, as in growing or fattening animals; they can be changed into milk, as in the case of dairy cows; or they can be used for the production of work, as in the case of work horses and mules. The uses of the nutrients for these purposes are discussed in detail in Chapters VII and VIII.

The sugars serve as sources of heat and muscular energy and also as the chief source of the milk sugar in milk. They can also be transformed into body fat. The fats, like the sugars, can furnish heat and energy, and they can possibly also be changed indirectly to glucose, if necessary.

If there is a greater supply of amino acids than is needed for body repair or the building of new protein tissues, the excess is deaminized in the liver. In this process the nitrogen (in the form of ammonia) is split off from the amino acid molecules and converted, in the case of mammals, chiefly into urea. This and similar nitrogenous waste products are then excreted by the kidneys into the urine. The nitrogen is therefore entirely wasted in this process. The non-nitrogenous parts of the amino acids that remain can, however, be used in the body for the same purposes as the sugars; i.e., for the production of heat and energy, or even for the formation of body fat.

Even when the supply of protein in the food is scanty, a considerable wastage of protein unavoidably occurs for some unknown reason, through the deaminization of amino acids in the liver. Therefore, as is explained in Chapter V, more protein must be supplied in maintenance rations than is theoretically needed to replace the daily breakdown of the protein tissues of the body.

It has been previously pointed out that most of the changes in the digestion of food are brought about by enzymes. It is now believed that most other body processes, both the building-up processes and the tearing-down processes, are likewise brought about through enzyme action.

62. Oxidation of nutrients in the body.—Nutrients are constantly being oxidized in the body tissues to provide the energy for all muscular movements and also to furnish heat for maintaining the body tempera-

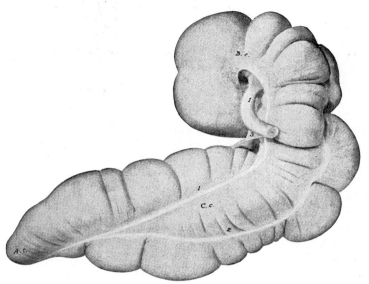

CAECUM OF HORSE

The entrance of the small intestine is designated (I). The opening of the cæcum into the large intestine is hidden from view. (From Sisson, "Anatomy of the Domestic Animals.")

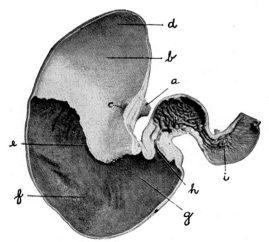

LONGITUDINAL SECTION OF STOMACH OF THE HORSE

A, Œsophagus, or gullet; b, œsophageal region of stomach, in which no gastric juice is secreted; c, entrance of gullet; d, left extremity of stomach; e, boundary between œsophageal region and portion of stomach secreting gastric juice; f, g, fundus gland region and pyloric gland region, in which gastric juice is secreted; h, pylorus, or ring of muscles closing the stomach; i, entrance of pancreatic and bile ducts. (From Sisson, "Anatomy of the Domestic Animals.")

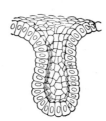

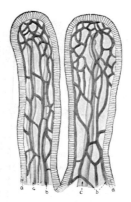

LEFT AND CENTER—THE PRINCIPLE OF THE STRUCTURE OF GLANDS

Left.—A vertical section of a simple microscopic gland. The cells are seen to surround a recess, into which they discharge their secretion.

Center.—The same structure with the encircling blood-vessels. (From Stiles, "Nutritional Physiology.")

RIGHT—VILLI OF THE SMALL INTESTINE

A, lining cells of intestine; b, net work of capillaries; c, lacteals.

For the sake of simplicity the muscle fibers in the villi are not shown in this diagram. (After Cadiat.)

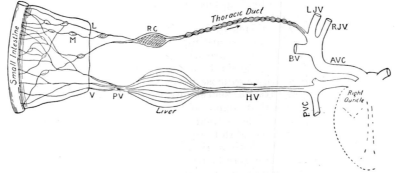

DIAGRAMMATIC REPRESENTATION OF THE TWO PATHS OF ABSORPTION

V, Veins from the small intestine, which unite to form the portal vein, P. V.; H. V., hepatic vein, passing from the liver to the posterior vena cava, P. V. C.; L, lacteals, which join and drain into the mesenteric lymph glands, M, and then pass to the lymph receptacle (receptaculum chyli), R. C.; L. J. V., left jugular vein; R. J. V., right jugular vein; B. V., brachial vein; A. V. C., anterior vena cava. (From Hadley, "Principles of Veterinary Science.")

ture.   These oxidations are produced in the tissues in the following manner:

In the lungs the blood is brought into close contact, inside the thin-walled capillaries, with oxygen in the air that is breathed into the lungs. The oxygen is absorbed by the hemoglobin in the red blood cells, and is held in loose combination.   The blood, transporting this oxygen, then passes back to the heart and is carried by the arteries to all the tissues of the body.   As the oxygen-laden blood permeates the capillaries, it gives up oxygen to the body cells.

Many investigations have been conducted by physiologists to determine, if possible, the exact changes that occur in the oxidation of the various nutrients in the body.   Considerable interesting information has been gained, and various theories have been advanced concerning the steps that occur.   For a discussion of these theories the reader is referred to texts on physiology or biochemistry.

For our purposes it is sufficient to state that by intricate processes the carbohydrates, fats, and other nutrients can be oxidized in the tissues to produce energy and heat.   In these changes the carbohydrates and fats are eventually oxidized completely to carbon dioxide and water. The carbon dioxide is absorbed by the blood and carried in the veins to the heart, and thence to the lungs.   Here it passes off into the air in the lungs and is exhaled, the blood then becoming again charged with oxygen, before it flows back to the various parts of the body.

The discovery made in 1921 that insulin, a hormone produced by the pancreas, is necessary for the oxidation of glucose in the body, has been of untold benefit to humans suffering from diabetes.   Without an adequate supply of insulin, which is carried from the pancreas to all parts of the body in the blood, glucose can not be utilized, but is excreted unchanged in the urine.

In diabetes there is a lack of insulin, and hence the body is unable to utilize carbohydrates, with resulting serious consequences.   By means of hypodermic injections of a carefully purified and standardized solution of insulin, relief is brought to a patient affected with the disease, for the body can then utilize glucose normally.

63. Hormones, or internal secretions.—Physiologists have found by extensive investigations that many of the body processes are controlled and regulated by substances called *hormones,* or *internal secretions.* These are produced by the glands of internal secretion, also called the endocrine glands, or the ductless glands.

The secretions of these glands are discharged directly into the blood, or indirectly into the blood by way of the lymph, and are not poured out through a duct, as in the case of the bile and the pancreatic juice. This is the reason why they are referred to as the ductless glands.   The hormones are carried in the blood to the parts of the body where they perform their functions.

The effect of *insulin,* a hormone produced by the pancreas, has been mentioned in the previous paragraphs.   A hormone, called *secretin,* which is produced by the lining of the small intestine, is important in the digestion of food.   As soon as the acid, partly-digested food passes from the stomach into the small intestine, the acidity causes the mucous membrane of the small intestine to form secretin.   This is absorbed by the blood and carried to the pancreas, where it causes this gland to pour out the pancreatic juice just when it is needed.

Among the other important glands of internal secretion are the thyroid gland, the parathyroid glands, the pituitary body, the adrenal glands, and the sex glands. All of these perform essential functions.

The *thyroid gland,* located in the neck, produces *thyroxine,* a hormone that regulates the rate of body metabolism. This hormone has been separated in pure form and found to be an iodine-containing amino acid. As is pointed out in Chapter VI, when there is insufficient iodine in the food, the gland enlarges in a desperate effort to manufacture enough thyroxine, and the disease called goiter results.

The *parathyroid glands* are very small glands, usually located close to the thyroid gland or imbedded in it. They secrete a hormone called *parathormone,* which regulates the calcium metabolism of the body and controls the concentration of this mineral in the blood. If for any reason the calcium content of the blood is too low, convulsions or paralysis may be caused, as in milk fever of dairy cows.

The *pituitary body,* or hypophysis, a small gland at the base of the brain, has several essential functions. A hormone produced by the anterior, or forward, part of the gland controls the growth and development of animals and therefore determines the mature body size. If the gland is too active, the body may be of giant size, and on the other hand an insufficiency of the hormone will dwarf the size.

As is explained in Chapter VIII, this part of the gland also produces a hormone that is necessary to start milk secretion in the female. It is also believed to be concerned with the activity of the thyroid gland. The posterior, or rear, portion of the gland secretes a hormone that stimulates the contraction of the smooth, or involuntary, muscles.

The *adrenal glands,* or suprarenals, which are small glands located on top of the kidneys, produce two hormones. One of these, called adrenalin, helps to keep the glucose content of the blood constant by regulating the rate at which glycogen is changed into glucose. It likewise aids in controlling blood pressure. The other is in some manner essential for life.

The *sex glands* secrete hormones that have important functions. Thus, as is explained in Chapter VIII, hormones produced by the ovaries are necessary for the growth and development of the mammary glands and for the secretion of milk.

64. Disposal of body waste.—It has been pointed out previously that the undigested portions of the food are voided as feces, along with the residues from the digestive juices, worn-out cells from the mucous membrane lining the digestive tract, bile salts and other excretory products, and bacteria.

Nearly all of the nitrogenous waste, representing the breaking-down of protein material in the body, is excreted in the urine through the kidneys, though a trace is given off in the sweat and a more appreciable amount in the feces. In mammals this waste chiefly takes the form of urea.

A great variety of other end-products of metabolism are likewise eliminated by the kidneys through the urine. Most of the mineral matter, such as common salt, is excreted in large part or principally in the urine.

However, calcium, magnesium, iron, and phosphorus are voided chiefly in the feces. Small amounts of most of the substances eliminated in the urine are also excreted by the skin through the sweat glands.

A large amount of carbon dioxide is formed in the oxidation of the nutrients within the body for the production of heat and energy. Most of this passes into the capillaries and is carried in the blood by the veins to the lungs, where it is eliminated in breathing. A portion, however, escapes by way of the skin. Some of the methane produced by fermentations in the stomach of herbivora is absorbed into the blood and thrown out by the lungs.

65. Importance of quiet, kindness, and regularity.—Farm animals are creatures of habit, and when once accustomed to a routine of living, show unrest at any decided change. The stable or feed lot should therefore be free from disturbance, and the administration of feed and water should be uniform in time and manner. The system of feeding and watering and the character of the rations should be changed gradually and only for good cause.

Animals know when meal time has come and fret if feeding is delayed. Investigations with humans have shown that worry and excitement cause a definite decrease in the completeness with which foods are digested. It is reasonable to believe that the same is true in the case of farm animals. In any event, there is no question but that unusual disturbance and excitement may markedly reduce the gains of fattening animals, especially sheep, and cut down the milk production of dairy cows.

66. Importance of palatability.—In closing this discussion of the digestion and use of food, it is well to emphasize the importance of palatability in animal nutrition and stock feeding. It is a matter of common knowledge that the mere sight or smell of appetizing foods may start the flow of saliva in our mouths. At least in the case of some animals, such a stimulus also causes a flow of gastric juice. Though it is a disputed question, it seems possible that well-liked feeds are digested somewhat better than others which may be equally nutritious but less palatable.

From an entirely different standpoint, however, palatability of feeds is of great importance in feeding animals for large production. Unless the ration is palatable, dairy cows, fattening cattle or sheep, and growing and fattening pigs will not consume sufficient feed to permit them to produce milk or meat efficiently. Therefore, feeds which are unpalatable should be used chiefly for stock not being fed for production. For example, idle horses can be wintered largely on straw or hay of rather inferior quality. Often by mixing a limited amount of an unpalatable feed with some well-liked ingredient stock may be induced to eat the entire mixture readily.

Sometimes the failure of animals to continue to eat a normal amount of feed may indicate a serious nutritive deficiency. For example, if thrifty pigs are fed a ration made up of palatable feeds, but which is deficient in vitamin A or in certain minerals, they may eat normal amounts of food for a time and make satisfactory gains. Then, when the body reserves of the particular nutrient are exhausted, they will usually consume much less feed, due to an impairment of their health and a consequent lack of appetite. Provided that the deficiency is not continued so long that the pigs are injured permanently, they will usually recover their appetites, if some feed is added which supplies the nutritive lack and makes the ration complete.

Familiarity and habit are important factors concerned with the palatability of feeds. Not infrequently, when corn silage is first placed before cows, after sniffing it they will let it alone for a time. They then usually begin nibbling at it, and later eat it with great relish. In such cases, food that at first seems unpalatable finally becomes palatable. Sometimes animals which are used to yellow corn will at first refuse white corn, or vice versa. If they are used to whole grain, it may take them a little time to become accustomed to ground grain.

Usually feeds that are palatable are safe and nutritious. However, in rare instances this may not be true. For example, sorghum which has been stunted by drought may contain sufficient prussic acid to kill stock in a few minutes, and yet it will be palatable and will be consumed with eagerness. As a rule, however, stock generally avoid poisonous plants instinctively and eat them only when impelled by hunger.

QUESTIONS

1. Define *digestion*. State the nature of the general mechanical and chemical changes produced in food during digestion.
2. Define *enzymes*. Describe a typical enzyme action.
3. Describe the digestive tract of cattle and compare it with that of pigs and of horses.
4. State the essential facts concerning the circulation of the blood; of the lymph.
5. Describe the villi of the small intestine. What is their function in digestion?
6. Of what importance is thorough mastication of the food?
7. Describe briefly the process of rumination.
8. Describe the digestion and absorption of carbohydrates in non-ruminants. State the enzymes or agents concerned, the place where digestion takes place, the substances acted on, and the products formed.
9. Discuss the formation and function of glycogen.
10. Describe the digestion of cellulose and pentosans by ruminants and by horses. Follow the same outline as for carbohydrates, above.
11. Describe the digestion and absorption of protein, following the same outline.
12. Describe the digestion and absorption of fats, following the same outline.
13. What can be said concerning the digestion of minerals?
14. Describe the disposal of undigested food.
15. Define *metabolism*.
16. How are the absorbed nutrients distributed to the body tissues?
17. What functions are performed by the absorbed sugars; the fats; the amino acids?
18. Describe the oxidation of nutrients in the body.
19. What functions are performed by each of the following hormones: insulin; secretin; thyroxine; parathormone; the secretions of the pituitary body; the secretions of the adrenal glands?
20. Describe the disposal of the various waste products from the body.
21. Discuss the importance of quiet, kindness, and regularity in stock feeding.
22. Of what importance is the palatability of feeds?

REFERENCES

1. Sherman, Chemistry of Food and Nutrition, 4th ed., p. 86.
2. Fuller, N. H., Tech. Bul. 35.
3. Bergman and Dukes, Jour. Amer. Vet. Med. Assoc., 69, 1926, p. 600; Dukes, The Physiology of the Domestic Animals, 3rd ed., pp. 264-270.
4. Schalk and Amidon, N. D. Bul. 216; Nevens, Jour. Agr. Res., 36, 1928, pp. 777-794.

CHAPTER III

MEASURING THE USEFULNESS OF FEEDS

I. Determining the Relative Values of Feeds

67. Methods of measuring the values of feeds.—In the computation of balanced rations for livestock, it is necessary to know the amounts of nutrients furnished by each of the available feeds. Also, in order to plan an efficient cropping system on a stock farm, one must have accurate data concerning the actual feeding value of the various crops that can be grown.

The simplest method of measuring the usefulness of any feed is to determine the amounts of digestible nutrients it supplies. This method is therefore discussed first in this chapter. A method that is theoretically more accurate, but which is much more complicated and expensive, is to determine the amount of net energy furnished by the feed. The energy values are discussed later in the chapter.

68. Determining nutritive values by feeding experiments.—Neither of these chemical methods, however, can take into consideration all the factors which determine the true value of any feed for a particular class of livestock. The only way in which this can be done is to conduct actual feeding experiments under practical conditions with that class of animals. In such investigations the relative value of the feed in question can be determined, in comparison with that of a standard feeding stuff.

To warrant definite conclusions, such experiments must be carefully planned and they must be conducted under controlled conditions and for a considerable period. Also, the trials must be repeated several times, because individual animals differ in their productive capacities and various lots of any feed may also differ in composition, as is emphasized in Chapter IV.

The animal husbandry investigators in the American experiment stations have fully appreciated the importance of such experiments. Therefore many hundreds of feeding trials have been carried on to determine the values of the various feeds and of specific rations for the different classes of stock.

In the preparation of this volume, much time has been spent in compiling and studying the results of these investigations. This has been done in order to present accurate data concerning the actual nutritive worth, and therefore the real money value, of the many feeds which are available on our farms. A detailed study of all the data concerning each feed is necessary for safe conclusions, because the results of any one experiment may not provide a correct measure of the value of the ration or feed in question.

69. Value of a feed for various animals may differ.—It is of great financial importance to stock farmers to have definite information readily available concerning the real value of the many important feeds for each class of animals. Therefore considerable space is devoted to such data in the chapters of Part II and especially in Part III of this volume.

In order to use the different feeds efficiently, one must have full knowledge about their particular merits and also concerning any deficiencies. Many feeds have a very high value when fed in rations that are complete in all the nutritive essentials, but their value is exceedingly low when they are improperly used. For example, corn grain is one of the best stock feeds, if it is combined with others that correct its deficiencies in protein, minerals, and vitamins. However, it is of low value when fed with no regard for these lacks.

Particular attention is therefore given in the later chapters to the individual characteristics of feeds that must be considered in order to use them effectively. Especial emphasis is placed on their content of vitamins and minerals and also on the quality of the protein that they provide. These factors may often be fully as important in stock feeding as the amounts of digestible nutrients or of energy that are supplied.

The information presented later concerning the usefulness and value of the different feeding stuffs shows clearly that the actual worth of a particular feed for two classes of stock may differ widely. For example, a ton of good corn silage is worth about 33 to 40 per cent as much as a ton of legume or mixed hay for dairy cows. Numerous experiments have shown definitely that for fattening cattle and lambs silage has an even higher value, being worth fully one-half as much per ton as good hay.

Similarly, the relative value of barley, in comparison with that of corn, differs for the various classes of stock. For dairy cows ground barley is about equal to ground corn, pound for pound, but for fattening lambs and for swine its relative value is appreciably lower. Also, barley injured by the scab disease is satisfactory for cattle and sheep, but it is unsuited to horses and pigs.

Another interesting example is the fact that cottonseed meal can safely be fed to cattle in large amounts, if plenty of vitamins and minerals are provided. On the other hand, pigs should be fed only limited amounts of cottonseed meal, or disastrous results may follow. Again, uncooked field beans give satisfactory results when forming not too large a part of the ration for dairy cows and fattening lambs, but pigs do poorly on beans unless they are cooked.

These are but a few examples of the manner in which the usefulness or value of a feed may be decidedly unlike for the several classes of stock. Such differences are not shown at all by determinations of the amounts of digestible nutrients or of the energy value of the feed. They can only be revealed by actual experiments with the particular kind of animal in question.

II. Digestible Nutrients in Feeds

70. A digestion experiment.—The digestibility of a particular feed for any class of stock is determined by means of digestion experiments with that kind of animal. The chemist first determines by analysis the percentage of each nutrient the feed contains. The animal is then fed weighed quantities of the feed for a preliminary period of a few days, in order that all residues of former food may pass from the alimentary tract.

During the digestion experiment the same amounts each day of the feed are then given to the animal and the feces voided are collected and weighed, and samples are analyzed. The difference between the amount of each nutrient fed and that found in the feces resulting therefrom represents the digested portion.

To show the manner in which the digestibility of a feed is determined, let us suppose that during a 10-day trial a cow was fed 20 lbs. of clover hay each day, containing the amounts of nutrients shown in the table. During this time she excreted, on the average, 47.3 lbs. of feces, containing the amounts of undigested protein, fiber, fat, and nitrogen-free extract shown in the table:

Digestion trial with cow fed clover hay; average for 1 day

	Protein	Fat	Fiber	N-free extract
Fed 20 lbs. hay, containing, lbs...............	2.6	0.62	5.1	7.7
Excreted 47.3 lbs. feces, containing, lbs.........	1.1	0.28	2.4	2.6
Digested, lbs.	1.5	0.34	2.7	5.1
Per cent digested.............................	57.7	54.8	52.9	66.2

Subtracting the amounts of the different nutrients in the feces from the amounts in the feed, we find the amounts digested. From this we compute the percentage of each which is digested. For example, there were 2.6 lbs. of protein in the 20 lbs. of hay the cow ate each day. Of this, 1.1 lbs. were excreted in the feces, leaving 1.5 lbs., or 57.7 per cent, as the part digested.

71. Determining digestibility by difference.—Some feeds cannot be fed alone, as was done in this trial. For instance, horses and ruminants are not fed concentrates alone, without hay or other roughage. Again, while pigs may be fed on grain only, such feeds as tankage and linseed meal are too rich in protein to be used thus. The digestibility of such feeds must therefore be found by difference, instead of directly.

For example, in an experiment to determine the digestibility of oats for horses, the horse is first fed hay for several days, and the digestibility of the hay found. Then oats are added to the ration, and the total amounts of nutrients are determined that are digested from the combination of oats and hay. The amounts of digestible nutrients coming from the hay are then subtracted from the total, leaving the amounts which are assumed to be digested from the oats.

72. Digestion coefficients.—The average percentage of each nutrient digested in a feeding stuff is termed the *digestion coefficient* (also called the *coefficient of digestibility*) for that nutrient in the feed.

As has been explained in the previous chapter, due to the fact that cattle and sheep are ruminants, they digest feeds high in fiber more completely than do horses and swine. In spite of this difference, the digestion coefficients obtained with ruminants are commonly used also in computing rations for horses and swine, because but few digestion trials have been carried on with the latter animals. However, no error of consequence is involved in this, for the recommendations in modern feeding standards are designed to meet these conditions.

Individual animals of the same species vary somewhat in their ability to digest any given feed. For this reason, it is essential, when computing the digestible nutrients in feeds as a basis for balancing rations for livestock, to use average digestion coefficients which are based on all representative digestion trials that have been conducted. The author has therefore compiled and averaged the coefficients for the various feeding stuffs, as determined in the many trials by the experiment stations. These average coefficients of digestibility are presented on the right-hand pages of Appendix Table I. In the case of feeds for which American data are not available, coefficients from European sources have been included.

An inspection of the digestion coefficients in this table will show that feeds which contain but little fiber, such as corn and wheat, are highly digestible, because the cell walls are thin and easily penetrated by the digestive juices. The higher the fiber content of feeds, the thicker and more resistant are the cell walls, and consequently the less digestible are the feeds, as a rule. Thus, oats and wheat bran are less digestible than corn or wheat, and the roughages, such as hay and straw, have still lower digestion coefficients.

In general, the nitrogen-free extract of feeds is slightly more digestible than the protein or the fat, and much more digestible than the fiber. It has been pointed out in Chapter I that the nitrogen-free extract in cereal grains and most other seeds is nearly all starch, which is readily digested. As a result, 80 to 90 per cent or even more of the nitrogen-free extract of such feeds is digested. On the other hand, much of the nitrogen-free extract of roughages consists of pentosans and hemicelluloses, which are less digestible. Therefore only 50 to 60 per cent of the nitrogen-free extract of certain hays is digested and even less in the case of such feeds as wheat or rye straw.[1]

73. Digestible protein; total digestible nutrients.—To find the percentages of digestible nutrients in any feeding stuff, the percentage of each nutrient is multiplied by the digestion coefficient for that nutrient. For example, dent corn contains 9.7 per cent of protein (See Appendix Table I), of which 76 per cent is digestible. Therefore the percentage of digestible protein in corn is 7.4. In this manner the data have been computed which are given in the second and third columns of figures in Appendix Table I.

Since protein has special functions in the body which can be performed by none of the other nutrients, the percentages of *digestible protein* are shown separately in the second column. Next are given the percentages of *total digestible nutrients* in the various feeds.

The *total digestible nutrients* include all the digestible organic nutrients—protein, fiber, nitrogen-free extract, and fat (the latter being multiplied by 2.25, because its energy value for animals is approximately 2.25 times that of protein or carbohydrates). The abbreviation T.D.N. is often used for *total digestible nutrients*.

The percentages of total digestible nutrients therefore represent the approximate heat or energy value of the feed. The digestible protein is included in this total, since protein serves as a source of heat and energy when more is provided than is required to meet the protein needs of the body.

In former editions of this book, the digestible carbohydrates and the digestible fat were given separately, but there is no longer necessity for these additional figures.   The old Wolff-Lehmann feeding standards, once widely used as guides in computing rations for livestock, were based on the amounts of digestible protein, digestible carbohydrates, and digestible fat in feeds.   In the Morrison feeding standards and the other modern feeding standards based on digestible nutrients, the recommendations are stated more simply in terms of dry matter, digestible protein, and total digestible nutrients.   Therefore the amounts of digestible carbohydrates and of digestible fat are necessary only in computing the amounts of total digestible nutrients, as has been done in this table.

An inspection of Appendix Table I will show the wide differences there are in the amounts of digestible protein and of total digestible nutrients in the various feeds.   The cereal grains and other seeds and also the by-products low in fiber are rich in total digestible nutrients. The roughages have much smaller amounts of total digestible nutrients than the grains and other concentrates, the straws being especially low.

A few feeds, such as flaxseed, which are unusually rich in fat, supply more than 100 lbs. of total digestible nutrients per 100 lbs. of the feed. This is due to the fact that the digestible fat is multiplied by 2.25 when it is included in the sum, "total digestible nutrients."   The high figure of 108.7 per cent total digestible nutrients for flaxseed means that 100 lbs. of flaxseed furnishes as much heat or energy as would be supplied by 108.7 lbs. of digestible starch.

74. Nutritive ratio.—As protein serves special uses in the body, in discussions of feeding stuffs and rations the term *nutritive ratio* is employed to show the proportion of digestible protein.

By *nutritive ratio* is meant the ratio, or proportion, between the digestible protein and the digestible non-nitrogenous nutrients (including fat multiplied by 2.25).

When the percentage of total digestible nutrients is given, as in Appendix Table I, the nutritive ratio is computed as follows: The percentage of *digestible protein* is subtracted from the percentage of *total digestible nutrients* to obtain the percentage of digestible *non-nitrogenous nutrients*. This remainder is divided by the *digestible protein*, the quotient being the second term of the ratio.

The manner of computing the nutritive ratio of dent corn is as follows:

Total dig. nutrients Per cent		Dig. protein Per cent		Dig. non-nitrogenous nutrients Per cent
83.7	—	7.4	=	76.3

Dig. non-nitrogenous nutrients Per cent		Dig. protein Per cent		Second factor of nutritive ratio
76.3	÷	7.4	=	10.3

Nutritive ratios are expressed with the colon, thus, 1:10.3.   The nutritive ratio of dent corn is therefore 1:10.3 (read as 1 to 10.3).   This means that for each pound of digestible protein in corn there are 10.3 lbs. of digestible non-nitrogenous nutrients, including fat multiplied by 2.25.

A feed or ration having much crude protein in proportion to non-nitrogenous nutrients is said to have a *narrow nutritive ratio;* if the reverse, it has a *wide nutritive ratio*. Oat straw has the very wide nutritive ratio of 1 :48.0, because of its low content of digestible protein compared with the carbohydrates and fat. Oat grain has the medium one of 1 :6.6, and protein-rich linseed meal the very narrow ratio of 1 :1.6, the digestible non-nitrogenous nutrients being less than twice the crude protein.

Another method of computing the nutritive ratio, which is even simpler than the preceding, is as follows: Divide the percentage of *total digestible nutrients* by the percentage of *digestible protein,* and subtract 1.0 from the quotient. The result will be the second term of the nutritive ratio. For example, the nutritive ratio of dent corn is found as follows:

Total dig. nutrients Per cent		Dig. protein Per cent		
83.7	÷	7.4	=	11.3

				Second factor of nutritive ratio
11.3	—	1.0	=	10.3

75. Limitations of digestion trials.—The data secured in digestion trials provide the general basis for our knowledge concerning the amounts of digestible nutrients furnished by the many different feeding stuffs. Such data are therefore highly important in the science of stock feeding.

Even the net energy values of feeds, which are discussed later in this chapter, are usually computed from tables of digestible nutrients, such as Appendix Table I of this volume, by applying certain factors to the values for digestible nutrients. However, in studying tables of digestion coefficients and digestible nutrients it is well to bear in mind the following facts concerning the limitations in securing data of this sort:

In digestion trials it is commonly assumed that all matter appearing in the feces represents the part of the food which is actually indigestible. This is only approximately correct, for the feces always contain in addition some waste from the body itself, such as unabsorbed residues from the bile and other digestive juices, worn-out cells and mucus from the membranes lining the digestive tract, and waste mineral matter. The feces also include innumerable living and dead bacteria.

In herbivora, such as cattle and horses, which eat much roughage, these products form but a small part of the feces, while in carnivora, such as dogs, they form a considerable portion. All these constituents of the feces are waste products. Therefore, although they do not represent undigested food, it is entirely correct from a practical standpoint to deduct them, along with the food that is actually undigested, in determining the digestible nutrients which are of use to an animal. These intestinal waste products which are excreted in the feces are a part of the cost of digesting the feed, as they represent the "wear and tear" of the digestive organs.

In nutrition studies, when it is desired to determine how much of the protein of the feed has actually been digested, the feces may be treated with an acid solution of pepsin. This dissolves practically all the protein compounds in the feces except the true undigested food protein.

It has been pointed out in the preceding chapter that in the digestion of cellulose and pentosans by bacteria in the paunch of ruminants and to a less extent in the large intestine of other animals, more or less of the carbohydrates are broken down into carbon dioxide and methane, which gases have no nutritive value. Yet, due to the method of computing digestible nutrients, these are commonly included in the amount of carbohydrates considered digestible. This does not involve any serious error even with ruminants, and with other classes of stock the discrepancy is usually negligible.

Errors are apt to occur in determining the digestibility of the ether extract, or so-called "fat," for fat is usually present in feeding stuffs in much smaller amounts than protein and carbohydrates. Furthermore, as has been pointed out in Chapter I, ether dissolves not only true fat but also such plant compounds as chlorophyll and waxes. It also dissolves such products in the feces as the bile residues.

The true fats are highly digestible, but the waxes, etc., are of rather low digestibility. Fraps and Rather, on studying the ether extract obtained from 18 different forage plants, found that only 42 per cent was true fat.[2] Of this, 66 per cent was digested, while only 29 per cent of the remainder (not true fat) was digestible.

The ordinary digestion trials give little information concerning the extent to which the mineral matter is actually digested and absorbed, for calcium, magnesium, phosphorus, and iron are chiefly excreted from the body in the feces. Therefore, in a digestion trial these compounds would be reported as largely undigested, though they may really have been digested and absorbed, and later excreted in the feces after being used in the body.

76. Determining digestibility by other methods.—In addition to the direct determination of the digestibility of the various nutrients by means of a digestion trial, other methods are sometimes used to estimate the digestibility of the nutrients in a feed. A fair index to the digestibility of the protein can be gained, in the case of concentrates, by digesting a finely-ground sample of the feed with a solution of pepsin and hydrochloric acid in an incubator under standardized conditions. This method is used in Europe to some extent in valuing oil meals of various grades. It is less accurate in the case of roughages.

Attempts have also been made to estimate the digestibility of the fiber and other nutrients by treating samples of the feed with various solvents. These are apparently of less value than the artificial determination of digestibility of the protein.[3]

Attempts have also been made to reduce the cost of actual digestion experiments by methods in which the feces are not collected and weighed, but are merely sampled at intervals and analyzed. Since the silica in feeds is not digested to an appreciable extent, it is practically all voided in the feces. The digestibility of the various nutrients can be estimated approximately from the percentage of silica and the percentage of the nutrients in the feed and the percentages of each in the feces.[4]

In another method iron oxide is added to the ration, and the digestibility of the various nutrients is estimated from the iron content of the feed and of the feces.[5] These methods have not as yet proven sufficiently exact to be used instead of the usual method of determining digestion coefficients.

III. Energy Values of Feeds

77. All losses not deducted in digestible nutrient values.—Tables showing the amounts of digestible nutrients in feeds tell approximately what part of the food is digested and absorbed, and thus really enters the body of the animal. However, in addition to the loss of undigested material in the feces, there are other losses of energy in the mastication, digestion, and assimilation of feed. These other losses cannot be considered at all in the digestible-nutrient values for the various feeding stuffs. To obtain information on these losses and also to study the use of food energy in the body, various types of *respiration apparatus* and *respiration calorimeters* have been devised.

78. Respiration apparatus.—A respiration apparatus is a device by means of which an animal's intake and outgo of carbon dioxide and oxygen gas can be accurately determined, or sometimes merely the amount of oxygen consumed in the oxidations that take place in the body.

In one type of respiration apparatus the animal breathes through a mask placed over the nose and mouth, and the amounts of carbon dioxide and oxygen in the incoming air and in the outgoing air are found by chemical methods. In addition to the carbon dioxide given off in the breath, a small amount is excreted through the skin. Also, there is a small excretion of carbon in the form of the combustible gas, methane. Since these losses are small and relatively constant for any particular kind of animal, mathematical corrections can be made for them.

Simple apparatus of this type is now commonly employed in most large hospitals to determine the rate of metabolism in humans suffering from certain diseases. Extensive studies have also been made with farm animals with such apparatus. For example, Zuntz, a German scientist, conducted such investigations many years ago to find the amounts of nutrients expended by horses in different types of work.

In the most simple kind of respiration apparatus, only the amount of oxygen is ascertained that is consumed in the oxidations that take place in the body, the amount of carbon dioxide not being determined. This method has been used in recent studies by Brody and associates at the Missouri Station, to find the energy expenditure of farm animals of various classes and under different conditions. In these experiments special sleeve-like masks were used which fitted over the nose and mouth of the experimental animals.

The more complete type of respiration apparatus is an air-tight chamber in which the animal is placed. This is so equipped that all the air entering the chamber and all leaving it can be accurately measured and analyzed. All food, feces, and urine are likewise carefully weighed and analyzed. In some cases mechanical work is performed by the animal within the chamber, while in others it is at rest.

In this manner there can be determined the exact amount of carbon and also of nitrogen that the animal has either gained or lost during the experimental period. From this information the amounts of body protein and of fat that have been stored or lost can be computed, and likewise the gain or loss in energy.

Extensive investigations have been made by Kellner, Mollgaard, and other European scientists with apparatus of this type, and by Ritzman and Benedict at the New Hampshire Station. More recently, respiration studies with the larger farm animals have been conducted by Mitchell and associates at the Illinois Station and by Kleiber and associates at the California Station.

79. Determining the chemical gain or loss in the body.—To illustrate the manner in which a respiration apparatus is used to gain information on the use of food in the body, let us assume that a steer has been fed a normal fattening ration during a respiration experiment. The feed given the animal during 24 hours contained 0.75 lb. of nitrogen, and the feces and urine voided during the same day contained 0.68 lb. of nitrogen. Therefore in this experiment the steer had stored 0.07 lb. of nitrogen in its body in the form of protein tissue. Multiplying this by the factor 6.25, it is found that the animal made 0.44 lb. of body protein during the day.

Similarly, if the feed contained 13.44 lbs. of carbon, and the steer voided 12.71 lbs. during the day in the feces, in the urine, and in carbon dioxide and methane gas, then 0.73 lb. of carbon must have been stored in his body. Since the average carbon content of body proteins is known, the amount of carbon in the 0.44 lb. of body protein stored can be computed, and this can be subtracted from the total carbon stored. Practically all the rest of the carbon must have been stored in the form of body fat, because the glucose and glycogen content of the body does not ordinarily change appreciably from day to day. Then from the average carbon content of body fat, there can be computed the amount of body fat stored during the experiment.

By means of respiration studies of this kind definite information can be gained concerning the use an animal can make of the total nutrients in a ration. For example, in the case of a growing or fattening animal, one can determine the actual amount of energy that is stored in the newly-formed body tissues. In experiments with a horse the proportion of the food energy can be found that is converted into useful work. In experiments with dairy cows there can be similarly ascertained the proportion of the total energy in the ration which is transformed into the energy of the milk. Such investigations have therefore been of great value in furnishing information on many important problems.

80. The respiration calorimeter.—Another means of measuring the usefulness of feeds is furnished by the respiration calorimeter. This is an exceedingly complicated form of the respiration apparatus, in which not only the feces, urine, and gaseous waste products can be collected, but in which the heat given off by the animal can also be directly determined. By means of this apparatus, it is possible to find how much of the energy of the feed the animal has been able to use in growth, fattening, or work.

The first and only respiration calorimeter built in this country for carrying on experiments with large farm animals was erected years ago by Armsby at the Institute of Animal Nutrition of Pennsylvania State College. Following the death of Armsby, the investigations with this respiration calorimeter have been in charge of Forbes.

81. Gross energy of feeds.—A mature animal may be compared to a steam engine, in which a part of the energy derived from the fuel is used for the operation of the engine itself, while the surplus may perform useful work. The steam engine derives its energy from coal, oil, or wood; the animal, from the feed it consumes. Both require a small amount of repair material—steel, brass, etc., for the engine, and protein and mineral matter for the animal—but the largest demand with engine and mature animal alike is for energy. It is therefore both important and interesting to consider the relative value of feeds in terms of the energy they can furnish the body.

The gross energy value of any feeding stuff for the animal depends on the amount of energy that it will furnish when burned. As with coal, the gross energy value of a feed is determined by burning a weighed quantity of it in pure oxygen gas under pressure in an apparatus called a calorimeter. The heat given off is taken up by water surrounding the combustion chamber and is determined with an exceedingly accurate thermometer.

The units of measurement employed in measuring heat and energy in such investigations are the Calorie and the therm. A *Calorie* (C.) is the amount of heat required to raise the temperature of 1 kilogram of water 1° C., or to raise the temperature of 1 lb. of water nearly 4° F. A *therm* (T.) is 1,000 Calories.

The Calorie, known as the large, or great Calorie, is written with a capital C, to distinguish it from the calorie (small calorie). The Calorie is 1,000 times the calorie.

The gross energy of 100 lbs. of various substances, or the heat evolved on burning them, is as follows:

Therms

Anthracite coal 358.3
Corn meal, average water content..............................180.3
Linseed meal, average water content...........................210.3
Timothy hay, average water content............................181.2
Wheat straw, average water content............................184.6
Pure digestible protein...263.1
Pure digestible carbohydrates..................................186.0
Pure digestible fat...422.0

The table shows that, on burning, 100 lbs. of anthracite coal yield 358.3 therms, or enough heat to raise the temperature of 358,300 lbs. of water 4° F. One hundred pounds of timothy hay likewise burned yield 181.2 therms, or about half as much as coal. Linseed meal has a higher fuel value than corn meal, because it contains more oil. Digestible protein yields considerably more heat than the carbohydrates, and fat over twice as much as the carbohydrates.

82. Metabolizable or available energy.—The gross energy of a feed does not measure its nutritive value to the animal, because feeds which yield the same number of heat units in the calorimeter may differ in the amount of energy which they can furnish to the body. Certain portions of the gross energy are entirely lost by the following means:

1. A part of the food passes through the digestive tract undigested.

2. The carbohydrates, especially woody fiber, undergo fermentations in the intestines and paunch, in which combustible gases, especially methane, are formed that are without fuel value to the animal.

3. When the protein substances in the body are broken down, they form urea and other nitrogenous compounds that are excreted by the kidneys. These have fuel value which is lost to the body.

The *metabolizable energy* of any feed, which is the only portion that is of use to the animal, is the amount of energy left after deducting from the gross energy of the feed these three losses; i.e., (1) the energy lost in feces, (2) the energy lost in urine, and (3) the energy lost in combustible gases. The metabolizable energy is also sometimes called available energy.

83. Additional losses of energy.—The metabolizable energy of a feed measures the value for heat production in the body, but does not represent its true value for other purposes. The animal must spend part of the metabolizable energy from any food in the work of masticating and digesting it and assimilating the digested nutrients. Obviously, energy is required for the movements of the jaws in chewing, the movements of the digestive tract, and the increased work of the heart and lungs during the digestive process. Also, the secretion of the digestive juices requires energy and there are losses of energy in the heat produced through the bacterial action upon carbohydrates.

The energy consumed in these processes all takes the form of heat, and it may help to warm the body. However, it cannot be used for other body purposes, because the body has no ability to convert heat into other forms of energy.

In addition to these losses of energy due to the actual work of masticating, digesting, and assimilating the food, a further loss occurs through the speeding up of the general metabolism in the body, which always follows the consumption of food. It has been found that the rate of metabolism is at once increased, when nutrients are absorbed from the digestive tract following a meal. As a result, more heat is produced. This additional production of heat is sometimes called the "specific dynamic effect" of the food nutrients.

The effect is familiar to all of us, for we know that if we eat a meal when we are chilly, we will soon feel decidedly warmer. Likewise, if we eat too heartily in hot weather, we will suffer even more from the heat.

All these losses of energy in the form of heat are often grouped together under the term "work of digestion." Investigators in this field more commonly use the term *heat increment* to include all these losses, for they are due to an increase, or increment, in the heat production of the body, which is caused by the consumption of food.

84. Net energy.—The *net energy* of any feed is the amount of energy left after deducting from the metabolizable energy the energy lost in the so-called "work of digestion," or "heat increment."

This net energy is used by the animal, first of all, to meet its daily maintenance needs. Even when an animal consumes no food, a certain amount of energy is required for the necessary functions of the body. These include the work of the heart, lungs, and other internal organs, as well as the work done by the muscles in producing the movements of the body. A certain amount of the net energy furnished by the food must, therefore, be used by the animal for these daily maintenance needs.

In case a surplus of net energy remains after meeting the requirement of the animal for merely maintaining the body, the surplus may be used for producing growth, fat, milk, or wool, or in the performance of external work.

85. Equations for metabolizable energy and net energy.—To fix in mind the definitions for metabolizable energy and net energy, they may be stated thus, in the form of equations:

Metabolizable energy = gross energy minus energy lost in (1) feces, (2) urine, (3) combustible gases.

Net energy = metabolizable energy minus energy lost in work of digestion.

86. Net energy values of typical feeds.—Our knowledge concerning the net energy values of different feeds and of the use of net energy by the various farm animals has largely been obtained through the painstaking and laborious experiments conducted by Armsby and later by Forbes at the Pennsylvania Institute of Animal Nutrition with a respira-

tion calorimeter and by Kellner and others with various types of respiration apparatus. Most of these investigations have been with mature
steers, and but little information of this character is available concerning
the net energy values of feeds for other classes of stock. Also, on account
of the great expense involved in these experiments, it has been possible
for the investigators to study but relatively few feeding stuffs. While
the data are therefore limited in nature, these determinations have
brought out facts of great interest and importance in animal nutrition
and in practical stock feeding.[6]

The losses of energy that occur in the utilization by cattle of the
pure nutrients and of typical feeds are shown in the following table:

Net energy from 100 lbs. of digestible nutrients and
typical feeding stuffs

Nutrients or feeding stuffs	Gross energy	Energy lost in			Meta-bolizable energy remaining	Heat increment	Net energy remaining
		Feces	Methane	Urine			
Digestible nutrients	Therms	Therms	Therms	Therms	Therms	Therms	Therms
Peanut oil (fat)........	399.2	0.0	0.0	0.0	399.2	174.4	224.8
Wheat gluten (protein).	263.1	0.0	0.0	49.2	213.9	118.3	95.6
Starch (carbohydrate)..	186.0	0.0	18.8	0.0	167.2	68.7	98.5
Common feeding stuffs							
Ground corn	180.3	21.2	15.9	8.1	135.1	52.2	82.9
Timothy hay	181.2	86.2	13.6	7.1	74.3	31.3	43.0
Wheat straw	184.6	107.5	15.3	4.4	57.4	47.3	10.1

As the pure nutrients were entirely digestible, no losses occurred
in the feces. There was no loss of energy in the form of methane in
the case of peanut oil or wheat gluten, because fat and protein do not
undergo the fermentations in the paunch and large intestine which
produce this gas. With starch, a loss of 18.8 therms of energy occurred
in methane gas for each 100 lbs. of the nutrient. A loss of energy in
the urea and other nitrogenous compounds in the urine resulted only in
the case of the wheat gluten, since fat and starch do not contain protein
or other nitrogenous compounds.

Deducting these losses, there remained 399.2 therms of *metabolizable
energy* for the fat, 213.9 therms for the protein, and 167.2 therms for
the starch. The losses in the heat increment, or so-called "work of digestion" were highest in the case of the fat and lowest for the starch.
Deducting these losses, there remained 224.8 therms of *net energy* from
the 100 lbs. of fat; 95.6 therms from the same weight of protein, and
98.5 therms from the starch.

It should be noted that, although the protein contained considerably more gross energy than the starch, the losses were so much larger
that it supplied a trifle less net energy. This net energy value of protein represents merely its worth as a substitute for starch or fat in
the production of heat, energy, or body fat. Protein has its full value
only when used for the repair of protein tissue or for the building of
new body protein.

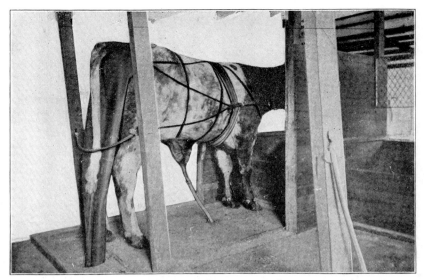

A STEER IN A DIGESTION STALL

In digestion trials the feces may be collected in several ways. A common manner is by means of the harness and rubber duct here shown. When it is desired merely to determine the digestibility of a feed, the urine need not be collected, as is being done in this trial. (From Pennsylvania Station.)

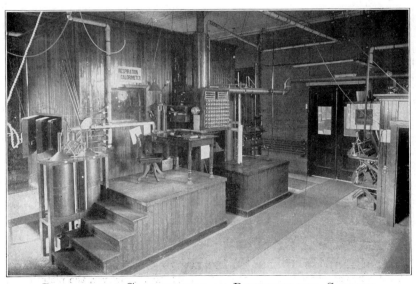

RESPIRATION CALORIMETER AT PENNSYLVANIA STATION

Much important information concerning the nutritive values of different classes of feeds has been secured through the investigations conducted with this apparatus. (From Pennsylvania Institute of Animal Nutrition.)

ANIMALS FED FOR PRODUCTION REQUIRE CONCENTRATES

Horses at hard work, dairy cows in milk, and fattening animals all must have a considerable amount of concentrates to keep up high production.

MATURE ANIMALS CAN BE MAINTAINED CHIEFLY ON ROUGHAGE

This is not an economical method of feeding straw. However, the picture well emphasizes the fact that mature horses, cattle, or sheep which are merely being maintained can live chiefly on cheap roughage.

87. Net energy values of concentrates and roughages.—Studying the data for corn meal, timothy hay, and wheat straw, we note that in the case of the corn only 21.2 therms of energy were lost in the feces, while this loss amounted to 86.2 therms for the hay. The loss in the feces was still greater for the straw, 107.5 therms being lost, or more than half of the original gross energy content. Small losses occurred in methane with all three feeds, and the losses of energy in the urine were also small, for none of these feeds is high in protein.

Deducting the losses in feces, methane, and urine, there remained 135.1 therms of *metabolizable energy* from the 100 lbs. of corn, 74.3 therms from the hay, and only 57.4 therms from the straw.

Over one-third of the metabolizable energy in the corn, or 52.2 therms, was lost in the "heat increment," leaving 82.9 therms as the *net energy* value of 100 lbs. of the grain. In the case of the hay, there was a loss of 31.3 therms in the "heat increment." This left only 43.0 therms of net energy, or only about one-half as much as for the corn grain. In the mastication, digestion, and assimilation of the straw, there was used up nearly all the available energy it furnished, leaving only 10.1 therms of net energy from 100 lbs. of the straw.

These data therefore show that for productive purposes, such as the formation of body fat, 100 lbs. of wheat straw were worth less than one-eighth as much as 100 lbs. of corn grain and only one-fourth as much as 100 lbs. of timothy hay. For the production of heat in the body, the relative values of these feeds are measured by their metabolizable energy values. For this purpose, 100 lbs. of the straw were worth over one-third as much as the same weight of corn grain. The amounts of total digestible nutrients furnished by various feeds are also approximate measures of their relative values for the production of heat in the body.

88. Net energy does not measure value for maintenance.—For the reason just stated, net energy values should not be used in computing maintenance rations for wintering farm animals in sections where the winter climate is cold. It is shown in Chapter V that the chief maintenance requirement under such conditions is for heat to keep the body warm. Net energy values seriously undervalue the worth of roughages for this purpose. In the computation of rations for maintaining stock, it is therefore more accurate to use total digestible nutrients. Metabolizable energy values are also suitable for this purpose, but are not in common use.

The fact that roughages have a much higher relative value for warming the body than they do for productive purposes, is of great importance in livestock feeding. It is pointed out in later chapters that mature animals that are merely being maintained, such as idle horses in winter, can be satisfactorily kept on roughages alone, even those of rather low quality. On the other hand, high-producing dairy cows, fattening cattle or sheep, and horses at hard work can use but little low-grade roughage, such as straw or poor, woody hay.

89. Advantages and limitations of net energy values.—For many years there has been much discussion among scientists as to whether feeds should be compared and rations computed on the basis of net energy values or on the basis of digestible nutrients. There is no question but that the net energy value of hay or other roughage furnishes a more correct measure of its value for productive purposes than its content of digestible nutrients, when it is desired to compare the roughage directly with a grain or other concentrate. Therefore from this standpoint net energy values would be preferable to total digestible nutrients as a basis for evaluating feeds and computing rations for livestock.

However, there are great scientific and also practical limitations in the use of net energy values. First of all, on account of the great cost of such investigations, the values of but very few feeds have been actually determined by experiments with a respiration apparatus or a respiration calorimeter. For example, though most such studies have been with fattening steers, the net energy values of less than 20 feeds have been directly determined for this class of stock. Still less information is available in the case of the other farm animals.

For all the other many feeding stuffs, the net energy values must therefore be computed from their chemical composition or from their content of digestible nutrients. When this is done, it is often necessary to make arbitrary deductions, based on the judgment of the scientist, from the computed values, to produce a result that seems reasonable. Sometimes the computed values have not been corrected sufficiently on the basis of judgment, and figures have been published for certain feeds that are widely different from those that have been obtained in actual feeding experiments.

90. Net energy values differ with kind of animal and with individuals.—It has been found that the same feeds have decidedly different net energy values for some classes of stock than for others. Therefore net energy values determined in experiments with one class of animals may not furnish a correct index of the values of the same feeds for other stock.

Investigations to study this problem were begun by Armsby and continued by Forbes and associates after the death of Armsby. In these studies it was found that the net energy value of a ration for the fattening of cattle was only 76 per cent as great as the net energy value of the same feeds for the maintenance of cattle.[7] The net energy values of feeds for milk production by dairy cows, according to their investigations, are practically as high as for maintenance, averaging 98.5 per cent of the latter values.

European investigators found years ago that the net energy values of concentrates for fattening swine were much higher than the values for fattening cattle.[8] Recently Mitchell and Haines determined that the net energy value of corn grain for chickens was 128.5 therms per 100 lbs.[9] This is 52 per cent higher than the net energy value of the same grain for fattening cattle, determined earlier by Armsby. According to the investigations of Zuntz many years ago, the net energy values of corn, oats, and other concentrates for work horses are also much higher than the values of these same feeds for fattening cattle.[10]

The net energy values of the same feed, determined in experiments with individual animals of a particular class, sometimes differ very widely, due to the individuality of the experimental animals and the complexity of the methods of investigation.[11]

91. Other factors also affect net energy values.—The net energy value of a particular mixture of feeds for the same class of stock may differ, depending on whether the animals are fed liberally or scantily. For example, in an investigation by Forbes and associates the net energy value of a combination of corn grain and alfalfa hay was 20 per cent less when steers were fed 2.5 times as much as they needed for maintenance, than when they were fed only 1.5 times their maintenance requirements.[12] It is pointed out later in this chapter that the amount of feed consumed also affects the digestibility of a ration, although to a less degree.

Investigations by Forbes and associates have shown that the net energy value of a ration which is nutritively complete is markedly higher than that of a ration which has certain deficiencies.[13] For instance, in experiments with rats the net energy value of a ration was decreased if it was too low in protein or if there was a lack of cystine, which is one of the essential amino acids. A deficiency of vitamins B, D, or G also reduced the utilization of the energy of a ration.

In another experiment with a fattening steer they found that the net energy value of corn grain was decidedly higher when it was fed in a balanced ration with alfalfa hay than when it was given to the animal as the only feed. Likewise, from a study of the results secured in experiments with fattening lambs, Fraps concluded that cottonseed meal had a considerably higher net energy value when small amounts were added to a ration low in protein, than when it was used in a ration already containing ample protein.[14]

92. Relative values of legume hay and timothy hay.—One of the most-discussed problems in the net-energy system of valuing feeds has been the relative net energy values of legume hay, especially alfalfa hay, and of timothy hay. The feeding experiments reviewed in later chapters show clearly that, even when timothy hay is fed with supplements that provide an abundance of protein, minerals, and vitamins, it is certainly not superior to alfalfa or other legume hay for animals fed for production. Early-cut, well-cured timothy hay from properly-fertilized fields may equal alfalfa hay in feeding value per ton for some classes of stock, except for the difference in content of protein and calcium and perhaps in vitamins. However, it is not superior to alfalfa hay.

Nevertheless, in investigations by Armsby and later by Forbes and associates net energy values of 42.8 to 48.7 therms were found for timothy containing 88 per cent dry matter, in comparison with net energy values of only 30.0 to 36.5 therms for alfalfa hay containing the same percentage of dry matter.[15] Alfalfa hay likewise had a decidedly lower net energy value than timothy hay for lambs in experiments by Mitchell and associates at the Illinois Station.[16]

On the other hand, in early investigations by Zuntz with work horses alfalfa hay had a considerably higher net energy value than timothy hay.[17] Likewise, in recent experiments by Ritzman at the New Hampshire Station with dairy cows alfalfa hay had a higher net energy value than timothy hay.[18]

93. Net energy values vs. total digestible nutrients.—From the preceding discussion it is apparent that the net energy values of individual feeds have very marked limitations as a practicable basis for evaluating feeds or computing rations for livestock. However, it should be recognized that most of the discrepancies in this system of valuing feeds also occur in comparisons based on total digestible nutrients. It is therefore natural that the opinions of scientists differ widely as to which system is preferable.

In the United States the net energy values have been used much less than in Europe. This is perhaps because their limitations have been realized more clearly. In this country the actual values of most of our important feeds have been determined by means of the extensive feeding experiments conducted by the experiment stations. Animal husbandmen have therefore relied chiefly on the results of these experiments in deciding on the relative values of the various feeds, instead of upon computed net energy values.

The author of this book has preferred and still prefers total digestible nutrients to net energy values for most purposes. The chief reasons for this preference are the very limited amount of data on the actual net energy values of different feeds, and the wide differences in net energy values that have been pointed out in this discussion. Also, it is apparently easier for most students and farmers to understand pounds of digestible nutrients than therms of net energy.

In this connection the conclusions of Meigs and Forbes are of interest. From experiments with dairy cows, Meigs of the United States Department of Agriculture concluded that the existing figures for total digestible nutrients in feeds were a better measure of their relative values under practical conditions than net energy values.[19]

After extensive investigations in this field with a respiration calorimeter, Forbes concluded: "(1) that in a critical sense, foodstuffs cannot be evaluated individually, (2) that the net energy values of individual foodstuffs are fundamentally variable and hence are not practicable standard measures of reference, and (3) that the most nearly logical, single, conventional measure of whole nutritive value is the net energy of the nutritively complete ration."[20]

The opposite point of view, that net energy values are a more accurate means of comparing the values of individual feeds, is well summarized in recent statements by Fraps and by Mitchell.[21]

The conclusion by Forbes is substantially that which the author has held for many years. It has long been his opinion, as expressed at the beginning of this chapter, that the best measure of the actual value of any feed for a particular class of stock can be secured only through carefully planned feeding experiments. In such studies the feed concerning which information is desired should be fed as part of a *complete* ration and under practical conditions, in direct comparison with another feed that is taken as the standard of value.

When such trials are repeated a sufficient number of times, definite and reliable conclusions can be made concerning the actual relative values of the two feeding stuffs for this particular class of stock. It should be pointed out that in order to determine which of several available feeds are the most economical to use in stock feeding, there must be considered other factors than the amounts of energy or total digestible nutrients that each furnishes.

The amounts of digestible protein, the vitamin and the mineral content, and the general suitability of each feed for that class of stock must all be given due attention. The methods of determining the money values of different feeds are discussed in Chapter X.

94. Net energy values in Appendix Table II.—It has been pointed out previously that net energy values, in spite of their limitations, are more accurate than total digestible nutrients as a basis for a direct comparison of the value of a concentrate and of a roughage. This is also true in a comparison of a high-grade concentrate, containing but little fiber, with a low-grade concentrate which is high in fiber. Also, it is fully recognized that some prefer to use net energy values in computing rations for live stock.

The author has therefore computed net energy values for some of the most important feeds, from the data on the average composition of these feeds which is presented in Appendix Table I. These net energy values are presented in Appendix Table II with full recognition that they are approximate values only, but with the hope that they may serve a useful purpose.

In the computation of these net energy values, considerable use has been made of the Fraps' "production coefficients" for estimating the net energy values of feeds from the chemical composition.[14] From extensive studies of the results of feeding experiments in which various feeds have been compared, Fraps of the Texas Station has computed net energy values for these feeds. He has also derived "production coefficients" for a considerable list of feeds, by means of which approximate net energy values can be computed from the chemical composition. In computing the net energy values these "production coefficients" are used in a manner similar to the way in which the amounts of digestible nutrients are computed from the chemical composition and the digestion coefficients.

These net energy values in Appendix Table II are primarily for the fattening of livestock. As has been shown previously in this chapter, the various feeding stuffs have materially higher net energy values for milk production than for the fattening of animals. However, the *relative* net energy values of different feeds for milk production and for fattening are probably not far different in most cases.

Therefore, those desiring to compute rations for dairy cows on the net energy basis can safely employ these net energy values, using the figures for net energy requirements given in Appendix Table III, which are designed for use with these net energy values. These values can also be used in computing rations for work animals.

It has been stated before in this chapter that net energy values should not be used in computing maintenance rations for wintering stock in sections having a cold winter climate. (**88**) It is much more accurate to use for this purpose feeding standards and tables of composition based on total digestible nutrients.

95. Starch values.—Kellner, who conducted extensive investigations with steers in a respiration apparatus many years ago in Germany, measured the values of feeds for productive purposes in terms of *starch values,* instead of net energy values expressed as therms.[22] In this system 1 lb. of digestible starch is taken as the net energy unit. The net energy value of any feeding stuff is expressed as the number of pounds of starch which, it is believed, would have the same net energy value for productive purposes. Thus, the starch value of dent corn, according to the Kellner method, is 81.5 lbs. starch equivalent. In comparison with this, Armsby estimated that dent corn had a net energy value of 85.5 therms.

Except for the difference in the manner in which the results are expressed, starch values are similar to Armsby's net energy values, which are stated in therms. In fact, the starch value for any feed, expressed in pounds of starch equivalent, can readily be converted into therms of net energy, by multiplying the pounds of starch equivalent by the factor 1.071. (One pound of starch equivalent has an average net energy value of 1.071 therms, according to Armsby.)

Kellner determined by experiments in his respiration apparatus with fattening steers the starch values of a few typical feeds, and then computed a table of starch values for all important feeds on the basis of these results and the amounts of digestible nutrients furnished by the respective feeds. He also prepared feeding standards in which the requirements for the various classes of livestock were stated in terms of digestible true protein and starch values.

Taking 1 lb. of digestible starch as his unit, Kellner found that 1 lb. of digestible pure protein had a starch value of 0.94 lb.; i. e., it would produce 94 per cent as much body fat as 1 lb. of digestible starch. Further, in oil-bearing seeds and oil meals, in which the ether extract, or so-called "fat," is practically all pure fat, 1 lb. of digestible fat had a starch value of 2.41 lbs., while in roughage, roots, etc., it had a starch value of only 1.61 lbs. Fat in cereals and factory and mill by-products had a starch value of 2.12 lbs., which was nearly as high as in oil-bearing seeds.

Kellner also found that the productive value of certain concentrates, such as grains and seeds, oil cakes, roots, and slaughter-house by-products, was about the same as that obtained when the several pure nutrients in them were fed separately. It was therefore possible to calculate the approximate starch values of such feeds from the amounts of each class of digestible nutrients they contained.

However, it was not possible to compute the starch values of feeds high in fiber with any degree of exactness whatsoever. From the few typical feeds which he actually studied, Kellner found that with such feeds it was necessary to make deductions from the starch values computed as before, ranging all the way from 5 to 30 per cent with mill and factory by-products and from 50 to 70 per cent with straw, to get reasonable starch values.

The system of valuing feeds on the basis of starch values, or starch equivalents, is widely used in Germany and also in Great Britain, but in the United States the net energy values, expressed in therms, are commonly employed by those who desire to compute rations according to the net energy system.

96. Scandinavian feed-unit system of valuing feeds.—A system of feed equivalents, based mainly on the experiments with dairy cows and swine by Fjord and his successors in Denmark and the investigations of Hansson in Sweden, has been widely used in the Scandinavian countries.[23] It has been employed especially by the cow-testing associations for measuring the relative values of different feeds and the productive efficiency of various herds and of individual cows. For the reasons pointed out later, it has never been used widely in the United States.

In the feed-unit system the value of the different feeds is compared with the value of 1 lb. of standard grain feed, such as corn and barley, which are taken as the unit of value.

The feed-unit value for any other feed is the amount of that feed which is estimated to have the same productive value as 1.0 lb. of corn or barley. For example, the feed-unit value of cottonseed meal for dairy cows is given as 0.8 lb. This means that, according to the estimate, it requires 0.8 lb. of cottonseed meal to equal 1.0 lb. of corn or barley in productive value. Similarly, the feed-unit value of wheat bran, oats, dried beet pulp, or malt sprouts for dairy cows is given in this system as 1.1 lbs. This indicates that 1.1 lbs. of one of these feeds will be required to equal 1.0 lb. of corn or barley.

The feed-unit values for a few other typical feeds for dairy cows are: linseed meal, distillers' dried grains, corn gluten feed, and soy beans, 0.9 lb.; alfalfa hay, clover hay, 2.0 lbs.; timothy hay, prairie hay, 3.0 lbs.; corn silage, 6.0 lbs.; turnips, mangels, wet beet pulp, 12.0 lbs. The feed-unit values of feeds for pigs and for horses differ from those for dairy cows to some extent, in accordance with the estimated productive values of the individual feeds for each class of stock.

The feed-unit values are not true expressions of net energy, for in this system feeds rich in protein are given a higher value than feeds low in protein which furnish the same amount of net energy. Thus, as has been mentioned before, the feed-unit value of cottonseed meal is 0.8 lb. and that of linseed meal and corn gluten feed, 0.9 lb. This means that it is estimated that it takes only 0.8 lb. or 0.9 lb., respectively, of these feeds to equal 1.0 lb. of corn or barley in productive value.

However, the actual net energy values of these protein-rich feeds are probably slightly lower than the net energy values of corn or barley. When these protein supplements are added to a ration that already contains an abundance of protein, each pound will not have a higher value than a pound of corn or barley.

Similarly, in the feed-unit system timothy hay is rated 50 per cent below clover or alfalfa hay. If added to rations too low in protein, feeds rich in protein have a higher value than those supplying an equal amount of net energy, but which are low in protein. However, when the ration already contains plenty of protein, any additional amount will have no higher value for the formation of fat or the production of milk or work than an equal amount of net energy supplied by carbohydrates or fat.

The high net energy value assigned to protein in the feed-unit system is undoubtedly the result of the character of the rations employed in the experiments in which the feed-unit values were determined. In the Scandinavian countries there is a shortage of protein in the home-grown feeds, and considerable amounts of protein supplements are imported. Therefore, the common rations are often rather low in protein. When added to rations which are somewhat below the optimum in protein content, 1.0 lb. of a protein supplement will manifestly have a higher productive value than 1.0 lb. of corn or barley.

The conditions in the various parts of the United States are much more diverse than in the Scandinavian countries. In the corn belt there is commonly a shortage of protein in the farm-grown feeds. On the other hand, in the alfalfa districts of the West, the shortage is often one of carbohydrates, and not of protein. Similarly, in the cotton belt of the South cottonseed meal is frequently cheaper per ton than grain. Under these latter conditions, protein-rich feeds obviously do not have a higher feeding value than corresponds to the amounts of net energy or of total digestible nutrients that they provide.

The feed-unit system has been developed in a comparatively small region, where similar crops are grown on the various farms and the price of purchased feeds is uniform throughout the entire district; hence this difficulty has not arisen there. As is pointed out in Chapter X, no arbitrary values for feeding stuffs, expressed in terms of feed units, money, or other fixed units, can be devised that will hold good under such widely differing conditions as are found in the different sections of the United States.

QUESTIONS

1. Show, by examples, why the information gained by extensive feeding experiments is the most reliable method of estimating the relative value of different feeding stuffs for the various classes of stock.
2. Define *digestion coefficient*. How are the digestion coefficients determined directly, and also by difference, in digestion trials?
3. Discuss the relative digestibility of feeds low in fiber and of those high in fiber.
4. Define *total digestible nutrients*. State how the amount of total digestible nutrients is computed.
5. Define *nutritive ratio* and show how it is computed. What is meant by the term *narrow nutritive ratio;* the term *wide nutritive ratio?*

6. Discuss briefly some of the limitations of digestion trials.
7. Describe a respiration apparatus. How can the gain or loss of protein and fat to the body be determined in a respiration experiment?
8. How does a respiration calorimeter differ from a respiration apparatus?
9. Define by means of equations *metabolizable energy; net energy.*
10. Through what 4 different means is energy lost when a cow eats corn grain? Why is the net energy value of corn grain much higher than that of timothy hay?
11. What is meant by the terms *heat increment; work of digestion?*
12. Why may considerable straw be fed advantageously to an idle horse, but not to one at hard work?
13. Why does not the net energy value of a roughage measure its value for maintaining stock in the winter in most sections of the United States? On what basis should maintenance rations for such animals be computed?
14. Discuss the relative usefulness of *net energy values, total digestible nutrients,* and the *results of feeding experiments* for comparing the values of different feeds.
15. In what terms are net energy values expressed in the Kellner starch-value system?
16. Explain what is meant by a feed-unit, according to the Scandinavian system. Why has this system of valuing feeds not been adopted in the United States?

REFERENCES

1. Fraps, Tex. Bul. 418.
2. Fraps and Rather, Tex. Bul. 150.
3. Waentig and Gierisch, Ztschr. Physiol. Chem., 103, 1918, pp. 87-103; 107, 1919, pp. 213-224; Thomann, Mitt. Lebensmtl. Untersuch. u. Hyg., Schweiz. Gsndhtsamt., 11, 1920, pp. 227-236.
4. Gallup and Kuhlman, Jour. Agr. Res., 42, 1931, pp. 665-669; Knott, Murer, Hodgson, and Ellington, Wash. Buls. 275, 305.
5. Bergeim, Jour. Biol. Chem., 70, 1926, pp. 29-58; Cal. Rpt. 1928.
6. For a detailed discussion of the net energy values of feeds, see: Armsby, The Nutrition of Farm Animals.
7. Forbes, Fries, Braman, and Kriss, Jour. Agr. Res., 33, 1926, pp. 483-492.
8. Armsby, The Nutrition of Farm Animals, p. 662.
9. Mitchell and Haines, Jour. Agr. Res., 34, 1927, pp. 927-943.
10. Zuntz, Landw. Jahrb, 27, 1898, Sup. III.
11. Meigs, Jour. Dairy Sci., 8, 1925, pp. 523-536.
12. Forbes, Braman, Kriss, et al., Jour. Agr. Res., 40, 1930, pp. 37-78; see also Forbes, Braman, Kriss, et al., Jour. Agr. Res., 37, 1928, pp. 253-300; Forbes, Kriss, and Miller, Penn. Bul. 308; Mitchell et al., Jour. Agr. Res., 45, 1932, pp. 163-191; Brody and Procter, Mo. Res. Bul. 193.
13. Forbes, Braman, Kriss, et al., Jour. Agr. Res., 43, 1931, pp. 1015-1026; Braman, Black, Kahlenberg, Voris, Swift, and Forbes, Jour. Agr. Res., 50, 1935, pp. 1-38; Forbes et al., Jour. Nutr., 8, 1934, pp. 197-219; 8, 1934, pp. 295-308.
14. Fraps, Tex. Bul. 436; see also: Fraps, Tex. Buls. 185, 329, 402, 461.
15. Armsby and Fries, Jour. Agr. Res., 3, 1915, pp. 435-491; Forbes and Kriss, Jour. Agr. Res., 31, 1925, pp. 1085-1099.
16. Mitchell, Kammlade, and Hamilton, Ill. Bul. 317.
17. Zuntz, Landw. Jahrb., 27, 1898, Sup. III.
18. Ritzman, N. H. Bul. 256.
19. Meigs, Jour. Dairy Sci., 8, 1925, pp. 523-526; see also: Meigs and Converse, Jour. Dairy Sci., 8, 1925, pp. 177-195.
20. Forbes, Science, 77, 1933, pp. 306-307.
21. Fraps, Texas Bul. 461; Mitchell, Science, 80, 1934, pp. 558-561.
22. For a detailed explanation of starch values see Kellner's books, *Ernährung landw. Nutztiere* and *Futterungslehre,* and the English translation of the latter book by Goodwin, entitled *The Scientific Feeding of Farm Animals.* This method is also discussed in some detail in Wood's book, *Animal Nutrition.*
23. For a discussion of the feed-unit system see: Woll, Wis. Cir. 37; Hansson, Utfodringslära; Hansson, Fühling's Landw. Zeit., 65, 1916, p. 314.

The Whole Family Helps to Grind Grain

Even when grain is ground on the farm, the cost is quite an item. Therefore it is important to know whether the feeding value will be increased enough to make grinding profitable.

Shredding Corn Stover Increases the Feeding Value

Shredding or cutting stover or dry fodder from corn or the sorghums is usually profitable, as the stock then waste much less of it.

SLOP-FEEDING OF PIGS HAS BEEN LARGELY DISCARDED

Feeding ground grain and other meals to swine in the form of slop was formerly common. However, experiments have proved that just as efficient results are secured when the same feeds are given dry, and much bother is saved.

SELF-FEEDING CONCENTRATES TO PIGS SAVES MUCH LABOR

The self-feeder has largely displaced the slop bucket in swine feeding. The self-feeding of dry concentrates not only saves labor, but also actually saves feed, in comparison with hand-feeding. In addition, it is more sanitary than slop-feeding. (See Chapter XXXV.)

CHAPTER IV

FACTORS AFFECTING THE VALUE OF FEEDS

I. The Preparation of Feed

97. When does preparation of feed increase the nutritive value?— It is of much financial importance to stockmen to know whether any particular method of preparing feed for farm animals is actually economical. In other words, for a certain class of stock does it pay to grind, crush, cut, soak, cook, or ferment the grain or the roughage? Extravagant advertising claims are frequently made concerning the supposed savings that will result from the method of preparation that is being advocated. Therefore, before spending money for equipment, it is highly important that a farmer have unbiased information about such preparation of feed.

It is often assumed that by grinding, cutting, or cooking feeds much labor is saved the animal, and its output of flesh, milk or work thereby increased. This idea is based on the theory that the less work the animal does in mastication and digestion, the greater will be the amount of nutrients left for useful production.

However, this is apparently not true. The muscles of the body do not grow strong through idleness, and activity and exercise are necessary for health and strength. Likewise, the organs of mastication and digestion should be kept working at their normal capacity. Making feeds so fine and soft that they can be swallowed with little chewing, not only fails to pay for the cost of such preparation, but it may actually lower the value of the feed.

The value of grinding, crushing, or cutting feed depends on the character of the particular feed in question and also on the kind of animal to which it is to be fed. Therefore the economy of these methods of preparing feed for each class of stock is discussed in detail in the respective chapters of Part III. In this chapter there are discussed only the general principles that apply to the various classes of feeding stuffs and to the different kinds of farm animals.

In some cases, feeds that are unpalatable to stock will be consumed readily if they are ground and mixed with those that are well liked. For example, rye gives better results with most classes of stock if it is mixed with more palatable grains.

To induce animals that are being fitted for show to consume a little more feed than they might otherwise, the grinding of grain, the chopping of hay, or the soaking of feed may sometimes be helpful, even though the expense of such preparation would not be justified for other stock. There will naturally be more saving in grinding feed for animals with poor teeth than for those that can chew their food normally.

98. Grinding grain or other seeds.—In the case of grain or other seeds, grinding, crushing, or soaking is usually profitable only when the particular animals fail to chew the seeds thoroughly. Seeds that escape mastication may pass through the digestive tract without appreciable digestion, and the nutrients are lost. Whether it will pay to grind grain for any class of stock is therefore a problem that can be determined only by feeding experiments.

Such preparation may be advantageous for very young animals, before their teeth are well developed, but later it may not be beneficial. Also, in certain instances animals chew their feed less thoroughly as they grow older, and the grinding of grain is then advisable, even though it may not have been worth while for the same animals when somewhat younger.

For example, after they are a few weeks old, calves chew corn or oats thoroughly up to about 6 or 8 months of age, and there is hence no advantage in grinding these grains for them. After this age, it usually pays to grind the grains. Similarly, growing and fattening pigs chew corn with such thoroughness up to the usual market weights, that it does not generally pay to grind it for them. However, older pigs chew corn less thoroughly, and therefore the saving through grinding is greater.

In general, sheep masticate their feed the most efficiently of all the larger farm animals. As a result there is generally no advantage in grinding grain or other seeds for them, except in the case of seeds that are unusually small or hard. All grains should commonly be ground for dairy cows. Grain should also be ground for beef cattle, with the exception that it does not pay to grind corn for them if pigs follow the cattle to salvage the unmasticated corn kernels in the manure. All grains except corn and oats should be ground or crushed for horses and mules.

99. Fineness of grinding; crushing or rolling vs. grinding.—Grain should be ground only to a medium degree of fineness for stock. In other words, it should be ground so that it is gritty, and not mealy or floury. Fine grinding not only takes more time and power, but it often actually makes the grain less palatable, on account of its dusty nature.

It was found in Indiana experiments that the cost was over twice as much for fine grinding of oats as for medium grinding.[1] In Wisconsin trials it took nearly four times as much power for fine grinding of barley as for medium grinding.[2] With corn, the power consumption was about twice as great for grinding to a fine, floury meal as for grinding to a medium-fine, gritty meal. In experiments with dairy cows and also with pigs, the medium-fine barley produced better results than that ground more finely.

The cost of grinding is somewhat less when grain is merely cracked than when it is ground to a medium degree of fineness. However, the utilization of the cracked grain is enough lower to make medium-fine grinding preferable.

The relative merits of crushing or rolling grain, compared with grinding, have been much discussed. Rolled grain is preferred by many horsemen to ground grain, probably because it is more bulky and perhaps somewhat less apt to cause colic. For fattening cattle, on the other hand, a mixture of ground wheat and oats produced better gains in an Illinois trial than a mixture of the same grains which had been rolled.[3] The rolled feed was so bulky that the cattle failed to eat as much as was desired.

When grain screenings, which consist to a considerable extent of weed seeds, are fed to stock, many of the smaller seeds may pass through the digestive tract unchewed and alive. Fine grinding of such screenings is therefore desirable to prevent infesting the field with weeds through the manure.

100. Grinding or cutting hay or other roughage.—In the case of hay, stover, and straw, there are no hard seed coats to be broken. Therefore the ordinary chewing by livestock tears the forage into particles that can readily be penetrated by the digestive juices. Hence additional expense for grinding or cutting of such roughage is usually advisable only if it induces animals to eat coarse, stemmy portions that they would otherwise waste; or if they will consume a greater total amount of the roughage than when fed without the preparation.

In general, for dairy cows, beef cattle, and horses, it does not pay to go to additional expense to cut or grind hay of such quality that it will be consumed with but little waste. If the long hay is not fed in mangers that prevent undue refuse, there may be considerable saving in cutting or grinding it. For example, in the West fattening lambs are commonly fed in open lots, and the alfalfa hay is frequently put on the ground, simply being rolled up against the fence of the feedlot. Under such conditions there is a considerable wastage. It is therefore not surprising that the trials reviewed in Chapter XXXII show that cutting or grinding the hay makes a sufficient saving to justify the expense.

If hay is coarse and stemmy or otherwise of poor quality, there will be much more advantage from cutting it than with hay of good quality. Not only will the wastage be reduced, but also the stock will usually eat a greater amount of such roughage if it is cut.

In the case of corn or sorghum stover, it usually pays to cut or shred it to lessen the refuse, and also because the waste is then much better for bedding. Cut, shredded, or ground stover or fodder will heat or mold in storage unless thoroughly dry. For this reason, in humid districts such roughages frequently cannot be kept for more than a few days, even in cool weather.

For cattle and horses cutting hay is preferable to grinding it. Not only is much less time and power required to cut it by means of a silage cutter or a special hay cutter, but also the cut hay is actually more desirable than hay ground to a meal. The ground hay is often so dusty that it is disagreeable to handle in the barn, and it is often less palatable to stock than cut hay.

In addition, the fine grinding of hay does not increase its digestibility for cattle, and it may even decrease it. In an experiment with a steer at the Pennsylvania Institute of Animal Nutrition finely-ground alfalfa hay was less digestible than cut hay, probably due to a suppression of rumination.[4] Also the ground hay did not have any higher net energy value than the cut hay.

If it is desired to feed corn fodder to cattle without removing the ears, or to feed sorghum fodder without removing the heads, it may be desirable to grind the fodder in a roughage mill that will crack most of the grain and prevent it passing through the animals unchewed. However, as is shown in later chapters, the crop generally has a considerably higher value when fed in the form of silage instead of as ground fodder.

Recently many farmers have adopted the practice of chopping hay as it is stored in the barn by running it through a silage cutter or a special hay cutter, equipped with a blower. This method of handling hay is discussed in Chapter XI, and the precautions that should be taken in the storage of cut hay are emphasized. Often hay can be thus stored in a barn at little or no more cost than by the usual methods of storing the uncut hay with a hay fork or hay sling.

101. Mixing cut or ground roughage with concentrates.—Claims have often been made that the value of a ration will be greatly increased if the roughage is cut or ground and mixed with the grain or other concentrates. Assertions are made that such mixtures are digested more completely than when the roughage and the concentrates are fed separately. In spite of these claims, the experiments reviewed in Part III show in general that such mixing of the feed does not increase its digestibility or its nutritive value. Farm animals have digestive systems which mix very thoroughly the feeds they eat.

However, in special cases the mixing of roughage with grain may be desirable from other standpoints. For example, horses are apt to have colic if fed a heavy grain, such as ground wheat or barley, as the only concentrate. Mixing with the ground grain a small proportion of a bulky feed, such as chopped or ground hay, ground oats, or wheat bran, will largely prevent the trouble. Lambs fed a very liberal allowance of a heavy feed, like corn, so that they will fatten rapidly, often suffer from digestive troubles. Mixing chopped or ground hay or some other bulky feed with the grain aids in preventing such difficulties.

It is highly desirable, when pigs are not on pasture, that they eat some legume hay to provide vitamins A and D. If legume hay, even of good quality, is fed uncut in a rack, young pigs will frequently not eat any appreciable amount. It is therefore advisable to mix about 5 per cent of chopped or ground legume hay in their concentrate mixture in order to force them to eat it.

102. Cooking or steaming feed.—Many years ago it was firmly believed that cooking or steaming feed greatly increased its value. Careful trials have shown, however, that in general such preparation of either grain or roughage does not increase its digestibility or its nutritive value, and it may decrease the digestibility of the protein.[5] In a recent Ohio test, for example, steaming alfalfa hay and corn stover for fattening cattle decreased the gains and reduced the profit, even though no charge was made for the fuel or the labor in steaming the feed.[6]

Though cooking feed for cattle was abandoned years ago, it is still occasionally done for swine. Fortunately this question has also been settled by numerous tests at several experiment stations, as is pointed out in Chapter XXXV. These experiments showed that instead of there being a gain from cooking feed, there was a loss in most cases. The only exceptions are a few feeds, such as potatoes and field beans, which can be fed satisfactorily to swine only when cooked. Soybeans also give better results in swine feeding when cooked, and soybean oil meal which has been thoroughly cooked in the manufacturing process is preferable to raw-tasting meal for swine.

103. Soaking feed; feeding slop.—When grain with small or hard kernels cannot be conveniently ground or crushed, it may be advisable to soften it by soaking before feeding. Care should be taken that such soaked grain does not become stale by long standing. Old corn often becomes hard and flinty in summer and sometimes causes sore mouths in cattle or other stock if fed whole. It should then be ground or soaked.

Many farmers still feed ground grain and other meals to their hogs in the form of slop, believing that slop-feeding produces much better results than dry-feeding. It is pointed out in Chapter XXXV that generally just as satisfactory results are secured when the same feeds are given dry, and much labor and bother is saved.

104. Fermenting, pre-digesting, malting, or sprouting feeds.— From time to time various processes of fermenting or pre-digesting feeds have been exploited by clever promoters. Claims have been made that these processes would save one-third to one-half the feed usually supplied livestock and would result in even better production than normal rations. In these methods the roughage is chopped, treated with a solution containing the "converter," and then allowed to remain in a tank or other container for several hours, where it undergoes fermentation. In some of the methods the concentrates must be mixed with the chopped roughage.

The converter, which usually contains malt, yeast, etc., is supposed to pre-digest the feed and cause other changes. In one process it was even claimed that the converter would change the carbohydrates into protein!

Experiments were conducted by the Ohio and Wisconsin Stations and by the Canadian Department of Agriculture in which three of these processes were carefully tested.[7] Dairy cattle, fattening cattle, and work horses were used in the investigations. In none of the experiments did these expensive methods of feed preparation cause any saving of feed or result in increased production. In the Canadian trials it was found that the fermentation of the roughage resulted in an actual loss of 20 per cent of the protein and 12 per cent of the carbohydrates in the feed.

In an Ohio test malting the entire ration for dairy cows did not improve it.[8] Likewise, in a Wisconsin trial malted corn fodder, including the ears, was decidedly inferior to corn silage.[9] Many years ago it was concluded from English experiments that the malting of barley for dairy cows or fattening cattle decreased its value, instead of increasing it.[10] This was due to the fact that some of the nutrients, chiefly starch, are oxidized in the process of germination.

Before spending money for equipment for any method of fermenting, pre-digesting, or malting feed, the wise farmer will consult the experiment station or agricultural college in his state.

Recently a method of sprouting grain, called the "Spangenberg process," has been advertised as "an 8-day method of growing succulent nutritious livestock food in cabinets without the aid of soil or sunlight." The grain is first soaked and then sprouted on trays in a cabinet, a nutrient solution being supplied. In a magazine article it has been inferred that such processes will do away with the present type of crop production. This entirely disregards the fact that organic matter is made by plants only through the action of sunlight on chlorophyll.

In English tests there was a loss of 25 per cent of the dry matter in grain in the process, instead of a gain.[10a] Such sprouted corn was worth no more for dairy cows than silage or green kale. It is advertised that in the process 10 lbs. of corn will "grow to 40 lbs. of health succulent food." However, this increase is due to the increase in water, and is not an increase in dry matter.

It is shown later that sprouted oats, which has sometimes been recommended as a cure for sterility in cattle, has not produced decisive results. (**533**) The purchase of equipment for sprouting grain does not therefore seem wise, unless at some future time impartial investigations have definitely proved that such feed is superior to the common stock feeds.

II. Factors Influencing the Nutritive Value of Feeds

105. Differences in the composition of feeding stuffs.—Except in the case of feeding stuffs which have undergone changes in composition in recent years, the figures in Appendix Table I are averages of practically all complete analyses of American feeds that have been reported by the experiment stations, the feed control laboratories, and the United States Department of Agriculture. It is obviously important to learn how much the actual composition of any particular lot of a given feed may vary from the average shown for it. Lack of space prohibits any detailed discussion of this question, but the following summary will give a general idea of the range in composition of typical feeding stuffs.[11]

From this summary it will be evident that average figures for the composition of any feeding stuff are but approximately correct when applied to a particular lot of the feed. This likewise applies to any expression of its nutritive value, whether stated in terms of digestible nutrients or of net energy. In other words, different lots of any feeding stuff vary in feeding value, the same as different samples of coal vary in fuel value.

Owing to the expense of obtaining chemical analyses, it is out of the question for any but the most extensive feeders to have their particular feeds analyzed, just as only the large manufacturer can afford to have samples of coal analyzed to determine their fuel value before purchasing. With the cereals and the roughages most stockmen must therefore rely on that average given in tables of digestible nutrients or of net energy values which corresponds most closely in his judgment to the feed at hand.

In purchasing commercial concentrates it is now fortunately possible in most sections of the country to secure standard brands, whose composition is fully guaranteed by the manufacturer.

106. Differences in water content.—Obviously the amount of moisture in grain or any other feed directly affects its nutrient content. Of the cereals, corn commonly varies most in water content. Therefore separate averages are given in Appendix Table I for dent corn of the various Federal grades, which are based largely on the water content.

Such roughages as corn fodder, corn stover, sorghum fodder and sorghum stover also vary widely in water. For example, analyses of corn fodder and corn stover show a water content ranging from over 50 per cent in field-cured material in wet seasons, down to 10 per cent or less in arid regions or when cured under cover in a dry season.

To show the difference in nutritive value of these extremes it may be stated that corn fodder or stover containing 10 per cent water will carry 80 per cent more nutrients per 100 lbs. than a sample of the same forage containing 50 per cent water! To overcome this error so far as possible, separate averages are given for very dry and for ordinary field-cured samples of these feeds in Appendix Table I.

107. Differences in composition of roughages.—Roughages are more variable in composition than most concentrates. Their composition may be greatly affected by the stage of maturity; the water content; the amount of plant food in the soil, especially nitrogen, calcium and phosphorus; and, in the case of hay and other cured forage, by weathering, shattering of the leaves, or leaching during the curing process.

On account of the great differences in the composition of the same variety of hay or other forage, separate averages are given in Appendix Table I for the various grades or qualities of the most important roughages, wherever sufficient data are available. The effects of various factors on the composition and feeding value of hay and other roughage are discussed in some detail in Chapter XI.

It is there pointed out that there may be more actual difference in the feeding value of two lots of the same variety of hay than there is between hay of two entirely different kinds. For example, two loads of alfalfa hay may differ more in value than a load of alfalfa hay and another of timothy hay.

108. Differences in composition of grains.—The climate and the variety are the most important factors influencing the composition of the grains. It is shown in Chapter XVII that there is a wide variation in the percentage of hulls in oats, and therefore in the fiber content and the feeding value of the grain. Oats with shrunken kernels may be fully one-half hulls, while there should not be over 30 per cent of hulls in grain of good quality. Barley also varies in percentage of hulls, though not so much as oats.

The protein content of wheat, oats, and barley is affected very materially by climate, and to a much smaller extent by the variety and other factors. It is pointed out in Chapter XVII that these grains are especially low in protein when grown in certain districts of the Pacific Coast region. Separate averages are therefore given in Appendix Table I for these grains from certain sections of the country.

The composition of corn grain is affected by climate much less than that of these small grains, provided the crop matures. Fraps has shown that under Texas conditions in seasons with abundant rainfall from January to June, the protein content of corn is apt to be slightly less than in dry seasons.[12]

Samples of corn and wheat from the same region may vary 10 per cent and sometimes even more in their content of protein or fat.[13]

The nitrogen-free extract is less variable.

109. Differences in composition of by-product feeds.—Many of the milling and other by-products are composed of a mixture of various portions of the grains or other seeds, and these portions may differ widely in value. Therefore a particular by-product may differ to a considerable extent in composition, depending on the exact process of manufacture. For example, the composition and the nutritive value of such feeds as buckwheat feed and oat mill feed depend on the proportions of hulls and of the more nutritious by-products from the kernels of the seeds. Averages are therefore given in Appendix Table I for the various grades of by-product feeds, where there is a marked difference in their composition.

110. Control of commercial feeding stuffs.—Nearly all the states in this country now have laws regulating the sale of commercial feeds. The inspection and regulation of commercial feeds under these laws are of great benefit, not only to stockmen but also to honest and conscientious feed manufacturers. In most states the laws require that each brand of commercial feed sold in the state be licensed, and that the chemical composition and the various ingredients be definitely guaranteed.

Commonly, there must be attached to each sack of the feed a tag stating the guaranteed composition and the exact ingredients which are contained in the feed. Sometimes the guarantee required by the law covers only the percentages of protein and fat, but more usually the manufacturer must guarantee that the feed contains at least the percentages of protein and fat stated, and also that it does not contain a larger percentage of fiber than is guaranteed.

Samples of the various brands of commercial feeds on the market are taken each year by inspectors sent out by the state department entrusted with the enforcement of the feeding stuffs laws. These samples are analyzed chemically to determine whether the composition conforms to the guarantee. They are also examined by a skilled microscopist to find whether the ingredients actually present in the feed are the same as those guaranteed. In case of violation of the laws, prosecution is brought against the offending manufacturer or dealer.

The results of the examinations of each brand of feed are usually published in detail by the state department in charge of the inspection and control work. These publications supply valuable information to the stockman, for they show him whether or not any particular manufacturer is living up to the guarantees he makes concerning the composition and ingredients of his various brands of feed.

111. A guide in purchasing commercial feeds.—In purchasing unmixed commercial feeds, the guaranteed composition should be compared with the average composition given for the same feed in Appendix Table I. It should be borne in mind that the feeds put on the market by reliable manufacturers are usually slightly higher in protein and fat and slightly lower in fiber than indicated in the guarantee. This is a necessary precaution on the part of the manufacturer, so that any particular lot of feed may not happen to fall below the guarantee.

If the guarantee of the feed is markedly lower in protein or fat, or noticeably higher in fiber than the average shown in Appendix Table I, the feed should be viewed with suspicion. Care must also be taken that the feed be fresh, that it is free from mold or rancidity, and that it corresponds with the descriptions given in later chapters.

In buying commercial mixed feeds, the precautions mentioned in Chapter XIX should be taken.

112. Importance of keeping safely within the guarantee.—It is exceedingly important for the permanent success of any feed manufacturer that his feeds at all times conform strictly to the guarantees of chemical composition and ingredients. Only when this is done, can a reputation for uniform high quality of product be gained.

If a mixed-feed manufacturer does not make actual chemical analyses at frequent intervals of the ingredients he uses and of his mixed feeds, he must take fully into consideration the normal variations in the composition of the ingredients. Otherwise, the mixed feeds may fall below their guarantees. To be safe, the guarantees for protein and fat must be sufficiently below the average composition, and the fiber guarantee enough above the average, so that the feeds will always meet the guarantees.

113. Effect of amount of feed eaten on its utilization.—Experiments have shown that farm animals digest their food somewhat more completely when fed a maintenance ration or a scanty ration, than when a liberal amount of the same feeds is supplied. This may be due to the more rapid movement of the feed through the digestive tract, or to a less complete absorption of the digested nutrients when present in large amount.

When the ration contains a considerable proportion of roughage, however, the difference is not large. In tests with cattle and sheep, from 3 to 9.5 per cent more of the dry matter in a definite mixture of feeds was digested when the animals were fed only enough for maintenance, than when they were fed liberally.[14] When fed hay alone, ruminants may digest a full feed as completely as a scanty feed.[14a]

If a maintenance ration consisting largely of roughage is compared with a liberal ration containing considerable grain, the dry matter in the liberal ration may be digested fully as well or even better than in the maintenance ration.[15] This is because much larger percentages of the nutrients in grain are digested than in hay or other roughage.

There is even more difference in the utilization of the digested nutrients in liberal and scanty rations than there is in the percentage digested. This is well shown in the experiments by Forbes and associates which have been mentioned in the preceding chapter.[16] They found that the net energy value of a feed mixture was 20 per cent less when steers were fed 2.5 times as much as they required for maintenance than when they received only 1.5 times their maintenance needs. Yet there was a difference of only 2.6 per cent in the percentage of dry matter digested in the two rations.

It might seem at first that these differences between the utilization of feed on a liberal ration and on a scanty ration would result in a greater efficiency of production on the scanty ration. It must, however, be borne in mind that an animal can use for the production of meat, milk, or work only the nutrients consumed in excess of the amount needed for the maintenance of its body. Therefore, as is shown in later chapters, if it is fed scantily, it will have available for production only a small proportion of the total feed eaten.

For example, a good dairy cow that is well fed needs about one-half her feed merely to maintain her body. She uses the remaining one-half for milk production. If she is fed only two-thirds as much feed, she will digest the scanty ration somewhat better, but she will still need about as much feed as before to maintain her body. Therefore she will probably have available for milk production only 30 per cent or less of the total feed she eats. It is of great importance in practical stock feeding that this factor usually more than offsets the increased digestibility and percentage utilization of a scanty ration.

Even if a slight reduction from full feeding causes a trifle better percentage utilization of the ration, as may perhaps be the case with fattening pigs, other factors usually make liberal feeding more profitable. Just as in the case of a factory which is run below its normal capacity, the overhead costs in stock feeding are greater when an animal is producing at a low rate. For example, the expense per pound of product for labor, for housing, and for interest on money invested are all much higher when the rate of production is low.

In certain cases it may be advisable for other economic reasons to feed animals less grain or other concentrates than normal. For example, when grain is very high in price in comparison with hay or other roughage, fattening cattle may return the most profit if their allowance of grain is reduced and they are fed all the roughage they will eat.

Again, it may sometimes be most profitable to fatten meat animals more slowly than usual, so as to have them ready for market at a time of the year when prices are usually high. These various matters are discussed in detail in Chapter X and in the chapters of Part III.

114. Effect of proportion of protein on digestibility.—It has been found in numerous investigations that when a ration contains too little protein in proportion to the amounts of easily digested carbohydrates, the digestibility may be seriously reduced.[17]

For example, a study by the author of the results of various digestion experiments shows that when kafir grain has been fed to ruminants in properly balanced rations 81 per cent of the protein, 55 per cent of the fiber, 92 per cent of the nitrogen-free extract, and 76 per cent of the fat were digested, on the average. On the other hand, when kafir has been fed in a ration low in protein, only 47 per cent of the protein, 44 per cent of the fiber, 51 per cent of the nitrogen-free extract, and 51 per cent of the fat were digested. Similar data might be cited for the other grains.

This *depression of digestibility,* as it is called, is obviously of much economic importance, for it is one of the factors causing poor utilization of feed on an unbalanced ration that contains too little protein. In the case of mature fattening cattle or mature work horses, the actual needs of protein for body repair or the making of new protein tissues are very small, as is explained in later chapters. However, because of this depression of digestibility, it is economical to feed such stock somewhat more protein than is needed for their theoretical protein requirements. These facts are fully taken into consideration in the Morrison feeding standards, which are discussed later.

The depression of digestibility occurs with ruminants when the nutritive ratio is wider than about 1:8 or 1:10, but with swine the nutritive ratio may apparently be even wider before the digestibility is affected.

One of the reasons for this poorer digestion of feed on such rations is that when a large proportion of soluble or easily digested carbohydrates is fed, those bacteria in the digestive tract which normally digest cellulose to secure food then attack instead the more readily available sugars or starch. Not only is the digestibility of the cellulose, or fiber, consequently lowered, but also that of the crude protein and nitrogen-free extract, for the unattacked cellulose cell walls protect the proteins and carbohydrates contained therein from the action of the digestive juices.

This depression does not occur when protein-rich feeds are added along with the starch or sugar, thus preserving the balance between protein and non-nitrogenous nutrients. It is assumed that this is due to a stimulation of the bacteria by the addition of more protein, so that, invigorated, they attack the fiber of the food again.

The decrease in the digestibility of protein on a ration low in protein is more apparent than real. The addition of non-nitrogenous food to a ration causes a greater excretion of protein in the feces. The amount of this additional loss depends chiefly on the amount of food added. This larger excretion of protein may consist chiefly, not of undigested protein, but of protein that has been assimilated, but then excreted as a waste. However, from the practical standpoint, the additional wastage of protein is just as truly a loss as though it represented solely a decrease in actual digestibility.

The addition of protein-rich feeds to roughages, such as hay or straw, does not usually increase the actual digestibility of the roughage. However, it may increase the apparent digestibility of the protein.

In conducting digestion trials to determine the digestibility of feeds that are rich in easily-digested carbohydrates, but low in protein, it is exceedingly necessary to add a sufficient amount of protein supplement to the ration to prevent any depression of digestibility. This is well shown in experiments by Holdaway and associates of the Virginia Station.[18] In previous digestion trials made by various investigators, the protein in apple pomace silage, which is very low in protein and very high in easily-digested carbohydrates, apparently was not digested to any appreciable extent. On the other hand, when a sufficient amount of protein supplement was included in the ration, along with the pomace silage, 37 per cent of the protein in the silage was digested, and the digestibility of the nitrogen-free extract was also slightly increased.

115. Effect of proportion of other nutrients.—The addition of molasses to a ration fed ruminants may slightly decrease the digestibility. However, Pennsylvania trials show that the difference is so slight that it is scarcely appreciable in ordinary rations.[19]

Adding fiber to a ration reduces the apparent digestibility of the protein, but not its actual digestibility.[20]

The addition of fat to a ration does not increase the digestibility of the other constituents. It has been found that feeding fat in excess of 1 lb. per 1,000 lbs. live weight or feeding pure fat or oil in unemulsified form may cause digestive disturbance.[21] Salt does not affect digestion, though it may cause animals to eat more food and may improve nutrition.

The addition of dilute acids, such as lactic acid (the chief acid in sour milk and in silage) or of sulfuric acid does not influence digestibility. This is important because silage contains considerable free acid.

116. Effect of other factors in feed.—If green forage is cured without waste and in a manner to prevent fermentation, the mere drying does not appreciably lower its digestibility. Ordinarily, however, losses of some of the finer and more nutritious parts occur in curing forage, and dews, rain, and fermentations cause changes which lower digestibility and decrease the content of nutrients. (See Chapter XI.) Also, more energy is required in masticating dry forage and passing it through the digestive tract than in the case of green fodder. These facts explain why green forage is somewhat more digestible and commonly gives better results than dry forage. The long storage of fodders, even under favorable conditions, decreases both their digestibility and palatability. In the making of brown hay, as is pointed out in Chapter XI, heavy losses of nutrients occur.

A comparison of the digestion coefficients for various kinds of silage with those for the green forages from which the silage was made shows that ensiling tends to decrease rather than increase the digestibility. The exceedingly favorable results from silage feeding are therefore due to the palatability of the silage, its beneficial effect on the health of the stock, and the fact that less feed is wasted than when dry fodder is fed.

If a feed is heated to an unduly high temperature in a manufacturing process, the digestibility may be considerably decreased, especially that of the protein. Thus, it is mentioned in Chapter XVIII that coconut oil meal that has a light color is more digestible than that which has been heated so hot that it is dark in color.

The digestibility of a few feeds is increased markedly by cooking, especially for swine. As is pointed out in later chapters, this is the case with beans, soybeans, and potatoes for swine feeding.

117. Effect of miscellaneous factors.—Neither the frequency of feeding, the time of watering, nor the amount of water drunk appears to influence digestibility. Moderate exercise tends to increase digestibility,[22] but excessive work lowers it.

The flow of saliva and the other digestive juices is checked by fright. On the other hand, kind treatment and palatability of food should favorably influence digestion. Under skillful care animals show remarkable relish for their food, and it is reasonable to conclude that better digestion ensues, though no confirmatory data can be given.

Ruminants—the ox, cow, sheep—digest most kinds of feed about equally well. Kellner, however, showed that cattle are able to digest as much as 11 per cent more of the less digestible roughages, such as straw, than are sheep. He ascribed this difference to the fact that the contents of the last part of the intestine of cattle remain more watery and hence are subject to more complete fermentation. The more easily digested a feeding stuff is, the less difference will there be in its digestion by these various animals.

The horse and pig digest less fiber than the ruminant, in whose paunch the coarse feeds undergo special preparation and digestion. The richer the feed, the more nearly do the digestive powers of the horse approach those of other farm animals. Swine digest the concentrates fully as well as do ruminants, but make only small use of the fiber.

In general, age does not, in itself, influence digestibility, though young farm animals cannot utilize much roughage until their digestive tracts are developed. The digestive power of old animals is often indirectly impaired by poor teeth, which make the proper mastication of their food impossible.

Breed has no influence upon digestibility. Individual animals may, however, show considerable difference in their ability to digest the same ration, though ordinarily the digestibility of a given ration by different animals of the same kind will not vary by more than 3 to 4 per cent.

QUESTIONS

1. What general principles determine whether or not it will pay to grind or crush a certain kind of grain for a particular class of stock?
2. To what degree of fineness should grain ordinarily be ground for stock feeding?
3. Discuss the chopping of hay or other roughage for livestock; the grinding of hay or other roughage.
4. Under what conditions may it be wise to mix cut or ground roughage with concentrates?

5. Discuss the cooking of feed for cattle; for swine.
6. When would you soak feed for stock or feed slop to pigs?
7. Discuss the fermenting, pre-digesting, and malting of feeds.
8. Give an example of the effect of a difference in water content on the value of a feed.
9. What factors affect the composition of roughages?
10. What is the chief factor affecting the composition of the wheat grain? State its effect.
11. Tell how a farmer should utilize the results of the feed inspection service in his state.
12. Discuss the effect of the amount of feed eaten on its utilization. Should dairy cows or fattening stock be fed scantily, in order that they will digest their rations most completely?
13. Discuss the "depression of digestibility" caused by a lack of protein in the ration.
14. State the effect on digestibility of: (a) adding molasses to a ration for ruminants; (b) adding fat to a ration; (c) adding dilute acids.
15. Why is green forage usually somewhat more digestible than the same forage after field curing?
16. What is the effect on digestibility of: (a) ensiling green forage; (b) heating feed to a high temperature; (c) cooking beans, soybeans, or potatoes for swine?
17. Discuss the effect on digestibility of time of watering; exercise; kind of animal; and age of animal.

REFERENCES

1. Vestal and Hienton, Ind. Rpt. 1929 and mimeo. rpts.; see also: Fenton and Logan, Kan. Engineering Expt. Sta. Bul. 27; Silver, Ohio Bul. 490.
2. Bohstedt, Roche, Fargo, Rupel, and Duffee, Wis. Bul. 421.
3. Rusk and Snapp, Ill. Rpt. 1931.
4. Forbes, Fries, and Braman, Jour. Agr. Res., 31, 1925, pp. 987-995; Penn. Bul. 196; see also: Kellner, Ernähr. landw. Nutztiere, 6th ed., p. 266.
5. Ladd, N. Y. (Geneva) Rpt. 1885; Hornberger, Landw. Jahrb., 8, p. 933.
6. Bohstedt, Bell, and Gerlaugh, Ohio Special Cir. 10.
7. Perkins and Monroe, Ohio Bimo. Bul. 134; Monroe and Hayden, Ohio Bimo. Bul. 150; Hayden and Monroe, Ohio Bul. 470; Bohstedt, Bell, and Gerlaugh, Ohio Special Cir. 10; Morrison, Humphrey, Fuller, Roche, and Wolberg, Wis. Bul. 396; Rupel, Roche, Bohstedt, and Fuller, Wis. Res. Bul. 102; Canada Dept. Agr. Bul. 96.
8. Hayden and Monroe, Ohio Bul. 446.
9. Morrison, Wis. Sta., unpublished data.
10. Lawes and Gilbert, Rothamsted Memoirs, Vol. IV.
10a. Rept. Nat. Instit. Res. Dairying, Reading, England; Mo. Bul. Agr. Sci. Pract. 26, 1935, 62T-86T.
11. For a more detailed discussion of the variations in the composition of feeding stuffs, see: Fraps, Texas Bul. 461.
12. Fraps, Texas Bul. 422.
13. Grindley, Ill. Bul. 165.
14. Jordan, N. Y. (Geneva) Bul. 141; Mumford, Grindley, Hall and Emmett, Ill. Bul. 172; Eckles, Mo. Res. Bul. 7; Perkins and Monroe, Ohio Bul. 376; Forbes, Braman, Kriss, et al., Jour. Agr. Res., 37, 1928, pp. 253-300; 40, 1930, pp. 37-78; Mitchell, Hamilton, et al., Jour. Agr. Res., 45, 1932, pp. 163-191; Schneider and Ellenberger, Vt. Bul. 270; Honcamp and Koch, Land. Vers. Stat., 96, 1920, pp. 45-120.
14a. Watson, Muir, and Davidson, Sci. Agr., Canada, 15, 1935, pp. 476-487.
15. Ritzman and Benedict, N. H. Tech. Bul. 26.
16. Forbes, Braman, Kriss, et al., Jour. Agr. Res., 40, 1930, pp. 37-38.
17. Armsby, The Nutrition of Farm Animals, pp. 616-622; Perkins and Monroe, Jour. Dairy Sci., 8, 1925, pp. 405-414; Schneider and Ellenberger, Vt. Bul. 270.
18. Holdaway, Ellett, Eheart, and Miller, Va. Tech. Bul. 32; see also: Holdaway, Ellett, and Eheart, Va. Tech. Bul. 38.
19. Williams, Jour. Dairy Sci., 8, 1925, pp. 94-104.
20. Titus, New Mexico Bul. 153.
21. Kellner, Ernähr. landw. Nutztiere, 1907, p. 51.
22. Schneider and Ellenberger, Vt. Bul. 262.

CHAPTER V

MAINTAINING FARM ANIMALS

I. Requirements for Heat and Energy

118. Maintenance needs of animals.—Farm animals are given food in order that they may convert it into useful products, such as meat, milk, wool, or work. However, before any continued yield of product is possible, they must first be supplied with sufficient food for their essential life processes.

The amount of food which is required merely to support the animal when doing no work and yielding no material product, is called the *maintenance ration*. When an animal is receiving a maintenance ration, its body will neither gain nor lose in protein, fat, or mineral matter. On the average, fully one-half of the feed consumed by farm animals is used simply for maintenance, only the remainder being turned into useful products. Thus it is highly important to understand the principles governing the maintenance requirements.

To maintain an animal at rest without losing or gaining in weight, it must have adequate supplies of the following: (1) Heat to maintain the body temperature; (2) energy to carry on such vital functions as the work of the heart, lungs, etc.; (3) protein to repair the small daily waste of protein tissues; (4) mineral matter to replace the small but continuous loss of minerals; (5) vitamins, which are necessary for the performance of the life processes; (6) water; and (7) air. As mentioned later, it is possible that small amounts of certain fatty acids are also needed for maintenance.

119. Maintaining the body temperature.—The average body temperatures of the various classes of larger farm animals range from 100.2° F. for horses to 103.5° F. for sheep. Since these are temperatures which the air reaches only on the hottest summer days, it is evident that heat must continuously be produced in the bodies of farm animals to keep them warm.

Heat is produced by all the oxidations which take place in the body, no matter whether of food yet within the digestive tract, or of nutrients in the muscles or other tissues of the body. It has been shown in Chapters II and III that considerable heat is generated, especially with ruminants, in the fermentations of cellulose and other carbohydrates that occur in the digestive tract. The rest of the heat is produced by the oxidation of nutrients in the tissues of the body. (**62**)

All the energy used up in the various forms of internal work of the body is finally changed to heat. Though this energy is lost so far as useful production is concerned, the heat formed helps to maintain the body temperature. The amount of heat so produced is considerable. Even with such an easily digested feed as corn, nearly one-half of the total energy which the digestible nutrients furnish is converted into heat in the processes of mastication, digestion, and assimilation. With roughages, such as hay and straw, the proportion is much larger.

However, in the case of animals exercising normally, the larger part of the body heat is produced in the muscles, since all muscular contraction is caused by the oxidation of nutrients in the muscles. Even when the muscles are not actively contracting, some heat is being generated in them.

When an animal is not moving about or even standing upright, the muscles are nevertheless in a state of some tension, and a small amount of nutrients must be continually oxidized to produce the force required for this tenseness.

Unlike the burning of fuel in a stove, the oxidations in the body take place at a comparatively low temperature. In still another respect, the body oxidations differ radically from ordinary burning of fuel. In a furnace the wider the draft is opened, increasing the supply of oxygen, the more rapid will be the combustion. However, in the body, so long as there is a normal supply of oxygen, the rate of burning of the food nutrients is independent of the supply of air. Hence the greater intake of oxygen in unusually deep breathing will not in itself cause an increase in heat production, though the increased muscular work in such breathing may lead to a slight increase in the production of heat.

120. Normal body temperatures of different farm animals.—The normal temperature of different animals of the same species may vary considerably. On the other hand, the temperature of an individual animal, if healthy, varies only within a narrow limit, a departure of even one degree from normal with farm animals generally indicating some bodily derangement.

The normal body temperature of mature horses ranges from 98.4°-100.8° F. (36.9°-38.2° C.) and averages about 100.2° F. For mature cattle the range is from 100.4°-102.8° F. (38.0°-39.3° C.) and the average about 101.5° F. The range of normal temperature is greater in sheep and swine than in horses and cattle. In sheep the range is 101.3°-105.8° F. (38.4°-41.0° C.) and the average about 103.5° F. In swine the range is 100.9°-105.4° F. (38.2°-40.7° C.) and the average about 102.6° F.

121. Regulation of body temperature.—Not only must heat be continuously produced in the body, but the temperature must be kept constant under varying external conditions and with supplies of food differing from day to day in amount and heat-producing power. This is done, first of all, by regulating the loss of heat from the body, which is called *physical regulation.* In cold weather insufficient heat may be generated in the normal processes of the body to maintain the temperature, and then there is an involuntary rise in the production of heat by increasing the oxidations of nutrients in the tissues. This is called *chemical regulation.*

The most important means of regulating the loss of heat is by varying the circulation of the blood near the surface of the body. When the body temperature rises, more blood flows to the capillaries of the skin, increasing the loss of heat by radiation and conduction from the surface of the body. It is this which causes the flushing of the skin commonly observed when one becomes heated. This means of regulation may be compared to opening the windows when a room becomes too hot.

If this means of control is not sufficient to keep the body temperature normal, sweat is produced, the evaporation of which cools the surface of the body. If the animal has only a few sweat glands, as in the case of swine or dogs, it will begin to pant. This increases the loss of heat by the vaporization of water from the lungs and mouth, and also increases the loss of heat through warming the large amount of air breathed in and out. The dog will not only pant, but also will extend his tongue so as to expose the wet surface to the air, in order to increase the loss of heat by the evaporation of water.

In addition to these means of regulating the loss of heat, the clothing of man, and the hair, wool, feathers, or thick skin of animals check and control its loss from the body. Also, when an animal is sleeping, it will tend to curl up if it is cold and to stretch out when it is hot, thus decreasing or increasing the amount of body surface exposed.

Even when an animal is not visibly sweating, a considerable part of the heat loss is through the evaporation of water from the surface of the body in the form of insensible perspiration, in which there is no visible sweat on the skin. From studies of milk cows at the New Hampshire Station, Ritzman and Benedict concluded that insensible perspiration was the safety valve by which the animal eliminated excess heat under high pressure of metabolism.[1]

In Illinois tests with steers Mitchell and Hamilton found that the percentage of heat lost by the vaporization of water (including the loss both from the skin and from the lungs) increased as the temperature rose.[2] Even at an air temperature of 69° F., which is not unduly warm, as much as 40 to 50 per cent of the total loss of heat was by this means.

When the temperature of the air is too cold, the chemical method of temperature regulation must be brought into action. The oxidation of nutrients in the tissues must be increased solely to keep the animal warm. This may be accomplished more or less voluntarily in part, but it may also be entirely involuntary. On cold days, for example, animals eat more heartily and take more exercise than in warm weather, both of which result in the production of more heat.

A low external temperature also causes an involuntary stimulation of the oxidations going on in the tissues, which may even become visible in the shivering of the chilled animal. This is the outward manifestation of increased muscular contractions, started to produce more heat.

The temperature of the air below which the oxidations in the body must be increased to keep an animal warm is called the *critical temperature* for that animal. The exact temperature will depend on the species of animal; on its coat of hair, wool, or feathers; on its degree of fatness; and, especially, on how liberally it is being fed.

In the case of a fattening animal given all it will eat, much heat is unavoidably produced in the mastication, digestion, and assimilation of the ration. Except in unusually cold weather, the heat thus formed is sufficient to keep the animal warm.

For this reason, except in cold climates, cattle and sheep fattened in winter will make just as economical gains when fed in an open shed as when housed in a warmer stable. The critical temperatures for farm animals with winter coats and which are fed maintenance rations are probably somewhat below 60° F. For fasting animals with normal coats the critical temperatures usually range between 60° and 70° F.[3] In the

One-half Their Feed Is Needed for Maintenance

Even good dairy cows require for the mere maintenance of their bodies about one-half the total feed they consume. Only the remainder can be used for milk production.

Fattening Stock Do Not Need Warm Shelter

Heavily-fed fattening steers need no winter shelter except an open shed, for an abundance of heat is unavoidably produced in the digestion of their liberal rations. On the other hand, animals being carried through the winter cn scanty rations may require less feed in warmer quarters.

Farm Animals Should Have Plenty of Water

All classes of stock should have all the water they will drink. Horses doing hard work in summer need an especially liberal supply, and they are benefited by watering them at reasonably frequent intervals.

A Fine Herd in a Well-Ventilated, Well-Lighted Stable

An efficient ventilation system is important in closed stables. Likewise, the stable should be well lighted, and the cows should be housed so that they are comfortable. (Jersey herd at Indiana Station, Purdue University.)

case of a man wearing ordinary clothing, the critical temperature is about 49° F., and for swine it is 68° F. or more.

Any external conditions that increase or decrease the loss of heat from the body affect the critical temperature. For example, wind striking the body continuously removes the layer of partially-warmed air next to the skin, and thus increases the loss of heat. Therefore a cold temperature is felt much more on a windy day, and wind makes hot weather less uncomfortable.

Moistness of the air increases the conducting power of the hair, wool, or clothing, and therefore animals feel the effects of damp, cold weather much more than of dry cold. In hot weather a high humidity, or moisture content of the air, lessens the rate of evaporation of water from the body, and therefore the loss of heat. This is why animals suffer much more on a humid, or "sultry," hot day than on a day equally hot, when the air is drier.

Because the loss of heat is largely controlled by the clothing he wears, man has, in some measure, lost his power of heat regulation. With many of the warm-blooded animals, however, this power is highly developed, and they can adapt themselves to great extremes of external temperature.

122. Energy required for vital functions.—In a maintenance ration a certain amount of net energy must be supplied for the various activities of the body when it is idle. Even when an animal is not eating food or digesting or assimilating a meal, energy is required for the work of the heart, lungs, and other internal organs. Also, as has been pointed out previously, nutrients are constantly being oxidized in the muscles to keep them in a state of tension.

When an animal is standing, more nutrients must be oxidized than when it is lying at rest, as the muscles are under greater tension. If it moves about, a still larger amount is needed to furnish the energy required for the movements. All of the energy used for these body needs is finally transformed into heat, and thus aids in keeping the animal warm.

Experiments have shown that with a mature animal being maintained at rest in the stall the requirement for fuel to keep up the body temperature is usually much greater than the amount of net energy needed for the internal work of the body organs. For example, to maintain the horse at rest only one-third of the total energy of the ration need be supplied in the form of net energy, the remainder serving simply as body fuel.

Maintenance rations for livestock, except swine and poultry, may therefore consist largely of roughages, such as hay and straw, which furnish abundant heat, but do not yield much net energy. Since the ration must furnish at least a minimum amount of net energy, animals cannot be maintained without loss of weight on such a feed as wheat straw alone, which furnishes no net energy to the horse and but little to the ruminant.

123. Total digestible nutrients required for maintenance.—Numerous studies have been made of the amounts of total digestible nutrients or of net energy required for the maintenance of animals. One method of conducting such experiments is to determine the minimum amount of a suitable ration that will actually maintain the animal over long periods of time in a thrifty condition, without gain or loss in weight. In such experiments care must be taken that the ration tested contains adequate supplies of protein, minerals, and vitamins.

Unless such investigations are continued for long periods, the results may not be entirely accurate. This is because the animal may not decrease in body weight, even when there is some loss of protein or fat, because there may be a compensating increase in the water content of the body. However, when such experiments are conducted for many months and with a sufficiently large number of animals, they provide the most reliable data concerning the actual amounts of nutrients required for proper maintenance.

The most extensive of such studies are those of Hills, who conducted investigations on the maintenance requirements of dairy cows at the Vermont Station over a period of 13 years.[4] The experiments included tests upon 20 different cows for periods ranging from 391 to 2,701 days. From these studies Hills concluded that a ration supplying 6.48 lbs. of total digestible nutrients, or 6 therms of net energy per day was sufficient for the maintenance of the 1,000-lb. dry, non-pregnant cow.

This is the same recommendation for the maintenance of cattle made somewhat earlier by Armsby, based upon his investigations with steers and upon a study of the results secured by others. This amount of nutrients is somewhat smaller than the 7.925 lbs. of total digestible nutrients recommended by Haecker for the maintenance of the 1,000-lb. dairy cow, based on his investigations at the Minnesota Station.[5]

It has been shown in the previous chapter that a liberal ration is not digested and utilized quite so completely as a scanty ration. (**67**) For this reason, as is pointed out in Chapter XXIV, a cow in milk which is fed with the liberality necessary to produce a good yield of milk undoubtedly needs more feed for mere body maintenance than she would if she were fed a scanty ration that would be sufficient to maintain her weight when dry. (**796**)

The data secured in investigations on the maintenance requirements of other classes of stock are summarized in the chapters of Part III.

Another method of studying the maintenance requirements for energy is to determine in a respiration apparatus or a calorimeter the amount of heat produced by an animal when at rest, and when a sufficient time has elapsed since the last meal so that there is no longer an increased production of heat due to the digestion and assimilation of food. This is called the *basal metabolism,* or the fasting metabolism, of the animal. Such determinations cannot be made until considerable time has elapsed since food has been eaten, because the heat production of the body is greatly increased while food is being assimilated. Thus in New Hampshire experiments dry cows produced 50 to 60 per cent more heat on a maintenance ration than on the second day of fast.[6] In determinations of the basal metabolism of humans, the experiments are made 12 to 18 hours after the last meal. In the case of farm animals, especially ruminants and horses, a much longer period of fasting is required to reach the same state. This is because of the slow passage of feed through their digestive tracts. Therefore, what is termed the *resting metabolism* is sometimes determined, the experiments being conducted 12 hours after the last meal. This resting metabolism may be considerably higher than the theoretical basal metabolism.

The basal metabolism does not represent the total amount of nutrients or energy required for maintenance, but only the minimum amount of energy expended by the animal when at rest and consuming no food. To this amount must be added the amount used in the so-called "work of digestion," which has been discussed in Chapter III. (86) Also the amount of energy expended in the normal motions of the animal must be added to the basal metabolism.

From studies at the Missouri Station, Brody and associates have concluded that the maintenance requirements of mature animals at air temperatures above the critical temperature are about twice the basal metabolism.[7] At lower temperatures, as in the case of animals exposed to winter temperatures in the northern states, the maintenance requirements would be higher.

124. Maintenance requirements not proportional to weight.—If we compare the maintenance requirements for total digestible nutrients or energy by animals of various sizes, it is found that they are more nearly proportional to body surface than to live weight. For example, a cow weighing 1,600 lbs. does not require twice as much total digestible nutrients for maintenance as one weighing 800 lbs. Similarly, the 800-lb. cow does not require anywhere near eight times as much nutrients for maintenance as a sheep weighing 100 lbs.

This difference is due to two factors: First, the chief loss of heat from the body is by radiation and conduction from the body surface. Therefore this loss is proportional to the surface. Large bodies have less surface per pound of weight than smaller ones. Thus the 1,600-lb. cow has much less body surface than two 800-lb. cows.

Second, as Brody and others have pointed out, the weight of the most active tissues of the body (the internal organs, the glands, etc.) in animals of different sizes is more nearly proportional to the surfaces of their bodies than to their live weights.[8] Thus the 1,600-lb. cow does not have twice as great a weight of these more active tissues (called the *active protoplasmic mass*) as does the 800-lb. cow.

It was concluded from earlier investigations that the maintenance requirements of animals of various live weights were proportional to their body surfaces. These are proportional to the two-thirds powers of their live weights (the cube roots of the squares of the live weights). From recent studies at the Missouri Station, Brody and associates have concluded that the basal metabolism, and therefore the maintenance requirements for energy or total digestible nutrients, of animals of various sizes are proportional to the 0.73 power of their live weights.[9] Kleiber of the California Station has reached similar conclusions.[10]

On the basis of his studies, Brody has presented feeding standards for the maintenance of animals of various weights. These data have been taken into consideration in the recommendations presented in the Morrison feeding standards for the maintenance of the various classes of stock. (Appendix Table III.)

It will be noted that in these standards somewhat more nutrients are advised for maintaining the 1,000-lb. horse than for the 1,000-lb. cow or steer. This is because idle horses which are being maintained must be allowed plenty of exercise, and not be closely confined for long periods, or their legs may be injured by inactivity. When allowed to exercise, they are much more restless and active than cattle, and therefore use up more nutrients per day.

125. Factors affecting maintenance requirements.—Any of the factors, discussed in the previous chapter, which decrease the digestibility or utilization of the food will obviously increase the amount of feed required for maintenance. (**114-117**) Also, any condition that increases the oxidation of nutrients in the body tissues will likewise increase the maintenance requirements.[11]

Differences in temperament and activity may produce marked variations in the maintenance requirements of individual animals of the same size and species, kept under identical conditions. As restlessness causes greater muscular activity, a quiet animal requires less food for maintenance than a nervous, active one. This is one of the main reasons why a fattening animal that will "eat and lie down" makes the most economical gains. This effect of difference in temperament also explains why some horses are much "easier keepers" than others.

When an animal that has been more liberally fed is first put on a maintenance ration, more feed may at first be required to maintain its weight than later. Apparently, after it has been on the scanty food supply for some time, it gets on a more economical basis and is able to digest and utilize its feed more efficiently. However, if an animal is unthrifty, because of semi-starvation or illness, its maintenance requirements will be higher than normal.

An animal requires more feed to maintain its live weight after it is fattened than before. This is partly because it is heavier and has a larger body surface. Also, the fat condition itself may increase the maintenance requirement per unit of weight or body surface.[12] In very cold weather, however, a blanket of fat might reduce the maintenance need, by insulating the animal against the cold.

Young animals require considerably more feed to maintain them at constant weight than mature animals of the same size or body weight.[13] This is due to a higher rate of metabolism and at least partly to their greater activity. Males of dairy cattle and swine have higher maintenance requirements than females per unit of weight, according to Missouri tests.[14] Castrated male cattle or sheep had about the same maintenance requirements as females.

As has been mentioned previously, more nutrients must be oxidized when an animal is standing up than when lying down. In the case of cattle and sheep the increases in heat production when standing averaged only about 9 per cent in numerous Missouri tests.[15] In other experiments the increases have often been much greater, perhaps due to greater restlessness of the animals when standing.[16]

In the northern states the maintenance requirements of animals are generally higher in winter than in summer, unless they are warmly housed.[17] Exposure of animals to cold air temperatures increases the loss of heat by radiation, especially if they have scanty coats. If their coats are wet by cold rain or snow, still more heat is lost, for the cold water must be warmed and evaporated by heat generated through the burning of food.

With the well-fed fattening animal, the greater loss of heat through these causes may not produce any waste of food, for much more heat is being generated in the mastication, digestion, and assimilation of the heavy ration than is normally needed to warm the body. In the case of animals on a maintenance ration, whose chief demand is for body fuel, such exposure will necessitate an increased consumption of feed to serve as fuel. On the other hand, too high a temperature may increase the maintenance requirements, for energy may actually be expended in keeping the body from becoming too warm. Therefore the maintenance requirement may be higher in hot summer weather than in spring or autumn.

126. Source of nutrients during starvation.—When an animal is given no food, the heat needed to warm the body, the net energy required to carry on the vital processes, and the protein and mineral matter necessary for the repair of the active tissues must all come from nutrients previously stored within the body. The small supply of glycogen in the liver and muscles is probably first used as fuel, but this is soon gone. Fat is the animal's chief reserve fuel, stored when food is abundant, against times of scarcity, and is therefore the main source of both heat and energy during starvation.

When the supply of fat begins to fail, the muscles and other protein tissues are broken down more rapidly to furnish heat and energy, and the animal finally perishes through the impairment of its organs and the lack of body fuel to carry on the functions of life. Carnivora, or flesh-eating animals, withstand hunger longer than herbivora. While dogs and cats have lived until their weights were decreased 33 to 40 per cent, horses and ruminants will die when their weight has been reduced 20 to 25 per cent.

Men have survived fasts of 30 to 75 days, and dogs have endured fasts of from 90 to 117 days without permanent ill effects. The age of the animal influences the time at which death occurs from starvation, young animals losing weight more rapidly and dying after a smaller loss of weight than old ones.

II. Requirements for Protein, Minerals, and Vitamins

127. Protein required for maintenance.—The needs of the body for heat and energy can be met through feeding carbohydrates and fat. However, an abundant amount of these nutrients alone will not prevent starvation, for there must also be a supply of protein to replace the daily break-down or wear of the protein tissues of the body. Likewise, protein must be provided for the growth of the hair or wool and of the skin and hoofs, which are all chiefly composed of protein.

Since protein-rich feeds are generally more expensive than those rich in carbohydrates, it is of much importance to know the minimum amount of protein needed to maintain animals in good health. Fortunately, the daily need of protein for mere body maintenance is relatively small. Thus, it has been estimated that in humans only 0.1 to 0.2 per cent of the total protein tissues of the body is broken down each day. At this rate the entire amount of protein would be replaced in 500 to 1,000 days.

While we generally speak of the protein requirements of the body, undoubtedly what the body actually needs is not certain proteins, but definite amounts of the various essential amino acids. These amino acids, as has been stated in Chapter II, are carried from the digestive tract to nourish the various body tissues. (**60-61**) Each tissue selects from the mixture of amino acids in the blood the particular amounts and kinds of amino acids that it needs. If any excess of amino acids is furnished by the digested food, the nitrogen is split off as ammonia by the liver, and then converted chiefly into urea in the case of most mammals. This nitrogenous waste is excreted by the kidneys. The non-nitrogenous residue from the excess amino acids can then be used as a source of heat or energy, just as in the case of the carbohydrates.

It is evident from the foregoing that not only must the food provide a sufficient amount of digestible protein for maintenance, but that the protein must be of proper quality. In other words, there must be adequate amounts of each of the essential amino acids.

The knowledge on this subject is still far too fragmentary to warrant estimates of the exact amounts of the various essential amino acids required for maintenance or other body functions. All that can be done in feeding standards is to advise certain amounts of digestible protein, on the assumption that reasonable care will be taken to provide protein of a quality that is satisfactory for the particular class of animal. The quality or kind of proteins in various feeds and rations is discussed in detail in the following chapter.

128. Determining the minimum protein requirement.—In determining the minimum amount of protein needed for maintaining any particular class of animals, care must first be taken that they receive sufficient carbohydrates and fat to meet the needs of the body for heat and energy. If this is not done, some of the amino acids resulting from the digestion of the protein will be oxidized as a source of heat or energy. Thus the nitrogen will be wasted, and therefore will not be available for the repair of the protein tissues of the body.

Also, feeding an abundance of carbohydrates has a special "protein-sparing" effect. In other words, less protein is needed for maintenance when the ration contains a liberal amount of carbohydrates. This may be due to some ability of the body tissues to synthesize or make certain amino acids. Possibly this can be done by combining organic acids formed from the carbohydrates, with ammonia or other simple nitrogenous compounds produced in the break-down of body tissues.

When ample amounts of carbohydrates and fats have been fed, animals have been maintained on relatively small amounts of digestible protein, without loss of protein from the body. Dry cows and steers have even been maintained on only 0.21 to 0.27 lb. digestible protein daily per 1,000 lbs. live weight. Armsby, who devoted much study to this question, considered such results exceptional, and reported that in other similar trials by various investigators from 0.43 to 0.75 lb. of digestible protein daily per 1,000 lbs. live weight had been required for the maintenance of cattle, with an average of 0.55 lb.[18] On this basis Armsby recommended 0.6 lb. digestible protein or 0.5 lb. digestible true protein daily per 1,000 lbs. live weight for the maintenance of cattle.

From extensive investigations at the Vermont Station with dairy cows, Hills concluded that 0.6 lb. digestible protein daily is sufficient for the maintenance of dry cows which are not pregnant.[19] Experiments at the Ohio Station and in Germany also indicate that this allowance of protein is sufficient for the maintenance of dry, non-pregnant cows.[20] Obviously cows that are pregnant will need a somewhat larger amount, at least during the latter part of gestation, when growth of the fetus is most rapid.

The protein requirements for the maintenance of other classes of livestock are discussed in the respective chapters of Part III. The requirements per 1,000 lbs. live weight for horses are apparently about the same as for cattle, but sheep need more protein on account of the growth of the wool. Swine likewise require more protein per 1,000 lbs. live weight than do cattle.

Studies on the protein requirements of animals have also been conducted by determining the amounts of protein lost from the body on a ration containing no protein, but which supplies an abundance of carbohydrates and fat. On such a ration, the amino acids needed for maintenance must be secured by a gradual tearing down or wasting away of the protein tissues of the body.

From such experiments and from similar investigations of others, Mitchell and associates have concluded that the 1,000-lb. animal will lose about 0.175 lb. protein daily on a protein-free ration, and that twice this amount of digestible protein in the food, or only 0.35 lb., is enough for maintenance.[21] This conclusion is based on the assumption that the proteins in the usual maintenance ration can be used for the repair of body tissue with an efficiency of 50 per cent.

Since it has not been proved by long-time feeding experiments that animals can actually be maintained in good health on this small amount of protein, the author has preferred not to recommend such small amounts in the feeding standards presented in Appendix Table III. Instead, the more conservative recommendations of Armsby and Hills have been followed.

Before feeding any class of stock a ration exceedingly low in protein, the following should be fully considered. First, in such a ration the digestibility of the protein and other nutrients is often seriously decreased. (**114**) This causes a wastage of feed. Also, it is the belief of many that a supply somewhat above the minimum promotes the health of the animal.[22]

129. Relation of protein requirements to live weight.—Until recently it has been generally believed that the amounts of digestible protein required for the maintenance of animals of various sizes, were proportional to their live weights. Thus, it was assumed that the 1,600-lb. cow would require twice as much protein for maintenance as an 800-lb. cow.

Recent investigations indicate, however, that the maintenance requirements for protein may be more nearly proportional to the body surface than to the live weight.[23] Brody and associates concluded from experiments at the Missouri Station and from a study of other available data that the maintenance requirements for digestible protein for mature animals of various sizes and species are proportional to the 0.72 power of their live weights.[24] This was the same trend that was found in the case of the energy requirements. However, in the case of growing rats the maintenance requirement for protein was more nearly proportional to live weight than to the energy requirement or body surface.

130. Protein loss in starvation.—To secure information on the requirement for protein by various animals, experiments have been conducted in which all feed has been withheld for varying lengths of time. When an animal is given no food, the nitrogen excretion (representing the loss of protein from the body) decreases rapidly at first, until the supply of amino acids in the blood and tissues, which have not yet been built into body protein, is lowered to a minimum.

The nitrogen waste in the urine then slowly decreases until it reaches a level that remains quite constant so long as heat and energy are furnished by the body fat. When the supply of the latter begins to fail, the muscles and other protein tissues must thereafter not only furnish protein for the repair of the vital body machinery, but they must also supply the necessary heat and energy; consequently they waste more rapidly until death follows.

We might expect that when protein only is fed to a fasting animal, in an amount corresponding to the quantity lost daily during starvation, it would replace the protein wasted from the tissues, and the animal thus be brought to nitrogen equilibrium; that is, it would excrete as much, but no more, nitrogen than was contained in the food. However, when protein is fed under such conditions, the amount of nitrogen excreted at once rises, and though the loss of nitrogen from the tissues is reduced, nitrogen equilibrium is not reached.

When practically pure protein is fed, the loss of nitrogen can be stopped only if the supply is far in excess of the waste from the starving body. It is assumed that this increase in nitrogen waste when protein is fed in such large proportions is due to a flooding of the tissues with amino acids, the products of protein digestion.

When animals are fed exclusively on nitrogen-free nutrients, such as the sugars, starches, fats, etc., the wasting away of the nitrogenous tissues of the body, such as the muscles, is somewhat reduced, though not entirely stopped. Therefore, animals forced to live on such a diet survive longer than those wholly deprived of food. Yet because of the continuous small waste of protein from the tissues of the body, animals nourished solely on fats and carbohydrates cannot long survive.

131. Mineral requirements for maintenance.—The necessity of an adequate supply of minerals in maintenance rations has been shown by giving animals sufficient food, but food from which the minerals have been removed as completely as possible. Even though the rations contain an abundance of protein, carbohydrates, and fat, the animals will die from mineral starvation, and generally the end will come sooner than if no food at all is given.

Mineral matter is found in all the vital parts of the body and in some mysterious manner the mineral compounds direct and control all the life processes. The life centers of all the cells are rich in phosphorus, and the skeleton is largely composed of calcium combined with phosphorus. As we have seen, the power of the blood to carry oxygen is due to hemoglobin, an iron protein compound in the red blood corpuscles. (**62**) In the stomach, the pepsin acts only in the presence of hydrochloric acid, a compound formed from mineral salts contained in the blood.

When an animal is merely being maintained, it is making no growth in skeleton or in protein tissues and is yielding no product. Therefore the mineral requirements for maintenance are relatively small, particularly in comparison with those for growth or milk production. But little definite information is available on the requirements for the different minerals. There is no question, however, but that common salt should ordinarily be supplied, even when livestock are not being fed for production. Care must also be taken that the ration provides the small amounts of calcium and phosphorus needed to replace the daily losses from the body. The other necessary minerals are usually furnished in sufficient amounts by the ordinary feeding stuffs.

The importance and functions of each of the necessary mineral nutrients are treated in detail in the following chapter, and recommendations are given with reference to the use of mineral supplements for the various classes of stock.

132. Vitamin requirements for maintenance.—The functions of each of the several vitamins are discussed in the following chapter, and information is given on the vitamin requirements of the various classes of stock, so far as it is available. Most of the vitamin investigations have been conducted to determine the vitamin needs for growth, for milk production, and for egg production, and but little specific information has been secured on the maintenance requirements.

It is known, however, that mature animals can be maintained in good health on considerably smaller supplies of vitamins than are required by young growing animals or by mature animals that are producing milk or eggs. Nevertheless, to insure against injury due to a lack of these nutritive factors, one should be sure that even maintenance rations provide an ample supply of the necessary vitamins, especially vitamins A and D.

III. Additional Requirements

133. Air requirements; ventilation of stables.—While animals can go without food for considerable periods, complete lack of air brings sudden death, since a continuous supply of oxygen is required for all vital processes. (**62**) There is no lack of oxygen in the air of any ordinary stable, even if it is not especially ventilated. However, for other reasons an efficient ventilation system should be provided in closed stables. This will not only make the animals much more comfortable, but it will also prevent undue moisture in the barn and will get rid of foul odors. Proper ventilation consists in maintaining a comfortable stable temperature and a relatively low humidity of the air, without drafts in the stable.[25]

We have all experienced the ill effects of poorly-ventilated rooms. These effects include depression, drowsiness, headache, and a reduced ability to do mental or physical work. It was believed earlier that the evil results of a lack of ventilation were due to an increase in the carbon-dioxide content of the air and a decrease in the oxygen, and also to a poisonous or injurious substance in the air breathed out by animals. More recent investigations have proved that these beliefs were untrue.

Outdoor air contains 20.93 per cent oxygen by volume and only 0.03 per cent carbon dioxide. The carbon-dioxide content of air can be increased to a much higher percentage than occurs in most poorly-ventilated stables, without causing any appreciable discomfort to stock. Likewise the oxygen content of the air can be reduced more than occurs in such stables, without producing any observable effect.

The discomfort experienced in poorly-ventilated quarters is apparently due, not to the change in the carbon-dioxide or oxygen content of the air, but chiefly to an increase in the humidity, produced by the water vapor in the air exhaled. Also, in warm weather the air temperature may rise to an uncomfortable level, because of the heat given off by the animals.

One of the most important benefits from proper ventilation of a stable, along with suitable insulation of the walls, is that it prevents the condensation of moisture in the barn. Without a ventilating system in a closed stable, water will often condense on the walls and windows to such an extent that serious rotting of the timber will result. Also, so much water may condense in the hay mows as to cause spoilage. The coats of the animals may also become damp, causing discomfort or even disease.

Dryness checks bacterial growth, while dampness favors it. For this reason alone, there is apt to be more trouble from disease when the stable is poorly ventilated.

134. Water requirements.—An abundant supply of water is necessary for all the vital processes of the body, such as the digestion and absorption of food nutrients and the removal of waste from the body. As already shown, water is also an agent in regulating the body temperature, both through the vapor given off by the lungs and the evaporation of sweat from the surface of the body. **(2, 121)**

Scientists agree that farm animals should generally have all the water they will drink. When horses are very warm after working, they should not have much water until they cool off. The water should be accessible to the stock, so that they can drink whenever they are thirsty, or they should be watered at regular intervals. To avoid disease, the water should be of good quality and not contaminated. Also, if the water is not palatable, animals may not drink enough for the best results.

All water that is drunk must be raised to the temperature of the body, thus requiring heat. Warming cold water taken into the body does not necessarily mean that more food must be burned, for animals produce a large amount of heat in the work of digesting food and converting the digested matter into body products or work. Due to this, many animals have an excess of heat and the excess may go to warm the water they drink, so that no food is directly burned for that purpose.

However, when animals are watered but once a day they then drink a large amount. In winter, if the water is cold, this makes a sudden demand for a large amount of heat, which may exceed the amount of excess heat being produced in the body. Food must then be burned simply to warm the water, even though thereafter an excess of heat may be produced in the body. For this reason, feed may be saved by allowing animals that are exposed to cold and those fed scanty rations to have frequent access to water, or else by warming the water.

Under normal conditions animals consume a fairly uniform quantity of water for each pound of dry matter eaten. If some of the feed is succulent, such as silage, roots, or green forage, the amount of water that is drunk will be correspondingly reduced.

When entirely oxidized in the body, 100 lbs. of carbohydrates will yield 55.5 lbs. of water and 163 lbs. of carbon dioxide, and fats over twice as much water. The nitrogenous compounds yield a little less than the carbohydrates, because they are not entirely oxidized in the body. This shows that the animal gets some water from the dry matter of the food.

The water requirements of each class of stock are discussed in detail in Part III. It is there pointed out that individual drinking cups are highly advisable for dairy cows, as they increase milk production and save labor.

135. Saline and alkaline water.—In the drier districts water sometimes contains so much soluble mineral salts that it is unsuitable for stock. It was found in studies by the Oklahoma Station that the limit of tolerance depended on the kind of animal, the age, and the season of the year.[26] It made little difference whether the total quantity of dissolved salts was made up of a single salt or a number of salts.

It was concluded that 1.5 per cent of total salts in the water was about the safe upper limit for satisfactory maintenance. For lactating animals the limit was lower. Sheep were able to exist when the water contained 2.0 per cent or more of minerals. Animals can become accustomed to drinking waters that are unsatisfactory at first. If good water is accessible, they never choose to drink water that contains a harmful amount of minerals.

136. Are certain fatty acids necessary for farm animals?—Careful experiments have shown that animals can grow on rations containing very small amounts of fat, but which supply sufficient amounts of protein, minerals, vitamins, and carbohydrates.[27] Recent investigations of Burr and others have shown that, at least for the growth of rats, small amounts of certain unsaturated fatty acids (linoleic acid or linolenic acid) must be present in the food, or the animals fail to grow, become unthrifty, and die.[28]

These experiments have been conducted with rats, used as laboratory animals, because they could be readily fed the expensive, highly-purified diets necessary in such investigations. Whether or not farm animals need these fatty acids is still an open question. In any event, the usual rations fed stock in all probability provide sufficient amounts of any such essential nutrient substances.

It is shown in Chapter VIII that the milk and fat production of dairy cows and milk goats is reduced unless there is a certain minimum amount of fat in the ration.

137. Feeding concentrates alone to herbivora.—It would not ordinarily be economical to feed the herbivora of the farm, or the plant-eating animals, on nothing but grain and other concentrates, for usually concentrates are more expensive than roughages. Also, good roughage, especially well-cured legume hay, is exceedingly important as a source of vitamins and minerals, as is pointed out in the following chapter.

However, as a matter of scientific interest, experiments have been conducted to find whether cattle and horses can live on concentrates alone. Many years ago dry dairy cows were fed for an 8-week period in winter on corn meal alone, without injury.[29] Feeding such an unbalanced ration for a long time would have led to disaster on account of the nutritive deficiencies of corn which are discussed in Chapter XVII. A 2-year-old steer was fed for about 8 months on only grain and water and made fair gains.[30] An attempt to feed horses on oats alone ended in failure, for in a few days the horses refused the oats and drank but little water.[31]

Until recently, all attempts to raise calves on milk and concentrates or on milk alone ended in failure, because the experiments were conducted before the importance of vitamins and minerals was fully understood.[32] Later trials have at length been successful, when great care has been taken to add mineral and vitamin supplements to the ration.[33]

The chief deficiencies of a ration of only milk and concentrates for continued feeding to calves or young cattle are vitamin D and iron. In recent Michigan studies calves fed only milk and starch with mineral and vitamin supplements finally died from convulsions or tetany due to a lack of magnesium in the blood.[34] This was finally prevented by adding magnesium salts to the ration. It is shown in Chapter VI, however, that there is no deficiency of magnesium in any ordinary ration for livestock.

Pigs have been raised with fair success on whole milk alone without grain or other roughage in trials at the Wisconsin Station.[35] However, failure will result unless they get iron and traces of copper from some other source, and also milk is often too low in vitamin D to prevent rickets. As is pointed out in Chapters VI and XXXVI, under practical conditions it is exceedingly important to furnish swine with well-cured legume hay whenever they are not on pasture. This provides vitamins A and D, as well as increasing the amount of calcium and protein in the ration.

138. Succulent feeds.—Numerous scientific trials and common farm experience have abundantly demonstrated the value of adding succulent feeds to the rations of farm animals. The beneficial effects of succulence, whether supplied as pasturage, silage, soiling crops, or roots, are many. Just as our own appetites are stimulated by fruits and vegetables, succulent feeds are relishes for the animals of the farm, inducing them to consume more feed and economically convert it into useful products.

It is reasonable to hold that such palatable feeds stimulate digestion, and it is well known that their beneficial laxative effect aids in keeping animals healthy. Among the most important contributions of the experiment stations are their demonstrations of the economy of feeding silage to milk cows, fattening cattle and sheep, and of the possibilities of cheapening the cost of producing pork through the use of pasture. The merits of the various kinds of succulent feeds for the different kinds of farm animals are discussed at some length in later chapters.

When silage is added to a satisfactory ration made up of dry feeds for the winter feeding of milk cows or for the fattening of cattle or sheep, generally the production will be very appreciably increased. Unless the dry roughage is of decidedly superior quality, the increase in the milk yield or the rate of gain will be marked.

On the other hand, if the stock are fed an abundance of high-quality legume hay or even mixed hay, there may be but little improvement through the addition of silage or any other succulent feed. The matter then becomes purely an economic one. The decision as to whether or not to feed silage under such conditions should be reached after considering the various factors discussed in Chapter XII.

139. Exercise; light.—For the maintenance of health, exercise is essential. The only exceptions to this rule are fattening animals, soon to be marketed, which make more rapid gains if not allowed to move about too freely. Abundant exercise is of special importance with breeding animals. The exercise requirements of the various farm animals are discussed in the respective chapters of Part III.

Sunlight is an effective germicide. To prevent the contraction and spread of disease, it is therefore important that the stables be well-lighted. It is pointed out in the next chapter that sunlight which has not passed through window glass produces vitamin D in the body, and therefore aids in the assimilation and use of calcium and phosphorus and in preventing rickets.

QUESTIONS

1. Define a *maintenance ration.* Name 7 essentials for the maintenance of an animal.
2. Describe the production of heat in the body and state how it differs from the burning of fuel in a stove.
3. How do farm animals regulate the temperature of their bodies?
4. Explain what is meant by the *critical temperature.*
5. In maintaining a mature animal, for what is most of the feed needed?
6. How can the amount of total digestible nutrients be determined that is required to maintain a mature animal?
7. What is the relationship between the amounts of total digestible nutrients required for maintenance by animals of various live weights?
8. How do the following affect the amount of feed an animal requires for maintenance; restlessness; a fat condition of the animal; exposure to cold weather?
9. Discuss the protein requirements for the maintenance of mature animals.
10. What 3 mineral nutrients should be considered in maintenance rations?
11. Compare the vitamin requirements for maintenance with those for growing animals or for those producing milk.
12. Why is a good system of ventilation advisable in closed stables?
13. Discuss the water requirements of farm animals.
14. Are certain fatty acids essential for farm animals?
15. What nutritive deficiencies are encountered when calves are raised on nothing but milk and concentrates?
16. Discuss the importance of succulent feeds; of exercise; of sunlight.

REFERENCES

1. Ritzman and Benedict, N. H. Bul. 250.
2. Mitchell and Hamilton, Ill. Rpt. 1932.
3. Capstick and Wood, Jour. Agr. Sci., England, 12, 1922, pp. 257-268; Magee, Jour. Agr. Sci., England, 14, 1924, pp. 506-515; Forbes et al., Jour. Agr. Res., 33, 1926, pp. 579-589; Mitchell and Haines, Jour. Agr. Res., 34, 1927, pp. 549-557.
4. Hills, Vt. Bul. 226.
5. Haecker, Minn. Bul. 140.
6. Ritzman and Benedict, N. H. Bul. 250.
7. Brody, Procter, and Ashworth, Mo. Res. Bul. 220.
8. Brody, Procter, and Ashworth, Mo. Res. Bul. 220; Ashworth and Brody, Mo. Res. Bul. 190.
9. Brody, Procter, and Ashworth, Mo. Res. Bul. 220.
10. Kleiber, Hilgardia 11, 1932, No. 11.
11. For a discussion of the factors affecting maintenance requirements see: Brody, Annual Review of Biochemistry, 1934, pp. 328-336; Armsby, Nutrition of Farm Animals, pp. 304-312.
12. McCandlish and Gaessler, Iowa Res. Bul. 60; see however: Trowbridge, Moulton, and Haigh, Mo. Res. Bul. 18.
13. Trowbridge, Moulton, and Haigh, Mo. Res. Bul. 18; Brody et al., Mo. Res. Bul. 166.
14. Brody et al., Mo. Res. Bul. 166.
15. Hall and Brody, Mo. Res. Bul. 180.
16. Forbes, Kriss, Braman, et al., Jour. Agr. Res., 35, 1927, pp. 947-960; Mitchell and Hamilton, Ill. Rpt. 1927; Ritzman and Benedict, N. H. Tech. Bul. 45.
17. Hogan, Salmon, and Fox, Mo. Res. Bul. 18.
18. Armsby, The Nutrition of Farm Animals, pp. 323-332.
19. Hills, Vt. Bul. 226.
20. Perkins, Ohio Bul. 389; Buschmann, Landw. Vers. Stat., 101, 1923, pp. 1-216.
21. Mitchell, Nat. Research Council, U. S., Bul. 67; Smuts, Jour. Nutr. 9, 1935, pp. 428-430.
22. McCollum and Simmonds, The Newer Knowledge of Nutrition, 4th Ed., p. 108.
23. Smuts, Jour. Nutr., 9, 1935, pp. 402-433; Terroine and Sorg-Matter, Arch. Internat. Physiol., 29, 1927, p. 121; 30, 1928, p. 115; Sorg-Matter, Arch. Internat. Physiol., 30, 1928, p. 126.
24. Brody, Procter, and Ashworth, Mo. Res. Bul. 220; Ashworth, Mo. Res. Bul. 223.
25. For a more detailed discussion of the ventilation of barns, see: Kelley, U. S. Dept. Agr., Tech. Bul. 187; Armsby and Fries, Jour. Agr. Res. 21, 1921, pp. 343-368.
26. Heller, Okla. Bul. 217; see also, Ramsay, Agr. Gaz., N. S. Wales, 35, 1924, pp. 339-342.
27. Osborne and Mendel, Jour. Biol. Chem., 45, 1920, pp. 145-152; Drummond, Jour. Physiol., 54, 1920, pp. xxx-xxxi.

28. Burr and Burr, Jour. Biol. Chem., 82, 1929, pp. 345-367; 86, 1930, pp. 587-621; Burr, Burr, and Miller, Jour. Biol. Chem., 97, 1932, pp. 1-19; Burr and Brown, Soc. Expt. Biol. and Med. Proc., 30, 1933, pp. 1349-1352; see also: McAmis, Anderson, and Mendel, Jour. Biol. Chem., 82, 1929, pp. 247-262; Evans and Lepkovsky, Jour. Biol. Chem., 96, 1932, pp. 143-156; 99, 132, pp. 231-234; Tange, Imp. Acad., Japan, Proc., 8, 1932, pp. 190-193.
29. Miller, Rpt. Am. Dairyman's Assoc., 1874.
30. Sanborn, Utah Bul. 21.
31. Patterson, Md. Bul. 51.
32. Davenport, Ill. Bul. 46; McCandlish, Iowa Res. Bul. 48, Sanborn, Utah Bul. 21.
33. Mead and Reagan, Cal. Rpts. 1930, 1931, 1932, Mead and Reagan, Jour. Dairy Sci., 14, 1931, pp. 283-293; Mead and Goss, Jour. Dairy Sci., 18, 1935, pp. 163-170; Fitch, Hughes, and Cave, Kan. Rpt. 1930-32; Cave, Riddell, Hughes, Whitnah, and Lienhardt, Kan. Rpt. 1932-34; Reed and Huffman, Mich. Quar. Bul. 8, 1926, No. 3; Huffman, Mich. Quar. Bul. 11, 1928, No. 1; Huffman, Mich. Rpt. 1930-32; Knoop, Krauss, and Washburn, Ohio Bul. 548.
34. Duncan, Huffman, and Robison, Jour. Biol. Chem. 108, 1935, pp. 35-44; Huffman and Duncan, Jour. Dairy Sci., 19, 1936, pp. 440-441.
35. McCollum, Hart, and Steenbock, Wis. Sta., information to the author.

CHAPTER VI

PROTEINS—MINERALS—VITAMINS

I. Proteins in Livestock Feeding

140. Importance of proper amount and kind of protein.—That animals must receive at least certain minimum *amounts* of protein in their food was recognized by the early investigators in animal nutrition. As early as 1864 Wolff set forth in his feeding standards the amounts of digestible crude protein he believed were necessary for the various classes of livestock.

The numerous later investigations on this subject have naturally shown that these early estimates concerning the amounts of protein required were inaccurate in many instances. They have also proved that the *quality* or *kind* of protein in a ration may be fully as important as the amount. We now know that for proper nutrition of any animal not only must the food provide a sufficient amount of protein, but also the proteins must be of the right kind. .

The minimum amounts of protein required for the maintenance of farm animals have been discussed in the preceding chapter, and the amounts needed for the various types of livestock production are considered in those which follow. Further information on the protein requirements of each class of stock is presented in the respective chapters of Part III. The amounts of digestible protein advised by the author for the different classes of stock are shown in the feeding standards presented in Appendix Table III.

In estimates of the minimum amounts of protein required by farm animals, such as are given in feeding standards, it is assumed that typical rations are fed, which provide proteins of average quality. If the proteins are of superior quality, a somewhat smaller amount of protein will suffice. On the contrary, if the proteins are of inferior nutritive value, a greater amount will be needed, and generally even then the production of the animals will be lowered, in spite of the liberal supply of the inefficient proteins.

141. Effect of excess of protein.—In livestock feeding protein-rich feeds are usually more expensive than those low in protein but rich in carbohydrates and fat. We are, therefore, commonly interested solely in the minimum amounts of protein that farm animals require for optimum results.

Under certain conditions, however, protein-rich feeds may be cheaper than carbohydrate-rich ones, as in the case of cottonseed meal in the South and alfalfa hay in sections of the West. The question then arises as to how much protein animals can be fed without injury. This problem is of great interest, because the consumption of a large amount of protein above that required by the body throws an increased load on the liver and kidneys in getting rid of the excess nitrogen.

A number of experiments have been conducted with laboratory

animals to study this question. In certain tests, rats have been grown normally on rations containing more than 90 per cent of protein. Also, it is well known that Eskimos live largely on meat. In a recent careful experiment two men in this country lived exclusively on meat (including some fat) for 11 months and remained in excellent health.[1]

It is shown in Chapter XVIII that dairy cows have been fed successfully for long periods on cottonseed meal, which is very high in protein, as the only concentrate, provided roughage was fed that supplied ample vitamins and mineral matter. It is also shown in Chapter XXIV that dairy cows have been fed other rations extremely high in protein without injury. In spite of statements sometimes made to the contrary, there is no scientific evidence that the heavy feeding of cottonseed meal or other protein-rich concentrates increases trouble from mastitis or other diseases in cattle.

From these results it seems safe to conclude that there is no danger from feeding farm animals a considerable excess of protein over the amounts that they actually require.

142. Essential and non-essential amino acids.—It has been explained previously that proteins are exceedingly complex substances. (**15**) The proteins of the bodies of animals and of the common feeding stuffs are made up of 22 or more different amino acids. In the digestion of food within the body, the proteins are cleaved or broken down into these amino acids, which are absorbed from the digestive system and enter the blood stream as free amino acids.

The mixture of amino acids is then carried in the blood to the various body tissues, where each organ or tissue removes the quantities of the individual amino acids that it needs for its repair or functioning. As has been explained previously, the nitrogen is split off from the excess amino acids by the liver and this waste nitrogen is excreted in the urine by the kidneys. (**61**)

The body is able to make certain of the simpler amino acids, forming them either from some of the more complex amino acids or producing them by combining ammonia or other simple nitrogenous compounds with organic acids formed from other food nutrients. However, the body is not able to synthesize or make several of the more complex amino acids which are present in the body tissues. These must, therefore, be provided in the proteins of the food.

The amino acids which are required by the body and which cannot be made from other substances are called the *essential amino acids*. Those which can be made from other substances are called the *non-essential amino acids*.

Many experiments have been conducted with laboratory animals fed rations of highly purified nutrients to determine which of the amino acids are essential. On account of the complexity of such investigations the information on the problem is still incomplete. It has been definitely proved, however, that certain amino acids are essential for growth and that others are not essential. The data concerning some of the amino acids are still too limited to warrant definite conclusions as to whether or not they are necessary in the food.

According to the present information, the following amino acids are apparently essential for the growth of rats, used as laboratory test animals: lysine, tryptophane, histidine, phenylalanine, valine, leucine,

QUALITY OF PROTEINS MAY BE AS IMPORTANT AS THE AMOUNT

Animals need not only plenty of protein in their food, but also proteins of the right kind or quality. The pig on the left received plenty of protein, but his ration consisted of only grain and grain by-products, supplying proteins of poor quality. The pig on the right, which is of the same age, received a ration of grain plus skimmilk, which supplied proteins of good quality. (From Hart, Wisconsin Station.)

DETERMINING NUTRITIVE VALUE OF PROTEIN IN RATIONS

Experiments are being conducted with lambs in these metabolism cages to determine the nutritive value of the protein in different rations. The feed is accurately analyzed and weighed, and all feces and urine are collected and analyzed. (From New York, Cornell, Station, Cornell University.)

GOOD GRASS IS NOT DEFICIENT IN QUALITY OF PROTEIN

The excellent growth made by sheep, cattle, and horses on abundant grass pasture shows that there are no decided lacks in the proteins supplied by most kinds of young grass.

LEGUME FORAGE INSURES GOOD PROTEIN FOR RUMINANTS

A fine crop of red clover in the foreground, with corn in the background. Such a combination as clover or alfalfa hay and corn grain provides good quality protein for ruminants.

isoleucine, alpha-amino-beta-hydroxybutyric acid, and methionine. Cystine, the chief sulfur-containing amino acid, was formerly considered essential, but recent data indicate that it may not be needed if the ration has enough methionine, which also contains sulfur.

Glycine and some of the other common amino acids can readily be formed in the body from other amino acids, and these amino acids are therefore not essential. For further information on this subject and also for a detailed discussion of the nutritive value of the various proteins, the reader is referred to recent exhaustive reviews of the experiments in this field.[2]

Protein tissue cannot be built by an animal unless the food provides an adequate supply of each of the essential amino acids. A shortage in a single necessary amino acid will limit the utilization of all the others, and therefore will reduce the rate of growth made by the animal.

For example, let us suppose that an animal is building protein body tissues that contain 5 per cent of a certain essential amino acid. However, the mixture of amino acids furnished by the food contains only 1 per cent of this same amino acid. Then 5 times as much food protein will be required to form a given amount of body protein, as would be needed if the food protein supplied the same percentage of this essential amino acid as was contained in the body tissue.

The nutritive value of a protein is not affected if it is entirely lacking in one of the non-essential amino acids. Thus casein, the chief protein of milk, is a protein of high nutritive value. Nevertheless, it does not contain any glycine, which is the simplest in structure of all the amino acids and is readily made in the body from other sources.

143. Differences in amino acid requirements.—It is possible that certain amino acids which are necessary for growth may not be essential for the maintenance of a mature animal. In the daily break-down of the protein tissues of the body, perhaps entire protein molecules are not destroyed, but only certain groups split off. Then the needs for maintenance would not involve building entire proteins, but only in replacing these simple groups.

The opinions of scientists differ with reference to this matter. Early experiments led Osborne and Mendel to conclude that, although lysine was essential for growth, it was not necessary for maintenance.[3] However, it was later found that the lysine-poor ration they had used contained considerably more of this amino acid than had been supposed.

So far as is known, the amino acid requirements for milk production are similar to those for growth.

Nearly all of the investigations to determine whether or not the various amino acids are essential for animals have been conducted with rats as the test animals. This is because such experiments with farm animals would be excessively expensive, since the rations employed must be made up of highly-purified, very costly nutrients. Enough of such a ration to feed a large animal over a sufficient period would cost a large sum. Also small laboratory animals, such as rats, have a short life cycle in comparison with farm animals. Therefore, it is not necessary to conduct experiments with them for such long periods as would be required with large animals.

1956

These facts naturally raise the question as to whether or not various species of animals differ materially in their ability to synthesize in their bodies the various amino acids that they need. While there is not much definite information on this question, it is probable that the ability of humans, of swine, or of poultry to synthesize amino acids does not differ greatly from that of rats. On the other hand, there may be a considerable difference in the case of ruminants.

It has been shown previously in Chapter II that the digestion of cellulose and pentosans by ruminants is caused by the bacteria and other micro-organisms which thrive and multiply in great numbers in the paunch. (45) These bacteria can probably use certain other simple nitrogenous compounds, in addition to the amino acids, for making the proteins in the cells of which they are composed. Further on in the digestive tract of the ruminant, these bacterial cells may be digested, and the protein that has been synthesized by the bacteria thus made available to the animal. This bacterial protein may hence provide all the essential amino acids, even though they were lacking in the nitrogenous food used by the bacteria in their growth.

Though several investigations have been conducted, especially in Germany, to determine the extent to which various non-protein nitrogenous compounds can be used by ruminants as a substitute for protein, the results differ so greatly that no definite conclusions can be drawn as yet.[4] However, there is unquestionably less difference in the nutritive value for ruminants of the proteins supplied by various feeds than there is in the case of humans or of swine and poultry.

For example, linseed meal gives excellent results when fed as the only protein supplement with grain and hay to cattle or sheep. On the other hand, it is shown in Chapter XXXVI that linseed meal is not very satisfactory when used as the only supplement to grain for pigs, even when they are on good pasture. Much better results are secured when they are fed in addition a limited amount of some protein supplement that furnishes protein of high quality, such as meat scraps, tankage, fishmeal, or dairy by-products.

144. Amino acid content of proteins as a measure of value.— By elaborate chemical methods of extraction and purification it has been possible to separate in pure form some of the chief proteins in seeds and certain other foods. These proteins can be broken down into amino acids by digestion with chemicals or with enzymes. The amounts of the various amino acids that they contain can then be determined with more or less accuracy.

Attempts have been made to ascertain the amounts of the different amino acids in the mixture of proteins present in normal foods. But little accurate information of this kind has thus far been secured. This is because it is very difficult to separate the total proteins completely from the carbohydrates, and the latter interfere with the chemical determination of the amino acids. It seems possible that more accurate data in this field can be obtained by a method recently developed by the United States Department of Agriculture.[5]

The data gained by finding the amounts of the individual amino acids in pure proteins are very interesting from a scientific viewpoint. However, such determinations cannot be used as reliable guides to the quality or value of the entire protein furnished by any feeding stuff. This is because the total protein in any natural feed does not consist of only one protein, but of a mixture of several different proteins. Some of these may be present in large proportions, while others are contained in small amounts.

The chief protein in a feed may have an entirely different amino acid composition than the other proteins that the feed contains. Thus zein, which is the chief protein of corn grain, lacks both lysine and tryptophane. These are two of the amino acids that are essential for growth. Fortunately, the other proteins in corn make up this lack to some extent.

Although a young animal is not able to make any growth whatsoever on corn zein as the only source of protein, it can make slow growth on the entire corn grain, used as the sole kind of protein. However, for efficient utilization of the total corn proteins, some protein supplement must be added to the ration that provides a larger proportion of lysine and tryptophane.

145. Measuring the nutritive values of proteins.—Because it is impossible to determine accurately the amounts of each amino acid in a food, definite information concerning the actual nutritive value of a feed as a source of protein can be gained only through feeding experiments. In such investigations animals are fed rations in which the protein is supplied by the feed or combination of feeds that are to be tested. Care must be taken that the experimental rations fully meet all requirements for minerals, vitamins, and energy. Otherwise, the utilization of the protein will be decreased by a lack of other nutrients.

Several different methods have been used in the experiments to determine the relative efficiency of various pure proteins or of the mixture of proteins in natural feeds or in complete rations. One of the simplest methods is to feed the experimental animals rations containing the same percentage of protein from various sources, and then compare the rates of growth produced on the different rations. When this method is used, the results are sometimes expressed in terms of the amount of gain produced from each gram or other unit weight of protein in the feed.

Much useful information has been gained through this method by Osborne and Mendel, McCollum and associates, and others, in experiments chiefly with rats. In this method it is assumed that a unit of gain in weight on each ration will contain approximately the same amount of protein. This is not always strictly true, but no serious errors are usually involved if the experiments cover a sufficient length of time. This is also the method commonly employed in feeding experiments with growing and fattening farm animals, when it is desired to measure the relative efficiency of various feeds as protein supplements.

A method theoretically more accurate is to conduct this type of investigation in such a manner that the feces and urine voided by the experimental animals are carefully collected and analyzed. From the analyses of the rations and the excreta, the exact amount of protein stored in the body can be determined. The results of such investigations are usually stated in terms of the percentage of total food protein that is stored by the animal. In similar experiments with lactating animals, the percentage can be found of the total food protein that is secreted in the milk produced. This method has been employed especially in experiments with farm animals by McCollum and by Hart and associates.

In a third method, recently used by McCollum and associates in experiments with rats, uniform young are carefully selected. Some of them are slaughtered at the beginning of the experiment, and the amounts of protein are determined in their entire carcasses. The remaining animals are fed the rations to be tested, and then after they have made considerable growth, they are likewise killed and analyzed. The average amount of protein stored on each ration is found by subtracting the average amount in the bodies of the check animals, killed at the beginning of the experiment, from the average amount of protein in the animals that have been fed each ration. Then the percentages of the total food protein stored on each ration can be computed.

In a fourth method, used extensively by Mitchell and others, the experimental animals are fed in metabolism cages, so that all the feces and urine can be collected. During a period at the beginning and one at the end of the experiment, they are fed a ration containing practically no protein, so that the basal excretion of nitrogen in the urine and in the feces can be determined. The animals are fed the rations to be tested consecutively for brief periods, the amounts of nitrogen that are excreted in the feces and the urine being determined in each period.

From these data so-called "biological values" are computed, which measure the percentage of the protein absorbed from the food that is used both for maintenance and growth. The term "biological value" is also used for other measures of the values of proteins. In this volume the term is used only for values determined by the preceding method.

A protein that could be used with perfect efficiency for maintenance and growth would have a biological value of 100 per cent, according to this method. Few feeds even approach this theoretical efficiency, and biological values of 90 per cent or more prove that the protein of a feed has an unusually high nutritive efficiency. Biological values of 75 to 90 per cent indicate that the proteins are of considerably better than average value, while a value below 65 to 70 per cent indicates that the protein is not of high quality.

It must be remembered that in computing the biological value, credit is given for the use of the protein in maintenance as well as for growth. In determining the biological values of proteins for growing animals it is very important that the animals actually make satisfactory gains in protein tissues during the experiment. Otherwise, the biological value will not at all represent use of the protein for growth, but merely its value for maintenance, which may be considerably different.

146. Conditions affecting utilization of proteins.—No matter what method is used in studying the nutritive values of proteins, certain fundamental principles must be observed, or the results of the investigation may be of little value. Unfortunately, these principles have been overlooked in certain of the experiments in this field. As a result, it is difficult to draw conclusions concerning the value of the proteins in some feeds which have been studied.

First of all, sufficient non-nitrogenous nutrients (carbohydrates and fats) must be provided so that the animal will not be forced to use protein as a source of heat or energy. If this principle is neglected, the nutritive value of the protein will appear to be low, merely because a considerable part of it has been wasted.

Second, the amount of protein in the ration must be below the optimum level for the particular kind of animal used. Otherwise, the animal may receive in its feed more protein than it can possibly use for protein purposes. As has been shown previously, the nitrogen will unavoidably be split off from any excess and the non-nitrogenous part used for heat and energy, this nitrogen being entirely wasted. (**61**)

Third, it must be realized at all times that protein is used with greater *percentage efficiency* for maintenance when the amount in the feed is below the optimum amount for the animal. Within certain limits, the lower the level of protein, the greater will be the apparent efficiency. Therefore, in any series of experiments in which it is desired to compare the nutritive value of the proteins in various rations, there must be the same percentage of protein. Erroneous conclusions may be drawn, for example, if one kind of protein is studied when forming 15 per cent of the experimental ration, and another kind of protein is fed at a level of 10 per cent.

In the case of growing animals the rate of gain will be slower if the amount of protein fed is slightly below the optimum, but the percentage utilization, as measured by the biological-value method, will be higher. On the other hand, in the methods in which the results are expressed as the percentages of protein stored in the body, the values will be low, if too little protein is fed.

The general principle just discussed—that in a comparison of the nutritive value of the proteins in various rations, there should be the same percentage of protein in each ration—is of great importance in practical feeding experiments. If two protein supplements are being compared which contain considerably different percentages of protein, correspondingly less of the supplement richer in protein should be used.

If enough of the low-protein supplement is fed to balance the ration in protein content and the same amount of the high-protein supplement is included in the other ration, it should be evident that there will then be an excess of protein in the latter ration. Part of the supplement will then be wasted, so far as its use as a protein supplement is concerned. On the other hand, if just enough of the high-protein supplement is used to balance one ration and no more of the low-protein supplement is included in the other ration, it will not supply enough protein for optimum results.

Therefore, whenever this fundamental principle is neglected, either one or the other of the rations will be made less efficient than it should be, solely because the experiment was not properly planned. Unfortunately, this simple principle has not been considered in certain of the comparisons of protein supplements that have been made, even during recent years.

147. Supplementary effects of protein.—Many of our common feeds contain too small amounts of one or more of the essential amino acids to produce good results when used as the only source of protein. Such feeds are said to have *protein of poor quality.*

On the other hand, a few feeds, such as milk, meat, and eggs, supply the various amino acids in very nearly the proper proportions for complete utilization. These feeds are said to contain *proteins of high quality.*

Fortunately, the feeds that have proteins of poor quality are not all deficient in the same amino acids. For this reason the proteins in two feeds, each of which furnishes poor-quality protein when fed alone, may supplement each other in a very important manner. For example, it has been mentioned that the proteins in corn grain are low in lysine and tryptophane, which are two of the essential amino acids. Corn is also low in total amount of protein. However, corn has an ample amount of cystine, the chief sulphur-containing amino acid. In strong contrast to corn are soybeans. They are not only rich in amount of protein, but also supply plenty of lysine and tryptophane. However, they are not rich in cystine, or else the cystine in uncooked soybeans is chiefly present in a form that cannot be utilized by some animals, such as swine and rats. (594-595)

Because these two feeds are not deficient in the same essential amino acids, they supplement each other to a considerable extent. It has thus been shown in recent Indiana experiments that the proteins supplied by a combination made up of proper proportions of corn and soybeans have a much higher nutritive value than those of corn grain alone.[6] In efficiency of proteins the mixture even excels soybeans alone, the proteins of which rank high in nutritive value among feeds of plant origin.

No common food surpasses milk in quality of protein, when used as the only source of protein in the diet. This shows that milk provides adequate amounts of all the essential amino acids. In experiments in which animals have been fed scanty amounts of milk, along with non-protein food, it has been found that milk does not have a very liberal supply of the sulfur-containing amino acids (cystine and methionine).

However, milk is so rich in lysine and tryptophane that it is able effectively to correct the deficiencies in the proteins of corn or other grains. This is shown by Wisconsin experiments in which young pigs were fed rations containing protein from various sources. When pigs were fed only wheat, corn, or oat grain, they stored in their bodies but 23 to 28 per cent of the total protein in their feed.[7] On the other hand, when skim milk was the sole source of protein, they were able to store 66 per cent of the protein supplied by the milk.

A mixture of one-third each of corn, wheat, and oats was only a trifle better than any one of the cereals alone, for they are all deficient in lysine. However, when pigs were fed 1.3 lbs. of skim milk to each pound of corn, they made 62 per cent of the total protein in their feed into body tissues. Thus the milk was rich enough in lysine and tryptophane to make the combination of corn and milk nearly as efficient as milk, which is often called the ideal food.

This well illustrates the fact that it is entirely unnecessary for each feed in a ration to furnish protein of high quality. All that is needed for efficient use of protein is that the entire ration has sufficient of each of the essential amino acids.

With the rapid increase during recent years in the knowledge concerning the nutritive characteristics of the various feeds, nutrition experts have been able to combine them into more efficient rations than ever before. In making up such rations the strong points and also any deficiencies of each feed are fully recognized. Through skillful combination, advantage is taken of the special merits of the feeds in the ration, and any deficiencies are corrected.

148. Proteins of cereal grains and their by-products.—Since cereal grains and their by-products form such a large proportion of the food of farm animals, it is essential that the character of their proteins be thoroughly understood. When fed as the only source of protein, the cereal grains all fall decidedly below such a food as milk in the quality of protein. The biological values of the proteins of the grains (the efficiency of the proteins for maintenance and production combined) have usually ranged between 60 and 70 per cent in experiments with pigs, chicks, and rats, when the rations have contained 8 to 10 per cent protein. In comparison with this, the protein in milk has generally had a biological value of 85 to 90 per cent or more.

The results have differed considerably in the experiments which have been conducted to compare the efficiency of the proteins in the various grains. It seems probable, however, that the protein in corn grain is usually slightly less efficient for growth than the proteins in wheat, oats, or barley. Also corn generally contains considerably less protein than these other grains.

As has been stated previously, corn grain is deficient in both lysine and tryptophane, and this is also apparently the case with oats. On the other hand, wheat grain is probably deficient only in lysine.[8]   The proteins of the grain sorghums seem to have the same general nutritive characteristics as those of the other cereals.[9]

In general, the germs of the cereal grains apparently have proteins of much better quality than the endosperm, or starchy part.   Also, in the case of the wheat grain, the bran layers provide protein of higher nutritive value than the endosperm.   Wheat bran, wheat middlings, and red dog flour therefore furnish protein of considerably better quality than does wheat flour or even the entire wheat grain.[10]   This helps to explain the popularity of wheat by-products for stock feeding.

Although the wheat by-products apparently furnish protein of somewhat better quality than the entire cereal grains, the protein does not completely correct the deficiencies of cereal proteins for swine and poultry.   Therefore, as is shown in Chapter XXXVI, the results are greatly improved in swine feeding, when skimmilk, meat meal, or fish meal is added to a ration of grain, wheat middlings, and minerals, even for pigs on pasture.

Rice bran has proteins of good quality and it effectively supplements the proteins of corn.[11]

149. Feeds of animal origin.—As has been stated previously in this chapter, the proteins of milk have an especially high nutritive value. Casein, which forms over three-fourths of the protein in milk, is but slightly inferior in value to the entire mixture of proteins milk contains.

Lactalbumin, or milk albumin, which forms most of the remainder of the milk protein, is also of high nutritive value and in some experiments has even been superior to casein.   The protein of whey is chiefly lactalbumin.   It therefore is not surprising that whey has proven to be very effective in correcting the deficiencies in the cereal grains, even though whey is low in percentage of protein.   (See Chapters XIX and XXXVI.)

The proteins of meat, fish, and eggs are also of unusually high nutritive value, a fact that is of great importance in human nutrition. Those of eggs and fish are probably about equal to milk proteins in efficiency, and meat proteins rank but slightly below.   In live stock feeding the meat and fish by-products are excellent protein supplements, especially for swine and poultry.

Animal tissues that consist mostly of gristle and connective tissue are apparently of considerably lower nutritive value than muscles or most glandular tissues, such as liver or kidney.[12]   Therefore if meat scraps consist too largely of such material, its value will probably be reduced.

Also, fish meal consisting chiefly of fish heads has a slightly lower value than that made largely of muscular tissue.[13]

If animal by-products are subjected to too high a temperature during the manufacturing process, the digestibility and the nutritive value of the proteins is decreased somewhat.[14]   Therefore the protein of vacuum-dried fish meal is of greater value than that dried at a higher temperature.   Also, as is stated in Chapter XIX, dry-rendered tankage, or meat scraps, containing 50 to 55 per cent protein has generally been equal or superior in feeding value to digester tankage containing 60 per cent protein.

Tankage and meat scraps are excellent protein supplements for swine, and meat scraps are one of the most important supplements for poultry. These feeds are not only very high in protein, usually containing 50 per cent protein or more, but also their proteins correct the deficiencies in those of the grains. However, their proteins rank in efficiency somewhat below those of fish meal or milk by-products as supplements to the grains.[15]

Blood meal of the usual kind is not high in digestibility, and the protein is apparently not of as high nutritive value as that of meat scraps or tankage.[16]

150. Proteins of legume seeds.—The proteins of the various legume seeds differ to a surprising degree in nutritive value. At the one extreme are soybeans and peanuts, which apparently make good the deficiencies of proteins in the cereal grains to a greater extent than other common feeds of plant origin.

For this reason, when no feeds of animal origin are included in rations for swine and poultry, these legume seeds and the oil meals made from them produce better results than other protein supplements of plant origin. However, the results are generally still better when a small amount of such feeds as meat scraps, tankage, skimmilk, or fish meal is included in the ration.

It has been pointed out previously in this chapter that although soybeans alone are somewhat deficient in cystine, this is corrected when they are combined with cereal grains. Recent investigations indicate that the quality of the proteins in various varieties of soybeans may differ to some extent.[17]

At the other extreme in quality of protein are most beans and also cowpeas and lentils, which are decidedly deficient in cystine. Though this lack is corrected when these seeds are fed with cereal grains, they do not seem to be efficient as the sole protein supplement to the grains for swine or poultry. Beans are poorly utilized by swine unless they are thoroughly cooked, and soybeans are also improved considerably for swine by thorough cooking.

Peas are an excellent feed for stock, except for the fact that they are usually expensive. However, the experiments reviewed in Chapter XVIII show that they are not efficient as the only supplement to grain for pigs not on pasture. This is probably because their proteins do not supplement those of the cereals as completely as do the proteins of soybeans or peanuts.

In recent English experiments the proteins of horse beans and of peas ranked high in nutritive value when these feeds were fed to dairy cows as supplements to a ration of oats, straw, and beet pulp.[18]

151. Proteins of other concentrates.—On account of the great importance of cottonseed meal and linseed meal as protein supplements in stock feeding, the nutritive value of their proteins is of especial interest. It is pointed out in later chapters that these feeds are excellent supplements for dairy cattle, beef cattle, sheep, and horses. For swine or poultry they should be used only in combination with such supplements as meat scraps, tankage, fish meal, or milk products, which provide protein of better quality.

There has been little or no difference in the quality of the proteins in linseed meal and cottonseed meal when these feeds have been fed as the only source of protein; when they have been fed with corn to non-ruminants; or when they have been fed with grain and hay and other roughage to dairy cows.[19] The biological values of the proteins in linseed meal and cottonseed meal have usually ranged between 60 and 70 per cent.

Coconut oil meal has proteins of higher quality than those of the cereal grains but not equal to those of soybeans or peanuts.[20] There-fore, as is explained in Chapter XVIII, it should not be used as the only supplement for pigs not on good pasture.

152. Proteins of green forage and other roughages.—In spite of the great importance of hay, pasture, and other forages in livestock feeding, there is but little information concerning the exact efficiency of the proteins these feeds provide. From the fact that young cattle, colts, or lambs, after the suckling period, can make good growth on an abundance of good forage, it is evident that there are no decided nutri-tive lacks in the proteins that such forage provides. Though swine cannot make as large a use of roughage as these other animals, mature sows that are not nursing pigs can be maintained on nothing but good pasture or even on legume hay.

One of the exceedingly important facts in livestock feeding, which is emphasized in Chapter XIII, is that legume forages admirably supple-ment the cereal grains. They are not only rich in protein, but the protein is of such character that it largely corrects the deficiencies in the proteins of the grains.

153. Proteins of legume roughages.—The experiments summarized in later chapters show clearly that a ration consisting only of farm grain and an abundance of well-cured alfalfa hay is excellent for dairy cattle, beef cattle, sheep, and horses. As is pointed out later in this chapter, the first lack that may be met in this ration, if fed to high-producing dairy cows, is not in the amount or in the quality of the protein, but in the amount of phosphorus.

The experiments reviewed in Chapter XXXVI show that even for growing pigs a combination of good pasture and cereal grain furnishes protein of fairly satisfactory quality. Pigs fed only corn and other grain on excellent pasture, such as alfalfa, clover, or rape, will make reasonably good growth. However, such a ration is too low in protein for the most rapid growth. Also, the quality of the protein can be made still better by adding to the ration such a protein supplement as skimmilk, tankage, or fish meal.

154. Legume hay insures good-quality protein for ruminants.— That alfalfa hay and clover hay furnish proteins of satisfactory quality for ruminants is definitely shown in recent investigations at the New York (Cornell) Station.[21] When growing lambs were fed either alfalfa hay or red clover hay as the sole source of protein in a ration supplying plenty of carbohydrates and fat, the biological value of the proteins averaged 79 per cent for alfalfa hay and 81 per cent for clover hay. When these hays were fed in combination with corn grain, the biological values of the proteins were approximately the same, being 77 per cent for alfalfa hay and corn and 80 per cent for clover hay and corn. In all probability, similar results would be secured with cattle.

When alfalfa hay was fed as the only feed to growing lambs in Washington trials, much lower biological values were secured for the protein, the average being only 56 per cent.[22] This low figure was probably due to the fact that alfalfa hay is low in total digestible nutrients in comparison to the amount of protein it furnishes. Therefore, when it is fed alone, as is often done in the alfalfa districts of the West, it does not provide sufficient non-nitrogenous nutrients to enable lambs or other animals to use the protein with maximum efficiency. A still lower biological value was secured for alfalfa leaves in other experiments, when they were used as the only feed for lambs.[23] This was apparently due to the fact that the leaves are even much higher than the hay in protein, and therefore the lambs had a large excess of protein which they could not utilize.

The fact that good-quality protein is furnished for ruminants by alfalfa or clover hay as the only source of protein, or by either of these hays and corn grain, is of great importance in stock feeding. It seems probable that for cattle or sheep there is not apt to be any deficiency in the quality of protein in the ration whenever a large part of the roughage consists of properly-cured legume hay. This means that if sufficient legume hay is fed to ruminants, good results can be secured when there is used as the only protein supplement such a feed as corn gluten meal or corn gluten feed, both of which have proteins that are unbalanced in nature.

This is shown by Wisconsin experiments in which dairy cows were fed rations supplying proteins from various sources.[24] When cows were fed cereal grain with clover or alfalfa hay and corn silage, there was little difference in the efficiency of corn gluten feed, linseed meal, cottonseed meal, or distillers' corn grains as protein supplements. On the other hand, when corn stover was the only roughage, corn gluten feed was distinctly inferior to the protein supplements that provided protein of better quality.

The proteins of legume forages are apparently somewhat less efficient for non-ruminants than they are for cattle and sheep. In Illinois tests the proteins of a ration of alfalfa hay and corn had a biological value of only 62 per cent for rats.[25] Although alfalfa leaves apparently contained ample cystine (the chief sulfur-containing amino acid) in English tests, in Oregon experiments with rats alfalfa proteins seemed to contain too little cystine for highest efficiency.[26]

It is of interest to note that in the New York experiments with lambs there was no indication of a lack of cystine. Wool is particularly high in cystine, which is the chief sulfur-containing amino acid. Therefore it might have been supposed that a lack of cystine in alfalfa hay would have lowered the efficiency with which the lambs utilized the protein, or would have resulted in poor growth of wool. No such effect was produced.

This may have been due to the fact that alfalfa is rich in other sulfur-containing compounds, even though it may be low in cystine. Perhaps sheep can utilize, through the action of the bacteria in the paunch, sulfur in other forms for producing the cystine they need for wool production. (**143**)

155. Proteins in non-legume forages.—There is so little information concerning the nutritive value of the proteins in non-legume rough-ages that only very general statements can be made on the subject. From the excellent growth made by young cattle, sheep, and horses on abundant grass pasture, we can conclude that there are no decided lacks in the proteins supplied by most kinds of young grass.

That there may be considerable difference, however, in the nutritive value of the proteins from various grasses and from fertilized and unfertilized grasses is indicated in a recent experiment by Crampton.[27] For rabbits the protein in young timothy grass was of decidedly higher nutritive value than that of reed canary grass. Also, the protein in the mixed grasses from a fertilized plot was of higher value than in the grass from an unfertilized area of the same field.

When grass hay is fed to ruminants in a ration with a considerable variety of concentrates, the quality of the protein may be as good as when the roughage is legume hay. In New York experiments, dairy cows utilized the protein just as efficiently for milk production from a ration of timothy hay, corn silage, corn grain, oats, wheat bran, and linseed meal, as they did when clover hay was fed in place of the timothy.[28]

Even when various single protein supplements of widely differing character are fed to ruminants as supplements to grain and non-legume hay, there is apparently much less difference in their nutritive value than there would be in the case of swine or poultry. Thus in recent experiments at the New York (Cornell) Station with growing lambs there has not been any appreciable difference in the nutritive value of the protein when either soybean oil meal, linseed meal, or corn gluten meal was used as the supplement to a ration of corn grain and timothy hay or corn stover.[29]

The biological values obtained when roughages very low in protein are fed as the only source of protein cannot be compared with the values secured for the proteins in balanced rations. As has been pointed out before, the biological value of the protein will be unduly high in such protein-poor rations. For this reason, the very high biological value of 92 per cent has been obtained for the proteins of corn silage fed alone to lambs, and a value of 81 per cent for the proteins of wheat straw fed as the only feed to steers.[30] Though these values cannot be compared with the biological values secured when balanced rations have been fed, it is evident from these experiments, that for the *maintenance* of ruminants, the quality of the protein provided by these roughages is not inadequate, though they are both low in quantity of protein.

II. MINERALS IN LIVESTOCK FEEDING

156. Importance of minerals.—It has long been known that minerals are necessary for the health of animals and even for life itself. However, only recently have investigations revealed the causes and methods of prevention of certain serious diseases which are due to mineral deficiencies. These discoveries have caused much popular interest in the subject of mineral nutrients and have led to extensive use of mineral supplements in stock feeding.

Although decided deficiencies of other minerals often occur that must be corrected by the use of a suitable mineral supplement, common salt is the only mineral that is generally insufficient in the feeds consumed by farm animals. To avoid expenditures for unnecessary mineral supplements, it is therefore important that stockmen know definitely the conditions under which there may be a lack of other essential minerals, and also know how to correct any deficiency at minimum cost. The use of mineral supplements when they are not needed is not only a waste of money, but also may in some cases be actually injurious, as is shown later.

157. Vital functions of minerals.—Minerals have many vital functions in the body, some of which are well understood, while there is but little definite knowledge concerning others. The skeletons of vertebrate animals is composed chiefly of minerals (nearly all calcium and phosphorus), and minerals are essential constituents of the soft tissues and fluids of the body. A few examples of the functions of minerals will serve to show how indispensable they are:

Phosphorus is a vital ingredient in the proteins that characterize the nuclei of all body cells, and also is a component of certain other important proteins, such as the casein of milk. The phospholipids, which are phosphorus-containing fat-like substances, are essential parts of all living protoplasm. The power of the blood to carry oxygen is due to hemoglobin, the iron-protein compound in the red blood corpuscles.

The soluble mineral compounds in the blood and other body fluids are essential in giving these fluids their characteristic properties and in regulating the life processes. The acidity or alkalinity of the digestive juices is due to mineral compounds. Thus, the acidity of the gastric juice in the stomach, which is necessary for the action of the enzyme, pepsin, is due to hydrochloric acid, derived from sodium chloride and other chlorides present in the blood. The osmotic pressure which is necessary for the transfer of nutrients and waste products through the cell walls is largely dependent on the concentration of mineral salts in the lymph and in the cells. The maintenance of an approximately neutral reaction in the body tissues, or the prevention of acidity or alkalinity, is due chiefly to a delicate adjustment of the mineral compounds in the body fluids. A serious lack of calcium in the blood, such as occurs in milk fever of cows and in certain advanced cases of rickets, causes convulsions and tetany.

The importance of minerals in controlling life processes is well illustrated by an experiment often performed in physiological laboratories. If the heart, still beating, is removed from a frog and placed in a solution of pure sodium chloride (common salt), its beats soon fade out. If a small amount of a calcium salt is now added to the solution, the heart will at once begin to beat again. However, unless a small amount of a potassium salt is also added, the beat will not be normal, but the heart will fail to relax quickly and completely enough after each contraction. Thus, if potassium is not added, the relaxations become more and more feeble, until the heart stops in a contracted state. Not only must potassium be present, but there must be a correct proportion between the amounts of calcium and potassium. If too much potassium is added, the heart will fail to contract properly, and finally will again stop beating, but this time in a state of complete relaxation.

Similarly, other vital processes are dependent not only on the presence of various mineral salts, but also on a proper relationship between them. It is therefore evident that unless the amount of these mineral salts in the blood is kept normal, serious consequences will follow. The kidneys are usually able to protect the animal against an unbalanced mineral content in the blood by promptly excreting any excess of various salts which may be present. However, if the food continually furnishes an excessive amount of certain minerals, the body may be unable to keep the blood composition normal, and injury will result.

In the paragraphs which follow brief summaries are presented concerning: (1) The requirements for each of the essential mineral nutrients; (2) the conditions under which there may be a lack of the mineral in the rations commonly fed farm animals; and (3) the mineral supplements that should be used to correct any such lack. Further information about the mineral needs of each class of stock is given in Part III. The amounts of calcium and phosphorus in various feeds are shown in Appendix Table I, so far as data are available, and the amounts of the other important minerals in typical feeds are given in Appendix Table IV.

158. Sodium and chlorine; common salt.—Herbivorous animals (those that live chiefly on plants) need a considerably larger amount of common salt than is supplied by their usual feeds. Thus, horses, cattle, and sheep show great hunger for salt when it is not provided for them. On the other hand, carnivora (flesh-eating animals) secure sufficient salt in the flesh and blood they consume and therefore need no additional salt. Though swine and poultry need less salt than herbivora, it is generally advantageous to supply them with it. If swine are fed tankage or fish meal as the chief or the only protein supplements, these feeds may supply sufficient salt for their needs, as is shown in Chapter XXXV.

The requirements of the various classes of stock for salt are discussed in detail in the respective chapters of Part III. The salt requirements will vary to some extent in different localities, depending on the salt content of the feeds grown there and on whether the water contains an appreciable amount of salt. Occasionally, the alkali deposits in arid districts contain so large a proportion of salt that it is not necessary to provide additional salt for livestock grazing on these areas.

Salt may be supplied to stock in the form of loose salt, lumps of rock salt, or salt blocks, the choice depending on which form is cheaper or more convenient. A common method of furnishing salt is to provide a supply where the stock can take what they desire. They will not eat too much unless they have previously received an insufficient supply. In such a case they may at the start take so much as to cause indigestion, and therefore the amount must be limited at first.

Both sodium and chlorine are essential for animal life.[31] They perform important functions in maintaining the osmotic pressure in the body cells, upon which depends the transfer of nutrients to the cells and the removal of waste materials, Chlorine is also required for the formation of the hydrochloric acid in the gastric juice. Blood is much richer in sodium and in chlorine than in other minerals and contains about 0.17 per cent of each, most of these amounts being present in the form of sodium chloride, or salt.

Normally, considerable sodium and chlorine are excreted daily, chiefly in the urine. Also, sweat is high in these minerals. It is of interest to note that when men are doing hard labor at unusually high air temperatures, as in deep mines, they suffer less from fatigue if they drink water containing a small amount of salt. This replaces the quantity lost in the profuse sweat. This shows that the salt supply should be liberal for horses performing severe work and therefore losing unusually large amounts of salt from their bodies.

If animals receive insufficient salt, the body retains its supply tenaciously, and the excretion in urine is greatly reduced. However, if the lack is long continued, injury will result. This is well shown in Wisconsin experiments conducted many years ago with dairy cows.[32] Cows that were well fed otherwise were given no salt for a year. After 2 or 3 weeks, they showed abnormal appetites for salt, but their health was not usually affected for a much longer time. Finally, a complete break-down occurred, marked by loss of appetite, lusterless eyes, rough coat, and a very rapid decline in both live weight and yield of milk. If salt was supplied, recovery was rapid.

In one case potassium chloride was given instead of common salt (sodium chloride). Recovery followed as quickly as when common salt was supplied, showing that the lack of chlorine was chiefly responsible for the trouble, and not a lack of sodium.

It has been claimed that salt is very poisonous to poultry, and that injury will result if their rations contain more than very small amounts. While too large a dose of salt will, without question, kill chickens, in Illinois tests they grew normally on rations containing as much as 8 per cent of salt, which is an extremely large percentage.[33]

159. Calcium and phosphorus.—Farm animals are more apt to suffer from a lack of phosphorus or of calcium than from any of the other minerals except common salt. These two minerals make up about three-fourths of the mineral matter in the entire bodies of farm animals and over 90 per cent of that in their skeletons. They also form more than half the minerals in milk. Therefore liberal amounts of calcium and phosphorus are needed by growing animals, by those that are pregnant, and by those which are producing milk. Even for the mere maintenance of mature animals, sufficient amounts of these minerals must be provided to replace the daily losses from the body, or injury will eventually result.

In order to assimilate and use the calcium and phosphorus in their food for the formation and renewal of the bones and for other purposes, animals must have an adequate supply of vitamin D. As is shown later in this chapter, this may be furnished either in the feeds they eat or through the effect of sunlight or other light that contains ultra-violet rays. Also, the ratio, or proportion, between the amount of calcium and the amount of phosphorus in the ration should be within certain limits. A great excess of one of these minerals may be detrimental, even though the supply of the other is ample. The importance of this factor is discussed later.

Under present conditions farm animals suffer from a deficiency of phosphorus or of calcium much more frequently than in early days. This is because of two different factors. First, the supply of these minerals in the common feeds, especially in roughages, has decreased in the older farming districts as the calcium and phosphorus content of the soil has been depleted. Second, the requirements of farm animals for these minerals have become much greater, as their rates of production of meat or milk have been increased through breeding and through improved and more intensive methods of feeding and management.

Under many conditions the supply of both these minerals is entirely adequate in the usual rations for farm animals, without the addition of any special calcium or phosphorus supplements. On the other hand, a lack of one or both of these minerals may sometimes occur which lowers production or even causes serious injury to the animals. It is therefore essential for efficiency in stock farming that one understand the requirements of livestock for phosphorus and for calcium, and that he know whether or not there are adequate amounts of these minerals in any particular ration.

Stock require somewhat greater amounts of calcium than they do of phosphorus, for the amount of calcium in their bodies is much greater than of phosphorus. Also, milk contains slightly more calcium than phosphorus. In spite of these facts, there is less apt to be a lack of calcium than of phosphorus in the rations of horses and of ruminants, including cattle and sheep. This is because roughages generally make up a large part of the feed consumed by these animals, and most roughages contain much more calcium than they do of phosphorus. Only when such animals are fed largely on grain and other concentrates or when the roughage is of unusually poor quality, is there apt to be a deficiency of calcium.

The condition is, however, far different in the case of swine and poultry. They are commonly fed chiefly on grain and grain by-products, all of which are very low in calcium, but fair or even high in phosphorus content. There may therefore be a decided lack of calcium in their rations, unless protein supplements of animal origin are fed which are rich in calcium, such as meat scraps, tankage, fish meal, or milk.

160. Calcium and phosphorus content of various feeds.—The information on the exact amounts of calcium and phosphorus in the many different feeding stuffs is even yet very limited, in comparison with the large number of analyses that have been made for protein, fat, fiber, nitrogen-free extract, and total mineral matter. This is because the real importance of these minerals in stock feeding has been appreciated only during recent years. To furnish as complete information as possible on the calcium and phosphorus content of various feeds, the author has made an extensive compilation of such data. The average percentages of these minerals in different feeding stuffs, as determined in this compilation, are shown in Appendix Table I.

In using these average figures it must be remembered that the amounts of these minerals in any particular lot of feed, especially of a roughage, may differ considerably from the average. (**107**) When grown on soil low in available phosphorus or in calcium, roughages will generally contain decidedly less of the mineral than when grown on fertile soil. Thus, timothy hay grown on calcium-rich land may contain more than twice as much of this mineral as hay cut at the same stage of maturity, which has been grown on soil very deficient in calcium.

It will be noted that the legume hays and all other legume forages, including legume straws, are rich in calcium. This is one of the most important facts with reference to the calcium content of feeding stuffs. Alfalfa hay contains 1.43 per cent calcium; red clover hay, 1.21 per cent; and soybean hay, 0.96 per cent. Even alfalfa stems have 0.79 per cent calcium. Though the calcium content of legume forage is influenced to some extent by the amount of this mineral in the soil, one can always safely count on its being relatively rich in calcium. If the soil is too deficient in calcium, legume crops will not grow.

At early stages of growth forage plants contain much more calcium and phosphorus, on the dry basis, than at later stages. Thus immature grass from a closely-grazed pasture will be much richer in these minerals, if dried, than the grass would be if allowed to grow up for hay.

Non-legume roughage in general contains much less calcium than that from legumes, and if grown on soil deficient in calcium, such roughage may be considerably lower in this mineral than indicated by the average figures. Timothy hay of average quality has 0.27 per cent calcium; good-quality hay from mixed grasses, 0.48 per cent; and dry corn stover, 0.46 per cent. Cereal straw is slightly lower than grass hay in calcium content. Silage from corn or the sorghums contains approximately as much calcium, on the dry basis, as does hay from the grasses. Roots and tubers are generally low in calcium.

None of the common roughages are rich in phosphorus, the amounts in various hays usually ranging from 0.15 per cent or even less, up to 0.25 per cent. Early in their growth, grasses and legumes have a larger percentage of phosphorus on the dry basis than at the hay stage. Thus, dried pasture grass from well-grazed, fertile pastures has 0.41 per cent phosphorus. Legume hay contains but little more phosphorus than grass hay of similar quality. Fodder and silage from corn or the sorghums have about the same content of phosphorus, on the dry basis, as grass hay. The stover from these crops and the straws from the small grains are very low in phosphorus, having only 0.09 to 0.13 per cent. Likewise, such feeds as cottonseed hulls and flax straw are very low in phosphorus. On the dry basis, roots and tubers tend to have slightly more phosphorus than the hay crops.

All the cereal grains are exceedingly low in calcium, the content ranging from only 0.01 per cent for corn and 0.03 per cent for wheat to 0.09 per cent for oats. On the other hand, the grains are fair in phosphorus content, the percentage ranging from 0.27 per cent in corn to 0.43 per cent in wheat. Beet pulp, beet molasses, and cane molasses are very low in phosphorus.

A very important fact is that most of the protein-rich concentrates of plant origin are much higher in phosphorus than the grains or the roughages, but none of them are rich in calcium. Wheat bran is especially rich in phosphorus, containing 1.32 per cent. Standard

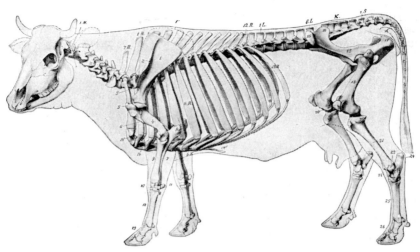

Farm Animals Need an Ample Supply of Mineral Matter

Over 90 per cent of the mineral matter in the skeleton consists of calcium and phosphorus. In certain rations the amount of these mineral elements may be insufficient for health. (From Ellenberger.)

Pigs Suffering From Severe Cases of Rickets

These pigs received a ration of white corn and skimmilk, without pasture or legume hay. This ration was deficient in vitamin D and also in vitamin A. Note the stiff and paralyzed condition of the pigs. The pig on the left died within a week after the photograph was taken, while the one on the right gradually recovered when a vitamin supplement was added to the ration. (From Wisconsin Station.)

CALF SUFFERING FROM SEVERE RICKETS

Rickets may be produced by a deficiency of calcium, of phosphorus, or of vitamin D. Note crippled condition, severe stiffness, bent and swollen knees, swollen hocks, and arching of back. (From Huffman, Michigan Station.)

CALF WITH MILD CASE OF RICKETS

This calf is beginning to show the arching of the back and the swollen knees and stiffness characteristic of rickets. Note the tendency to develop long toes. (From Huffman, Michigan Station.)

wheat middlings has 0.94 per cent; cottonseed meal, 1.11 to 1.24 per cent; and linseed meal, 0.86 per cent. Wheat flour middlings has considerably less phosphorus than standard middlings, containing only 0.72 per cent, and wheat red dog flour contains still less.

The protein-rich legume seeds are not very high in phosphorus, soybeans having 0.60 per cent; field peas, 0.40 per cent; and cowpeas, 0.47 per cent. Soybean oil meal contains 0.66 per cent phosphorus and peanut oil meal only 0.55 per cent. Corn gluten meal and corn distillers' grains are relatively low in phosphorus for protein-rich concentrates, containing but 0.38 and 0.31 per cent, respectively.

Milk is high both in calcium and phosphorus, dried skimmilk having 1.24 per cent calcium and 0.96 per cent phosphorus. Fish meal, meat scraps, and tankage are the richest of all common feeds both in calcium and in phosphorus, due to the bone they contain. For example, fish meal has 5.37 per cent calcium and 2.98 per cent phosphorus. On the other hand, dried blood has only 0.33 per cent calcium and 0.26 per cent phosphorus.

161. When do lacks of calcium or phosphorus occur?—From these data showing the calcium and phosphorus content of various classes of feeds, certain general conclusions may be drawn: When legume hay or mixed hay containing considerable legumes forms any important part of the ration for cattle, sheep, and horses, they will ordinarily have an abundance of calcium. Even when no legume roughage is fed to these classes of stock, there will usually be no deficiency of calcium unless the roughage is grown on soil very low in calcium, or unless they are fed largely on grain and other concentrates, with but a limited amount of roughage.

Even though good dairy cows need large amounts of calcium for the milk they produce, it is shown in Chapter XXIV that generally there is no marked deficiency of calcium in their rations if they are fed roughage of good quality, even when none of it comes from the legumes. However, when no legume roughage whatsoever is fed to high-producing cows, it is probably wise to supply a calcium supplement as insurance against any possible lack, unless the non-legume roughage comes from soil well supplied with calcium.

It is shown in Chapters XXIX and XXXII that when young cattle or lambs are fattened on liberal amounts of grain, with non-legume roughage and such protein supplements as cottonseed meal or linseed meal, there may be a decided lack of calcium in the ration. This is because they do not eat enough roughage to meet their calcium requirements. In such cases there will generally be a great benefit in rate and economy of gain from feeding a calcium supplement, such as ground limestone.

If the animals have been raised previous to the fattening period in an area where the forage is high in calcium, they may have in their bodies a sufficient store of the mineral to meet their needs during the usual fattening period. They may then show little or no benefit from the addition of a calcium supplement to such a ration. This may also sometimes be the case when fattening stock are fed a ration low in phosphorus.

There will be a serious lack of calcium in the rations of swine and poultry if they are fed on grain and protein supplements of plant origin, without such calcium-rich animal by-products as meat scraps, tankage, fish meal, or milk. Even when on legume pasture, swine may not consume enough of the calcium-rich forage to meet their requirements if fed only grain and protein supplements low in this mineral. On the other hand, when meat scraps, tankage, fish meal, or milk are used as the chief supplements, there will be no lack of calcium in the ration.

Since the cereal grains are fair in phosphorus content and most protein-rich concentrates are rich in this mineral, there will generally be no lack of it when stock are fed a considerable proportion of such feeds in a well-balanced ration. However, when the ration is balanced only by those protein supplements which are not rich in phosphorus, there may be a lack of the mineral.

The phosphorus supply for cattle, sheep, and horses will be ample even when they are fed entirely on roughage, if the forage has been grown on soil reasonably well supplied with the mineral. On the other hand, there may be a serious deficiency of phosphorus if stock are fed chiefly on phosphorus-poor forage, without any supplement that is high in this essential.

On account of the high phosphorus requirements of dairy cows, they may not receive sufficient of the mineral when fed a ration of legume hay and corn or other grain, unless the hay comes from land having an ample supply of phosphorus. Since beet pulp and beet molasses are especially low in phosphorus, a deficiency must be guarded against when these feeds form any large part of the ration, by using a phosphorus supplement or by feeding a protein supplement like cottonseed meal, which is high in the mineral.

Much of the phosphorus in seeds and their by-products is in the form of phytin and related organic compounds. In recent studies with rats, used as laboratory test animals, phosphorus in such form has not been as well utilized as that in the form of phosphates, as supplied by bone meal.[34]

These studies have raised the question as to the relative value for farm animals of the phosphorus furnished by the grains and other seeds and their by-products. However, in Utah experiments with fattening cattle, wheat mixed feed and cottonseed meal both proved just as efficient as bone meal when added to a ration very deficient in phosphorus.[35] Also, in other experiments with various classes of stock which are mentioned in Part III, there has been little or no advantage from adding bone meal to a ration containing a liberal amount of phosphorus supplied chiefly by seeds and their by-products. It therefore seems safe to conclude that there is no need of adding a phosphorus supplement to a ration for stock that contains an ample total amount of phosphorus, even though much of it is provided by seeds and their by-products.

The requirements of each class of stock for calcium and phosphorus are discussed in detail in the respective chapters of Part III. Specific information is also there presented as to whether or not various common rations are deficient in these minerals, and recommendations are given for the correction of any such deficiencies.

162. Calcium-phosphorus ratio.—It has been mentioned previously that not only must animals receive adequate amounts of calcium and phosphorus, but also there should be a suitable proportion or ratio between the amounts of these two minerals.[36] If there is a great excess of calcium or of phosphorus, detrimental effects may be produced, even when there is an amount of the other mineral that would be adequate under usual conditions. Also less vitamin D is needed in the ration when there is a desirable calcium-phosphorus ratio.

As yet there have been but few investigations to determine the optimum ratios between the amounts of calcium and of phosphorus for the various classes of farm animals.[37] An ideal proportion of these minerals is probably from 1 to 2 parts of calcium to each part of phosphorus, or a calcium-phosphorus ratio ranging between 1:1 and 2:1. However, especially when there is an ample supply of vitamin D, satisfactory results are secured when the proportion of calcium is much greater than this. For example, rations having a calcium-phosphorus ratio as wide as 6.5:1 have been entirely satisfactory for raising dairy calves in Michigan experiments.[38]

163. Effects of calcium or phosphorus deficiency; rickets.—A decided deficiency of calcium or phosphorus or a lack of vitamin D will cause rickets in growing animals and will also produce serious trouble in mature animals. Even a moderate lack may result in a weak skeleton that can not withstand the usual strains and shocks.

The term *rickets* is commonly used for the deficiency disease produced in young animals by a lack of calcium, phosphorus, or vitamin D. (Sometimes the term is used also for similar bone diseases in mature animals.) In rickets the blood becomes deficient in phosphorus or calcium or in both of these minerals. As a result, normal deposition of calcium and phosphorus can not occur in the growing bones. They therefore are weak and are readily broken or fractured. In an attempt to overcome the weak structure, the long bones become abnormally large at the ends, where the growth takes place. Characteristic enlargement or "beading" at the ends of the ribs often results. If rickets develops at an early age, the legs may become decidedly bowed.

Among the larger farm animals, rickets occurs most frequently in young cattle and pigs. The methods of preventing this trouble are therefore given especial consideration in Chapters XXVIII and XXXV.

In young cattle characteristic symptoms of rickets are stiffness, bent and swollen knees, swollen hocks, and an arching of the back, except immediately at the rear of the shoulders, where there is often a sag. The animal frequently stands humped up with middle drawn up, and is often easily excited and may have attacks of fits. Respiration is rapid, and the animal becomes exhausted from slight exertion. A depraved appetite may develop, as shown by the chewing of bones, wood, or hair. In severe cases the animal may show a decided lack of appetite, especially for roughage.

The most marked symptom of rickets in pigs is stiffness of the legs. This is usually accompanied by a general unthrifty appearance and a failure to make good gains in weight. Eventually, paralysis of the hind legs often occurs. This is due, at least in certain cases, to a fracture of one of the vertebra and the resulting crushing or constriction of the spinal cord.

If the disease has not advanced too far, the animal will usually recover when supplements are added to the ration that furnish liberal amounts of vitamin D, calcium, and phosphorus. However, recovery may be slow if it has reached the stage where there is a marked lack of appetite. Also, it may be impossible to overcome malformations of the skeleton produced by the disease.

164. Effect of calcium or phosphorus lack on mature animals.— In the case of mature animals a deficiency of calcium or phosphorus or a lack of vitamin D produces mineral-deficiency diseases which are somewhat different from rickets. Calcium and phosphorus are withdrawn from the bones to meet the needs for these minerals by the body. As a result the bones become porous and weak and are therefore easily broken. The animals often become lame or stiff, because of injury to the joints.

Due to the porous condition of the bones, these deficiency diseases are often called *osteoporosis*. Other names given to these troubles are pica, stiffs, and osteomalcia. Sometimes these diseases are included under the term rickets, but this term is properly used only for the similar disease in growing animals.

Stock suffering from these mineral deficiencies usually have depraved appetites and gnaw bones, wood, or other objects or eat dirt in an instinctive effort to secure the needed minerals. Through eating decayed bones or flesh, animals on range pastures may become infected with botulism or other diseases, or be poisoned by toxic substances in such material.

It has been found during recent years that there are many areas in this and other countries where stock suffer seriously from a deficiency of phosphorus in pasturage, hay, and other feeds.[39] In these areas the soil is so lacking in available phosphorus that the crops grown thereon have a much lower content of this mineral than normal.

Fertilization with superphosphate or other phosphorus fertilizers not only greatly increases the yields of crops in such areas, but also produces feeds of normal phosphorus content and therefore prevents injury to stock from a lack of the mineral. Wherever fertilization of the land is not practicable, as on range areas, trouble from phosphorus deficiency may be prevented by supplying bone meal or some other safe phosphorus supplement.

Common symptoms of phosphorus deficiency are depraved appetite, stiffness of the joints, lack of appetite, and a run-down, unthrifty condition. The bones sometimes become so soft or brittle that they are readily broken. In severe cases of phosphorus deficiency the animals may no longer show a depraved appetite, but appear listless and have little desire for food. High-producing cows and young stock are usually most affected by the deficiency, due to their greater needs for the mineral. In phosphorus-deficient areas cows frequently fail to come in heat regularly and often do not calve more than once in two years.

In cases of phosphorus deficiency, animals not only have poor appetites and eat less feed than normal, but also they utilize poorly that which they do consume. Kansas and Minnesota studies show that the lack of the mineral does not lessen the digestibility of the ration, but it deranges metabolism so that the digested nutrients are used inefficiently.[40]   This is perhaps because phosphorus compounds are probably involved in the conversion of carbohydrates into body fat or the fat of milk.

As has been previously stated, there is much less apt to be a deficiency of calcium than of phosphorus in the common roughages. However, in a few areas, as in certain sections of Florida, the soil is so deficient in calcium that serious trouble results unless stock are supplied with a calcium supplement.[41]   While dairy cows suffering from phosphorus deficiency are commonly thin and run-down in condition, those affected by a lack of calcium may be in good flesh if fed liberally on concentrates.   However, their milk yield may be greatly reduced, and their bones may be broken without any unusual strain or shock.

If breeding females are fed rations seriously deficient in phosphorus or calcium, the body of the mother does its utmost to protect the young against the lack by withdrawing the mineral from the skeleton.   In extreme cases, normal reproduction may be prevented and the young may be born weak or even dead.   This is much more apt to occur in the case of brood sows than with herbivora, for sows fed on only grain and grain by-products receive a ration that is disastrously deficient in calcium.

165. Calcium supplements.—When a ration is fed that is deficient in calcium, in phosphorus, or in both of these minerals, the lack should be corrected by the use of a suitable mineral supplement.   In deciding what supplement to use, one should first determine which mineral is lacking.   If the ration is deficient only in calcium and has plenty of phosphorus, it is uneconomical to use a supplement like bone meal, which furnishes both of these minerals.   Such supplements cost much more than ground limestone or other calcium supplements.

Also, if there is already an abundance of phosphorus in the ration, it may be injurious to add considerably more.   For example, the addition of a phosphorus supplement to a ration for chicks which is already rich in this mineral may cause the serious trouble known as "slipped tendon."

The calcium supplement most commonly used when this mineral alone is lacking, is *ground limestone*.   This is generally cheap in price and is readily available in most sections.   *High-calcium limestone,* or calcitic limestone, is to be preferred as a mineral supplement, as the value depends on the actual amount of calcium present.   *Dolomitic limestone,* which contains considerable magnesium carbonate, is also fairly satisfactory, though it has been somewhat inferior to calcitic limestone in certain tests.[42]   Its value per ton is of course lower than that of calcitic limestone, due to the smaller amount of calcium it supplies.

Ground oyster shells and *ground clam shells* are excellent calcium supplements.   As shown in Appendix Table IV, these supplements are slightly higher in calcium than high-calcium limestone.

Marl is also satisfactory as a calcium supplement when it does not contain too large a proportion of clay or sand. Its value per ton will obviously depend on the amount of calcium it supplies.

Precipitated calcium carbonate, a by-product from soap and sugar factories, is sometimes available for use as a mineral supplement and is entirely satisfactory for the purpose.

Wood ashes contain about two-thirds as much calcium as does ground limestone and may be used in place of it as a calcium supplement, when available on the farm.

Gypsum supplies calcium in the form of calcium sulfate instead of calcium carbonate, as in limestone and the other calcium supplements that have been mentioned. It is apparently satisfactory for use as a calcium supplement in stock feeding.

Unslaked lime or *water-slaked lime* (hydrated lime) should not be fed to stock because of their caustic nature.

166. Phosphorus supplements.—The mineral supplement used most commonly to correct deficiencies of phosphorus is steamed bone meal. Other satisfactory phosphorus supplements are so-called "raw bone meal," spent bone black, dicalcium phosphate, and phosphates of rock origin from which practically all of the fluorine has been removed. These phosphorus supplements all supply calcium as well as phosphorus, bone meals and spent bone black containing twice as much calcium as phosphorus.

As is stated later, superphosphate or untreated rock phosphate or phosphorized limestone cannot be recommended for use as mineral supplements in stock feeding over extended periods, on account of their fluorine content. (**171**)

167. Steamed bone meal.—In the production of steamed bone meal for feeding purposes, fresh bones of suitable quality are cooked under steam pressure very thoroughly. This extracts most of the protein and fat, which are used for other purposes. The residue is pressed and dried, and then ground for sale as steamed bone meal, often called merely "bone meal." Steamed bone meal contains an average of 32.6 per cent calcium and 15.2 per cent phosphorus, with only 7.1 per cent protein and 3.3 per cent fat.

Raw material of much better quality should be used in making bone meal for stock feeding than for fertilizer bone meal. Therefore it is wise to buy for feeding only products that are known definitely to have been made especially for this purpose. Fertilizer bone meal often has a rank, disagreeable smell, while a good grade of feeding bone meal should have but little odor, and should be nearly white in color.

168. Raw bone meal—This by-product was formerly often used for poultry, but it has now been almost entirely replaced by steamed bone meal. It is not a raw or uncooked product at all, but is thoroughly cooked in open kettles instead of under steam pressure, as in the making of steamed bone meal. Due to the lower temperature, the protein is removed less completely, and raw bone meal is therefore lower in phosphorus and calcium. It has an average of 25.8 per cent protein, 2.9 per cent fat, 23.0 per cent calcium and 10.9 per cent phosphorus. Raw bone meal is sometimes ground more coarsely than steamed bone meal and screened into various sizes for poultry of different ages.

169. Spent bone black, or bone char.—Bone black is a granular product made by charring bone in closed retorts and grinding it coarsely. It is employed especially for clarifying and decolorizing the sirup in the manufacture of cane or beet sugar and in making table sirups. After the bone black has once been used and has taken up organic impurities, it is re-charred and used again. Finally, it becomes too powdery for further use, and is then dried and sold as *spent bone black,* or bone char, for stock feeding or for fertilizer.

Though black in color, spent bone black contains about two-thirds as much phosphorus and calcium as steamed bone meal, having 10.9 per cent phosphorus and 22.0 per cent calcium. It may be used in the same manner as steamed bone meal in stock feeding.

170. Dicalcium phosphate; other phosphate products.—*Dicalcium phosphate* is made either from rock phosphate or bone, the phosphate being dissolved in acid and then precipitated. If the fluorine in rock phosphate is nearly all removed in the process of manufacture, the product made from rock phosphate is just as satisfactory as that made from bone. Dicalcium phosphate contains about 18 per cent phosphorus, in comparison with 15.2 for bone meal. Per pound of phosphorus, dicalcium phosphate is no more valuable than steamed bone meal as a mineral supplement.

Monocalcium phosphate is a product somewhat similar to dicalcium phosphate, except that it contains much less calcium and more phosphorus. If the fluorine has been sufficiently removed in the process of manufacture, monocalcium phosphate is a satisfactory mineral supplement when only phosphorus is lacking in the ration, but it furnishes relatively little calcium.

Other phosphate products made from rock phosphate or from phosphorized limestone are satisfactory for use in stock feeding, provided that practically all of the fluorine has been removed in the manufacturing process. One should, however, be sure that such products do not contain dangerous amounts of fluorine. It is not advisable to feed fertilizer superphosphate or untreated rock phosphate to stock for any long period, due to their content of fluorine.

171. Fluorine; rock phosphate, phosphorized limestone, superphosphate.—It has long been known that fluorine is a violent poison when taken into the body in any considerable amounts.[43] Recent investigations have shown, furthermore, that even very small amounts of this mineral have a poisonous effect if these amounts are steadily consumed over a long period of time. The chief effect is upon the teeth and bones. It is of interest to mention that the presence of more than a mere trace of fluorine in the drinking water is the cause of the serious condition of the teeth of humans which is known as "mottled enamel."[44]

These investigations upon the toxic effects of fluorine are of great importance in stock feeding, for rock phosphate (sometimes called "lime phosphate"), which has been used to some extent as a mineral supplement for farm animals, usually contains 3 to 4 per cent of fluorine. Due to this fluorine content, when 1.5 per cent of rock phosphate was included in the concentrate mixture for dairy cattle in Michigan investigations, the teeth became so soft that they wore down to such an extent within 2 years that the cattle were unable to chew their feed properly.[45] Also, the teeth were so worn that the animals were unable to drink cold water, because of the pain, but lapped it with the tongue, like cats or dogs. There was also marked derangement and injury to various bones of the body. Similar results were produced when a proprietary mineral mixture was fed that included rock phosphate as one of the ingredients.

In Wisconsin experiments in which only 0.6 lb. of rock phosphate was included in each 100 lbs. of the concentrate mixture for dairy cattle, they showed no apparent effects during the first 3 years. However, during the next 2 years their teeth showed the same changes as in the Michigan experiments, and the cows had poor appetites, lost weight, and declined in milk production.[46] Also, oestrum was delayed following calving, and the calves were smaller than normal at birth.

In the Wisconsin experiments swine were also fed for three generations on rations containing various percentages of rock phosphate. A ration containing 1.6 per cent of rock phosphate was distinctly harmful, and one containing 0.8 per cent did not produce normal results when fed to pigs in dry lot. However, there was no apparent injury to swine when only 0.4 per cent rock phosphate was included in the ration. Injury has also resulted in experiments at other stations when much rock phosphate has been included in rations for swine.[47] In Ohio experiments poor results were secured with chicks when the ration contained more than 1 per cent rock phosphate, while satisfactory results were obtained in Wisconsin tests with a ration carrying 2 per cent rock phosphate.[48]

Phosphorized limestone, which is part way between limestone and rock phosphate in chemical composition, has been used to some extent as a mineral supplement for stock feeding.[49] Though the actual percentage of fluorine in this product is lower than in rock phosphate, the proportion between the amount of phosphorus and the amount of fluorine is nearly the same as in rock phosphate. Therefore, if enough phosphorized limestone is fed to supply a certain amount of phosphorus, the ration will have nearly as much fluorine as though rock phosphate had been used. In an instance which came under the observation of the author, disastrous results were produced in a dairy herd which, according to the owner, had been fed phosphorized limestone as a mineral supplement for 3 to 4 years. This had been done in a mistaken and vain effort to eradicate infectious abortion, or Bang's disease, by the use of a mineral supplement, instead of eradicating the disease by means of the blood test.

In the manufacture of superphosphate for fertilizer from rock phosphate most of the fluorine is not removed. Therefore continued use of much superphosphate as a mineral supplement would undoubtedly produce the same effects as rock phosphate.

Since there is but little definite information as to how much of these products which contain appreciable amounts of fluorine can be safely fed to the various classes of stock, it is the best plan to use instead a phosphorus supplement which is entirely safe, such as steamed bone meal. It would seem especially unwise to feed these fluorine-containing products in appreciable amounts to breeding animals for any extended length of time.

GOITER SOMETIMES CAUSES HEAVY LOSSES

A litter of pigs affected with goiter, or "hairlessness," caused by a lack of iodine in the ration of the sow. Some of the pigs are dead, while others are still alive, although very weak. After this sow had been given iodine in the form of potassium iodide during her next gestation period, she produced a litter of thrifty pigs. (From Hart, Wisconsin Station.)

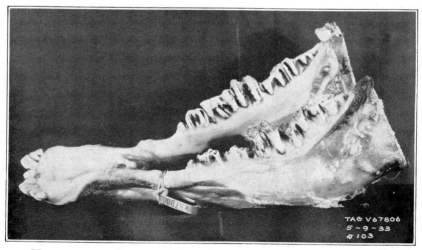

FLUORINE IN CERTAIN ROCK PRODUCTS MAY POISON STOCK

Jaw bone and teeth of cow which had been fed a mineral supplement containing fluorine for three years. The teeth were worn down to such an extent that the cow was unable to chew her feed normally. In spite of liberal feeding she became a pitiful wreck. (From Udall, New York State Veterinary College, Cornell University.)

The Pig on the Left Has Severe Anemia

These pigs are litter mates. The one on the left was raised by its mother in a hog house and a small paved exercise lot, without access to the soil. It has severe anemia, due to the lack of iron and copper in milk. (See Chapter XXXV.) The thrifty pig on the right was transferred soon after birth to a sow whose udder was swabbed with a solution of ordinary iron sulfate. (From J. P. Willman, New York, Cornell, Station.)

Experiments With Rats Have Solved Many Problems

Much of our knowledge concerning proteins, vitamins, and minerals has been gained through experiments with small laboratory animals. Equipment for investigations with rats and other small animals in the Animal Nutrition Laboratory, Animal Husbandry Department, Cornell University. (From McCay and Maynard.)

172. Iodine; goiter in farm animals.—It has been explained previously that the rate of metabolism of the body is controlled through the action of thyroxin, an iodine-containing compound secreted by the thyroid gland in the neck. (**63**) If an animal secures insufficient iodine in its food to make possible the production of the normal amount of thyroxine, the thyroid gland may enlarge in the attempt to make sufficient thyroxine, and the ordinary type of goiter will result.

Formerly, there were heavy losses of new-born pigs, lambs, kids, calves, and foals from goiter in certain sections of the northwestern states, in western Canada, and in other iodine-deficient areas. For some unknown reason the severity of the trouble varied greatly from year to year.

The young thus affected are born dead or weak, the losses being especially severe in the case of pigs and lambs. Such pigs usually are practically hairless, and the disease in swine is often called "hairless pigs." The pigs have thick, pulpy skin and large necks, and seem unusually large and fat because of a bloated condition. In lambs and calves affected with goiter, the enlarged thyroid gland is readily seen. In foals there is seldom a visible goiter, the only symptom usually being extreme weakness at birth.

Experiments have proved conclusively that goiter in new-born farm animals can be entirely prevented by supplying small amounts of iodine to the pregnant animals during at least the last half of the pregnancy period.[50] The simplest method of furnishing iodine is to supply iodized stock salt during this period, instead of ordinary salt. Such salt should contain 0.02 per cent of potassium iodide, which is equivalent to 1 ounce of potassium iodide in each 300 lbs. of salt. If iodized salt made by a reliable manufacturer is not readily available, it can be easily mixed on the farm.

If for any reason salt is not fed to brood sows, potassium iodide tablets can be used instead of iodized salt. Once a week enough of the tablets to supply each sow with 2 grains of potassium iodide should be dissolved in water, and the solution mixed with the feed.

There is no need of thus supplying additional iodine to pregnant animals in areas where there has been no trouble from goiter in new-born animals. It is rather surprising that goiter does not commonly occur among livestock in many areas where goiter among humans is common. For example, relatively few cases of goiter in stock have been reported in this country east of the Mississippi river. Also, mature farm animals rarely have any pronounced goiters, even in areas where losses of new-born animals from goiter are severe.

There is very little evidence that there is any benefit from adding iodine to the rations of live stock except where this may be necessary to prevent goiter in the new-born young, or possibly to prevent navel-ill in foals, as is mentioned later. Several experiments have been conducted to study this question, including trials with dairy cows, dairy calves, pigs, lambs, and chickens.[51] In the majority of the tests there has been no distinct benefit from the addition of iodine to a normal ration. Even in the trials where an iodine supplement has apparently been beneficial, the advantage has usually been slight.

In spite of these results, extravagant advertising claims are still made for the widespread use of various iodine supplements. **For** example, statements are made that such products will build up resistance to various diseases, will prevent sterility and other breeding troubles, will eradicate or prevent infectious abortion (Bang's disease), will cause a great increase in product, or markedly increase the efficiency with which feed is utilized.

In areas where iodine deficiency is most serious, it may possibly be wise to use iodized salt regularly in place of common salt for all stock, and not merely for pregnant animals. On the other hand, in districts where there has been little or no trouble from goiter in live stock, the general use of iodized salt or other iodine supplements for farm animals does not seem to be warranted. There is no positive evidence that organic forms of iodine are more effective than iodized salt for preventing goiter, or that such iodine compounds are of especial benefit to stock.

A very limited amount of data indicates that navel-ill and weakness of foals may be lessened by feeding brood mares during pregnancy as much as 14 to 15 grains of potassium iodide daily, with their grain.[52] Further results are needed before final conclusions can be drawn concerning the merits of this treatment.

173. Iron and copper.—An adequate supply of iron is essential for animals, because the oxygen needed by the tissues for the life processes is transported in the blood by the hemoglobin, which is an iron-containing compound. (**62**) Iron is also usually present in the nuclei, or life centers, of the body cells, which control their activities. Iron compounds are, moreover, believed to play an important part in the oxidation of nutrients in the cells.

In spite of the importance of iron, the animal body contains but a very small amount. Indeed, iron forms only about one part in twenty-five thousand, by weight, of our bodies. The tissues of a full-grown, healthy person contain only one-tenth ounce of this mineral.

Recent investigations by Hart and associates at the Wisconsin Station have shown the surprising fact that for hemoglobin formation in the body small traces of copper must be provided in the food, as well as an ample supply of iron.[53] These results have been confirmed by several other scientists. Traces of copper are therefore essential for animal life, although this mineral is a violent poison when any considerable amount is taken into the body.

It has been found that the copper is not a part of the hemoglobin, but that it is necessary to enable the body to produce this compound.[54] When the essential traces of copper are not present, the animal can still assimilate iron from the food, but it merely stores it in the liver and is unable to manufacture hemoglobin.

If animals are fed a diet that is too low in iron, or in iron and copper, nutritional anemia will result. In this disease there is a serious lack of hemoglobin in the blood. Such nutritional anemia is very different from the disease in humans called pernicious anemia, and also differs from anemia caused by great loss of blood, as from a wound.

There is usually no lack of iron or copper in the rations of farm animals, except perhaps during the suckling period, as is discussed later. (**174**) However, in a few localities the forage is so low in one or both of these minerals that serious anemia of stock results.

It was long known that cattle would not thrive on certain areas of very poor, sandy land in Florida. They lost their appetites, they became emaciated and weak, and their blood was very low in hemoglobin. Young cattle were most affected by the disease and were often badly stunted. Many of the animals died from the disease. Goats, sheep, and swine were also affected in certain of the areas.

In experiments by Becker, Neal, and Shealy it has finally been proved that this disease, which is called "salt sick," is due to a serious lack in the forage of iron, or of both iron and copper.[55] Recovery follows rapidly when the animals are allowed to take as much as they wish of a mineral mixture composed of 100 lbs. common salt, 25 lbs. of red oxide of iron, and 1 lb. of finely-ground copper sulfate. The mixture must be mixed very thoroughly so no animal will get too much copper sulfate. In a few localities the forage is also deficient in phosphorus. In such cases it is also necessary to include bone meal or some other phosphorus supplement in the mineral mixture.

It has been found that baffling diseases of stock in certain other parts of the world are likewise probably due to a lack of iron, or of iron and copper. Similar anemias have been found in areas of New Zealand, of Tasmania, of Southern Scotland, and in Kenya Colony, British East Africa. With the knowledge that has recently been gained concerning these troubles, it will undoubtedly be found that iron deficiency exists in the forage of certain other localities.

Many investigations have been conducted to determine which sources of iron were most readily available for hemoglobin building, especially in the human body. With the recent discovery that copper is also necessary in this process, it has at length been possible to secure more definite information on this subject. In recent Wisconsin experiments it has been found that simple inorganic iron salts, such as ferric chloride, are readily utilized, while the iron in the complex organic iron compound in the hemoglobin of blood was much less readily used.[56] This indicates that iron in organic compounds must be broken down in the body into simple inorganic iron salts, before it can be utilized. It was also found in these studies that the organic iron in the cereal grains was not as available for hemoglobin building as that in inorganic salts.

The green-leaved parts of plants, especially of young plants, are rich in iron. Other feeds and foods relatively high in iron are most meats, legume seeds, cereal grains, and cane molasses.

174. Anemia of suckling animals.—Milk is exceedingly low in iron and also in copper, and it is not possible by any method of feeding a lactating animal to increase the amounts of these minerals in her milk.[57] To offset this lack, young mammals are born with a store of the minerals in their bodies which normally suffices until they begin to eat other food that supplies ample amounts of these minerals. If they are continued on milk as an exclusive diet for an abnormal length of time, disaster will follow on account of these and other deficiencies, as is pointed out in the next chapter. (**208**)

When young farm animals are raised under normal conditions

and are allowed to eat other feed as soon as they will take it, there is generally no trouble whatsoever from anemia, the lack of red blood cells, except in the case of suckling pigs which are not on pasture but are confined away from the soil. Under such conditions the lack of iron, or of iron and copper, sometimes causes serious anemia, which is often called "thumps." As shown in Chapter XXXVII this disease, often fatal to young pigs, can readily be prevented by swabbing the udder of the sow daily with a solution of an iron salt or by dosing the pigs once a week with the iron solution.

175. Sulfur.—Sulfur is necessary for the life of animals, for it is an essential part of most proteins. Also, recent investigations indicate that an important part in the oxidations of nutrients in the body tissues is played by a compound called glutathione. This is composed of cystine (the chief sulfur-containing amino acid) and two other amino acids.

Most of the sulfur used by animals in the formation of proteins and for other purposes probably comes from the cystine and other organic sulfur compounds in their feed. It has been shown previously in this chapter that certain common feeds are low in cystine, and therefore do not produce good results unless this lack is corrected. (150)

Since wool is especially rich in cystine, sheep have a higher sulfur requirement than other classes of stock.[58] It has been shown previously, however, that although alfalfa hay is apparently rather low in cystine, the proteins have a high value for growing lambs. (154) This indicates that sheep can use other sources of sulfur for the formation of the cystine in wool, perhaps through the action of the bacteria in the paunch.

So far as has been shown by experiments there is no advantage in adding sulfates or other inorganic sources of sulfur to the rations of livestock.[59]

176. Other essential minerals.—In addition to the minerals that have been discussed in detail, there are required by animals appreciable amounts of potassium and also traces of magnesium, manganese, and zinc. These minerals need no special consideration in the feeding of humans or of livestock, for the usual foods and feeding stuffs supply adequate amounts.

Further information concerning the functions and importance of these minerals is given in the following paragraphs. It is possible that minute traces of still other minerals are required by animals. Thus, according to a recent report, studies in Australia indicate that a mineral deficiency in certain areas of southern and western Australia may be due to a lack of traces of cobalt. This mineral has not hitherto been considered essential for animal life. Until further investigations are conducted, no final conclusions can be made concerning its importance in animal nutrition.

177. Potassium.—Potassium is essential to animal life, and the bodies of animals contain more potassium than they do of either sodium or chlorine.[60] However, the usual feeding stuffs supply ample amounts, and therefore there is no need of adding potassium supplements to livestock rations.

It has been a disputed point as to whether the presence in a ration of a considerable amount of potassium will cause an increased excretion of sodium, and therefore a greater need for common salt.[61] Though this often does not seem to be the result, nevertheless herbivora, which live largely on forage plants, that are high in potassium, require more salt than swine and poultry, which consume rations lower in this mineral.

178. Magnesium.—Magnesium is present in only very small amounts in the bodies of animals, forming about 0.05 per cent of the human body. Nevertheless, recent investigations have proved that it is necessary for life.[62] If experimental animals are fed rations from which the magnesium has been removed as completely as possible, they will show increasing irritability after a few days and a little later die in convulsions. Most all normal foods contain the small traces of magnesium needed for life. Therefore, there is no lack of it, so far as is known, in any ordinary ration fed livestock.

It was formerly believed that magnesium had a decidedly antagonistic action against calcium in the body, and that an excess of magnesium would cause a large loss of calcium, thus producing injury. Recent experiments have shown that unless the amount of magnesium is very large, no bad results will be produced.[63] As has been stated earlier in this chapter, dolomitic or magnesian limestone is fairly satisfactory as a mineral supplement for stock.

179. Manganese.—Manganese is present in the animal body only in traces. However, recent studies show that if experimental animals are fed for a considerable period on rations from which the manganese has been removed, growth is lessened and also reproduction and lactation are impaired.[64] Certain experiments conducted a few years ago indicated that manganese was necessary, along with iron, for the formation of the hemoglobin in the blood, but other investigations have finally disproved this.[65]

Manganese is essential for plant growth, and a few soils have been found that are so lacking in it that some crops are injured, the normal development of chlorophyll being prevented. On such soils the addition of manganese salts produces striking improvements. So far as is known, the small traces of manganese needed by farm animals are always provided by ordinary rations. Cereals, legume seeds, green plants and vegetables, and fruits are the most important sources in foods of this mineral.[66]

180. Zinc.—It has been known for a considerable time that the bodies of animals always contain traces of zinc, but the opinions of scientists have differed as to whether zinc is necessary for life.[67] In recent experiments in which rats have been fed diets freed as thoroughly as possible from zinc, it has been found that traces of this mineral are essential for good growth and also apparently for normal hair development.[68]

On account of the wide use of galvanized (zinc-coated) containers for liquids, studies have been conducted to find whether sour foods would dissolve sufficient zinc to be poisonous to animals. In Oklahoma tests buttermilk stored in galvanized tanks for some time was not poisonous to rats.[69] Probably most cases of poisoning attributed to zinc have been due to lead, which is present in most zinc coatings.

181. Mineral mixtures; methods of using mineral supplements.—

When a ration is fed that is deficient in calcium or in phosphorus, this lack should be corrected by the use of a suitable mineral supplement, as has been shown previously. When a mixture of ground concentrates is being fed, the proper amount of the mineral supplement may be mixed with the concentrates. In other cases, the mineral supplement is best mixed with salt to make it more palatable, and the mixture then supplied where the stock can have access to it. The instinct of farm animals guides them to consume sufficient of the mineral mixture to correct the deficiency in the ration.

If the only deficiency is of calcium, such a mixture as 2 parts by weight of ground limestone or some other calcium supplement and 1 part of common salt is satisfactory.

If phosphorus is deficient and there is plenty of calcium in the ration, such a mixture as 2 parts or more by weight of bone meal or other safe phosphorus supplement and 1 part common salt is excellent.

When both phosphorus and calcium are deficient, a suitable mixture is 2 parts by weight of steamed bone meal or other safe phosphorus supplement, 2 parts ground limestone or other calcium supplement, and 1 part common salt.

In using one of these mixtures, it is wise to supply common salt separately in addition, so that the animals will not have to consume more of the mineral mixture than they need in order to get sufficient salt. If no salt is supplied separately, a mineral mixture for cattle should contain one-half salt and one for swine at least one-third salt. A suitable mixture for cattle when no additional salt is provided, is 1 part by weight of bone meal, 1 part ground limestone, and 2 parts common salt. A good mixture for swine is made up of equal parts by weight of these three supplements.

In areas where there is trouble from goiter in livestock, 1 ounce of potassium iodide should be included in each 300 lbs. of mineral mixture for pregnant animals, unless iodized salt is fed separately. In the very rare localities where there is a deficiency of iron or of iron and copper, these minerals should be supplied, as previously advised.

182. Complex mineral mixtures.—Many complex proprietary mineral mixtures are on the market that contain several other minerals, in addition to those that have been advised in the preceding recommendations. Among the additional substances used in such complex mineral mixtures are sulfur, Epsom salts, Glauber's salts, sodium carbonate, potassium salts, manganese salts, silicates, charcoal, coal, and kelp.

To determine definitely whether there is an advantage in adding any of these substances to good rations for livestock would require several experiments, in each of which one lot of animals was fed a well-balanced ration without the supplement, while the particular supplement to be tested was added to the ration for the other lot. Several experiments would be needed before definite conclusions could be drawn, because excellent results are secured without any of these substances, and they cannot therefore be expected to produce any marked improvement in the ration.

In a few experiments, especially with swine, complex mineral mixtures have been compared with simple mineral mixtures, and in other tests such substances as sulfur, charcoal, coal, sodium carbonate, or kelp have been added to good rations.[70] From a study of the data thus far secured, the author has come to the conclusion that there is no positive evidence that it is advantageous to include in mineral mixtures for livestock other minerals than those in the mixtures previously advised in this chapter.

Practically all of the animal husbandmen in this country evidently have the same point of view on this matter, for they recommend simple mineral mixtures, instead of complex preparations. For example,

Weber reports that of 32 animal husbandmen in 29 agricultural colleges who replied to a questionnaire concerning minerals for swine feeding, all except two recommended only simple mineral mixtures supplying merely common salt, calcium, and phosphorus, with iodine in addition for goitrous sections.[71]

183. Acid-base balance.—It is the belief of some investigators in nutrition that care should be taken to have a proper balance of bases and acids in the human diet. This means that the food should provide a sufficient amount of bases, or alkalies, to neutralize the acid supplied by such acid mineral constituents of the food as phosphates, sulfates, and chlorides. However, the body possesses much power to maintain the neutrality of the blood in spite of considerable differences in the intake of alkalies and acids in the food. (The manner in which this is done is explained in texts on biological chemistry.) The importance of the acid-base balance in normal diets for humans is therefore doubted by other investigators.

Farm animals, especially ruminants, have great ability to produce ammonia in the body tissues to neutralize any ordinary excess of acid. Therefore any amount of acid that may be present in an ordinary ration will probably not be at all injurious, provided that the ration furnishes sufficient amounts of calcium and other essential minerals.

It has been abundantly proven that the continued feeding of liberal amounts of corn silage to dairy cows for several years has no injurious effect whatsoever, though silage has a considerable amount of organic acids. Cows in Ohio tests were fed 50 lbs. of corn silage per head daily for several months without any harmful effect.[72] Also, they were fed without injury larger amounts of lactic acid and acetic acid than they would ever get in a normal ration. In other tests calves and swine have been fed without injury greater amounts of dilute mineral acids or organic acids than would be contained in any normal ration.[73]

III. Vitamins in Stock Feeding

184. Vitamin discoveries of profound importance.—In no other field of nutrition have the discoveries during recent years been as surprising or important in our daily lives as those dealing with the vitamins and their functions. Through the results of these investigations it has been possible to increase the general health and vigor of humans and to prevent entirely such diseases as rickets and beri-beri. These discoveries have also had a profound effect upon livestock farming by increasing the efficiency of animal production and preventing serious nutritional diseases.

For example, before the functions of vitamins were known, pigs that were born in the fall often failed to thrive and many became paralyzed or died from pneumonia or other diseases. This fall-pig problem has been solved through the use of improved rations that provide an ample supply of the essential vitamins. Similarly, before the necessity of vitamins in poultry feeding was understood, it was difficult to grow thrifty chicks during the seasons of the year when they could not get out in the sunshine and secure green forage. Now they can be raised efficiently at any season of the year.

In the southern states cattle fed heavily on cottonseed meal often died from what was thought to be "cottonseed meal poisoning." It is now known that the trouble was due to deficiencies of vitamins and minerals. As a result, it is now possible to feed dairy cows for long periods on cottonseed meal as the only concentrate without any injurious results whatsoever.

The discoveries concerning the occurrence and functions of vitamins have all been made in a surprisingly short period. Previous to 1911 even the existence of vitamins as definite food essentials was unknown. It was then generally believed that the only requirements for a satisfactory diet for humans or a complete ration for farm animals were adequate supplies of proteins, carbohydrates, fats, and mineral matter.

Certain investigators had previously reported that laboratory test animals, such as rats or mice, did not thrive on a diet made up of the highly-purified nutrients that were then known. They had furthermore found that when certain natural foods, like milk, were added to such a diet the animals would thrive. They therefore concluded that certain other substances must be essential for animal life, in addition to the recognized classes of nutrients. It is rather surprising that these interesting observations attracted little attention at the time from other investigators.

Beginning in 1911, important discoveries came with great rapidity. It was first discovered that a mysterious substance (now known as vitamin B) was able to prevent or cure experimental beri-beri in laboratory animals. The following year it was announced that scurvy in experimental guinea pigs could be cured by feeding small amounts of fresh green feeds that supplied the anti-scorbutic factor, which we now call vitamin C. Then in 1913 investigators in two different laboratories discovered a food essential in butter fat that was necessary for growth and even for life itself. Since that time hardly a year has passed without some discovery of major significance in this field.

The existence of at least 6 different vitamins has been definitely proved, and their functions and occurrence in foods have been studied in detail. These are known as vitamins A, B, C, D, E, and G. As is indicated in the discussion of the vitamin B complex, it is probable that there are still other vitamins which are essential for certain species of animals. The recently-discovered vitamin K is apparently needed by poultry but seems to be provided amply by ordinary rations.

Vitamin A and vitamin D are necessary for all classes of farm animals and are of great importance in stock feeding. They are therefore considered first in the discussions which follow. The requirements of the various classes of stock for these two vitamins are discussed in detail in Part III. There is apparently no lack of any of the other vitamins in the usual rations fed livestock, with the exception of vitamin G for poultry. Their requirement for this vitamin is particularly high, and it therefore must be given especial consideration in making up poultry rations.

Only the briefest summary can be presented here concerning the nature, the functions, and the occurrence in various feeds of the different vitamins. For further information the reader is referred to recent texts on biological chemistry and to the books dealing exclusively with this subject.[74]

185. Vitamin content of various feeds.—The available information on the relative amounts of the different vitamins in various important feeding stuffs is summarized in Appendix Table V. Data of this kind are still exceedingly scanty, since most of the investigations in this field have been conducted upon human foods, rather than on

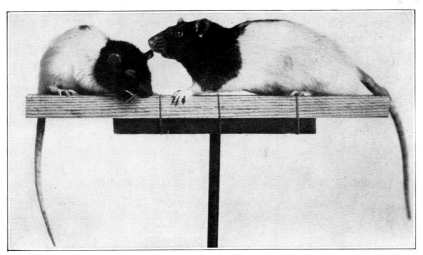

Vitamin A Was Discovered in Experiments With Rats

The thrifty rat on the right received plenty of vitamin A in the form of butter fat. The rat on the left, which received oleomargarine instead of butter, is of the same age, but has been stunted, due to a lack of the vitamin. Also, it is nearly blind. (From Steenbock and Hart, Wisconsin Station.)

Vitamin G Is of Much Importance in Poultry Feeding

The chick on the left received plenty of vitamin G. The one on the right is the same age, but it has been stunted by a lack of this vitamin. Especial attention must be given to vitamin G in poultry feeding, but other classes of livestock apparently receive an ample supply in ordinary rations. (From Halpin and Hart, Wisconsin Station.)

YOUNG CHICK PARALYZED BY LACK OF VITAMIN B

This 9-day-old chick was fed an experimental ration lacking vitamin B and is suffering from severe polyneuritis. (From Norris and Heuser, New York, Cornell, Station.)

EFFECT OF A LACK OF VITAMIN C ON GUINEA PIGS

Above—A thrifty guinea pig, which received ample vitamin C. Below, a guinea pig suffering from scurvy, produced by a lack of the vitamin. (From Wisconsin Station.)

feeds for livestock. Also, the amount of a particular vitamin in a certain kind of feed may vary widely, depending on the quality of the feed, on the stage of growth, and, in the case of hay or other dry forage, on how it has been cured.

Therefore no attempt is made in this table to express the amounts of the various vitamins in the terms of the quantitative units that are employed by investigators in their measurement. By appropriate symbols it is merely indicated whether a given feed is a fair, a good, or an excellent source of the particular vitamin, or whether it has no appreciable amount.

Though the number of feeds included in this table is very limited, the data will indicate the approximate vitamin content of other feeds of the same general nature.

186. Vitamin A; its importance and its functions.—Vitamin A is of very great importance in animal husbandry, for it is required by all classes of livestock, including poultry. Unless care is taken to include in the rations fed farm animals a sufficient amount of feeds rich in the vitamin, unsatisfactory production will result and disaster may follow.

Vitamin A is essential even for the maintenance of mature animals. For growth, reproduction, and lactation, greater amounts are required than for the mere maintenance of the body. The experiments by McCollum at the Wisconsin Station and by Osborne and Mendel at Yale University in which vitamin A was first discovered were with growing animals. The importance of the vitamin for growth therefore received the most attention for some years, and as a result it was often called "the growth vitamin." This designation should not be used, however, for its other functions are just as important. Moreover, vitamins B and G are also necessary for growth.

One of the chief functions of vitamin A is to keep the epithelium, or surface tissues, of the mucous membranes of the body in a healthy condition so that they will resist bacterial infection. A deficiency of the vitamin causes these tissues to become so changed and weakened that bacteria can readily invade the body. Due to this effect, animals suffering from a lack of vitamin A are especially subject to diseases of the respiratory system. For example, pigs fed rations lacking vitamin A often die from pneumonia. The characteristic eye disease, known as xerophthalmia, which is often produced by a severe deficiency of the vitamin, is due to injury of the mucous membranes of the eye. These membranes can no longer resist bacteria, and infections occur that eventually cause blindness.

A lack of vitamin A also results in degeneration of the nervous system. This is characterized in advanced stages by a striking lack of co-ordination of the legs, by severe spasms or paralysis, and by impairment of vision (not due to xerophthalmia). Kansas experiments show that such symptoms are especially marked in swine fed for long periods on rations lacking in the vitamin.[75] It is shown in Chapter XVIII that the disastrous effect on cattle of a ration consisting of cottonseed meal and poor-quality roughage is due chiefly to the lack of vitamin A.

A lack of this vitamin also prevents successful reproduction. In males it causes sterility. Females fed rations seriously deficient in vitamin A may not conceive, and if they do, the young are usually born dead or so weak that they perish.

In humans a lack of vitamin A causes the disease known as night blindness. The person is unable to see in a dim light, due to an effect upon the retina of the eye. The condition is also found in stock suffering from vitamin A deficiency. In recent Texas experiments pigs from sows fed a ration devoid of the vitamin have been born without any eyeballs.[76]

Blindness of calves at birth has resulted in Michigan experiments when cows have been fed on poor-quality roughage lacking vitamins and probably also other nutritive essentials. Normal calves fed poor rations also became blind. In these cases the blindness was due to a constriction of the optic nerve.[77] Other factors than lack of vitamin A were apparently concerned, at least in part, in these tests, for calves still went blind on the poor rations, even when a vitamin A supplement was fed.

That disastrous results due to a lack of vitamin A may occur in livestock even when they are on range pasture is shown in a striking manner by recent California investigations.[78] During the dry season in some of the range districts of that and certain other western states, no green feed may be available for several months. The stock must then subsist on dry and bleached grass and other forage, which is practically devoid of vitamin A.

When stock are kept on such feed alone for too long a time, disaster usually occurs. The calves are born dead or so weak that they die soon after birth, and the cows often abort long before the normal calving time. After calving, the cows may fail to come in heat until green feed is again available. Young cattle also suffer seriously, showing a general unthrifty appearance, intermittent diarrhea, and respiratory infections. If exposed to inclement weather such animals usually die from pneumonia. Unless the animals have been too seriously affected, they recover when supplied with feed rich in vitamin A, such as fresh green forage.

Opinions of investigators differ as to whether or not resistance to infectious diseases is increased by providing a greater supply of vitamin A than is needed to prevent any actual symptoms of deficiency. There is no question, however, but that animals fed rations deficient in the vitamin are much more susceptible to certain infections, especially those of the respiratory tract, than animals receiving an ample supply.

Animals are able to store considerable amounts of vitamin A in their livers and other tissues when they receive a liberal supply. Therefore, if they are later fed a ration deficient in the vitamin, the length of time it will take for the lack to produce injurious results will depend on whether or not they have a store in their bodies. Also, because of their greater requirements for vitamin A, young animals suffer from a deficiency much sooner than those which are mature.

187. Vitamin A and carotene.—Recent investigations have shown that vitamin A, which is colorless, can be formed in the body of animals from carotene supplied in their food. Carotene is the yellow-colored, fat-soluble substance that gives the characteristic color to carrots and to butter fat. The conversion of carotene into vitamin A occurs chiefly in the liver. When an animal receives in its food an abundant supply of vitamin A or of carotene, it stores vitamin A in the liver, and to a lesser extent in other body tissues. Also, unchanged carotene from the food may be similarly stored in the body.

With foods of plant origin it is probable that all or nearly all of the vitamin A value is due to the carotene they contain, and that they have little or no actual vitamin A. The general term "carotene" is applied to the different forms of carotene that occur in plants, and also to closely-related compounds from which vitamin A can also be formed.

Those foods of animal origin that possess a vitamin A value may contain both the yellow carotene and the colorless vitamin A. The carotene has been assimilated by the animals from foods of plant origin. The vitamin A has been formed by the animals from carotene supplied by their food. In the white milk from Holstein or Ayrshire cows there is more vitamin A and less carotene than in the yellow milk from Guernseys or Jerseys. However, even in the latter, the amount of carotene is generally less than that of vitamin A.

Since carotene can be converted into vitamin A in the body and thus indirectly performs the same functions, the terms "vitamin A value" or "vitamin A content" are commonly used to indicate the combined effect of the carotene plus the actual vitamin A in a food. Therefore in this volume when reference is made to the vitamin A content of a feed, it will mean its total value as a source of vitamin A to the animal, irrespective of whether this value is due to carotene or to vitamin A in the feed.

Both carotene and vitamin A are readily destroyed by oxidation. For this reason a great loss of vitamin A value occurs in the making of hay from green forage. A considerable loss also takes place when dry roughage or a concentrate mixture containing vitamin A is stored for any long period.

188. Vitamin A content of various feeds.—All green parts of growing plants are very rich in carotene, and therefore they have a high vitamin A value. The yellow color in such plant tissues is masked by the green color of the chlorophyll, but may be seen if the plant becomes etiolated or blanched. Due to the richness of the green parts of plants in vitamin A value, stock on good pasture always have an abundance of the vitamin.

There is but little information concerning the relative vitamin A content of various pasture crops. The limited data available indicate that certain grasses at the pasture stage may be fully as rich as alfalfa and other legumes, or even richer. In Idaho tests green brome grass was unusually high in vitamin A, and red top was richer than timothy.[79] All green pasture crops can, however, be considered excellent sources of the vitamin.

A considerable part of the carotene is destroyed in the field-curing of hay or other dry roughage, but if the forage is cured so that it retains a green color, it will still be an excellent source of vitamin A. On the other hand, forage that has been bleached or weathered in the curing process will have its vitamin A content seriously reduced, and it may even have only a negligible amount.

The relative amount of carotene in any particular lot of hay and therefore its vitamin A value may be estimated from its color, for the amount of carotene is generally proportional to the degree of greenness. Hay that is brown in color has but little carotene. In recent investigations by the United States Department of Agriculture, alfalfa hay of United States Federal Grade No. 3 contained only about one-eighth as much carotene as did alfalfa hay of Grade No. 1.[80] Even the latter excellent hay contained only one-seventh as much carotene per pound of dry matter as was present in the green alfalfa before it was cured into hay.

In these studies clover hay and timothy hay were somewhat lower in carotene content than alfalfa hay of equal quality. Poor-quality timothy hay (Grade No. 3) had practically no carotene. In Indiana studies good-quality soybean hay was somewhat lower in vitamin A value than good alfalfa hay.[81]. As is shown in Chapter XI, artificially-dried hay is very rich in vitamin A if it is dried at proper temperatures, but it has only a small amount of vitamin D.

The green leaves of plants contain much more carotene than the stems, alfalfa leaves containing over 6 times as much as alfalfa stems in the tests by the United States Department of Agriculture. In Texas studies some samples of alfalfa leaf meal were excellent in vitamin A value, while alfalfa stem meal supplied but little of the vitamin.[82]

Early-cut hay is higher in carotene than that cured equally well which has been cut at a later stage of growth.[81] Severe heating of hay in the mow or stack undoubtedly reduces the carotene content seriously. Indiana tests indicate that the fermentation that takes place in hay during ordinary hay making is also an important factor in the lowering of the carotene content.[83]

Corn forage is rich in carotene when the plants are still green, but the content decreases rapidly as they mature.[80] The carotene content of silage varies widely, due to differences in maturity and to differences in the proportion of the carotene destroyed in the ensiling process. Per pound of dry matter, good corn silage may be fully as rich in carotene as well-cured hay. In Washington tests silage made from mixed clovers and grasses was even higher in carotene than hay made from the same forage.[84]

With the single exception of yellow corn, the cereal grains are all practically devoid of vitamin A value. Yellow corn is an important source of the vitamin, even though the chief coloring matter is not carotene, but a related compound called xanthophyll. However, yellow corn contains only about one-tenth as much carotene as well-cured hay. Corn gluten feed, corn gluten meal, and hominy feed that are made from yellow corn are richer than yellow corn in carotene content. Only a very few of the other seeds used in stock feeding have any appreciable vitamin A value. Ripe peas of green varieties equal yellow corn in vitamin A content, and millet seed supplies some of the vitamin.

With the exception of carrots and yellow sweet potatoes, roots and tubers probably supply no appreciable amounts of vitamin A. Yellow pumpkins and yellow squash have considerable.

Among human foods whole milk, butter, and all other dairy products containing the butter fat are perhaps the most important sources of vitamin A. The richness of milk in this vitamin is undoubtedly one of the chief reasons why it is necessary, in raising dairy calves on milk substitutes, to continue the feeding of whole milk until the calf is old enough to eat considerable hay. If lactating animals have been fed for long periods on rations seriously deficient in vitamin A, the content of the vitamin in the milk will be low. (**189**)

Practically all the vitamin A in milk is present in the butter fat. Therefore skim milk and other milk products from which nearly all of the fat has been removed will have but little of the vitamin. Indeed, skim milk may contain only one-twenty-fifth as much vitamin A as whole milk.[85]

The yolks of eggs from properly-fed poultry are rich in vitamin A, and liver is also an excellent source. Tankage and meat scraps supply little or no vitamin A. If fish meal has not been processed at too high a temperature, it will usually supply some vitamin A. However, the content is so variable that reliance cannot be placed upon it as a source of the vitamin, unless the source and method of manufacture are definitely known. Cod-liver oil and other fish-liver oils are the richest common source of vitamin A, and other fish oils are also generally rich in it.

In the discussions of the vitamin requirements of the various classes of stock in Part III, it is shown that it is not generally necessary to use any special vitamin supplements, such as cod-liver oil or vitamin concentrates, in the feeding of horses, cattle, sheep, or swine. Their vitamin needs can be amply supplied by the use of good roughage, fed as is there advised. On the other hand, in the feeding of poultry in confinement or during the winter, vitamin supplements supplying both vitamin D and vitamin A are now commonly used.

189. Effect of feed and breed on vitamin A content of milk.— Recent investigations have shown that the vitamin A content of milk depends on the supply of the vitamin provided in the ration of cows or other lactating animals.[86] The highest possible vitamin A content is present in the milk of cows which are on good pasture, and a low content is found in milk from cows that have received for a considerable period no pasture, or well-cured, green-colored hay, or other feeds rich in vitamin A. Often the vitamin A content of pasture-produced milk will be twice as high as that from cows fed the usual kinds of winter rations.

By feeding dairy cows on plenty of well-cured, green-colored hay, the vitamin content of the milk may be maintained at a satisfactory level during the winter. The feeding of good legume hay will aid in maintaining a higher content of vitamin A than the use of grass hay of similar quality. Silage will also help keep the content of the vitamin at a good level, providing the silage is of good quality and if it has been made from corn, sorghums, or other crops harvested while the leaves are still green.

When cows have been fed rations extremely low in vitamin A for long periods, the milk has contained only one-fifth as much vitamin A as milk produced on pasture or even less. In trials by the United States Department of Agriculture cows fed poor-quality grass hay as the only roughage for long periods produced milk so low in vitamin A that calves raised on it by the usual whole milk-skimmilk method would not thrive unless they received the vitamin from some other source.[87]

For many years there has been much interest in the relative vitamin A value of milk from cows of various breeds. This was especially the case after it was discovered that vitamin A was made by animals from carotene supplied in their feed, since carotene is the coloring substance in butter fat.

Recent investigations have shown conclusively the surprising fact that there is no marked difference between the vitamin A value of yellow-colored butter fat from Guernsey or Jersey cows and that of the much paler butter fat from similarly-fed cows of other breeds.[88] Indeed, in certain tests the butter fat from Holstein milk was a trifle higher in vitamin value than the yellow fat from Guernsey or Jersey milk.

This surprising fact is due to the following conditions: Guernseys and Jerseys do not convert into colorless vitamin A so large a proportion of the carotene they assimilate as do cows of the other breeds. They therefore secrete more carotene and less vitamin A in their milk. This makes it yellower in color. Likewise, their body fat is colored yellow by carotene stored in the fatty tissues. Holsteins, Ayrshires, and Shorthorns convert most of the carotene into vitamin A, and therefore their milk and their body fat have but little yellow color. It seems probable that, due to the much higher fat content, a given weight of normal Guernsey and Jersey milk will contain more vitamin A than the same weight of normal Holstein or Ayrshire milk. However, this question has apparently not yet been studied in detail.

190. Vitamin D, its functions and importance.—It has been shown earlier in this chapter that animals must have an adequate supply of vitamin D to enable them to assimilate and utilize the calcium and phosphorus in their food. (**159**) Since vitamin D is necessary for the prevention of rickets, it is often called the anti-rachitic vitamin.

The requirements for vitamin D are especially great during growth, when the skeleton is being developed. The vitamin is also essential even for mature animals, though lesser amounts are required. During pregnancy there is a special need by the mother for vitamin D and also for calcium and phosphorus, to enable her to build the skeleton and other tissues of the fetus without depleting her own skeleton. During lactation there is an even greater demand for the vitamin, due to the large amounts of calcium and phosphorus that must be assimilated and utilized in the production of milk.

The discoveries concerning the functions and sources of vitamin D have been of untold value to humans and also to the livestock industry. It has been estimated that a generation ago nearly 80 per cent of the children in the large cities of western Europe and of America were afflicted to a greater or less degree with rickets. As a result of the discoveries made since 1918, human rickets is fast disappearing in countries where the results of such research are widely adopted by the people.

In livestock farming the knowledge recently gained concerning vitamin D is of similar significance. By utilizing the information now available, it is possible to prevent the disastrous results from rickets that were once common, especially among pigs, calves, and poultry. The effects upon animals of a lack of vitamin D or of an inadequate supply of calcium or phosphorus have been described earlier in this chapter. (**163**) In the respective chapters of Part III the requirements of the various classes of stock for vitamin D are considered in detail.

191. Nature of vitamin D and its relation to light.—Before 1918, the exact cause of rickets was unknown. Previously it had been attributed to many different factors, including insanitary surroundings, infection, and hereditary influences, as well as to improper diet. Mellanby, an English scientist, then proved that rickets definitely could be prevented in experimental animals by certain foods. It had earlier been observed that cod-liver oil seemed to aid in curing rickets and also that exposure to direct sunlight had a beneficial effect. However, opinions differed greatly as to the effectiveness of these widely differing methods of treatment, which seemed to have no relationship to each other.

It was soon found that rickets in experimental animals could be cured by exposing them to ultra-violet light (light of such short wave length that it is invisible). The next great steps came rapidly. In 1922 McCollum of Johns Hopkins University showed, by passing heated air through cod-liver oil to destroy vitamin A, that it contained a second vitamin which prevented and cured rickets. This vitamin was named vitamin D and is also known as the anti-rachitic vitamin.

In 1924 Steenbock of the Wisconsin Station and also Hess of Columbia University reported nearly simultaneously that the exposure to ultra-violet light of certain foods which contained no vitamin D produced the vitamin in them. It was later found that the production of vitamin D in this manner was due to the effect of the ultra-violet light upon very small amounts of ergosterol, a compound contained in traces in many common foods and stock feeds. (**12**)

Ergosterol itself has no anti-rachitic effect. However, upon exposure to ultra-violet light, the atoms are apparently rearranged in the molecules of ergosterol, thereby converting it into vitamin D. Too long exposure will destroy some of the vitamin D that has been produced. Recent studies indicate that small amounts of vitamin D can also be formed from cholesterol by certain methods. (**12**)

The prevention and cure of rickets when animals are exposed sufficiently to direct sunlight result from the ultra-violet light in the sunlight penetrating the skin and producing vitamin D from traces of ergosterol in the tissues. If the light passes through ordinary window glass, practically all the ultra-violet rays are removed. Such light does not therefore have an anti-rachitic effect. Some special kinds of glass and also certain glass substitutes permit the passage of more or less of the ultra-violet rays.

The ultra-violet rays in sunlight are absorbed to some extent as they pass through the atmosphere, before reaching the earth. In the North the sunlight therefore has much less anti-rachitic effect during the winter months when the rays are very slanting and must penetrate a greater distance of atmosphere. Also, the ultra-violet rays are largely screened out by clouds or smoke. Owing to the reflection of the ultra-violet light, the indirect light from "sky shine" on a clear day has a slight anti-rachitic effect, even though the direct rays of the sun do not reach the body.

During the growing season livestock that are out in the sunshine much of the time will be amply provided with vitamin D through the effect of sunlight on their bodies. Even during the winter, exposure to sunlight will have considerable anti-rachitic effect. When stock are exposed but little to sunlight that has not passed through ordinary window glass, it is necessary to give attention to their vitamin D requirements. This is of particular importance during winter in the northern states, especially in those districts where the sky is clouded much of the time.

Vitamin D is not readily destroyed even by heating at temperatures much above the boiling point of water. It is soluble in fat and is therefore classed as one of the fat-soluble vitamins.

192. Sources of vitamin D.—Among the common stock feeds the only important sources of vitamin D are hay and other dry roughages that have been field-cured by exposure to sunlight. Even such sun-cured forages unfortunately have only a rather limited amount of the vitamin.

There is as yet but little information on the relative amount of vitamin D in various grades and kinds of sun-cured hay and other dry roughage. It would seem probable that the amount will be higher in good-quality, leafy hay than in that of lower grade. In experiments by the United States Department of Agriculture timothy hay of Federal Grade No. 1 seemed to have greater vitamin D potency than timothy hay of Grade No. 3.[89]

Green, growing plants contain little or no vitamin D, but it is formed during the sun-curing process by the action of the ultra-violet rays upon traces of ergosterol in the plant tissues. As is shown in Chapter XI, artificially-dried or dehydrated hay or other forage has little or no vitamin D, but it is exceedingly rich in vitamin A, if it is properly dried.

Whole milk from cows fed normal rations contains a significant though a relatively small amount of vitamin D, and milk and butter fat are of considerable importance as sources of the vitamin for humans. As is shown later, the vitamin D content of milk can be greatly increased by certain methods. Skimmilk and other dairy products containing but little fat have only traces of the vitamin. The yolks of eggs from poultry receiving a plentiful amount of vitamin D are rich in it.

An exceedingly important fact in human nutrition and also in stock feeding is that cereal grains and all other seeds contain no appreciable amounts of vitamin D. Also, roots and tubers have little or none.

The livers of fish are strikingly rich in vitamin D, and also the body oils of most fish contain considerable amounts. For this reason cod-liver oil and certain other fish oils are widely used as vitamin D supplements for infants and in poultry feeding.

Fish meal is variable in vitamin D content, some fish meals being a fair source and others containing but little. The content depends on the source of the raw material and on the degree of heat used in the process of manufacture.

Meat scraps and tankage supply no appreciable amounts of vitamin D. In general, meat from mammals contains no significant amounts of the vitamin, with the exception of such organs as the liver and kidneys, which may supply limited amounts. Clams and oysters are a good source of vitamin D.

By removing the true fat or oil (which contains no vitamin D) from cod-liver oil or other fish oils, vitamin concentrates are now prepared which are much more potent in vitamin D than the original fish oils. These contain more or less vitamin A, as well as being high in vitamin D, and are commonly sold on definite guarantee of vitamin potency.

Vitamin D concentrates that are very potent are also manufactured by the Steenbock process of irradiation with ultra-violet light. In the production of the product known as viosterol, purified ergosterol is, separated from yeast, which is rich in it, and then irradiated. Irradiated yeast is also made for use as a vitamin D supplement through the direct radiation of yeast with ultra-violet light by the Steenbock process.

It has been found in recent investigations that the potency of the vitamin D in irradiated ergosterol and irradiated yeast is much lower for chicks than for rats, in comparison with cod-liver oil. This indicates that there are various related forms of vitamin D, some of which are more potent for certain species of animals than for others.

193. Vitamin D milk.—Special vitamin D milk for human use is now produced commercially by various methods.[90] One of these methods is the feeding of irradiated yeast to the cows. Since cows are able to transfer into their milk only a small portion of the vitamin D in their feed, the amount of irradiated yeast that is fed must be standardized to insure milk of the desired vitamin D potency. Vitamin D milk is also produced by the direct irradiation of the milk with ultra-violet light, or by the addition to the milk of a vitamin D concentrate.

When cows are fed normal rations, irradiating the cows with ultra-violet light or exposing them to sunlight does not usually cause any appreciable increase in the vitamin D content of the milk.[91] Neither does it have any appreciable beneficial effect on the cows. The vitamin D potency of goat's milk can, however, be increased somewhat by irradiating the animals with ultra-violet light.

If dairy cows are fed good rations which supply a normal amount of vitamin D, there is apparently no significant benefit to the cows themselves through feeding them irradiated yeast or other vitamin D supplements.[92]

194. Effect of cod-liver oil on herbivora.—Recent investigations have raised the question as to whether cod-liver oil should be fed to herbivora as a vitamin supplement over a long period. In experiments at the New York (Cornell) Station fatal results were produced when sheep, goats, rabbits, or guinea pigs were fed cod-liver oil for an extended time, though the amounts were no greater than are sometimes recommended.[93] In these animals there was a degeneration of various muscles, including the heart in certain instances. Paralysis and eventually death ensued if the animals were continued too long on the rations.

The results were apparently not due to vitamin A or vitamin D, but to some constituent in the fat of the cod-liver oil. The injury was most marked and occurred soonest in animals fed rations composed of purified nutrients. However, disaster finally resulted when cod-liver oil was fed to animals on pasture at the rate of one-half ounce daily per 100 lbs. live weight. Similar injurious results to various animals, including calves, have also been reported by other investigators.

Cod-liver oil has been widely used as a vitamin supplement for humans and also in poultry feeding. It has been extensively employed with entire success as a source of vitamins A and D in nutrition experiments with rats. It therefore seems possible that the effect is entirely different in the case of herbivora than with other animals. In this connection the fact that cod-liver oil markedly depresses the fat percentages in the milk of cows is of interest. (See Chapter XXIV.)

Because of these results it does not seem wise to use appreciable amounts of cod-liver oil over long periods as a vitamin supplement for herbivora (including cattle, sheep, goats, and possibly horses). In the few cases where it is advisable to add a vitamin supplement to rations made up of ordinary feeds for these classes of stock, it is apparently safer to use a vitamin concentrate instead.

195. The vitamin B complex.—In the regions of the Orient where polished rice was the chief food of the people, the disease known as beri-beri had been wide-spread for many years before the cause was finally discovered. The symptoms of this disease are loss of appetite, fatigue, depression, and other nervous symptoms, including numbness and stiffness of the legs and a tingling or burning sensation in feet, legs, and arms.

Through studies by several investigators from 1897 to 1911 it was learned that a disease similar to beri-beri could be produced in pigeons, chickens, and rats by feeding them entirely on polished rice. If young pigeons were fed such a diet they failed to grow and became paralyzed after only 15 to 20 days. It was then found that administering the water extract of rice polishings to these animals would bring recovery in a short time. For example, pigeons would recover from the paralysis in only a few hours.

Through these investigations it was definitely proved that the disease in humans was due to the lack of some factor in polished rice which was supplied by the inner skin and germ of the rice kernel. It was next found that this nutritive factor was widely distributed in natural foods, but was lacking in certain highly-milled products, such as polished rice and patent wheat flour. By including in the diet a sufficient amount of foods rich in this factor, it was possible to cure beri-beri and prevent its recurrence.

Until recently it was believed that the lack of a single vitamin was the cause of this disease, and also of the failure of young animals to make normal growth. This vitamin was called vitamin B. It has been discovered recently, however, that what was formerly considered to be one vitamin actually consists of separate vitamins that have different functions. The term "vitamin B complex" is therefore now used for the group of vitamins included in what was formerly considered to be the single factor, vitamin B. Two of these vitamins have been definitely separated and studied in detail.

The first of these is the vitamin now known as vitamin B in the United States and as vitamin B_1 in Great Britain. (This vitamin was first called vitamin F in the United States, but this name has been discarded.)   The second is the vitamin known as vitamin G in this country and as vitamin B_2 in Great Britain.   These two vitamins are discussed in detail in paragraphs that follow.

In addition to vitamins B and G, it is the belief of some investigators that there are at least 4 other vitamins in the vitamin B complex. However, the knowledge concerning them is still fragmentary and indefinite.   So far as is known, these other vitamins in the B complex are not of importance in human nutrition or in livestock feeding.   To these vitamins the designations vitamin B_3, vitamin B_4, vitamin B_5, and vitamin B_6 are usually given.

196. Vitamin B.—Vitamin B prevents the polyneuritis (nervous symptoms) in beri-beri.   It is therefore often called the anti-neuritic vitamin.   A lack of vitamin B also causes loss of appetite, a failure to grow, emaciation, and general weakness.   Experimental animals fed a ration devoid of the vitamin finally die as the result of the deficiency.

Vitamin B is widely distributed in natural human foods and stock feeds.   The unmilled cereal grains are all rich in it.   Fresh green forage contains a fair supply, as do well-cured hay and other dry forages of good quality.   It is supplied in fair amounts by milk and whey.   Yeast is especially rich in vitamin B.

Though vitamin B can be destroyed by prolonged heating at temperatures above the boiling point, it is stable in ordinary feeds.   For example, whole rice stored in an arid climate for 100 years was found to be still rich in it.

Due to the wide distribution of vitamin B in common feeding stuffs, livestock undoubtedly secure ample amounts when fed any usual ration that would be otherwise satisfactory.   Also, it has been found that the vitamin B complex can, at least in certain instances, be synthesized in the paunch of ruminants through the action of bacteria.[94]

197. Vitamin G.—In addition to vitamin B, vitamin G (or vitamin B_2) is also required for growth.   This vitamin is of much importance in the feeding of poultry, as they have very high requirements for it.[95] On the other hand, it is apparently supplied in ample amounts in the rations of other farm animals, or perhaps it is not required by them. Vitamin G is not injured by heating at temperatures that will destroy vitamin B.

Especially rich sources of vitamin G are milk and dairy by-products, including dried skimmilk, dried buttermilk, and dried whey.   This gives dairy by-products a particularly high value for poultry feeding. Yeast is also very high in vitamin G, and liberal amounts are furnished by green forages and well-cured hay.

198. Yeast as a vitamin B or vitamin G supplement.—From the statements that have been made in the preceding paragraphs, it is evident that the usual rations of farm animals will furnish plenty of vitamin B and vitamin G, with the exception that special care is necessary to provide ample vitamin G in poultry rations.

The effect of adding yeast, which is rich in both these vitamins, to various rations for calves, pigs, and poultry has been tested in several experiments.   In the trials with calves and pigs, which are summarized in Chapters XXVIII and XXXV, there has generally been no benefit from the feeding of yeast, and its use has been uneconomical.

This has been the case no matter whether the yeast has been mixed with the dry feed, or whether it has been mixed with moist feed and fermentation allowed to take place before the mixture was fed.

In the case of poultry, milk by-products and alfalfa meal or alfalfa hay are generally fed in sufficient amounts to provide enough vitamin G. There will then generally be no improvement from the addition of yeast to the ration.

199. Vitamin C.—Vitamin C, the anti-scorbutic vitamin, is apparently not of importance in the feeding of farm animals. However, it must be supplied in the food of humans, monkeys, and guinea pigs, or scurvy will result. In 1932 vitamin C was definitely separated in pure crystalline form and identified as the substance now called ascorbic acid. This has the chemical formula $C_6H_8O_6$. The terms vitamin C, anti-scorbutic vitamin, and ascorbic acid are therefore synonymous and designate the same chemical substance. Vitamin C is soluble in water.

The striking difference in the vitamin C requirements of various kinds of animals is due to the fact that many species can synthesize this vitamin in their bodies from other compounds normally present in their foods. On the other hand, humans (except very young infants), monkeys, and guinea pigs do not possess this power. Consequently they must receive adequate amounts of the vitamin in their food.

For centuries scurvy had been one of the most common human diseases in northern Europe. It gradually came to be recognized that fresh fruits and vegetables would prevent the disease, but it was not until 1912 that the existence of vitamin C was discovered. If this vitamin is not provided in the food of man, monkeys, and guinea pigs, disastrous results follow, due to scurvy. The chief symptoms of this nutritional disease are loosening of the teeth, inflammation of the gums, hemorrhages, brittleness of the bones, slow healing of wounds, and loss of vigor. In this country scurvy among humans has now become rare, because of the universal inclusion of fruits and vegetables in the diet, and the use of orange juice or tomato juice for young infants before they can consume other foods rich in vitamin C.

Farm animals probably require vitamin C, but they can synthesize it from other substances in their feed. In experiments with rats and chickens it has been definitely proved that they can make the vitamin within their bodies and store it in the liver and kidneys on a diet on which guinea pigs would soon die.[96] In these studies rats were raised successfully for two generations on a diet lacking vitamin C. They were then killed, and it was found they had synthesized sufficient of the vitamin and stored it in their livers, so that these livers cured scurvy in guinea pigs. Recent investigations indicate that human infants may possess some power of synthesizing vitamin C up to about 5 months of age, but they then lose this ability.

All fresh fruits and vegetables and also green forages supply vitamin C, the content in citrus fruits, tomatoes, spinach, cabbage, and peppers being especially high. The vitamin is destroyed by heating in the presence of air and by the drying of forage. Mature seeds and their by-products, and also hay and other dry forage, are all devoid of vitamin C. Silage may contain appreciable amounts. The vitamin is formed during the germination of seeds, and therefore sprouted seeds have an anti-scorbutic effect.

200. Vitamin E.—Vitamin E, discovered by Evans and Bishop of California in 1922, is necessary for reproduction in rats and at least in certain other animals. If rats are fed on a ration made up of highly-purified nutrients containing none of this vitamin, the females will conceive normally, but the fetuses die at an early stage of development and are absorbed. A lack of vitamin E also causes sterility of male rats, and it may also be concerned with lactation in the rat. Vitamin E is soluble in fat and fat solvents, such as ether.

Experiments show that vitamin E is necessary for good reproduction in poultry, but the usual poultry rations provide sufficient amounts of it.[97] In recent experiments at the Iowa Station goats reproduced normally on a ration in which the vitamin E had been destroyed, and which would not permit reproduction in rats.[98] This indicates either that goats require little or no vitamin E, or that they are able to synthesize it from other substances in their food.

Vitamin E is widely distributed in stock feeds and also in human foods that have not been artificially refined. It is abundant in the cereal grains and other seeds, where it is present in the oil of the embryo and not in the endosperm. It is also abundant in the green-leaved parts of plants and in good-quality hay, and is supplied by milk, butter, egg yolk, and meat. Wheat germ oil is especially rich in vitamin E and most vegetable oils contain it, although some are not rich in the vitamin.

Nebraska experiments indicate that even if farm animals require vitamin E, the usual rations will furnish ample amounts of it.[99] Fertility was restored to female rats when the ration contained only 20 to 25 per cent of any of the following common feeds: Wheat bran, wheat shorts, linseed meal, hominy feed, white or yellow corn, kafir grain, or alfalfa hay. On the other hand, corn gluten meal, corn gluten feed, and dried beet pulp provided very little vitamin E.

Most rations for livestock which are otherwise satisfactory will include at least 20 to 25 per cent of cereal grains and other seeds or their by-products rich in vitamin E, or this proportion of good hay. Therefore it seems very doubtful whether there is an advantage from adding wheat germ oil or any other vitamin E concentrate to the usual rations for farm animals, in spite of certain claims that such supplements cure sterility and produce other benefits.

QUESTIONS

1. Discuss the effects of feeding livestock more protein than is needed to meet their requirements.
2. Explain what is meant by essential and non-essential amino acids.
3. What is known about differences in the amino acid requirements for various kinds of stock and for different body functions?
4. Why is not the value of the protein in a feed determined by analyzing it for the percentages of various amino acids it contains?
5. What different methods are used to measure the nutritive values of proteins?
6. What three principles must be observed in determining the nutritive value of the protein in a ration?

7. Discuss the supplementary effects of protein.
8. What quality of protein is furnished by the cereal grains; by wheat bran?
9. Discuss the quality of the protein in milk, meat, fish, and eggs.
10. Explain the wide difference in the values of the proteins in various legume seeds.
11. What is the quality of the protein furnished by the following: (a) Linseed meal; (b) cottonseed meal; (c) coconut meal?
12. Discuss the quality of the proteins in legume forage and other roughages.
13. What are some of the vital functions of minerals?
14. Discuss the importance and use of common salt in stock feeding.
15. Why are calcium and phosphorus of especial importance in stock feeding? Why is there now more often a lack of these minerals than formerly? Which of these minerals is most frequently deficient?
16. State the relative calcium content of the following: (a) Legume forage; (b) non-legume forage; (c) cereal grains and other seeds and their by-products; (d) roots and tubers; (e) milk; (f) meat scraps, tankage, and fish meal.
17. State the relative phosphorus content of each of the above groups of feeds.
18. When do lacks of calcium or phosphorus occur in stock feeding under farm conditions?
19. What is the importance of the calcium-phosphorus ratio?
20. What is the cause of rickets? Describe its effects.
21. What are the effects on mature animals of a lack of calcium or of phosphorus?
22. Name 5 satisfactory calcium supplements.
23. Name 5 satisfactory phosphorus supplements and state their origin.
24. Discuss the effects of fluorine upon livestock.
25. Discuss the importance of iodine for farm animals. Would you feed an iodine supplement to stock in a non-goitrous area?
26. Explain the functions of iron and copper in the animal body. Under what definite conditions may there be a lack of these minerals for livestock?
27. From what source do farm animals get most of the sulfur they need?
28. Is there a need of adding potassium, magnesium, manganese, or zinc to the rations for livestock?
29. State a satisfactory mineral mixture for use under each of the following conditions: (a) When only calcium is lacking; (b) when both calcium and phosphorus are lacking; (c) for cattle fed no additional salt, and when both phosphorus and calcium are lacking.
30. Discuss the use of complex mineral mixtures.
31. Mention 3 instances where the discoveries concerning vitamins have solved important livestock problems.
32. Discuss vitamin A briefly, stating: (a) Its importance for farm animals; (b) its functions and the effects of a deficiency; (c) relative content of the vitamin in various classes of feeds.
33. Explain the relationship between carotene and vitamin A.
34. What is the effect of feed and of breed of cattle upon the vitamin A content of milk?
35. Discuss vitamin D, following the same outline as for vitamin A. (Question 32.)
36. Explain the relation of light to vitamin D.
37. State 3 methods by which vitamin D milk is produced.
38. What effect may cod-liver oil have on herbivora?
39. Explain what is meant by the vitamin B complex.
40. Discuss vitamin B, following the same outline as for vitamin A.
41. Discuss vitamin G, following this same outline.
42. Would you feed yeast to livestock as a vitamin supplement under usual conditions?
43. Discuss vitamin C, following the same outline as for vitamin A.
44. Discuss vitamin E, following the same outline as for vitamin A.

PROTEINS—MINERALS—VITAMINS 137

REFERENCES

1. Lieb and Tolstoi, Soc. Expt. Biol. and Med. Proc., 26, 1929, pp. 324-325.
2. Mitchell and Hamilton, The Biochemistry of the Amino Acids, 1929; Boas-Fixsen, Nutr. Abstracts and Reviews, 4, 1935, pp. 447-459; McCollum and Simmonds, The Newer Knowledge of Nutrition, 4th Ed., 1929; see also Rose, Jour. Biol. Chem., 109, 1935, pp. lxxvii-lxxviii.
3. Osborne and Mendel, Jour. Biol. Chem., 12, 1912, p. 473.
4. Mitchell and Hamilton, Biochemistry of the Amino Acids, pp. 574-588.
5. Csonka, Jour. Biol. Chem., 109, 1935, p. xxv.
6. Shrewsbury and Bratzler, Jour. Agr. Res., 47, 1933, pp. 889-895; see also: Maynard, Fronda, and Chen, Jour. Biol. Chem., 55, 1923, pp. 145-155.
7. McCollum, Jour. Biol. Chem., 19, 1914, p. 323; Hart and Steenbock, Jour. Biol. Chem., 38, 1919, p. 267; 43, 1924, p. 923.
8. Mitchell and Smuts, Jour. Biol. Chem., 95, 1932, pp. 263-281.
9. Smith, Ariz. Rpts. 1932, 1933.
10. Osborne and Mendel, Jour. Biol. Chem., 37, 1919, p. 557; Jones and Gersdorff, Jour. Biol. Chem., 64, 1925, pp. 241-251; Murphy and Jones, Jour. Biol. Chem., 69, 1926, pp. 85-99; Klein, Harrow, Pine and Funk, Am. Jour. Physiol., 76, 1926, pp. 237-246.
11. Maynard, Fronda, and Chen, Jour. Biol. Chem., 55, 1923, pp. 145-155.
12. Mitchell and Hamilton, The Biochemistry of the Amino Acids, p. 533.
13. Wilgus, Norris, and Heuser, Indus. and Engin. Chem., 27, 1935, pp. 419-422; Wilgus, Ringrose, and Norris, Fifth World's Poultry Congress, Rome, Italy, 1933.
14. Maynard, Bender, and McCay, Jour. Agr. Res., 44, 1932, pp. 591-603; Schneider, Jour. Agr. Res., 44, 1932, pp. 723-732.
15. Hart and Steenbock, Jour. Biol. Chem., 38, 1919, pp. 267-285; Mitchell and Kick, Jour. Agr. Res., 35, 1927, pp. 857-864; Mussehl, Nebr. Res. Bul. 55; Wilgus, Ringrose, and Norris, Fifth World's Poultry Congress, Rome, Italy, 1933; Johnson and Brazie, Jour. Agr. Res., 48, 1934, pp. 183-186.
16. Carr, Spitzer, Caldwell, and Anderson, Jour. Biol. Chem., 28, 1917, pp. 501-509; Winter, Ohio Bul. 436.
17. Csonka and Jones, Jour. Agr. Res., 46, 1933, pp. 51-55; 49, 1934, pp. 279-282.
18. Morris and Wright, Jour. Dairy Res., 4, 1933, pp. 177-196; 5, 1933, pp. 1-14.
19. Hart and Humphrey, Jour. Biol. Chem., 21, 1915, p. 239; 26, 1916, p. 457; 31, 1917, p. 445; 35, 1918, p. 367; Nevens, Jour. Dairy Sci., 4, 1921, pp. 552-588; Maynard, Fronda, and Chen, Jour. Biol. Chem., 55, 1923, pp. 145-155; Bethke, Bohstedt, et al., Jour. Agr. Res., 36, 1928, pp. 855-871; Braman, Jour. Nutr., 4, 1931, pp. 249-259; Mitchell and Hamilton, 43, 1931, pp. 743-748.
20. Maynard and Fronda, N. Y. (Cornell) Memoir 50; Jones, Finks, and Johns, Jour. Agr. Res., 24, 1923, pp. 971-977.
21. Morrison and Turk, N. Y. (Cornell) Rpts. 1933, 1934; Turk, Morrison and Maynard, Jour. Agr. Res., 48, 1934, pp. 555-570.
22. Sotola, Jour. Agr. Res., 40, 1930, pp. 79-96.
23. Sotola, Jour. Agr. Res., 47, 1933, pp. 919-945.
24. Hart and Humphrey, Jour. Biol. Chem., 21, 1915, p. 239; 26, 1916, p. 457; 31, 1917, p. 445; 35, 1918, p. 367.
25. Nevens, Jour. Dairy Sci., 4, 1921, pp. 552-588.
26. Pollard and Chibnall, Biochem. Jour., 28, 1934, pp. 326-335; Haag, Jour. Nutr., 4, 1931, pp. 363-370.
27. Crampton, Am. Soc. Anim. Prod., Proc. 1934, pp. 69-70.
28. Maynard, Miller, and Krauss, N. Y. (Cornell) Memoir 113.
29. Morrison and Miller, N. Y. (Cornell) Station, Unpublished data.
30. Sotola, Jour. Agr. Res., 40, 1930, pp. 79-96; Watkins, New Mex. Bul. 194.
31. St. John, Wash. Buls. 175, 180, 187; St. John, Jour. Biol. Chem., 77, 1928, pp. 27-32; Mitchell and Carman, Jour. Biol. Chem., 68, 1926, pp. 165-181; Miller, Jour. Biol. Chem., 70, 1926, pp. 759-762.
32. Babcock and Carlyle, Wis. Rpt. 1905; see also: Evvard, Brown, Culbertson, and Hammond, Iowa Res. Bul. 94.
33. Mitchell, Card, and Carman, Ill. Bul. 279.
34. Bruce and Callow, Biochem. Jour., 28, 1934, p. 517; Harris and Bunker, Jour. Nutr., 9, 1935, pp. 301-309; Lowe and Steenbock, Wis. Bul. 430.
35. Maynard, Am. Soc. An. Prod., Proc. 1933, pp. 86-89.
36. Haag and Palmer, Jour. Biol. Chem., 76, 1928, pp. 367-389; Guilbert and Hart, Hilgardia, Cal. Sta., 5, 1930, pp. 101-118; Blum, Tex. Bul. 441; Bethke, Kick, and Wilder, Jour. Biol. Chem., 98, 1932, pp. 389-403; Kramer and Howland, Jour. Nutr., 5, 1932, pp. 39-60; Cox and Imboden, Jour. Biol. Chem., 105, 1934, pp. xviii-xix.
37. Colo. Rpt. 1934; Nebr. Rpt. 1934; Nev. Rpt. 1934; Mussehl and Ackerson, Poultry Sci., 1932, pp. 293-296; Titus, McNally, and Hilberg, Poultry Sci., 12, 1933, pp. 5-8; Bethke, Edgington, and Kick, Jour. Agr. Res., 47, 1933, pp. 331-338; Turner, Meigs, Shinn, and Hale, Jour. Agr. Res., 48, 1934, pp. 619-630.
38. Lamb et al., Jour. Dairy Sci., 17, 1934, pp. 233-241.
39. Theiler, Green, and du Toit, Jour. Dept. Agr. (Union of South Africa) 8, 1924, pp. 460-504; Eckles, Becker, and Palmer, Minn. Bul. 229; Eckles, Gullickson, and Palmer, Minn. Tech. Bul. 91; Hart, Beach, Delwiche, and Bailey, Wis. Bul. 389; Becker, Neal, and Shealy, Fla. Bul. 264. Other references are cited in the reviews given in these articles.
40. Riddell, Hughes, and Fitch, Kan. Tech. Bul. 36; Eckles and Gullickson, Am. Soc. Anim. Prod., Proc. 1927.
41. Becker, Neal, and Shealy, Jour. Dairy Sci., 17, 1934, pp. 1-10.
42. Hostetler and Nance, N. C. Rpt. 1932; Ohio Bul. 417; Tully and Franke, S. D. Bul. 287; Hart, Wis. Bul. 388.

43. McCollum, Simmonds, and Becker, Jour. Biol. Chem., 63, 1925, pp. 553-562; Schulz and Lamb, Science, 61, 1925, pp. 93-94; McClure and Mitchell, Jour. Biol. Chem., 90, 1931, pp. 297-320; McClure, Physiol. Rev., 13, 1933, pp. 277-300.
44. M. C. Smith, Lantz, and H. V. Smith, Ariz. Tech. Buls. 32, 43, 45.
45. Reed and Huffman, Mich. Tech. Bul. 105.
46. Phillips, Bohstedt, Fargo, Hart, and Halpin, Wis. Bul. 428; Phillips, Hart, and Bohstedt, Wis. Res. Bul. 123.
47. McClure and Mitchell, Jour. Agr. Res., 42, 1931, pp. 363-373; Kick, Bethke, and Edgington, Jour. Agr. Res., 46, 1933, pp. 1023-1037; Kick and Bethke, Ohio Bul. 516.
48. Kick, Bethke, and Record, Ohio Bul. 532; Halpin and Holmes, Wis. Bul. 425.
49. Tolle and Maynard, N. Y. (Cornell) Bul. 530.
50. Welch, Mont. Bul. 214; Mont. Cir. 145; Bell, Ohio Bul. 470; Kalkus, Wash. Bul. 156; Hart and Steenbock, Wis. Bul. 297; Hadley, Wis. Bul. 352.
51. Hamilton and Kick, Ill. Sta., Jour. Agr. Res., 41, 1930, pp. 135-137; Evvard and Culbertson, Iowa Res. Bul. 86, Iowa Rpt. 1928; Vinke, Mont. Sta., mimeo. rpt.; Russell, N. J. Rpt. 1928; Bartlett, N. J. Rpt. 1930; Severson, N. D. Sta., information to the author; Krauss and Monroe, Ohio Bul. 470; Forbes, Karns, Bechdel, Williams, Keith, Kallenbach, and Murphy, Penn. Sta., Jour. Agr. Res., 45, 1932, pp. 113-128; Hart, Hadley, and Humphrey, Wis. Res. Bul. 112; Holmes, Pigott, and Packard, Jour. Nutr., 8, 1934, pp. 583-595.
52. Rodenwold and Simms, Am. Soc. Anim. Prod., Proc. 1934, pp. 89-92; Harvey, Am. Soc. Anim. Prod., Proc. 1929.
53. Hart, Steenbock, Waddell, and Elvehjem, Jour. Biol. Chem., 77, 1928, pp. 797-812; 83, 1929, pp. 251-260; 84, 1929, pp. 115-130; 95, 1932, pp. 363-370.
54. Elvehjem and Sherman, Wis. Bul. 425; Jour. Biol. Chem., 98, 1932, pp. 309-319; Josephs, Jour. Biol. Chem., 96, 1932, pp. 559-571; see also: Mitchell and Hamilton, Ill. Rpt. 1932.
55. Becker, Neal, and Shealy, Fla. Bul. 231; Neal and Becker, Jour. Agr. Res., 47, 1933, pp. 249-255.
56. Elvehjem, Wis. Buls. 421, 425; Elvehjem, Hart, and Sherman, Wis. Bul. 428; Elvehjem, Jour. Am. Med. Assoc., 98, 1932, pp. 1047-1050; see also: Mitchell and Vaughn, Jour. Biol. Chem., 75, 1927, pp. 123-127.
57. Elvehjem, Herrin, and Hart, Jour. Biol. Chem., 71, 1927, pp. 255-262; Hamilton, Mitchell, and Nevens, Ill. Rpt. 1929; Elvehjem, Steenbock, and Hart, Jour. Biol. Chem., 83, 1929, pp. 27-34.
58. Marston and Robertson, Australian Council Sci. and Indus. Res. Bul. 39.
59. Evvard et al., Iowa Rpt. 1924; Lewis and Lewis, Jour. Biol. Chem., 74, 1927, pp. 515-523.
60. Miller, Jour. Biol. Chem., 55, 1923, pp. 61-78; 70, 1926, pp. 587-591.
61. Miller, Jour. Biol. Chem., 55, 1923, pp. 45-59; 67, 1926, pp. 71-77; 70, 1926, pp. 593-598; Evvard, Brown, Culbertson, and Hammond, Iowa Res. Bul. 94.
62. Kruse, Orent, and McCollum, Jour. Biol. Chem., 96, 1932, pp. 519-539; Orent, Kruse, and McCollum, Am. Jour. Physiol. 101, 1932, pp. 454-461; Cramer, Lancet, 1932, II, No. 4, pp. 174-175; Brookfield, Brit. Med. Jour. No. 3827, 1934, pp. 848-849.
63. Elmslie and Steenbock, Jour. Biol. Chem., 82, 1929, pp. 611-632; Eckles, Gullickson, and Palmer, Minn. Tech. Bul. 91; see also: Buckner, Martin, and Insko, Poultry Sci., 11, 1932, pp. 58-62.
64. Kemmerer, Elvehjem, and Hart, Jour. Biol. Chem., 92, 1931, pp. 623-630; Skinner, Van Donk, and Steenbock, Am. Jour. Physiol., 101, 1932, pp. 591-597; Ky. Rpt. 1931; Orent and McCollum, Jour. Biol. Chem., 98, 1932, pp. 101-102; Miller, Am. Jour. Bot., 20, 1933, pp. 621-631; Keil, Keil, and Nelson, Soc. Expt. Biol. and Med. Proc., 30, 1933, pp. 1153-1155.
65. Titus, Cave, and Hughes, Jour. Biol. Chem., 80, 1928, pp. 565-570; Waddell, Steenbock, and Hart, Jour. Biol. Chem., 84, 1929, pp. 115-130; Krauss, Jour. Biol. Chem., 90, 1931, pp. 267-277.
66. Peterson and Skinner, Jour. Nutr., 4, 1931, pp. 419-426.
67. Bertrand and Benzon, Compt. Rend. Acad. Sci., Paris, 175, 1922, pp. 289-292; Hubbell and Mendel, Jour. Biol. Chem., 75, 1927, pp. 567-586; Newell and McCollum, Jour. Nutr., 6, 1933, pp. 289-302.
68. Elvehjem, Hart, and Todd, Wis. Bul. 428; Stirn, Elvehjem, and Hart, Jour. Biol. Chem., 109, 1935, pp. 347-359.
69. Heller, Okla. Rpt. 1924-26; Heller and Burke, Jour. Biol. Chem., 74, 1927, pp. 85-93.
70. Carroll, Hunt, Mitchell, and Hamilton, Ill. Rpt. 1931; Evvard, Culbertson et al., Iowa Sta., mimeo. rpts; Morrison and Fargo, Wis. Bul. 405.
71. Weber, Nebr. Sta., mimeo. rpt.
72. Perkins, Ohio Bimo. Bul. 159.
73. Wells and Ewing, Ga. Bul. 119; Lamb and Evvard, Iowa Res. Buls. 70, 71; Steenbock, Nelson, and Hart, Jour. Biol. Chem., 19, 1914, pp. 399-419; Blatherwick, Jour. Biol. Chem., 42, 1920, pp. 517-539.
74. For more complete discussions of the vitamins and extended bibliographies, see the following: Sherman and Smith, The Vitamins, 2nd. ed.; Vitamins, Essential Food Factors, 2nd. ed.; Sure, Vitamins in Health and Disease; McCollum and Simmonds, The Newer Knowledge of Nutrition, 4th ed.
75. J. S. Hughes, Aubel, and Lienhardt, Kan. Tech. Bul. 23; see also: E. H. Hughes, Jour. Agr. Res., 49, 1934, pp. 943-953.
76. Hale, Jour. Heredity, 24, 1933, pp. 105-106.
77. Moore, Huffman, and Duncan, Jour. Nutr., 9, 1935, pp. 533-551; Moore, Huffman and Duncan, Jour. Dairy Sci., 18, 1935, p. 435.
78. Hart and Guilbert, Cal. Bul. 560.
79. Woods, Shaw, Atkeson, and Johnson, Jour. Dairy Sci., 15, 1932, pp. 475-479; Id. Buls. 197, 205.

80. Shinn, Kane, Wiseman, and Cary, Am. Soc. Anim. Prod., Proc. 1934, pp. 190-192; see also: Sewell and Cottier, Ala. Rpt. 1931; Russell, Taylor, and Chichester, N. J. Bul. 560; Bethke and Kick, Ohio Bul. 431; Smith and Briggs, Jour. Agr. Res., 46, 1933, pp. 229-234.
81. Hilton, Hauge, and Wilbur, Jour. Dairy Sci., 16, 1933, pp. 355-361; Hilton, Wilbur, and Hauge, Jour. Dairy Sci., 18, 1935, p. 434.
82. Fraps and Treichler, Tex. Bul. 477.
83. Hauge, Ind. Sta., Jour. Assoc. Off. Agr. Chem., 17, 1934, pp. 304-307; Hilton, Wilbur, and Hauge, Jour. Dairy Sci., 18, 1935, p. 434.
84. Hodgson, Knott, Murer, and Graves, Jour. Dairy Sci., 18, 1935, p. 433; see also: Gillam et al., Biochem. Jour., 27, 1933, pp. 878-888.
85. Hathaway, Nebr. Res. Bul. 69.
86. Hilton, Hauge, and Wilbur, Jour. Dairy Sci., 16, 1933, pp. 355-361; Hilton, Wilbur, and Hauge, Jour. Dairy Sci., 18, 1935, p. 434; Krauss, Ohio Bul. 470; Fraps, Copeland, and Treichler, Texas Bul. 495; Baumann and Steenbock, Jour. Biol. Chem., 101, 1933, p. 547; Meigs and Converse, Jour. Dairy Sci., 16, 1933, pp. 317-328; Converse, Wiseman, and Meigs, Am. Soc. Anim. Prod., Proc., 1934, pp. 50-54; Scheunert, Milchw. Forsch., 3, 1926, pp. 117-121.
87. Converse, Wiseman, and Meigs, Am. Soc. Anim. Prod., Proc. 1934, pp. 50-54.
88. Davis and Hathaway, Nebr. Res. Bul. 54; Hathaway and Davis, Nebr. Res. Bul. 69; Sutton and Krauss, Abstr. of Papers, 29th Annual Meeting, Am. Dairy Sci. Assoc., 1934; Baumann, Steenbock, Beeson, and Rupel, Jour. Biol. Chem., 105, 1934, pp. 167-176; Beeson, Am. Soc. Anim. Prod., Proc. 1934, pp. 54-56.
89. Turner, Kane, and Hale, Jour. Dairy Sci., 15, 1932, pp. 267-276.
90. For a discussion of the various methods of producing vitamin D milk, see: Krauss and Bethke, Ohio Bimo. Bul. 162; Russell, N. J. Cir. 285. See also: Steenbock, Hart, and Hanning, Jour. Biol. Chem., 88, 1930, pp. 197-214; Thomas and MacLeod, Science, 73, 1931, pp. 618-620; Russell, Wilcox, Waddell, and Wilson, Jour. Dairy Sci., 17, 1934, p. 445.
91. Bartlett, N. J. Rpt. 1926; Hart et al., Jour. Biol. Chem., 66, 1925, pp. 441-449; 67, 1926, pp. 371-383; 73, 1927, pp. 59-68; 87, 1930, pp. 103-126, 127-137; S. D. Rpt. 1932; Knott and Garver, Wash. Bul. 260; Luce, Biochem. Jour., 18, 1924, pp. 716-739, 1279-1288; Boas and Chick, Biochem. Jour., 18, 1924, pp. 433-447.
92. Krauss and Bethke, Ohio Bul. 516; Krauss, Bethke, and Wilder, Jour. Dairy Sci., 16, 1933, pp. 549-555; Hart et al., Wis. Bul. 410; Knott and Garver, Wash. Bul. 260.
93. Madsen, McCay, Maynard, Davis, and Woodward, N. Y. (Cornell) Memoir 178. Also see this publication for a summary of other work on this subject.
94. Bechdel, Honeywell, Dutcher, and Knutsen, Jour. Biol. Chem., 80, 1928, pp. 231-238.
95. Hauge and Carrick, Jour. Biol. Chem., 69, 1926, p. 403; Norris, Heuser, Ringrose, Wilgus, and Heiman, Rpt. of Fifth World's Poultry Congress, Rome, Italy, 1933, pp. 512-520.
96. Parsons, Jour. Biol. Chem., 44, 1920, pp. 587-602; Parsons and Hutton, Jour. Biol. Chem., 59, 1924, pp. 97-105; Parsons and Reynolds, Jour. Biol. Chem., 59, 1924, pp. 731-736; Lepkovsky and Nelson, Jour. Biol. Chem., 59, 1924, pp. 91-96; Carrick and Hauge, Jour. Biol. Chem., 63, 1925, pp. 115-122; Hart, Steenbock, Lepkovsky, and Halpin, Jour. Biol. Chem., 66, 1925, pp. 813-818.
97. Card, Poultry Science, 8, 1929, pp. 328-334; Adamstone, Jour. Morph. and Physiol., 52, 1931, p. 47; Barnum, Jour. Nutr., 9, 1935, pp. 621-635.
98. Wilson, Thomas. and Cannon, Jour. Dairy Sci., 18, 1935, p. 431.
99. Hathaway and Davis, Nebr. Res. Bul. 73.

CHAPTER VII

GROWTH—REPRODUCTION—FATTENING

I. GROWTH

201. Importance of thrifty growth.—Growth is one of the most important forms of livestock production. While the maximum productive possibilities of any animal depend on its inherited characteristics, its full capacity cannot be reached unless it is properly fed during the growing period.

Growth is the foundation of meat production in all classes of stock. Young cattle, sheep, and swine will not make economical gains while being fattened, unless they have been raised so that they are thrifty and vigorous. One cannot expect good yields of milk from dairy cows, unless they have been well developed as heifers.

Similarly, brood mares, beef cows, and ewes may have their productive ability seriously reduced if they have been raised improperly. Work horses and mules cannot perform the maximum amount of labor if their growth has been stunted or if their skeletons have been injured by inadequate rations during the growth period.

202. Nutritive requirements for growth.—The nutritive requirements for growth are in strong contrast to those for the mere maintenance of the body. Not only are far greater amounts of certain nutrients required, but also a young, growing animal suffers sooner and much more seriously from nutritive deficiencies than does a mature animal. The requirements for growth differ from those for maintenance in the following respects:

1. A much larger amount of total digestible nutrients or net energy must be provided in the ration for a growing animal than for an animal of the same size that is being maintained at constant weight. An animal can use for the formation of new body tissues only the amount of nutrients that remains after the requirements for maintenance have been fully met.

Therefore, for normal growth the ration must be much more liberal than for maintenance, and also it must generally be more concentrated in nature. It has been pointed out in Chapter V that mature cattle, sheep, and horses can be maintained largely or entirely on roughage, even that which is rather inferior. On the other hand, young calves, lambs, and foals cannot make good growth on roughage alone, even if it is of high quality.

2. Since growth consists largely of an increase in the size of the muscles and other protein tissues, it is obvious that far more protein is needed for growth than for maintenance. Also, as has been emphasized in the preceding chapter, the quality or kind of protein is probably more important in rations for growing animals than for those that are mature and are not producing protein in milk.

MILK IS THE NATURAL FOOD FOR YOUNG MAMMALS

A study of the composition of milk shows that young animals should have rations which provide: (1) a liberal amount of easily-digested nutrients; (2) an abundance of protein of high quality; (3) plenty of minerals, especially calcium and phosphorus; and (4) an adequate supply of vitamins. (From Wisconsin Station.)

LIBERAL FEEDING IS NECESSARY FOR RAPID GROWTH

In addition to their mothers' milk, these early-spring lambs are being supplied with a mixture of grain and other concentrates in a lamb creep, so they will make rapid growth. (From J. P. Willman, New York, Cornell, Station.)

Legume Forage Is Unexcelled for Growing Stock

Shorthorn cattle on clover pasture. An abundance of good legume forage is excellent insurance against any deficiency of protein, of calcium, or of vitamins for calves, lambs, or foals.

Fattening Stock Need a Liberal Supply of Concentrates

Hereford cattle being fattened on an Iowa farm. The first requirement of a ration for fattening animals is an abundance of total digestible nutrients or net energy. These steers are being fed a liberal amount of corn.

3. For the building of the skeleton and also in the formation of the protein tissues, large amounts of minerals are required, especially calcium and phosphorus. Therefore the mineral needs for growth are very great in comparison with those for maintenance.

4. The growing animal has a much greater requirement for vitamins than an animal which is being maintained without gain in weight. For normal growth of all farm stock it is especially important, as has been pointed out in the previous chapter, that the ration provide a plentiful supply of vitamins A and D. With the exception of poultry, which require an unusually large amount of vitamin G, the other vitamin requirements are met by the rations usually fed growing animals.

203. Rates of growth.—The different kinds of farm animals have rates of growth which are characteristic for the species. Also, the various breeds of the same species differ to some extent in the mature size that is reached and in the earliness of maturity. Tables showing the normal weights and heights of young stock at various ages, such as are presented in Chapter XXIII for horses and in Chapter XXVIII for dairy cattle, serve as convenient guides in determining whether stock have made normal growth.

Studies by Brody and associates at the Missouri Station, as well as the investigations of others, have shown that the rate of growth by farm animals generally increases up to the age of puberty, or sexual development.[1] After this, the rate gradually decreases as maturity is approached.

These studies also show that in proportion to their mature size and the length of time taken to reach it, the rates of growth of most species of animals have great similarity. However, the rate of growth in humans differs in a striking manner from the rates for farm animals, humans having a much longer juvenile period in proportion to their average length of life.

204. Utilization of food by young animals.—It is well known that young animals make decidedly more rapid gains, considering their size, than those made by older animals, even when the latter are fed liberal fattening rations. A month-old calf which is fed liberally on milk will gain more than 1 lb. a day per 100 lbs. live weight, while a daily gain of 0.3 to 0.4 lb. per 100 lbs. of weight is large for a 2-year-old fattening steer.

The amount of protein built into body tissues per 100 lbs. live weight is high for the very young animal and rapidly decreases as it becomes older. Thus, a calf 8 days old will store nearly 0.40 lb. of protein daily per 100 lbs. live weight.[2] At a month of age it will store only about 0.28 lb. per 100 lbs. live weight; at 2 months, about 0.16 lb.; and at 10 months, only about 0.05 lb.

Young animals can retain and build into their protein tissues and skeleton a large part of the protein and mineral matter in their rations. For example, up to a month of age thrifty calves may store 70 per cent or more of the protein, calcium, and phosphorus supplied by the milk they consume. As they grow older, the percentages of these nutrients which are stored decrease. Thus 2-year-old fattening steers, fed a liberal ration in Illinois experiments, stored only 13 per cent of the total protein in their ration.[3]

After growth is completed, but little storage of protein or mineral matter can take place, for the skeleton, the muscles, and the internal organs have reached full development. The muscular fibers, of which the muscles are composed, increase in number only during youth. Indeed, it is believed that the muscles of the new-born young of some animals contain as many fibers as those of the mature animals. As the fibers can thicken only to a limited extent, the muscular tissues, or lean meat, of a mature animal can be increased but little in comparison with the great storage of fat that may occur.

If an animal is healthy but has poor muscular development, the size of the muscles can be increased somewhat through a thickening of the individual fibers produced by suitable exercise and food. Also, an animal whose muscles have wasted through sickness or starvation will rapidly repair its tissues upon a return to favorable conditions, thereby storing protein. With these exceptions the only storage of protein and mineral matter which can occur in mature animals is in the growth of the nitrogenous hair and hoofs, and in the small amount of protein and mineral matter in the fatty tissues.

205. Importance of utilizing growth capacity.—From the practical standpoint, it is of prime importance in feeding animals for meat production to take advantage of the great stimulus to growth while they are young. Young animals should always be fed rations rich enough in total nutrients, in protein, in minerals, and in vitamins to permit rapid and economical growth of body tissues and skeleton.

The rate of growth and the efficiency with which the nutrients are utilized depend not only on the adequacy of the ration, but also on the inherited growth capacity of the animal. By skillful breeding, much improvement can undoubtedly be made in the efficiency with which farm animals transform food into body tissue.[4] An excellent illustration of such possibilities is the improvement of swine in Denmark, which is mentioned in Chapter XXXV. Through careful selection of breeding stock, based on feeding and slaughter tests of the progeny, the amount of feed required per 100 lbs. gain has been materially reduced and the quality of the carcasses also markedly improved.

206. Comparative efficiency of young and older animals.—Numerous feeding trials reviewed in Part III show that young animals require considerably less feed for 100 lbs. of gain in body weight than those which are older. Because of this, they have a marked economic superiority in the production of meat. There are several reasons for the more rapid gains and the more economical meat production of young animals.

Their gains are more watery than those of older animals, and also contain more protein and far less fat, which has a much higher heat value than protein. More net energy is therefore required to make a pound of gain on a mature fattening animal than on one which is young and growing.

Furthermore, the food consumed by young animals is ordinarily lower in fiber, and hence more digestible and higher in net energy, than that eaten by older animals. In addition, since young animals consume more feed in proportion to live weight, they have left for building into body tissues a much larger part of their feed, after the maintenance requirements have been met.

These factors account fully for the greater economic efficiency of young animals. Contrary to common popular opinion, there is no evidence that a young animal makes any better percentage utilization of the net energy supplied in the feed than an older one, after the maintenance requirements are deducted.[5]

207. Milk the natural food for young mammals.—Milk is indispensable for mammals during the earliest stages of growth, and it is unexcelled as a food throughout the entire suckling period. A study of the composition of milk will therefore aid in showing the nutritive requirements for growth. Information on the composition of the milk of the various farm animals is given in the respective chapters of Part III and in Appendix Table I. While the milks of various species differ considerably in content of the various nutrients, especially of fat, all milk has certain general characteristics.

First of all, milk is easily digested and assimilated. The nutrients are supplied in forms that are particularly adapted to the undeveloped digestive systems of mammals at birth.

Milk is rich in protein, and the protein is of exceptionally high quality, supplying an ample amount of all the essential amino acids. On the dry basis, cow's milk generally contains 25 per cent or more of protein, and on the average it has the very narrow nutritive ratio of 1:3.9.

Milk is high in minerals, on the dry basis, and it is especially rich in calcium and phosphorus, the two minerals needed in largest amounts by growing animals. There is therefore no deficiency of these important minerals when young animals receive liberal amounts of milk.

There is but little iron in milk, but this lack is offset, as has been pointed out in the preceding chapter, by the fact that the young are born with a considerable store of iron in their bodies. Before this store is depleted, young animals normally begin to consume other foods which supply much more iron than does milk. Only in the case of suckling pigs not on pasture is this lack of iron in milk apt to cause serious anemia.

Milk also contains less copper, manganese, and magnesium than do most foods. This does not cause any difficulty, unless animals are continued on milk as an exclusive diet during a far longer period than normal.

When the mother receives a ration ample in content of vitamin A, her milk is rich in this vitamin, which is needed in particularly liberal amounts for growth. Milk from properly-fed animals is also high in vitamin G, fair in content of vitamin B, and supplies an appreciable amount of vitamin D.

The fat and the sugar in milk furnish concentrated energy in readily-assimilated form and provide the nutrients for the formation of the fatty tissues in growth.

It has long been known that the shorter the time it takes new-born young of different species to double their birth weights, the greater are the percentages of protein, calcium, and phosphorus in the milk.

Thus, for the young of each species there is provided milk of the composition particularly adapted for their growth.

208. Deficiencies of milk as exclusive diet for long periods.— Under normal conditions young mammals begin to eat solid food in addition to milk early in the suckling period, and this food makes good the lack of iron and copper in milk. Attempts to raise animals on milk as an exclusive diet have ended in failure, unless small amounts of these minerals have been added.[6] (**174**)

The results have been still further improved in Wisconsin studies when traces of manganese were also added.[7] However, in recent Michigan experiments mentioned previously, failure finally resulted when calves were fed no roughage, but only milk and starch plus mineral and vitamin supplements.[8] (**137**)

Since milk, even whole milk, is not high in vitamin D, there will generally be a lack of this vitamin when an exclusive milk diet is continued for an abnormal length of time, unless the young animal is exposed to sunlight or other ultra-violet rays.[9]

It should not be concluded from these studies that milk is not an ideal food for young farm animals under normal conditions. It is only when milk is continued as an exclusive diet for an unusual length of time that these nutritive lacks manifest themselves.

209. Rich and poor milk for young animals.—A very young animal has only a limited ability to digest and assimilate fat. If it is fed milk containing a greater percentage of fat than is normal for that species, digestive disturbances may therefore result. Since human milk is lower in fat content than cow's milk, this fact must be borne in mind in feeding very young infants. For delicate infants cow's milk too high in fat may produce unsatisfactory results.

Even for very young calves, particularly those that are not vigorous, it is best to use milk that is not unduly rich in fat. Thus, in a Jersey or Guernsey herd it is wise to use milk from a low-testing cow for a week or two, or to add warm skimmilk or even water to lower the fat percentage.

In Connecticut and Vermont experiments with young pigs, better results have been secured when they were fed milk moderate in fat content than when milk high in fat was used.[10] Milk moderate in fat content was also more valuable per pound for young calves and lambs in the Connecticut tests than milk high in fat. For species of young animals, such as rats, that are able to utilize large proportions of fat, Illinois tests show there is no difference in the digestibility of cow's milk rich and poor in fat content.[11]

210. Importance of colostrum for the new-born.—Colostrum, which is the milk yielded by the mother for a short period following the birth of the young, differs from ordinary milk in containing much more protein and also somewhat more minerals. The high protein content, which in the case of cow's milk may be 17 per cent or more, is due chiefly to a large amount of globulin. This is a protein that occurs in the blood, but which is present in ordinary milk only in traces. The albumin content of colostrum is also considerably higher than that of normal milk.

Recent investigations have shown that, at least in the case of farm animals, colostrum has an exceedingly important function.[12] It contains specific antibodies, or immunizing substances which temporarily protect the new-born against certain diseases, especially infections of the digestive system. The young animal is born with very slight ability to resist these diseases, and, if it does not secure the colostrum, is apt to succumb to infection. Later in life the young animal itself develops more or less immunity to such infections.

Colostrum is also especially rich in vitamin A, and, because of a laxative action, it is believed to aid in cleansing the digestive tract of accumulated fecal matter present at birth.

211. Protein requirements for growth.—It has previously been emphasized that relatively large amounts of protein are required for growth, and also that the protein in the ration must be of suitable quality. If there is an inadequate supply of any of the essential amino acids, an animal will be unable to make normal growth, even though the *amount* of digestible protein is plentiful. (**142**)

Definite information is presented in Part III on the protein requirements of the various kinds of young stock, both as regards the quantity and the quality of protein needed. Many different rations are also suggested which will produce good growth and development.

In the opinion of the author, the only safe method of determining the minimum amount of protein required for normal growth by any class of stock is to conduct experiments in which the animals are actually raised to maturity on rations containing various proportions of protein. Only by such long-time investigations can it be definitely ascertained whether the results are better from one proportion of protein than from a smaller amount.

Unfortunately, relatively few experiments of this type have thus far been conducted. Our knowledge concerning the minimum amounts of protein needed for growth by the various classes of stock is therefore still very limited. In the Morrison feeding standards, presented in Appendix Table III, the author has followed the plan of not recommending less protein than has actually produced good growth in careful tests. It has been borne in mind that the actual amount of protein in individual feeding stuffs of the same kind may vary considerably, and therefore recommendations have been made which should be safe under varied practical conditions.

A method sometimes used in studying the protein requirements for growth is to determine the amounts of protein stored daily in the bodies of growing animals. From what limited data are available, it is then estimated that the animals should utilize the digestible protein in their feed with a certain percentage of efficiency. On this basis, amounts of digestible protein are computed, which, it is believed, should produce normal growth.

Based upon this method, Mitchell and associates of the Illinois Station have recommended amounts of protein for growing animals which are much lower than are commonly fed.[13] The author considers it unsafe to follow such recommendations in practical stock feeding until it has been proven by actual experiments with a sufficient number of animals that these amounts of protein are entirely adequate under practical conditions.[14]

If the ration of a young animal supplies protein of proper quality, but the amount of protein is insufficient, the only result may be to check the rate of growth, without causing permanent stunting, unless the lack is too great or too long continued. On the other hand, more serious consequences may follow when the total amount of protein is liberal, but the supply of one or more of the essential amino acids is decidedly inadequate.

212. Mineral requirements for growth.—On account of the large amounts of minerals, especially calcium and phosphorus, that are required to build the skeleton and other parts of the body, normal growth cannot be expected unless the ration amply meets these mineral needs. A lack of minerals may be much more serious to a young animal than a lack of protein or a lack of total digestible nutrients or net energy.

If the ration is very deficient in calcium or phosphorus, rickets may result, and the animal may be permanently crippled or deformed if the deficiency continues too long. (**163**) Also, the skeleton may be seriously reduced in strength, and the bones may be so fragile that they will break under ordinary stresses and strains in later life.

For calves, lambs, and foals the best insurance against a lack of calcium is to feed sufficient legume hay throughout the winter and to provide good pasture during the growing season. Well-cured legume hay not only has an abundance of calcium, but also sun-cured hay is the best source among common feeds of vitamin D, which animals must have in order to assimilate the calcium and phosphorus in their rations.

Whenever there is any possibility that the rations for young stock may be lacking in phosphorus, a safe phosphorus supplement should be added, as advised in the preceding chapter and in Part III, where recommendations are made for each class of stock.

In the case of suckling pigs not on pasture, there may be disaster from anemia caused by lack of iron, unless the precautions explained in the previous chapter are taken. (**174**) In districts where there is a definite deficiency of iodine, it is wise to supply this mineral in the form of iodized salt, or by other means. (**172**)

213. Vitamins required for growth.—In the discussions of the vitamins in the preceding chapter, it has been emphasized that it is just as necessary that the rations of growing animals furnish an adequate supply of these substances as it is that they provide ample protein and minerals.

Suckling animals will receive plenty of vitamin A in the milk if their dams are fed suitable rations. When they are weaned, care must be taken that sufficient of this vitamin is furnished by well-cured hay, good pasture or other green feed, or by yellow corn. In the case of calves changed from whole milk to skimmilk or milk substitutes at an early age, it is especially important that they be furnished with choice, green-colored hay as soon as they will eat it, to provide both vitamin A and vitamin D.

Young stock on pasture will not suffer from a lack of vitamin D, because of the effect of the ultra-violet rays in sunlight. (**191**) Under winter conditions, however, young pigs are often severely crippled or even paralyzed by rickets, caused by a lack of this vitamin.

Also, calves often suffer from rickets, and they may be stunted and badly deformed as a result. These conditions can usually be entirely prevented by the use of well-cured legume hay, as described in the chapters of Part III. Lambs rarely have rickets, probably because they eat much hay, and all good shepherds make a special effort to supply them with hay of good quality.

With the exception of poultry, which need particularly liberal amounts of vitamin G, there is generally no lack of the other vitamins in the rations commonly fed to young stock.

214. Requirements for total digestible nutrients or net energy.— It is a fundamental fact that an animal can use for growth only the amounts of nutrients that are left after its maintenance needs have been met. Reasonable liberality of feeding is therefore necessary for normal growth. If a young animal is fed a ration that does not furnish sufficient total digestible nutrients or net energy, its rate of growth will be slow, and it may be permanently stunted in size if the under-feeding is continued too long.

The amounts of total digestible nutrients recommended in the Morrison feeding standards for the different kinds of young stock are based upon the results of the feeding experiments conducted by the experiment stations. (Appendix Table III.) Recommendations in terms of net energy are also included in these standards, for use by those who prefer to compute rations on this basis. Specific information is presented in Part III of this book concerning rations suitable for raising each class of stock, especial attention being given to the amounts of concentrates that are required under various conditions.

Young stock are not so apt to be permanently injured by a moderate deficiency of total digestible nutrients or energy as they are to be hurt by a lack of minerals or vitamins. As is shown in the following paragraphs, young animals have a remarkable power to recover from a period of scanty feeding when again fed with liberality.

However, under practical conditions young female animals are apt to be stunted in size unless they receive sufficient feed to make normal growth up to the time they bear their first young. If they are under-sized at this time, they will usually get no opportunity to make up for the lost growth. In milk production there are heavy demands on their bodies for nutrients, and these demands take precedence over any use of nutrients for continued growth of the mother. Because of re-peated reproductions and lactations, the animals are unable to complete their growth, and they therefore never reach normal size.

This is especially apt to occur with dairy heifers that have not made normal development by the time of first freshening. Because of the large amount of milk a good heifer produces, she will not be able to make much growth while in milk, unless she is fed with con-siderable liberality. In many a herd the cows are under-sized and lack high productive capacity, largely because the owner has fed his heifers too scantily.

215. Effects of restricting the feed of growing animals.—It has been emphasized previously that young animals may be permanently injured or even killed by a serious lack of minerals or vitamins. A severe deficiency in the amount or the quality of protein may also have grave effects. The question then arises as to what the effect will be if young animals are fed a ration that does not provide enough total digestible nutrients for normal growth, but which furnishes an adequate supply of protein, minerals, and vitamins. Does such scanty feeding permanently stunt the animal?

The question is of great practical importance, especially in the western range districts. Under range conditions the feed during the winter is often so scanty that the young cattle weigh considerably less in the spring than they did in the fall. Also, under farm conditions young stocker steers which are to be fattened for market the next summer are often wintered on a ration consisting chiefly of cheap roughage, on which they will make but little gain in weight.

On account of the importance of this problem, extensive investigations were conducted at the Missouri and Kansas Stations to determine the effects of severely restricting the feed of young cattle.[15] In these trials some steers were grown to maturity on liberal rations, while others for periods of several months were fed rations so scanty that they could make no gain in live weight. Still others were fed sub-maintenance rations, supplying so little feed that they steadily lost weight. After the steers had been under-nourished for periods of various lengths, some were fed liberal rations to determine whether they would reach normal size.

For 70 to 120 days, depending on how vigorous they were and how much fat they carried, steers, weighing 573 to 740 lbs. at the start, which were fed only enough to maintain their weights, gained as rapidly in height as others that were liberally fed. After this period the increase in height became less rapid, ceasing altogether in from 6 months to a year and a half, by which time the animals had become very thin and had used up all the fat in their bodies which was not absolutely necessary to life.

Striking changes were produced in the composition of the carcasses of the steers by this severe under-feeding. The carcass of a steer fed for 5 months so as to gain 0.5 lb. per head daily had a considerable amount of fatty tissue, and this contained 73 per cent fat and only 18 per cent water. In strong contrast to this, the fatty tissue had practically disappeared from the carcass of a steer which had been losing 0.5 lb. per head daily for 12 months. What little "fatty tissue" was left contained only 5 per cent fat and had 81 per cent water. The lean flesh was changed much less in percentage composition than the fatty tissue, but this steer had lost nearly 40 per cent of the lean meat from his body during the year of under-feeding.

The skeleton is not affected by scanty feeding until practically all the fat has been removed from the fatty tissues and the muscles. In this steer, however, the withdrawal of fat had gone so far that nearly all the fat had been removed from the marrow of the bones and replaced with water.

216. Effects of checking growth.—It was found in these investigations that unless the under-feeding of the young steers was continued for a long time, they were not permanently stunted. When liberal feeding was resumed, they recovered to a surprising degree, and unless they had been under-fed for 3 years or more, usually reached full mature size. Also, the under-nutrition did not seem to result in any abnormal body conformation.

These experiments and also investigations at the New Hampshire Station show that unless the under-feeding has been so severe as to cause the animal to become unthrifty, it will make very rapid gains in weight when again liberally fed.[16] During this period of rapid gains the amount of feed required per 100 lbs. gain will generally be less than normal.

The growth periods of animals may be prolonged to a surprising extent when they are fed a ration that is limited in amount, but which supplies sufficient protein, minerals, and vitamins. In New York experiments rats had not lost the capacity to grow after they had been under-fed to an age of 911 days, which is much more than their normal length of life.[17]

These studies on growth are highly significant to the stockman. They show that under certain conditions it may be profitable to carry growing animals through the winter on roughages alone. Even though they lose slightly in weight during the winter, they will make rapid and economical gains when they go to pasture, if they are in thrifty condition. However, the livestock breeder who seeks to develop his animals toward an ideal should supply ample feed during the whole growth period.

II. REPRODUCTION

217. Importance of adequate rations for breeding animals.—It is essential that breeding cows, mares, ewes, and sows receive rations that fully meet the needs of their own bodies and also supply sufficient amounts of the various nutrients for the unborn young. Without question, many of the failures in raising young stock are due to improper nutrition of the breeding females.

If the mother is fed inadequately, the offspring are apt to be weak or undersized at birth, and also the supply of milk may be scanty or of low vitamin content. Occasionally the ration is so deficient that the young are born dead. Fortunately, the mother is able to protect the unborn offspring to a certain extent against temporary or small deficiencies in her food by drawing on her own skeleton for calcium or phosphorus and on her muscular tissues for protein. Such maternal protection is, however, at the expense of the female's own body.

On account of the importance of the subject, especial attention is given in the chapters of Part III to the requirements during pregnancy of each kind of breeding stock. Rations, adapted to various parts of the country, are suggested that will produce satisfactory results. Breeding females should be so fed that they are in thrifty condition. However, they should not be allowed to become too fat, or their breeding efficiency may be seriously decreased. Abundant exercise is essential for the best results.

Especial care should be taken that the rations of pregnant animals furnish ample amounts of those nutrients which are particularly needed in the development of the fetus. Sufficient protein and protein of good quality must be provided for the formation of the body tissues.

There must be plenty of calcium and phosphorus for the development of the skeleton, and also a liberal amount of vitamins A and D.

The nutritive requirements of male breeding animals have thus far been studied but little. Practical experience shows, however, that the sires must be kept in thrifty condition to retain their breeding powers. Exercise is especially important. Information on the feeding and care of sires of each class of stock is given in Part III.

It has been pointed out in the previous chapter that if there is a serious lack of vitamin A in the mother's ration, her milk may be so deficient in this vitamin that the offspring cannot be raised upon it. So far as known, there is no deficiency of vitamin E, the reproductive factor, in the usual rations fed cattle, horses, sheep or swine. (**200**)

While it is essential that mature pregnant animals receive sufficient protein, calcium, phosphorus, and vitamins A and D, their requirements for these nutrients are not nearly so high as in the case of animals that are growing rapidly. Also, the requirements during pregnancy are much lower than for milk production.

Most of the growth of the fetus is made during the last third of pregnancy. Up to this time it is not necessary to give the pregnant animal much more feed than would be needed to maintain her in thrifty condition, if unbred. However, more care should be taken to provide sufficient protein, minerals, and vitamins. During the last third of pregnancy the ration should be somewhat more liberal, in order to provide for the rapid growth of the fetus at this time and also to get the dam in condition to produce a liberal flow of milk. In the case of an immature female, which is still growing, the supply of feed must, of course, be more liberal than for a mature animal.

The total amount of nutrients contained in a fetus are considerably less than many realize. At birth the body of the young animal is very high in water content, new-born calves containing 71 to 75 per cent water. In Missouri experiments new-born 65-lb. Jersey calves contained about 11.8 lbs. protein, 2.5 lbs. fat, and 2.7 lbs. mineral matter; and 80-lb. Hereford calves, 14.6 lbs. protein, 2.9 lbs. fat, and 3.6 lbs. mineral matter.[18] These are no greater amounts of nutrients than are contained in 400 to 500 lbs. of milk of average composition. To these amounts of nutrients must be added those contained in the fetal membranes and fluids.

III. Fattening

218. The object of fattening.—We all know that the lean meat from a well-fattened animal is better flavored and more juicy and tender than that from a lean one. This improvement in the quality of the lean meat, and not the storage of thick masses of fat, is the main object in fattening animals before they are slaughtered for meat.

To some extent during growth and especially during fattening, fat is stored in the lean-meat tissues, chiefly between the bundles of fibers of which the muscles are composed. This storage of fat, which forms the so-called "marbling" of meat, adds to its tenderness, juiciness, and flavor, besides increasing the digestibility and nutritive value. There is also an increase in the soluble protein and in other extractives of the muscles, resulting in a further betterment of the quality of the meat, as an additional advantage obtained from fattening.

219. What fattening is.—The fattening of animals is what the term implies, chiefly the laying on of fat. Many years ago Lawes and Gilbert of the Rothamsted (England) Experiment Station found, by analyzing the bodies of animals slaughtered at various stages of fattening, that the gains of steers when nearly full grown were about two-thirds fat, and only 7.7 per cent protein and 1.5 per cent mineral matter.[19] With pigs the proportion of fat was even greater.

The younger the animals are when they are fattened, the greater will be the storage of protein and mineral matter. This is shown in the following table, which presents the results of experiments at the Missouri Station.[20] There is first given the composition of the carcass of a 755-lb. steer in thrifty growing condition, followed by the composition of the gains made by similar steers during fattening.

Composition of unfattened steer and gains during fattening

	Fat Per ct.	Protein Per ct.	Mineral matter Per ct.	Water Per ct.
Carcass of unfattened steer	18.0	18.5	5.7	57.3
First 500 lbs. of gain	46.1	11.8	2.0	39.8
Second 500 lbs. of gain	67.7	6.6	1.9	22.3

While the carcass of the steer killed before fattening contained only 18.0 per cent fat, the first 500 lbs. of gain were nearly one-half, and the last 500 lbs. over two-thirds fat. During the first 500 lbs. of gain, 11.8 per cent of the increase was protein, but in the last 500 lbs. of gain only 6.6 per cent was protein. The storage of mineral matter was likewise less as the animal matured.

The fact that the proportion of fat in the gain made by an animal steadily increases during the fattening period is of much practical importance. It is the chief reason why the feed cost per pound of gain increases rapidly after an animal has become fairly well fattened. Such flesh contains much more fat and less water, and it is correspondingly more expensive to produce.

The fat animal also needs a greater proportion of its feed for maintenance than one which is not yet well fleshed, because of two factors: First, the maintenance requirement of a fat animal per 1,000 lbs. live weight tends to be higher than for a thinner one; and second, the fat animal eats less feed per 1,000 lbs. live weight, consequently having less nutrients left for meat production after the maintenance requirements have been met.

For these reasons, one should have the demands of the market very definitely in mind in fattening stock for sale. The animals should be fattened sufficiently to produce the best net returns, considering the probable sale price for animals of various degrees of fatness. However, they should not be made fatter than necessary, or the additional cost of the gains will generally reduce the profits.

220. Composition of steers of different ages.—For several years Haecker of the Minnesota Station conducted extensive investigations on the food requirements of steers of different ages, in which the entire carcasses of many animals were analyzed.[21]   The following table shows the average composition of the steers slaughtered at various stages of growth.

*Average composition of steers at various stages**

Normal weight	No. of steers	Water	Dry matter	Protein	Fat	Ash
Lbs.		Per cent	Per cent	Per cent	Per cent	Per cent
100	5	71.84	28.16	19.89	4.00	4.26
200	4	70.43	29.57	19.14	6.01	4.42
300	4	65.72	34.26	18.77	11.19	4.30
400	5	65.79	34.21	19.31	10.56	4.34
500	5	62.90	37.10	19.15	13.73	4.22
600	3	61.20	38.80	19.40	15.04	4.36
700	4	60.35	39.65	18.60	16.58	4.48
800	3	58.44	41.56	18.80	18.52	4.24
900	3	54.10	45.90	17.66	24.08	4.16
1,000	4	52.03	47.97	17.11	26.91	3.95
1,100	3	47.77	52.23	16.38	32.03	3.82
1,200	3	47.96	52.04	16.02	32.32	3.70
1,300	2	47.93	52.07	15.79	32.50	3.78
1,400	1	47.76	52.24	16.15	32.58	3.51
1,500	1	43.48	56.52	15.72	37.59	3.21

*Not including contents of the digestive tract.

The table shows that the percentage of water steadily decreases as the animal matures, falling from 71 per cent in the calves to 43 per cent in the 1,500-lb. steer.   The percentage of fat increases rapidly during the growth and fattening of the animal, increasing from 4.0 per cent soon after birth to over 37 per cent in the 1,500-lb. steer. The protein and ash show less change than the water and fat, but the percentages decrease gradually as the animals grow older.

Haecker found that the storage of protein by the animal, which is rapid in early life, shows a marked slowing up when the animal reaches a weight of about 800 lbs.   On the other hand, the gain in fat is most rapid after the steer reaches a weight of 600 lbs.

221. How body fat is formed.—Since fattening is chiefly a storage of body fat, in studying the feed requirements of fattening animals it is important to learn from what substances in the feed this body fat may be formed.   By numerous feeding experiments it has been shown that after enough nutrients have been supplied to maintain the body, any excess—no matter whether of fat, carbohydrates, or protein —may be transformed into body fat.

The largest part of the fat stored in the bodies of farm animals is undoubtedly formed from the carbohydrates of the food, for these are the most abundant nutrients in all common rations.   When more protein is furnished than is needed for the repair of the body tissues, the remainder may, after the nitrogen is split off, likewise be changed into body fat.   The fat in the food can also be transformed into body fat, after more or less change.

The relative values of different feeds for the formation of body fat depend on the amounts of net energy or of total digestible nutrients that they furnish.   For this reason, such a feed as corn grain is unexcelled for the fattening of stock.

222. Effect of food fat upon character of body fat.—Each species of animals produces a characteristic kind of body fat, differing in melting point and chemical properties from those formed by other species. These characteristics are due to differences in the proportions of the various fatty acids. It is well known that the tallow produced by cattle and the mutton suet formed by sheep have much higher melting points than lard from swine. This is because lard contains much more oleic acid, which is liquid at ordinary temperatures, and less stearic acid and palmitic acid, which melt at higher temperatures.

In the case of some animals the character of the body fat can be changed greatly if rations are fed which contain considerable amounts of certain fats. This is because the fatty acids in these food fats are to some extent deposited unchanged in the body fats. Thus, if swine are fed any considerable amount of soybeans or peanuts, both of which are rich in fat containing much oleic acid, the lard will be much softer than normal. Indeed, the pork will be so soft that the quality of the carcass will be decidedly injured from the market standpoint. Just opposite in effect, cottonseed meal and coconut meal tend to produce hard pork. On account of the great practical importance of this matter, it is discussed at length in Chapter XXXV.

The character of the fat in feeds also greatly affects the properties of the body fats produced by chickens and rats,[22] and likewise the character of the milk fat produced by cows. **(242)** However, recent Georgia and Iowa experiments indicate that, for some unknown reason, the character of the body fat formed by ruminants, including cattle, sheep, and goats, is not appreciably affected by the kind of fat in the feed.[23] In this respect these animals seem to differ from swine in a striking manner.

223. Total digestible nutrients required for fattening.—The first requirement of a ration for fattening animals is an abundance of total digestible nutrients or net energy. Unless a large surplus of nutrients is left after the maintenance requirements of the body have been met, the rapid formation of fatty tissues is impossible.

The supply of total digestible nutrients must be considerably more liberal for fattening than for normal growth. Thus a beef calf, after weaning, will make good growth during winter on roughage alone, if it is of excellent quality. On the other hand, a calf being fattened for baby beef needs a large amount of grain and other concentrates, in addition to good roughage. In the fattening of young animals it is especially necessary that they have an abundant supply of nutrients. If their ration is not liberal, they may merely continue to grow, because of their strong growth impulse, and may fail to put on the desired amount of body fat.

As is explained in Chapter IV, animals digest and assimilate a slightly smaller percentage of the nutrients in their ration when they are given liberal rations than when their feed is limited. However, in the fattening of stock this difference is generally more than offset by other factors. **(113)**

The animal that is fed liberally will have a much larger proportion of the total nutrients in its ration available for fattening, after the amount needed for maintenance is deducted. Less feed is therefore commonly required per 100 lbs. of gain when an animal is fed with sufficient liberality to produce good gains than when the feed supply is so scanty that slow gains result. Also, slow gains greatly prolong the fattening period, and so increase the cost of labor and the other expenses.

Especial consideration is given in Part III to the amounts of feed required for fattening the various classes of stock. The factors that should determine the proportions of concentrates and of roughages in the rations for fattening cattle and sheep are fully explained in Chapters XXIX and XXXII.

224. Protein requirements for fattening.—In the fattening of mature animals there is but little storage of protein in the gain produced. Much less protein is therefore needed than for growing animals. Indeed, experiments have shown that mature fattening animals will make fairly satisfactory gains on rations supplying only 0.75 to 1.5 lbs. of digestible protein daily per 1,000 lbs. live weight.[24] However, it is probably not advisable in the practical fattening of mature animals to reduce the protein supply to this low level.

It has been pointed out in Chapter IV that the digestibility of a ration is considerably reduced if it contains too large a proportion of carbohydrates and fat and too small a proportion of protein. Also, a ration is usually more palatable if it has a reasonable amount of protein, and therefore animals will eat a greater amount of it than of a ration very low in protein. This is important in producing rapid gains.

If fattening animals are fed rations that are rich in carbohydrates and fat, but too low in protein, they are apt to "go off feed" and may even suffer from digestive disturbances. Considering all these factors, it is recommended that even for mature animals a ration for fattening should not generally have a wider nutritive ratio than 1:10.0.

225. More protein needed for young fattening animals.—Most of the animals raised for meat in this country are now fattened for market at relatively young ages. For instance, but few steers are older than 3 years when slaughtered, and a large proportion are only 1 to 2 years old. Likewise, practically all the lambs not retained for breeding are fattened and marketed before they are a year old. Most of the pigs reach the market at weights of 200 to 225 lbs. or less, when much less than a year of age.

All these animals are thus growing rapidly during the fattening period, and therefore they are making considerable amounts of protein tissues. These young animals consequently need much more protein in their feed than do mature fattening animals. For example, while mature fattening cattle make good gains when their ration has a nutritive ratio as wide as 1:10.0, the nutritive ratio should not be wider than 1:6.0 to 1:7.3 for the fattening of calves for baby beef.

226. Mineral and vitamin requirements for fattening.—Mature fattening animals do not require a much greater amount of minerals than they need for mere maintenance, and their vitamin requirements are also low. On the other hand, young fattening animals have even greater needs for minerals and vitamins than those that are merely making normal growth. Particular care must therefore be taken that

RESULTS OF FEEDING GROWING PIGS A DEFICIENT RATION

These pigs were raised at the Wisconsin Station on grain and grain by-products without pasture or legume forage. They became stunted and finally developed the severe rickets shown here. The proteins in such a ration are of poor quality; there is a deficiency of mineral matter, especially calcium; and there is also a serious lack of vitamin D. Unless the grain is yellow corn, there will also be a deficiency of vitamin A. (From Hart, Wisconsin Station.)

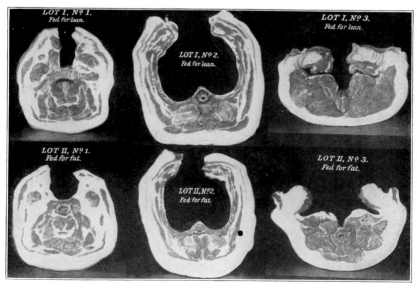

PIGS FED CORN ALONE DO NOT DEVELOP NORMAL CARCASSES

Upper row, cross sections of carcasses of pigs fed for lean; i. e., on well-balanced ration, by Henry at the Wisconsin Station. Left, section at shoulder; middle, section between fifth and sixth ribs; right, section at loins. Lower row, carcasses of pigs fed corn alone. Note larger size of muscles of pigs fed well-balanced ration.

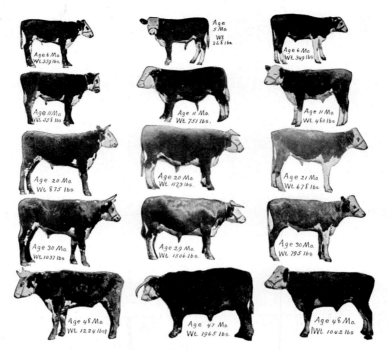

SCANTY FEEDING STUNTS GROWING ANIMALS

The steer in the middle row of pictures, fed a full ration, weighed 1,965 lbs. when 4 years old. The steer at the left, fed a medium ration, weighed only 1,224 lbs. and the one at the right, fed a scant ration, but 1,042 lbs. Note the stunted appearance of the latter steers at the end of the trial. (From Missouri Station.)

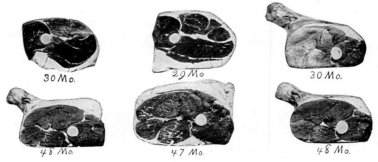

ROUND STEAKS FROM STEERS VARIOUSLY FED

Left, from steers fed medium ration; middle, from steers fed full ration; right, from steers fed scant ration. Note large size and well-marbled appearance of muscles from the full-fed steers and the scarcity of fat in the meat from the steers fed the scant ration. (From Missouri Station.)

they have an ample supply of these nutrients, or the gains will be unsatisfactory, and the animals may even become decidedly unthrifty.

The recent investigations which are reviewed in Chapters XXIX and XXXII have shown in a striking manner that the poor gains often made by fattening cattle or lambs when there is no legume hay in the ration may be due chiefly to a lack of calcium. As is pointed out there and in the previous chapter, this can readily be provided in such forms as ground limestone or ground oyster shell. (**165**)

227. Rations for fattening animals.—The nutritive requirements for fattening each class of stock are explained further in Part III, and many practical rations are recommended that are adapted to conditions in various districts. The amounts of nutrients advised for fattening the different classes of stock and at various ages are stated in the Morrison feeding standards. (Appendix Table III.) These recommendations are based upon a study of the results of the investigations by various experiment stations and also upon experiments by the author and associates.

228. Factors influencing fattening.—In addition to the suitability and the liberality of the ration, certain other factors have a great influence on the rapidity and economy of gains during fattening.

Unthrifty animals make slow and expensive gains. Young animals that are thin and even somewhat small for their age, due to a previous scanty supply of feed, may make rapid and cheap gains when fed a liberal fattening ration. It will, of course, require considerably longer for them to reach a desired market condition than for animals which are in better flesh at the start of fattening. If young animals have been stunted by a lack of minerals or vitamins, they are apt to be unthrifty and therefore unprofitable in the feed lot.

The ability of an animal to make economical gains and reach a good finish also depends upon temperament. While a wild animal, nervous and active, can be fattened only with extreme difficulty, domesticated animals are more quiet and usually fatten readily. The restless animal is rarely a good feeder, while the quiet one, which is inclined to "eat and lie down," will show superior gains. This is not due to difference in digestive or assimilative powers, but rather to the fact that the quiet animal has, from a given amount of food, a greater surplus of nutrients available for fat building.

Fattening animals must not be allowed to exercise too much, as this wastes nutrients which they might store in their bodies.

IV. Studies on Growth and Fattening

229. Effects of inadequate rations on young animals.—Several experiments have been conducted to determine the effects on the growth of animals and on the composition of their bodies of feeding unbalanced rations, which supplied too little protein or mineral matter. These studies are of much practical importance, as they show clearly the folly of failing to provide proper rations for young animals.

Many years ago experiments were carried on at the Missouri, Wisconsin, Kansas, and Alabama Stations, and also in France, in which pigs that were already fairly well grown were then fed corn alone, in comparison with well-balanced rations made up of corn and various protein supplements.[25] If younger pigs had been used in the trials, those fed only corn would have made practically no growth or would have died or been permanently stunted.

The partly-grown pigs fed only corn made poor gains and required much more feed per 100 lbs. gain than those fed the balanced rations. Also, the feeding of corn alone greatly modified the carcasses. The pigs fed the balanced rations had much larger muscles, and therefore their carcasses had a greater proportion of lean meat. The carcasses of the pigs fattened on corn alone had a wastefully high proportion of fat, with correspondingly less lean meat.

It was also found that the pigs which had been fed only corn had a smaller amount of blood and also smaller livers and other internal organs per 100 lbs. of carcass than did those fed the rations containing ample protein and mineral matter. Moreover, the bones of the corn-fed pigs were abnormally weak. In the first Wisconsin trial their thigh bones broke at an average pressure of 380 lbs. for each 100 lbs. of carcass, while the bones of pigs fed milk, dried blood, and wheat middlings broke at 500 lbs., a difference of 32 per cent.

To determine whether the poor results from corn alone were due to the lack of minerals, Henry conducted 3 experiments at the Wisconsin Station in each of which one lot of pigs was fed corn alone; a second lot, corn and hard-wood ashes, which are rich in calcium; and a third lot, corn and bone meal.[26] The pigs were confined in pens, with exercise yards floored with boards, so they could eat no dirt. The pigs fed corn alone soon failed to grow and became unduly fat and dwarfed. Those receiving wood ashes or bone meal in addition grew quite well for a time, but later their gains were poor.

On corn alone 629 lbs. of corn were required for 100 lbs. gain in weight, while only about 490 lbs. of corn were required when wood ashes or bone meal was added. Also, the bones of the pigs fed corn alone were only half as strong as those of the others. These trials clearly showed that adding a liberal supply of minerals to the ration was of some benefit, but it did not entirely remedy the deficiencies of corn for growing animals.

In later years numerous trials have been conducted to study this matter further. These investigations have clearly shown that to make a complete and satisfactory ration for growing animals, there must be added to corn not only a supply of minerals, but also an additional supply of protein, and furthermore, protein which is better balanced in composition than that which the corn grain furnishes. For pigs not on pasture, white corn is unsatisfactory, unless a supplement is furnished that provides vitamin A. Also, the pigs must receive vitamin D, unless they are exposed to direct sunlight.

The earlier trials with corn alone were carried on chiefly with pigs which were fairly well grown when the experiments began. That young pigs cannot be raised on corn alone is shown by extensive experiments at the Kansas Station.[27] In these trials pigs weighing about 25 lbs. were fed corn with various supplements. On corn plus a mixture of mineral matter containing an ample supply of calcium, pigs made practically no growth, gaining only 12 lbs. on the average in 180 days! In comparison with this, the pigs fed corn supplemented not only with mineral matter but also with milk casein, a protein of high quality, made an average gain of 179 lbs. in the same time.

It should not be concluded from these experiments that corn is not an excellent feed for pigs and other stock. On the contrary, as is shown in later chapters, it is unexcelled for feeding all classes of stock when it is properly supplemented.

230. Influence of soil upon breeds of livestock.—It is a common belief among those familiar with the livestock of various countries that the fertility of the soil in any district has a marked effect on the size and ruggedness of a breed of livestock which originates there.

Ashton, who recently studied this subject in Europe, concluded that the dwarf size of the Brittany breed of cattle in France was due largely to the great deficiency of calcium and phosphorus in the district where the breed was developed.[28] This dwarfed condition is apparently a result of the cumulative effort on the part of animals through successive generations to adapt themselves to their environmental conditions. If the animal cannot get enough calcium and phosphorus to build a strong skeleton of large size, there is a tendency to reduce the size of the bones.

Ashton concluded that, on the other hand, the large size and rugged frames of the Brown Swiss breed were due in part to the high calcium content of the soil in Switzerland. Also, for generations the cattle have secured their living from roughage, with little or no concentrates. This roughage has undoubtedly supplied a goodly amount of calcium, and of phosphorus as well.

It was also pointed out that in the Island of Jersey the soil is more deficient in calcium and phosphorus than in Guernsey, where the cattle are larger. Breeders of the "Island type" of Jerseys in the United States recognize that there is a tendency for their cattle to become somewhat larger and more rugged in bone when they are amply fed and kept on soil rich in minerals.

It is also well known that the small size of the Shetland pony is due to the rigorous climate of the Shetland Islands and the lack of fertility in the soil. In marked contrast are the Percheron, Belgian, Clydesdale, and Shire breeds of horses, all of which were developed in districts where the soil was rich and the climate was moderate.

231. Comparative economy of animal production.—The economy with which the various classes of farm animals produce human food is discussed in detail in the respective chapters of Part III, but it will be interesting to compare directly in the following paragraphs the economy of each class of animals with the others.

Cooper and Spillman of the United States Department of Agriculture[29] computed the following instructive estimates of the amounts of human food produced from an acre of crops fed to livestock and also from an acre of various crops consumed directly for human food. In each instance the pounds of digestible protein and the therms of energy furnished by an acre are shown.

The production of livestock per acre was arrived at by assuming that the land was devoted to crops suitable for feeding the kind of animal under consideration, and in the proper proportion to make a well-balanced ration. For instance, in the case of hogs, four-fifths of the acre was in corn and one-fourth in clover, and it was estimated that an acre used in this manner would produce 350 lbs. of live-weight increase in hogs. In order to make an efficient ration, it was assumed in some cases that a part of the product of the acre was exchanged for a high-protein feed not produced on the farm, such as cottonseed meal.

The estimates given for the various farm animals are for merely the edible human food, after all waste in the carcass and in slaughtering has been deducted. The figures for corn, wheat, and soybeans are for the entire seeds and not for the milled product, such as corn meal and wheat flour. The estimates for rice are for polished rice and those for oats are for the hulled kernels.

Human food from an acre of staple farm products

	Yield per acre	Human food per acre	
		Digestible protein	Energy
	Lbs.	Lbs.	Therms
Dairy products			
Milk	2,190	72.3	711.8
Cheese	219	56.7	427.0
Butter	99	1.0	355.3
Meat			
Pork, 350 lbs. live wt...........................	273	22.7	672.9
Poultry, 267 lbs. live wt........................	171	33.0	178.7
Mutton, 205 lbs. live wt.........................	113	14.7	137.3
Beef, 216 lbs. live wt...........................	125	18.5	130.0
Eggs, 122.4 dozen...............................	184	24.6	132.2
Food crops			
Corn, 35 bu......................................	1,960	147.0	3,124.2
Sweet potatoes, 110 bu...........................	5,940	53.5	2,851.2
Irish potatoes, 100 bu...........................	6,000	66.0	1,908.0
Wheat, 20 bu.....................................	1,200	110.4	1,788.0
Rice, polished (40 bu. rough rice)...............	1,086	50.0	1,581.2
Soybeans, 16 bu..................................	960	294.7	1,534.0
Peanuts, 34 bu...................................	524	126.2	1,265.0
Oats, 35 bu......................................	784	89.4	1,254.4

The table shows that if whole milk is used for food, the dairy cow leads all other classes of livestock in the economy with which she produces human food from a given area of land. In producing milk the cow yields 711.8 therms (711,800 Calories) of energy from 1 acre, and 72.3 lbs. digestible protein. Where only the cheese or the butter produced from milk is used for human food, the acreage yield of food nutrients is correspondingly reduced.

Among the meat-producing animals, the hog greatly excels in economy of production. In pork there are produced per acre in edible human food 672.9 therms of energy and 22.7 lbs. digestible protein. It will be noted that in amount of energy in human food produced per acre, the hog even excels the cow if only butter or cheese is used for human food. Far below the hog in amount of food produced per acre come poultry, beef cattle, and sheep.

The food crops all surpass the livestock products in amount of food energy furnished per acre. This is the reason why animal products cannot form any considerable part of the human diet in countries where there is a great congestion of population.

Among the food crops, corn excels in yield of energy, producing 3,124.2 therms per acre. Wheat, rice, and oats fall far below corn in the economy with which they furnish both protein and energy. Though ranking relatively low as a producer of energy, soybeans lead all the crops in yield of protein per acre.

In comparing the yields of the various classes of livestock and in studying the returns from the food crops consumed directly as human food and the returns from farm animals, the following facts should be borne in mind: Beef cattle and sheep can be maintained largely, except for the fattening period, on cheap roughages. They can even utilize considerable of such feeds as corn stover, straw, stubble-field pasturage, etc., much of which would otherwise be wasted. Though dairy cows require a liberal amount of concentrates for high production, they can dispose of much roughage, even some of relatively low value. The farm flock of poultry can secure much of its feed from kitchen scraps, insects, and farm waste in general.

Furthermore, in studying data of this character one must have in mind the relative expense for labor and other items with the various classes of stock. For instance, more labor is required for each dollar's worth of product in the case of dairy cattle than with beef cattle, sheep, or swine. These estimates present but one side of a most complicated economic question, as they show merely the relative efficiency with which the various animals and the various food crops utilize land in the production of human food.

In this connection the fact that the colored laborers in the cotton fields of the South live largely on corn meal and pork products is of interest. By the force of circumstances they have been driven in their struggle for existence to live mainly on the crop producing the largest amount of human food per acre—Indian corn, the king of the cereals—and for the sake of variety in their food and an additional supply of protein, the most efficient meat-producing animal of the farm—the pig. Undoubtedly, better nutrition and an even more economical diet would result if they made greater use of milk.

QUESTIONS

1. Discuss the importance of thrifty growth for farm animals.
2. Compare the food requirements for growth and maintenance, considering: (a) Amount of total digestible nutrients; (b) amount and quality of protein; (c) minerals; (d) vitamins.
3. Discuss the utilization of feed by young animals.
4. Why do young animals make cheaper gains than older ones?
5. Why is milk such an excellent food for young animals?
6. What deficiencies does milk have as an exclusive food over long periods?
7. Discuss the use of rich versus poor milk for young animals.
8. Why is it important that new-born animals receive the colostrum?
9. Discuss the requirements of growing animals for the following (a) Protein; (b) minerals; (c) vitamins; (d) total digestible nutrients or net energy.
10. What are the effects of restricting the feed of growing animals?
11. Of what practical importance are the results of the experiments in which growing animals have been fed scanty rations for a time?

12. Discuss the nutrient requirements of pregnant animals.
13. What is the object of fattening meat-producing animals?
14. Discuss the composition of the gains during the various parts of the fattening period.
15. Why is it generally uneconomical to carry an animal to a greater degree of fatness than necessary to meet the market demands?
16. From what nutrients may body fat be formed? From what source is most of it usually made by farm animals?
17. Discuss the effect of food fat upon body fat in swine and in ruminants.
18. Discuss the requirements of fattening animals for the following: (a) Total digestible nutrients or net energy; (b) protein; (c) minerals; (d) vitamins.
19. What factors, other than the ration, influence the rapidity and economy of gains during fattening?
20. Discuss the effects of feeding young pigs such a ration as corn alone.
21. How may the soil of a region influence the size of a breed of livestock developed there?
22. Discuss the relative economy with which various farm animals produce human food.

REFERENCES

1. Brody et al., Mo. Res. Buls. 96, 97, 98, 99, 101, 102, 103, 104, 105, 116; see also, Mumford et al., Mo. Res. Bul. 62; Brody and Ragsdale, Mo. Res. Buls. 67, 80; Hammond, Growth and Development of Mutton Qualities in the Sheep.
2. Armsby, Nutrition of Farm Animals, pp. 376-377.
3. Grindley, Mumford, Emmett, and Bull, Ill. Bul. 209; Bull and Grindley, Jour. Agr. Res. 18, 1919, pp. 241-254.
4. Morris, Palmer, and Kennedy, Minn. Tech. Bul. 92.
5. Armsby, Nutrition of Farm Animals, pp. 390-396; Hogan, Weaver, Edinger, and Trowbridge, Mo. Res. Bul. 73.
6. Becker and McCollum, Amer. Jour. Hyg., 12, 1930, pp. 503-510; Matill and Stone, Jour. Biol. Chem., 55, 1923, pp. 443-455; Palmer and Kennedy, Soc. Exptl. Biol. and Med. Proc., 20, 1923, pp. 506-508; Underhill et al., Jour. Biol. Chem., 99, 1933, pp. 469-472; Waddell, Steenbock, and Hart, Jour. Nutr., 4, 1931, pp. 53-65.
7. Hart, Steenbock, et al., Wis. Bul. 425.
8. Duncan, Huffman, and Robinson, Jour. Biol. Chem., 108, 1935, pp. 35-44.
9. Knoop and Krauss, Ohio Bul. 532.
10. Beach, Conn. (Storrs) Bul. 31; Washburn and Jones, Vt. Bul. 195.
11. Nevens and Shaw, Jour. Agr. Res., 46, 1933, pp. 463-472.
12. For a detailed discussion of the function of colostrum, see: Fundamentals of Dairy Science, by Associates of Rogers, 2nd ed., pp. 466-474.
13. Mitchell, Amer. Soc. Anim. Prod., Proc. 1933; Mitchell, Hamilton, and Kammlade, Ill. Rpt. 1932.
14. Morrison, Amer. Soc. Anim. Prod., Proc. 1933, pp. 27-34.
15. Waters and Trowbridge, Soc. Prom. Agr. Sci., Proc. 1908; Trowbridge, Moulton, and Haigh, Mo. Res. Buls. 28, 43; Moulton, Trowbridge, and Haigh, Mo. Res. Buls. 54, 55; Ritchie, Moulton, Trowbridge, and Haigh, Mo. Res. Bul. 59; Hogan, Mo. Res. Bul. 123; Waters, Cochel, and Vestal, Kansas Industrialist, May 10, 1913, Apr. 18, 1914, and information to the author.
16. Ritzman and Benedict, N. H. Tech. Bul. 26; Benedict and Ritzman, Carnegie Inst. Washington, Publications 324, 377.
17. McCay, Crowell, and Maynard, Jour. Nutr., 10, 1935, pp. 63-79; see also, Osborne and Mendel, Jour. Biol. Chem., 18, 1914, pp. 95-106; Carroll, Amer. Soc. Anim. Prod., Proc. 1922; Jackson and Stewart, Jour. Expt. Zool., 30, 1920, pp. 97-128.
18. Haigh, Moulton, and Trowbridge, Mo. Res. Bul. 38; see also, Yapp, Ill. Rpt. 1932; Yapp, Amer. Soc. Anim. Prod., Proc. 1931, pp. 133-136.
19. Lawes and Gilbert, Jour. Roy. Agr. Soc., England, 1860.
20. Trowbridge, Moulton, and Haigh, Mo. Res. Bul. 30; see also: Moulton, Trowbridge, and Haigh, Mo. Res. Bul. 61.
21. Haecker, Minn. Bul. 193.
22. Kan. Rpt. 1920-22; Anderson and Mendel, Soc. Expt. Biol. and Med. Proc., 21, 1924, pp. 436-437; Mendel and Anderson, Science, 64, 1926, pp. 384-386; Eckstein, Jour. Biol. Chem., 81, 1929, pp. 613-628.
23. Ga. Rpt. 1934; Thomas, Culbertson, and Beard, Amer. Soc. Anim. Prod., Proc. 1934, pp. 193-199.
24. Mitchell, National Res. Council, United States, Bul. 67.
25. Sanborn, Mo. Buls. 10, 14, 19; Henry, Wis. Rpts. 1886, 1887, 1888, 1889; Shelton, Kan. Bul. 9; Duggar, Ala. Bul. 82; Fortier, Ext. Trav. Soc. Cent. d'Agr., Dept. Seine-Inf., 1889, 1890; see also: Forbes, Mo. Bul. 81; Grindley et al., Ill. Buls. 168, 169, 171, 173.
26. Henry, Wis. Rpt. 1890, Wis. Bul. 25.
27. Hogan, Jour. Biol. Chem., 29, 1917, pp. 485-493; see also, Reed and Huffman, Mich. Quar. Bul. 6, 1924, No. 4.
28. Ashton, Mo. Res. Bul. 141.
29. Cooper and Spillman, U. S. Dept. of Agr., Farmers' Bul. 877.

CHAPTER VIII

PRODUCTION OF MILK, WORK, AND WOOL

I. Production of Milk

232. Secretion of milk.—Milk, the marvelous fluid designed for the nourishment of the young of all mammals, is secreted by the special organs called *mammary glands*.[1] The fully-developed mammary gland consists of a multitude of small, sac-like secreting bodies (called alveoli) and the duct system into which the milk is poured. The alveoli are grouped into clusters, somewhat like bunches of grapes. The alveoli may be compared to the grapes and the small ducts to the stems in the bunch of grapes.

The smallest ducts, into which the alveoli secrete the milk, unite to form large ones. The ducts are not uniform in size throughout their length but are greatly enlarged in places, to provide greater storage capacity for the milk as it is secreted. In some animals the large milk ducts open directly on the surface of the teat, but in other animals, including the cow, they open into a small cavity, called the milk cistern, which is just above the teat.

Our information is still incomplete concerning the exact process by which milk is produced in the alveoli, which form the secreting tissue of the udder. However, we do know that the blood, laden with nutrients, is brought by the capillaries of the udder to the alveoli. The nutrients then pass through the walls of the capillaries into the lymph and thence enter the cells of the alveoli. Here, by one of nature's wonderful processes they are converted into milk, which differs greatly in composition from the blood whence it is made.

Casein, the chief protein of milk, is unlike all other proteins of the body, and the milk fat also has entirely different properties than the body fat of the same animal. Lactose, or milk sugar, the carbohydrate of milk, is found nowhere else in the body. While the blood contains more sodium than potassium, potassium predominates in milk.

The opinions of scientists have differed concerning the method by which the milk, as secreted, passes from the cells of the alveoli into the ducts. Some believe that the milk constituents pass through the intact cell wall, while others conclude that the cell wall ruptures to let the milk constituents, especially the fat globules, pass out.

In considering the food requirements for milk production it should be borne in mind that the mammary gland does not receive a particular kind of blood suited to its special needs. It receives the very same kind of blood that flows to the other body tissues, and therefore it must compete with the other organs for its supply of nutrients. Recent investigations have proved, as would be expected, that, as the blood flows through the udder, the content in the blood of amino acids, glucose, and fats is appreciably decreased.

161

233. When is milk secreted?—It was formerly believed that the greater part of the milk secured at any one milking was secreted during the milking process. Recent investigations have shown definitely, however, that the secretion is a continuous process and that most of the milk obtained at a milking is already present in the udder when milking begins.

The rate of secretion is probably most rapid for a time after milking is completed, for there is then little or no pressure in the udder.[2] As the milk gradually accumulates in the milk ducts before the time of the next milking, it is believed that the rate of secretion tends to slow up somewhat, due to the increasing pressure. Also, the pressure may tend to hold the fat globules back in the cell, the milk then secreted being lower in fat.

In some experiments to determine when milk is secreted, cows have been slaughtered immediately before the usual milking time. Their udders have then been removed, kept at body temperature, and milked out thoroughly in the usual manner. In experiments by Swett and associates of the United States Department of Agriculture an average of 70 per cent as much milk was secured from the udders that had thus been removed, as the cows had yielded previously at a milking.[3] This milk was, however, much lower in fat than normal.

Other investigations likewise show that most of the milk has already been formed in the udder when milking starts.[4] In some of these studies cows have been slaughtered just before the usual milking time and their udders analyzed for lactose. Even more lactose has been found in the udder than would be contained in the milk yielded at one milking. This was due to the fact that even after thorough milking some milk still remains in the smaller ducts of the udder.

234. "Letting down" and "holding up" of milk.—The secretion of milk is involuntary and cannot be prevented by the animal, any more than can breathing or the circulation of the blood. The yield may, however, be reduced considerably through nervousness caused by fright or unusual conditions.

Any experienced milker has learned that when he begins to milk a cow, a small quantity of milk can readily be obtained at the start. Then there may be a short period when it is more difficult to get the milk. If the cow responds to the milking process, soon there is a great inflow of milk into the milk cistern, and we say that the cow has "let down" her milk. If the cow is nervous or disturbed she may refuse to "let down" her milk, and sometimes she will "hold up" her milk, even after milking has been proceeding satisfactorily.

From experiments in which the pressure in the udder of cows was determined at various times, Turner of the Missouri Station explains these well-known occurrences as follows:[5] He believes that the "letting down" of the milk by the cow is due to the contraction of muscle fibers throughout the udder. This causes an internal squeezing action upon all the milk storage spaces, including the ducts and the alveoli. This forces the milk downward into the milk cistern and teats.

If the cow becomes excited, a relaxation of the udder tissues may occur, making it difficult or impossible for the milker to secure the normal amount of milk, and he says the cow has "held up" her milk.

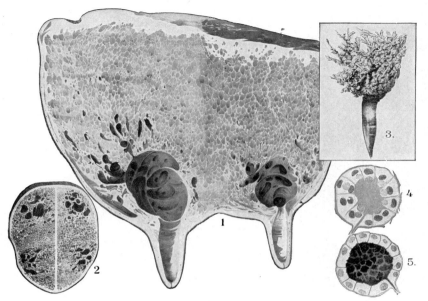

1. Longitudinal Section thru One Side of Udder and Teats of Cow

The narrow duct at the end of the teat, or the teat canal, may be seen, also the cavity in the teat, and the milk cistern. Altho there is no septum, or visible division, between the fore and hind quarters, no communication exists between the milk ducts in the two quarters. In this section the tissue of the fore quarter is colored slightly lighter than that of the hind quarter.

2. Horizontal Section of the Four Quarters of the Cow's Udder

The septum, or division, between the right and left halves of the udder is clearly visible. Note the size and distribution of the milk ducts.

3. Milk Cistern and Milk Ducts of a Fore Quarter of Udder

A metallic cast of the milk cistern and the larger milk ducts of one of the fore quarters.

4. Cross-section of an Alveolus Before Milking

The alveoli are small sac-like bodies, lined with secreting cells. The droplets of fat, indicated in the figure by the light-colored spots in the cells, are discharged into the cavity of the alveolus thru the cell walls when milk is secreted.

5. Cross-section of an Alveolus After Milking

This should be contrasted with Figure 4, as it shows the appearance of the cells of the alveolus following secretion. Note that the cells have lost their fat droplets and their fluid to a large degree. (Reproduced from charts by Rubeli, Berne, Switzerland.)

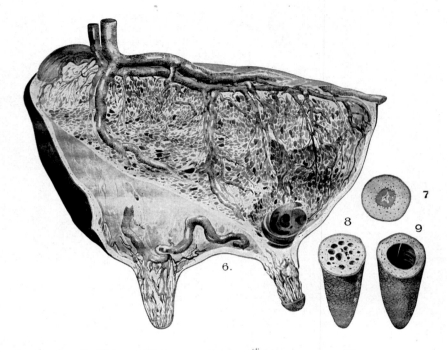

6. Blood Vessels of the Udder of the Cow

In this drawing both the arteries and the veins are shown. From the lower left-hand portion of the udder only the skin has been removed. In the portion above this and in all of the rear quarter the blood vessels and the secretory tissue of the udder have been exposed. Note the network of blood vessels in the teats.

7. Cross-section Near the End of a Cow's Teat

The triangular figure in the center is the narrow duct, or teat canal, at the end of the teat.

8. Cross-section of the Upper Part of a Cow's Teat Between Times of Milking

The round figures indicate the blood vessels and the irregular, slit-like figure at the center, the contracted cavity of the teat. Note the large size of the blood vessels and the small size of the teat cavity.

9. Cross-section at the Same Point During Milking

Note that the teat cavity is distended, while the blood vessels are contracted and carry relatively little blood. (From charts by Rubeli, Berne, Switzerland.)

Probably what has occurred is that she has failed to co-operate and "force down" the milk.

The largest yield of milk is usually obtained when the milker milks a cow rapidly, as soon as she has let the milk down. This is probably because the contraction of the muscular tissues will not continue for a very long period, and when the udder has relaxed, the milk cannot be drawn out as completely.

These recent studies provide an interesting explanation for the well-known fact that regularity in feeding and stable management is necessary to secure the largest yields from good cows. Also, the kind milker who gains the confidence of cows secures more milk from them than a rough or indifferent person.

235. The development of the mammary gland.[6]—In a young female before sexual maturity the mammary glands are but slightly developed. For example, in the case of dairy calves, the milk ducts leading out from the milk cistern are small and short, with but few branches. After sexual maturity is reached and the animal comes in heat, the duct system begins to grow and branch out into the fatty pad of tissue which at that time composes most of the udder. This growth is caused by a hormone which is secreted in the ovaries and carried in the blood to the udder. This hormone, usually called *theelin* or *estrin*, is the same hormone that is responsible for the heat period in females. With each successive heat period, further growth of the duct system occurs.

If the animal does not become pregnant, the duct system becomes fairly extensive, but there is not much development of the true secreting tissues, the groups of alveoli. When pregnancy occurs, a further growth takes place in the duct system, and also the secreting tissues develop rapidly. This is caused by theelin and also by a hormone secreted by the corpus luteum, or "yellow body," in the ovary of the pregnant animal. This hormone is called by various scientists *progestin, corporin,* or *lutein.*

At about the middle of the pregnancy period the growth of the glandular tissue has been largely completed. The cells of the alveoli then begin to secrete a fluid that resembles colostrum, which is the first milk yielded by the mother after the birth of the young. The beginning of secretion is brought about, not by either of the two hormones that have been mentioned, but by a hormone called *galactin* or *prolactin*, which is secreted by the forward, or anterior, part of the pituitary gland. (**63**)

Because of the rapid enlargement of the udder during the latter part of pregnancy, it has been commonly thought that the greatest growth in the gland takes place at that time. However, the opposite is true. The increase in size is chiefly due, not to a growth in the glandular tissue, but to the accumulation in the duct system and alveoli of the secretion. This colostrum is not commonly removed until the young are born and begin suckling.

The function of the colostrum in protecting the new-born against disease has been explained in the previous chapter. (**210**)

When the milk yield decreases during the latter part of the lactation period and the animal finally "goes dry," the alveoli disappear to a considerable extent, leaving only the cistern and duct system. Then the alveoli are rebuilt during the first half of the next pregnancy period.

Since the development of the udder tissues and the secretion of milk are controlled by hormones, it has seemed possible that the yield of milk might be increased by the injection of hormone extracts into the blood. It has been possible by such injections to cause the secretion of milk in non-pregnant females or even in those that had been spayed. However, attempts to cause any appreciable increase in the milk production of normal, high-yielding animals by the use of hormone extracts or tissues have not been successful.[7]

Young heifers often develop the habit of sucking each other, and this manipulation of the udder will sometimes start the secretion of milk, even in the unbred animal. In one instance at the Wisconsin Station a barren heifer produced over 5,000 lbs. of milk in 630 days, the maximum daily yield being 18.7 lbs.[8]

Such a milk flow is, however, much less than the animal would produce following pregnancy and the birth of young.

236. Nutrients required for milk production.—In the discussion of the composition of milk, which has been given in the preceding chapter, it was emphasized that milk is especially rich in protein of high quality and also in calcium and phosphorus. The ration of a lactating animal must therefore supply adequate amounts of these nutrients in order to make possible a satisfactory yield of milk. The large requirements of protein, calcium, and phosphorus for milk production are in strong contrast to the relatively small amounts needed by an animal that is being fattened, or one that is merely being maintained without yielding any product.

Milk is also rich in fat and in lactose, or milk sugar. The ration of an animal in milk must therefore supply liberal amounts of total digestible nutrients or of net energy. In this respect a ration for heavy milk production is similar to a ration for an animal that is being fattened rapidly or for a horse at hard work.

It has been shown in Chapter VI that the ration must contain an abundance of vitamin A to enable an animal to produce milk having the normal richness in this vitamin. There must also be a liberal supply of vitamin D to make possible the assimilation and use of the large amounts of calcium and phosphorus required in milk production.

It should be self-evident that the quantities of the various nutrients required by any particular milking animal will depend primarily on the amount of milk that is actually being produced. Thus, a cow yielding 60 lbs. of milk a day will require twice as great a supply of nutrients, above her maintenance requirements, as will a cow producing only 30 lbs. of milk of the same richness. This simple fact is disregarded by far too many dairymen, who allow the net returns from their herds to be seriously reduced because they do not feed the individual cows in proportion to their actual productions. This important question is discussed in detail in Chapter XXIV.

The heavy nutrient requirements for milk production are evident, if we compute the total amounts of nutrients produced by a good cow in a year. A cow that yields annually 8,000 lbs. of milk containing

3.5 per cent fat will produce in her milk about 270 lbs. protein, 280 lbs. fat, 390 lbs. lactose, and 55 lbs. mineral matter. This milk will have a total energy value of about 2,600 therms. In comparison with these figures, the entire body of a fat 2-year-old steer weighing 1,200 lbs. will contain about 190 lbs. protein, 390 lbs. fat, 45 lbs. minerals, and only an insignificant amount of sugar. The body of the steer will have a total energy value of about 2,275 therms.

Thus, each year such a cow yields a much greater quantity of protein and somewhat more energy and minerals than have been built into the body of the steer during its entire life. As has been shown in the previous chapter, the cow will also have built into the body of her calf during pregnancy nutrients which are equivalent to those in 400 lbs. or more of milk. (217)

237. Protein requirements.—The investigations on the protein requirements for milk production by farm animals have been chiefly with dairy cows. These investigations are reviewed in some detail in Chapter XXIV.

Satisfactory milk production is secured when cows receive in their feed, in addition to the amounts of protein that they need for maintenance, only 1.25 times as much digestible protein of a suitable quality as is actually contained in their milk. A supply that is somewhat more liberal than this allowance may, however, increase the yield of milk, as is pointed out in Chapter XXIV.

The great economy of the dairy cow in converting the protein of her feed into the high-quality protein of milk is evident from the fact that she needs, in addition to her maintenance requirements, only 1.25 lbs. of digestible protein in her food for each pound of protein in the milk. In the economy with which she converts the protein of feeding stuffs into protein of the highest nutritive value, the dairy cow far excels the other farm animals, as has been emphasized previously. (231)

The importance of supplying milking animals with proteins of suitable quality has been treated in the preceding chapter. Specific information on the protein requirements of dairy cows is presented in Chapter XXIV, and the protein needs of other stock when suckling their young are likewise discussed in Part III. The feeding standards presented in Appendix Table III show the amounts of digestible protein advised by the author for the various classes of milking animals.

238. Fat requirements.—At one time it was believed that an animal producing milk could form the milk fat only from the fat in her feed. That other nutrients could also serve as the source of milk fat was proved many years ago by Jordan and associates at the New York (Geneva) Station.[9]

For over 3 months a cow was fed on hay, corn meal, and oats, from which the fat had been extracted by naphtha, as is done in one method of extracting the oil from flax seed. During this time the cow received only 5.7 lbs. digestible fat in her feed, but yielded 62.9 lbs. of fat in her milk. She was fatter at the end of the trial than at the beginning and so could not have converted her body fat into milk fat. From the amount of digestible protein in her feed, it was computed that not over 17 lbs. of the milk fat could possibly have come from the food protein. Thus, the larger part of the fat must have been formed from the carbohydrates of the feed.

Later investigations, especially experiments by Maynard, McCay, and associates at the New York (Cornell) Station, have shown that lactating animals can apparently make most of the milk fat more readily from the fat digested from their feed than they can from carbohydrates or protein.[10] As a consequence, if the amount of digestible fat in the ration is too small, the milk yield will be decreased considerably.

In these experiments, which are reviewed in greater detail in Chapter XXIV, it was found that the milk and fat yields of high-producing cows receiving the usual type of roughage were reduced appreciably unless the concentrate mixture that they were fed contained at least 4 per cent total fat.

When the concentrate mixture was richer than this in fat, containing 6 or 7 per cent fat, there was a tendency for the production of milk and fat to be increased very slightly. It was concluded, however, that the difference was not sufficiently marked to be of practical importance. When a concentrate mixture containing 4 per cent fat was fed with corn silage and mixed clover and grass hay for roughage, the ration supplied about 70 per cent as much fat as there was in the milk. Somewhat more than 30 per cent of the milk fat was therefore made from other nutrients in the ration, for part of the so-called ''fat'' in feeds consists of other substances than true fats. (12)

When a low-fat ration was fed to dairy cows in these experiments, the percentage of fat in the milk was not appreciably affected, but the total yield of fat was decreased, due to the fall in milk yield. However, in the case of milk goats a ration very low in fat decreased the percentage of fat in the milk.

There is probably no deficiency of fat for efficient milk production in the rations commonly fed beef cows, brood mares, ewes of the common breeds, and brood sows. This is because their milk yield is relatively low in comparison with that of good dairy cows or milk goats. In feeding these last two classes of stock, due care should be taken that the ration furnishes at least the minimum amount of fat necessary for high production.

239. Mineral and vitamin requirements.—The mineral and vitamin requirements of farm animals have been discussed at some length in the preceding chapter. The importance was there emphasized of supplying sufficient calcium, phosphorus, vitamin A, and vitamin D to make possible a high yield of milk, without injury to the animal.

The mineral and vitamin requirements for milk production by the various classes of stock are considered further in Part III, and the influence of the vitamin supply in the ration upon the vitamin content of the milk is discussed later in this chapter.

240. Total digestible nutrient or net energy requirements.—The importance of rapid growth in young farm animals has been emphasized in the preceding chapter. To produce such growth in young mammals it is essential that the mother be so fed that her milk yield will be ample.

Many do not realize that the requirements during milk production for total digestible nutrients and also for protein, minerals, and vitamins are far greater than the requirements during pregnancy. On account of her strong impulse to secrete an ample amount of milk for her young, the mother will draw heavily on her body during the first part of lactation, if her food supply is insufficient. However, a good flow of milk cannot long be maintained unless the ration is fully adequate in nutrients.

For efficient milk production, dairy cows, beef cows, brood mares, and breeding ewes should, first of all, receive a liberal supply of good-quality roughage. This will not only furnish total digestible nutrients and net energy, but it is also important in providing minerals and vitamins. In addition to roughage, these animals should receive whatever amounts of concentrates are necessary to maintain a satisfactory flow of milk. Brood sows must get most of their nutrients for milk production from concentrates.

The amount of concentrates required for any class of stock will depend on the quality of the roughage they receive and on the amount of milk they are yielding. Thus, beef cows nursing calves need no grain in addition to good pasture, while high-producing dairy cows cannot secure enough nutrients from pasture alone, unless it is most excellent.

Specific information is given in the respective chapters of Part III on rations suitable for the various classes of lactating animals. The amounts of total digestible nutrients and of net energy recommended by the author for various classes of milking animals are stated in Appendix Table III.

241. Effect of various factors upon the composition of milk.— The effects of various factors upon the yield and composition of milk have been studied chiefly in experiments with dairy cows. These factors are therefore discussed in detail in Chapter XXIV.

In general, there is a strong tendency for a lactating animal to produce milk of normal composition under widely varying conditions. Any inadequacy in the ration or fault in the methods of care and management will generally manifest itself by a reduction in the yield of milk, rather than by a change in its chemical composition. However, certain factors have an effect on the fat percentage. Also, a continued lack of vitamin A will result in the milk being very deficient in this vitamin.

242. Effect of protein, fat, and sugar.— Cows that were fed rations unusually low in protein at the Ohio Station yielded milk that did not differ in any important respect from that produced by cows fed rations rich in protein.[11] Calves and also laboratory test animals made equally good growth on both kinds of milk. The only significant difference was that the milk from the high-protein feeding contained more of the non-protein nitrogenous compounds, including urea, which are found in traces in milk. Also this milk was slightly higher in the vitamin B complex. (**195**)

If the ration of a dairy cow does not contain a certain minimum amount of fat, the yield of milk will be reduced, as has already been shown in this chapter. The percentage of fat in the milk is not, however, reduced in the case of cows, but may be with goats. The experiments reviewed in Chapter XXIV show that the richness of the milk may be considerably increased for a few days by adding fat or fat-rich feeds to the ration. The fat content, however, tends to fall back to normal later, even though the feeding of fat is continued. Certain feeds, especially coconut meal and palm kernel meal, may cause a very slight increase in the fat content of the milk over a longer period. Cod-liver oil and certain other fish oils decrease the percentage of fat in the milk of cows.

When fed in considerable amounts, feeds that are rich in fat may have a decided effect on the character of the fat in milk, just as they do upon the body fat produced by swine. (**222**) Thus, soybeans and peanuts tend to produce soft butter, while cottonseed meal and coconut oil meal make hard butter with a high melting point.

The percentage of lactose in milk cannot be changed by any ordinary method. In a Kansas test it was increased somewhat when a glucose solution was pumped into the stomachs of cows.[12] On the other hand, in a Minnesota trial there was no change in the lactose content of the milk when a solution of glucose or lactose was injected into the blood.[13] When the glucose content of the blood was decreased abnormally by the injection of the hormone, insulin, the lactose percentage was reduced.

243. Effect of feed on mineral content of milk.—The mineral content of milk is not affected to any appreciable extent by the amounts of minerals in the ration, except in the case of iodine. A ration deficient in phosphorus or calcium will reduce milk production and may cause injury to the milking animal.[14] However, the milk that is produced will contain about the normal percentages of phosphorus and calcium.

As has been stated before, milk is low in iron and copper. (**174**) Experiments have shown that it is apparently impossible to increase the percentage of these minerals in milk by increasing the supply in the feed.[15] Likewise, increasing the manganese content of a ration does not appreciably increase the manganese content of the milk.[16]

Cow's milk normally contains only traces of iodine, the content ranging from less than 9 up to 40 parts per billion. By adding potassium iodide or some other source of iodine to the ration, the iodine content of the milk can usually be increased several-fold. However, the cow is very inefficient in transferring this expensive mineral constituent into her milk.[17] Only 3.5 to 29.0 per cent of the iodine supplied in the feed has been recovered in the milk when it has been added to the rations of dairy cows. Also, the feeding of iodine may lower the percentage and yield of milk fat.

It has been advocated by a few that iodine should be added to the rations of dairy cows so that their milk might be used as a goiter preventative for humans in iodine-deficient districts. The production of such "iodized" milk seems inadvisable and unnecessary. The use by humans of iodized salt as insurance against goiter is much cheaper, and the dosage of iodine in this form can be much more easily standardized.

In spite of claims sometimes made to the contrary, it has not been proved in controlled experiments that the addition of iodine to the rations of dairy cows is of any appreciable benefit to them in sections where there is no deficiency of iodine in the soil and water. (172)

244. Effect of feed on vitamin content of milk.—The effect of the ration upon the vitamin content of milk has been considered in the previous chapter, in which the functions and the occurrence of the various vitamins have been discussed.

While milk produced by an animal fed a suitable ration is rich in vitamin A, the amount of the vitamin will be low if the ration is deficient in this nutritive essential. This is an important matter, not only from the standpoint of the value of milk for humans, but also in rearing livestock.

It has been explained in the previous chapter that the vitamin D content of milk is not high from cows fed any ordinary rations. However, the amount of this vitamin can be increased several-fold by feeding cows irradiated yeast or irradiated ergosterol, as has been mentioned in the previous chapter. (193)

The vitamin B content in milk cannot apparently be increased, even by the addition of yeast, which is very rich in this vitamin, to a normal ration.[18] The amount of vitamin G may be slightly increased by this method. The results of experiments in which attempts have been made to increase the vitamin C content of milk have differed. However, it seems probable that the milk produced on a ration high in vitamin C will generally be somewhat richer in this vitamin than that produced from feeds containing but little vitamin C. Apparently cattle are able to synthesize the vitamin in their bodies, for the milk from cows kept for 7 years at the Wisconsin Station on a vitamin-C-free ration still contained the vitamin.[19]

II. Production of Work

245. The source of muscular energy.—It has long been known that muscular exertion or work greatly increases the amount of nutrients oxidized in the body, but scientists have disagreed as to the exact source of the energy required for the muscular contractions.[20]

By painstaking experiments it was at length proved that all the organic nutrients may serve as sources of the energy for muscular work. Under normal conditions the carbohydrates and the fats of the food are first drawn upon, and little more or no more protein is broken down than during rest. Should the carbohydrates and fats of the food not furnish enough energy, the body fat is next used. Finally, as a last resort, the muscles or other protein tissues can be called upon, if the energy can be secured from no other source. Since the greater part of the food of farm animals consists of carbohydrates, most of the energy they expend in muscular activity undoubtedly comes from them.

Many investigations have been conducted by physiologists and biochemists to determine whether there is any increase in the amount of protein broken down in the body during work, providing there are abundant supplies of carbohydrates and fat. Opinions on this question still differ, but it is agreed, at least, that even during hard work there is no material increase in the amount of protein used in the body, if the amounts of other nutrients are ample.

For this reason, a mature animal needs during work but little more protein than is required for satisfactory maintenance at rest. The protein requirements for work therefore differ greatly from those for growth, for milk production, or for wool production.

246. Production of muscular movements.—It is known definitely that the glycogen stored in the muscles while at rest is used up in muscular work. During work, increased amounts of oxygen are taken up from the blood, and the amount of carbon dioxide produced in the body is increased in proportion to the amount of work accomplished. Part of the energy contained in the nutrients used up in the muscular contractions is changed into the mechanical work produced, while part is set free as heat.

While glycogen, or animal starch, is undoubtedly the chief source of the energy for work under usual conditions, the exact process that occurs is still in question. In a marvelous manner some compound or compounds stored in the muscular fibers are broken down suddenly to provide the energy for the muscular contraction. A recent theory is that the compound which is chiefly broken down at the instant of contraction may not be glycogen or any derivative of it, but a compound called phosphagen, formed by the union of phosphoric acid and a nitrogenous substance called creatine.

It is thought that this compound breaks down during contraction, and then, during the relaxation of the muscle which follows, the compound is again formed in the muscle fibers by a complicated process. It is believed that the energy required for this process comes from some substance formed from the glycogen in the muscle, perhaps lactic acid.

The production of mechanical energy in the muscles is in a way similar to the production of power by a gasoline engine, where the fuel undergoes such a rapid breaking down that it becomes an explosion. In the gasoline engine and also in the muscle, part of the energy of the fuel is turned into useful work and part is set free as heat. This latter part yields no useful work.

During rest, glycogen is stored in the muscles, forming from 0.5 to 0.9 per cent of the weight of well-nourished muscle when resting. A smaller amount of glucose is also stored in the muscles. During muscular activity the stored glycogen is used up in proportion to the severity and duration of the work, and after prolonged hard work the supply may be entirely exhausted.

Though the amounts of glycogen and glucose in the muscular tissues at any one time are small, a supply of glucose is being continuously brought to them in the blood. This glucose is in part built up into glycogen in the muscle fibers.

247. Nutrient requirements for work animals.—From the preceding discussion it is evident that the primary need in rations for work animals is a sufficient supply of feeds rich in total digestible nutrients or net energy. The value of any particular feed for work production will depend strictly on the amount of net energy it yields. This is because the energy used up in the so-called work of digestion is all

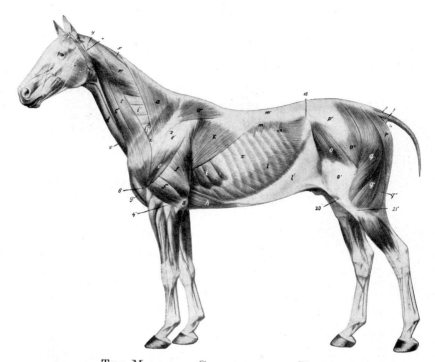

The Muscular System of the Horse

The work done yearly in this country by horses and mules is worth more than a billion dollars. (From Ellenberger.)

Left—Small Portion of Mammary Gland of Cow

Small portion of gland, greatly magnified. A, alveoli, in which milk is secreted; b, small milk duct; c, larger milk duct. (After Klein.)

Right—Wool Fibers

Appearance of fibers, greatly magnified, after dirt and yolk have been removed. Left, fiber of Merino wool; right, fiber of Down wool. Note the overlapping scales covering the fibers.

HORSES AT HARD WORK REQUIRE MUCH NET ENERGY IN FEED

On account of the large amount of energy they expend in the work they perform, horses at hard work must receive a liberal amount of concentrates high in net energy.

HIGH-PRODUCING DAIRY COWS ALSO REQUIRE MUCH NET ENERGY

Many people fail to realize that high-producing cows are expending as much energy in producing milk as horses at hard work expend in their labor.

converted into heat, and, as has been explained in Chapter III, is wasted so far as the production of work or the formation of body tissues is concerned. (86-87)

The amounts of digestible nutrients or net energy that are required for any particular work animal will obviously depend on the amount of labor performed. Accordingly, the proportion of concentrates in the ration must be increased as the work becomes harder. For severe work, horses and mules must be fed a liberal amount of such concentrates as the farm grains, and they can use only a limited amount of hay or other roughage. On the other hand, animals doing light work can be fed more largely on roughage.

It has been explained previously in this chapter that little or no more protein is needed during work than when the animal is at rest. A mature work animal therefore needs but little more protein when at work than when idle. In experiments mentioned in Chapter XXI, work horses have been successfully fed rations in which the nutritive ratio was as wide as 1:28.0. However, as has been stated in Chapter IV, the digestibility of a ration is usually decreased when the proportion of protein is too low. Also, it is believed that a supply of protein somewhat above the minimum requirements tends to give work animals better life and spirit.

In recent New York experiments, which are also mentioned in Chapter XXI, rations having nutritive ratios of 1:10.0 to 1:11.0 have been as satisfactory over long periods as a ration with a nutritive ratio of 1:8.0 for farm horses doing medium to hard work. These and other investigations have been taken into consideration in the recommendations for work horses and mules which are presented in the Morrison feeding standards. (Appendix Table III.)

The mature animal when at work does not need a much greater amount of minerals or vitamins than when merely being maintained at rest. However, since a long life of usefulness is important, it is wise to be sure that there is a plentiful supply of these nutrients in the ration.

An immature work animal that has not yet completed its growth will obviously need somewhat more protein, more minerals, more vitamins, and also more total digestible nutrients or net energy than a mature animal performing the same amount of labor. Likewise, the requirements of brood mares during pregnancy and especially during lactation are increased by these functions. It is therefore important that the brood mare receive a ration containing ample protein, minerals, and vitamins, as is emphasized in Chapter XXIII.

Detailed discussions of the nutrient requirements of horses and mules for various degrees of work are given in these later chapters. Typical rations which are adapted to various sections of the country are recommended in Appendix Table VII for idle animals and for those performing light, medium, and hard work.

248. Efficiency of the animal as a machine.—Numerous experiments have shown that animals at moderate labor can convert into the actual work produced one-quarter to one-third of the energy they expend, after deducting the amounts they need for body maintenance. The rest takes the form of heat within the body, and is lost so far as the production of work is concerned. These figures do not take into account the energy lost in the excreta, that expended for digestion and assimilation, or that used in maintaining the body when at rest.

Allowing for all of these, a horse doing a full day's work will turn about 9 per cent of the gross energy in the feed it eats during the 24 hours into actual useful external work, such as hauling a load. This does not count the energy expended in the work of moving his own body. It is shown in Chapter XXI, where the efficiency of the horse as a motor is discussed further, that this percentage is not far below that of the best farm tractors.

The efficiency of the animal is especially striking when it is borne in mind that the tractor is supplied with purified fuel (kerosene or gasoline) while the horse must secure its energy from crude materials, including hay, of which only about half is actually digestible. Furthermore, he must digest this feed, and himself separate out the useful from the waste material. Also, he must make all body repairs. Last, but not least, he must maintain his body during the part of the 24 hours that he is not working, while all expenditures of energy cease when the tractor stops work.

249. Factors influencing energy required for work.—The amount of energy required to produce a given amount of useful work depends upon many factors. Practice in doing a certain kind of work lessens the amount of energy expended. In one instance, training for two weeks decreased by over 20 per cent the energy used by a man climbing a tower.[21]

On the other hand, fatigue greatly increases the energy required to do a task. This is largely due to the fact that with increasing fatigue the muscles normally used, and which are thus most efficient in performing the given work, are put out of use. Then other less efficient muscles are called upon to a constantly increasing degree, and these cannot perform the work so economically.

Increasing the speed at which the work is done also lessens the efficiency with which it is performed. This is because the work of the heart is increased, the body temperature rises, and much heat is lost by the evaporation of water through the skin and lungs. This decreases the amount of work that a given quantity of feed will produce. Furthermore, when a horse trots or gallops, the rise and fall of the body is much greater than in walking, and therefore it has available for onward movement a smaller part of the total energy that is expended.

The part of the expended energy which is converted into useful work varies with the build of the animal, the development of its muscles, and the structure of its limbs. For example, a lame horse may use nearly twice as much energy in traveling a certain distance as one with sound legs. An animal which is able to perform one kind of work most economically may have to expend undue energy at other kinds of work. Thus, horses bred for generations to the saddle can carry the rider with a smaller expenditure of energy than those whose breeding and form specially fit them for draft purposes.

Additional discussions of the factors influencing the production of work, as applied to horses, are given in Chapter XXI.

III. Wool Production

250. Composition of wool.—Wool is made up of pure wool fiber and yolk, the latter including the suint and the wool fat. The wool fiber is practically pure protein, and it is of the same chemical composition as ordinary hair, but it differs in being covered with minute overlapping scales.

The suint, chiefly composed of compounds of potassium with organic acids, comprises from 15 to over 50 per cent of the unwashed fleece, being especially high in the Merino breed. As suint is soluble in water, most of it is removed by washing the unshorn sheep or the fleece, and less is present in the wool of sheep exposed to the weather. Wool fat, or lanolin, is really a wax and not a true fat. (**12**) It is often incorrectly called yolk. The wool fat is insoluble in water and may form 8 to 30 per cent of the weight of a washed fleece.

251. Requirements for wool production.—Owing to the large amount of protein stored by sheep in the fleeces, their rations should contain somewhat more protein than rations for cattle or swine at the same stage of maturity. This is taken into consideration in the feeding standards for the different classes of animals. (See Appendix Table III.) With ewes which are pregnant or suckling lambs, there is a double demand for food protein, which makes a liberal supply especially advisable.

The mohair produced by Angora goats has the same general chemical composition as wool fiber, though differing in structure. Therefore the nutrient requirements of these goats are similar to the requirements of sheep. The requirements of milk goats, on the other hand, are similar to those of dairy cows.

Adverse conditions, such as sickness, undue exposure, or a decided lack of feed, will decrease the yield of wool, will produce smaller and weaker fibers, and will sometimes cause weak spots in the fibers. Unless the undernutrition is severe, the amount of yolk (wool fat plus suint) will be decreased more than the yield of scoured wool (gross weight of fleece minus the suint, wool fat, and dirt).[22]

In a California trial sheep produced more than three times as much scoured wool when fed a liberal fattening ration for 6 months as when poor-quality alfalfa hay was fed in amounts not quite sufficient to maintain their weights.[23] The wool fibers were only half as strong on the sub-maintenance ration, and they were seriously lacking in crimp. In a Nebraska trial lambs fed a liberal ration for about a year produced more than twice as much scoured wool as others given slightly less than a maintenance ration.[24] The wool fibers produced on the scanty ration were shorter and much smaller in diameter.

Exposure and insufficient feed, such as ewes are often subjected to under range conditions during the winter, will considerably reduce the yield of scoured wool, in comparison with the yield under better conditions of feeding and shelter.[25] A Louisiana experiment indicates that underfeeding of sheep may even cause shedding of the wool, which sometimes occurs in sheep even when not infected with scab.[26]

If lambs are fed so that they make rapid gains, they will have larger bodies at a given age and be more mature than if fed somewhat less liberally. They will consequently shear heavier fleeces.

In most of the tests that have been reported, ewes have had heavier fleeces at 2 to 3 years of age than as yearlings, but in some trials the yearlings have shorn the most wool.[27] After 3 to 4 years the fleece weight gradually declines with increasing age. The diameter of the wool fibers, at least in Rambouillet sheep, remains relatively constant throughout the useful life of the sheep.[28]

QUESTIONS

1. Describe the structure of the udder, and tell what is known about the manner in which milk is secreted.
2. When is milk secreted?
3. Give an explanation of the way in which cows "hold up" and "let down" their milk.
4. Describe the development of the mammary gland after the animal reaches sexual maturity; after pregnancy occurs.
5. Compare the nutrient requirements of a lactating animal with the requirements for maintaining a mature animal. Consider protein, minerals, vitamins, and total digestible nutrients or net energy in your discussion.
6. Discuss the protein requirements for milk production. About how much digestible protein does a dairy cow require in her feed, in addition to the maintenance requirement, for each pound of protein she produces in her milk?
7. Discuss in detail the fat requirements for milk production. What is the minimum amount of fat that a concentrate mixture for dairy cows should contain?
8. Discuss the mineral and vitamin requirements for milk production.
9. Discuss the requirements of total digestible nutrients or net energy for milk production.
10. In what manner can the composition of milk be changed by the feed the animal receives? Consider: (a) Protein; (b) amount and character of fat; (c) minerals; (d) milk sugar; (e) vitamins.
11. What is your opinion concerning the production of "iodized" milk?
12. From what food nutrients can muscular energy be produced?
13. Describe some of the chief processes that occur in the production of muscular movements.
14. Compare the requirements for a work animal with those for maintaining the same animal when idle, considering (a) total digestible nutrients or net energy; (b) protein; (c) minerals and vitamins.
15. Discuss the efficiency of the animal as a machine for the production of work.
16. What are the effects of fatigue, speed, lameness, and build of the animal on the economy with which work is produced?
17. Of what is wool composed?
18. Discuss the food requirements for wool production, and state what effects unfavorable feed or conditions may have upon wool.

REFERENCES

1. For further information on the structure of the udder and the physiology of milk secretion see: Turner, Mo. Buls. 339, 344, 346; also, Fundamentals of Dairy Science, 2nd ed., Associates of Rogers, (Chapter by Meigs and Cary), pp. 555-602.
2. Cockefair, Jour. Dairy Sci., 11, 1928, pp. 230-239; Turner, Mo. Bul. 346.
3. Swett, Jour. Dairy Sci., 10, 1927, pp. 1-14; Swett, Miller, and Graves, Jour. Agr. Res., 45, 1932, pp. 385-419, 577-607.
4. Gaines, Am. Jour. Physiol., 38, 1915, pp. 285-312; Gaines and Sanmann, Am. Jour. Physiol., 80, 1927, pp. 691-701; Gowen and Tobey, Jour. Gen. Physiol., 12, 1928, pp. 123-128; Peterson, Palmer, and Eckles, Am. Jour. Physiol., 90, 1929, pp. 573-581; Ragsdale, Turner, Brody, Elting, and Gifford, Mo. Buls. 244, 256.
5. Turner, Mo. Bul. 346.
6. For detailed descriptions of the development of the mammary glands in animals, and the relation of hormones to the processes, see: Turner, Mo. Bul. 339;

Turner, Mo. Res. Buls. 140, 156, 160; Turner and Schultze, Mo. Res. Bul. 157; Turner and Gardner, Mo. Res. Bul. 158; Turner and Gomez, Mo. Res. Buls. 182, 194, 206; Allen, Sex and Internal Secretions; Woodman and Hammond, Jour. Agr. Sci., England, 13, 1923, pp. 180-191; Asdell, Jour. Agr. Sci., England, 15, 1925, pp. 358-374; Asdell et al., N. Y. (Cornell) Rpts. 1931, 1932, 1933, 1934; Nelson and Pfiffner, Anat. Rec., 51, 1931, pp. 51-83.

7. Bartlett, N. J. Rpt. 1924; Turner and Slaughter, Jour. Dairy Sci., 13, 1930, pp. 8-24; Asdell, Salisbury, Brooks, Woodward, Kelly, and Seidenstein, N. Y. (Cornell) Rpts. 1933, 1934.

8. Johannsson and Knudson, Jour. Dairy Sci., 16, 1933, pp. 523-528; see also: Becker and McGilliard, Jour. Dairy Sci., 13, 1930, pp. 372-379; Asdell, Jour. Agr. Sci., England, 15, 1925, pp. 358-374.

9. Jordan and Jenter, N. Y. (Geneva) Bul. 132; Jordan, Jenter, and Fuller, N. Y. (Geneva) Bul. 197.

10. Maynard and McCay, N. Y. (Cornell) Bul. 543; Maynard, McCay, Williams, and Madsen, N. Y. (Cornell) Bul. 593.

11. Perkins, Krauss, and Hayden, Ohio Bul. 515.

12. Whitnah, Riddell, and Hodgson, Jour. Dairy Sci., 16, 1933, pp. 347-353.

13. Petersen and Brown, Abstr. of Papers, 29th Ann. Meeting, Am. Dairy Sci. Assoc., 1934; see also: Gowen and Tobey, Maine Bul. 360.

14. Maynard, Cornell Veterinarian, 19, 1929, pp. 125-138; Associates of Rogers, Fundamentals of Dairy Science, 2nd Ed., pp. 584-587.

15. Elvehjem, Herrin, and Hart, Jour. Biol. Chem., 71, 1927, pp. 255-262; Elvehjem, Steenbock, and Hart, Jour. Biol. Chem., 83, 1929, pp. 27-34; Waddell, Steenbock, and Hart, Jour. Nutr., 4, 1931, pp. 53-65; Krauss and Washburn, Ohio Bul. 532.

16. Kemmerer and Todd, Jour. Biol. Chem., 1931, p. 317.

17. Maynard, Cornell Veterinarian, 19, 1929, pp. 125-138; Associates of Rogers, Fundamentals of Dairy Science, 2nd Ed., pp. 584-587.

18. Krauss and Hunt, Ohio Buls. 470, 516; Donelson and Macy, Jour. Nutr., 7, 1934, pp. 231-249.

19. Hart, Certified Milk, 6, 1932, No. 65, pp. 5-6; 6, 1932, No. 66, pp. 8-9.

20. For detailed information on this subject and on the chemical changes occurring in muscles during work, see the recent texts on biochemistry and physiology.

21. Gruber, Ztschr. Biol. 38, 1891, p. 466; see also, Lewis, Hewlett, and Barnett, Proc. Soc. Exptl. Biol. Med., 22, 1925, pp. 537-538.

22. Miller, Cal. Rpt. 1930; Snell, La. Rpt. 1929-31; Joseph, Jour. Agr. Res., 33, 1926, pp. 1073-89.

23. Wilson, Am. Soc. Anim. Prod., Proc. 1930.

24. Weber, Am. Soc. Anim. Prod., Proc. 1931.

25. Esplin, Utah Bul. 240.

26. Snell, Am. Soc. Anim. Prod., Proc. 1931.

27. Spencer, Am. Soc. Anim. Prod., Proc. 1925-26, pp. 97-101; Horlacher, Ky. Rpt. 1923; Snell, La. Rpt. 1929-31; Vaughan, Joseph and Vinke, Mont. Rpt. 1929; Jones, Tex. Rpt. 1929.

28. Jones, Am. Soc. Anim. Prod., Proc. 1933, pp. 170-173.

CHAPTER IX

BALANCED RATIONS—FEEDING STANDARDS

I. Balanced Rations

252. Purpose of feeding standards.—To guide farmers in selecting properly balanced rations for their livestock, scientists have prepared *feeding standards*. These are tables stating the amounts of nutrients which, it is believed, should be provided in rations for farm animals of the various ages and classes in order to secure the best results.

Before reviewing the history of feeding standards and comparing the recommendations made by various scientists, let us compute a ration, balanced according to the recommendations of a feeding standard, to show how these aids in stock feeding are used.

253. A balanced ration for a dairy heifer.—A dairy farmer wishes to compute a balanced winter ration for a dairy heifer weighing 400 lbs., which is no longer being fed milk. He has available plenty of good red clover hay, corn grain (No. 2 grade), and oat grain. A study of the practical recommendations in Chapter XXVIII for feeding dairy heifers shows that these feeds, in proper combination, are excellent for this purpose.

The next step is to find the amounts of nutrients recommended for heifers of this age in an up-to-date feeding standard. By turning to Appendix Table III, which presents the complete Morrison feeding standards, we find that the requirements of a 400-lb. dairy heifer per head daily, according to these standards, are as follows: Dry matter, 9.0 to 10.0 lbs.; digestible protein, 0.80 to 0.90 lb.; total digestible nutrients, 6.1 to 6.6 lbs.; and nutritive ratio, 1:6.5 to 1:7.0.

These recommendations mean that a heifer of this size has a digestive tract that is sufficiently large for her to consume 9.0 to 10.0 lbs. of dry matter a day in her feed, and that her ration should supply 0.80 to 0.90 lb. of digestible protein and 6.1 to 6.6 lbs. of total digestible nutrients. To be balanced properly, the ration should have a nutritive ratio between 1:6.5 and 1:7.0. In other words, there should be in the ration 1 lb. of digestible protein to each 6.5 to 7.0 lbs. of other digestible nutrients (including fat multiplied by 2.25). (**73**)

A range is indicated in the recommendations of the Morrison standards in recognition of the fact that feeding standards can only be approximate guides. They are thus very different from the exact figures in the multiplication table. As has been pointed out in the previous chapters, individual lots of the same kind of feed may differ very appreciably in chemical composition and in feeding value. Also, individual animals differ in ability to digest and use feeds. (**105-109**)

In general, a ration made up of suitable feeds will be satisfactory, if the amounts of dry matter and of digestible nutrients fall within the limits set in the standard for that particular animal.

For those desiring to compute rations according to the net energy system, the standards also give recommendations of the amounts of net energy, expressed in therms, for the various classes of stock. In this discussion, we will consider only the working out of a ration which is balanced according to the recommendations for dry matter, digestible protein, total digestible nutrients, and nutritive ratio, as this is the method most commonly used in America.

254. Computing the ration.—Before proceeding to compute a balanced ration, one should first write down in tabular form the requirements for the particular animal, as in the table on this page.

Let us next see how nearly a ration of only clover hay would come to meeting the requirements for this heifer. Appendix Table I shows that red clover hay of average quality (Clover hay, red, all analyses) supplies 88.2 per cent of dry matter, 7.0 per cent of digestible protein, and 51.9 per cent of total digestible nutrients. According to the standard, the heifer should receive 6.1 to 6.6 lbs. of total digestible nutrients a day. As we desire the heifer to make excellent growth, we will feed her a ration that will supply at least 6.5 lbs. of total digestible nutrients.

Since each pound of hay furnishes 0.519 lb. of total digestible nutrients, the amount of hay needed to provide approximately this amount of total digestible nutrients can be found by dividing 6.5 lbs. by 0.519 lb., which gives a result of 12.5 lbs. This amount of hay would furnish the amounts of dry matter and digestible nutrients shown in the table:

First trial ration for 400-lb. dairy heifer

	Dry matter	Digestible protein	Total digestible nutrients	Nutritive ratio
	Lbs.	Lb.	Lbs.	1:
Requirements	9.0-10.0	0.80-0.90	6.1-6.6	6.5-7.0
Red clover hay, 12.5 lbs...........	11.03	0.88	6.49	6.4

This ration supplies sufficient digestible protein and total digestible nutrients for the heifer, but it is too high in dry matter. This means that the ration is too bulky and that it is too low in digestible nutrients per pound of dry matter. In other words, the heifer will not be able to eat sufficient hay to meet fully her need for total digestible nutrients. To make the ration satisfactory it is therefore necessary to replace part of the hay by grain or other concentrates.

In the discussion of "Feeding heifers from 6 to 12 months of age" in Chapter XXVIII, it is stated, "The amount of concentrates required will depend on the quality of roughage fed. With good roughage 2 to 3 lbs. of concentrates per head daily should be enough, while with that of only fair quality 4 or 5 lbs. may be needed to keep the heifers gaining properly."

A mixture of equal parts, by weight, of corn and oats is excellent for dairy heifers, when fed with plenty of legume hay. Therefore let us see if the requirements will be met fully if we use 3 lbs. of a mixture of one-half corn and one-half oats, and reduce the amount of hay so that the amount of total digestible nutrients will be approximately the same as before. This will make possible the reducing of the hay allowance to 8 lbs. a day. The ration will then provide the following:

Balanced ration for 400-lb. dairy heifer

	Dry matter	Digestible protein	Total digestible nutrients	Nutritive ratio
	Lbs.	Lb.	Lbs.	1:
Requirements	9.0-10.0	0.80-0.90	6.1-6.6	6.5-7.0
Red clover hay, 8 lbs..............	7.06	0.56	4.15	
Corn, No. 2, 1.5 lbs................	1.28	0.11	1.21	
Oats, 1.5 lbs.......................	1.37	0.14	1.07	
Total.......................	9.71	0.81	6.43	6.9

This ration comes within the limits set in the standard in all particulars, and is therefore balanced. It will be noted that the amount of protein in the ration is but slightly above the minimum of the standard. Those who believe in supplying growing animals with an abundance of protein might therefore prefer to substitute a small amount of some protein-rich concentrate, such as wheat bran, linseed meal, cottonseed meal, etc., for a part of the corn and oats. However, this is not necessary for satisfactory results, as is pointed out in Chapter XXVIII.

255. A balanced ration with roughage lower in protein.—If good legume hay had not been used as the only roughage or at least as the chief roughage for this heifer, it would have been necessary to use some protein supplement to balance the ration. Let us suppose, for example, that the heifer is to be fed mixed clover and timothy hay, containing 30 to 50 per cent clover, as the only roughage. (Appendix Table I. Clover and timothy hay, 30 to 50 per cent clover.) If we feed 8 lbs. of this hay with the same amounts of corn and oats as in the preceding ration, we will have the following:

Ration too low in protein for 400-lb. heifer

	Dry matter	Digestible protein	Total digestible nutrients	Nutritive ratio
	Lbs.	Lb.	Lbs.	1:
Requirements	9.0-10.0	0.80-0.90	6.1-6.6	6.5-7.0
Mixed clover and timothy hay, 8.0 lbs.	7.35	0.38	4.11	
Corn, No. 2, 1.5 lbs................	1.28	0.11	1.21	
Oats, 1.5 lbs.......................	1.37	0.14	1.07	
Total.......................	10.00	0.63	6.39	9.1

This ration falls considerably under the requirements in amount of digestible protein, furnishing only 0.63 lb. of digestible protein and having a nutritive ratio of 1:9.1. Therefore let us replace some of the corn-and-oats mixture with linseed meal (33 to 37 per cent protein grade).

The next step is to find how much of the corn-oats mixture must be replaced with linseed meal. The preceding ration supplies only 0.63 lb. digestible protein, while 0.80 to 0.90 lb. is recommended.

An Unsatisfactory and Expensive "Balanced" Ration

This ration of 20 lbs. ordinary-quality timothy hay, 3 lbs. ground corn, 2 lbs. ground oats, 3 lbs. wheat bran, and 3.5 lbs. linseed meal, meets the standard for a 1,200-lb. cow yielding 30 lbs. of 3.5 per cent milk. However, timothy hay of ordinary quality is a poor roughage for dairy cows, and also the ration is expensive, due to the large amount of costly protein-rich concentrates needed. Cost, 30.2 cents. (From Wisconsin Station.)

A Ration Which Is Good, but Lacks Succulence

This ration of 24 lbs. red clover hay, 3 lbs. ground corn, 2.5 lbs. ground oats, and 2 lbs. wheat bran furnishes no more nutrients than the previous one, but it will produce more milk, because clover is far superior to ordinary timothy hay as a roughage. Cost, 26.6 cents. (From Wisconsin Station.)

An Excellent and Economical Ration for Milk Production

This ration of 12 lbs. red clover hay, 36 lbs. corn silage, 3 lbs. ground corn, 1.5 lbs. wheat bran, and 2.25 lbs. cottonseed meal is far superior to the two previous ones, for the feeds are all palatable and suitable for dairy cows, and the silage provides succulence. Cost only 25.9 cents, over 4 cents less than the first ration. (From Wisconsin Station.)

PIGS FED AN EFFICIENT BALANCED RATION

This lot of pigs received barley supplemented by whey. They were carried in dry lot, without pasture, from an initial weight of 128 lbs. to an average weight of 225 lbs., and made the most excellent gain of 2.53 lbs. a head daily. While this ration was excellent for fattening these well-grown pigs, it would have been deficient in vitamins A and D for feeding over a long period. (From Wisconsin Station.)

PIGS FED AN INEFFICIENT BUT "BALANCED" RATION

These pigs, fed barley and wheat middlings, without pasture, were just as thrifty at the start as the lot above. However, due to the inefficiency of their ration they gained only 1.27 lbs. a head daily, or only one-half as much as the others. This ration was seriously deficient in quality of protein and in calcium, as well as lacking in vitamins A and D. (From Wisconsin Station.)

Therefore we should add 0.17 to 0.27 lb. digestible protein to the ration to balance it properly. The 3 lbs. of corn-oats mixture has a total of 0.25 lb. digestible protein, as shown by the table. (0.11 lb. + 0.14 lb. = 0.25 lbs.) Thus each pound of this mixture supplies only 0.083 lb. digestible protein.

From Appendix Table I we find that each pound of linseed meal (33 to 37 per cent protein) has 0.307 lb. digestible protein. Therefore, by substituting 1.0 lb. of such linseed meal for 1.0 lb. of the corn-oats mixture, we will increase the amount of digestible protein in the ration by 0.224 lb. This happens to be just sufficient to bring the protein content of the ration well within the limits set in the standard.

We should hence have a suitable ration, if we feed 8 lbs. of the mixed hay, 2 lbs. of the corn-oats mixture (1 lb. of corn and 1 lb. of oats), and 1 lb. of linseed meal. That this ration meets the requirements of the standard is shown in the following table:

Second balanced ration for 400-lb. dairy heifer

	Dry matter	Digestible protein	Total digestible nutrients	Nutritive ratio
	Lbs.	Lb.	Lbs.	1:
Requirements	9.0-10.0	0.80-0.90	6.1-6.6	6.5-7.0
Mixed clover and timothy hay, 8.0 lbs.	7.35	0.38	4.11	
Corn, No. 2, 1.0 lb..................	0.85	0.07	0.81	
Oats, 1.0 lb........................	0.91	0.09	0.72	
Linseed meal, 1.0 lb...............	0.91	0.31	0.78	
Total......................	10.02	0.85	6.42	6.6

If it had not happened that the proper increase in the protein content of the ration was made by substituting just 1.0 lb. of linseed meal for 1.0 lb. of the grain mixture, we could have found the exact amount required by the following method: Let us suppose that it had been necessary to make an increase of 0.34 lb. in the protein content of the ration. It would then have been necessary to substitute for an equal weight of the grain mixture, the following amount of linseed meal:

$$\frac{0.34 \text{ lb. (amount of increase in dig. protein needed)}}{0.224 \text{ lb. (amount of increase by substituting 1 lb. linseed meal)}} = 1.52 \text{ lbs. linseed meal}$$

Thus, to make an increase of about 0.34 lb. digestible protein in the ration, it would have been necessary to replace 1.5 lbs. of the corn-oats mixture with linseed meal. If such a method as this is not used, it is often necessary to try out several combinations of feeds, before one finds the proper mixture to balance the ration. Time can also often be saved by using this method of computation when the ration is either too low or too high in total digestible nutrients, and one wishes to make a certain definite change in the amount of total digestible nutrients by changing the proportion of roughage and concentrates.

256. Finding the formula for a concentrate mixture.—In the practical feeding of livestock, it is not usually necessary to compute balanced rations for the individual animals in the herd or flock. Instead, a ration is found that will provide a proper supply of nutrients for the average animal, and then the amount of concentrates or the amounts of concentrates and of roughage may be varied for the individual animals.

For example, in feeding a herd of dairy cows, the same concentrate mixture is generally used for all the cows, except perhaps for those which are exceptionally high producers. However, the amount of the concentrate mixture fed each cow should be regulated in accordance with her actual production of milk and fat.

The following example will show the manner in which one should proceed to compute the formula for a suitable concentrate mixture to make a balanced ration: Let us find a good concentrate mixture for feeding to dairy heifers, averaging 400 lbs. in weight, with the same mixed clover and timothy hay for roughage as was used in the previous example. The previous table shows that such heifers require 0.80 to 0.90 lb. digestible protein per head daily, and that 8.0 lbs. of such hay, which is about the amount that the heifers will eat a day, contain 0.38 lb. digestible protein. The concentrate mixture should therefore furnish enough protein to bring the total between 0.80 lb. and 0.90 lb. It should supply 0.42 to 0.52 lb. of digestible protein.

Since 3.0 lbs. of concentrates should be sufficient for such heifers, if they are fed good roughage, the necessary minimum percentage of digestible protein in the concentrate mixture is found by dividing 0.42 by 3.0, which gives us 14.0 per cent. This means that the concentrate mixture must furnish at least 14.0 per cent of digestible protein to balance the ration properly.

Let us now find the proportions of corn, oats, wheat bran (all analyses), and cottonseed meal (43 per cent protein grade) in a concentrate mixture that will furnish this amount of protein. We will try first a mixture of 30 lbs. corn, 30 lbs. oats, 30 lbs. wheat bran, and 10 lbs. cottonseed meal. From Appendix Table I, we find on computation that the mixture will supply the following amounts of protein:

	Digestible protein Lbs.
Corn, No. 2, 30 lbs.	2.13
Oats, 30 lbs.	2.82
Wheat bran, 30 lbs.	3.93
Cottonseed meal, 10 lbs.	3.50
In 100 lbs. of mixture	12.38

Since 100 lbs. of this mixture contain 12.38 lbs. of digestible protein, the percentage of digestible protein is 12.38 per cent. This is less than is needed in the ration. Therefore, we must increase the proportion of a protein-rich feed in the mixture and decrease the amount of another feed correspondingly.

We desire to feed as large a proportion of home-grown corn and oats as is possible. Therefore, since cottonseed meal is much richer than wheat bran in protein, we will increase the proportion of cottonseed meal and reduce the proportion of wheat bran. By trying out various combinations we find that a mixture of 30 lbs. corn, 30 lbs.

oats, 20 lbs. wheat bran, and 20 lbs. cottonseed meal will contain 14.57 per cent of digestible protein. It should therefore be satisfactory in this ration.

To check the ration, let us now find the amounts of dry matter and of digestible nutrients in 1 lb. of the concentrate mixture. This is done as follows:

Finding the composition of a concentrate mixture

	Dry matter	Digestible protein	Total digestible nutrients
	Lbs.	Lbs.	Lbs.
Corn, 30 lbs.	25.56	2.13	24.18
Oats, 30 lbs.	27.33	2.82	21.45
Wheat bran, 20 lbs.	18.12	2.62	14.04
Cottonseed meal, 20 lbs.	18.70	7.00	15.10
In 100 lbs. of mixture	89.71	14.57	74.77
In 1 lb. of mixture	0.897	0.146	0.748

Having found the composition of the concentrate mixture, we can use these figures in working out a ration, just like the figures in Appendix Table I for the various single feeding stuffs. Let us now check this ration to see whether it fully meets the nutritive requirements of 400-lb. dairy heifers. We will then have the following:

Balanced ration, using preceding concentrate mixture, for 400-lb. dairy heifers

	Dry matter	Digestible protein	Total digestible nutrients	Nutritive ratio
	Lbs.	Lb.	Lbs.	1:
Requirements	9.0-10.0	0.80-0.90	6.1-6.6	6.5-7.0
Mixed clover and timothy hay, 8.0 lbs.	7.35	0.38	4.11	
Concentrate mixture, 3.0 lbs.	2.69	0.44	2.24	
Total	10.04	0.82	6.35	6.7

This ration fully meets the requirements and will prove very satisfactory for the heifers.

257. Finding the percentage of protein needed in a mixed feed.— If one desires to use a commercial mixed feed instead of a home-prepared concentrate mixture, the question arises as to the percentage of protein needed in the mixed feed to make a balanced ration with the roughage available.

In the case of most mixed feeds on the market, while the percentage of total protein is guaranteed, the percentage of digestible protein in the feed is not stated. Therefore it is necessary to find the approximate percentage of total protein required in the mixed feed to make a balanced ration with the roughage that is to be fed. This can be done as follows:

First, the percentage of digestible protein that is required in the mixed feed is found, as in the preceding example. In this example we found that 3.0 lbs. of the concentrate mixture should supply at least 0.42 lb. of digestible protein, and that therefore the concentrate mixture should contain at least 14.0 per cent of digestible protein.

In most good mixed dairy feeds from 75 to 80 per cent of the total protein is digestible. On this basis the necessary percentage of total protein in a mixed feed may be found by dividing 14.0 per cent by .75 and by .80. This gives us a result of 18.7 per cent to 17.5 per cent, which means that a good-quality mixed feed which supplies 14.0 per cent digestible protein will contain about 17.5 to 18.7 per cent total protein.

Therefore 3 lbs. of a good 18 per cent dairy feed, fed with 8 lbs. of such mixed clover and timothy hay as was used in the preceding example, will make a satisfactory ration for 400-lb. dairy heifers.

258. Guides in selecting efficient balanced rations.—Before attempting to compute economical balanced rations for any class of stock, it is important to read the explanations and general hints in the following paragraphs and in the next chapter. Also, one should study the information given in Part III on making up efficient rations for that particular class of stock. It is impossible to compute satisfactory and economical rations if reliance is placed only on the amounts of nutrients recommended in feeding standards.

As a guide to students and stockmen alike, the author has computed example balanced rations for the different classes of stock, which are adapted to various conditions. These rations are given in Appendix Table VII.

Often one will be able to find among these suggestions a ration that will exactly meet his particular conditions. Even when the feeds that are available differ somewhat from those included in these suggested rations, they will serve as convenient guides and will save much time in computation.

259. Proportions of concentrates and roughages.—Unless a person is experienced in stock feeding, he may not know what proportions or amounts of roughages and concentrates should be included in rations for any particular class of stock. It has been pointed out in the previous chapters that the proportions of concentrates and roughages in the ration should be regulated according to the kind and class of animal to be fed and the results sought.

For example, mature, idle horses may be maintained on roughage alone, if it is of fairly-good quality. On the other hand, work horses must receive considerable concentrates, and the proportion of concentrates will depend on the amount of work performed.

As has already been shown in this chapter, the amounts of dry matter and of total digestible nutrients recommended in a feeding standard for a particular class of stock furnish a guide to the proper proportion of roughages and concentrates in the ration. When the requirement of digestible nutrients or of net energy is high compared with the total amount of dry matter advised, the proportion of concentrates in the ration must be large to meet the standard. On the other hand, for the mere maintenance of horses, cattle, or sheep the standards call for much less digestible nutrients or net energy in comparison with the amount of total dry matter. This is because these animals can be maintained largely or entirely on roughage.

In Appendix Table III there will be found, immediately previous to the Morrison feeding standards, a set of convenient guides which shows the approximate proportions of roughages and concentrates required by the various classes of stock. By referring to these data, much time can often be saved in computing balanced rations for the different kinds of farm animals.

II. GENERAL REQUIREMENTS FOR SATISFACTORY RATIONS

260. Feeding standards only approximate guides.—It has been shown in Chapter IV that average figures for the composition of any feeding stuff are only approximately correct when applied to any particular lot of the feed. **(105)** Because of the various factors there discussed, which affect the composition and nutritive value, there may be considerable difference in the feeding value of two different lots of the same kind of feed. Such differences are apt to be greater in the case of roughages than with concentrates.

It has also been pointed out in Chapter IV that individual animals may differ somewhat in their ability to digest and utilize their feed. These facts must be taken into consideration in the preparation of feeding standards. The recommendations should be such that a sufficient margin of safety is provided to cover the usual variations in the composition of feeds and the differences in the individual animals to be fed. It should be borne in mind that tables of digestible nutrients, such as Appendix Table I of this volume, and also feeding standards, are averages and approximations.

The amounts of digestible protein stated in the standards are the minimum amounts recommended for efficient results. If protein-rich feeds are cheaper than those low in protein, it is usually economical to furnish a greater amount of protein than is called for by the standards. It is shown in Chapter VI that any ordinary excess of protein will not be injurious to farm animals. **(141)**

On the other hand, if protein-rich feeds are unusually high in price, in comparison with carbonaceous feeds, it may be economical to feed a ration containing somewhat less protein than is advised in the standards. However, it is rarely wise to depart far from the recommendations.

261. Quality of protein.—The recommendations in feeding standards concerning the amounts of digestible protein that should be fed the various classes of stock are made on the assumption that protein of average quality will be furnished by the ration. It has been emphasized in Chapter VI that the *quality* or *kind* of protein in a ration may be fully as important as the *amount*. In order to secure satisfactory results from livestock, it is therefore necessary to give due attention to the quality of protein in their rations. This is of especial importance in the feeding of swine and poultry and in raising dairy calves on milk substitutes.

Information on the quality of the protein in various feeds is presented in Chapter VI and in the detailed discussions of the individual feeds in Part II. Full consideration has been given to the importance of proper quality of protein in the rations suggested for the various classes of stock in Appendix Table VII and in the respective chapters of Part III.

262. Minerals and vitamins not included in feeding standards.—The various feeding standards make recommendations only in regard to the amounts the ration should furnish of dry matter, of digestible protein, and of total digestible nutrients or net energy. It has been emphasized in previous chapters that for health and for efficient production, it is just as necessary that farm animals receive an adequate supply of vitamins and minerals as that their rations be properly balanced in protein. While it is not yet possible to state the requirements of most classes of stock for vitamins and minerals in the set mathematical terms of a feeding standard, these substances must be given full consideration.

Detailed information concerning minerals and vitamins has been given in Chapter VI, and further data concerning the requirements of each class of stock will be found in Part III. In order to select rations that will amply meet the needs of livestock for minerals and for vitamins, it is necessary to have this information fully in mind.

263. Suitability of feeds; palatability.—The feeds selected for any animal should be such that they will not injure its health or the quality of the product yielded. Feeds which are suited to one class of farm animals may not be adapted to others. Again, a given feed may give satisfactory results when combined with certain feeds, yet in other combinations it may prove unsatisfactory. This matter has already been discussed in some detail in Chapter III. (69) One can readily learn whether any particular feed is suitable for a given class of stock by consulting the index to find the pages where detailed information is given on the subject.

The palatability of the ration is an important factor in feeding livestock for production, as has already been emphasized. (66) The wise farmer will utilize feeds of low palatability chiefly for animals which are being merely maintained, and will feed growing and fattening animals, milk cows, and horses at hard work rations made up, for the most part at least, of well-liked feeds.

Some concentrates, such as malt sprouts and dried distillers' grains, which may not be relished when fed alone, are entirely satisfactory if used in mixture with other better-liked feeds. Similarly, if such low-grade roughage as straw is combined with good hay that provides plenty of vitamins, a limited amount can be fed satisfactorily to dairy cows or to fattening cattle and sheep. In Europe such roughage is often chopped and mixed with the concentrates, the mass then being moistened and allowed to stand for a few hours, until the roughage becomes softer and more palatable.

Livestock will usually yield the maximum of product only on rations made up entirely or chiefly of palatable feeds. However, it should be borne in mind that an important function of our farm animals is to convert into useful products materials that would otherwise be wasted.

264. Cost of the ration.—The most important factor of all, for the farmer who must depend on the profits from his stock for his income, is the cost of the ration. In securing a ration which provides the nutrients called for by the standards and meets the other conditions previously discussed lies a great opportunity for exercising foresight and business judgment on every farm where animals are fed.

The wise farmer-stockman will consider the nutrient requirements of his animals in planning his crop rotations. Through the use of farm-grown grain, legume hay, and such cheap succulence as silage from corn or the soghums, it is possible in most sections of the country to go far toward solving the problem of providing a well-balanced, economical ration.

Simple methods of determining which feeds are most economical to use in making up balanced rations for the various classes of stock are described in the following chapter.

III. EARLY FEEDING STANDARDS

At the beginning of the last century almost nothing was known concerning the chemistry of plants and animals. The farmer then gave his livestock hay and grain without knowing what there was in this feed that nourished them. But science soon permeated every line of human activity, and agriculture was benefited along with the rest. Davy, Liebig, Boussingault, Henneberg, Wolff, Lawes and Gilbert, and other great scientists were early laying the foundations for a rational agricultural practice based on chemistry.

265. Hay equivalents.—The first attempt to express the relative value of different feeding stuffs in a systematic manner was by Thaer of Germany, who in 1810 published a table of hay equivalents with meadow hay as the standard.[1] For example, in this table, 91 lbs. of clover hay, 200 lbs. of potatoes, or 625 lbs. of mangels were considered equal to 100 lbs. of meadow hay in feeding value. Naturally, opinions on feed values varied, and so there were about as many tables of hay equivalents as there were writers on the subject.

266. The first feeding standard.—Chemistry having paved the way, Grouven in 1859 proposed the first feeding standard for farm animals, based on the crude protein, carbohydrates, and fat in feeding stuffs.[2] This, however, was imperfect, since it was based on the total instead of the digestible nutrients.

267. The Wolff feeding standards.—In 1864 Wolff, a German scientist, presented the first table of feeding standards based on the digestible nutrients in feeds.[3] These set forth the amounts of digestible crude protein, carbohydrates, and fat required daily by the different classes of farm animals. The Wolff standards were brought to the attention of American farmers 10 years later and their value and importance were soon recognized. With their adoption came the first wide-spread effort toward the rational feeding of farm animals.

268. The Wolff-Lehmann feeding standards.—In 1896 the Wolff standards were somewhat modified by another German scientist, Lehmann, as further scientific facts were then available regarding the nutrient requirements of livestock.[4] These standards, known as the Wolff-Lehmann feeding standards, were widely used for many years in Europe and also in America in computing balanced rations for livestock, but have now been superseded by more accurate, modern standards. It should be noted, in particular, that these standards recommended considerably more protein than later investigations have shown to be necessary.

The Wolff-Lehmann standards have been given in full in previous editions of this book. They are omitted from this edition, as they are now only of historical interest. To show the form in which these standards were presented, the daily requirements of a dairy cow, yielding 22 lbs. of milk, were as follows per 1,000 lbs. live weight: Dry matter, 29 lbs.; digestible crude protein, 2.5 lbs.; digestible carbohydrates, 13.0 lbs.; digestible fat, 0.5 lb.; nutritive ratio, 1:5.7.

It is of interest to note that in these standards the amounts of nutrients recommended for dairy cows depended only on the amount of milk produced. No consideration was given to the fact that more nutrients are required to produce a pound of milk rich in fat than for a pound of milk low in fat. Also, it will be observed that in these standards separate recommendations were made not only for digestible protein, but also for digestible carbohydrates and for digestible fat. Balancing rations according to these standards therefore required more computation than when the modern and more simple method is used in which the requirements are stated in terms of digestible protein and of total digestible nutrients.

IV. LATER FEEDING STANDARDS

269. Standards based on net energy or starch values.—The net energy method of measuring the nutritive values of feeding stuffs and rations has been explained in Chapter III. Also a full discussion has been presented of the advantages and disadvantages of this system in comparison with the system based on digestible nutrients. **(81-94)**

In the method developed by Armsby the net energy values of feeds are expressed in *therms of net energy*. On the other hand, in the Kellner starch-value system, which is also explained in Chapter III, the productive values of feeds, which are net energy values, are expressed in *pounds of starch value*. **(95)**

In 1907 Kellner formulated feeding standards in which the recommendations were stated in terms of dry matter, of digestible true protein (not digestible crude protein), and of starch value.[5] For example, his standard for maintaining a mature steer calls for 15 to 21 lbs. dry matter, 0.6 to 0.8 lb. digestible true protein, and 6.0 lbs. starch value.

The Kellner starch values and feeding standards have been widely used in Europe, especially in Germany and in Great Britain, but were never employed to any large extent in the United States.

Somewhat later Armsby presented feeding standards expressed in terms of digestible true protein and of therms of net energy.[6] In 1917 these standards were amplified and revised in his book, The Nutrition of Farm Animals.[7] In the United States the Armsby standards have usually been employed instead of the Kellner standards by those desiring to compute rations according to the net energy system.

It should be pointed out that in both the Kellner standards and the Armsby standards the amounts of protein recommended were stated in terms of digestible true protein, instead of digestible protein (digestible crude protein). These standards did not therefore credit the simpler nitrogenous substances in feeds with any value as a substitute for proteins. This point of view has now generally been discarded, as has been mentioned previously. (18) It is therefore much preferable to express the protein requirements of animals in terms of digestible protein (digestible crude protein), as is done in most of the more recent feeding standards.

In the Armsby standards no recommendations were made concerning the amounts of dry matter to be included in the rations for the various classes of stock. Therefore, in computing rations according to these standards, it was necessary to rely, not on the standards, but on one's general information, in deciding on how many pounds of dry matter an animal could consume and in determining the proper proportion of roughage and of concentrates to include in the ration.

Recently Fraps has presented feeding standards expressed in terms of dry matter, digestible crude protein, and productive value, stated in therms of net energy.[8] These productive values are thus given in the same terms as Armsby's net energy values.

These net energy standards are not presented in this volume, but instead there is included in the revised Morrison standards (Appendix Table III) an additional column showing the amounts of net energy, expressed in therms, which are advised for the various classes of stock. Those desiring to compute rations according to the net energy system can readily use this column of figures instead of the column showing the amounts of total digestible nutrients advised.

In using these net energy standards for the computation of rations, the same general method is followed that has been described in the first part of this chapter. However, instead of using the values for total digestible nutrients, given in Appendix Table I, the net energy values of the various feeds are employed, which are given in Appendix Table II.

270. Standards based on Scandinavian feed units.—The feed-unit system of measuring the relative values of different feeds, which is used extensively in the Scandinavian countries, has been explained in Chapter III. (96) It has there been pointed out that in this system protein-rich feeds are given somewhat higher values than those which are lower in protein content, but which furnish approximately the same amounts of total digestible nutrients or of net energy.

The feed-unit values are therefore not true expressions of net energy. However, they are convenient measures of the approximate values of different feeds under the conditions in the Scandinavian countries, where the farm-raised feeds do not usually supply sufficient protein for well-balanced rations.

Hansson prepared feeding standards, based on the feed-unit system, for the various classes of farm animals, in which the recommendations are stated in terms of dry matter, digestible true protein, and feed units.[9] Slightly different standards have been widely used in Denmark, especially for dairy cows.

These feeding standards and the feed-unit method of valuing feeds have never been used to any appreciable extent in the United States, for the reasons mentioned in Chapter III.

271. Standards for dairy cows.—Several different feeding standards have been formulated for dairy cows, based either on digestible nutrients or on net energy values. These standards are explained in Chapter XXIV, and comparisons are there given of the recommendations made in the various standards.

It is of especial interest to note that Haecker of the Minnesota Station was apparently the first to recognize in feeding standards for dairy cows the fundamental fact that the amount of nutrients a cow requires depends not only on the amount of milk she produces, but also on its richness in fat.[10]

272. Special standards for certain other classes of stock.—Special standards have also been prepared by various scientists for certain other classes of stock. The more important of these are mentioned in the chapters of Part III which consider the nutrient requirements of each class of stock. These standards include the Zuntz standards for horses, the Eckles-Gullickson standards for dairy heifers, the Bull-Emmett standards for fattening lambs, and the Evvard standards for swine.

273. The Morrison feeding standards.—Until 1915 the old Wolff-Lehmann feeding standards were employed more commonly in the United States than any others, except for dairy cows. In computing rations for milk production these German standards had then been largely replaced by the more accurate American standards, especially by the Haecker standards, the Savage standards, and the Eckles standards. For other classes of stock the Wolff-Lehmann standards were commonly used, in spite of the facts that they advised larger amounts of protein than necessary and were not well adapted to American conditions.

At this time the need for modern standards for the various classes of stock was deeply impressed upon the author of this volume. He found that certain companies which fattened annually thousands of cattle and sheep were carefully computing rations according to these out-of-date standards. In order to balance the rations according to these standards they were spending large sums of money for entirely unnecessary amounts of protein supplements, thus considerably reducing their profits.

Neither the Kellner nor the Armsby feeding standards had been widely adopted in this country, for instructors and farmers seemed to prefer standards based on digestible nutrients instead of energy values. The author therefore endeavored to combine in one set of standards what seemed in his judgment to be the best guides available in the computation of rations for the various classes of stock. These standards were first presented in the fifteenth edition of Feeds and Feeding, published in 1915, and were then called the "Modified Wolff-Lehmann Standards."

To lessen the work of computing rations, the standards were expressed in terms of dry matter, digestible protein, and total digestible nutrients, instead of giving separate recommendations for digestible carbohydrates and for digestible fat, as in the Wolff-Lehmann standards. Also, since it was realized fully that feeding standards were only approximate and that they were not exact expressions of nutritive requirements, a range was given in the amounts of nutrients recommended.

Since the standards for most classes of stock were considerably different from the old Wolff-Lehmann standards, they have more recently been called the Morrison feeding standards. From time to time certain changes have been made in the standards, as additional information has been gained concerning the nutrient requirements of the various classes of stock.

274. Revised Morrison feeding standards.—Extensive changes have been made in the standards presented in Appendix Table III of this edition of Feeds and Feeding in order to incorporate the results of recent investigations. Also, a change has been made in the manner in which the recommendations are presented.

Previously the standards have shown the requirements of the various classes of animals *daily per 1,000 lbs. live weight.* To find the requirements for a particular animal of any other live weight, computation has been required. In order to save time in computing rations, the revised standards state the amounts of dry matter and of digestible nutrients required *per head daily* by animals of the various weights. For the use of those desiring to use net energy values instead of total digestible nutrients in the computation of rations, a column has been added to these revised standards which states the net energy requirements, expressed in therms.

The chief sources of the recommendations made in the standards are stated in the explanatory paragraphs which precede the standards in Appendix Table III.

275. Computing rations according to the Morrison standards.— The method of computing rations based on the digestible nutrient recommendations in the Morrison standards has been fully described in the first part of this chapter. In computing rations according to total digestible nutrients, one should entirely disregard the net energy values which are given in the last column of figures in Appendix Table III. He should base his computations solely on the recommendations given for dry matter, digestible protein, total digestible nutrients, and nutritive ratio, and should consult Appendix Table I to find the corresponding composition of the various feeding stuffs.

On the other hand, if one desires to compute rations according to the net energy system, he should disregard the columns giving the total digestible nutrients and nutritive ratios, and should use instead the net energy values shown in the last column of figures. The net energy values of the most important feeds, for use in this method of computing rations, are stated in Appendix Table II. This table also gives the percentages of dry matter and of digestible protein in these feeds. As has been emphasized in Chapter III, the net energy values given in this table are approximate values, which have been computed by the author from the limited data available. (**94**)

Except for the difference in the figures used, the method of computing a ration according to the net energy system is the same as when total digestible nutrients are used. It is therefore not necessary to present an example of the use of this method.

QUESTIONS

1. What are feeding standards?
2. Compute a ration for a 1,400-lb. horse at medium work according to the Morrison feeding standards. In this and the following problem use feeds available in your locality and find the cost of the ration.
3. Compute a ration according to the Morrison feeding standards for 1,200-lb. dairy cows producing an average of 40 lbs. of milk containing 3.5 per cent fat daily. Determine first the necessary percentage of digestible protein in the concentrate mixture to feed with the roughages you select, using the method shown in Article 256. Then work out a formula for a satisfactory concentrate mixture, containing this percentage of digestible protein. Finally, compute the dry matter, the digestible protein, the total digestible nutrients, and the nutritive ratio of the entire ration, to see whether or not it meets the requirements.
4. If you wished to use a good commercial dairy feed for these cows, approximately what percentage of total protein should it contain?
5. What guide do the Morrison feeding standards furnish as to the proper proportion of roughages and concentrates for a particular class of stock?
6. What factors not included in the recommendations of feeding standards must be considered in computing efficient rations for stock?
7. Why have the Wolff-Lehmann feeding standards been superseded by other feeding standards?
8. In what terms are the nutrient requirements expressed in the Armsby feeding standards; in the Kellner feeding standards?
9. What important advance did Haecker make in feeding standards for dairy cows?
10. In what terms are the nutrient requirements of livestock expressed in the Morrison feeding standards?
11. Why is a range indicated in the recommendations given in these standards for each class of stock, instead of only one figure being given for dry matter, digestible protein, and total digestible nutrients, respectively?

REFERENCES

1. Thaer, Landwirtschaft, new ed., 1880, p. 211.
2. Agricultur-Chemie, 1859, p. 603.
3. Mentzel and von Lengerke Agricultural Calendar, 1864.
4. Mentzel and von Lengerke Agricultural Calendars, 1896-1906.
5. Kellner, Ernährung landw. Nutztiere, 9th ed., pp. 650-651.
6. Armsby, U. S. Dept. Agr., Bur. Anim. Indus., Buls. 51, 74, 101; Farmers' Bul. 346.
7. Armsby, The Nutrition of Farm Animals, pp. 711-714.
8. Fraps, Tex. Bul. 461.
9. Hansson, Utfodringslära, 1916, pp. 707-709.
10. Haecker, Minn. Buls. 71, 79, 140.

CHAPTER X

ECONOMY IN FEEDING LIVESTOCK

I. Selecting Economical Rations

276. Providing efficient rations at minimum expense.—In order to secure the largest returns from his farm animals the stockman must, first of all, thoroughly understand the fundamental nutrient requirements of the various classes of livestock, which have been discussed in the preceding chapters. He must next study the possibilities of his farm for the production of crops, paying attention both to the probable yields and to the value of the various crops for feeding to stock or for sale. It is also necessary to consider the feeding value of the many feeds on the market and compare the prices at which they can be secured.

With this knowledge he is in a position to plan his rotations so that from the crops raised, supplemented when economical by purchased feeds, efficient rations for his stock may be provided at minimum expense. As a rule it will be found wise to raise all needed roughage on the farm. On the other hand, it is often economical to sell more or less of the farm-grown grains and replace them with purchased protein-rich concentrates which economically supplement the farm-grown feeds.

277. Market prices often not a guide to feeding values.—On studying the market prices of the different available feeds, it will often be found that the market prices are no index to the relative values of certain feeds. For example, one year there may be a short oat crop in this country, but a good crop of corn. This will make oats unusually expensive in comparison with corn. The next year the conditions may be reversed, and oats will then be an economical feed. Similarly, the relative prices of the various protein supplements vary considerably from year to year, and sometimes there are wide changes in the relative prices of feeds even during a single year.

To secure the maximum net returns from livestock, it is necessary to give careful attention to the changes in feed prices. One should not get into the habit of feeding the same combination of feeds year after year, regardless of whether these feeds are cheap or costly. Whenever feed prices change decidedly, the wise stockman will make whatever changes are necessary in his rations to take advantage of the new conditions.

Experiments have shown that there is no one best ration for any class of stock. It is therefore possible to increase the net returns by carefully selecting each season the particular combination of feeds that will make a well-balanced, efficient ration at the minimum cost. To aid stockmen in selecting balanced rations that will be economical under different conditions, there are presented in Appendix Table VII a considerable number of balanced rations for the various classes of animals. Any one of these should give excellent results when composed of good-quality feeds and fed to thrifty animals. Many additional suggestions will be found in the chapters of Part III.

By figuring out the cost of those rations or concentrate mixtures that seem adapted to the local conditions, one can readily determine which will be most economical.

278. Determining which feeds are actually cheap.—The amounts of total digestible nutrients (or net energy) and the amounts of digestible protein contained in various feeds provide general information concerning their values. Methods of determining the relative economy of feeds based on digestible nutrients are explained in paragraphs which follow.

In using such a method, it must be borne in mind, however, that tables of digestible nutrients or of net energy supply information concerning only a part of the factors that determine the actual relative values of different feeds for any particular class of stock. Numerous experiments have proved that there are marked differences in the values of the same feed for the various classes of animals. Such differences may not be shown at all by the amounts of digestible nutrients the feed supplies.

These differences may be due to several factors: One class of stock may have a much greater need than another class for vitamins or minerals that the particular feed furnishes. For example, a limited amount of choice alfalfa or other legume hay has an especially high value, not measured by its content of digestible nutrients, as a source of vitamins A and D in the winter feeding of pigs in the northern states. Similarly, excellent hay is nearly indispensable in the raising of dairy calves. On the other hand, idle horses and beef breeding cows can be wintered successfully on roughage of rather inferior quality. Another example is the fact that dairy by-products have an unusually high value for poultry on account of their richness in vitamin G.

Protein of high quality is of especial importance for swine, for poultry, and for dairy calves being raised on milk substitutes. Therefore feeds that furnish protein of excellent quality, such as meat scraps, tankage, and fish meal, have a much higher relative value for these animals than for other classes of stock.

Other differences in the relative values of a feed for various animals may be due to certain factors concerning which we have but little definite information. For example, ground barley is equal to ground corn for dairy cows, but for fattening cattle, sheep, or pigs it is worth appreciably less per ton than corn. Wheat is fully equal to corn for pigs and for fattening cattle, but it is worth only about 83 to 85 per cent as much as corn for fattening lambs. Oats have a much higher relative value for horses and for dairy cows than they do for fattening cattle or sheep, and especially for pigs.

For dairy cows and for fattening lambs, cottonseed meal is equal to linseed meal when fed in a suitable ration. On the other hand, for fattening cattle it is generally worth much less per ton than linseed meal when used as the only protein supplement. Soybeans are an excellent supplement for dairy cows, beef cattle, or sheep, but are not entirely satisfactory as the only protein supplement for pigs. They also tend to produce soft pork.

Such facts as these have convinced the author that by far the best guides to the relative values of different feeds for any particular class of stock are furnished by the results of the feeding experiments in which these feeds have been carefully compared. This has been emphasized previously in Chapter III. (**68-69**) Therefore in the preparation of this volume the author has spent much time in the compilation and analysis of the results of the many investigations of this kind that have been conducted by the experiment stations, particularly those in the United States.

Wherever data are available, definite statements based on these compilations are given in the respective chapters of Part III concerning the actual relative values of the different important feeds for each class of stock. By referring to the index, the pages can readily be found on which these data are presented for a particular kind of farm animal.

279. Selecting feeds on the basis of cost of total digestible nutrients.—While the results of feeding experiments are the most reliable guide in showing the relative values of different feeds for any particular class of stock, definite data of this kind are as yet available only for some of the most important feeding stuffs. For other feeds the decision as to whether they are economical or not at a given market price must be based on their content of digestible nutrients (or net energy) and also on the general information concerning their usefulness for the particular kind of animal.

In making up a balanced ration for stock we commonly base our computations primarily on the amounts of digestible protein and of total digestible nutrients (or net energy) required by the particular class of stock. It has been emphasized in previous chapters that other factors, such as quality of protein, amount of calcium or phosphorus, or vitamin content, may sometimes be just as important as the content of digestible nutrients, in determining whether or not a particular feed should be used in the ration. However, these factors cannot well be taken into consideration in feeding standards.

In most parts of the United States feeds that are rich in digestible protein generally cost more than those which are low in protein but rich in digestible carbohydrates. Under such conditions digestible protein has a greater value per pound than digestible carbohydrates, or than digestible fat multiplied by the factor 2.25 to change it to the carbohydrate equivalent.

One method of comparing the economy of various feeds that has often been used is to compute the cost per pound of total digestible nutrients in each feed. This will readily show which feeds supply total digestible nutrients at least expense. It is a correct method of comparison of the relative values of feeds when protein-rich feeds cost no more than those rich in other digestible nutrients.

However, it has very decided limitations under more usual conditions, where digestible protein is more expensive than other nutrients. This is because this method does not take into consideration the differences in the amounts of digestible protein that the various feeds supply. This lack is of particular importance when one wishes to decide which of several protein supplements is most economical for balancing a ration low in protein.

To overcome this difficulty partly, one can likewise compute for each feed the cost per pound of digestible protein. Both the cost per pound of total digestible nutrients and the cost per pound of digestible protein can then be taken into consideration in determining which protein supplements are cheapest.

Even when both these methods of comparison are used, however, one will often have difficulty in deciding which supplements are most economical. One supplement may furnish digestible protein at the least cost, while another is a cheaper source of total digestible nutrients. Considerable experience is necessary to balance one factor against the other in estimating the actual relative economy of the two feeds. To obviate this difficulty, the methods described in the following paragraphs have been devised.

280. Valuations based on both digestible protein and total digestible nutrients.—Several methods have been suggested for considering both digestible protein and total digestible nutrients (or net energy) in determining the relative values of feeds. In one method a definite money value is assigned to each pound of total digestible nutrients (or net energy) in the feed and an additional value is assigned to each pound of digestible protein the feed contains.[1] These values are determined from the price of a standard, common carbohydrate-rich feed, such as corn grain, and the price of a common protein supplement, such as cottonseed meal.

The value of any other feed is then computed by adding together the valuation for the amount of total digestible nutrients it supplies and the valuation for its content of digestible protein. Tables can be worked out on this basis which show the relative values of various feeds in comparison, for example, with corn and cottonseed meal at certain fixed prices. However, any such table can be used only so long as corn and cottonseed meal stay at approximately these set prices. The method therefore has only limited usefulness.

281. The Petersen method of valuing feeds.—Petersen of the Minnesota Station has recently devised an ingenious method which can readily be used to determine the relative values of various feeds with changing prices for the base feeds. Corn and cottonseed meal are taken as the base feeds, since corn is the most widely used carbohydrate-rich concentrate in this country and cottonseed meal the most important high-protein supplement. However, other base feeds may be similarly used in any section where corn and cottonseed meal are not important.

It is evident that whenever protein-rich feeds cost more than carbohydrate-rich feeds, as is usually the case, then the actual relative value of any other feed will depend partly on the price of the standard or base carbohydrate-rich feed and partly on the price of the base protein-rich feed. Two factors are therefore computed for each feed to be valued. One of these, called the "constant for corn," shows the extent to which the price of corn per ton affects the value of the given feed. The other factor, called the "constant for cottonseed meal," shows the extent to which the price of cottonseed meal per ton affects the value of the particular feed in question.

Constants of this kind for the most important concentrates are given in Appendix Table VIII, together with constants for certain roughages. These constants have been computed according to the Petersen method from the data for each feed in Appendix Table I. In the case of roughages or of low-grade concentrates high in fiber, the constants are modified to take into consideration the fact that each pound of total digestible nutrients in such feeds has a lower value than a pound of total digestible nutrients in a high-grade concentrate.

To illustrate the method of using these constants, let us determine the value of corn gluten feed as a source of digestible protein and of total digestible nutrients, in comparison with ground corn (Grade No. 2) at $22.00 per ton and cottonseed meal (43 per cent protein grade) at $36.00 per ton.

By referring to Appendix Table VIII, it will be seen that for corn gluten feed the "constant for corn" is 0.443 and the "constant for cottonseed meal" is 0.557. To find the value of corn gluten feed we multiply the price of corn by 0.443, the "constant for corn;" then multiply the price of cottonseed meal by 0.557, the "constant for cottonseed meal;" and finally add the products. This gives us $29.80 as the value of corn gluten feed with corn and cottonseed meal at the particular prices stated.

282. Graphs for finding the relative values of feeds.—In order to obviate the need for these computations, Petersen has also devised convenient graphs, from which the relative values of feeds can be easily read, with corn and cottonseed meal at any particular prices. Such graphs have distinct advantages over the use of the "constants." First, no computation whatsoever is required. Second, if some other protein-rich feed is decidedly cheaper than cottonseed meal, it may be taken as the standard protein-rich feed in using the graphs. Likewise, barley or one of the other small grains may be used as the standard low-protein feed, if one of these grains is cheaper or more available locally than corn.

To be used accurately, graphs of this kind must be of larger size than can be included in such a volume as this. Also, only a few feeds can be given in each graph, as otherwise the lines for various feeds would fall too close together to be legible.*

It has been pointed out previously that when protein-rich feeds cost no more or even less than those low in protein, the amount of total digestible nutrients (or net energy) should be used as the basis for determining the relative values of various feeds. To make such comparisons possible without any need for computations, graphs have also been devised from which the relative values of the important feeds can be determined at a glance, taking as a standard of comparison one of these feeds at any particular price.*

283. A comparison of corn-belt feeds for dairy cows.—To illustrate the manner in which the relative economy of different feeds may be determined by using the constants in Appendix Table VIII, let us assume that a dairyman in the corn belt has plenty of the following farm-grown grains: Shelled corn (Grade No. 2), worth 56 cents a bushel, or $20.00 a ton, on the farm; oats, worth 40 cents a bushel, or

---

*Pamphlets containing graphs for valuing the most important feeds by these methods, with directions for their use, may be obtained from the Animal Husbandry Department, Cornell University, Ithaca, New York. There is a small charge to cover the cost of publication.

$25.00 a ton; and barley, worth 50 cents a bushel, or $20.83 a ton. He wishes to feed his herd the grain which is cheapest, considering its feeding value, and sell that which is highest priced. It will cost $2 a ton to grind these grains, as should be done for dairy cows. This will bring the farm price of ground corn to $22.00 a ton; ground oats, $27.00 a ton; and ground barley, $22.83 a ton.

To balance the ration the following supplements are available on the local market: Corn gluten feed at $30.00 per ton; cottonseed meal (43 per cent protein grade), $36.00 per ton; distillers' dried corn grains, $33.00 per ton; linseed meal, $37.00 per ton; soybean oil meal (old process), $34.00 per ton; and wheat bran, $23.00 per ton. Limited amounts of these feeds can be hauled home on return trips from town without much of any additional cartage expense. It is not assumed that these prices represent average conditions in any section of this country, but they are merely taken to illustrate the manner in which the relative economy of various feeds may be compared.

We will assume that this farmer has for his cows plenty of good mixed clover and timothy hay containing one-third to one-half clover, and in addition has sufficient corn silage to feed throughout the winter. It is shown in Chapter XXIV and in Appendix Table VII that with such roughage a concentrate, or "grain," mixture containing about 14.5 per cent digestible protein or 18.0 per cent total protein will provide ample protein for good dairy cows. Let us therefore compute an economical concentrate mixture which will supply this amount of protein.

First, we will compute from the constants in Appendix Table VIII the values per ton of the various feeds, taking corn and cottonseed meal as the base feeds, or the standards of comparison. We will set these values down in tabular form, along with the market prices of the various feeds. We will then set down for each feed the amount by which its computed value per ton is greater or less than the market price. Though it is not at all necessary in the actual use of this method, we will also include in the table, in order to show certain facts, the percentages of digestible protein and total digestible nutrients in each feed. This table is given on the next page.

The table shows that ground barley is worth $22.77 per ton, with corn at $22.00 per ton and cottonseed meal at $36.00 per ton. Thus, ground barley is worth for feeding purposes within 6 cents of its market price. On the other hand, oats are worth only $21.22 per ton, which is $5.78 less than the market price. It is clear, therefore, that this dairyman should sell the oats and feed the corn and barley to his stock.

It is of interest to note that with protein-rich feeds considerably higher in price than corn, as is the case in this example, barley becomes worth slightly more per ton than corn. This is due to the following: Though barley furnishes slightly less total digestible nutrients than does corn, it has 9.3 per cent digestible protein, in comparison with only 7.1 per cent for corn. When protein is relatively high in price the value of barley will be higher, in comparison with that of corn, than when protein is cheap.

The data for the protein supplements likewise show clearly that at these particular prices soybean oil meal is by far the cheapest supplement. This is evident from the fact that its value is $5.08 per ton higher than its cost, in comparison with cottonseed meal and corn. In this example the other supplements all rank much below soybean oil meal in economy.

Comparison of the economy of various concentrates at the prices stated

	Digestible protein	Total digestible nutrients	Price per ton	Value of feed per ton	Difference per ton between price and value
	Per cent	Per cent	Dollars	Dollars	Dollars
Farm grains					
Barley, ground	9.3	78.7	22.83	22.77	— 0.06
Corn, dent, ground......	7.1	80.6	22.00	22.00	....
Oats, ground	9.4	71.5	27.00	21.22	— 5.78
Protein supplements					
Corn gluten feed........	22.7	77.4	30.00	29.80	— 0.20
Cottonseed meal (43% protein)..............	35.1	74.9	36.00	36.00	....
Distillers' dried corn grains	22.3	85.0	33.00	31.30	— 1.70
Linseed meal...........	30.6	78.2	37.00	34.29	— 2.71
Soybean oil meal........	37.7	82.2	34.00	39.08	+ 5.08
Wheat bran	13.1	70.2	23.00	22.96	— 0.04

284. Choosing an economical concentrate mixture.—With feeds at these prices the cheapest concentrate mixture can therefore be made up from proper proportions of ground corn, ground barley, and soybean oil meal. This would, however, make a much heavier mixture than most dairymen like to use. Such a mixture could be fed satisfactorily by distributing it over the silage, except perhaps in the case of very high producing cows that were receiving a large allowance of concentrates. To make the mixture much more bulky, it would be necessary to include oats, distillers' grains, or wheat bran, for these are the only decidedly bulky feeds in the list. Of these, wheat bran is the most economical, for its value, merely on the basis of the nutrients it supplies, comes the closest to its market price.

We will therefore find the proportions of ground corn, ground barley, soybean oil meal, and wheat bran that will give us a concentrate mixture containing 14.5 per cent digestible protein. Let us assume that the dairyman has about twice as much corn to feed his cows as he has of barley. A little figuring will show us that the formula shown in the following table will make up an exceedingly economical concentrate mixture under these particular conditions.

An economical concentrate mixture with feeds at the prices stated

	Digestible protein Lbs.	Total digestible nutrients Lbs.	Cost Dollars
Ground corn, 450 lbs...............................	32.0	362.7	4.95
Ground barley, 200 lbs............................	18.6	157.4	2.28
Soybean oil meal, 200 lbs.........................	75.4	184.4	3.40
Wheat bran, 150 lbs..............................	19.7	105.3	1.73
Total in 1,000 lbs.............................145.7		809.8	12.36
In 100 lbs..................................... 14.6		81.0	1.24

This mixture supplies 14.6 lbs. digestible protein per 100 lbs., or 14.6 per cent. It costs only $1.24 per 100 lbs., or $24.80 per ton, and is one of the most economical mixtures containing the desired percentage of protein that can be made up with these feeds at the particular prices that have been assumed in this discussion.

Some dairymen may prefer a concentrate mixture with greater variety, or a greater number of different feeds in it. At these particular prices other feeds could not be included in the mixture without increasing the cost. However, this mixture will produce first-rate results, for all the feeds in it are excellent for dairy cows. The mixture will provide excellent quality of protein, and it will be thoroughly palatable.

285. Changing the ration to meet changed feed prices.—To show how a ration should be modified to meet changed feed prices, let us assume that the next year the prices for the same feeds used in the preceding example are as follows: The price of barley has risen from 50 cents per bushel to 65 cents, while the price of oats has declined from 40 cents per bushel to 29 cents. Corn has remained at 56 cents per bushel. Adding $2.00 per ton for grinding, as before, the prices for the ground grains will be: Ground barley, $29.08 per ton; ground oats, $20.13 per ton; and ground corn, $22.00 per ton. The prices for the protein supplements have also changed, as shown in the first column of the following table. Cottonseed meal, the base protein-rich feed, is now $34.00 per ton.

Let us now see which feeds are most economical, in comparison with corn and cottonseed meal at these prices. Using the same method as before, we will have:

Effect of changed prices on economy of various feeds

	Price of feed per ton Dollars	Value of feed per ton Dollars	Difference per ton between price and value Dollars
Farm grains			
Barley, ground	29.08	22.60	— 6.48
Corn, dent, ground	22.00	22.00	....
Oats, ground	20.13	21.00	+ 0.87
Protein supplements			
Corn gluten feed	28.50	28.68	+ 0.18
Cottonseed meal (43% protein grade).........	34.00	34.00	....
Distillers' dried corn grains.................	31.00	30.26	— 0.74
Linseed meal	32.50	32.62	+ 0.12
Soybean oil meal	38.00	36.94	— 1.06
Wheat bran	25.00	22.47	— 2.53

The rank of the various feeds in economy has changed very decidedly. Thus oats are now even more economical than corn. Barley is very expensive, as is shown by the fact that its feeding value is $6.48 less per ton than its selling price on the farm. At these prices barley should be sold, and oats and corn used for feeding. Though corn is not quite so economical as oats, some corn had best be used in the concentrate mixture, as oats are rather bulky and high in fiber to be fed as the only grain to high-producing cows.

Among the protein supplements, linseed meal, corn gluten feed, and cottonseed meal are the most economical, there being but little difference between them in this regard. Wheat bran is now an expensive source of nutrients. If there were no other bulky feed in the concentrate mixture, it might be advisable to include a little bran, merely for bulk. However, since oats are this year the cheapest grain, the concentrate mixture will contain considerable oats, and will therefore have plenty of bulk without any need of bran.

With feeds at these changed prices, an economical concentrate mixture furnishing 14.5 per cent digestible protein would be: Ground corn, 300 lbs.; ground oats, 410 lbs.; corn gluten feed, 100 lbs.; cottonseed meal, 90 lbs.; and linseed meal, 100 lbs. It will be noted that this concentrate mixture is quite different from the one suggested for the previous price conditions. However, it is likewise an excellent mixture and well adapted for feeding high-producing cows.

These two examples well show that no particular combination of feeds should be used year after year, regardless of the changes in feed prices. On the contrary, the ration should be modified whenever necessary to adapt it to changed price conditions.

286. Relative economy of feeds when protein is cheap.—In the preceding examples protein-rich feeds have been more expensive than those rich in carbohydrates. Protein has therefore had an additional value beyond the amount of total digestible nutrients it furnishes. However, this is not always the case.

For example, in the cotton belt cottonseed meal is often lower in price per ton than farm grain. Also, in the alfalfa districts of the West alfalfa hay is frequently so cheap that it supplies total digestible nutrients at much less cost than the grains or other carbohydrate-rich feeds. During the past few years, even in the northeastern states, protein-rich concentrates have occasionally been decidedly lower in price than the farm grains.

Whenever such conditions exist, the relative economy of various feeds will depend on the amounts of total digestible nutrients (or of net energy) that they furnish, and will not be affected by their content of digestible protein. It is therefore not correct under such circumstances to use the constants given in the first and second columns of figures of Appendix Table VIII in comparing the values of various feeds. Instead, one should make such comparisons on the basis of the amounts of total digestible nutrients in each feed, as shown in Appendix Table I, or on the basis of the amounts of net energy, as shown in Appendix Table II.

To facilitate comparisons of feeds on the basis of total digestible nutrients, there are given in the third column of figures in Appendix Table VIII "total digestible nutrient factors." The method of using these factors is explained in the paragraphs that precede the table.

287. Comparing the economy of various roughages.—Methods of comparing the relative values of various feeds, such as the method used in the preceding example, are much better adapted to comparisons of various concentrates than to comparisons of roughages. This is because such factors as palatability and the content of vitamins and minerals are often of great importance in determining the actual value of a roughage.

Thus a valuation on the basis of digestible nutrients, or even on the basis of net energy, may not measure at all the actual difference in feeding value between well-cured, green-colored hay and that which is weathered and bleached. The poor hay will, of course, be considerably lower in digestible nutrients and in net energy than the good hay. However, unless the stock get plenty of vitamin A from some other source, the poor hay may have a value much less than indicated by its content of digestible nutrients, due to its deficiency in this vitamin.

While comparisons of various roughages can be made by using the constants in Appendix Table VIII, it must be remembered that such a method of evaluation may have great shortcomings for these feeds. A much safer basis for valuing roughage is provided by the information presented in the respective chapters of Parts II and III, concerning the value and usefulness of the various roughages for the different classes of stock.

II. Adapting Systems of Feeding to Local Conditions

288. Amount of protein to supply.—It will be noted that in the Morrison feeding standards a range is indicated in the amounts of protein which are advised for the various classes of farm animals. When protein-rich feeds cost but little or no more than those low in protein, it is well to feed as much protein as is indicated by the higher figures. On the other hand, when corn or the other grains are relatively cheap, it may be better economy to feed no more protein than called for by the lower figures. Rarely is it advisable to feed decidedly less protein than shown in the lower figures.

Whether or not to add a protein-supplement to certain rations will depend on the relative price of such a supplement in comparison with the prices of the farm grains. For example, it is shown in Chapters XXIX and XXXII that corn and clover hay alone make a fairly well-balanced ration for fattening cattle or fattening lambs. However, the gains are usually slightly increased and a higher finish secured when a small allowance of some suitable protein supplement is added to the ration. Whether such addition will be profitable or not depends on the relative price of the supplement and on whether the market will pay an appreciably better price for the more highly-finished animal.

When protein-rich feeds supply nutrients more cheaply than those carbonaceous in character, as is often the case in the cotton belt and the alfalfa districts of the West, it will be economy to feed much more than the amounts of protein set forth in the standards. (**141**)

289. Proportion of concentrates to roughages.—To meet the recommendations of the feeding standards for milk cows and for fattening cattle and sheep, fairly liberal amounts of concentrates are required. This is because these animals need, for a high level of production, rations rich in digestible nutrients and net energy. Unless concentrates are unusually high in price in comparison with roughages, it is generally advisable to feed as large a proportion of concentrates as is called for by the feeding standards.

Young cattle and lambs cannot be made fat enough to meet the demands of the large markets on harvested roughage alone, even if it

BEEF CATTLE ON THE WESTERN RANGE

In the range districts of the West pasturage is cheap, but concentrates are high in price. Hence beef cattle are raised on the range and sold as feeders to be fattened in grain raising districts. (From *Breeder's Gazette*.)

A BEEF FARM IN NORTHEASTERN KANSAS

The bottom lands are in corn and the sloping hillsides in hay, while the broken limestone hills in the background are pastured. Here beef calves are raised and also fattened for market. (From U. S. Department of Agriculture.)

FATTENING BEEF CATTLE ON GRASS IN THE CORN BELT

On high-priced land, with few acres unsuited for tillage, the stockman has generally found it more profitable to fatten feeder cattle brought from the ranges than to raise his own feeders.

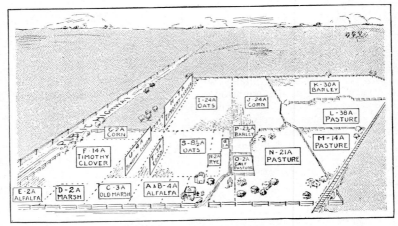

A Poorly Planned Farm

This dairy farm was poorly arranged for economical cultivation, for it was cut up into many fields, irregular in size and shape. There was no well-planned rotation system, and but little legume hay was grown. (From Wisconsin Station.)

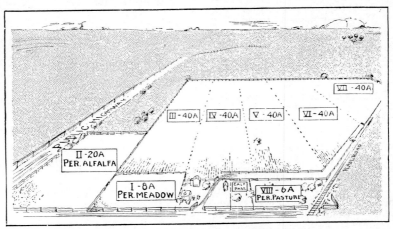

The Same Farm Efficiently Laid Out

This shows the same farm as laid out by an expert in farm management. Fields III to VII are in the following definite 5-year rotation: First year, grain seeded to alfalfa; second year, alfalfa; third year, alfalfa; fourth year, alfalfa; fifth year, corn. This rotation provides a well-balanced ration for the milk cows without much purchased feed, for there is plenty of legume hay. Note that the fields are of equal size and that they are large and so shaped that time is saved in tilling them. Fields I and II are permanently in hay and Field VIII is in permanent pasture. (From Wisconsin Station.)

is of excellent quality. On the other hand, little or no premium is paid on some local markets of the West for animals that have been well fattened by feeding them grain. Under such conditions it may not pay to feed any concentrates in addition to good hay or hay and silage.

With dairy cows much depends on the productive capacity of the animal. Except when concentrates are unusually high in price, the cow of good productive capacity will pay for at least a fair allowance of concentrates. On the contrary, for a low-producing cow the most economical ration, when concentrates are relatively high in price, may be silage and legume hay with no concentrates whatsoever.

The feeding standards for growing cattle are based upon continuous thrifty growth, and hence call for the feeding during winter of a limited allowance of concentrates, unless a liberal amount of excellent roughage is fed. The breeder of pure-bred animals who wishes to develop the best there is in his young stock will feed sufficient concentrates to keep them growing rapidly. On the other hand, the western ranchman may find it most profitable to carry young stock through the winter on roughage alone, or with but a very small allowance of concentrates. Thus fed, they will gain in frame and, though losing in flesh, will be thrifty enough in the spring to make good gains on the cheap pasturage.

It is a matter of great financial importance in stock farming to make a wise decision concerning the amounts of concentrates to feed the different classes of stock under varied conditions. This matter is therefore given especial consideration in Part III of this volume.

290. When roughage is scarce.—Occasionally there is a serious shortage of roughage in some part of the country due to severe drought. Hay and other roughage may then be so high in price that digestible nutrients in roughages will be much more expensive than digestible nutrients in grain and other concentrates. In some districts of the United States this was the condition, for example, in 1934, on account of the serious and wide-spread drought in the North Central and Plains States.

Under such conditions, it is most economical to increase the proportion of concentrates somewhat and to feed no more roughage than is necessary to provide sufficient bulk in the ration and a sufficient supply of vitamins.

291. Finish animals to meet demands of the market.—The wise stockman will keep in close touch with the demands of the market and adjust his feeding operations accordingly. If the market pays a sufficient premium for thoroughly fattened animals he will finish his stock well before marketing them. On the other hand, on local markets which pay no more for a prime carcass than for one carrying less fat, it will not pay to prolong the fattening process or to feed as heavy an allowance of concentrates as is necessary to make the carcass "ripe," or thoroughly fat.

292. Adapt type of farming to local conditions.—It is outside the field of this volume to discuss in detail the many factors which the stockman should take into consideration in deciding the type of livestock husbandry in which to engage and the systems and methods to follow. The foregoing paragraphs serve to illustrate how the farm operations and practices should be suited to local conditions, taking into consideration the prices of land and labor, the nearness to market, and the available crops.

For example, the beef producer on high-priced land in the eastern part of the corn belt will often crowd his calves to rapid growth on a heavy allowance of grain and fatten them as baby beeves. Perhaps he will raise no cattle, but fatten feeder steers from the western ranges on a liberal allowance of corn.

On the other hand, in the West where pasture is cheap compared with grain, the ranchman will usually follow a much less intensive system of beef production. Even during the winter his breeding herd will be maintained as largely as possible on the range and will be fed harvested feeds only when the range forage is covered by snow. Instead of fattening his steers for market, the ranchman will commonly sell them in the fall as feeder cattle, to be shipped to the districts where grain is cheaper. When he does fatten cattle, he will feed them chiefly on roughage, with but a limited amount of grain.

Dairymen producing market milk on high-priced land near large cities often use only a minimum acreage of land for pasture, but instead may rely to a considerable extent on corn silage or soiling crops for feed during the summer months. They often buy most of the concentrates for their cows, including grain as well as protein supplements. They do this because grain can be grown on land farther from market and shipped in at less expense than it may be possible to grow it on their farms. Such a system is not, however, economical for the dairyman remote from the large markets, whose milk is used in the manufacture of butter or cheese. Since with him land is relatively less expensive than labor, he must adopt a less intensive system of dairying, in which the herd is maintained chiefly on pasture in summer, and in which just as much as possible of the feed for the remainder of the year is produced on the farm.

293. Principles of successful livestock farming not complex.—The reader will come to realize as he goes on in this book that, while there are no hard and fast rules for successfully managing livestock, a clear understanding of the principles of the nutrition of animals is essential to the highest success. This must be supplemented by good judgment and by a thorough knowledge of the farm animals themselves, which can only be gained by actual experience. He will further find that expensive buildings for housing stock and complex devices for feeding and caring for them are not necessary; that there are no "best" feeds for all conditions; that elaborate and laborious preparation of feed is often wasted; that patent stock foods guaranteed to work miracles enrich, not the farmer, but the manufacturer.

On the other hand, he will come to appreciate that a proper balancing of the rations for his stock not only benefits the animals, but also increases his profits. He will further realize that animal husbandry is generally most successful when combined with general farming and the raising of crops; that it rests upon pasture lots which are well fertilized and upon tilled fields which are so managed that the fertility is maintained and bumper crops are grown, a large part of which is marketed through the animals of the farm.

Having discussed in the preceding chapters the fundamental principles governing the rational feeding and care of the various classes of farm animals, let us now consider in detail the value of the many different feeding stuffs for livestock.

QUESTIONS

1. Using local prices for feeds, see if you can find instances where the market price of a feed does not represent its actual feeding value compared with other feeds which are available.
2. Give examples which show that the results of feeding experiments may be a much more reliable guide to the relative values of feeds for different classes of stock than the amounts of digestible nutrients the feeds supply.
3. What difficulties are there in comparing the relative economy of various feeds on the basis of the cost per pound of total digestible nutrients and the cost per pound of digestible protein?
4. How is the relative value of a feed determined by the Petersen method?
5. Find the local prices of at least 3 farm grains and 5 protein supplements suitable for dairy cows. Then determine, by using the Petersen method, which of these feeds are actually the cheapest. Finally, work out the most economical concentrate mixture you can that will supply 16.0 per cent digestible protein and be excellent for dairy cows.
6. On what basis should feeds be compared when protein-rich feeds cost no more than those low in protein?
7. Why are comparisons of the values of various roughages, based solely on digestible nutrients or net energy, less reliable than similar comparisons of concentrates?
8. How would you adapt the amount of protein in the ration to local conditions?
9. When would you feed less concentrates than called for in the feeding standards?
10. Under what conditions are beef calves fattened for baby beef?
11. Discuss other ways in which you would adapt your type of farming to local conditions.

REFERENCES

1. Hayden, Ohio Cir. 128; Fraps, Texas Buls. 323, Texas Control Cir. G.
2. Petersen, Jour. Dairy Sci., 15, 1932, pp. 293-297; Petersen, Minn. Exten. Pamphlet 33.

PART II

FEEDING STUFFS

CHAPTER XI

PASTURE AND HAY

I. FACTORS AFFECTING THE VALUE OF FORAGE

294. Importance of forage crops and pasture.—In discussing the nutritive properties and the uses of the various feeding stuffs in this volume, forage crops and pasture are considered first, on account of their outstanding importance in this country. For all classes of farm stock except swine and poultry, good forage, including pasturage, is the foundation for efficient production.

Commonly, livestock are provided with what forage they will consume, and then are fed in addition whatever grain or other concentrates they need to meet their specific requirements. Even for swine and poultry, high-quality forage is important as a source of vitamins, minerals, and other nutrients.

The value of pasture, hay, and other forage in the United States is shown clearly by the Census data. In 1930 there were on our farms and ranches 464,154,524 acres in pasture, out of a total of 986,771,016 acres of farm and ranch land. This does not include the vast areas of grazing lands in the National Forests and other public lands of the West. In addition to the acreage of pasture, 82,467,990 acres were used for the production of hay, silage, and other forage crops, the total value of such forage being $1,186,000,000 for 1929.

Before discussing the value and use of the various forage crops in the following chapters, it is important to consider the different methods of utilizing forage, and the factors that affect the nutritive value.

295. Influence of stage of maturity on composition.—It is exceedingly important to understand fully the wide differences in the composition of young, immature plants and of the same plants when mature. Young plants are much more watery and lower in dry matter than those at later stages of growth; hence to find the true relative content of various nutrients, it is necessary to make comparisons on the dry-matter basis.

Immature, actively-growing plants are much richer in protein, on the dry basis, than the same plants when usually cut for hay. Young plants are also soft and tender, but become more woody as they mature, due to the increase in fiber. Their dry matter is therefore more digestible than that of plants whose growth is far advanced. In addition, young plants contain more calcium and phosphorus, on the dry basis, and are higher in vitamins, especially vitamin A.

204

These differences in composition have been shown in numerous investigations and are clearly apparent in the data given in Appendix Tables I and V, for different crops at various stages of maturity. For example, young, actively-growing pasture grass from well-grazed pastures contains an average of over 17 per cent protein when dried to a hay basis, while hay from mixed grasses, cut at the usual stage of maturity, has only about 7 per cent protein. Young legumes, such as clover and alfalfa, are even higher than the grasses in protein content.

Dried pasture grass from fertile, closely-grazed pastures supplies 64.7 per cent total digestible nutrients, in comparison with 51.7 per cent for mixed hay of good quality, cut at the usual stage of maturity. Likewise, the dried pasture grass from such pastures has, on the average, 0.66 per cent calcium and 0.29 per cent phosphorus, while mixed grass hay of good quality has only 0.48 per cent calcium and 0.17 per cent phosphorus.

296. Immature grass not a concentrate.—These figures show clearly that very young forage, such as immature pasturage on good pastures, is a protein-rich feed, and furthermore, that it is much higher in total digestible nutrients, on the dry basis, than most roughages. Indeed, with one important exception, the best of such immature forage is similar in composition and nutritive value to the protein-rich concentrates, such as wheat bran, corn gluten feed, linseed meal, etc.

This exception is that even young forage is somewhat higher in fiber, on the dry basis, than are these concentrates. Therefore it is correspondingly lower in total digestible nutrients and net energy than the concentrates. Consequently, although such forage is often called a protein-rich concentrate, it cannot fully take the place of concentrates in stock feeding.

For example, dairy cows of high productive capacity need some concentrates in addition to excellent pasture, or their production will be reduced. Likewise, young beef cattle will not generally reach the same degree of fatness on pasture alone as they will when fed grain in addition. In the case of pigs, the difference in the effects of young forage plants and of concentrates is still greater. This is because the digestive tracts of pigs do not enable them to eat a great amount of roughage. Even on the best of pasture as the only feed, pigs will not make normal growth, to say nothing about fattening.

297. Utilizing the abundant protein in pasturage.—It is highly important in efficient stock feeding that full advantage be taken of the richness in protein of excellent pasturage and other immature plants. Since young pasture grass contains even more protein, on the dry basis, than alfalfa hay, it is obvious that animals on excellent, well-grazed pasture receive a liberal supply of protein. This fact is often entirely overlooked in stock feeding.

For example, dairy cows on such pasture are often fed a concentrate or grain mixture containing much more protein than is necessary. This does not increase their production, and it is usually decidedly uneconomical.

298. Effect of rate of growth and season of the year.—Pasture grass is generally high in protein, on the dry basis, as long as it is kept growing actively and is prevented from heading out. Therefore proper fertilization and good pasture management are important in producing pasturage rich in protein throughout as much of the season as is possible.

The grass will usually be somewhat richer in protein in the spring and early summer when the growth is most rapid than later in the summer. If growth is decidedly checked in midsummer by drought, by a lack of available plant food, or by the hot weather, the protein content of the grass will be decidedly lower than that of grass at the same stage of maturity earlier in the season.[1] Often such pasturage will contain 12 to 14 per cent or less of protein, on the dry basis, in comparison with 16 to 18 per cent or more for rapidly-growing grass.

If the grass resumes rapid growth in the autumn after the fall rains come, the protein content may be nearly as high as early in the season. In case the grass is allowed to head out and go to seed at any time, the protein content will be relatively low.

299. Certain forage crops richer in nutrients when mature.—The only exceptions to the general rule that immature plants are richer in protein, lower in fiber, and higher in total digestible nutrients, on the dry basis, than when mature, are such crops as corn, the small grains, the sorghums, and soybeans. In these crops large amounts of highly digestible nutrients are stored in the seeds as they approach maturity. Therefore the percentages of protein and of digestible nutrients are commonly higher when the seed has fully developed in such crops (considering both the seed and the stover or straw) than at an earlier stage.

300. Effect of frequent cutting or grazing on yield.—When grasses are cut at frequent intervals throughout the season, as on a well-kept lawn, the total yield of dry matter is much less than when they are allowed to grow to the usual hay stage.[2] This is because there is then a smaller leaf surface exposed to the sunlight. Therefore the production of carbohydrates through the action of sunlight on the chlorophyll of the leaves is decreased. The same effect is produced by close grazing of the crop.

On the other hand, the total yield of protein during the season may be greater when the crop is cut frequently or grazed than when it is cut for hay. Also, since very immature plants are lower in fiber and more digestible than at the hay stage, the yield of total digestible nutrients is not reduced as much as the dry matter.

The actual reduction in yield through frequent cutting or through grazing will depend on the kind of plants and also on other factors. The yield of tall-growing plants, such as alfalfa, red clover, alsike clover, orchard grass, and the ordinary kinds of timothy, is reduced much more than that of low-growing, spreading pasture plants, such as bluegrass, Bermuda grass, and white clover. In general, grasses cut at intervals of 2 to 3 weeks will yield only 50 to 65 per cent as much dry matter and 60 to 75 per cent as much total digestible nutrients during the season as when they are harvested at the usual stage of growth for hay.

When grasses are continuously grazed very closely by stock or are cut every week, the yield is reduced much more than when they are grazed or cut at intervals of 2 to 4 weeks.[3] Also, under good pasture management and fertilization, this latter method does not greatly decrease the protein content and digestibility of the grass, in comparison with weekly cutting. For this reason, as is pointed out later, the yield of pasture is generally increased somewhat when a system of rotation or alternate grazing is practiced, instead of continuous close grazing on the same plot. (312)

301. Influence of soil fertility on composition.—Not only is the yield of a forage crop dependent on the amount of mineral nutrients in the soil, but also its composition may be greatly affected. It has been pointed out in Chapter VI that grass or other forage grown on soils very deficient in phosphorus may be so low in this mineral that stock grazed on it suffer disastrously, unless supplied with a phosphorus supplement. (160-164)

Pasture grass on phosphorus-deficient soil may contain only 0.10 per cent phosphorus on the dry basis, in comparison with 0.20 to 0.40 per cent or more for that from fertile pastures. Legume forage is also much lower in phosphorus content than normal when grown on phosphorus-deficient soil, but the content does not usually drop to quite such a low level as in the case of the grasses. However, most legumes are exceedingly sensitive to a lack of this mineral nutrient and do not thrive or yield well unless there is an ample supply of phosphorus.

The percentage of calcium in non-legume forage crops is greatly reduced when the crops are grown on soil deficient in calcium. However, the calcium content is not often so low that livestock suffer from a lack of calcium in pasture grass and other forage. (161) While the percentage of calcium in legume forages depends to some extent on the calcium content of the soil, they are always relatively high in the mineral. When the soil is too deficient in calcium, the legume crop will not thrive, but the small amount of forage produced will be fairly high in calcium.

It has been pointed out in Chapter VI that in a few sections there is such a deficiency of iron in the soil that cattle on pasture may suffer seriously from a lack of this mineral. (173) Likewise, in certain districts the forage and the water are so deficient in iodine that goiter in stock may be produced. (172)

The yield of non-legume forage crops often depends largely on the amount of nitrogen in the soil. However, the protein content of forage crops is not affected by the supply of soil nitrogen to any such extent as the supply of soil phosphorus or calcium changes the amounts of these minerals.

In the case of the grasses, the protein content at immature stages of growth is usually increased materially by nitrogenous fertilization, unless the soil is already well supplied with nitrogen. This increase may be sufficient to add appreciably to the feeding value of grass pasture or early-cut grass hay. Also, nitrogen fertilization increases the palatability of the grasses.

Proper inoculation and also liming, when necessary, not only increase the yield of alfalfa and other legume forages, but in addition make them richer in protein.[4] If such crops are well inoculated with the proper bacteria, nitrogenous fertilization will not produce much increase in the percentage of protein in the plants. In New Jersey experiments the protein content of corn silage was not appreciably increased by nitrogen fertilizers.[5]

Grass grown in partial shade, as in open woods, not only produces much less forage than that fully exposed to sunlight, but also is less palatable to stock. This is probably because it contains less sugars and starch.[6]

302. Early-cut hay richer in protein and more digestible.—Early-cut hay is much richer in protein and also is higher in total digestible nutrients than that which is cut at a late stage of maturity. Even a slight difference in time of cutting may make a considerable difference in the actual feeding value, especially in hay from the grasses.

For example, it is shown in Appendix Table I that timothy hay cut in early bloom contains an average of 7.6 per cent protein and 51.6 per cent total digestible nutrients. In comparison with these amounts, timothy hay cut in full bloom contains 6.2 per cent protein and 48.0 per cent total digestible nutrients, and that cut from late bloom to early seed, only 5.8 per cent protein and 44.4 per cent total digestible nutrients.

Similarly, alfalfa cut before bloom contains 19.0 per cent protein, in comparison with 14.9 per cent for that cut when one-tenth to one-half in bloom, and 14.0 per cent for the three-fourths-bloom to full-bloom stage. The importance of cutting hay reasonably early is discussed further in the following chapters, especially with reference to alfalfa, clover, and timothy.

303. Improvement of grass hay by nitrogenous fertilization.—Unless the soil is already unusually rich in available nitrogen, the application of a nitrogenous fertilizer to a grass-hay meadow will not only make a large increase in yield, but also it will commonly make an appreciable increase in the percentage of protein in the hay. For example, on 15 New York farms the application of a commercial nitrogenous fertilizer in the early spring to old timothy fields increased the yield of hay 1,065 lbs., or 35 per cent, in the first cutting, and also resulted in much more aftermath.[7] The hay from the nitrogen-fertilized fields, cut in early to full bloom, contained 9.4 per cent protein, while that from the plots not fertilized with nitrogen, cut at the same stage of maturity, contained only 8.0 per cent.

It is pointed out in later chapters that such early-cut grass hay from nitrogen-fertilized land closely approaches legume hay in feeding value per ton for dairy cows and other stock. Where alfalfa, clover, or other good legume hay crops thrive, obviously they are superior to grass hay, since they aid in maintaining soil fertility and also usually produce larger yields than the grasses.

304. Mature, weathered forage may be of low value.—In the semi-arid range districts stock get most of their feed during the winter or during the dry season by grazing on forage which has matured and dried. Mature grass is always relatively low in protein, and if it is weathered by exposure to rains, there will be a large loss of nutrients through leaching. Also, the vitamin A value is destroyed by the exposure to the sunlight and by the weathering. Where there is little or no rainfall after the grass matures, much less loss through weathering will occur, and the dried mature grass may furnish satisfactory feed for stock.

Weathered, mature forage resembles straw in composition and feeding value, being very low in protein, vitamin A, calcium, and phosphorus.[8] It is also lacking in palatability and is low in digestibility.

When badly weathered, the forage may not even furnish sufficient nutrients for body maintenance. If stock receive no other feed, they may suffer severely from the lack of these nutrients. For example, it was found in California studies that, on account of the lack of vitamin A, cattle or sheep which had only such weathered forage for long periods might be unable to produce normal, strong offspring, or might themselves suffer from deficiencies. (**186**)

Some forage plants lose much less nutrients by weathering than others. For example, the wire grasses and sedges of the West often furnish much more nutritious winter feed than other grasses. Also, bur clover furnishes good feed even when mature, and winter fat (sometimes called white sage) and some of the true sages have a high feeding value in winter.

II. THE UTILIZATION AND IMPROVEMENT OF PASTURE

305. Economy of pasture.—Good pasture generally supplies the cheapest and most economical feed for cattle, sheep, and horses during the growing season. Even for swine, pasturage is an important means of reducing the cost of feeding. This is in spite of the fact, already discussed in this chapter, that the yields of dry matter and total digestible nutrients are usually reduced when grasses and other hay crops are pastured, in comparison with their yields for hay.

The difference in yield is much more than offset by the greater expenses for labor, seed, and machinery in planting, tilling, and harvesting forage crops. In well-managed permanent pasture the annual expense is reduced to a minimum.

The economy of pasture is well shown in studies conducted by the United States Department of Agriculture in seven dairy districts of this country.[9] In these areas pasturage furnished nearly one-third of the total nutrients consumed by the milk cows during the year, but the cost of the pasturage was only one-seventh of the total annual feed cost. In similar studies on 478 corn-belt beef farms, the breeding cows obtained practically all their feed from pasture for 200 days of the year. While the pastures furnished a little more than one-half the total feed for the whole year, the cost of pasture was only one-third of the annual feed bill.

On dairy farms in southern Indiana pasture furnished total digestible nutrients at 27 per cent of the cost of harvested feeds, although each acre of pasture produced only one-half as much actual feed per acre as an ordinary yield of corn or legume hay on the same land.[10]

306. Importance of pasture improvement.—In spite of the dominant place that pasturage occupies in livestock production in this country, the improvement of permanent pastures has received little attention until the past few years. All too commonly, farmers made little effort to increase the productivity and value of their pastures. If the soil was fertile and the summer rains were timely, their stock thrived during the season. On the other hand, if lack of fertility or drought caused a serious shortage of feed in midsummer, the returns from their stock were much decreased.

During recent years, experiments and demonstrations on pasture fertilization and management have been conducted by most of the agricultural colleges and experiment stations and also by other agencies. In addition, much excellent work has been done abroad. The results of these studies show convincingly that in most localities a great improvement can readily be made in the productivity of pastures, and that wise expenditures for this purpose are usually highly profitable.

It is outside the scope of this volume to discuss in detail the fertilization and management of pastures under the various conditions throughout the country, or to review the results that have been secured in the numerous pasture investigations. All that can be done is to summarize briefly certain of the most important findings. For further information the reader is referred to the publications of his state experiment station or agricultural college, or to those of the United States Department of Agriculture.[11]

307. Pasture improvement through proper grazing.—In any plan of pasture improvement, proper management of the pasture is essential for good results. The chief objects of such management are: (1) To keep the plants growing actively over as long a period as possible, so they will provide palatable feed of high nutritive value; and (2) to encourage the growth of desirable grasses and clovers, while crowding out weeds, brush, and inferior grasses. In general, the protein content of pasturage depends much more on proper management than on fertilization.

It is pointed out later in this chapter that in the semi-arid districts it is important not to graze the range pastures so closely that the plants fail to develop seed occasionally. On the other hand, in humid districts much better results are usually secured when the pasture is so managed that the grasses do not head out and go to seed.

Both under-grazing and over-grazing should be avoided. If the plants mature, the forage becomes unpalatable and of low nutritive value. Also the new growth is diminished, and what there, is may be wasted, because stock will refuse to eat the mature grass along with it, unless impelled by hunger. In addition, if the grasses grow so high as to shade the low-growing white clover, they will drive it out. Weeds, brush, and coarse grasses are, moreover, apt to gain a foothold when the pasture is grazed insufficiently. A good rule for maintaining a uniform turf is to graze the pasturage all down closely at least once a year.

Over-grazing throughout the season will reduce the yield. Also it will weaken many of the best pasture grasses, because there will be no opportunity for the plants to store reserve nutrients in their roots.[12] Injury is especially apt to result if heavy grazing is begun before sufficient growth is made in the spring, and if the fall growth is grazed so closely that no cover is left for winter protection.

The stock should be turned on the pasture in the spring just as soon as the plants have made sufficient growth and the soil is firm enough to stand trampling. If grazing is delayed longer, it may be impossible, during the period of rapid growth which follows, to prevent much of the grass from becoming too mature.

308. Other points in pasture management.—Even when the pasture is properly managed, the stock are apt to graze unevenly, and some of the grass will head out and then will not be eaten during the rest of the season. If the land is not too rough or stony, it is wise to mow all such spots at least once a year at the usual hay-making time or before, to get rid of the old grass and to encourage new growth. It is especially important to cut all weeds and brush.

The field will be grazed more uniformly if more than one kind of stock is pastured on it. Rotating two or more species of stock not only helps to control grazing, but also aids in reducing the trouble from internal parasites.

Stock will not graze the rank rings of grass around piles of droppings in the pasture, unless forced to it by hunger. Therefore in heavily-stocked cattle or horse pastures, there is considerable wastage of feed unless droppings are spread at least once a year with a harrow or otherwise.

For efficient use of the pasture, it is important to provide a good supply of water and also shade. Since stock on good pasture spend much of their time in the shade, if it is available, fertility is conserved when shade trees are located at the top of a slope, instead of at the bottom of the slope or on the banks of a stream.

If the pasture is very weedy and has only a small proportion of desirable forage plants, it is usually best to plow and reseed it, unless it is too rough or stony. Improvement by fertilization and management alone may be unduly slow.

309. Pasture fertilization.—Pasture fertilization is of two general types. The first is fertilization with phosphorus and perhaps with calcium or potassium, if these minerals are necessary. The purpose of this type of fertilization is not only to increase the growth of the grasses, but especially to increase the proportion of white clover and other legumes. The legumes are relied upon as the source of additional nitrogen. The second type of fertilization is the more intensive system in which some nitrogenous fertilizer is also applied, in order to produce the maximum yield of nutrients per acre.

The choice between the two systems will depend, first of all, on the amount of pasturage already available. Where the area is limited and there is need for the greatest possible amount of feed over a long pasture season, the second system will naturally be followed. On the other hand, where the pasture acreage is large, the first method should generally be followed on most of the area, perhaps with more intensive fertilization on a small separate pasture to provide early grazing. An intensive system of fertilization generally has much greater advantages and is more profitable for high-producing dairy cows than for other classes of stock.

310. Fertilization without nitrogen.—On most pastures lacking in fertility throughout the United States, the first need is for phosphorus. On such soil, phosphorus fertilization greatly increases the yield and the nutritive value of the grasses. Also, if grazing is properly managed, it will increase the proportion of legumes. However, the latter result will not be secured when the grasses grow up so tall that they shade the legumes too much.

Under good pasture management with this system of fertilization, the white clover often forms a dense mat over much of the pasture. This not only furnishes excellent feed over a long season, but also aids in keeping the soil temperature lower in hot weather than in a sod of pure grass.[13] As a result the growth of the grass is increased, for most grasses grow best at moderate temperatures.

Whether or not it will be advisable to apply lime or potash under this system of fertilization, will depend entirely on the supply in the soil. Superphosphate and the other common phosphorus fertilizers furnish calcium as well as phosphorus. Also, the pasture grasses and such legumes as white clover, lespedeza, yellow trefoil, and bur clover will thrive in a soil much more acid and lower in lime than will alfalfa, red clover, or sweet clover.

311. Intensive pasture fertilization.—Soil and crop experts differ greatly in their opinions on the use of commercial nitrogen fertilizers and of farm manure on pastures. Except in the case of pastures having a large proportion of legumes, the application of nitrogen will, without question, produce a large increase in yield. Furthermore, it will result in earlier growth in the spring, so that grazing can begin one to two weeks earlier. This is important, as it shortens the expensive barn-feeding period. On account of these benefits, nitrogen fertilization should usually be included in any *intensive* system of pasture development.

Liberal fertilization with nitrogen is apt to decrease the proportion of legumes, as it greatly stimulates the taller growing grasses. However, many farmers are able to keep a goodly proportion of white clover in such a pasture by careful management of the grazing and proper fertilization with phosphorus.

Since most of the effect of commercial nitrogen fertilizers is secured in the first season, annual applications are usually made early in the spring. Such fertilization produces earlier pasturage and usually results in a much greater yield. However, it does not generally aid in supplying more feed during the scant pasture season of midsummer.

In seasons of ample rainfall throughout the summer, the growth during this period can be increased by one or more later applications of nitrogen. However, there is often insufficient rainfall during midsummer in the northern states to gain any great advantages from this method. Therefore it is generally better to rely on supplementary grazing crops or other feed for this season.

When more farm manure is available than is needed for the crop land, it is an excellent nitrogenous fertilizer for pasture, when properly used. The manure should be applied in the fall or by early spring and the entire field must be covered uniformly. Otherwise, during the first season the stock are apt not to graze on the manured portion. Phosphate should be applied along with the manure, as manure is much richer in nitrogen than in phosphorus.

312. Rotation or alternate grazing; the Hohenheim system.—If the animals are kept on a single pasture throughout the season, it is often difficult to secure uniform grazing of all areas. Also, the yield of forage is usually less than when a system of rotation or alternate grazing is used.

In such a system, there are two or more separate fields which are pastured in succession. After each area is grazed down, the animals are removed, and the forage is allowed to grow up to a height of 4 to 6 inches, before it is grazed again. Most of the feed is therefore eaten when it is rich in protein and digestible nutrients, and before it becomes less palatable. If the rainfall is abundant and the grass grows so fast the stock cannot graze it all, one of the areas should be cut early for hay, to prevent the bad effects of under-grazing. This plan will provide pasture during the midsummer season.

Additional fencing is required under this system, and each plot must be accessible to a water supply. This can often be provided best by having the plots open into a common lane, where water is available. If it is necessary to go to much extra expense to adopt this system, it is doubtful whether the outlay will be warranted, except under an intensive system of pasture fertilization, such as the Hohenheim system, described later.

Though the yield of forage is increased by rotation grazing, the increase is not generally large. For example, in experiments in western Washington on excellent pasture the estimated production of total digestible nutrients in the forage was only 9 per cent greater on pastures grazed in rotation by dairy cows, than with continuous grazing.[14] The cows on the rotated pasture also produced only 9 per cent more milk than those on the continuously-grazed area.

This system is of especial value for high-producing dairy cows, which must secure a great amount of nutrients each day to maintain their production. Rotation grazing is also important for sheep, as it aids in reducing infestation with stomach worms and other internal parasites.

In the most intensive system of pasture utilization, rotation grazing is combined with liberal fertilization, including applications of nitrogen fertilizers each spring. Often nitrogen is also applied during the growing season to keep the forage growing rapidly over as long a period as possible. This system is often called the "Hohenheim system," from the Hohenheim Agricultural College in Germany, where it was developed. The system is most frequently used for dairy cattle.

In this system the pasture is divided into 4 to 8 paddocks, about equal in size, and often the herd is divided into two or more groups. The first group, consisting of the cows in milk, are pastured first for a few days on each plot in succession, thus getting the most liberal supply of forage. Then the dry cows and the heifers are turned into the plot to complete the grazing. Sometimes the cows in milk are divided into two groups, and the high producers grazed first on each plot.

In this system it is important to distribute the droppings by harrowing at least once a year. Also, a plot should be mowed whenever necessary to prevent the grass going to seed. Even under this system, it is difficult to provide ample forage on the pasture area itself during midsummer. Therefore, additional grazing should be furnished at that time, if necessary, by a field that has been cut early for hay, by Sudan grass pasture, or otherwise.

Experiments with this system in this country have shown that the yield of nutrients can often be increased 2 to 4 times over that on unfertilized pastures grazed by ordinary methods.[15] The cost of such a system of fertilization and management may seem considerable, but where the pasture area is limited, the method yields large net returns, on account of the saving of other feed. For example, in New Jersey trials over a five-year period, the annual cost of fertilizer was $13.52 per acre in this intensive system, but the additional forage produced by the fertilization saved $39.27 per acre in barn feeding.[16]

When the moisture supply is ample, the greater part of the nitrogen in the annual application is recovered that same year in the additional high-protein forage produced. Thus, in Wisconsin tests the recovery was 80 per cent or over.[17] Liberal nitrogenous fertilization does not greatly increase the amount of inorganic nitrogen compounds in the grass, or of other compounds simpler than the proteins. In the Wisconsin tests, 72 to 77 per cent of the total nitrogen was protein, and most of the remainder consisted of the simpler organic-nitrogen compounds, such as amino acids.

313. Range management and improvement.—While it is generally best in humid districts to graze pastures sufficiently close so that the grasses do not go to seed, the conditions are entirely different on the western ranges.[18] On account of the limited rainfall, care must be taken there not to over-graze the land. Otherwise, the desirable forage plants will be killed and only those left which are relatively unpalatable and of low value. Also, the land will then be much more subject to injury by erosion.

To produce the most feed, the grasses must have a chance to form seed at least every 3 or 4 years, and the following spring the young seedlings should be given a chance to grow. No range should be grazed in the spring until the grass has made sufficient growth and the soil is reasonably dry. Poisoning of stock often results from forcing the animals to graze the scanty growth too early, for some of the poisonous plants start growth earlier than the grasses or other good forage and are therefore eaten, when they would otherwise be left untouched.

The range should not be grazed so heavily that the forage is injured badly by trampling or unduly close cropping. Otherwise, not only will the grasses and other herbaceous plants be destroyed, but also the shrubby browse will be injured, which forms a large part of the feed on some of the mountain ranges. Watering places should be developed close enough together to avoid over-grazing near the water supplies. Salting the stock at certain places will aid in relieving areas that are being injured by too close grazing. In normal years, when the stock come off a range, it should be in good condition and with some feed left.

Through improper management and unrestricted grazing, the carrying capacity of many of the ranges has been seriously reduced. Where a range has been thus injured, reseeding may sometimes be advisable. More commonly, methods are used in which the grazing on part of the area is deferred until after the grasses have matured seed. The following year, another area is similarly treated. This method of deferred and rotation grazing usually increases the carrying capacity of the range, unless the pasturage is already better than the average.[19] The great improvement that results from controlled grazing and proper management has been abundantly demonstrated in the National Forests, where the grazing is under very definite regulation.

III. HAY-MAKING

314. Importance of hay.—Throughout the temperate regions hay from the grasses and legumes is the most important harvested roughage for livestock. The value of the hay crop in the United States is shown by the fact that in 1933 there were made 65,852,000 tons of tame hay and 8,633,000 tons of wild hay from a total of 66,144,000 acres. This hay had an estimated total value of $578,279,000. In 1934 the total yield was considerably below normal, on account of the severe drought, but the value of the crop was increased to $724,520,000.

Many millions of dollars are lost each year by farmers through lack of sufficient care in hay-making and also because they do not understand certain of the principles involved in the process. In addition, it is estimated that the yearly losses in this country through farm fires caused by spontaneous combustion have been as high as $30,000,000.[20] The greater part of this huge loss is due to the storage of hay when it contains an unsafe amount of moisture. To avoid such losses and to prevent possible disaster to his buildings, it is highly important that every farmer understand clearly the processes that occur in hay-making.

315. Objects in hay-making.—The primary object in hay-making is to reduce the water content of the green plants enough so that the hay can be safely stored in mass without undergoing pronounced fermentation or becoming moldy. This object must be accomplished in such a manner that the hay is not bleached unduly by exposure to sun and weather, that it is not leached by rain, that the loss of leaves is kept at a minimum, and that the hay does not become moldy.

316. Importance of quality in hay.—High-quality hay is leafy; it is not made from plants cut at too late a stage of maturity; it is green in color; the stems are soft and pliable; it has but little foreign material, such as weeds and stubble; it is free from mustiness or mold; and it has an attractive fragrance typical of the particular crop from which it is made. Such hay is much more nutritious and also more palatable than that which is deficient in these characteristics. Indeed, there may be much more difference in feeding value between good and poor hay of any particular kind than there is between the different kinds of hay made from the common hay crops.

The Federal hay grades, by which hay is sold on the larger markets in the United States, are based on the above qualities.[21] Any person who produces hay for such markets should familiarize himself with these grades, for the price paid for any lot of hay depends strictly on the quality as indicated by the Federal grade.

In the following paragraphs the various factors in hay-making are discussed and the various methods are explained by which high-quality hay is produced.

317. Reduction in water content.—At the stages of growth when usually cut for hay, most legumes contain 70 to 75 per cent water or more, and most grasses 60 to 75 per cent. For the hay to keep safely in barn or stack the water content must be reduced at least to 25 per cent,[22] and preferably to not more than 22 per cent if it is to be stored in a large mass. Hay containing more moisture than this when stored is apt to undergo pronounced fermentation and become very hot. The value may be greatly decreased due to mold or to the losses of nutrients which occur in the extensive fermentations. Also, there is always grave danger of spontaneous combustion when hay is stored with too high a moisture content.

It is a common belief that it is safer to store hay with a high moisture content when this is due to the moisture content of the plants, than when the hay has been dampened by rain or dew. It is not wise to rely much on this as a factor of safety. The only safe way to avoid serious loss is not to store any hay when it is too high in moisture, no matter what the cause.

It is somewhat difficult to estimate the water content of hay by feeling of it, but experience will soon enable one to know when hay is well cured. Alfalfa or clover will usually be dry enough for storage when the leaves are thoroughly dry and the stems show only a slight toughness when twisted, but with no trace of sap exuding. In excellent curing weather the hay may appear drier than it really is, especially if cured chiefly in the swath. This is because the leaves will be dry and brittle, while the stems are still too high in moisture.

If it seems wise, because rain is threatening, to haul hay to the barn before it has reached the desired dryness, it should be spread out well in a mow to a depth not greater than about 3 to 5 feet. Especial care should be taken not to leave any large, compact masses where the hay falls from the hay fork or sling. If possible, such hay should not be covered with other hay until it has cured out somewhat in the mow.

318. Losses of nutrients in hay-making.—Some nutrients are always lost in the field-curing of hay, but under favorable conditions this loss is not large. However, the wastage may be great unless proper care is taken. These losses are not due to the mere drying out of the forage plants. Experiments have shown definitely that the drying of green grass or other green forage at ordinary temperatures does not reduce its digestibility.[23] Also, when plants are dried without any bleaching or fermentation, they retain a high content of the vitamins that are of importance in stock feeding.

The losses in nutritive value that occur in hay-making are: (1) Mechanical losses of leaves and other finer parts by shattering; (2) losses of vitamins by bleaching and fermentations; (3) losses of carbohydrates by fermentations; and (4) losses of soluble nutrients by leaching, in case of heavy rains.

319. Losses by shattering.—The losses by shattering of the leaves and other finer parts during hay-making are highly important, especially in the case of the legumes. The leaves of alfalfa, for example, contain two to three times as high a percentage of protein as the stems. Also, the leaves are much richer than the stems in minerals and vitamins and are lower in fiber. Therefore the proportion of leaves is one of the important factors in determining the feeding value of any particular lot of hay.

Unless great care is taken, the losses of leaves are apt to be especially great in the making of alfalfa hay in dry climates. Thus in Colorado tests, when the conditions were unfavorable and the hay was handled carelessly, half the total weight of the alfalfa and a much larger part of the feeding value was lost.[24] Even under favorable conditions the loss amounted to 350 lbs. of leaves and stems for each ton of alfalfa hay taken off the field. By the methods described later, the losses by shattering can be reduced to a minimum.

320. Losses of vitamins.—While the drying of forage plants artificially may not cause any great loss in the vitamin A value (carotene content), there is always considerable destruction of carotene in the field curing of hay, even under the best of conditions. However, as has been shown in Chapter VI, well-cured hay is still one of the best sources of vitamin A among the roughages available for the feeding of stock under barn conditions. **(188)** When the hay is badly bleached in curing, the losses of vitamin A are serious. Thus, alfalfa hay of No. 3 Federal grade contains only about one-eighth as much vitamin A, on the average, as that of No. 1 grade. Some samples of such hay contain practically no vitamin A.

In general, the amount of vitamin A in hay is proportional to the greenness in color. Good green-colored hay is always rich in the vitamin, and straw-colored or brown hay very poor in it. The wide difference in vitamin A content of hay is naturally of especial importance when legume hay is used as a vitamin supplement, as in the feeding of swine and poultry not on pasture.

Fortunately, the exposure of green hay plants to the direct sunlight in the ordinary curing process increases the vitamin D content, instead of decreasing it. Therefore hay cured with reasonable exposure to the sun is always a good source of this vitamin.

321. Losses by fermentations.—Even under favorable conditions the usual curing of hay in the field is not merely a simple process of drying. Fermentations take place in which some of the organic nutrients, especially the sugars and starch, are oxidized into carbon dioxide and water, thus being lost. Also, fermentation has a very destructive effect on the carotene in hay. If the weather is favorable and the hay is cured by proper methods, without undergoing pronounced heating, the losses by fermentation will be relatively small.

On the other hand, when extensive fermentation takes place, as in the production of brown hay, the losses are much larger than many realize. As is shown later, in the making of brown hay 40 per cent of the total dry matter may be lost through oxidation into carbon dioxide, water vapor, and other gases. **(333)** Similar losses occur when hay suffers from extensive heating and molding in the windrow or cock. These fermentations not only waste the carbohydrates but also largely destroy the vitamins in the hay.

322. Losses by leaching.—If hay that is already nearly cured is exposed to heavy and prolonged rain, especially when it is in the swath, severe losses may occur through leaching. For example, in a Colorado test in which alfalfa hay was exposed to 3 rains, aggregating 1.8 inches, there was a loss of 31 per cent of the dry matter.[25] The loss in nutritive value was even greater than this, for the fiber is not dissolved by rain, but the more soluble parts are leached out. In this test 60 per cent of the protein and 41 per cent of the nitrogen-free extract were lost on account of the rains.

Unless the rain is so heavy that the hay is thoroughly soaked and washed by the rain, important losses by leaching will not occur. In Nebraska experiments with alfalfa hay, exposure to a rainfall of an inch did not lower the protein content, though the rain of course injured the color of the hay and prolonged the time required for curing.[26] For this reason the losses will be much less, even in a heavy rain, if the hay is in cocks or good-sized windrows than if it is in the swath.

323. Modern hay-making methods.—Extensive investigations have been conducted recently by several experiment stations to determine the best methods of making hay, especially legume hay.[27] In these the object has been to produce high-quality hay, leafy and green in color, with a minimum of labor. These experiments have supplied information of much value to farmers on the principles of efficient hay-making. In particular, these investigations have shown that many common beliefs are apparently not true.

324. Curing hay in swath and windrow.—Hay dries much more rapidly in the swath than in a windrow, even if the windrow is small and loose. However, claims are often made to the contrary. The larger the windrow is, the slower will be the curing, and the rate is still slower in cocks.

Though hay cures with maximum rapidity in the swath, it is not advisable to cure it entirely there, except perhaps with grass hay in cool, dry weather. When curing is completed in the swath, the leaves become dry and brittle long before the stems have dried out sufficiently for safe storage. With legume hay, especially alfalfa, a heavy loss by shattering of the leaves will then take place when the hay is raked and handled. Also, the prolonged exposure of most of the leaves to the sunlight will bleach the hay and destroy much of the vitamin A.

On the other hand, if the green forage is raked into a windrow, even a small, loose one, immediately after it is mowed, an unduly long time will be needed for curing, except in a very dry climate. Fermentation and molding may occur, which will seriously damage the hay. Moreover, in humid climates such slow curing greatly increases the risk of damage from rain.

For reasonably rapid curing and the production of high-quality hay, it is usually best to let the crop lie in the swath for a few hours after mowing, until it is well wilted, or about one-fourth to one-third cured. Then it should be raked into small, loose windrows, preferably with a side-delivery rake. If good weather continues, the curing should be completed in the windrow and the hay hauled to the barn or stack directly from the windrow. To avoid serious loss of leaves in very dry climates, it may be necessary to handle the hay only early in the morning before it has become too dry.

When the weather is such that the hay cures rather slowly, it may be advisable to turn the windrows partly over in a few hours, in order to hasten the curing. Turning may also be necessary if the hay is wet by rain when in the windrow.

It is a common belief that the windrows made by a side-delivery rake cure more rapidly than those made with a dump rake. This is probably only because they are usually smaller. In Nebraska tests there was apparently no difference in rate of curing in windrows made by the two methods when they were of the same size.[28] The hay tedder was formerly often used to hasten the curing of heavy cuttings of hay in the swath. In recent years this has been largely abandoned, because it tends to shatter the leaves of legume hay.

325. Curing hay in cocks.—Not many years ago it was generally advised that when the best quality of hay was desired, regardless of expense, it should be put in good-sized, well-made cocks as soon as it had

Immature, Actively-Growing Grass Is Rich in Protein

On excellent, actively-growing grass pasture, such as this, dairy cows do not need a concentrate mixture high in protein, for the young grass is rich in protein.

Later, the Grasses and Cereals Are Lower in Protein

When the grasses and cereals have headed out, the percentage of protein, on the dry basis, is much lower than at early stages of growth. Hereford cattle on rye pasture which has headed out.

Making High-Quality Hay with Efficient Machinery

The side-delivery rake and the hay loader not only decrease labor in hay making, but they are also important in improving the quality of the hay.

Storing Alfalfa Hay That Is Leafy, but Dry Enough for Safety

To secure full feeding value from a legume hay crop, it must be cured so that the hay will be leafy and green-colored, yet it must be dry enough when stored to prevent molding or serious heating.

dried enough so it would not heat or mold. This method of curing preserves the color and vitamin A content, but it involves too much labor for use when there is any considerable acreage of hay. Also, in a humid climate there is much risk of damage from rain before the cocks dry out, unless one goes to the further considerable expense of covering the cocks with hay caps. Therefore the cocking of hay has become much less general than a few years ago.

However, it is probably wise to cock hay sometimes as an emergency measure to lessen damage from rain. Hay is injured most by heavy rain when it is nearly dry enough to store. Therefore, if there is every prospect of a hard storm at that time, it is a good plan to hurry and put the hay into large, well-made cocks. Unless the rain is unusually heavy, these will not wet through, there will be practically no loss from leaching, and the color and vitamin A content will be largely preserved.

When the weather clears and the outside of the cocks has dried, it may be necessary to open them somewhat to dry out the interior before the hay is hauled.

326. Do leaves aid in the curing process?—It has been a common belief that, as long as the leaves remain alive, the evaporation of water from them pulls water from the stems, thus helping to dry out the stems. This has been given as a reason for raking the hay into windrows with a side-delivery rake before the leaves have been killed by drying. A large proportion of the leaves would then be inside the windrows, where they would be protected from rapid drying, and they would aid in curing the stems.

Investigators who have recently studied this matter differ in their opinions concerning the importance of this factor.[29] In some of the experiments the stems have apparently dried about as fast when the leaves have been removed from the plants as when they were attached, even though the wounds were sealed with paraffin, so no loss of sap could occur through the wounds.

Even though the leaves may not aid materially in removing water from the stems, it is highly important for the other reasons which have been mentioned to rake the hay into windrows after it is well wilted in the swath.

327. Time of day to mow hay.—There has been much discussion concerning the best time of day to mow hay. The experiments on this question show that when there is a dew, mowing should not start in the morning until it has dried off. In Ohio tests the amount of water from dew still on legume hay crops at 7 o'clock a.m. sometimes actually amounted to more than one-fourth of the green weight of the plants.[30] Mowing at that time would greatly delay the curing process.

After the dew has evaporated, there is no advantage in waiting longer before mowing, in the hope that the sunlight will reduce the water content of the growing plants by afternoon. Unless the soil is so dry that the plants wilt, they will contain nearly as much water in the afternoon, even in hot weather, as in the forenoon.

328. Good equipment reduces cost and increases quality.—Proper equipment for efficient hay-making not only greatly decreases the labor cost, but also is important in improving the quality of the hay. The value of the side-delivery rake in the rapid curing of hay has already been pointed out. It is just as advantageous to have efficient machinery that will make it possible to store the hay rapidly as soon as it is dry enough. If this is not done, some will become too dry and a serious loss of leaves may result, or the hay will be bleached and its value thereby lessened.

329. Hauling and storing hay.—On most farms in the central and eastern states, hay is loaded on wagons and hauled to the barn for storage. When the hay is cured in the windrows, a hay loader is nearly essential, at least on large farms, to save labor and increase the speed of haying. At the barn the hay is generally unloaded with a hay fork or hay sling and mowed away. Care should be taken to distribute the hay well in the mow and not leave it in large, compact masses where it falls from the fork or sling. Such masses are especially apt to heat, if the hay is not thoroughly dry.

Good judgment should be used in putting the various kinds and qualities of hay in a place where they will be available when wanted, and not be covered with other hay. On a dairy farm, it is a mistake to put all the late-cut hay on top of the higher-quality, early-cut hay. If this is done, the cows may drop off severely in production in the fall when they get only the poorer hay.

There is considerable difference of opinion as to whether the sprinkling of salt on hay that contains a rather high percentage of moisture will aid appreciably in preventing molding or undue heating.[31] Many farmers use 10 to 20 lbs. of salt per ton of such hay, believing that the hay is then more apt to be of good quality. However, the salting of hay is no insurance against spoilage or even against spontaneous combustion if the hay is much too damp. Too great reliance on salting may, in fact, be dangerous. The only safe plan is not to store hay in a barn unless it is dry enough for safety.

In the dry climate of the West most of the hay, even alfalfa, is stacked in the fields. Where hay is made on an extensive basis, it is usually hauled to the stack with a push or sweep rake, and then stacked with some type of mechanical stacker. Especially in dry climates, the hay is sometimes baled directly from the windrow or cock.

Windrow pick-up balers have recently been developed which bale hay directly from the windrow. To cure satisfactorily, the hay must not be too moist when baled and it must not be packed too tightly in the bales. The bales are piled under cover with air spaces between them, or in arid climates may be placed on end in the field. As the handling of the hay is reduced to a minimum by this method, the maximum of leaves is saved in such a hay as alfalfa.

330. Chopping hay into the barn.—Recently some farmers have adopted the system of chopping the hay as it is hauled from the field, in a special hay cutter or a silage cutter, which blows the chopped hay into the barn. In the semi-arid districts the hay is sometimes similarly chopped and stacked in the open. The chopped hay occupies only one-half to one-third as much space as long hay, and thus barn storage space is saved. However, care must be taken not to overload the joists of the barn when this method is used. Chopped hay is convenient to feed, and especially in the case of hay of inferior quality it is eaten with less wastage.

The relative cost of chopping hay into the barn and of the usual methods of storing it will depend on several factors, especially the arrangement of the barn. Generally the cost of storing it by chopping will be little or no higher, where sufficient hay is raised to justify the expense of the cutter.[32]

In spite of some statements that have been made to the contrary, it is dangerous to store chopped hay in a mow or a stack when it contains more moisture than would be safe in the case of uncut hay. On the contrary, for safe storage chopped hay should contain less moisture than might be permitted in uncut hay. In Ohio tests chopped hay heated more than uncut hay, when stored with the same water content.[33] Dry chopped hay should not be put on top of hay that is somewhat damp, or dangerous heating may result.

Chopped hay should not be stored in ordinary silos, unless it is considerably dryer than would be necessary in the case of uncut hay stored in a mow or stack. Otherwise it is apt to heat greatly and it may even char.

331. Ventilated hay-storage structures.—There has recently been considerable interest in the storage of hay in ventilated hay mows and other structures, and a special type of ventilated hay-storage structure has been developed in this country. Tests at the Wisconsin and New York (Cornell) Stations indicate that to keep properly in such structures, chopped hay must be practically as dry as would be necessary if it were to be stored uncut in an ordinary mow.[34]

332. Aids in curing hay.—Especially with such crops as cowpeas and peanuts, which are thick stemmed and succulent, devices are often used, under unfavorable weather conditions, to allow the air to penetrate the cocks. The simplest is the perch, which is a stake about 6 feet high with cross arms 2 to 3 feet long. This is driven into the ground so that the cross arms do not touch the earth, and the green or partly-cured plants are then piled on the frame so as to make a tall, slender cock.

A somewhat more elaborate device, the pyramid, consists of 3 or 4 legs joined at the top and sometimes shaped so they can be driven firmly into the ground. This permits making a larger cock with an air space in the interior. Other frames combine the characteristics of the perch and the pyramid. Often such crops as cowpeas are stacked before thorough curing, rails supported at the ends being used to separate the stack into layers with air spaces between.

In districts with heavy rainfalls during the haying season, as in some sections of the South, the hay is often stacked in the field on cheap two-wheel trucks or on sleds, when dry enough to cock.[35] It is then covered with canvas or muslin covers and allowed to stand until thoroughly cured. When dry, the hay is drawn directly to the barn or baler on these trucks or sleds.

A machine has recently been developed in which the forage is passed between rollers after it is cut by the cutter bar of a power mower, to crush the stems and hasten the drying. After the crushing, the hay is dropped to the ground and cured in the usual manner.

Soybean hay is often difficult to cure by the usual methods, because it is cut late in the season, when the weather is cooler and rains are frequent. If too many weeds are not present, soybean hay can be cut with the grain binder and cured satisfactorily in small shocks, especially if harvested when the seeds are well developed.[36]

333. Brown hay.—When weather conditions render it impossible to make good hay by the usual methods, the crop is sometimes made into "brown hay." The forage is allowed to wilt thoroughly (until the water content has been reduced to about 50 per cent) and then is well packed in piles or a stack.

Extensive fermentation soon takes place in the damp mass and considerable heat is developed. If the process proceeds satisfactorily, the temperature should not exceed about 175°F.[37] The heat drives off the water in the mass and at length it becomes dry. In the fermentations a considerable part of the dry matter in the hay is oxidized and converted into carbon dioxide, water vapor, and other gaseous products. These losses may be as high as 40 per cent of the total dry matter.[38] In addition, the digestibility of the hay is generally decreased, especially of the protein.

The forage must not be too dry when stacked, or it cannot be packed firmly enough to prevent extreme heating and possible charring or burning. If the forage is too moist, it will spoil or be converted into stack silage. On account of these dangers and also because of the great loss of nutrients, the method cannot be recommended under usual conditions.

The product will vary in color from dark brown to nearly black, depending on the extent of the fermentation. The darker the color the lower will be the feeding value. Brown hay of good quality has an aromatic odor and is well liked by stock. It is probably very low in vitamins, and should therefore not be used as the only roughage for stock throughout the entire winter. Brown alfalfa hay of good quality has been about equal to good green-colored alfalfa hay for fattening steers and fattening lambs in Kansas and Utah tests, but black hay was of little value.[39] For dairy cows brown alfalfa hay was distinctly inferior to green-colored alfalfa hay in Kansas experiments.[40]

334. Spontaneous combustion.—If hay or other dry forage containing too much moisture is put into a mow or stack, rapid fermentations take place in which a large amount of heat is produced. In a large mow or stack most of this heat is retained in the mass, causing a rapid rise of temperature. In these fermentations highly unstable organic compounds are apparently formed which are readily oxidized.[41]

At temperatures of 150° to 175° F. all bacteria or molds are killed or made inactive, but the oxidations continue, and the mass may become extremely hot. Finally, the hay begins to char and at a temperature of from 300° to 400° F. spontaneous combustion may occur and the mass burst into flames. This generally happens a month or six weeks after the hay is stored, but it may occur sooner.

The only way to avoid such loss is never to store hay in a large mass unless it is thoroughly cured. If hay in a mow or stack heats unduly a day or two after storing, and pungent odors, with much vapor and gas, are given off, it should be removed at once and spread out to dry. Removing the hay later may only hasten spontaneous combustion. All that can usually be done then is to compact the hay as much as possible and cover it with other material, so as to keep the air out.

In some instances compressed carbon dioxide gas from the containers used in soda fountains has been introduced into the mow through a pipe to reduce the heating and prevent fire.

To avoid spontaneous combustion the following points should be given attention: The hay should be well distributed in the mow, as has been pointed out previously. After the crop is placed in the barn no water should be permitted to fall on it, as from leaks in the roof. Stacks should never be built on old, rotten stack bottoms. Baled hay, grain in the sheaf, or other heavy material should not be put on top of hay in a mow which is going through the sweat, for it will prevent the escape of heat and gases. Crops upon which rain has fallen should receive extra care, and should not be housed until completely dry.

335. Measurement and shrinkage of hay.—Farmers, ranchers, and hay dealers buy and sell large quantities of hay in the stack according to the estimated weight. The stack is measured and the volume and tonnage are then computed by one of several rules in common use. The density of the hay and therefore the number of cubic feet required per ton are affected by many factors. Hay that was stored when slightly damp will be more compact than that which was very dry. The coarseness of the hay also affects its density.

The following rules are recommended by the United States Department of Agriculture for estimating the tonnage of hay in stacks from the volume in cubic feet:[42] For hay 30 to 90 days in the stack, 485 cubic feet per ton for alfalfa; 640 for timothy and timothy mixed hay; and 600 for wild hay. For hay over 90 days in the stack, 470 cubic feet per ton for alfalfa; 625 for timothy and timothy mixed hay; and 450 for wild hay. The same approximate figures may be used for hay in a mow.

The volume of hay in a mow can readily be computed, but it is more difficult to determine the volume of a stack. Different rules for estimating this have been used in various sections of the country. The following are recommended by the United States Department of Agriculture after much investigation on the subject:[43]

The volume of a rectangular or oblong stack in cubic feet is:
For low, round-topped stacks: $(0.52x0) — (0.44xW) \times W \times L$.
For high, round-topped stacks: $(0.52x0) — (0.46xW) \times W \times L$.
For square, flat-topped stacks: $(0.56x0) — (0.55xW) \times W \times L$.
The volume of a round stack is: $(0.04x0) — (0.012xC) \times C^2$.

In these formulas O is the "over" (the distance from the base on one side of the stack, over the stack, and to the base on the other side); W is the width; L is the length; and C is the circumference of a round stack, or the distance around it. In measuring a round stack the "over" should be measured in two positions, at right angles to each other.

Hay stored in the mow will shrink in weight, due to drying out and also to fermentations taking place during the sweating process, in which nutrients are broken down into carbon dioxide and water.[44] The shrinkage will vary, depending on the water content of the hay when placed in the mow, and may reach 20 per cent or over. When hay is stacked the shrinkage is greater, since the outside of the stack is exposed to the weather. A stack 12 feet in diameter has about one-third of its contents in the surface foot.

336. Artificial drying of hay or other forage.—Recently various driers have been developed for the artificial drying of hay crops or other forage, and this new method has attracted much attention. The green forage is commonly first chopped in a hay cutter or silage cutter and then passed through the drier. Here it is exposed by various methods to a current of hot air or a mixture of hot air and gases from an oil burner or furnace. Sometimes the green material is partly dried in the field to reduce the cost of dehydrating it.

Though the temperature of the hot gases may be 600° F. or more, the forage itself does not become so hot as to be injured in a good drier. This is due to the cooling effect produced when the water evaporates from the plant tissues. In this method there is no loss of leaves, and therefore a maximum yield of dry matter and of protein and other nutrients is secured. Also, the green color is preserved, and the hay is of a very high market grade.

Such dehydration does not materially lower the digestibility, in comparison with the fresh green material, if the temperature is not too high. **(116)** Otherwise, the digestibility may be decreased considerably, especially that of the protein.

Experiments have shown that the artificially-dried, or dehydrated, hay is much higher in vitamin A value (carotene content) than that which is sun-cured in the field.[45] Even in favorable hay-making weather, field-cured hay usually contains only one-half to one-fifth as much vitamin A as dehydrated hay. The content of vitamin E is also greater in the dehydrated hay.[46]

On the other hand, dehydrated hay is generally much lower than sun-cured hay in vitamin D, as are all green plants before they are exposed to the sun during field-curing.[47] Sometimes dehydrated hay contains practically no vitamin D. Therefore it cannot be relied on as a vitamin D supplement in stock feeding, as for swine in winter.

On account of the large cost of the hay driers, the considerable amount of fuel required to dehydrate each ton of hay, and the power required in the process, the cost of drying hay artificially is much higher than that of curing it in the field. For these reasons, the method will probably have very limited use in sections where good hay can be made by ordinary methods.

In certain regions where rains are frequent during the summer, much of the field-cured hay is seriously damaged, in spite of good management. Thus Snell estimates that in certain areas of Louisiana from 40 to 60 per cent of the hay is damaged by rain, considerable of it being a total loss.[48] Also, much forage that could be made into hay is never harvested on account of the heavy rainfall. Under such conditions either the dehydration of hay or ensiling it offers especial advantages.

337. Feeding experiments with dehydrated hay.—But few experiments have yet been reported in which the actual feeding value of dehydrated hay for the various classes of stock has been determined in comparison with that of field-cured hay made from the same crop. The data available show, as would be expected, that the dehydrated hay has a higher value per ton than field-cured hay when fed as part of the usual ration.

In several Pennsylvania experiments with dairy heifers dehydrated alfalfa, red clover, timothy, and mixed timothy-and-clover hay have been directly compared with field-cured hay from the same field.[49] The dehydrated hay was more palatable, and the heifers made more rapid gains on it, when equal weights of the two kinds of hay were fed.

A Louisiana test shows that dehydrated hay, even though it is of high value, cannot serve as a complete substitute for concentrates in feeding dairy cows.[50] When fed a good concentrate mixture as a supplement to pasture, cows produced 20 per cent more milk than when fed dehydrated soybean hay as the pasture supplement. In other Louisiana trials dehydrated soybean hay was much superior to field-cured soybean hay for fattening steers.[51] However, the field-cured hay was of poor quality, containing over 45 per cent fiber. This was due to difficulty in curing it, because of frequent rains.

In Wisconsin tests dehydrated pea-vine hay from a canning factory was equal to field-cured alfalfa hay for dairy cows and dairy heifers.[52] However, it did not produce quite as rapid gains on fattening lambs as did the alfalfa hay.

It is perhaps not safe to feed dehydrated hay as the only roughage for a long period of time, without pasture during the growing season. This is indicated by the results of Missouri tests in which dairy heifers were fed only on alfalfa hay, either dehydrated or field-cured, from the time they were yearlings until they had calved.[53] The heifers fed the field-cured hay had normal calves, but all except one of those fed the dehydrated hay produced dead or weak calves. Similar results were also secured with rabbits.

The heifers were housed in an open shed and were exposed to sunlight in an exercise yard, and therefore should not have suffered from a lack of vitamin D in the dehydrated hay. In fact, they showed no indications of rickets. Perhaps some unknown nutritive factor had been destroyed in the dehydrated hay which was still present in that which had been field-cured.

338. Dehydrated young forage not a concentrate.—On account of the high nutritive value of young grasses and legumes, experiments have been conducted to determine whether such forage, when dehydrated, could be used satisfactorily as a substitute for grain and other concentrates.

Appendix Table I shows that dried grass from frequently-clipped plots contains, on the average, 18.0 per cent protein and only 20.1 per cent fiber, in comparison with 28 to 30 per cent fiber for most hay. The dried grass is considerably more digestible than hay and supplies 64.7 lbs. total digestible nutrients per 100 lbs. However, it is lower than most concentrates in total digestible nutrients and especially in net energy.

In Vermont and Washington experiments the production of good dairy cows was well maintained when dehydrated young grass was substituted for part of the concentrates usually fed.[54] However, when the dehydrated grass replaced all the concentrates, and the usual amounts of hay or hay and silage were fed, the production was reduced.

The ration was then so bulky that the cows could not consume sufficient nutrients to keep up the maximum milk flow.

In a Vermont test cows fed a reduced amount of hay and silage, with a large allowance of dehydrated grass (greater than the weight of concentrates usually fed), produced as much milk as on a normal ration of concentrates, hay, and silage.[55] The dehydrated grass was also satisfactory as a silage substitute.

On account of the high cost of harvesting the immature grass at frequent intervals and of dehydrating the watery material, the use of such dehydrated grass as a substitute for concentrates does not appear to be practicable under ordinary conditions.

QUESTIONS

1. Discuss the influence of stage of maturity of forage crops on per cent of protein in the dry matter, on content of calcium and phosphorus, and on amount of vitamin A.
2. Why will immature forage, such as pasture grass, not fully take the place of concentrates in livestock feeding?
3. What is the effect of rate of growth and season of year on protein content of grass, on the dry basis?
4. State three forage crops which are richest in nutrients when mature, and tell why this is so.
5. What is the effect of frequent cutting or continuous close grazing upon the yield of dry matter by pasture or hay crops?
6. Discuss the influence of soil fertility on the composition of forage crops, considering content of protein, phosphorus, and calcium.
7. What is the effect of early cutting on the protein content and digestibility of hay?
8. In what respects may grass hay be improved by nitrogenous fertilization?
9. Discuss the composition of mature, weathered grass, and the effects upon stock receiving only such feed.
10. Why is pasturage usually the most economical feed for cattle, sheep, and horses during the growing season?
11. Discuss the importance of pasture improvement.
12. State the essentials of proper grazing management for the improvement of pastures.
13. Explain the two general types of pasture fertilization. How would you decide which system to use on a particular farm?
14. Discuss the fertilization of pastures without the use of a nitrogen fertilizer.
15. What are the two points of view with reference to nitrogenous fertilization of pastures? Under what conditions would you fertilize a pasture with nitrogen?
16. Discuss the use of manure on pastures. If it is used, what precaution must be taken, so that stock will eat the grass the first season?
17. What are the benefits from rotation grazing?
18. Describe the intensive system of pasture fertilization, called the Hohenheim system.
19. What methods can be used for providing feed to supplement short pasture in mid-summer? Discuss the advantages or disadvantages of: (a) Annual spring fertilization with nitrogen and later applications of nitrogen during the season; (b) growing special emergency pasture crops, such as Sudan grass; (c) grazing second-crop growth on hay meadows, where hay has been cut early; (d) use of silage or hay.
20. In what respects does the improvement of a range in the West differ from the improvement of pastures in a humid district?

21. What are the objects in hay-making?
22. State 7 qualities that good hay should possess.
23. How can you tell when hay is dry enough to put in the barn?
24. Discuss the following losses of nutritive value in hay-making, and tell how each can be minimized: (a) By shattering; (b) by fermentation; (c) by leaching.
25. How can you tell whether a given sample of hay is high or low in vitamin A value?
26. How would you cure hay, where there is a considerable acreage, so as to keep the losses of vitamins at a minimum, to produce hay of a high protein content, and to reduce other losses?
27. Under what conditions may it be wise to put hay in cocks?
28. Discuss the hauling and storage of hay.
29. What precautions are necessary when hay is chopped into the barn as it is hauled from the field?
30. What special methods may be used in curing hay under unfavorable conditions?
31. Why is not the making of brown hay advisable under usual conditions?
32. How may losses through spontaneous combustion of hay be reduced to a minimum?
33. Discuss the artificial drying of hay, particularly with reference to the vitamin content and general nutritive value.
34. What is the relative vitamin D content of field-cured and artificially-dried hay?

REFERENCES

1. Brown, Conn. (Storrs) Buls. 187, 190; Ind. Rpt. 1933; Kan. Rpt. 1930-32; Lush, La. Rpt. 1929-31; Elting, La Master, and Mitchell, S. C. Rpt. 1933; Newlander, Jones, and Ellenberger, Vt. Bul. 362; Dustman and Van Landingham, Jour. Amer. Soc. Agron., 22, 1930, pp. 719-724; Woodman, Blunt, and Stewart, Jour. Agri. Sci., England, 16, 1926, pp. 205-274; 17, 1927, pp. 209-263.
2. Crozier, Mich. Bul. 141; Wiggans, N. Y. (Cornell) Bul. 424; Newlander, Jones, and Ellenberger, Vt. Bul. 362; Aldous, Jour. Amer. Soc. Agron., 22, 1930, pp. 385-392; Wolfe, Jour. Amer. Soc. Agron., 18, 1926, pp. 381-384; Schutt, Hamilton, and Selwyn, Jour. Agr. Sci., England, 22, 1932, pp. 647-656; Davies and Sim, Australian Council Sci. and Indus. Res. Pamphlet 18. See also: White, Jour. Amer. Soc. Agron., 21, 1929, pp. 589-594.
3. Brown, Conn. (Storrs) Bul. 190; Elting, La Master, and Mitchell, S. C. Rpt. 1930; Woodman, Norman, et al., Jour. Agr. Sci., England, 18, 1928, pp. 269-296; 19, 1929, pp. 236-265; 20, 1930, pp. 587-617; 22, 1932, pp. 852-873; Stapledon, Welsh Plant Breeding Sta., Aberystwyth, Ser. H, No. 3.
4. Walker and Brown, Iowa Bul. 305.
5. Bender, N. J. Bul. 363.
6. Wilton and Morris, Ohio Bimo. Bul. 136.
7. Morrison, Salisbury, et al., N. Y. (Cornell) Rpts. 1933, 1934; see also: Prince, Blood, and Percival, N. H. Cir. 41; Prince, Blood, Phillips, and Percival, N. H. Bul. 271; Musbach, Mortimer, and Fink, Wis. Bul. 428.
8. Hart, Guilbert, and Goss, Cal. Bul. 543; Hart and Guilbert, Cal. Bul. 560; Wilson, New Mex. 189; Lantow, New Mex. Bul. 202; Watkins, New Mex. Bul. 212; Hopper and Nesbitt, N. D. Bul. 236; Christensen and Hopper, N. D. Bul. 260; McCall, Wash. Buls. 260, 275, 305; Roberts, Wyo. Bul. 146; McCreary, Wyo. Buls. 157, 184.
9. Semple and Woodward, U. S. Dept. Agr., Misc. Pub. 194; Piper, et al., U. S. Dept. Agr. Yearbook, 1923.
10. Young, Ind. Bul. 359.
11. See especially: U. S. Dept. Agr., Misc. Pub. 194, A Pasture Handbook, by Semple, Vinall, Enlow, and Woodward.
12. Graber, Wis. Buls. 396, 405, 410; Aldous, Ecology, 11, 1930, pp. 752-759; Kan. Rpt. 1926-28; Sprague, Soil Sci., 36, 1933, pp. 189-209; Jones, Empire Jour. Expt. Agr., 1, 1933, pp. 43-57.
13. Johnstone-Wallace, N. Y. (Cornell) Bul. 612.
14. Hodgson, Grunder, Knott, and Ellington, Wash. Bul. 294; see also: Brown, Conn. (Storrs) Bul. 190; Comfort and Brown, Mo. Bul. 328; Gerlaugh, Salter, and Welton, Ohio Bul. 470; Hulme, Utah Bul. 237; Hutcheson and Wolfe, Va. Rpts. 1918, 1928-31; Semple, Vinall, Enlow, and Woodward, U. S. Dept. Agr. Misc. Pub. 194.
15. Foley, Montague, and Parsons, Mass. Bul. 262; Archibald, Nelson, and Bennett, Jour. Agr. Res., 45, 1932, pp. 627-640; Bender, N. J. Bul. 564; Salter and Yoder, Ohio Bimo. Bul. 152; Fink, Mortimer, and Truog, Wis. Bul. 421; Jour. Amer. Soc. Agron., 25, 1933, pp. 441-453; Mortimer, Ahlgren, Graul, and Rupel, Wis. Bul. 428.
16. Bender, N. J. Bul. 564.
17. Mortimer, Graul, and Ahlgren, Wis. Buls. 421, 428.
18. For further information on this subject see: Sampson, Range and Pasture Management; Sampson, Livestock Husbandry on Range and Pasture; Barnes, Western Grazing Grounds; and the publications of the western experiment stations and of the United States Department of Agriculture.

19. Hanson, Love, and Morris, Colo. Bul. 377; Aldous, Cattleman, 14, 1928, pp. 71, 73, 75, 77, Kan. Rpts. 1928-30, 1930-32; Shepperd, N. D. Bul. 233; Blizzard, Hawkins, and Kiltz, Okla. Rpt. 1930-32; Sarvis, U. S. Dept. Agr. Buls. 1170, 1337.
20. Browne, U. S. Dept. Agr., Tech. Bul. 141.
21. U. S. Dept. of Agr., Handbook of Official Hay Standards.
22. Parker, U. S. Dept. Agr., Farmers' Bul. 1539; Kiesselbach and Anderson, U. S. Dept. Agr., Tech. Bul. 235; Iowa Rpt. 1929.
23. Armsby, Penn. Rpt. 1888; Newlander and Jones, Vt. Bul. 348; Hart, Kline, and Humphrey, Jour. Agr. Res., 1932, pp. 507-511; Woodman, Bee, and Griffith, Jour. Agr. Sci., England, 20, 1930, pp. 53-62; Watson and Ferguson, Jour. Agr. Sci., England, 21, 1931, pp. 235-246.
24. Headden, Colo. Bul. 110.
25. Headden, Colo. Bul. 111; see also: Mead and Jackson, Hilgardia, Cal. Sta., 6, 1931, No. 1; Ames and Boltz, Ohio Bimo. Bul. 2, 1917, pp. 178-180.
26. Kiesselbach and Anderson, U. S. Dept. Agr., Tech. Bul. 235.
27. Diseker, Ala. Rpts. 1932, 1933; Hughes, et al., Iowa Rpt. 1933; Rather and Morrish, Mich. Quar. Bul. 17, 1935, No. 4; Kiesselbach and Anderson, Nebr. Res. Bul. 36, U. S. Dept. Agr., Tech. Bul. 235; Willard, Ohio Bul. 470; Parker, U. S. Dept. Agr., Farmers' Bul. 1539; Reynoldson and Kinsman, U. S. Dept. Agr., Farmers' Bul. 1525.
28. Kiesselbach and Anderson, U. S. Dept. Agr., Tech. Bul. 235.
29. Iowa Rpt. 1928; Higgins, Mich. Tech. Bul. 83; Jones and Palmer, Miss. Rpt. 1932, Agr. Engin., 15, 1934, pp. 198-201; Willard, Jour. Amer. Soc. Agron., 18, 1926, pp. 369-375; Kiesselbach and Anderson, U. S. Dept. Agr., Tech. Bul. 235; Westover, U. S. Dept. Agr., Bul. 1424.
30. Willard, Ohio Bul. 470.
31. Stuart and James, Jour. Agr. Res., 42, 1931, pp. 657-664; Shutt, Canada Expt. Farms, Div. Chem. Rpt. 1927.
32. Cannon, Hansen, and Collins, Iowa Rpts. 1931, 1932, 1933; Harrison, N. Y. (Cornell) Station, unpublished data; Selby, Ore. Bul. 248.
33. Batchell, Miller, Silver, and Weaver, Ohio Bul. 516; Miller, Silver, and Willard, Ohio Bul. 532.
34. Duffee, Graber, Bohstedt, Roche, and Hart, Wis. Bul. 430; Morrison and Salisbury, N. Y. (Cornell) Sta., unpublished data.
35. McClure, U. S. Dept. Agr., Farmers' Bul. 956.
36. Mich. Rpt. 1930-32; Irvin, Penn. Bul. 293.
37. Mangold, Handb. Ernähr. und Stoffwechsels, Vol. I, pp. 287-289.
38. Swanson, Call, and Salmon, Jour. Agr. Res., 18, 1919, pp. 299-304; Honcamp, Landw. Vers. Sta., 100, 1922, pp. 79-88.
39. McCampbell, Jour. Agr. Res., 18, 1919, pp. 303-304; Maynard, Esplin, and Boswell, Utah Bul. 238; see also: Folger, Cal. Bul. 575.
40. Kan. Rpts. 1926-28, 1928-30.
41. Browne, U. S. Dept. Agr., Tech. Bul. 141; U. S. Dept. Agr., Rpt. of Conference on Spontaneous Heating and Ignition of Agricultural and Industrial Wastes, 1930; Lamb, Iowa Cir. 36; James and Price, Science, 67, 1928, pp. 322-324.
42. Hosterman, U. S. Dept. Agr., Leaflet 72, Tech. Bul. 239; see also: Adams, Cal. Bul. 570; Mont. Rpt. 1929; Sotola, Wash. Bul. 243.
43. Hosterman, U. S. Dept. Agr., Leaflet 72, Tech. Bul. 239.
44. McClure, U. S. Dept. Agr., Bul. 873; Sotola, Wash. Bul. 243.
45. Ind. Rpt. 1930; Hathaway, Davis, and Graves, Nebr. Res. Bul. 62; Russell, Taylor, and Chichester, N. J. Bul. 560; Miller and Bearse, Wash. Bul. 292.
46. Hathaway, Davis, and Graves, Nebr. Res. Bul. 62.
47. Penn. Bul. 293; Hart, Klein, and Humphrey, Wis. Bul. 425; see also: Hodgson and Knott, Wash. Bul. 291.
48. Snell, La. Bul. 257.
49. Bechdel and Williams, Penn. Buls. 266, 279, 293; Bechdel, Clyde, Cromer, and Williams, Penn. Bul. 308.
50. Snell, La. Rpt. 1929-31.
51. Snell, La. Bul. 257.
52. Rupel, Rocke, and Bohstedt, Wis. Bul. 420.
53. E. B. Powell of Ralston Purina Co., address before Certified Milk Producers' Assoc., January, 1935.
54. Newlander, Vt. Buls. 348, 350; Knott and Hodgson, Wash. Bul. 291, Jour. Dairy Sci., 17, 1934, pp. 409-415; see also: Watson, Jour. Agr. Sci., England, 21, 1931, pp. 414-424.
55. Camburn, Vt. Buls. 359, 368.

CHAPTER XII

SILAGE AND SOILING CROPS

I. SILAGE AND THE SILO

339. Importance of silage.—In most of the leading stock-farming districts of the United States silage is one of the very important feeds.* According to the Census, in 1929 there were grown on 379,364 farms in this country a total of over four million acres of corn for silage, and the acreage had increased to 4,565,000 acres in 1935. This does not include the large acreage of sorghums grown for silage and the acreage of other silage crops, exact figures for which are not available.

The widespread use of silage in this country is easily explained when we consider the following advantages which it offers in livestock feeding:

1. Over the greater part of the United States either corn or the sorghums surpass other forage crops in actual yield of total digestible nutrients per acre. Alfalfa is the only close competitor in yield of nutrients, and then only for areas well adapted to its growth. Corn or sorghum forage may readily be made into silage of excellent quality, and a far greater feeding value is secured when these crops are used for this purpose than when they are fed as dry fodder or when the grain is removed and the grain and stover are fed separately. The use of silage therefore permits the keeping of more stock on a given area of land.

2. At a low expense silage furnishes high-quality succulent feed for any desired season of the year. For winter feeding, silage is far cheaper than roots and is just as efficient a feed, except possibly in the case of animals being fitted for shows or milk cows on advanced registry test. For summer feeding, silage furnishes succulent feed with less bother and expense than do soiling crops.

3. In the case of such crops as corn and the sorghums, which almost invariably make good silage, there is a smaller loss of nutrients in making silage than usually occurs when the forage is cured as dry fodder or hay.

4. Silage, even from plants with coarse stalks, such as corn and the sorghums, is eaten practically without waste. On the other hand, a considerable part of dry corn or sorghum fodder is usually wasted, even if it is of good quality.

5. Crops may be ensiled when the weather does not permit of curing them into dry fodder. In some sections of the South it is almost

---

*The first experimental silos built in the United States for investigations on silage were erected in 1881 by W. A. Henry at the University of Wisconsin and by I. P. Roberts at Cornell University in New York. Through their pioneer experiments and those of F. H. King at the University of Wisconsin, the value of silage was first called prominently to the attention of the farmers of the United States. It is of interest that Wisconsin still leads in number of silos, with New York second.

impossible to preserve the corn crop satisfactorily as grain and stover, on account of the humidity and also because rodents and weevils cause great loss in the stored grain.

Also, in some districts, particularly in the South, frequent heavy rains make it exceedingly difficult to produce hay of good quality. Preserving the crop as silage avoids these difficulties.

6. Weedy crops which would make poor hay may produce silage of good quality, the ensiling process killing practically all the weed seeds present.

7. The product from a given area can be stored in less space as silage than as dry forage. A cubic foot of hay in the mow, weighing less than 5 lbs., contains not over 4.3 lbs. of dry matter. An average cubic foot of corn silage from a 30-foot silo, weighing about 39.0 lbs., will contain 11.0 lbs. dry matter, or over 2.5 times as much. Dry corn fodder takes up even more space per pound of dry matter than hay. In climates where it is necessary to store corn fodder under cover this may be an added reason for the use of the silo.

8. When the corn or sorghum crop is ensiled, the forage is removed from the land early, so that it may be prepared for another crop.

9. In sections where there is considerable damage from the European corn borer, it is important to bear in mind that cutting the stalks close to the ground and then ensiling the crop is one of the best methods of controlling the pest and lessening the damage.

340. Value and use of silage.—On account of the importance of silage for feeding dairy cattle, beef cattle, and sheep, its value and use for these classes of stock and also for horses and mules are discussed in detail in the respective chapters of Part III. Information is also presented in the following chapters on each of the important silage crops.

Apart from the nutrients it contains, good silage has certain desirable qualities not possessed by most dry roughages. It is highly palatable, and therefore stock will usually eat more roughage on the dry basis when fed both silage and hay or other dry forage than when receiving only dry feed. This will often make possible a considerable saving in the amount of concentrates required for good production.

Silage made from corn, the sorghums, and most other crops is also slightly laxative. This effect is especially advantageous when little or no legume hay is available. If cattle or sheep are fed only dry non-legume roughage during the winter they are apt to become constipated and unthrifty.

Occasionally the statement is still made that on account of the acidity of silage injurious effects are produced when stock are continuously fed liberal amounts. This statement is entirely unfounded. The organic acids in silage are similar to those normally produced in the digestive tract of ruminants in the digestion of the fiber and pentosans of the feed through bacterial action. These acids are utilized by the animal for food in the same manner as are the sugars.

Experiments by the Ohio Station have shown conclusively that the feeding of large amounts of corn silage continuously for long periods to dairy cows does not tend to produce acidosis, or any other undesirable condition. (**183**) In fact, corn silage and other corn forage have a residual alkaline effect on the body, just opposite to a condition of acidosis. In the making of silage by the A. I. V. method that is mentioned later, mineral acids are added to the green forage as it is ensiled. (**347**)   Ground limestone or some other form of calcium carbonate should be fed with such silage, to neutralize the mineral acids.

Silage is used most extensively for the feeding of dairy cattle, especially dairy cows. Cows will generally produce more milk on a ration containing both silage and good hay than they will when only dry roughage is fed. The only exception is when they have an abundance of excellent legume hay of considerably better quality than the average. Silage is particularly important for milk production when the dry roughage available is rather inferior.

Silage is just as useful and economical for beef cattle and sheep as it is for dairy cows. In fact, as is pointed out in Chapter XIV, the value per ton of well-matured corn silage for fattening cattle or sheep is even slightly higher, in comparison with that of hay, than it is for dairy cows. Silage aids in keeping beef breeding cows and breeding ewes in thrifty condition during the winter, as well as being a cheap feed for them. Good silage may also be used in a limited way with idle horses and those not hard worked in winter, especially brood mares and colts.

Spoiled, moldy silage should always be discarded, and special care taken to feed no such material to sheep or horses, which are much more easily affected by it than cattle. Silage which is unusually sour may cause digestive disturbances with sheep. For all animals, only as much silage should be supplied as will be cleaned up at each feeding. Care should be taken to remove any waste, for it spoils in a short time on exposure to the air. Frozen silage must be thawed before feeding.

The amounts of silage commonly fed per head daily to the various classes of stock are about as follows: Dairy cows, 30 to 50 lbs. for those in milk, with somewhat less for dry cows; dairy heifers, 12 to 20 lbs.; beef breeding cows, 30 to 50 lbs.; fattening 2-year-old steers, 25 to 30 lbs. at the beginning of the fattening period, the allowance decreasing as they fatten until only 10 to 15 lbs. are fed; fattening calves, from 10 to 20 lbs. at the beginning of the feeding period to 8 to 10 lbs. or less during the latter part; brood mares and idle horses, 15 to 30 lbs.; breeding ewes, 2 lbs. per 100 lbs. live weight (sometimes more is safely fed); fattening lambs, 1.5 to 3.0 lbs.

341. Silage for summer feeding.—Many farmers who fully appreciate the value of silage for winter feeding do not realize its value for supplementing dried-up pastures in the summer. It is also economical as a partial substitute for pasturage on high-priced land where all the stock possible must be kept per acre. It is pointed out later in this chapter that silage is generally a much cheaper and more satisfactory feed than green soiling crops for these purposes. (**356**)

Silage can be used for summer feeding only if enough animals are fed to use 2 inches or more of silage daily from the entire surface of the silo, to keep it from spoiling.

342. Cost and economy of silage.—The experiments with dairy cows, beef cattle, and sheep, which are reviewed in Part III, show clearly that much more economical and efficient feed is furnished when a corn or sorghum crop is ensiled than when it is fed as dry fodder. There is, however, considerable argument as to whether silage is actually a cheaper stock feed than good hay.

In this connection the table in the following chapter is of special interest, since it shows the average yield of digestible nutrients per acre for the United States from corn silage, alfalfa hay, clover hay, and mixed hay or timothy hay. (**368**) This table shows that corn silage, with an average yield of 7.28 tons per acre, exceeds all these hay crops in average yield of total digestible nutrients.

Corn silage furnishes more than twice as much digestible nutrients per acre as timothy or timothy-and-clover mixed hay, and 65 per cent more than red clover. Only alfalfa even approaches it in yield of digestible nutrients per acre. These facts are of great importance to the farmer who desires to produce as much feed as possible on his farm.

The following table presents the results of cost accounting records on farms in various states in which the relative cost of corn silage and of the common kinds of hay has been determined. In considering these data it should be borne in mind that on the farms where all of the land was not adapted to alfalfa, this crop was probably grown on the fields best suited to it. The average yield of corn silage on the particular Wisconsin farms included in the studies was considerably lower than the state average, and the cost per ton was therefore high.

Yield and cost per ton of corn silage and hay

	Iowa*		Wisconsin†		New York‡	
	Yield per acre	Cost per ton	Yield per acre	Cost per ton	Yield per acre	Cost per ton
	Tons	Dollars	Tons	Dollars	Tons	Dollars
Corn silage	8.2	3.95	5.66	5.35	9.7	4.86
Alfalfa hay	2.5	13.69	2.48	7.85	2.3	10.31
Clover and timothy hay.....	1.2	11.84	1.73	9.71	1.6	10.90

*Hopkins, Iowa Bul. 261. Data for 1925-27.
†McNall and Ellis, Wis. Res. Bul. 83. Data for 1922-24.
‡Findlen, N. Y. (Cornell) Exten. Bul. 318. Data for 1931-33.

On the Iowa farms the cost per ton of corn silage was only one-third that of hay or less, while on the Wisconsin and New York farms the cost of silage was somewhat higher in proportion to that of hay. The experiments summarized in Part III show that for dairy cows corn silage is worth 33 to 40 per cent as much per ton as good legume hay, and for beef cattle or sheep one-half as much per ton.

It might be concluded from these data that it is not economical to feed corn silage to dairy cattle when the cost per ton is more than 40 per cent as much as that of good hay. However, other factors must be considered than merely the relative costs per ton as determined in cost-accounting studies. First, all labor is valued at a uniform price per hour in such studies, regardless of whether it is in a rush season or not. When both corn silage and hay are produced, the demand for labor is distributed much better than when only hay is used for winter roughage. Therefore the need of extra hired labor during hay-making may often be avoided.

Growing a cultivated crop, such as corn or sorghum, in the rotation may have a special value for the control of weeds.

In humid sections a considerable part of the hay crop will usually be injured by rain, in spite of good management. It cannot be assumed therefore that the average hay actually fed on stock farms is of a high market grade. Much of it is, in fact, decidedly inferior. On the other hand, corn or sorghum silage is generally of high quality, if even moderate care is taken in ensiling the crop.

Last, but not least, it is often difficult in humid sections to cure, without serious damage from rain, a large acreage of hay before it becomes too mature. This difficulty is much greater when hay is the only roughage than if silage is also produced.

Considering all these factors, it seems reasonable to conclude that silage is an economical feed for cattle and sheep over most of the United States. However, in the irrigated alfalfa districts of the West there are many areas in which the cost of producing high-quality alfalfa hay is very low in comparison with the cost of silage. In these areas the hay is decidedly more economical as a feed. Hay is also more economical than silage in some sections of the northern states which are particularly adapted to hay production, but where the growing season is too short or too cool for corn or other good silage crops.

The cost per ton of silage will obviously depend largely on the yield per acre. Therefore corn or sorghum for silage should be grown on land well adapted to the crop, and the field should be so fertilized and tilled that it will produce a large yield per acre.

The cost of ensiling the crop should be reduced as much as possible by using efficient methods. For example, it took only two-thirds as long to haul corn forage from the field on low-rack wagons in Massachusetts tests as it did on high-rack wagons.[1] Where the acreage is sufficient, the expense is reduced materially by using a corn binder. On large farms an ensilage harvester may be economical. Care should be taken to run the silage cutter at the proper speed for the most efficient results and to keep the knives sharp and properly adjusted.

343. How ensiling preserves green forage.—When green forage from a suitable silage crop is placed in a compact mass in a silo the following characteristic changes take place which convert it into silage:[2] For a time the living plant cells continue to respire, or breathe, rapidly using up the oxygen in the air within the mass and giving off carbon dioxide (carbonic acid gas). Within 5 hours practically all the oxygen has disappeared, and this prevents the development of molds, which are unable to grow in the absence of oxygen.

Certain acid-forming bacteria multiply enormously in the silage, as conditions are favorable for their growth. At the end of 2 days each gram of silage juice (about one-fourth of a teaspoonful) may contain one hundred billion bacteria. These bacteria attack the sugars in the green forage, producing organic acids, chiefly lactic acid (the acid of sour milk), with some acetic acid (the acid of vinegar), and traces of other acids. This production of acid is the most important change in the silage process, for the acidity prevents the growth of undesirable bacteria, such as cause rotting, or putrefaction.

When the acidity has reached a certain degree, the fermentation is checked, and finally the action practically ceases. If air does not gain entrance into the mass of silage, it will then keep for long periods with but little change. Instances are on record where corn silage made 12 to 14 years before has been found to be of satisfactory quality. If air does penetrate, as at the top of the silo or adjacent to a crack in the wall, mold will grow and destroy the acid. Putrefactive bacteria can then develop and cause further spoilage.

While the sugars are the chief compounds acted upon by the bacteria in the acid fermentations, the starch and pentosans may be attacked to some extent. However, the amount of acid developed in the silage depends largely on the percentage of sugar in the ensiled crop. If the forage is very high in sugar, as in the case of corn or sorghum which is too immature, so much acid may develop that the silage will be unpalatable to stock. Also, the feeding value will be lowered, because there will be a greater loss of nutrients in the fermentations. Normally the amount of acid in good silage is not greater than 1.0 to 2.4 per cent of the total weight.

In addition to the acids, some ordinary or ethyl alcohol is produced and traces of other alcohols. The alcohols largely combine with the acids to form compounds that aid in producing the characteristic aroma of good silage. Yeast cells develop in the silage to some extent in the early stages of the process, but are relatively unimportant.

In the silage formation the proteins in the green forage are broken down or digested to a considerable extent, probably by the enzymes in the plant cells. This is very similar to the changes that occur when proteins are digested into simpler compounds in the animal body, and therefore the action is not detrimental.

During the fermentations in silage the temperature rises somewhat, but if the mass has been well compacted, so that but little air is present, the temperature in the interior of the silo rarely reaches 100° F. The changes are therefore far less extensive than those which occur in the making of brown hay. (**333**)

344. Losses of nutrients in silage and in dry forage.—In the fermentations and other changes which occur in the ensiled forage, a certain part of the nutrients, chiefly sugars and other carbohydrates, is oxidized into carbon dioxide and water and therefore lost. The extent of this loss will differ considerably, depending on the kind of forage crop, the depth of the silo, and other factors.[3] It is usually lower in silage from well-matured corn or sorghum than in legume silage or silage from the grasses or small grains. When the mass of silage is not well compacted, as in a shallow silo, the loss is higher than in a deep silo.

With forage from well-matured corn or sorghums which is ensiled in deep, well-built, cylindrical silos, not more than 5 to 10 per cent of the nutrients should be lost through this means. In addition there is a loss through the spoilage of silage at the top of the silo, unless feeding begins as soon as the filling is completed. If the forage is too immature and watery, a further waste will occur through the loss of juice.

SAVING ALL OF THE CORN CROP BY ENSILING IT

Over a great part of the United States silage has well-nigh revolutionized stock feeding. The silo provides high-quality succulent feed for any season of the year, with a low expense for labor and a minimum wastage of nutrients.

SOILAGE IS USUALLY LESS ECONOMICAL THAN SILAGE

Providing succulent feed in summer by a succession of soiling crops is usually more expensive than the use of silage, chiefly because it requires more labor. (From Wisconsin Station.)

CRUDE PROTEIN
FIBER
NITROGEN-FREE EXTRACT
FAT

FIRST TASSELS   SILKS DRYING   GLAZING STAGE   SILAGE STAGE

NUTRIENTS IN CORN PLANTS AT VARIOUS STAGES

The shaded areas in the legend represent the amounts of crude protein, fiber, nitrogen-free extract, and fat in corn plants at various stages. Note especially the large storage of nitrogen-free extract as the crop matures. (From Indiana Station.)

THE SILO CONSERVES THE FULL VALUE IN THE CORN CROP

When the corn crop is ensiled at the proper stage of maturity, the full value of both grain and stover is secured for dairy cattle, beef cattle, and sheep.

In silos 30 feet deep or more the total loss should not exceed 10 to 15 per cent for well-matured corn or sorghum silage, if reasonable care is taken to reduce the surface wastage and if there is little or no loss of juice. This is considerably less than usually occurs when such forage is cured as dry fodder.

Even when cured in well-made shocks, corn fodder or stover standing in the field for a few months loses at least 15 per cent and usually 20 per cent or more of the dry matter it contains, due to weathering and to fermentations which gradually waste the forage.[4] With unfavorable conditions the waste is much greater. The losses fall chiefly on the most valuable parts of the plant—the protein, sugar, and starch —which are less resistant and more soluble than the fiber.

If the forage is too immature and watery when it is ensiled, a considerable loss of juice will occur unless the silo is water-tight. Even if the juice does not run out, the silage will often be very sour and not as palatable as that from crops lower in water.

The actual loss of nutrients in the juice escaping from a silo filled with watery corn forage is often much greater than realized, for it represents nutrients not only from the stalks and leaves, but also from the kernels. A considerable part of the protein of the kernels is dissolved in the silage processes and this portion tends to pass out of the kernels into the juice. In a silo studied by the Dairy Division of the United States Department of Agriculture, about 9,500 lbs. of juice were lost, which contained as much protein as 7,500 lbs. of silage.[5]

Very rarely, many spots of rotten silage occur in the midst of good silage. Such spoilage can be produced by certain bacteria which are not checked by the acidity or the absence of air, but destroy the acid and rot the silage.[6] Where there has been this trouble, it is recommended that the silo walls be cleaned and painted with hot tar before filling, in order to kill the bacteria.

345. Requisites for good silage.—To produce satisfactory silage the green forage crop must have certain definite characteristics. First of all, it must be neither too dry nor too high in water content. If it is too dry, it will not pack sufficiently in the silo, and enough air will remain to permit the development of mold. If the forage is too high in water, the silage is apt to be very sour or it may even spoil.

To make the best silage, the forage crop should have solid stems, so that only a small amount of air will remain in the mass after it is settled. The small grains with their hollow stems do not possess this quality. Hence, in ensiling such green forage it is especially important that the cut material be packed well by sufficient tramping.

It is essential that enough acid be produced in the silage to prevent the growth of undesirable bacteria that will cause rotting or putrefaction. The forage must therefore contain sufficient sugar or other carbohydrates which can be attacked by the acid-forming bacteria.

346. Crops for silage.—The suitability of the various crops for silage is discussed in some detail in the following chapters. Where it thrives, Indian corn is usually the best silage crop. Next in value and importance for silage are the sweet sorghums and the grain sorghums. Where the growing season is too short or too cool for corn, sunflowers are often used for silage, though producing silage that is worth considerably less per ton than that from well-matured corn or sorghum. Another good silage crop for these sections is such a combination as oats and peas.

The green small grains are fairly satisfactory for silage when grown alone, if ensiled before the stems become woody, and if the cut forage is well tramped to force the air out of the hollow stems. Green grass or mixed grasses and clovers will usually make fair silage, if cut at the usual hay stage and packed thoroughly.

When ensiled alone, most legumes tend to produce unsatisfactory silage if the ordinary methods are followed. This is due either to a lack of sufficient sugars in these plants or to the fact that the forage is more alkaline in nature than corn or sorghum forage, and this alkalinity neutralizes some of the acid which is produced.[7] If the legume forage is allowed to wilt somewhat before it is ensiled, it will contain more sugar per pound of the forage, due to the removal of part of the water. This will usually make possible the development of a great enough degree of acidity to prevent spoilage.

Alfalfa, red clover, or sweet clover should be in the medium-late-bloom stage when cut for silage. It should usually be allowed to wilt well in the swath before it is ensiled, so that the water content will be reduced from the 70 to 75 per cent present in the fresh green forage when cut to 50 to 65 per cent when ensiled.[8] If it dries out too much, however, the silage will mold or will heat unduly. Legumes make satisfactory silage if mixed with such forages as green corn or sorghum. Other methods of ensiling legumes are discussed in following paragraphs.

Soybeans often make satisfactory silage when ensiled alone and without any wilting after cutting, provided they have reached the seed stage and the lower leaves are beginning to turn yellow.[9] Likewise cowpeas alone may make good silage if mature enough. A still safer plan is to ensile both these crops with corn or sorghum forage. Wherever alfalfa, clover, soybeans, cowpeas, and other legumes can be cured into satisfactory hay, there is no need of ensiling them, for other more reliable silage crops can usually be grown.

The pea vines from canning factories and the green husks, cobs, and other waste from sweet-corn canneries make good silage. Soft or immature ear corn can be saved for feeding by ensiling it. Such substances as beet pulp, beet tops, apple pomace, and sorghum bagasse may be successfully preserved in silos, or placed in heaps and covered with earth, or even massed in large heaps without covering, in which case the outside portion on decaying forms a preserving crust.

Weeds and other waste vegetation may sometimes be advantageously ensiled. Cabbage, rape, and turnips make unsatisfactory silage, ill-smelling and watery. Chopped potatoes can be ensiled satisfactorily, if inoculated by adding corn meal, or if they are mixed with corn fodder.

347. Special silage methods.—Many experiments have been conducted to find methods that will produce good silage with greater uniformity from such crops as the legumes and grasses, or that will reduce the losses which occur through fermentations. No special methods are needed in the case of corn or sorghum silage, for these crops almost invariably make excellent silage if reasonable care is taken in the usual method.

A patented method developed by Virtanen of Finland (after whose initials it is called the A. I. V. method) is to add dilute mineral acids to the forage as it is ensiled.[10] The resulting acidity prevents the growth of undesirable bacteria, just as does sufficient acidity developed in the normal silage processes. It also tends to diminish the bacterial fermentations considerably and thus to reduce the loss of nutrients. In this method the vitamin A value of the silage is preserved more completely than in normal silage. The method is used to a considerable extent in Finland and has also attracted attention in other countries of northern Europe where corn or sorghums cannot be grown, because of the climate.

In this process special equipment is necessary to distribute the acid solution over the forage. Also, the amount of acid required apparently varies considerably with different lots of forage, depending on the nature of the crop and on the soil on which it was grown. In some cases alfalfa silage made by this method has been none too palatable to stock. To neutralize the considerable amounts of mineral acid in this silage, ground limestone or some other form of calcium carbonate should be fed with it.

Another method of ensiling legumes recently tested is the addition of a molasses or sugar solution to the forage as it is ensiled.[11] This increases the sugar content of the forage so that enough acid is formed in the fermentations to preserve the silage and prevent the growth of the bacteria that cause putrefaction or rotting.

The amount of molasses needed per ton of green forage will depend on the kind of crop and on its stage of maturity. Legumes contain less sugars when very immature than at later stages of growth. With alfalfa it is wise to use 40 to 60 lbs. of molasses per ton of forage, in order to insure good-quality silage. In the case of soybeans cut after the pods have developed, 20 lbs. of molasses per ton may be sufficient. The molasses can be run from an elevated barrel through a good-sized pipe and onto the green forage on the feed table of the silage cutter. The molasses can also be diluted with an equal weight of water, and the solution run into the blower pipe or sprinkled over the chopped forage in the silo.

The additional expense involved in either of these two methods must be considered, as well as the advantage gained from the method. These methods have not yet been tested sufficiently in this country to warrant final conclusions concerning their economy and advisability under American conditions.

In a method developed in Italy, grasses or legumes are allowed to dry until the water content is only 30 to 40 per cent when ensiled.[12] The forage is placed in cylindrical silos much like the American silos, except that means are provided at the top for raising and lowering heavy wooden covers. After the silo is partly filled, the cover is lowered on the mass and weighted down with large stones. When more forage is to be ensiled, the cover is raised and the process repeated.

By this means most of the air is forced out, and the fermentations are therefore much reduced. Forage as dry as is used in this method would mold or heat unduly, perhaps to the charring point, if put into an ordinary silo without special weighting.

Attempts have also been made to improve the quality of silage by inoculating the forage with acid-producing bacteria.[13] No benefit has usually resulted, except in the case of potatoes and of potato pomace from potato-starch factories, which usually lack sufficient of the proper bacteria to produce the desired acid fermentation. Methods of treating the ensiled forage with currents of electricity[14] or steaming it[15] to kill the bacteria have not proven advantageous.

348. Requisites of a good silo.—The satisfactory above-ground silo must possess the following characteristics:

1. Air tight walls. The walls must prevent the entrance of air and the doors must fit snugly. If air enters, the fermentations will continue and molds will grow, spoiling the silage.

2. Cylindrical shape. In the early silos, which were rectangular, it was exceedingly difficult to pack the mass in the corners so that it would not spoil. The cylindrical silo has no corners, the sides are strong and unyielding, and it provides the largest possible cubic capacity for a given amount of building material.

3. Smooth, perpendicular, strong walls. Unless the walls of the silo are smooth and perpendicular, cavities will form along the walls as the mass settles, and the adjacent silage will spoil. The walls must be strong and rigid, for while the silage is settling a great outward pressure is developed.

4. Depth. By making the silo deep, the great pressure compacts all but the uppermost layers, so that the losses through fermentation are reduced to a minimum. While over 30 per cent of the dry matter may be lost in the layer of silage just under the spoiled material on the surface, the loss in the rest of the silo should not be greater than 5 to 10 per cent.

The loss through the surface spoilage, after the silo is filled and before feeding is begun, is also a much smaller percentage of the total contents in the case of a deep silo than in a shallow one.

349. Types of silos.—Satisfactory permanent silos can be constructed of wood, solid concrete, concrete staves or blocks, glazed tile, bricks, or galvanized sheet iron or steel. The choice between the various types of construction will depend on local conditions. Anyone in doubt as to the best types for his use should consult his agricultural college or experiment station.

During the past few years wide use has been made of trench and pit silos. These provide a cheap and satisfactory means of ensiling crops where the soil is well drained. The losses of nutrients in trench silos are apt to be considerably greater than in the case of deep cylindrical silos,[16] but this is more or less offset by the small cost.

On account of the shallowness, the forage must be packed very thoroughly in a trench silo by driving a tractor or a team of horses back and forth over it, and when filling is completed the surface should be covered with wet straw or with straw and earth. Feeding is begun at one end, the silage being removed in vertical slices of a size which can be fed out in about two days.

Emergency silos are also made of slat or picket fencing, such as is used for snow fences. This is lined with a tough, reinforced paper made especially for the purpose.

350. Filling the silo.—Green forage packs more densely in a silo when it is chopped into short lengths by running it through a silage cutter, and therefore such cut forage usually makes better silage than if uncut. This is especially important in such coarse material as corn or sorghum forage and in the hollow-stemmed forage from small grains. Also, the silage can be removed much more readily if the forage is cut.

The safest plan to insure good silage is to have a reliable man in the silo as it is filled, who distributes the forage uniformly by moving the flexible distributor pipe around. In walking about, he will also help pack the forage. Toward the top of the silo the material should be tramped especially well near the wall and should be kept higher there than at the center, as the friction of the wall retards the settling.

To save labor many have adopted the plan of tying the distributor pipe so it is directed toward the center of the silo. The forage is then allowed to "cone up" as it falls. Sometimes a man levels it off every hour or so, but others do no levelling except toward the top of the silo. To avoid a large amount of spoilage at the top, it is important that for the last few feet the silage be levelled off and that it be thoroughly tramped. Good results are secured by this method, if the forage contains sufficient water to pack well, but if it is a little dry, the silage is apt to be poor, especially near the wall.

No matter what method is followed, if the forage is too dry to pack well when it is ensiled, water should be added. This may be done by running it into the blower-fan case or into the blower pipe just above the blower. If the water is under sufficient pressure, it may be allowed to run into the flexible distributor pipe in the silo, or the man who tramps the forage can carry the hose and wet the forage as he packs it.

The forage will settle considerably after the silo is filled, and more may then be put in, any spoiled surface material being first removed. If feeding is not to begin immediately, the surface should be wet down thoroughly and tramped well several times the first week, when the rotting forage will form a layer on top that protects the rest. To lessen the waste, it is well to remove the ears from the last few loads of forage and to cover the top with a foot or so of cheap refuse such as straw or weeds, wet with water. Sometimes oats are sown on the surface. On growing, the roots form a dense mat which aids in keeping out the air.

The loss at the surface can be reduced to a minimum if the forage is covered (after it is levelled, thoroughly wet down, and well tramped) with cheap roll-roofing, the joints being lapped about 4 inches and the ends turned up against the side wall 4 or 5 inches.[17] Then the roofing is covered with a thick layer of cut straw, sawdust, or other material.

351. Danger from carbon dioxide.—On going into the silo after an intermission in filling, one should always beware of the danger from carbon dioxide. This may accumulate in sufficient quantities to prove fatal. If a lighted lantern or candle lowered into the silo continues to burn, it is safe, but if the light goes out it means death to one entering. Opening a door low down in the silo will allow the poisonous gas to pour out, as it is heavier than air. When the filling of the silo is resumed, the inrush of the cut forage will create a circulation of air that will soon remove the danger.

352. Weight of silage and capacities of silos.—The most extensive investigations reported on the weight of silage at various depths in a silo and on the capacities of silos are those at the Kansas, Missouri, and Nebraska Stations.[18] The silage is more compact and heavier as the depth from the surface increases. The exact weight per cubic foot at any depth will vary considerably, depending on the percentage of water in the crop when ensiled, the amount of grain in the fodder, and other factors.

In the Kansas and Missouri studies, the average weight of a cubic foot of corn silage at the surface foot was 32.0 lbs.; at a depth of 5 feet, 34.8 lbs.; at 10 feet, 38.0 lbs.; at 20 feet, 41.0 lbs.; and at 30 feet, 43.0 lbs. The average weight of the silage for the whole depth was 33.4 lbs. per cubic foot for the first 5 feet, 35.0 lbs. for a depth of 10 feet, 37.5 lbs. for a depth of 20 feet, and 39.0 lbs. for a depth of 30 feet.

The first part (A) of the following table shows the estimated capacity of silos according to these investigations for well-matured corn or sorghum silage, when the silage has been well-tramped and allowed to settle one day and the silo then refilled. The second part (B) shows the estimated tonnage when the silage has settled for one month or more.

The depth indicated is the actual depth of the silage, not the height of the silo wall. It is therefore necessary to have the silo about 5 feet higher than the depth given to allow for settling. The table shows, for example, that in a silo 16 feet in diameter, if there is 30 feet of settled silage one month after settling, there will be about 118 tons of silage.

Approximate capacity of cylindrical silos in tons of corn silage

A. Capacity when filling is completed.*

Inside diam. in feet	Depth of silage in feet											
	18	20	22	24	26	28	30	32	34	36	38	40
10.............	20	23	26	30	33	37	41	...	...	...	...	...
12.............	28	33	38	42	48	53	58	64	70	...	...	...
14.............	38	45	51	58	65	72	80	87	95	103	111	120
16.............	50	58	67	76	85	94	104	114	124	135	145	156
18.............	64	74	84	96	107	119	132	144	157	171	184	198
20.............	78	91	104	118	132	147	162	178	194	211	227	244
22.............	95	110	126	143	160	178	196	215	235	255	275	296

B. Capacity after silage has settled one month or more.**

Inside diam. in feet	Depth of silage in feet											
	8	10	12	14	16	18	20	22	24	26	28	30
10.............	11	14	17	20	23	26	29	33	36	39	43	46
12.............	16	20	24	29	33	38	42	47	52	56	61	66
14.............	21	27	33	39	45	51	58	64	70	77	83	90
16.............	28	35	43	51	59	67	75	84	92	100	109	118
18.............	35	44	54	64	75	85	95	106	116	127	138	148
20.............	43	55	67	80	92	105	118	130	144	157	170	184

*A. If corn is unusually dry when ensiled, deduct 10 per cent from the capacity given. If corn is dry and very little grain is present, deduct 15 per cent. If silo is filled rapidly and no time is allowed for settling, deduct 10 per cent.

**B. For corn ensiled when less mature than usual add 10 to 15 per cent to the capacity given. If corn is unusually rich in grain, add 5 to 10 per cent. If corn is unusually dry when ensiled, deduct 10 to 15 per cent. If very little grain is present, deduct 10 per cent.

When the bundles of corn or sorghum are loaded with a bundle elevator onto the wagon as the corn is cut, the forage will be higher in water than when the bundles are allowed to dry out somewhat on the ground. Therefore the silage will be heavier per cubic foot, and the silo will contain more tons of silage. However, each ton of silage will have a correspondingly lower feeding value, because of the higher water content.

Sunflower silage is much heavier than corn silage, weighing from 1.5 to 3 times as much per cubic foot. A silo for sunflower silage must therefore be strongly constructed to withstand the great lateral pressure when the silage is settling.

353. Estimating the amount of silage left in a silo.—To estimate the amount of silage remaining in a silo after part has been fed out, find the actual depth left and estimate the original total depth of silage after settling. Then compute the amount as follows: Let us suppose that 10 feet of silage are left in a silo having a diameter of 14 feet, and that after settling one month the entire depth of silage was about 28 feet before feeding started.

From the table we find that at first the silo contained 83 tons. The first 18 feet of silage, which were fed out, would weigh about 51 tons, according to the table. The difference, or 32 tons, is the approximate weight of the silage left.

354. Proper size of silo.—The diameter of the silo should be gauged by the number and kind of animals to be fed from it, and its height by the length of the feeding period. The silo should be of such diameter that in the cooler part of the year at least 1.5 inches, and preferably 2 inches, of silage will be removed from the entire surface daily to prevent spoilage. When silage is used for summer feeding somewhat more should be removed daily.

The exact size of silo required may be computed from the length of the feeding period and the amount required daily for the different kinds of stock, as shown previously in this chapter and in the respective chapters of Part III. Knowing the number of animals of each kind to be fed, the entire amount of silage which will be consumed daily may be ascertained. The maximum diameter which the silo should have may then be determined from the following:

Two inches in depth of ordinary corn silage weigh about 5 lbs. per surface square foot near the top of the silo and 7 lbs. near the bottom, averaging about 6.5 lbs. in a silo filled to a depth of 30 feet. To use 2 inches daily from the surface, approximately the following amounts must be fed from silos of various diameters: Diameter 10 feet, 510 lbs. silage; 11 feet, 615 lbs.; 12 feet, 735 lbs.; 14 feet, 1,000 lbs.; 16 feet, 1,305 lbs.; 18 feet, 1,655 lbs.; 20 feet, 2,045 lbs.; 22 feet, 2,470 lbs.; 24 feet, 2,940 lbs.; 26 feet, 3,450 lbs. In cold weather and when the silage is well packed, a somewhat smaller amount may be removed daily.

When the maximum diameter which the silo should have has thus been determined, the total amount of silage required for the desired feeding period may be computed and the dimensions for a silo of this capacity found by referring to the table given previously. (**352**) It should be borne in mind that silage in a relatively deep silo keeps better than in a shallow one, as has been pointed out previously. Care must be taken not to have the diameter so great that the silage cannot be fed rapidly enough to keep it from spoiling. Also, when a silo is more than 18 or 20 feet in diameter, increased labor is involved in carrying the silage to the silo door as it is removed for feeding.

II. SOILING CROPS

355. The place of soiling crops on American farms.—*Soiling crops* are green forage crops that are cut in the field and fed in fresh condition to livestock. Green forage fed as a soiling crop is also sometimes called "soilage." Due to the high expense of growing special soiling crops and harvesting them for feeding while green, this method of providing feed is rarely followed throughout the summer in this country. However, soiling crops are often fed to dairy cattle and less frequently to sheep for limited periods when pastures become parched during drought. Occasionally, a farmer on high-priced land near a city, who desires to keep as much stock as possible on his farm, will grow a succession of soiling crops for feeding throughout the season as a substitute for pasture.

It has been pointed out in Chapter XI that a considerably larger yield of nutrients is secured when a crop is allowed to grow to the hay stage than when it is kept grazed during the season. (**300**) For this reason, and also because none of the forage is wasted by the trampling of stock, an acre of land will usually furnish much more feed when used for soiling crops than for pasture. For example, in early Wisconsin experiments by Henry an acre of soiling crops equalled about 2.5 acres of bluegrass pasture for feeding dairy cows.[19] In Kansas trials there was an even greater difference in the yield from pasturage and from soiling crops.[20] Another merit of soiling crops is that less fencing of fields is required than where all the feed is furnished by pasturage.

When a properly-planned succession of soiling crops is grown by a person with experience, it is usually possible to provide an abundance of palatable feed throughout the entire growing season, while permanent pastures often become scanty during midsummer. However, it takes considerable experience to have each crop ready for harvest just when it is needed. Drought may interfere seriously with the proper succession of feed.

Under usual conditions these advantages of soiling crops for furnishing feed throughout the season are more than offset by their high cost. The expense is large for labor, seed, and fertilizer in producing the crops. To provide a succession of green feed by means of soiling crops, it is necessary to fit and plant comparatively small areas to different crops at various times. Much labor is also needed to cut the crop daily or every other day, to haul the heavy green feed to the stock, and to feed it. This comes throughout the busiest time of the year and interferes seriously with other farm work.

The cost per ton in harvesting soiling crops is very high in a herd of average size, for only a small amount of the crop can be cut and hauled at a time, or it will spoil before it is fed. In warm weather it may be necessary to harvest the green feed each day. When but a few animals are fed, the forage may be spread thinly on the barn floor, so it will not heat, but it will then dry out and be less palatable. During wet spells, it may be difficult to harvest and haul the crop without injury to the land.

For these reasons soiling crops are not commonly relied upon in the United States for feed throughout the season. They are used more often to supplement permanent pastures during a midsummer drought or at any other time when the pastures provide insufficient feed. Even for this purpose, it is usually much cheaper to grow such crops as Sudan grass or sweet clover to be used for temporary pasture, or to pasture the second crop on a hay field, or to feed silage or hay as the supplement to scanty pasture.

In case the pasture becomes parched and none of these other provisions has been made, it is certainly wise to cut and feed green some crop that has been raised in the regular rotation and which is ready for use at that time. Excellent crops for this purpose are green alfalfa, clover, the hay grasses, or corn.

Such green feed, fed as a supplement to short pasture, will often have a much higher value per ton than if it is harvested in the regular manner and fed to the stock the following winter. This is especially true in the case of dairy cows. It is essential that they be provided with plenty of feed at all times, or their milk yield will be seriously reduced and even liberal feeding later will fail to bring it back.

In Europe, where labor is relatively cheap in comparison with the price of land, a much wider use can economically be made of soiling crops than in this country.

356. Soiling crops vs. silage or pasture.—Where enough dairy cows are kept to consume silage in summer fast enough to keep it from spoiling, silage generally furnishes succulent feed which is much cheaper than soiling crops and just as satisfactory. Also, corn or sorghum silage will usually be relished by the cows as well or even better than a succession of different soiling crops.

Silage furnishes feed of uniformly high quality throughout the season, a goal which is difficult to attain with soiling crops, for one crop is often exhausted or too mature before the next is in prime condition for feeding. The years when drought is severe and pastures are unusually short are the very times when soiling crops will be scanty or may even fail. By means of the silo, a crop may be carried over from one year to the next, thus providing insurance against drought.

Experiments by the Iowa, Nebraska, and Wisconsin Stations show that the production of dairy cows is maintained just as well on good silage plus limited pasture and a suitable supply of concentrates, as when soiling crops are fed in place of the silage.[21] In the Iowa trials it required 180 lbs. of soiling crops to equal 100 lbs. of corn silage in value, because the soiling crops contained a much smaller percentage of dry matter and total digestible nutrients.

In the Nebraska experiments it took only 1.2 hours of labor per 100 lbs. of milk produced to raise the silage crop, harvest it, and feed it, while it required 1.8 hours per 100 lbs. of milk to grow and feed the soiling crops. In addition, a much larger area was needed per cow to provide feed when soiling crops were used than when corn silage and alfalfa hay were fed.

It was found in Montana experiments that when all the items of expense were considered, the net return per acre was decidedly higher when irrigated land was used for pasturing dairy cows than when it was used for soiling crops.[22]

357. Suitable soiling crops.—Several crops are well suited for use as soiling crops. Alfalfa, the clovers, peas and oats, soybeans, and cowpeas are all excellent for the purpose. In humid sections corn is generally the best soiling crop for use during the latter part of the season, on account of its palatability and its high yield. Except for the danger of prussic acid poisoning, the sorghums are also excellent. This danger is slight in humid regions, except when the crop is injured by drought or frost. Sudan grass is usually entirely safe, though a close relative of the sorghums.

Very satisfactory green feed is also furnished by green grass or mixed grass and legumes from the hay fields, cut when in bloom or before. The green small grains—rye, wheat, oats, and barley—all may be used as soiling crops. The value of these crops for this purpose is discussed in the following chapters.

Soiling crops should not be fed until reasonably mature. Plants that are too young are composed largely of water, and often cattle cannot consume enough of them to secure the required nourishment. For this reason, where very immature crops are fed, some dry forage should also be supplied.

QUESTIONS

1. State nine advantages of silage for livestock feeding.
2. Discuss the use and value of silage for dairy cattle, beef cattle, and sheep.
3. Under your local conditions should a dairy farmer raise silage for his cows, or should he use hay as the only roughage?
4. Describe in detail the changes that occur when a green crop is ensiled.
5. What are the relative losses of nutrients in corn silage and in the field-curing of corn fodder?
6. What characteristics should a good silage crop have?
7. Discuss the suitability of the following crops for silage: Corn, the sorghums, the small grains, alfalfa.
8. What special methods are used to produce better silage from legume crops? Describe three methods.
9. State four requisites of a good silo.
10. State the advantages and disadvantages of trench silos.
11. Discuss the various methods of filling a silo with corn forage. Under what conditions might you allow the forage to "cone up" in the silo?
12. How can you determine approximately how much silage is left in a silo after part of it has been fed out?
13. Discuss the advantages and disadvantages of soiling crops, in comparison with pasture or the use of silage for summer feeding.
14. Name four good soiling crops.

REFERENCES

1. Mighell and Barrett, Mass. Bul. 293.
2. Peterson, Hastings, and Fred, Wis. Res. Bul. 61; see also: Nevens, Ill. Bul. 391; Neidig, Iowa Res. Bul. 16; Lamb, Iowa Res. Bul. 40; Lamb, Iowa Bul. 168; Kan. Rpts. 1924-26, 1929-30; Hunter, Penn. Bul. 170; Hunter, Jour. Agr. Res., 21, 1921, pp. 767-789.

3. Kan. Rpt. 1926-28; Ragsdale and Turner, Mo. Res. Bul. 65; Cook, N. J. Bul. 19; Perkins, Ohio Bul. 370; Armsby, Penn. Rpt. 1889; King, Wis. Bul. 59; Peterson, Hastings, and Fred, Wis. Res. Bul. 61; Shaw, Wright, and Deysher, U. S. Dept. Agr. Bul. 953; Neal and Becker, Jour. Agr. Res., 46, 1933, pp. 669-673; Gaines, Jour. Dairy Sci., 5, 1922, pp. 507-509; Amos and Williams, Jour. Agr. Sci. (England), 12, 1922, pp. 323-336; Woodman and Hanley, Jour. Agr. Sci. (England), 16, 1926, pp. 24-50; Woodman and Amos, Jour. Agr. Sci. (England), 16, 1926, pp. 539-550; Boyle and Ryan, Roy. Dublin Soc. Econ. Proc., 2, 1933, pp. 515-528.
4. Osland, Colo. Bul. 380; Ragsdale and Turner, Mo. Buls. 179, 189, Mo. Res. Bul. 65; Cook, N. J. Bul. 19; Armsby, Penn. Rpt. 1889; King, Wis. Bul. 59; Woll, Wis. Rpt. 1891.
5. Shaw, Wright, and Deysher, U. S. Dept. Agr. Bul. 953; see also: Perkins, Ohio Bul. 370; Gadden, Jour. Agr. Sci., England, 13, 1923, pp. 462-466.
6. Hastings, Wis. Bul. 388.
7. Wilson, N. Y. (Cornell) Sta., Jour. Dairy Sci., 18, 1935, pp. 317-325.
8. Eckles, Mo. Bul. 162; Perkins, Ohio Bul. 370; Wright and Shaw, Jour. Agr. Res., 28, 1924, pp. 255-259; Shutt, Rpt. Dominion Chemist, Canada, 1927.
9. Becker, Neal, Dawson, and Arnold, Fla. Bul. 255; Wright and Shaw, Jour. Agr. Res., 28, 1924, pp. 255-259.
10. Imperial Bur. of Anim. Nutr. (Scotland) Tech. Communication 1; Peterson, Bohstedt, Bird, and Beeson, Jour. Dairy Sci., 18, 1935, pp. 63-78; Bohstedt, et al., Wis. Bul. 430; Hughes, Woodruff, and Cave, Kan. Sta., mimeo. rpt.; Hayden, Perkins, et al., Jour. Dairy Sci., 18, 1935, pp. 439-440.
11. Casalis, Hoard's Dairyman, 79, 1934, pp. 141, 142; Elting, Jour. Dairy Sci., 18, 1935, p. 440; Bartlett, et al., N. J. Sta., information to the author.
12. Gorini, Atti accad. Lincei, 3, 1926, pp. 629-632; Samarani, Hoard's Dairyman, 63, 1922, p. 806; Hastings, Fred, and Peterson, Wis. Bul. 362.
13. Ore. Rpt. 1918-1920; Wyant, Mich. Rpt. 1920.
14. Withycombe and Bradley, Ore. Bul. 102; Wyant, Mich. Rpt. 1920; Peterson, Hastings, and Fred, Wis. Res. Bul. 65.
15. Woll and Hoffman, Cal. Rpts. 1922, 1923; Mangold, Handb. Ernährung u. Stoffwechsels, Vol. I, pp. 368-370.
16. Dawson and Van Horn, U. S. Dept. Agr. Cir. 274.
17. Nevens, Ill. Cir. 409.
18. Eckles, Reed, and Fitch, Mo. Bul. 164 and Kan. Cir. 89; Chase, Nebr. Cir. 1; see also: King, Wis. Bul. 59.
19. Henry, Wis. Rpt. 1885.
20. Otis, Kan. Press Bul. 71; see also: Voorhees, Forage Corps; Quincy, The Soiling of Cattle.
21. McCandlish, Iowa Bul. 201; Frandsen, et al., Jour. Dairy Sci., 4, 1921, pp. 124-157; Woll, Humphrey, and Oosterhuis, Wis. Bul. 235.
22. Tretsven, Mont. Bul. 282.

CHAPTER XIII

LEGUMES FOR FORAGE

I. Superiority Of Legume Forage

358. Importance of legume roughages.—Legume roughages occupy a place of particular importance in the feeding of livestock, because of the several superiorities they have over all other forage crops. Legume roughages excel in the following respects:

1. They lead in yield of palatable hay produced per acre.
2. They are the richest in protein of all common roughages.
3. The protein which they provide supplements in a very effective manner the deficiencies in the proteins of the cereal grains.
4. They are the highest in calcium among common feeds, and although not rich in phosphorus, they are generally a little higher in this mineral than forage from corn, the sorghums, or the grasses.
5. Well-cured legume hay is the richest source of vitamins A and D among the common feeds available for winter feeding.
6. Such legumes as alfalfa and the clovers increase the yield and protein content of the grasses when grown in combination with them.
7. They are highly important from the standpoint of the maintenance of soil fertility.

On account of these virtues legume roughages are admirable supplements to the cereal grains. They are in marked contrast to forage from corn and the sorghums and to hay from the grasses, all of which, if cut at the usual stage of maturity, furnish forage low in crude protein and only poor to fair in calcium.

Through the proper utilization of roughage from the legumes, the amount of protein-rich concentrates needed to provide balanced rations for farm animals may be greatly reduced. Indeed, for many classes of animals merely legume hay and grain from the cereals, or else legume hay, silage, and grain, furnish very satisfactory rations. The numerous recent experiments which have proved the great importance of the quality or kind of proteins in rations and of a plentiful supply of vitamins and minerals, have emphasized more than ever before the need for sufficient legume forage on well-organized stock farms.

In considering the legumes it must be kept in mind that these crops build up the nitrogen content of the soil only when the proper nodule-forming bacteria are present. Where these nitrogen-fixing germs are lacking, it is essential that the soil be inoculated.

359. Legume roughages excel in yield of palatable feed.—In nearly every livestock section of the United States some kind of legume hay will produce a greater yield of dry matter per acre than other common hay crops. Moreover, this hay is so much more palatable than hay from the grasses, cut at the usual stages of maturity, that livestock will eat larger amounts of it and get a greater proportion of their nourishment from this cheap source. Due to the high palatability of legume hay, it is consumed by livestock with much less waste than is hay of the usual quality from the grasses or such roughage as corn or sorghum fodder. The superiority of legumes, especially alfalfa, in furnishing a large yield of palatable dry matter and of digestible nutrients is shown in the table presented later in this chapter. (**368**)

360. Legume roughages excel in amount of protein.—The fact that legume hays and pasturage are the richest in protein of all common roughages is of great importance in providing economically the large amount of protein needed by dairy cows for high milk production, and in the efficient feeding of beef cattle, sheep, horses, and swine.

In most dairy sections the cereal grains and corn or sorghum forage provide the cheapest source of energy or digestible nutrients for dairy cows. These feeds, which commonly form a large part of dairy rations, are all decidedly low in protein. To provide most economically the additional protein dairy cows need for efficient production, it is generally of first importance to grow an abundance of good legume hay. This will go far toward supplying the cows with sufficient protein and will reduce greatly the amount of protein supplements like linseed meal, cottonseed meal, and gluten feed, which must be purchased.

Legume hay occupies a position of nearly as great importance in the efficient and economical feeding of beef cattle and sheep. A liberal supply of good legume hay will not only usually result in greater production, but will also reduce very considerably the amount of expensive protein-rich concentrates needed to balance the rations. Even for feeding farm horses legume hay helps reduce the feed bills. Since swine, with the exception of brood sows, will not eat much legume hay, the high value of legume hay for feeding swine in winter is due chiefly to the quality of the protein it furnishes and to its supply of vitamins and minerals, rather than to the amount of protein it supplies. For swine of all classes legume pasture is unexcelled. The value and use of legume roughages for each class of stock are discussed in detail in the respective chapters of Part III.

The protein content of the leaves of legumes is much higher than that of the stems. For example, dried alfalfa leaves average 21.9 per cent in protein, while the stems contain only 10.0 per cent. The nutrients in the leaves are also much more digestible than those in the stems.[1] As a result, dried alfalfa leaves furnish 16.9 per cent of digestible protein, in comparison with only 5.1 per cent for alfalfa stems. (Appendix Table I.) These figures show that when a considerable part of the leaves is lost through shattering in making legume hay, the loss is much more serious than is indicated by the mere reduction in the yield of hay.

361. Legume roughages excel in quality of protein.—Not only are legume roughages rich in protein, but also the proteins are of good quality and effectively supplement and make good the deficiencies in the proteins of corn and the other cereals. This fact, which is one of the most important truths in practical stock feeding, has been discussed in detail in Chapter VI. (**153**)

In order to secure satisfactory results with swine and poultry, it is necessary that the rations contain a sufficient amount of protein supplements which provide complete proteins such as are furnished by dairy by-products, tankage, meat scraps, or fish meal. This is because swine and poultry, on account of the nature of their digestive tracts, cannot consume any considerable amount of dry roughage, even good legume hay.

Cattle and sheep, with their capacious four-fold stomachs, are much more fortunate. If they are fed an abundance of good legume hay with cereal grains, and with or without corn or sorghum silage, the combination will furnish a very efficient and adequate quality of proteins. But relatively little attention need then be paid to the *quality* of protein furnished by the additional protein supplements that may be needed to provide the necessary *amount* of digestible protein.

For example, gluten feed, which is a corn by-product and therefore supplies unbalanced protein, may not make an efficient ration when added as the only protein supplement to such a combination as corn, oats, timothy hay, and corn silage for dairy cows or for fattening cattle or lambs. (**154**) On the other hand, gluten feed is fairly satisfactory as the only supplement, if legume hay replaces a considerable part of the timothy hay in this ration. This is because the legume hay makes good the deficiencies in the quality of the protein. However, still better results will usually be secured if some other protein supplement, providing better-quality protein, is fed in combination with the gluten feed.

362. Legume roughages excel in calcium and are fair in phosphorus.—Legume roughages are the richest sources of calcium among common feeds. (**160**) Indeed, they furnish calcium so liberally that they will provide adequately for the calcium requirements of dairy cows, even those of high productive capacity, if an ample amount of legume hay or other legume roughage is fed. When beef cattle or sheep are fed plenty of legume hay, there is likewise no need to add a calcium supplement to the ration.

Legume roughages are not rich in phosphorus, containing less of this mineral nutrient than do the cereal grains. However, their phosphorus content is generally a little higher than that of forage from corn, the sorghums, or the grasses. It is pointed out elsewhere that unless the legume hay is grown on phosphorus-rich soil, it is advisable, in feeding dairy cows, to add a phosphorus supplement to home-grown rations of legume hay and farm grain, with or without corn silage or sorghum silage. (**161**)

363. Legume roughages excel in vitamins A and D.—As has been pointed out in Chapter VI, well-cured legume hay is the best source of vitamins A and D among ordinary stock feeds, and these are probably the only vitamins that may be deficient in any usual good ration for dairy cows, beef cattle, horses, sheep, or swine.

The less the hay is exposed to sunlight, the greener will be its color and the higher the content of vitamin A. It has been shown previously that all or nearly all of the vitamin A value of feeds of plant origin is due to the carotene they contain. (**187**) The effect of curing methods upon the carotene content (vitamin A value) of hay has been discussed in the previous chapter. (**320**) Curing hay with a reasonable exposure to sunlight increases its content of vitamin D. (**191**)

The richness of well-cured legume hay in vitamins A and D makes it especially important for dairy cows, for all young growing animals, particularly pigs, and for poultry. As is pointed out in Part III, adding only 5 per cent of good legume hay to the rations of young pigs in the winter time may make all the difference between profit and disaster.

364. Legumes increase yield and protein content of grasses.—Not only do legume forages excel in yield and protein content when grown alone, but they also increase the yield and the percentage of protein in the grasses when grown in combination with them. Therefore for pasture or for hay a combination of grasses and legumes is usually far preferable to any mixture of grasses alone, without legumes.

In Ohio experiments over several years a combination of timothy with red clover, alsike clover, or alfalfa yielded over 40 per cent more hay than timothy alone. Also, the percentage of protein in timothy or orchard grass (not including the legumes) was 44 to 50 per cent higher when grown with alfalfa than when the grass was grown alone.[2]

365. Legumes important in maintenance of fertility.—The importance of legumes, grown in proper rotation, for the maintenance of soil fertility and the increase in yield of succeeding crops is too well known to necessitate lengthy explanation. When properly inoculated, the legumes are able, through the action of the legume bacteria in the nodules on their roots, to use in their growth free nitrogen from the air.

Due to this, these crops are not only able to secure indirectly from the air most of the nitrogen in the crop harvested, but the stubble and roots may add nitrogen to the soil. Therefore, even when the legume forage is harvested for feeding, the nitrogen content of the soil will be increased, or at least there will be much less depletion of soil nitrogen than when a non-legume is grown. The yield of succeeding non-legume crops is consequently much higher as a rule than when no legume crop is grown in the rotation.

Obviously, when the entire legume crop is plowed under as green manure, as is often done for special truck crops, much more nitrogen will be added to the soil than when the forage is removed. In livestock farming legume forage is too valuable to be plowed under, except in very unusual circumstances. However, by feeding the legume forage to livestock and taking proper care of the manure, most of the nitrogen and other fertilizing constituents can be returned to the soil, thus getting a double advantage from the crop.

In trials over 8 years at the Arkansas Station corn was grown continuously, in comparison with corn followed by legumes grown for forage and removed, or grown for green manure and plowed under.[3] Converting the legumes into hay gave the greatest annual net return, in spite of the fact that no manure was returned to the soil.

Not only do legume crops aid in maintaining the nitrogen supply in the soil, but also they increase the yield of succeeding crops by rendering the soil nitrogen more active and available.[4] This effect does not continue for many years after the growth of the legume crop. It is therefore advantageous from this standpoint, as well as for the maintenance of the nitrogen supply of the soil, to grow the legumes chiefly in regular crop rotations, instead of growing such a crop as alfalfa for a long time on the same field. In addition to these effects upon the nitrogen of the soil, experiments indicate that the good effects of legumes on subsequent crops may be due in part to an improvement in the mechanical and bacterial conditions in the soil and to an increase in the availability of the soil potassium.[5]

When crop residues low in nitrogen, such as straw, are incorporated in the soil, the growth of certain soil bacteria may be increased to such an extent that the supply of available soil nitrogen is locked up temporarily in the bacterial cells. Though the nitrogen becomes available again after the crop residue has decomposed, the yield of a non-legume crop which immediately follows may be decreased. This sometimes results if no manure or other nitrogen fertilizer is applied when a crop of soybeans is removed from the land and only the stubble and roots, which are low in nitrogen, are returned to the soil.[6]

366. Inoculation of legumes.—It is well known that legumes are unable to use in their growth the free nitrogen gas in the air, except as this nitrogen is fixed or built into organic compounds by legume bacteria in nodules on their roots. Therefore, unless the proper bacteria are present in the soil, the legume will utilize only the soil nitrogen, just as is the case with such a crop as corn or timothy. On soil low in nitrogen the legume crop may even fail utterly unless it is inoculated.

Even in a soil well supplied with nitrogen, the growth of the legume will quite commonly be much more vigorous when large numbers of the proper bacteria are present. It is therefore essential that the seed be inoculated with reliable cultures, unless one is sure that the soil contains an abundance of the right bacteria.

The legume bacteria which develop in the various legume crops are of different varieties, and a given variety will inoculate only certain legumes. For example, one variety inoculates alfalfa and sweet clover; another, red, crimson, and white clover; a third, field and garden peas, vetches, sweet peas, and horse beans; a fourth, only soybeans.

It has been discovered that there are various strains of the same variety of legume bacteria, and that these strains may differ widely in their ability to stimulate the growth of the legume crop.[7] Some strains are highly beneficial, while others produce but little benefit. Inoculating legume seed with an efficient culture may decidedly increase the growth of the crop, even when there are enough of this variety of legume bacteria in the soil to produce many nodules on the roots of the particular kind of legume. In purchasing legume cultures for any crops, it is therefore important to secure them from a source which is absolutely reliable and which can provide cultures of proven high efficiency.

367. Soil conditions for good legume crops.—For legumes to thrive it is necessary on many soils to apply ground limestone or some other form of calcium, in order to neutralize or to lessen the soil acidity and to provide the calcium needed by the legume crop in building its calcium-rich tissues. It was formerly believed necessary to apply enough lime to neutralize soil acidity completely, but recent investigations indicate that, at least on some soils, just as good results are secured when less lime than this is applied.[8] On many soils the application of a phosphate fertilizer will greatly increase the growth of legumes and make them surer crops. Often a soil which is said to be "clover sick" merely lacks lime and phosphorus.

Not only is the yield of a legume forage increased when it is prop-

CUTTING ALFALFA IN A WESTERN IRRIGATED DISTRICT

Wherever it thrives the acreage of alfalfa is rapidly increasing, due to its heavy yield of protein-rich hay. (From U. S. Reclamation Service.)

RED CLOVER—A BOON TO FARMERS OF THE NORTHERN STATES

Red clover is the most important legume in the humid parts of the northern two-thirds of the United States. The stock farmer who grows broad acres of clover such as this has a foundation for economical rations.

LEGUMES CAN USE NITROGEN OF AIR ONLY WHEN INOCULATED

When the nitrogen-fixing bacteria or germs are lacking, it is essential that the soil be inoculated to secure maximum crops. At left, are Ito San soybeans on sandy soil which were inoculated with proper bacteria; at right, soybeans which were not inoculated. (All photographs on this page from Wisconsin Station.)

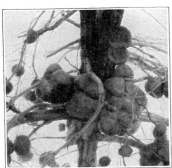 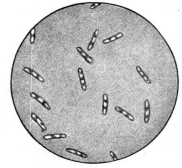

SOYBEAN NODULES (Left) AND SOYBEAN BACTERIA (Right)

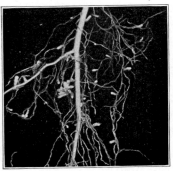 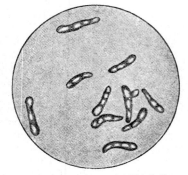

ALFALFA NODULES (Left) AND ALFALFA BACTERIA (Right)

erly inoculated and, if necessary, fertilized with lime and phosphorus, but also the percentage of protein and of calcium in the crop is often increased, thus making each ton of the crop more valuable. For example, in experiments by the Wisconsin Station the inoculation of alfalfa on a limed, virgin silt-loam soil increased the protein content 1.5 per cent, and on a sandy soil, 4.0 per cent.[9] In a few districts where the soil is unusually low in sulfur, fertilization with sulfur may not only greatly increase the growth of legumes but also may considerably increase the percentage of protein.[10]

II. ALFALFA

368. Alfalfa.—Alfalfa (*Medicago sativa*) stands at the head of the list of all common hay crops and is commonly taken as the ideal with which other hay is compared. The excellence of alfalfa hay and other alfalfa forage is due to its high yield, its palatability, its richness in protein, its unusually high content of calcium, and its value as a source of vitamins A and D. Though alfalfa is especially adapted to the semi-arid plains and the irrigated districts of the West, it can be profitably grown in most districts of the United States where the soil is deep, well-drained, and not so acid as to make the cost of liming prohibitive.

According to the United States Census 11,515,811 acres of alfalfa were grown in this country in 1929 with an average yield of 2.04 tons of hay per acre, making a total production of 23,493,505 tons of hay. During the period from 1909 to 1935 the acreage of alfalfa has nearly trebled, and in 1935 over one-third of all the tame hay raised was alfalfa.

The reasons for this steady increase in the popularity of alfalfa are revealed in the following table. This shows the average yield per acre throughout the country of alfalfa hay, of clover hay (red, alsike, or mammoth) grown alone, of timothy and mixed timothy-and-clover hay, and of corn silage.

Average returns per acre from alfalfa hay and other crops

	Yield per acre Tons	Dry matter Lbs.	Digestible protein Lbs.	Total dig. nutrients Lbs.
Alfalfa hay	2.04	3,688	432	2,052
Clover hay	1.48	2,601	207	1,536
Timothy and timothy-clover hay	1.23	2,173	90	1,167
Corn for silage	7.28	3,888	160	2,533

This table, computed from the average yields for the whole country, shows that alfalfa produces a much larger yield of hay and of dry matter per acre than clover or timothy and mixed timothy-and-clover. It is but slightly excelled in yield of dry matter per acre by corn grown for silage.

In furnishing protein the superiority of alfalfa is striking. It provides over twice as much digestible protein per acre as clover hay, about five times as much as hay from timothy and mixed timothy-and-clover, and 2.7 times as much as corn silage. In yield of total digestible nutrients (including fat multiplied by 2.25) it is excelled only by corn silage, and it furnishes nearly twice as much total digestible nutrients per acre as timothy or mixed hay and one-third more than clover hay. When we consider in addition the facts that alfalfa hay is much richer in calcium and is also higher in vitamin A than these other crops, its importance in stock farming becomes fully apparent.

Considerably larger yields of alfalfa hay are secured under favorable conditions than the average shown in the table. Even under conditions in the eastern states, yields of 3 to 4 tons per acre during the season are not uncommon. In the West very heavy yields are often secured when the crop is amply watered by irrigation. In the hot irrigated districts of the Southwest 9 or even more cuttings are sometimes made in a year. Where both soil and climate are suitable, this long-time perennial returns good crops for many years without reseeding. When high temperature is combined with a humid climate, alfalfa generally fails unless the soil is unusually favorable.

The good yields of alfalfa in some of the non-irrigated, semi-arid sections of the West are due to the fact that alfalfa sends its roots deep into the subsoil, drawing from a great depth moisture which has gradually been stored over a long period. In a dry climate this brings about a decided depletion in the moisture of the subsoil. For example, in Nebraska experiments it was found that in a 6-year-old field of alfalfa the moisture in the soil had been reduced to a depth of 35 feet.[11] During 15 years of cropping to cereals after breaking up the alfalfa sod, the water content of the soil increased so slowly that it was estimated 225 years would be needed to restore the subsoil moisture removed by 6 years of alfalfa.

This depletion of subsoil moisture is one of the chief reasons why alfalfa often fails to thrive in such dry districts when seeded on land which previously has been in alfalfa several years. The very efficiency of the crop in obtaining water thus proves its undoing on that particular field. This probably has been the chief cause of a decrease in alfalfa acreage in certain western states during the past few years.[12]

Where alfalfa thrives best, it will produce a larger yield when seeded alone than when sown with timothy or other grasses. In sections where alfalfa is a somewhat uncertain crop, a mixture, especially alfalfa and timothy, is often advantageously used, as an insurance against total loss of the crop in case the alfalfa should winterkill.[13] Also, growing the alfalfa in mixture with timothy or other grass may aid in preventing winter injury, as the fibrous roots and the fall growth of the grass will lessen the heaving of the soil. Early-cut mixed alfalfa-and-timothy hay containing a good proportion of alfalfa is very satisfactory for feeding dairy cattle, beef cattle, sheep, and horses.

369. Varieties and types of alfalfa.—The *variegated alfalfas* are of much importance in the northern-most states and in Canada, as they are much more winter hardy than ordinary alfalfa. These varieties, which have various-colored and variegated blossoms, are hybrids between ordinary alfalfa and the yellow-flowered or Siberian alfalfa (*Medicago falcata*). To this class belong the well-known Grimm, Cossack, Ontario-Variegated, Baltic, Ladak, and Hardigan varieties. *Turkestan alfalfa* is indistinguishable from ordinary alfalfa in growth. It is somewhat hardier but usually yields less hay. *Peruvian alfalfa* is a rapidly-growing, non-hardy type, which is particularly well adapted to the southern-most alfalfa districts.

Numerous trials have been conducted by the various experiment stations to determine the best varieties and the best sources of seed for the various regions. Any person in doubt as to the best kind of seed to sow should secure advice from his state experiment station, agricultural college, or county agent. In general, for the extreme northern sections the hardy variegated strains are by far the best. A little farther south, northern-grown common alfalfa seed is entirely satisfactory, and is much superior to seed from mild sections. In the central part of the corn belt and southward the ordinary strains of common alfalfa may be used safely.

370. Differences in composition and value of alfalfa hay.—Alfalfa hay, like all other kinds of hay, varies widely in value, depending, first of all, on how it was cured. Bright, "pea green" hay, cured when there was no rain and with little shattering of leaves, has the highest feeding value per ton and commands the highest price. Since the leaves contain about 3 times as high a percentage of protein as the stems, a considerable loss of leaves in hay-making not only decreases the yield of hay but also decidedly lowers the value per ton. When alfalfa was harvested at various stages from before bloom to full bloom in Nebraska trials, the leaves formed 49 to 57 per cent of the hay, but on account of their richness in protein they contained 70 to 75 per cent of the protein in the entire crop of hay.[14]

Exposure to rain, particularly when the hay is nearly cured, will leach out a considerable part of the most soluble nutrients, as has been shown in Chapter XI. (**322-325**) Hay which is of good quality but not bright green in color may be about as valuable, except from the vitamin standpoint, as the more prized kind, provided it is as leafy and has not been leached by rain.

With hay cured equally well, the chief factor affecting the composition is the stage of maturity at which it is cut. The earlier the hay is cut, the higher will be the percentage of protein, the lower will be the percentage of fiber, and the greater will be the digestibility. (Appendix Table I.) In general, hay cut reasonably early (when from one-tenth to one-half in bloom) is preferred for dairy cows, beef cattle, sheep, swine, and poultry. Hay cut in full bloom is preferred for horses, as early-cut hay may be too laxative. Hay cut too early may also cause scours in young calves.

If alfalfa is cut for hay before full bloom, the feeding value depends more on proper curing than upon extreme earliness of cutting. In 5 Arizona trials alfalfa hay cut at the bud stage was somewhat more palatable to dairy cows than that cut when one-third in bloom, but there was little difference in the feeding value per ton.[15] In Kansas tests with beef steers, hay cut when one-tenth in bloom produced twice as much gain per ton as hay cut in the seed stage.[16] Hay cut at the blossom-bud stage made 18 per cent more gain per ton than hay cut when one-tenth in bloom. For poultry and rabbits hay cut at an early stage of maturity is decidedly preferred.

The protein content of alfalfa hay varies considerably, even in hay harvested at the same stage of maturity and well cured. Occasionally it will contain no more protein than clover hay. The value of brown alfalfa hay has been discussed in Chapter XI. (**333**)

371. Effect of stage of cutting on longevity of alfalfa.—In deciding upon the stage of maturity at which to cut alfalfa for hay one must consider not only the quality of the hay, but also the effect upon the vigor and length of life of the plants. Extensive experiments have shown conclusively that, except perhaps where the conditions are most favorable to alfalfa, repeated cutting of a field much earlier than full bloom will weaken the plants and shorten their life.[17] This is due to a depletion of reserve food in the alfalfa roots, brought about by the early and frequent cutting. These reserves are built up in the roots during the blossoming period and later.

Cutting a vigorous stand occasionally as early as the tenth-bloom stage will not usually produce any noticeable injury, but the same field should not be cut early repeatedly. Where the winters are not severe and the soil is well adapted to alfalfa, continued early cutting (not earlier than about one-tenth bloom) will be even less injurious and may produce the largest yield.

In the northern states it is usually best not to cut alfalfa repeatedly earlier than the tenth-bloom stage, and preferably not earlier than the half-bloom stage when it is desired to keep the stand for several years. The same area should not be cut first each year, and it is wise to cut a new seeding after the cutting of the older stands has been completed. When leafhopper infestation is severe, cutting the crop at a particular time may aid in preventing damage. If alfalfa has been injured by severe winter weather, cutting it at the full-bloom stage the following spring will aid it to recover.

Where the winters are severe, the stand is maintained better if the alfalfa is not cut for hay in the fall or grazed closely, but a growth 6 inches or more in height is left for winter protection. Wisconsin experiments show that when it is desired to cut alfalfa or to graze it in the fall, the stand is injured less if this is delayed until late October, by which time the fall growth will have been made and the storage of nutrients in the roots will have taken place.[18]

Since the best practice will differ considerably in the various sections of the country, any person in doubt as to the best time to cut the crop should consult his agricultural college, experiment station, or county agent.

372. Value of different cuttings of alfalfa.—The relative value of the different cuttings of alfalfa hay will depend on climatic conditions. In the corn belt and eastward the first cutting of alfalfa is commonly coarser and less leafy than the later cuttings and is hence of somewhat lower value, when the different cuttings are equally well cured. Also, the weather is often less favorable for curing the first crop.

In many sections a decided prejudice exists among stockmen in favor of a certain cutting, while the actual difference in value may be slight. For example, on account of a wide-spread opinion among Utah dairymen in favor of first-cutting alfalfa, two comparisons were made of first-, second-, and third-cutting hay.[19] To make the test as much as possible upon the different cuttings of hay, the alfalfa was fed as the only roughage, with a very limited amount of concentrates. It was found that the actual advantage of any one cutting over the others was almost negligible.

In Washington, where there was a decided prejudice against second-cutting hay, there was no appreciable difference in the feeding value for lambs between the first, second, and third cuttings cut at the same stage of maturity.[20] Similar results were secured in Utah tests.[21]

In certain sections of the West wild foxtail, or squirrel-tail grass *(Hordeum jubatum)*, injures the quality of the first cutting on account of its objectionable beards. As this grass makes palatable hay when cut early, the crop may be harvested then or may be ensiled, which will soften the beards.

373. Value and use of alfalfa hay.—Alfalfa hay is considerably richer than red clover in protein, averaging 14.7 per cent in comparison with 11.8 per cent for red clover, and the protein in alfalfa is also more digestible than that in clover hay. This results in alfalfa furnishing one-half more digestible protein than clover hay. It supplies 10.6 lbs. digestible protein per 100 lbs., on the average, against 7.0 lbs. for red clover.

There is therefore a decided difference in the amount of protein supplements required to balance the ration when dairy cows, beef cattle, and sheep are fed alfalfa hay in place of clover hay. Indeed, as pointed out elsewhere, sometimes no supplement whatsoever may be needed with alfalfa, while a supplement may be required with clover hay to make a properly-balanced ration. The fact that the proteins of alfalfa combine efficiently with the proteins of the cereals and of such forage as corn silage has been discussed earlier in this chapter. (**361**)

Alfalfa hay is exceptionally high in calcium, containing 1.43 per cent, on the average. This adds to its value, particularly for dairy cows, breeding stock, and young growing animals. It is only fair in phosphorus content, the average being only 0.21 per cent. Well-cured alfalfa hay is very rich in vitamin A value (carotene content), and it is also one of the best sources of vitamin D among common stock feeds.

Alfalfa hay supplies practically as much total digestible nutrients as does red clover hay, and is appreciably higher than timothy hay. However, investigations by Armsby and later by Forbes and Kriss with cattle and by Mitchell and associates with sheep have shown that alfalfa hay is slightly lower in net energy than clover hay and decidedly lower than timothy hay.[22]

This lower net energy value of alfalfa hay is apparently due to a stimulating effect on heat production and body metabolism produced by the protein compounds it furnishes so liberally. These investigations do not mean that timothy hay is superior to legume hay in general nutritive effect. This is the only respect in which timothy hay of the usual quality equals alfalfa or clover in nutrition. Perhaps this stimulating effect on metabolism produced by hay from alfalfa and other legumes (which stimulation reduces its energy value) is one of the very reasons why such excellent production is secured when dairy cows and other stock are fed plenty of good alfalfa hay.

Occasionally cattle or sheep fed leafy, good-quality alfalfa hay as the only roughage will tend to bloat. Such a tendency may usually be prevented by feeding some non-legume roughage, such as corn or sorghum silage, along with the alfalfa.

The value and use of alfalfa hay for the various classes of stock are discussed in detail in the respective chapters of Part III. The use of alfalfa straw or chaff is treated later in this chapter.

374. Alfalfa meal; alfalfa leaf meal; alfalfa stem meal.—In certain of the western alfalfa sections the production of *alfalfa meal* is of considerable importance. Alfalfa meal should be made from a good grade of hay, with no addition of alfalfa straw. A good green color is desirable, as this indicates it has been made from hay of satisfactory quality.

Compared with hay, the meal is easier to transport to distant markets, and for animals having poor teeth the grinding is undoubtedly beneficial. In feeding dairy cows the bulky meal may also be helpful in diluting heavy concentrates, which, if carelessly fed, may cause digestive disturbances. However, hay can be readily chopped sufficiently fine for this purpose by running it through an ordinary silage cutter. Alfalfa meal is used chiefly as an ingredient in mixed feeds, and is especially desirable in poultry feeds and in mixed swine feeds for winter feeding, on account of the vitamins and the calcium and protein it furnishes.

If legume hay is not available for livestock, the purchase of alfalfa meal as such may be warranted, but most farmers can grow good legume hay more cheaply than they can buy it in feed sacks. It must be borne in mind that fine grinding does not transform a roughage into a concentrate, nor does it increase its digestibility for animals with good teeth. Any advantage from grinding or chopping hay probably results from a saving in wastage or in getting animals to eat more than they would otherwise consume. The effect of grinding or chopping hay for the various classes of stock is discussed in detail in Chapter IV and in Part III.

It is often impossible to determine without chemical or laboratory analysis whether alfalfa meal has been made from leafy, early-cut hay or from over-ripe, stemmy material. Hence the meal should be purchased on guarantee of composition, special attention being paid to the fiber content, which in first-class meal should not be higher than in good-quality hay, or 29 to 30 per cent. According to the definitions of feeding stuffs adopted by the Association of American Feed Control Officials, alfalfa meal must not contain more than 33 per cent of crude fiber.[23]

Alfalfa leaf meal, made from the finer parts of alfalfa hay, is considerably higher in protein content than ordinary alfalfa meal or hay and commands a high price for poultry feeding. For other classes of stock its use is not economical, except perhaps for very young pigs in the winter. The definition for alfalfa leaf meal adopted by the Association of American Feed Control Officials states that it must not contain more than 18 per cent of crude fiber.

Alfalfa stem meal is the product screened from ground alfalfa hay in making alfalfa leaf meal. It is considerably lower in protein and higher in fiber than good alfalfa meal, and has a correspondingly lower feeding value. When very finely ground, it may be difficult to distinguish alfalfa stem meal from alfalfa meal, without laboratory examination.

As has already been mentioned alfalfa meal is used quite extensively as an ingredient in commercial mixed feeds. These and also alfalfa-molasses feed are discussed in Chapter XIX.

375. Alfalfa for pasture.—Alfalfa provides a large yield of highly nutritious pasture, but it has definite limitations as a pasture crop. In humid regions heavy grazing is very apt to injure the stand, especially if the fall growth is grazed closely in the North. Also, cattle and sheep are subject to bloat on alfalfa. Horses are rarely affected. In spite of these limitations alfalfa provides such excellent pasture that it is grazed extensively, even in the eastern states.

To avoid serious injury to the stand, fields should never be pastured until they have become well established, and animals should be kept off when the ground is frozen, soft, or muddy. Heavy stocking of the pasture is decidedly injurious, especially with horses and sheep, which gnaw the plants to the ground. Except in districts to which alfalfa is particularly well adapted, it is best to provide a sufficient area of pasture so that considerable will grow up to be cut for hay once or twice during the season. A still better plan is to pasture a given area during only part of the growing season, making one or more cuttings of hay at the usual stage of maturity.

The danger to cattle and sheep from bloat varies greatly with climate and other factors. Though it is always present to some degree, in such sections as the irrigated districts of the Southwest but trifling loss is experienced. Sheep are more subject to bloat than cattle. Where cattle or sheep are grazed on alfalfa, the following precautions should be taken:

For permanent pasture sow with the alfalfa, such grasses as bluegrass, brome grass, or others adapted to your conditions. Use upland in preference to lowland for pasture, and have a constant supply of water for the stock. Frosted alfalfa is especially dangerous, but in the late fall after the crop has dried, it may be grazed again. Before turning animals on alfalfa for the first time, allow them to fill up on hay or on grass pasture, with grain in addition, if they have been accustomed to it. Then in the middle of the forenoon turn them on the alfalfa.

Though some advise allowing the stock to graze only a few minutes the first day and gradually increasing the length of time on the following days, it is probably safer to keep them on the pasture continuously, for then they will never consume undue amounts at one time. When alfalfa pasture is being used for cows in milk, they should be kept on the pasture except at milking time and should never be allowed to get very hungry before being turned back on the pasture. Many advise keeping some hay or straw in a rack where it is always accessible.

Watch the stock closely for the first few days and remove permanently any animals which exhibit symptoms of bloat, for individuals show great differences in their susceptibility to the trouble. A method sometimes used in starting cattle on alfalfa, is to cut part of a field and turn the cattle upon this portion after the alfalfa is half dry. Then after they are well filled, they are allowed to eat whatever of the green crop they wish.

376. Bloat.—Bloat is caused by an extremely rapid production of gases, chiefly carbon dioxide, in the paunch through the fermentation of the succulent forage. The gas is produced faster than it can escape through the gullet, and thus the paunch becomes greatly distended.

This distension may entirely close the exit and the increasing pressure may rupture the paunch and hence kill the animal.

In severe cases of bloat prompt measures of relief are necessary. Sometimes vigorous rubbing and kneading of the abdomen will help the animal to get rid of the gas. If possible the animal should stand on an incline, with its head up the slope.

In severe cases of bloat care must be taken not to waste much valuable time before resorting to the tapping of the paunch by means of the trocar, or if this handy instrument is not available, with a clean knife.

377. Alfalfa as a soiling crop.—Alfalfa is one of the most valuable of all soiling crops, owing to the large yields and to the fact that under proper management it will furnish good feed throughout the entire summer. Much more forage, even twice as much in some cases, is secured from a given acreage as a soiling crop, than when pastured.

In certain hot irrigated sections of the West where no grasses make satisfactory summer pasture, dairy cows are often maintained chiefly on green alfalfa during much of the year. The use of soiling crops has been discussed in detail in the preceding chapter. (**355-357**)

378. Alfalfa silage.—Alfalfa is apt to produce poor-quality, vile-smelling silage, unless one of the special methods is used which have been discussed in the preceding chapter. (**347**) Owing to the palatability and high nutritive value of good-quality alfalfa hay, there is little reason for ensiling the crop, except when weather conditions are such that it cannot be made into good hay. Satisfactory silage is made when alfalfa is mixed with crops rich in sugars, such as green corn or sorghum, or else rye or wheat cut when just past the milk stage.[24] Such a mixture as alfalfa and timothy usually makes better silage than alfalfa alone.

II. Medium Red Clover

379. Medium red clover.—Medium red clover (*Trifolium pratense*), commonly known merely as red clover, is still the most important legume in the humid sections of the northern two-thirds of the United States. It is chiefly seeded in combination with timothy, only 4,202,607 acres of clover (red, alsike, and mammoth) being grown alone in this country in 1929, in comparison with 25,547,279 acres of timothy and mixed timothy and clover. Grown in rotation with corn and other cereals, clover is not only excellent for hay, for pasturage, and as a soiling crop, but it is also important in maintaining soil fertility.

The value of clover and other legumes in increasing the yields of other crops through the nitrogen they add to the soil is shown in a striking manner by experiments covering 30 to 40 years conducted by the Ohio, Pennsylvania, and Missouri Stations.[25] In these studies short-time rotations which included clover have been compared with continuous cropping to corn, oats, wheat, etc. The increases in the value of the grain crops due to the growing of clover were worth even more than the actual value of the clover harvested. Thus the hay value of the clover crop was less than half its total value.

Red clover does best on well-drained soils rich in lime, but it grows satisfactorily on fields which are a little too acid or not quite well enough drained for alfalfa. It stands severe winters better than alfalfa but does not endure drought so well, as the roots do not go so deep. But few plants live over three years, and when grown alone the crop is usually treated as a biennial. Pastured plants persist longer than those cut for hay, and in the Pacific Coast States and northern Europe satisfactory yields are often secured for three years. Alsike clover is commonly seeded with red clover where the soil drainage is not ideal, for alsike will thrive better on any poorly-drained spots in the field.

Red clover generally yields a heavy first crop of hay and a much lighter second crop, which is often allowed to mature for seed. When red clover is seeded in the spring with a small grain crop, as is the common practice, it will furnish some pasturage the same fall, or even a hay crop if the season is especially favorable. In the southern states, where it does not thrive during the heat of summer, red clover is sometimes grown as a winter annual, the first crop being cut in the spring and the second in early summer. At the northern limits of its culture but one cutting is produced.

The average yield of clover hay per acre, according to the Census of 1930, was 1.48 tons, but under favorable conditions much higher returns are secured, the yield in 2 cuttings ranging from 2 to 3 tons or even more per acre. Where it flourishes, alfalfa out-yields red clover. However, red clover is better adapted for short-time rotations than the longer-lived alfalfa, which is often difficult to establish and is then grown in the same field for many years, if possible.

In many cases the growing of red or mammoth clover has been abandoned on account of failure to secure stands. Such "clover sickness" of the soil may be due to certain diseases, but in most cases it means that lime, phosphate, and possibly potash are needed, or that unsuitable seed has been used. Farmers who willingly prepare fields thoroughly for alfalfa often fail to make reasonable efforts to get good stands of clover.

Sometimes clover is badly covered with a powdery mildew and farmers wonder whether there will be any danger in using it for hay or pasture. Apparently, this will not injure stock at all.[26]

380. Sources of seed.—Many trials have been conducted by the experiment stations and by the United States Department of Agriculture to compare red clover seed from various sources. These investigations show that it is very important to use a strain of seed that is well adapted to the particular district where sown. Seed from Italy or other southern European countries has been found unsuitable for any section except the Pacific Northwest, for it is not hardy. In the northern states, except in this Pacific district, seed from these same states or Canada should be used, if possible, instead of any imported seed, for these plants stand the winters better.

Of the imported seed, that from northern Europe and Chile has given much better results than southern European seed. In the southern part of the clover belt seed of a strain resistant to anthracnose should be used, if possible. It is easy to distinguish American strains of red clover from the European, for the leaves of the former are covered with fine hairs, while the leaves of the latter are practically hairless.

381. Stage to cut clover for hay.—Unless the weather is decidedly unfavorable, the first crop of red clover should be cut for hay not later than full bloom, and preferably when two-thirds in bloom. The quality of the hay will then be much better, it will be richer in protein, and the yield of hay or seed in the second crop will be much larger than if cutting is delayed.[27] The yield of hay in the first cutting made at this stage will not usually be quite so great as when the cutting is delayed a few days, but the total yield of both crops will be greater and the hay is of higher value.

382. Value and use of red clover hay.—Red clover hay is second only to alfalfa hay in value for livestock, and for certain classes of stock is fully equal to alfalfa. When cut at the usual stage of maturity, it supplies only about two-thirds as much digestible protein as alfalfa hay. Therefore in feeding dairy cows and other classes of stock, a somewhat larger amount of protein supplements is often needed with red clover hay to balance the ration. If clover hay is cut early it may be practically as rich in protein as ordinary alfalfa.

The difference in protein content and a slightly greater palatability are the chief reasons why alfalfa hay usually sells at a somewhat higher price than clover hay of equal quality, for clover hay supplies a trifle more total digestible nutrients than alfalfa and slightly surpasses it in net energy. The use and value of clover hay for the various classes of stock are discussed in the respective chapters of Part III. It is there shown that well-cured clover hay is excellent for all classes of stock. While it is not quite so valuable as alfalfa per ton for dairy cows, for growing cattle and lambs, and for swine, it apparently equals alfalfa for horses and for fattening steers and lambs.

The value of mixed clover-and-timothy hay will depend on the proportion of clover present and on the stage of maturity at which it is cut. The more clover there is in the hay, the greater will be its value for all classes of stock except horses. Many farmers greatly overestimate the actual proportion of clover present in mixed hay. Late-cut mixed hay is a poor roughage for dairy cows or sheep.

The use of clover straw or chaff is discussed later in this chapter.

383. Clover for pasture.—Red clover does not usually persist in permanent pastures, but it is one of the best pasture crops to be grown in rotations. Where alfalfa thrives, it will furnish more feed per acre than red clover, especially in the dry time of midsummer. However, for pasturing cattle and sheep red clover is safer than alfalfa, because there is less danger from bloat. Even with clover the precautions stated previously in this chapter should be taken to avoid trouble. With mixed clover-and-timothy pasture, which is used for such stock much more commonly than pure clover, there is little danger from bloat. In the northern and central states, red clover is one of the most valuable pasture crops for swine, being excelled only by alfalfa.

Like alfalfa, red clover will not stand too close pasturing. Much more feed per acre will be produced if care is taken to avoid this. Clipping the pasture at the usual time for the first cutting of hay will stimulate the new growth.

384. Clover as a soiling crop and for silage.—Clover is particularly valuable as a soiling crop, ranking next to alfalfa among legumes available for this purpose. When clover is cut early, it at once starts growth again if the weather is favorable, and it may furnish three or even four cuttings of green forage a year.

In some cases clover has made good silage, but so many failures have occurred that this plant cannot be recommended for this purpose, except where weather conditions prevent its being properly cured into hay. The same precautions should then be taken as with alfalfa. (**347, 378**) Mixed clover and timothy will usually make much better silage than clover alone.

Red-clover silage was a satisfactory winter feed for dairy cows in trials at the Montana Station, but in summer it became darker in color and acquired a strong odor.[28] Cows at the Pennsylvania Station maintained their yield better when fed red-clover silage and mixed hay as roughage than when the only roughage was the mixed hay.[29]

IV. OTHER CLOVERS

385. Mammoth clover.—Mammoth clover *(Trifolium pratense perenne)* grows ranker than medium red clover, has coarser stems, and blooms 1 to 2 weeks later. It usually lives 3 years or more and thrives better on poor or sandy soil than does red clover. As it is coarser, the hay is more difficult to cure and somewhat less palatable. Since it yields but a single cutting during the season, this clover is frequently pastured for several weeks in the early spring. After the stock is removed, the plants shoot up and are soon ready for the mower.

386. Alsike clover.—This variety of clover *(Trifolium hybridum)*, once supposed to be a hybrid between red clover and white clover, flourishes on land too acid or too wet for other clovers and is a hardier, longer-lived plant, enduring 4 to 6 years on good soil. Since it yields but one cutting with some fall pasturage, it is excelled by red clover where the latter thrives. It should be seeded with timothy or other grasses to support the weak stems. Many farmers include some alsike in their seedings of red clover and timothy. Alsike hay is fine-stemmed and fully equal to red clover in value.

387. White clover.—This creeping perennial *(Trifolium repens)* has the widest range of any of the clovers, thriving in almost any soil from Canada nearly to the Gulf of Mexico, if moisture is ample. In the North it is an important plant in mixed pastures, forming a dense mat of herbage and furnishing feed throughout the growing season. On account of its creeping growth it forms seed even when grazed closely, and thus spreads rapidly in pastures when conditions are favorable. In the South it nearly disappears in summer but reappears in the fall, furnishing winter pasturage and thus combining well with Bermuda grass. Owing to the low, creeping growth of ordinary white clover, it does not yield hay.

The white clover which often appears spontaneously in many pastures under favorable conditions is usually a wild type with smaller leaves than the common variety (known as "white Dutch clover"). This wild white clover is longer-lived and apparently better adapted for seeding in permanent pasture mixtures, when the seed is available.

388. Ladino clover.—Ladino clover, a large-growing variety of white clover from Italy, has recently attracted considerable attention in the United States. It is of much promise for pastures in the sections where it thrives, and it is apparently adapted to soils on which alsike clover will do well.[30] It has given especially good results in the irrigated sections of the northwestern states, where it is one of the most productive pasture crops. Continuous close grazing will kill it, and also there is some danger of cattle and sheep bloating on Ladino clover pasture.

389. Sweet clover.—Recently sweet clover has become an important crop, especially for temporary pasture, over extensive areas in the United States. In 1929 there were 1,759,479 acres of sweet clover pasture in the country. The kind most grown is the biennial white sweet clover *(Melilotus alba)*, also known as melilot and Bokhara clover. Yellow-flowered biennial sweet clover *(Melilotus officinalis)*, two weeks earlier in blossoming and somewhat smaller in growth, has usually given lower yields than the white kind. These biennial varieties are usually seeded in spring grain, and reach maturity and die in August of the following year.

An annual variety of the white sweet clover, called Hubam clover, is useful as a green-manuring crop to be seeded in spring grain and plowed under in the fall. When the biennial varieties are used for this purpose or even plowed under very early in the spring, they are apt to volunteer and cause difficulty in the succeeding crop. For hay or pasture the first year, Hubam has not in general been superior to the biennial kinds.

Sweet clover stands drought nearly as well as alfalfa and will grow on soil which is so poorly drained or so low in fertility and humus that alfalfa or red clover will not thrive. However, it is about as particular as alfalfa about soil acidity, an ample supply of lime, and proper inoculation. In the West it is a good crop for alkali soils or hard adobe. In the North sweet clover is subject to injury from heaving during the winter, the same as alfalfa.

390. Sweet clover for pasture.—Sweet clover is primarily a pasture plant, and in the second year of its growth will usually produce, from spring to mid-August, a larger yield of dry matter than any other pasture crop. It is therefore useful to supplement permanent pastures, especially for dairy cows.

At first stock usually dislike sweet clover, on account of the bitter taste due to the cumarin it contains, but generally they soon become accustomed to it, especially if started on it in the spring, when it is less bitter. Often they will industriously search out every spot of grass and even weeds in the pasture, grazing them to the ground before hunger forces them to the sweet clover. In spite of this lack of palatability, stock usually thrive on sweet clover. Sweet clover is less apt than alfalfa to cause bloat in cattle or sheep, but the danger should be guarded against by taking the precautions discussed earlier in this chapter. (**376**)

The first season's growth of sweet clover may be pastured after it is 8 to 10 inches high and until frost, but close grazing may reduce the yield the following year. The second season the crop will furnish grazing from early spring until the plants die in August, or until they become too woody. By seeding sweet clover in the spring grain each year, it is often possible, if the growth of the first-year crop is good, to pasture the stock on it by the time the second-year crop is exhausted. It will sometimes be necessary to furnish other feed for a brief period. In some cases sweet clover has been established successfully in permanent-pasture mixtures by seeding two successive springs.

Some farmers seed sweet clover in the spring without a nurse crop, as a hay or pasture crop for the first season. When thus seeded alone, yields of 1 to 3 tons of hay per acre are secured under good conditions.

Sweet clover grows so rapidly in the spring of the year that it will often carry more animals per acre at this time than has been estimated. If it grows up too rapidly, more stock should be turned in, for otherwise it will become woody or will set seed and die. At the lush period of its growth sweet clover may tend to scour cattle receiving no other feed. Due to this, beef cattle made poorer gains on sweet clover early in the season than they did later in Illinois and North Dakota trials.[31]

Sweet clover has been used with great success on thousands of farms as a pasture for dairy cows, and with a good stand on fertile soil it will carry more than a cow to the acre. It is particularly useful in providing good feed in July and early August when bluegrass pasture is apt to become parched. To furnish pasture at this season a second-year crop must be kept closely grazed in the period of lush growth in the spring. There has been but little trouble from sweet clover producing a noticeable flavor in milk, though sometimes there is a slight change on sweet-clover pasture.

In tests during four seasons at the Wisconsin Station yearling heifers did poorly on sweet-clover pasture in comparison with others on mixed timothy-and-alsike-clover pasture or on bluegrass-and-red-top pasture.[32] This suggests that sweet-clover pasture may generally be less useful for heifers than for dairy cows.

Both second-year and first-year sweet-clover pasture is satisfactory for swine, though they take to it a little less readily than do cattle. However, alfalfa, red clover, or rape is superior where these crops thrive.

391. Sweet clover for hay.—As a hay crop sweet clover is inferior to alfalfa or red clover, without considering the possible danger from sweet-clover poisoning referred to later. In sections where sweet clover seeded in spring grain makes sufficient growth after the grain is harvested, it may be cut for hay the same fall. This crop, which is rather fine stemmed, cures much more readily than the rank growth of the second season and may make hay nearly equal to alfalfa, except for the grain stubble present.

The second year two cuttings of hay can be made if the first crop is cut early, before the blossoms appear or at least by the beginning of bloom. If the cutting is delayed, the rank growth is apt to kill the buds on the lower parts of the stems, and practically no second growth may be made. This cutting should be made with the mower set so as to leave a very high stubble, to save as many buds as possible.

At this immature stage the plants are very succulent, and it is difficult to cure them into good hay, particularly with the unsettled weather usual at that time in the humid sections. To make matters worse the stems are large and solid, while the leaves are fine and shatter readily. Therefore, except with a combination of care and good luck, the hay is apt to be stemmy and of poor quality. Sometimes the crop is cut with a grain binder and the bundles cured in small shocks. In the corn belt this first cutting is apt to come just when farmers are busiest with their corn crop. There is much less difficulty in curing the second cutting, as the weather is better for hay-making and the plants are less succulent.

392. Sweet-clover disease.—With the spread of sweet-clover growing there have been serious outbreaks among cattle of a strange poisoning caused by sweet clover hay or silage.[33] This disease, which occurs most commonly in young cattle and which rarely, if ever, affects horses and sheep under farm conditions, causes a loss of the clotting power of the blood. Animals affected die from internal hemorrhages or from bleeding to death from minor wounds, such as those from dehorning or castration.

The cause of the disease is in doubt, but it is usually produced only by moldy or spoiled hay or silage, though spoilage is not always visible.[34] The disease has not apparently been caused by hay from the first-year crop, perhaps because there is usually little difficulty in curing this properly.

The sweet-clover disease is most apt to occur when cattle are fed exclusively on sweet clover hay and when it is fed for a considerable period, though the hemorrhages may occur in 15 days after the feeding of sweet clover hay is begun.

Trouble from the disease may be prevented or minimized by feeding sweet clover hay with at least twice as much other roughage, or by feeding it for only a week or 10 days and then feeding other roughage for two weeks or more.[35]

393. Sweet clover as a soiling crop or for silage.—Sweet clover is sometimes used as a soiling crop, especially for dairy cows, to supplement short pasture. It is not commonly ensiled, on account of the difficulty of making good silage. When this is attempted, the method advised for alfalfa should be used, the sweet clover being allowed to dry out somewhat after cutting. It should be borne in mind that the sweet-clover disease may be caused not only by spoiled sweet-clover hay but also by spoiled silage.

394. Crimson clover.—Crimson clover *(Trifolium incarnatum)*, an annual that is adapted to mild climates, is grown chiefly in the Atlantic seaboard states from New Jersey southward. Sown in the late summer or early fall, it blossoms the following spring and dies by early summer. It is grown chiefly as a green-manure and winter-cover crop, but is also used for pasture and hay and to some extent as a soiling crop. Crimson clover thrives on both sandy and clay land, if well drained, and has the advantage that the crop may be harvested or plowed under as manure early enough so that other crops may be raised the same year.

When grown for hay, it is important that crimson clover be cut by the time the flowers at the base of the most advanced heads have faded. After this the minute barbed hairs of the blossom heads and stems become hard and wiry. If hay from over-ripe crimson clover is fed to horses or mules, these hairs sometimes mat together in the digestive tract, forming felt-like masses which plug the intestines, causing death. When over-ripe hay must be fed to horses or mules, which are usually the only animals affected, it should be given with other roughage to reduce the danger, and preferably with succulent feeds, or else it should be wet thoroughly 12 hours before feeding.

Cut at the right stage, crimson-clover hay is about equal to that from red clover. According to Piper, yields of hay from good stands average about 1.25 tons per acre.[36]

During a short period in the spring before it matures, crimson clover furnishes good pasturage earlier than grass or other clovers, and in warm sections it may be utilized as late fall or winter pasture.

395. Bur clovers.—The *southern* or *spotted bur clover (Medicago arabica)* and *California* or *toothed bur clover (M. hispida)* are winter annuals that furnish valuable pasturage in mild regions. The former, which is the hardier, is found chiefly in the southern states, and the latter in California and Texas. They are admirable supplements to Bermuda pasture, furnishing feed when that grass is resting and re-seeding unless grazed too closely. Even on land where summer-cultivated crops are grown, bur clover volunteers in the fall, if once sown. Though not commonly so used, it may be seeded for hay with fall grain.

396. Other clovers.—The *hop clovers (Trifolium procumbens* and *dubium)* are annual, low-growing clovers that are of importance in permanent pastures in some sections of the South and on the northern Pacific slope.[37] They furnish good early grazing, but disappear in summer.

Berseem, or Egyptian clover *(Trifolium alexandrinum),* is an annual clover which is adapted to hot climates, growing during the winter season when alfalfa is dormant. It is of much importance in Egypt as a hay crop, as a green soiling crop, and for green manure. Berseem is adapted to such sections of the United States as the Imperial Valley in California. It may be cut several times a season and produces heavy yields under favorable conditions.

Subterranean clover (Trifolium subterraneum) is a winter annual which somewhat resembles bur clover. It is an important pasture crop in certain districts of Australia and is adapted to some areas in the southern states.

V. Other Legume Forages

397. Soybeans.—Though soybeans *(Soja max)* have long been one of the most important crops of Manchukuo, Northern China, and Japan they have only recently gained an important place in the agriculture of the United States. Prior to 1917 less than 500,000 acres of soybeans were grown annually in this country, including the equivalent acreage on which soybeans were raised in combination with corn or other crops. As farmers have become familiar with the merits of soybeans during recent years, the acreage has increased with great rapidity, and it is estimated that in 1930 it reached 3,758,000 acres.[38] Of the entire acreage in that year about 56 per cent was used for hay, 14 per cent was grazed, and 30 per cent harvested for the seed.

Though soybeans have now become an important crop in this country, especially in the heart of the corn belt, the percentage of crop land devoted to their culture is small in comparison with the soybean districts of the Orient. There they are put to many uses and serve largely as a substitute for meat and other animal foods in the diet of the people. In several districts of Manchukuo, the most important center of foreign production, soybeans occupy between 40 and 65 per cent of the cultivated area. In Illinois, which is the center of soybean production in the United States, the 1930 Census showed that the highest percentage of the cultivated land occupied by soybeans in any county was 11 per cent.

Soybeans are annual legumes, bushy to twining in habit, and grow 2 to 5 feet high or more. They thrive in practically all localities where corn may be grown and will stand considerable frost, both in spring and autumn. Due to this and also to the relatively short growing season of early varieties, soybeans may be grown in the northern part of the cornbelt, where cowpeas are not a success.

Soybeans are markedly drought resistant, and are adapted to a wide range of soils, even doing well on poor sandy land if the seed is properly inoculated. On very poor land in the South, they are excelled by cowpeas. The fondness of rabbits for the plants is a serious drawback in the plains states. Though soybeans are benefited by lime on lime-deficient soils, they will make a good crop on soil too sour for alfalfa. Unlike cowpeas, soybeans ripen their seed at one time, and the plants then die.

Soybeans produce the largest yield of seed of any legume suited to temperate climates, but until recently the crop has been grown in this country chiefly for forage. The acreage of soybeans grown for seed in the Central States has increased greatly during the past few years, the seed being raised both for direct feeding to livestock and for sale to oil mills for the production of soybean oil and soybean oil meal. From New England west to Minnesota, soybeans are of less importance as a grain crop than farther south, because the early varieties which mature seed there are not usually heavy yielders of seed.

For hay and other forage purposes, a relatively late-maturing variety of soybeans for the given locality is usually grown, as it will produce a larger yield for forage. Soybeans make excellent hay, grown alone, or sometimes in combination with Sudan grass, sorghum, or millet. They are often raised in combination with corn for silage, and they are a good soiling crop for fall feeding. The uses and value of soybean seed and of soybean oil meal for stock feeding are discussed in Chapter XVIII.

398. Soybeans for hay.—In most of the corn-growing districts of the United States, except in the most southern part, soybeans are the most valuable and important annual legume crop for hay. They yield 1 to 2 tons or more per acre of palatable, protein-rich hay, which is an excellent substitute for alfalfa or clover in feeding all classes of stock.

The portion of well-cured soybean hay that is eaten by stock is about equal to alfalfa or clover hay in feeding value. However, there is generally more waste on account of the coarseness of the stems. Therefore, the usual value of the soybean hay per ton, as fed, is correspondingly less than that of alfalfa or clover hay.

In the wide region where soybeans thrive, farmers have found that soybeans are usually the best substitute crop for hay when clover or

WHITE CLOVER IS VALUABLE IN PERMANENT PASTURES

An excellent stand of white clover in permanent blue-grass pasture in the corn belt. This dwarf, creeping clover is an important plant in mixed pastures.

FIELD PEAS THRIVE IN THE NORTHERN STATES

In the cool climate of the northern states, field peas grow luxuriantly. Especially in combination with oats or barley, they provide good hay, soilage, or pasturage. (From Wisconsin Station.)

Loading a Fine Crop of Cowpea Hay

The cowpea, the most important legume in the cotton belt, grows on all types of soil, increasing the fertility of the soil and furnishing rich feed. Cowpea hay is even higher in protein than alfalfa hay.

Velvet Beans Grown with Corn

Velvet beans have become an important crop in some of the southern states. Note the velvet bean vines, which surmount the stalks of corn. (From U. S. Department of Agriculture.)

alfalfa winterkills, and many include it regularly in their rotations. Soybeans are also an excellent catch crop for late spring planting when early crops have been stricken by drought or otherwise destroyed. The fact that soybeans thrive over a wide range of soil conditions and on soils too acid or too low in lime for alfalfa makes the crop particularly useful. For hay, soybeans should be seeded quite thickly, so the stems will not be too coarse. For the same reason, the slender varieties are usually better for hay than the more bushy types.

Many experiments have been conducted to determine the best time to cut soybeans for hay.[39] They will make good hay at any stage from the time the pods are formed until the lower leaves are yellowing from maturity, but before they drop off. Most investigators have found that the largest yields of dry matter and nutrients are usually secured from the time the seeds are well formed until the lower leaves turn yellow. Also, it was found in experiments reviewed in Chapter XXV that soybean hay, cut when the seed had practically reached full development and the lower leaves were turning yellow, was of higher value per ton for dairy cattle than hay cut at an earlier stage of maturity.

This high value for the late-cut hay, which is coarser and less leafy, is due to the fact that a considerable proportion of such hay consists of soybean seed, rich in protein and fat. Appendix Table I shows that the late-cut hay is richer in protein and total digestible nutrients than hay cut when the seeds are first forming. The condition is thus entirely different than in the case of most kinds of hay, such as alfalfa, clover, or timothy, for generally early-cut hay is richer in protein and more nutritious than late-cut hay.

If cutting is delayed until too late, it may be difficult to cure the crop, on account of the cooler weather and the more frequent rains. Soybeans are more readily cured than cowpeas, and even though they may be discolored by rains that would spoil cowpea hay, they will usually make palatable hay. The best hay is made by curing it in cocks, but if labor is limited, good hay can be made under favorable conditions by the use of the side-delivery rake. If the soybeans do not contain too much grass or weeds, the crop can be cut with a binder and cured in the shock like small grain.

Combinations of soybeans with Sudan grass, sorghum, or millet are often grown, especially for hay. The combination of soybeans and Sudan grass has proved one of the best late-summer emergency hay and forage crops in the central corn belt. The mixture usually yields more forage than soybeans alone, and it is easier to cure into hay. Such hay has a considerably higher feeding value than hay from Sudan grass alone.

399. Soybeans for silage.—The use of soybeans alone for silage is not advisable when the weather permits making them into hay, as the silage may be rank-smelling and poor in quality. If the green soybeans are allowed to dry out somewhat, but not too much to pack well, are finely cut, and are carefully packed in the silo, good silage will probably result. (**346-347**) However, a mixture of green soybeans and corn or sorghum makes first-class silage without any trouble, and so the combination is decidedly preferable. The corn and the soybeans may be grown separately and mixed at the time of ensiling at the rate of 1 ton of soybeans with 2 to 4 tons of corn forage, or the corn and soybeans may be grown together.

In the several experiments in which the combination crop has been compared with corn alone, sometimes the combination has produced the larger yield of silage and in others there has been no increase in yield, or even a decrease.[40] The combination silage will be richer in protein than corn silage, but it is apt to be a little lower in total digestible nutrients, for the amount of soybean seed produced will usually not quite make up in weight for the reduction in the amount of corn grain resulting from growing the combination crop. If the conditions are ideal for corn, the soybeans will be shaded so much that they may not form any important part of the crop. Farmers often greatly over-estimate the weight of soybeans in the forage.

Considering the effect of the soybeans on soil fertility when they are properly inoculated and also the higher protein content of the silage, the growing of soybeans with silage corn, particularly for feeding dairy cattle, seems a sound practice where the total yield of silage is not reduced. The best rate of seeding varies with local conditions, but generally it is advisable to use nearly the normal amount of corn, with the soybean seed in addition.

400. Soybeans as a soiling crop and for pasture.—Soybeans provide a satisfactory soiling crop for fall feeding, though the green forage is usually less palatable to dairy cows than green corn fodder, green alfalfa, or green clover. Soybeans are not especially desirable for use as a pasture crop, for the growth of the plant is stopped as soon as the branches are eaten off, instead of growth continuing as it does in the case of rape, clover, or alfalfa. Soybeans should not be pastured until the plants are well grown; they will then furnish a fairly-heavy yield of feed, but only over a rather short period. For pasture, soybeans should be grown in rows to reduce the loss from trampling the plants. Soybeans are often planted with corn which is to be hogged-down or harvested with sheep, and they are only rivaled by rape for this purpose.

For swine pasture in the northern states rape, alfalfa, or clover is preferable to soybeans, for these crops provide good feed throughout a much longer season and produce more pork per acre. In the southern states pigs are used extensively to hog-down crops of soybeans in the fall, and this practice has recently spread into parts of the corn belt. Unfortunately, as is pointed out in Chapter XXXVI, this method of feeding soybeans produces soft pork.

401. Cowpea.—The cowpea (*Vigna sinensis*), a hot-weather annual that may be grown from the central part of the corn belt southward, is the most important legume in the cotton belt. Chiefly grown for forage and green manure, it also furnishes seed for humans and animals, though the seed is usually too high priced for stock feeding. The use of the seed for feeding is discussed in Chapter XVIII.

The especial value of cowpeas lies in the fact that they will grow on all types of soil and with but little attention, increasing the fertility of the land and furnishing excellent roughage. On the poorest soils in the cotton belt cowpeas will do better than soybeans, but on better soils, or even on poor soils when fertilized, soybeans are usually the more productive crop.

This vine-like plant does not mature in a definite time but continues to bear pods and put forth new leaves during a long period. Sown at corn-planting time or later, early varieties mature the first pods in 70 to 90 days. The crop may be then cut for hay or the harvesting considerably delayed without loss. Cowpeas yield from 1 to 2 tons per acre of a hay which is even richer than alfalfa in protein, though slightly lower in total digestible nutrients. It is excellent for dairy cattle, beef cattle, and horses. If well cured, it is equal in feeding value to red clover or alfalfa hay.

Because of the succulent leaves and thick stems, the cowpea is difficult to cure. It is therefore usually cured in high and narrow cocks, after it has dried out sufficiently in the windrow. Sometimes the hay is cocked about frames or pyramids of poles to permit better air circulation. (332) When raised for hay, cowpeas are often grown with Sudan grass, sorghum, Johnson grass, millet, or soybeans to support the vines and permit easier curing, as well as to increase the yield. Sudan grass generally excels for this purpose.

Cowpeas are extensively grown with corn or sorghum, and the crop grazed by cattle, sheep, or pigs. Sometimes more or less of the corn ears or cowpea seed is picked by hand before the stock is turned in.

402. Field peas; peas and oats.—Field peas *(Pisum arvense)*, the use of which as a grain crop is discussed in Chapter XVIII, are grown in Canada and the northern states to some extent for forage. They do not thrive where the season is hot. A combination of peas and oats, if cut early and well cured, makes nutritious hay, liked by all classes of stock. It is slightly richer than red clover hay in protein, but is usually not so palatable.

Field-pea straw, with its finer stems and often still carrying some seed, is worth more than the coarser straw from field beans or soybeans.

Peas and oats make satisfactory silage, if not ensiled until the oats are in the dough stage and the peas have hardened. Such silage is not quite equal to corn silage but is useful north of the corn belt. Dairy cows fed pea-and-oat silage with hay and concentrates produced 9 per cent less milk in a Pennsylvania trial than when corn silage was fed.[41] However, it was concluded that pea-and-oat silage was much better than no silage at all, and that it would often help out during the late summer months when pasture was short and the supply of corn silage exhausted.

Oats and peas are frequently sown as a spring soiling crop, especially for dairy cows, and are about the best early annual crop for this purpose. The combination is also sometimes used for pasture, particularly for swine. However, it does not furnish pasturage over a very long season, and stock may tramp down and waste considerable of the forage. Therefore, for pasture oats and peas are excelled by rape or by a combination of oats, peas, and rape. In certain sections of the Northwest field peas, usually with a small quantity of oats or barley to help support the vines, are grown extensively for hogging-down or sheeping-down when the crop is nearly mature.

In the southern states and in certain sections of the Pacific-coast district, Austrian winter field peas have given promising results as a winter cover-crop or as a winter pasture-crop when seeded with winter oats or other winter grain.[42]

403. Pea-cannery waste; pea-vine silage.—*Pea-cannery waste* consists of the pea vines and empty pods, left after the green peas are removed at the pea-canning factories. It is usually put in large stacks, where the decaying outside layer preserves the mass of silage within, or else it is put in silos.

The *pea-vine silage* has a strong odor, but it is relished by stock and is an excellent feed for dairy cows, beef cattle, and sheep. It contains considerably more digestible protein than corn silage, but it supplies only 86 per cent as much total digestible nutrients as well-eared corn silage. Where advantage can be taken of its richness in protein by saving on protein supplements that would otherwise be needed to balance the ration, pea-vine silage is worth fully 90 per cent as much as well-eared corn silage per ton.[43] If fed in a ration that contains more protein than is needed, pea-vine silage is probably worth only about 85 per cent as much as well-eared corn silage, but it is worth fully as much per ton as silage from corn cut when in the milk stage or earlier.

Though pea-vine silage has a strong odor, it does not injure the flavor of milk, if fed after milking in a well-ventilated barn and if spoiled portions are discarded.

If cannery waste is spread out thinly on a field where the grass is short, it may be cured into hay about equal to clover or alfalfa hay in feeding value, but this involves much more labor than placing it in the silo.[44]

404. Vetch.—Only *hairy vetch (Vicia villosa)*, also called sand or Russian vetch, and *common vetch (Vicia sativa)*, also known as tares or Oregon vetch, are important in the United States. Both are ordinarily annuals, though hairy vetch especially may live more than a year. Being cool-weather plants they do not thrive in the Central States. They are usually fall-sown in mild climates, but a spring strain of the common vetch is sometimes grown.

While common vetch is killed by zero temperatures, hairy vetch usually endures the winter in the northern states, if well established in the fall. Hairy vetch may be grown on poorer soil than its relative, is adapted to a wider range than crimson clover, and is markedly drought resistant. It is usually sown with small grain to support the weak vines, which clamber from 4 to 10 feet in a tangled mass. In the South and in western Washington and Oregon, where the winters are not severe, common vetch is preferred on soil rich enough for its culture, since the seed is cheaper and the vines grow less tangled.

Both kinds of vetch make good hay, usually being grown with oats or other small grain for this purpose and cut when the pods are well developed. Pure vetch hay is rich in protein, and yields of 2.5 tons per acre are secured under favorable conditions.

The vetches also furnish excellent pasture for stock, the crop sometimes being pastured when young and then being allowed to grow up for hay or seed. The combination of vetch and oats also makes good silage to use as a substitute for corn silage. In the coast sections of Oregon and Washington this combination is often sown in the fall and ensiled in early summer, thus making possible double use of silos during the year. In Oregon trials the average yield of vetch and oats for silage was 16 tons per acre, which was double that of corn.[45] The vetch-and-oats silage was as palatable as corn silage and equalled it in feeding value. In Canadian trials oats-vetch-and-pea silage was slightly inferior to corn silage for milk production.[46]

A smooth strain of hairy vetch, called *smooth vetch*, has given good results in the South, growing in colder weather than hairy vetch but not being as hardy.[47] *Hungarian vetch (Vicia pannonica)*, less viny than common vetch, is especially well adapted to the Pacific-coast section, as it is resistant to aphis and will grow on land more poorly drained than will common vetch.[48] *Monantha vetch (Vicia monan-*

tha) produces edible seed which may be used like lentils and appears promising in certain areas of the Gulf States and the Pacific-coast district.[49]

405. Lespedeza. — *Common lespedeza (Lespedeza striata),* sometimes called Japan clover, is a summer annual which has spread over most of the area from southern New Jersey and Pennsylvania westward to eastern Kansas, Oklahoma, and Texas. Here, even on poor soils, it appears spontaneously in mixed pastures and reseeds freely unless grazed too closely.[50]

Since lespedeza will grow on almost any soil without lime, fertilizer, or artificial inoculation, it has taken the place of red clover on many farms where it has become increasingly difficult to grow red clover. For this reason lespedeza is often grown in regular crop rotations, especially in Virginia, North Carolina, Tennessee, and Kentucky. In the district where it thrives, it is exceedingly valuable in permanent pastures, as it adds nitrogen to the soil, binds it together and prevents erosion, and furnishes pasturage well liked by stock. It apparently has not been known to cause bloat.

Common lespedeza and the varieties which have been developed from it grow tall enough for hay only on rich soils. On such soil the growth is so thick that the yield of hay is often surprisingly large. On rich bottom lands yields of 2 tons of hay per acre are not unusual.

Korean lespedeza (Lespedeza stipulacea), an earlier and taller annual species, can be grown somewhat farther north than common lespedeza.[51] It has been satisfactory as far north as central Ohio, Indiana, and Michigan and readily produces an abundance of seed where killing frosts do not occur before the middle of September. It is too early for the extreme southern part of the country.

Hay from the annual lespedezas is eaten readily by all classes of stock and may be used in the same manner as alfalfa or red clover hay. The annual lespedezas include common lespedeza and the varieties developed from it, and also Korean lespedeza. In experiments with dairy cattle, beef cattle, and mules, annual lespedeza has been about equal to alfalfa hay in feeding value.[52] In content of protein and total digestible nutrients it averages slightly higher than red clover hay.

Green lespedeza plants contain less moisture than alfalfa or red clover, and therefore are more readily cured. A light crop can often be cut and hauled the same day. To make the best hay, lespedeza should be cut not later than full bloom or shortly thereafter. If cut before bloom, a good yield of seed can often be obtained from the second growth. In the South mixed lespedeza-and-Bermuda-grass hay is often made. Lespedeza also combines well with orchard grass and red top, the first cutting being nearly all grass and the second practically all lespedeza.

Lespedeza sericea, a perennial species which is taller and has coarser stems than the annual kinds, is of promise as a perennial pasture and hay crop in sections adapted to common lespedeza.[53] The first cutting of hay should be made before bloom and when the plants are not more than about 20 inches tall, or the crop will become too woody. The stubble should be left 4 or 5 inches high, as the new growth comes from the lower part of the stems and not from the crowns, as in the case of alfalfa or red clover.

Hay from perennial lespedeza is somewhat less palatable than that from the annual varieties. Also the first cutting is more stemmy, and there may be some wastage in feeding it to dairy cattle, while horses and mules will eat it without much wastage. In Tennessee tests satisfactory results were secured when perennial lespedeza hay was fed to dairy cattle and horses.[54]

406. Yellow trefoil, or black medic.—Yellow trefoil, or black medic *(Medicago lupulina)*, a relative of alfalfa, is a creeping annual legume which is somewhat like white clover in habit of growth. It is usually not prominent in permanent pastures, except on the black prairie soils of Alabama and Mississippi, where it occasionally furnishes a considerable part of the pasturage in early spring.

407. Velvet bean.—Especially since earlier-maturing varieties were developed, velvet beans *(Stizolobium* spp.) have become an important southern crop. The early-maturing varieties, which are now usually grown, thrive throughout the cotton belt, except in the extreme northern part. Velvet beans grow well on poor, sandy soils and those deficient in lime, providing they are well drained. Even the early varieties make a tangled mass of vines 3 to 10 feet long, while the later ones run 15 to 40 feet.

Velvet beans are difficult to cure into hay, and over 90 per cent of the acreage is grown in combination with corn to support the vines. The crop is commonly used for grazing cattle or hogs during the autumn and winter, after most of the ears of corn and perhaps some of the ripe beans have been picked by hand. The velvet beans may decrease the yield of corn slightly, but their value for feeding purposes and green manuring will much more than offset any decrease. On sandy soil the leaves, vines, and pods do not decay readily after they are killed by frost, and the crop often furnishes feed until early spring. Silage may be made from the combination of velvet beans and corn. Though it has a very dark color, it is eaten readily by stock.[55]

Velvet beans furnish good grazing for cattle and sheep but not for swine. With fattening pigs the gains are usually satisfactory as long as the corn lasts, but then they are often poor, as is pointed out in Part III.

The use and value of velvet-bean seed, of velvet beans in the pod, and of velvet-bean feed are discussed in Chapter XVIII.

408. Forage from beans.—*Field* or *navy beans (Phaseolus vulgaris)* are grown for human food, instead of for feeding livestock, but the cull beans, discolored or otherwise unsuited for human consumption, are used for stock feeding, as is discussed in Chapter XVIII. The straw from field beans, often called "bean pods," is frequently fed to dairy cows or to fattening sheep or cattle. Its value will vary widely, depending on whether it has been damaged by weather. (418)

Pinto beans are raised for the seed in certain sections of the Southwest. The straw varies considerably in value, like that of field beans.[56]

Hay from *tepary beans (Phaseolus acutifolius)*, another crop of the Southwest, was equal to cowpea hay or alfalfa hay for dairy cows and heifers in Oklahoma tests.[57]

409. Moth or mat bean.—The moth or mat bean *(Phaseolus aconitifolius)* is an annual legume that somewhat resembles the cowpea in manner of growth. In northern Texas it was superior to the latter, being more drought resistant and curing more readily, and it was also promising in California tests.[58] It makes excellent, leafy hay, if cut when the first pods are ripe.

410. Mung bean.—The mung bean *(Phaseolus aureus)* also resembles the cowpea in growth, but is less viny. It is adapted to similar conditions as cowpeas, producing fair yields on poor soils where alfalfa will not thrive. Though introduced into the United States many years ago, it has never been grown extensively, apparently because cowpeas are usually a better crop. It was concluded from recent Oklahoma tests that mung beans were of promise as a hay crop for dairymen on poor upland soil. The hay is rather stemmy and there is often considerable waste in feeding it. In the Oklahoma tests mung bean hay was worth 75 to 90 per cent as much per ton for dairy cows as No. 1 alfalfa hay, and in an Arkansas trial chopped mung bean hay was equal to alfalfa hay for dairy heifers.[59]

411. Jackbean.—The jackbean *(Canavalia ensiformis)* is a vigorous-growing annual legume, producing a large yield of seed in pods 9 to 14 inches long. These beans are unpalatable and not well digested by stock, and as a forage plant the jackbean does not seem to offer advantages over the common legumes.[60]

412. Hyacinth bean.—The hyacinth bean, or bonavist *(Dolichos lablab)*, an annual which resembles the cowpea but is more viny, is often grown as an ornamental. Tests have not yet indicated that it is superior to cowpeas for general use.

413. Peanut.—As is pointed out in Chapter XVIII, peanuts *(Arachis hypogea)* are grown chiefly for the underground nuts. These are used for human consumption, for oil production, or for hogging-down. However, when peanuts are raised for market, the forage is a valuable by-product.[61]

The peanuts are usually harvested with a digger which cuts off the lower roots and lifts the plants with the nuts attached. After the leaves have wilted somewhat, the plants are stacked about stakes set in the ground. To keep the plants off the ground, two cross pieces are attached to each stake at right angles to each other and 8 to 12 inches from the ground. After curing for 3 to 6 weeks, the nuts are picked from the vines by a threshing machine, leaving as a by-product the cured forage, usually called "peanut hay."

Such peanut hay, if well cured and not moldy, is a good substitute for other legume hay, though it contains somewhat less protein. If it is moldy or if it carries much dirt or dust, it is not suitable for horses or mules. When the crop is grown for hogging-down, the peanut vines are sometimes mowed and cured into hay before the hogs are turned in. Such hay is about equal to soybean or cowpea hay in value, though lower in protein. To be grown primarily for hay, peanuts cannot compete in yield with soybeans or cowpeas.

The hogging-down of peanuts is discussed in Chapter XXXVI.

414. Kudzu.—Kudzu *(Pueraria thunbergiana)* is a rapid-growing perennial vine which dies back to the ground each year. It is often grown as an ornamental in the South, where it reaches a length of 60 feet or more. It is not hardy in the northern states but is of considerable promise as a perennial forage crop for the Gulf region.[62]

The seed does not germinate well, and the crop is propagated by layers, about three years being required for it to become fully established. Under field conditions the prostrate branches root at the joints and send up twining shoots 2 to 4 feet high, which may be cut with a mower without great difficulty. Kudzu cures into hay more readily than most legumes, and the hay is even richer than alfalfa in protein. Kudzu pasturage flavors the milk if cows are grazed on it shortly before milking.

415. Beggar weed.—Beggar weed *(Desmodium tortuosum)*, an annual legume which has rather woody stalks 3 to 10 feet high bearing abundant leafage, is used for green forage and hay production in the sub-tropical regions of our country.[63] It does well on sandy land. Beggar weed should be cut for hay at the beginning of the blooming period, before it becomes too coarse and woody or the lower leaves drop off. Such hay is relished by stock, but the greatest value of the crop is for grazing.

416. Serradella.—Serradella *(Ornithopus sativus)* is cultivated to some extent in Europe on poor sandy land, as it will grow on soil too acid for most legumes. Though it has been often tested in the United States, it has proven inferior to other crops even on acid, sandy soils.

417. Crotalaria.—Various species of crotalaria *(Crotalaria spp.)* are grown in the southern states for green manure, especially in Florida. Most species are apparently not palatable to stock and some may even be poisonous. However, recent tests by the Florida station indicate that *Crotalaria intermedia* may prove useful for stock feeding, especially as a silage crop.[64]

418. Legume straw or chaff.—The straw or chaff that is left after ripe legumes are threshed for seed is often used for stock feeding. Legume straw contains much less protein than hay made from the same crops and is much higher in fiber and therefore lower in total digestible nutrients. If the legume straw contains a considerable proportion of leaves, the protein content will be decidedly higher than that of straw from the small grains.

The value of legume straw or chaff varies widely, depending chiefly on the proportion of leaves and the manner in which it was cured. It can be fed satisfactorily as part of the roughage to dairy cattle, beef cattle, or sheep, but it is often too dusty for feeding to horses. Legume straw gives much better results when it is fed as only part of the roughage, along with good legume hay or else with silage, than when it is the only roughage.

Alfalfa or clover straw or chaff, when well cured, is of greater value than straw from the coarser legumes, such as soybeans or field beans. In an Idaho trial alfalfa or clover chaff was worth about one-half as much as alfalfa hay when it replaced part of the hay in a ration for fattening lambs.[65] On the other hand, when alfalfa chaff was fed as the only roughage in a Utah trial with fattening lambs the results were not satisfactory.[66]

Field-pea straw is also usually of higher value than straw from soybeans or field beans. Good-quality pea straw was fairly satisfactory as the only roughage for fattening steers and for wintering ewe lambs and pregnant ewes in Washington trials.[67] The value per ton will probably range from one-half to three-fourths that of alfalfa hay.

Lespedeza straw of excellent quality, cured without exposure to rain and containing a high proportion of leaves, was a satisfactory substitute for good soybean hay in an Illinois trial with dairy cows, when both were fed with corn silage and a suitable concentrate mixture.[68] Though the lespedeza straw did not seem so palatable as the soybean hay, the cows actually wasted a smaller percentage of it.

Straw from field or kidney beans, often called "bean pods," is used for feeding cattle, sheep or horses in the bean-growing districts. Its value varies widely, but straw of a good grade, preferably fed with some legume hay, may be considered worth about one-half as much per ton as alfalfa or clover hay, or about equal to such forage as well-cured corn or sorghum fodder.[69]

Soybean straw usually consists chiefly of the coarse stems with a very small proportion of leaves, and it therefore has a low feeding value. It should be fed as only part of the roughage, preferably along with some good legume hay. Also, it is better for animals that are not being fed for high production. For example, it is more satisfactory for dry cows or for heifers than for cows in milk.[70] When fed as the only roughage to fattening lambs in an Illinois trial, soybean straw gave poor results, even though sufficient protein supplement was fed to balance the ration.[71] The straw, which contained only 3.4 per cent protein, was worth but one-fourth as much as alfalfa hay. It was concluded that for sheep a soybean crop had a much higher value as hay, than when fed as soybean straw plus soybean seed.

QUESTIONS

1. State 7 advantages of legume roughages.
2. Discuss the importance of the inoculation of legumes and of proper fertilization.
3. Why should livestock farmers grow a large acreage of alfalfa wherever the soil and climate are adapted to the crop?
4. What varieties of alfalfa are best suited to your section? Why?
5. Discuss the effect of various factors on the composition and value of alfalfa hay.

6. What influence does the stage of maturity at which alfalfa is cut for hay have on its longevity?
7. Discuss the value and use of alfalfa hay.
8. What are *alfalfa meal, alfalfa leaf meal,* and *alfalfa stem meal?*
9. What precautions should be taken in pasturing cattle or sheep on alfalfa?
10. Discuss the use of alfalfa as a soiling crop; as a silage crop.
11. Compare the merits of red clover and alfalfa as hay crops for your locality.
12. At what stage of maturity should red clover be cut for hay?
13. Discuss the use of red clover for pasture; for silage; as a soiling crop.
14. Of what importance are the following in your locality: (a) Mammoth clover; (b) alsike clover; (c) Ladino clover; (d) crimson clover; (e) bur clover; (f) hop clover; (g) berseem; (h) subterranean clover?
15. Discuss the use of sweet clover for pasture and for hay.
16. Discuss the value of soybeans for hay, for silage, and for pasture.
17. Discuss the value as forage crops of any of the following that are important in your state: (a) Field peas; (b) vetch; (c) lespedeza; (d) velvet beans; (e) beans; (f) peanuts.
18. How can legume straw or chaff be used best in stock feeding?

REFERENCES

1. Sotola, Wash. Bul. 245, Jour. Agr. Res., 47, 1933, pp. 919-945.
2. Willard, Ohio Bul. 497; Bachtell and Allen, Ohio Bul. 538; Willard, Thatcher, and Cutler, Ohio Bul. 540.
3. Nelson, Ark. Bul. 246; see also: Mooers, Tenn. Bul. 142.
4. Lyon, N. Y. (Cornell) Bul. 500.
5. Headden, Col. Bul. 364; Löhnis, Soil Science, 22, 1926, pp. 355-389.
6. Turk, Mo. Bul. 173.
7. Fred, Baldwin, et al., Wis. Buls. 396, 405, 410.
8. Whitson and Chapman, Wis. Buls. 396, 405; Albrecht and Poirit, Jour. Amer. Soc. Agron., 22, 1930, pp. 649-657.
9. Fred, Whiting, and Hastings, Wis. Res. Bul. 72.
10. Neller, Indus. and Engin. Chem., 18, 1926, pp. 72-73.
11. Kiesselbach, Russel, and Anderson, Jour. Amer. Soc. Agron., 21, 1929, pp. 241-268.
12. Pearson, U. S. Dept. Agr., Yearbook 1931, pp. 96-99.
13. Bachtell and Allen, Ohio Bul. 538.
14. Kiesselbach and Anderson, Nebr. Res. Bul. 36.
15. Arizona Rpt. 1934.
16. Salmon, Swanson, and McCampbell, Kan. Tech. Bul. 15; see also: Foster and Merrill, Utah Bul. 61.
17. Salmon, Swanson, and McCampbell, Kan. Tech. Bul. 15; Grandfield, Jour. Amer. Soc. Agron., 26, 1934, pp. 179-188; Kiesselbach and Anderson, Nebr. Res. Bul. 36; Graber, Nelson, Luekel, and Albert, Wis. Res. Bul. 80; see also: Burlison, Sears, and Hackleman, Ill. Bul. 349; Ind. Rpt. 1932; Norton, Mont. Bul. 245; Willard, Thatcher, and Cutler, Ohio Bul. 540; Sotola, Wash. Bul. 220; Westover, U. S. Dept. Agr., Farmers' Bul. 1722.
18. Graber, Wis. Bul. 425.
19. Carroll, Utah Bul. 126.
20. Sotola, Wash. Bul. 220; see also: Ariz. Rpt. 1933.
21. Maynard, Esplin, and Boswell, Utah Bul. 238.
22. Armsby, The Nutrition of Farm Animals, p. 660; Forbes and Kriss, Jour. Agr. Res. 31, 1925, pp. 1083-1099; Forbes and Kriss, Jour. Agr. Res. 34, 1927, pp. 785-796; Mitchell, Kammlade, and Hamilton, Ill. Bul. 317.
23. Association of American Feed Control Officials, Official Pub., 1935.
24. Reed, Kan. Bul. 217.
25. Summarized by Thorne, Ohio Bimo. Bul. 167.
26. Jacobs, Tenn. Rpt. 1923.
27. Willard, Cutler, and McLaughlin, Ohio Bimo. Bul. 167; see also: Hunt, Ill. Bul. 5.
28. Clark, Mont. Bul. 94.
29. Bechdel, Penn. Bul. 178.
30. Madson and Coke, Cal. Exten. Cir. 81; Conn. (Storrs) Bul. 192; Headley and Wilber, Nev. Rpt. 1934; Semple, Vinall, Enlow, and Woodward, U. S. Dept. Agr., Misc. Pub. 194.
31. Snapp and Knox, Ill. Bul. 328; Shepperd, N. D. Bul. 211.
32. Mortimer and Rupel, Wis. Bul. 410.
33. Roderick and Schalk, N. D. Bul. 250; Schofield, Jour. Amer. Vet. Med. Assoc., 64, 1924, pp. 553-575; Fitch, Am. Soc. Anim. Prod., Proc. 1923.
34. Crosby and Kephart, U. S. Dept. Agr., Farmers' Bul. 1653.
35. Crosby, U. S. Dept. Agr. Tech. Bul. 380.
36. Forage Crops, rev. ed., p. 458.
37. Semple, Vinall, Enlow, and Woodward, U. S. Dept. Agr., Misc. Pub. 194; Elting, LaMaster, and Mitchell, S. C. Rpt. 1933.
38. Stewart, Burlison, Norton, and Whalin, Ill. Bul. 386.

39. Hackleman, Sears, and Burlison, Ill. Bul. 310; Nevens, Ill. Rpt. 1931; Hilton, Wilbur, and Epple, Ind. Bul. 346; Hughes and Wilkins, Iowa Bul. 228; Zahnley, Kan. Bul. 249; Metzger, Holmes, and Bierman, Md. Bul. 277; Uhland, Mo. Bul. 279; Thatcher, Ohio Mo. Bul. 8 (1923), Nos. 87 and 88; Noll and Lewis, Penn. Bul. 187; Moore, Delwiche, and Briggs, Wis. Bul. 375; Morse, U. S. Dept. Agr., Farmers' Bul. 1605.

40. Morse, U. S. Dept. Agr., Farmers' Bul. 1617; Dvorachek et al., Ark. Buls. 181, 196; Robertson, Kezer, and Deming, Colo. Bul. 392; Slate and Brown, Conn. (Storrs) Bul. 133; Hackleman, Sears, and Burlison, Ill. Bul. 310; Mighell, Hughes, and Wilkins, Iowa Bul. 309; Kan. Rpt. 1924-1926; Ky. Rpt. 1924; Etheridge and Helm, Mo. Bul. 220; King, Mo. Cir. 174; N. C. Rpt. 1932; N. D. Bul. 194; Wiggans, N. Y. (Cornell) Bul. 548; Borst and Park, Ohio Bul. 513; Noll and Lewis, Penn. Bul. 167; Hartwell, R. I. Bul. 183; Mooers, Tenn. Cir. 13; Wolfe, Va. Bul. 235; Odland, West Va. Bul. 227; Albertz, Wis. Bul. 388; Akers and Westover, U. S. Dept. Agr., Tech. Bul. 419; Zavitz, Ontario, Canada, Dept. Agr. Cir. 43.

41. Bechdel, Penn. Buls. 176, 178.

42. McKee, U. S. Dept. Agr., Yearbook 1931, pp. 104-6; Schoth, Ore. Bul. 286; Grimes, Sewell, and Taylor, Ala. Bul. 233.

43. Bohstedt, Roche, Rupel, and Fuller, Wis. Bul. 425; see also: Tretsven, Jour. Dairy Sci., 18, 1935, p. 438, and Mont. Rpt. 1931.

44. Rupel, Roche, and Bohstedt, Wis. Bul. 420.

45. Jones, Ore. Bul. 194.

46. Rothwell, Can. Expt. Farms, Anim. Husb. Div., Rpts. 1922, 1924.

47. McKee and McNair, U. S. Dept. Agr., Farmers' Bul. 1663.

48. McKee and Schoth, U. S. Dept. Agr. Bul. 1174.

49. Bailey, Williamson, and Duggar, Ala. Bul. 232; McKee, Schoth, and Stephens, U. S. Dept. Agr., Cir. 152.

50. Miller, U. S. Dept. Agr., Farmers' Bul. 1724; Pieters, U. S. Dept. Agr., Leaflet 100; Ga. Rpt. 1929; Pieper, Sears, and Bauer, Ill. Bul. 416; Ind. Rpt. 1932; Kinney and Kinney, Ky. Exten. Cir. 179; Willard, Dodd, Cutler, and Thatcher, Ohio Bimo. Bul. 166.

51. Pieters, U. S. Dept. Agr., Leaflet 100; Aldous, Kan. Cir. 163; Wenner, Mich. Quar. Bul. 16, 1934, No. 3; Ethridge, Helm, and King, Mo. Bul. 280.

52. Nevens, Ill. Stat., Jour. Dairy Sci., 18, 1935, pp. 593-598; Rusk, Ill. Sta. mimeo. rpt.; Moore and Cowsert, Miss. Bul. 235; Grinnells, N. C. Rpt. 1932.

53. Pieters, U. S. Dept. Agr., Leaflet 100; Helm and Etheridge, Mo. Bul. 331; Mooers, Tenn. Cir. 42; Texas Rpt. 1933.

54. Mooers and Ogden, Tenn. Bul. 154.

55. Piper and Morse, U. S. Dept. Agr., Farmers' Bul. 1276.

56. Titus, New Mex. Bul. 143.

57. Jacobs, Okla. (Panhandle) Sta., Buls. 26, 50.

58. Conner, Tex. Bul. 103; Kennedy and Madson, Cal. Bul. 396.

59. Kuhlman, McGilliard, and Weaver, Okla. Rpt. 1932-34; Dvorachek, Ark. Bul. 221.

60. Piper, Forage Plants, Rev. Ed., pp. 608-9.

61. Beattie and Beattie, U. S. Dept. Agr., Farmers' Bul. 1656; McNess, Tex. Bul. 381.

62. Conn. (Storrs) Bul. 142; Ill. Rpt. 1925; Ohio Bul. 382; Bailey and Mayton, Ala. Cir. 57; Ga. College of Agr., Exten. Bul. 356; La. Rpt. 1919; Pieters, U. S. Dept. Agr., Leaflet 91.

63. Tracy, U. S. Dept. of Agr., Farmers' Bul. 1125.

64. Becker, Neel, Dix Arnold, and Shealy, Jour. Agr. Res., 50, 1935, pp. 911-922; see also: McKee and Enlow, U. S. Dept. Agr. Cir. 137; La. Rpt. 1929-31.

65. Maynard, Esplin, and Boswell, Utah Bul. 238.

66. Rinehart, Hickman, and Johnson, Id. Bul. 194.

67. Hackedorn, Wash. Bul. 155; Hackedorn and Sotola, Wash. Bul. 157.

68. Nevens, Jour. Dairy Sci., 17, 1934, pp. 671-674.

69. Miller, Cal. Rpt. 1923; Morton, Osland, and Brandon, Colo. Press Bul. 80; H. W. Mumford, Mich. Bul. 136; Vinke and Hanson, Mont. Sta., mimeo. rpt.; Quayle, Wyo. Bul. 191.

70. Nevens, Ill. Cir. 369.

71. Kammlade and Mackey, Ill. Bul. 260; see also: Carmichael, Ohio Bul. 245.

CHAPTER XIV

INDIAN CORN AND THE SORGHUMS FOR FORAGE

I. INDIAN CORN

419. Indian corn excels as a forage crop.—Indian corn *(Zea Mays)* is the imperial agricultural plant of America. Wherever conditions are favorable for its growth, it excels all other forage crops in average yield of dry matter and of digestible nutrients. It has been shown previously that in these respects it even slightly surpasses alfalfa, the queen of the legume roughages. This giant annual grass reaches a height of from 7 to 15 feet in 4 or 5 months' growth, producing under favorable conditions from 10 to 15 tons of green forage per acre, containing from 4,000 to 9,000 lbs. of dry matter.

Corn is an exceedingly adaptable crop, and it is raised for grain or for forage on more than two-thirds of all the farms in the United States. It flourishes best in the corn belt—that great region between the Appalachian Mountains and the dry-farming districts of the West. Corn is a heat-loving plant and does not thrive if the nights are cool during the growing season. However, short, early-maturing varieties have been developed that will usually ripen in the northern-most states.

If the corn plants are grown the proper distance apart, a large yield of grain results, with good forage a secondary product. Wherever the climate and soil are suitable, it surpasses all other cereals as a feed grain. Not only is the average yield of grain much higher, but also corn grain ranks first in feeding value, and the corn stover is worth much more per acre for stock feeding than the straw from the small grains. The use and value of corn as a grain crop are discussed in Chapter XVII.

When corn is planted thickly, a tremendous yield of forage is secured under favorable conditions, with relatively little grain. This forage can be cured into nutritious dry fodder which approaches hay from the grasses in feeding value.

It is surprising indeed that this one plant excels not only as a grain crop but also as a forage crop that can be used as silage, fed as a green soiling crop, or even cured as dry fodder. Were a seedsman to advertise Indian corn by a new name, recounting its actual merits while ingeniously concealing its identity, either his claims would be discredited or he would have an unlimited demand for the seed of this supposed novelty.

420. Corn fodder; shock corn; corn stover.—In discussing the uses of corn as a forage crop, it is important to have definitely in mind just what is meant by the terms used in speaking of corn forage.

The terms *corn fodder* and *fodder corn* are commonly used for corn plants, either fresh or cured, which have been grown primarily for forage, with all of the ears, if any, originally produced. *Shock corn* and *bundle corn* are terms used for corn grown primarily for grain, but which is fed without husking. Sometimes shock corn is also called corn fodder.

Corn stover is the term applied to cured shock corn from which the ears have been removed. Corn stover is often called "corn stalks," but this term is misleading, for the greater feeding value is in the leaves and not in the stalks.

The terms fodder and stover are also applied to such crops as the sorghums. For example, kafir forage is called either kafir fodder or kafir stover, depending on whether or not the heads have been removed.

421. Thickness of planting.—The maximum yield of sound corn grain is secured when the kernels are planted at such a distance apart that all the plants may produce full-sized ears. The optimum number of plants per acre is greater on fertile soil and with ample rainfall than when conditions are less favorable. To secure the largest yield possible one must know the capacity of his land for corn and plant accordingly. A common rate for dent corn on good soil in the corn belt is 10,000 to 12,000 kernels per acre. Early-maturing, short varieties should be planted somewhat more thickly than larger varieties.

Under favorable conditions the largest yield of total dry matter and of digestible nutrients is secured from corn planted more thickly than when grown for grain, but the yield of grain will then be much less. Where the crop is raised for silage to be fed to such animals as dairy cows or fattening cattle or sheep, it is usually best to plant it at such a rate that there will be a large proportion of good ears. However, it is usually planted somewhat more thickly than when the crop is raised for grain. This will give a large yield of dry matter per acre, yet the silage will be high in digestible nutrients and net energy. These animals need a liberal supply of digestible nutrients, and if they are fed silage containing little grain, it will be necessary to provide larger allowances of concentrates.

If the silage is to be fed to beef breeding cows not nursing calves or to stocker cattle being carried through the winter to be fattened on grass the next summer, it may be desirable to plant the corn so thickly that the proportion of ears is small. Under favorable conditions this method may produce the largest yield of digestible nutrients per acre, though the amount of net energy may be less than when more grain is formed. A still more economical method would perhaps be to grow the corn at the usual rate for grain, husk out the ear corn for sale or for feeding to other classes of stock, and ensile the corn stover for feeding to the beef cows or stocker cattle.

422. Nutrients in grain and stover.—Even when grown for the grain a considerable part of the feeding value of the corn crop is in the stover. In trials at 4 northern stations an average yield of 4,415 lbs. of ear corn and 3,838 lbs. of stover was secured per acre.[1] The stover contained one-fourth of the digestible crude protein and over one-third of the total digestible nutrients in the crop.

The amount of total digestible nutrients measures the value of the stover for merely carrying animals through the winter. For dairy cows in milk, young growing animals, fattening cattle or sheep, and horses at hard work, a more accurate measure of its value is the net energy it supplies. Yet, even on this basis the stover furnished one-fourth the net energy of the crop. This shows clearly the loss of animal food which occurs each year when unnumbered acres of corn stover are allowed to decay in the fields.

423. Development of nutrients in the corn crop.—In raising corn as a forage crop, it is important to have clearly in mind the amounts of nutrients it furnishes at various stages of growth. By analyzing corn plants at different stages from July 24, when they were about 4 feet high, until Oct. 8, when the kernels were hard, Jones of the Indiana Station secured the following data, based on an average stand of 10,000 stalks per acre.[2]

Composition of an acre of Indian corn at different stages

Stage of growth	Total wt. of green crop Lbs.	Dry matter in crop Lbs.	Ash Lbs.	Crude protein Lbs.	Fiber Lbs.	N-free extract Lbs.	Fat Lbs.
Four feet high, July 24......	5,138	731	90	149	170	282	40
First tassels, Aug. 6.........	18,827	2,245	195	360	670	977	42
Silks drying, Aug. 28........	24,327	4,567	272	436	1,203	2,606	49
Milk stage, Sept. 10	26,710	6,174	328	544	1,361	3,846	95
Glazing stage, Sept. 24......	25,750	8,104	389	566	1,523	5,425	202
Silage stage, Oct. 1..........	25,275	8,929	369	660	1,602	6,084	215
Ready to shock, Oct. 8......	22,253	9,412	383	691	1,737	6,336	265

From July 24, at a stage when sometimes unwisely fed as soilage, to Aug. 28, when the silks were drying, the crop increased over 19,000 lbs. in total weight and over 3,800 lbs. in dry matter. The increase in total weight was thereafter less rapid, the maximum green weight being reached when the kernels were in the milk stage. After this the gross weight decreased by over 4,000 lbs. due to drying out as the crop matured. The dry matter, however, continued to increase rapidly until the plants were fully ripe. Indeed, in less than a month following Aug. 28 the acre of corn stored over 3,500 lbs. of dry matter!

When four feet high the crop was nearly 86 per cent water and only 14 per cent dry matter; while when the kernels were hard and the husks dry over 42 per cent was dry matter. The mineral matter, or ash, increased rapidly until the plants reached their full height.

The most rapid increase in crude protein occurred in the period before the plants were tasseled, when cell growth was most active, but some increase occurred until the plants reached maturity. Although the amids—the building-stones of the proteins—were constantly being formed during the development of the plants, they were in turn quickly built over into the more complex, stable proteins. Hence it was found in further studies that the amount of amids did not increase after the plants were silked, while there was a steady storage of protein up to maturity.

Since the stalk of the corn plant must be strong and sturdy to carry the abundant foliage and the heavy ear, the fiber increased rapidly until the woody framework was grown. Between tasseling and ripening, there was an increase of more than 2.5 tons in nitrogen-free extract. This increase was chiefly the starch which was deposited in the corn kernels.

At the milk stage, starch formed less than a fifth of the nitrogen-free extract, but after this it increased rapidly as it was stored in the maturing kernels. From the milk stage to the date when the corn was ready to shock, a period of less than a month, there was a gain of nearly 2,500 lbs. of nitrogen-free extract, over a ton of which was starch. This shows plainly the heavy losses of valuable nutrients which occur when a crop of corn is harvested too early.

424. Composition of corn forage.—Like the corn grain, corn forage is rich in carbohydrates and low in protein. As is shown in Appendix Table I, the nutritive ratio of corn silage or of corn fodder harvested at the glazing stage or later is 1:12 or wider. Corn stover is still lower in protein, having the very wide nutritive ratio of 1:21 or more.

When the corn crop is stricken with drought so that no ears develop and the plants are killed, the forage will contain a considerably higher percentage of protein than normal, but the total yield of nutrients will be low. Likewise, corn harvested in the milk stage or before will contain a higher percentage of protein, on the dry basis, than more mature forage. However, such immature forage is watery and low in nutrients on the green basis.

Nitrogenous fertilization will greatly increase the yield of corn forage when the soil is deficient in nitrogen, but it apparently has no appreciable effect on the percentage of protein in the corn forage.[3]

The calcium content of corn forage varies widely, depending on the amount of calcium in the soil on which it is grown. On soil reasonably well supplied with calcium, corn forage will be fair in calcium content and will usually be somewhat richer in this mineral nutrient than hay from the grasses. Where the soil is deficient in calcium, on the other hand, corn forage will be low in calcium. When corn forage is used as the only roughage or when it is fed with hay from the grasses, it is wise to add a calcium supplement to the ration to guard against a lack of this mineral.

Corn fodder and corn silage are rather low in phosphorus, containing about as much, on the dry basis, as hay from the grasses. Corn stover is very poor in phosphorus, having only 0.09 per cent.

Green corn forage, even from white corn, is high in vitamin A value. This is because the green corn leaves and stalks contain a greater total amount of carotene than the grain, even in the case of yellow corn. (**188**) The vitamin A value of dry corn fodder will vary widely, depending on whether the leaves and stalks were green when the crop was harvested, and on how well it was cured. Probably well-cured corn fodder or corn stover will supply considerable vitamin D.

425. Corn silage.—Indian corn is the premier silage plant. The solid, succulent stems and broad leaves, when cut into short lengths, pack closely and form a solid mass which keeps well, is greatly relished by stock, and is consumed with little waste. Although with enlarging experience the use of other crops for silage is increasing, by far the greater portion of all the forage stored in silos in this country is corn. In 1933 about 4,425,000 acres of corn were grown for silage in this country, with an estimated total production of 29,963,000 tons of silage.

The yield of silage per acre varies widely with the soil and season. A 50-bushel crop of corn should make from 8 to 10 tons of silage, depending on the size and leafiness of the stalks. The average yield of corn grown for silage during the 7-year period, 1927 to 1933 was **7.0** tons per acre for the entire United States.[4]   It is of interest to note that the highest yield per acre for any section of the country was secured in the North Atlantic States, this being 9.0 tons per acre. Here the acreage of corn is limited and the crop is usually grown on the areas best adapted to large yields. In the North Central States, which include most of the corn belt, the average yield was 6.6 tons per acre.

Corn makes the best silage if cut when the kernels have passed the dough stage and reached the glazing stage, but while most of the leaves are still green. At the glazing stage the dent varieties will be well dented. Ensiling the corn should not be delayed longer, or the corn will become too mature to make the most palatable and nutritious silage, and it may mold unless water is added to the cut forage as it is ensiled. On the other hand, it should not be ensiled earlier, except in case of necessity. If ensiled too early, a sourer silage is produced, and, still more important, a great waste of nutrients occurs. As has been pointed out previously in this chapter, the corn crop stores much of its highest quality nutrients during the late stages of growth.

426. Value of corn silage.—The use of corn silage has practically revolutionized the feeding of dairy cattle over a large part of the United States and is also of great importance in the feeding of beef cattle and sheep. Through its use the cost of producing milk and meat may be materially lowered over a large part of this country. Not only is corn silage excellent for cattle and sheep, but it may be used in a limited way with horses that are idle or at light work.

Corn silage is used most commonly as only part of the roughage for stock, usually being fed in combination with hay or dry fodder. It gives especially good results when used with legume hay or mixed hay rich in legumes. If corn silage is fed as the only roughage, a calcium supplement, such as ground limestone, should be added to the ration to insure a sufficient supply of this mineral. The importance of corn silage on American farms and the value and use of this feed for the various classes of stock are discussed in detail in the respective chapters of Part III.

Silage from well-matured corn supplies 18.7 lbs. total digestible nutrients per 100 lbs. on the average. This is about 35 per cent as much as 100 lbs. of good-quality hay furnish. In the experiments in which the relative values of silage and hay have been determined for dairy cows, good corn silage has actually been worth 33 to 40 per cent as much per ton as good legume or mixed hay. The feeding value of silage has therefore agreed well with the amount of digestible nutrients it furnishes.

For fattening cattle and fattening sheep corn silage has an even higher value per ton in comparison with hay. In the many experiments reviewed in later chapters it has been found that for these classes of stock good corn silage is usually worth half as much per ton as good legume or mixed hay. This difference in the relative values of silage and hay for dairy cows and for fattening cattle and fattening sheep is somewhat surprising. It may perhaps be explained as follows:

Lambs chew their feed very thoroughly and therefore no corn kernels in the silage escape digestion. In the experiments with fattening cattle, pigs have commonly followed the cattle to consume any kernels that passed through unmasticated. Thus the combination of fattening cattle and pigs completely utilized the grain in the silage. On the other hand, in the case of dairy cows there is some loss of nutrients due to kernels which escape mastication.

This difference in value does not mean that corn silage is an inefficient feed for dairy cows. As is pointed out later, wherever corn thrives it is usually the most economical succulent feed for winter feeding. The difference merely means that for fattening sheep and also for fattening cattle which are followed by pigs, well-eared corn silage has a considerably higher actual value than would be estimated from its chemical composition.

427. Corn silage vs. corn fodder.—It has been shown in Chapter XII that the losses of nutrients are about 5 per cent greater when the corn crop is cured as dry fodder, even under the most favorable conditions, than when it is ensiled. (**344**) The trials summarized in Part III show, however, that there is a much greater difference than this in the actual feeding value per acre of corn silage and dry corn fodder.

This is doubtless due to the fact that stock usually reject the butts of the dry corn stalks, even when finely cut, while in silage they are mostly eaten. Moreover, owing to the great palatability of this succulent feed, silage-fed animals consume a larger ration, and more nutrients are hence available for milk or flesh production after supplying the wants of the body. Just as important as these advantages is the fact that, like other succulent feeds, silage has a beneficial laxative effect, and is a valuable aid in keeping farm animals thrifty.

428. The type of corn for silage.—In the North an important question is whether to grow for silage a variety of corn that is early enough to reach the late-dough or the glazing stage in the average season and hence has a relatively large proportion of corn grain, or to grow instead a late, southern variety that will not reach these stages before frost. The results of the numerous experiments that have been conducted to study this problem differ somewhat.[5] However, in the majority of the investigations it has been concluded that it is best to grow a variety that will reach the dough stage or else the glazing stage in the average season.

The late varieties will of course produce a larger tonnage of green forage, but it will be much more watery than the more mature fodder. In actual amount of dry matter produced per acre there has usually been but little difference. Silage made from immature corn is apt to be much sourer that that from corn which has at least reached the dough stage, and it may not keep so well. Because of its higher water content and also because it contains little grain and is slightly less digestible, the value per ton will be considerably lower.

Forage from corn cut when the kernels are in the milk stage or earlier will supply only 60 to 75 per cent as much digestible nutrients per 100 lbs. as that which has reached the glazing stage. For each 100 lbs. of digestible nutrients in the silage, the expense of harvesting and ensiling the crop is therefore much greater in the case of the late varieties, and also much more silo space is required.

Usually the northern stockman with plenty of other roughage to

In Stock Farming Corn Stover Is Utilized

Corn stover contains at least one-fourth the feeding value of the corn crop. In well-planned stock farming this important feed is never wasted.

In Grain Farming Corn Stover Is Largely Wasted

In exclusive grain farming in the corn belt, the ears are picked from the standing stalks, and the stover is then often allowed to waste away in the field.

A FIELD OF KAFIR IN TEXAS

Because of their resistance to drought, the grain sorghums and the sweet sorghums are of great importance as forage crops in the semi-arid districts.

HARVESTING KAFIR FOR SILAGE WITH A CORN BINDER

The grain sorghums not only yield grain which closely approaches corn in feeding value, but also silage but little inferior to corn silage. (From U. S. Department of Agriculture.)

feed will wish to fill his silo with richer and more palatable feed than the late-maturing varieties supply. In case he has a very limited amount of corn land and desires to produce the largest possible amount of silage, he may decide to grow a late variety and plant it thickly. In feeding such silage, however, it must be remembered that it is low in dry matter. Therefore to prevent lower production of milk or meat, more hay or other dry roughage must be fed with it than in the case of silage from well-eared corn, cut at the glazing stage.[6]

It is important not to use for silage a variety that is so early that it will fail to utilize effectively the entire growing season. Such varieties produce much less feed per acre than a variety that just reaches the desired silage stage in the average season.

In late seasons it is best to let corn stand till after frost rather than ensile it too green, for satisfactory silage can be secured from frosted corn, and the crop may mature to a considerable extent before a severe frost comes. If the crop is killed by frost, it should be ensiled quickly, for the storm which usually soon follows will wash out much nutriment from the frosted forage, and the wind will also whip off the dried, brittle leaves. If the plants dry out before all the crop can be ensiled, water should be added as the silo is filled, to insure the necessary fermentations that preserve the silage.

When corn is ruined by drought, the silo is likewise the best means of saving all possible feeding value in the crop. Water should, of course, be added to the forage as it is ensiled, if it is too dry to pack well in the silo.

429. Corn-fodder or corn-stover silage.—Silage can be made from cured corn or sorghum forage if the forage is thoroughly wet as it is chopped into the silo and if it is well packed. It will undergo fermentation similar to that which occurs with green material and will be preserved in a satisfactory manner. Though usually less palatable than silage from green fodder, this product has an aromatic silage odor and is readily consumed by stock with less waste than is dry fodder or stover. Some farmers fill their silos in the fall with green corn or sorghum and then after this is fed out, refill them with the cured forage.

It is necessary to add enough water so that the material will pack well and then to tramp it down with especial thoroughness; otherwise the mass will spoil. Though the water may be added to the cut material in the silo, it can be distributed more evenly if a stream is run into the blower, and then more water sprinkled over the cut fodder in the silo as it is filled. Due to the widely varying water content of field-cured corn forage, it is impossible to state definitely the amount of water to be added. Some recommend adding about an equal weight of water to the forage, others add just enough so that water may be squeezed out of the cut material.

Since corn-stover silage lacks the grain, it is worth decidedly less per ton than normal corn silage. The experiments reviewed in later chapters show that stover silage can be used satisfactorily as the only or the chief roughage for wintering beef breeding cows (which are not nursing calves) or for wintering stocker cattle that are to be fattened on grass the next summer. This is because these animals do not need rations rich in digestible nutrients.

On the other hand, it is a mistake to remove the ears from corn forage for silage intended for dairy cows, dairy heifers, fattening beef cattle, beef calves, breeding ewes, or fattening sheep. These animals all need rations rich in digestible nutrients. Therefore if the ears are removed, it will be necessary to replace this grain by the feeding of larger amounts of concentrates. Even then, the results will usually not be so good as when the normal silage, rich in ears, is fed.

430. Dry corn fodder.—Though not so palatable and valuable as corn silage, corn grown thickly and cured as dry fodder while the leaves are yet green, makes a coarse forage which may be used as a substitute for hay from the grasses. Such fodder, with bright, nutritious leaves and small palatable ears that are easily masticated, has a value not appreciated by many stockmen. The importance of dry corn fodder as a feed in this country is shown by the fact that 6,263,881 acres of corn were cut for fodder in 1929, in comparison with 4,005,539 acres grown for silage.

As it is low in protein, corn fodder gives the best results when legume hay forms part of the roughage, such a combination giving satisfactory results with dairy cows, beef cattle, and sheep. Corn fodder is also an economical substitute for timothy hay with idle horses, brood mares, and growing colts.

Corn fodder and stover should be placed in large, well-made shocks, to reduce the losses by weathering. Since the stalks stand almost vertical in the shocks, when the leaves wilt there is ample room for the upward passage of air currents, which rapidly dry the interior and check molds and fermentations. When shock corn is pronounced "dry" by the farmer, it usually carries more water and consequently less dry matter than hay, a fact which should not be overlooked in feeding this forage. Care must be taken that corn fodder or stover is well cured before it is stacked, and especially before it is stored in the mow, for musty, moldy forage is not only unpalatable but even dangerous. In districts of the South where it is exceeding difficult to cure corn forage, the silo is particularly useful.

431. Shock corn.—Rather than husking corn and feeding the grain and stover separately, sometimes shock corn is fed, the animals doing their own husking. Shock corn is decidedly inferior to corn silage, and gives the best results with animals not being fed for high production, such as cattle being carried through the winter and idle horses. It is also sometimes used for fattening cattle or sheep, particularly at the beginning of the fattening period.

432. Corn stover.—Corn stover, the forage which remains after removing the ears from shock corn, has a higher feeding value than some realize. Stover produced in the northern part of the corn belt is superior in feeding value and palatability to that grown in the South. When corn develops but little grain, due to drought or to hot winds at silking time, the stalks and leaves will be higher in protein and total digestible nutrients than usual. As soon as corn stover is well cured, it should be stacked or placed under cover, rather than being left to waste away in the shock.

When fed with alfalfa or clover hay, good corn stover may often profitably form half the roughage allowance for fattening cattle or sheep. For stock cattle and breeding cows it may be utilized to an even larger extent, and it is also satisfactory as part of the roughage for breeding ewes.

While corn stover alone will not quite maintain the weight of growing steers during the winter, stover and legume hay with no grain will produce fair gains. Corn stover is also a satisfactory roughage for horses doing but little work. Most of the roughage for dairy cows should be more palatable and nutritious in character, but corn stover may sometimes be economically fed in limited amounts even to them.

In the corn belt the ears are commonly husked or snapped from the standing stalks, and the stover then left uncut in the field. On live-stock farms horses, cattle, or sheep are commonly turned into these stalk fields to utilize the stover and to get any remaining ears. Considerable feeding value can thus be saved, though the wastage is greater than when the crop is harvested and husked.

433. Shredding, cutting, or grinding stover or fodder.—When shock corn is husked by machinery, the stover is usually shredded or cut at the same operation. Corn fodder is also often passed through a feed cutter before feeding. This shredded or cut material is no more digestible than the uncut forage. However, cutting or shredding usually reduces the waste, as it induces the cattle to eat a greater part of the stalks, unless they are unusually coarse and woody. The cut or shredded forage is also easier to handle, and the waste is in better shape for bedding. Unless shredded or cut fodder or stover is thoroughly dry, it will heat and mold if a large quantity is stored for any considerable period.

Grinding fodder or stover to a meal requires much more power and time than shredding or cutting it, and does not increase the value enough to justify the expense. Finely ground forage may even be unpalatable on account of its dusty nature.

434. Pulling fodder.—In the South the tops of the ripening corn stalks are often cut off just above the ears, leaving the tall butts, each with an unhusked ear at its top. Next, the leaves are stripped from the butts, and these together with the severed tops are cured into a nutritious, palatable fodder, which is used for feeding horses and other stock.

The previous study of the development of the nutrients in the corn plant shows the folly of this practice. During the last stages of its life the corn plant is busiest in manufacturing and storing nutrients. Removing the top and leaves, at once stops all this work of food making. In a Louisiana trial pulling fodder caused a shrinkage of from 15 to 20 per cent in the yield of grain.[7]

435. Corn as a soiling crop.—Corn ranks high as a soiling crop on account of its palatability, the high yield of nutrients, and the fact that it remains in good condition for feeding over a much longer period than many of the other soiling crops. Green corn fodder is of especial value for feeding to dairy cows when pastures are short in late summer or early fall. (355) An acre of ripening corn thus fed in early fall may return twice as much profit as if it were held over until winter. For early feeding sweet corn may often be advantageously used.

436. Sweet corn stover; corn-canning-factory waste.—*Sweet corn stover*, left after the green ears have been removed for sale on the market or to a canning factory, is of somewhat higher value per ton, on the dry basis, than stover from ripe field corn. It is more leafy, and the leaves and stalks are more nutritious. Silage made from green sweet corn stover is worth nearly as much per ton as that made from immature field corn which contains but little grain.

Before cutting green sweet corn stover for silage, it should be allowed to mature a few days after the ears are removed. It will then be less watery and the silage will not be too acid. However, it should be harvested when the stalks and most of the leaves are still green, or it will not pack well in the silo, unless water is added.

The *canning-factory waste* at corn canneries consists of the husks and cobs, with some ears of unsatisfactory quality for canning. This waste is usually ensiled, either in stacks at the factory or in silos on the farms of the growers. Such silage is lower in protein and in total digestible nutrients than silage made from well-matured field corn that has a good proportion of ears. Judging from its composition and digestibility, it is worth about 60 per cent as much per ton as well-eared field-corn silage and about 90 per cent as much as silage from immature field corn that has but little grain.[8] Silage made from canning-factory waste is sometimes very acid, and may then be rather unpalatable to stock.

II. The Sorghums

437. Importance of the sorghums.—In the central and southern parts of the western plains states the sorghums *(Adropogon sorghum,* or *Sorghum vulgare,* vars.) are of great importance as feed crops, both for forage and for grain. In fact, success in stock farming throughout this great section depends largely on the sorghums. Because they are much more drought-resistant than corn, they have largely taken its place in those portions of this region that have too little rainfall for corn.

Where there is sufficient rain, corn is usually more productive than the sorghums, for both grain and forage. However, corn requires a plentiful supply of moisture throughout the growing season, and the yield is always unsatisfactory if its growth is seriously checked by drought. The sorghums will cease growing and the edges of the leaves roll together during periods of drought and extreme heat. Yet, when rains come and the soil becomes moist again, the plants quickly resume growth, unless they have been killed by the drought. Like corn, the sorghums require warm weather throughout the growing season. In fact, they are even more particular than corn in this respect.

The importance of the sorghums in the drier districts is shown by the fact that 10,470,000 acres of grain sorghum were grown for all purposes in 1935 and 3,867,000 acres of sweet sorghum for forage. About 94 per cent of the acreage was in seven states—Texas, Kansas, Oklahoma, Nebraska, Colorado, New Mexico, and South Dakota. In Texas the acreage of the sorghums raised for forage is about four times the combined acreages of all tame hay crops and of corn grown for forage.

Sorghums are also important as forage crops in certain sections of the South where they yield much more forage per acre than corn. They will produce a fair crop on soil too poor or thin for corn. In the corn belt and eastward the acreage of the sorghums is small, because here corn usually outyields them.

The average yield of cured sorghum forage in the United States was 1.3 tons per acre for the 10-year period, 1924-1933. It must be remembered that much of the crop is grown where the rainfall is usually deficient, which greatly reduces the average yield for the whole country. On good soil and with ample rainfall, yields of 3 to 4 tons or even more per acre of dry fodder or 10 to 15 tons or more of silage should be secured.

The sorghums are important in India, China, Manchukuo, and Africa. In these countries the grain is used widely for human food in place of wheat or rye. In Africa, where sorghum grain is one of the chief foods of the natives, the sorghums are grown on the dry plains, in the oases of the Sahara, on high plateaus, in mountain valleys, and in tropical jungles. Their forms are as diverse as the conditions under which they grow, the plants ranging in height from 3 to 20 feet, with heads of different shapes varying from 5 to 25 inches in length. Though sorghum originated in the tropics, it is now grown chiefly in the temperate zone.

The uses of sorghums for grain are discussed in Chapter XVII.

438. Types of sorghums.—The sorghums are of two general types —the *sweet sorghums,* which have stems filled with sweet juice, and the *grain sorghums,* which have juice that is sour or only slightly sweet and which usually have more pithy stems. *Broom corn* is another type of sorghum which is raised for the stiff brushes of which the heads are made.

The grain sorghums range in height from very early, dwarf varieties only 1½ to 2½ feet tall to later varieties about 5 to 7 feet tall. The sweet sorghums are usually 6 or 7 feet tall or more. The various varieties of sorghums and even the two types cross freely. Through crossing, certain hybrid varieties have been developed that combine some of the characteristics of the grain sorghums and the sweet sorghums.

The grain sorghums are used both for grain and for forage, and the sweet sorghums are grown for forage and also for the manufacture of sorghum sirup. When the term "sorghum" is used without the words "sweet" or "grain," in referring to silage, fodder, or stover, the product from sweet sorghum is usually meant.

439. Sweet sorghums. — The sweet sorghums, or sorgos, often called "cane" by farmers, are forage rather than grain producers. In most sections of the sorghum belt the varieties of sweet sorghum that are adapted to the particular locality give larger yields of forage per acre than the best grain sorghums. For forage they usually excel even kafir and hegari, which lead in forage production among the grain sorghums. In some districts the kafirs yield about as much forage as the sorghos, and are extensively grown for this purpose because they cure more quickly in the shock.

In the South late-maturing, tall varieties of sweet sorghums are often grown, but even in Texas the medium-maturing varieties are more common. In the North early varieties, such as the Amber sorghums, are raised, which will ripen wherever corn will mature. The early varieties are also grown extensively in certain western portions of the sorghum belt, because they evade drought better than the later types.

440. The grain sorghums.—The *kafirs,* highly important in this country among the grain sorghums for both grain and forage, are stout-stemmed, broad-leaved plants, having juicy stalks and long, erect, compact, cylindrical heads carrying small egg-shaped seeds. They do not sucker or produce undesirable side branches, nor do they lodge or shatter the grain. Since most of the kafirs are rather late in maturing, they are grown chiefly in the more humid sections of the grain-sorghum belt. Varieties which are dwarf and earlier have been developed that are of importance farther west.

The *milos* are earlier in maturing than the kafirs and are even more drought resistant. They are therefore especially adapted to the drier sections, where they are the most important type of grain sorghums. They have few leaves compared with the kafirs and the stalks are pithy, with little juice. Therefore milo is not so valuable as kafir for forage. The seeds are larger than those of kafir and are borne in short, thick heads, which are often goose-necked or drooping.

In order to make harvesting easier, particularly with the grain header or the combine, dwarf strains have been developed in which nearly all the heads are erect. Milo is fully equal to kafir in feeding value. The milos, and to a lesser extent the feteritas, are attacked to a greater extent by chinch bugs than are other types.

The *feteritas* are among the earliest of the grain sorghums, and for this reason are often used as a "catch" or emergency crop. They usually have slender stems carrying more leaves than milo, but less than kafir, and have erect heads bearing large whitish seeds. They are of importance in some of the western sections of the sorghum belt, especially towards the north.

The *kaoliangs* are early-maturing and slender, and have pithy stalks with few leaves. The heads are loose, open, and erect. They are grown chiefly in the northern sections where other types will not mature. Elsewhere milo, kafir, or feterita usually outyield kaoliang. The forage is scanty and of poor quality.

The *durras* were introduced early into the United States but are not extensively grown except in certain districts of California. They lodge readily, sucker badly, and have coarse stems with few leaves. Also, the grain shatters easily and the pendent, or "goose-necked," heads of the usual types make harvesting difficult.

Shallu, sometimes called "Egyptian wheat," "California wheat," or "desert wheat," is slender-stemmed, with spreading heads which shatter badly. It is apparently inferior to other types and has never become of importance in this country.

Hegari resembles kafir, having numerous broad leaves, sweet juicy stalks, and erect heads. It is popular in certain sections, especially in the western part of the sorghum belt, for grain and forage combined.

Darso is apparently a hybrid between kafir and a sweet sorghum. It is dwarf, being 3 to 4 feet tall, and has numerous leaves and juicy stalks. Darso produces a good yield of grain but less forage than kafir. The grain is somewhat bitter, on account of a high content of tannin, but this is an advantage where sparrows and other birds damage other types. Darso grain has given good results in feeding experiments.

Shrock is also probably a hybrid between kafir and a sweet sorghum and has some of the same characteristics as darso. *Sagrain* is the name given to a strain of shrock sorghum which has given excellent yields of grain and forage in the Delta district of Mississippi.

441. Sorghum hay or fodder.—For dry forage the sweet sorghums are usually grown, rather than the grain sorghums. This is because the yield is generally larger and the forage is also more palatable, due to the greater sugar content.[9] Where the rainfall is sufficient, the yield is commonly larger if the sorghum is seeded in close drills or is broadcast, than when it is grown in cultivated rows. Also, the forage is more palatable, because the stalks are much smaller. The proportion of seed is, of course, small when the crop is seeded thickly, but this is more than offset by the greater tonnage.

It is usually advisable to cut sorghum for hay or dry fodder when the seed is in the dough stage, unless the crop is badly injured before by drought or frost. Sweet sorghum cures much more slowly than most hay crops, since the stems are large and juicy. However, it is injured but little by rain and loses few leaves in the hay-making process. It must be thoroughly cured in cocks or windrows before it is stacked or stored in the barn, else it will sour or mold.

When the crop is grown in cultivated rows and cured in shocks, the shocks should be small, so the forage will dry out. In humid districts sweet sorghum fodder is apt to sour if left too long in the shock, due to fermentation of the sugar in the stalks.

Sweet-sorghum hay or fodder, often called "cane hay," is lower in fiber and a trifle richer in protein than average timothy or prairie hay, but there is more waste in feeding it unless it is cut or shredded. Due to its sweetness, it is somewhat more palatable than corn fodder. Fodder from the grain sorghums, including the grain, may have fully as high a value per ton as that from sweet sorghum. Though the stalks are less nutritious, this may be offset by the larger proportion of grain. The grinding of grain sorghum fodder has been discussed in Chapter IV. (**100**)

It is shown in Part III that well-cured sorghum hay or fodder is a satisfactory roughage for dairy cattle, beef cattle, sheep, and horses. For all these classes of stock, except work horses, it usually gives the best results when fed with some legume hay. If no legume hay is available, ground limestone or some other calcium supplement should be added to the ration to provide plenty of this mineral.

442. Sorghum stover.—Sorghum stover (sorghum fodder from which the heads have been removed) is similar to corn stover in composition and general value. Stover from kafir, hegari, darso, or the sweet sorghums is the best, as it is leafier and the stalks are more nutritious than in the case of stover from milo, kaoliang, or durra. Sorghum stover should be used in the same manner as corn stover.

443. Sorghum silage.—The sorghums make excellent silage if ensiled when the seeds are hard and ripe.[10] Such silage contains no more acid than corn silage, or even less, and it is well liked by stock. If the plants are immature, very sour silage will result, which is much less satisfactory.

If the crop does not mature before frost, fairly good silage can be made by allowing it to dry out somewhat before ensiling it. Also, immature sorghum which has been withered by drought can be used successfully for silage.[11] Water should be added, if the forage is too dry to pack well in the silo. A good way to determine whether sweet sorghum or kafir is mature enough for silage is to twist the stalk with the hands. If just a little juice is visible on the twisted cane, the proper stage has been reached.

A sorghum crop has a much higher feeding value per acre when ensiled than when fed as dry fodder or hay. For example, in Kansas trials the kafir silage from an acre, fed to yearling steers that were being carried over winter, produced 80 per cent more gain in weight than an acre of dry kafir fodder.[12]

Sorghum silage is excellent for dairy cattle, beef cattle, and sheep, as is pointed out in Part III. The value per ton is usually somewhat less than that of well-eared corn silage, such as is grown in the corn belt, due to the fact that sorghum silage is not so rich in grain. Also, cattle do not chew the seed in sorghum silage as thoroughly as they do corn grain. Therefore a considerable percentage passes through undigested.[13]

However, in the sorghum belt the yield of the sorghums per acre is so much greater than that of corn that they far surpass corn for silage production. This is also the case in the sections of the South where the sweet sorghums yield much more forage per acre than does corn. There is no danger from prussic acid poisoning in feeding sorghum silage to stock.

Pit or trench silos provide a cheap means of storing silage in the sorghum belt and are therefore widely used. (349) Since sorghum silage keeps well from one year to another, or even longer, many farmers in the dry-farming districts store silage in a good year to carry over to a time of drought.

444. The sorghums for pasture and as soiling crops.—It is pointed out in Chapter XVI that there is always some danger from prussic acid poisoning when cattle or sheep are pastured on the sorghums. (501) Therefore they are not commonly used for this purpose. Instead Sudan grass is generally employed, for this is not only much safer, but it is also a better pasture crop. Horses and swine can be safely grazed on sorghum, but other crops provide better pasture for swine. Young sorghum plants contain more prussic acid than do more mature ones, and sorghum that has been injured by drought or frost is especially apt to be dangerous.

Except for the danger of prussic acid poisoning, the sorghums are satisfactory as soiling crops. If the crop is allowed to reach the seed stage before it is fed, the danger is usually slight.

QUESTIONS

1. Discuss the excellencies of corn as a forage crop.
2. Define *corn fodder; shock corn* or *bundle corn; corn stover.*
3. What factors determine the best thickness of planting of corn for forage?
4. Approximately what part of the digestible protein, total digestible nutrients, and net energy of a corn crop grown for grain is in the stover?
5. Discuss the development of nutrients in the corn crop, explaining why corn should not generally be cut for silage until after it reaches the glazing stage.
6. State the main facts concerning the composition of corn forage, considering content of protein. total digestible nutrients, calcium, phosphorus, vitamin A, and vitamin D.

7. Discuss corn as a silage crop, comparing the value of corn silage and good hay for dairy cows; for fattening cattle or lambs.
8. Why does an acre of corn silage have a decidedly higher value than an acre of dry corn fodder?
9. Under what conditions might you advise a dairyman in the northern states to grow a late-maturing variety of corn for silage?
10. Discuss the making and the use of corn-fodder silage and of corn-stover silage.
11. Discuss the use in livestock feeding of the following: (a) Dry corn fodder; (b) shock corn; (c) corn stover.
12. Is it advisable to shred or cut corn stover or fodder; to grind it?
13. Discuss the use and value of corn as a soiling crop.
14. In what sections of the country are the sorghums superior to corn for forage?
15. What are the differences between the sweet sorghums and the grain sorghums?
16. If sorghums are important in your state, describe the characteristics of the 3 most important varieties raised there.
17. Discuss the use and value of sorghum hay or fodder; of sorghum silage; of sorghums for pasture.

REFERENCES

1. Summarized by Armsby, Penn. Rpt. 1887.
2. Jones, Ind. Bul. 175; see also: Ladd, N. Y. (Geneva) Rpt. 1899; Hopper, N. D. Bul. 192.
3. Bender and Prince, N. J. Bul. 563.
4. U. S. Dept. Agr. Yearbooks.
5. White, Chapman, Slate, and Brown, Conn. (Storrs) Bul. 121; White and Johnson, Conn. (Storrs) Bul. 159; White, Johnson, and Connelly, Conn. (Storrs) Bul. 167; Conn. (New Haven) Bul. 357; Nevens, Ill. Bul. 391; Ind. Rpt. 1926; Sax and Burgess, Maine Bul. 330; Hays, Minn. Bul. 40; Wiggans, N. Y. (Cornell) Memoir 152; Hayden and Perkins, Ohio Bul. 369; Ohio Spec. Cir. 29; Bechdel, Penn. Bul. 207; Noll and Irvin, Penn. Bul. 289; Henry, Wis. Rpt. 1888.
6. White, Johnson, and Connelly, Conn. (Storrs) Bul. 167.
7. Stubbs, La. Bul. 22 (old series).
8. Nevens, Ill. Bul. 391; McCandlish, Jour. Dairy Sci., 3, 1920, pp. 370-374; Beattie, U. S. Dept. Agr., Farmers' Bul. 1634.
9. Thompson and Gray, Ariz. Bul. 103; Laude and Swanson, Kan. Bul. 265; Cole, N. Mex. Bul. 130; Kiltz et al., Okla. Bul. 210; Quinby et al., Tex. Bul. 496; Vinall, Getty, and Cron, U. S. Dept. Agr. Bul. 1260.
10. Reed, Kan. Cir. 28; Fitch, Cave, and Latshaw, Kan. Rpt. 1930-32.
11. Laude and Swanson, Kan. Bul. 265.
12. Kan. Sta., Fort Hays Substa., Rpt. Beef Cattle Inves., 1931, 1934.
13. Cave and Fitch, Kan. Cir. 110, Moore, Miss. Rpt. 1927; Becker, Jour. Agr. Res. 35, 1927, pp. 279-282; LaMaster and Morrow, S. C. Bul. 254.

CHAPTER XV

THE HAY AND PASTURE GRASSES—THE CEREALS FOR FORAGE—STRAW

I. The Grasses; the Cereals for Forage

445. The hay and pasture grasses.—Unlike the cereal grains, which are all annuals, the hay and pasture grasses are mostly perennials. They therefore thrive without yearly tillage, producing roughage of good quality with little expense for labor. The grasses are also of great importance for building up the soil by adding humus, and binding it together so as to prevent erosion. In regions where the grasses flourish, the larger animals of the farm largely feed themselves during the summer, and milk, meat, and wool are produced at minimum expense.

In Chapter XI a detailed discussion has been presented on the effect of various factors upon the composition of pasture and hay crops. Also, information is there given concerning the utilization of pastures and on hay making.

The grasses are divided into two classes—the sod-formers and the non-sod-formers. The sod-formers, which spread by creeping rootstocks, either above or below ground, and make a smooth turf, include our most valuable pasture and lawn grasses, such as Kentucky bluegrass and Bermuda grass. The non-sod-formers, such as orchard grass, grow in tufts or bunches and increase only by seed or stooling, except in the case of a few, such as timothy, which also increase to some extent by forming new bulbs at the base of the stems.

446. Combinations for meadows and pastures.—No single variety of grass should ordinarily be sown for a meadow or permanent pasture, but instead a mixture of suitable grasses in combination with the clovers and other legumes. Such a mixture will produce a larger yield, and the stand will be more permanent than from a seeding of any single variety.

The kind and proportion of grasses and legumes for such a mixture will depend on the climate, the soil, and the fertility of the particular field. In case of doubt as to the best mixture to sow, advice can readily be secured from the local county agricultural agent, the agricultural college or experiment station in each state, or from the United States Department of Agriculture.

In general, for permanent pastures the chief reliance should be placed on those plants that are high-yielding and also permanent under the particular local conditions. However, grasses of this type, such as Kentucky bluegrass, require some time to become well established. Therefore it is generally advisable to include in the seeding mixture some quick-growing plants to furnish forage while the slower-developing kinds are becoming established. For this reason, such seeds as timothy and alsike clover are usually added to pasture mixtures, although these plants will usually be crowded out in a few years by the more tenacious species.

447. Timothy.—In the United States timothy *(Phleum pratense)* is by far the most important hay grass and also the most widely-used pasture grass for short-time pasture seedings. It is distinctly a northern grass and does not thrive where the summers are too hot and humid. It survives the winters practically up to the Arctic circle.

Timothy is commonly seeded with small grain, and, except when grown for a market where pure timothy hay sells at a premium, it is generally sown with red or alsike clover, or else with alfalfa. The mixture of timothy and clover usually produces a considerably larger yield than timothy alone, and the growing of clover is important from the standpoint of soil fertility. The hay is also usually less weedy than when timothy is seeded alone. Even more important, the mixed hay has a higher feeding value for all classes of stock except light horses and work horses or mules. Where alfalfa grows fairly well but is not a very sure crop, the combination of alfalfa and timothy is often grown, or else a combination of alfalfa, clover, and timothy. The advantages of growing legumes in combination with timothy are well shown by the Ohio tests that have been mentioned in Chapter XIII. (**364**)

If conditions are favorable for clover, the first cutting of hay, the year after seeding the combination of timothy and clover, will consist largely of clover. A still larger proportion of the second cutting will be clover, for timothy does not produce much aftermath, unless cut very early. Except in a few districts, most of the clover, especially the red clover, dies at the close of this year. The decaying clover roots then nourish the timothy that remains, so that a larger yield of the grass is obtained the next season than would otherwise be the case. On many farms timothy is regularly used for pasture for a year or more after it has been cut for hay one or two seasons.

The actual proportion of clover in the hay following the first year after seeding is often much less than is estimated by the grower. He may still think of the hay as mixed clover-and-timothy, even when it contains less than 10 per cent of clover.

The importance of timothy in the United States is shown by the fact that, according to the Census, in 1929 there were grown for hay 25,547,-779 acres of timothy and mixed timothy-and-clover, with a yield of 31,485,896 tons of hay, or 1.23 tons per acre. This was nearly half of all the acreage of tame hay in the country and more than 40 per cent of the total amount of tame hay produced. Over the great area from New England to Virginia on the east, across the country to and including Minnesota, Iowa, and Missouri on the west, timothy and timothy-and-clover are by far the most important hay crops. In the New England and Middle Atlantic states about three-fourths of all the tame hay is timothy or mixed timothy-and-clover.

The continued popularity of timothy, even though numerous experiments have shown the superiority for stock feeding of legume hay over the usual kind of timothy hay, is due to the following: Timothy is not as particular in its soil requirements as alfalfa or red clover, and it thrives on soil which is too acid or too poorly drained for these legumes. The seed is cheap and generally of good quality. A field of timothy is quickly established and usually holds well. The grass seldom lodges, it may be harvested over a longer period than most grasses, and it is easily cured into bright, clean hay which is free from dust and can be handled with little waste.

448. Stage to cut timothy for hay.—Much of the timothy grown in the United States is cut entirely too late to make good hay. Hay from timothy that is cut after full bloom is much lower in protein and vitamins, is less palatable, and also is less digestible than early-cut hay. (See Appendix Tables I and V.) Moreover, when the crop is cut early, considerably more aftermath is produced, which furnishes excellent late summer and fall pasture.

Recent experiments by the New Hampshire and Ohio Stations and also earlier Missouri trials show that when yield of hay, protein content, and amount of digestible nutrients are all considered, timothy should be cut not later than early to full bloom.[1] If the hay is cut later than this, the yield of hay may be a trifle greater, but the quality is much poorer, and the amount of aftermath is also less. The early-cut grass is somewhat more difficult to cure than that cut late, but this is much more than offset by the higher feeding value of the hay.

It is shown in Part III that while late-cut timothy hay is poor for dairy cattle, beef cattle, and sheep, early-cut hay from well-fertilized land produces satisfactory results when fed in a properly-balanced ration. For work horses and mules and for saddle and driving horses, hay cut not earlier than full bloom is preferable, for that cut too early may be unduly laxative. However, even for horses the cutting should not be delayed much after full bloom, or the grass will become tough and woody.

It has been pointed out in Chapter XI that when timothy or other grass is fertilized with a nitrogenous fertilizer (either farm manure or a commercial nitrogen fertilizer), not only is the yield greatly increased, but also the protein content of the hay is usually higher. (**303**) Therefore when early cutting is combined with nitrogenous fertilization, the hay often contains twice as much protein as late-cut hay from land deficient in nitrogen.

449. Value of timothy and mixed timothy-and-clover hay.—The value of timothy hay and of mixed timothy-and-clover hay for the various classes of stock is discussed in detail in Part III. It is there pointed out that for mature horses and mules timothy hay is the standard roughage with which others are compared. Timothy hay has this high value for such horses and mules because it is usually freer from dust and mold than legume hay. Also, these animals need but relatively little protein, calcium, and vitamins A and D. Therefore legume hay, which is much richer than timothy in these nutrients, does not have the same advantages for them that it does for dairy cows, growing animals, or sheep. For colts and brood mares mixed clover-and-timothy is superior to pure timothy hay on account of its higher content of protein, calcium, and vitamins.

Early-cut timothy hay from well-fertilized land is a satisfactory roughage for dairy cows, if fed with a concentrate mixture supplying sufficient protein, and preferably with silage as part of the roughage. On the other hand, late-cut timothy hay or that of poor quality because of damage in curing, is a poor roughage for milk production. Mixed clover-and-timothy hay that is high in proportion of clover, is superior to pure timothy hay for dairy cows, because it is not necessary to feed such large amounts of protein supplements with this hay as with pure timothy. Mixed hay is also decidedly preferable to pure timothy for dairy calves and heifers.

Timothy hay is fairly satisfactory for beef cattle, if it is cut early and cured well, but mixed clover-and-timothy hay is preferable. Timothy hay is least useful for sheep, and that of ordinary quality should not be fed to ewes or lambs, except in case of necessity, for it is constipating and unpalatable to them. If cut in early bloom and well cured, timothy hay gives satisfactory results when fed in combination with silage to breeding ewes or fattening lambs, provided that a sufficient amount of protein supplement is furnished and also a calcium supplement.

450. Timothy for pasture.—Where fields in the regular crop rotation are used for pasture, timothy is usually the most common pasture grass in the area where it thrives. It was formerly believed that timothy pasture was less palatable to stock than bluegrass. Recent studies have shown, however, that timothy surpasses bluegrass and many other common grasses in this respect, especially when the timothy is not more than 4 or 5 inches high.[2]

Timothy of the usual type does not generally persist in permanent pastures, due to its tall, upright growth. However, pasture types have been developed in England which are lower and more spreading in manner of growth and which withstand close grazing better.

451. Kentucky bluegrass.—Kentucky bluegrass *(Poa pratensis),* commonly known as bluegrass or as June grass, easily ranks first for pasture and lawns in the northern half of the United States, except where the climate is too dry. It thrives on well-drained fertile soils but is not so well suited to wet soils as red top. It does not thrive on soil too low in calcium or phosphorus.

Bluegrass is very resistant to cold in winter, but it also does well farther south than timothy. It does not grow as well in shade as orchard grass. The combination of blue grass and white clover makes an especially good permanent pasture. Therefore bluegrass should usually be grazed closely enough to encourage the growth of white clover.

The fact that bluegrass is one of the richest of grasses in protein helps explain the fondness for it shown by stock. Before heading out in the spring, bluegrass usually contains nearly 20 per cent protein, if dried to a hay basis. This is actually a larger proportion of protein than in alfalfa hay cut at the usual hay stages. Also, when the grass is kept actively growing by proper fertilization and management of the pasture and is not permitted to head out, the percentage of protein will be nearly as high later in the season. (**298**) On the other hand, bluegrass in blossom or at the still later stages of growth is low in protein and high in fiber. While bluegrass is much less nutritious at the later stages of growth, it is then grazed more readily by stock than most other mature grasses.

Bluegrass starts growth early in spring and soon provides excellent pasturage. When it is permitted to bear seed, it will enter a period of rest in midsummer, but starts growth again with the coming of the fall rains and furnishes excellent fall pasture. Even when it does not go to seed, it usually becomes parched and brown during the midsummer droughts. The growth continues much better if the pasture is properly fertilized, unless the drought is too severe.

In any efficient system of pasture management, plans should be made to provide plenty of other feed for stock during this period of scanty growth, especially for dairy cows. A temporary pasture, such as sweet clover, alfalfa, or Sudan grass, should be provided, if possible. If this is not done, the stock should be fed some silage, a green soiling crop, or else some hay. Sometimes a bluegrass pasture is stocked rather lightly in the spring, so there will be some grass left to provide feed later. However, such mature growth is not very palatable or nutritious. Also, if the bluegrass is allowed to grow up in this manner, the shade will tend to kill out the white clover, which is a most valuable part of the best permanent pastures.

Because of its low, spreading growth, bluegrass is not a good hay grass. If cut in early bloom, the hay is nearly equal to timothy. However, most bluegrass hay, such as is cut along the roadside after the tame hay has been made and the bluegrass has gone to seed, is of low feeding value.

452. Red top.—Red top (*Agrostis alba* or *palustris*) is suited to a wider range of climatic and soil conditions than any other cultivated grass. It ranks next to bluegrass in importance as a pasture grass in the United States. A couple of years after seeding it forms a close, smooth sod, almost as dense as bluegrass turf. It is an excellent grass for marshy and damp lands, and at the same time it will withstand considerable drought. It endures on poor uplands and on soils too acid for most other grasses, and it may be grown much farther south than timothy or bluegrass. It is important as a hay grass in New England.

Red-top pasture or hay is only fair in palatability. Therefore red top is usually grown only where better-liked grasses do not thrive. It is seldom seeded alone for hay or pasture, but is commonly grown with other grasses, chiefly timothy, and with the clovers.

453. Orchard grass.—Orchard grass (*Dactylis glomerata*) is a long-lived perennial that grows in nearly every state in this country. It does not stand cold winters as well as timothy, but it can endure more heat in summer and it does better on soil of low or moderate fertility. It is grown most widely in a broad belt south of the middle of the corn belt, reaching from North Carolina and Virginia to Missouri, Arkansas, and Kansas. Here it is used as a substitute for timothy, and is usually seeded with clover. Ripening two weeks before timothy, it fits in well with red clover. North of this belt, timothy is superior, chiefly because it is hardier and the seed much cheaper. In England orchard grass is commonly called cocksfoot.

Orchard grass grows in bunches or tufts, forming an uneven sod and hence should be sown with clovers or other grasses, both for hay and for pasture. It does better than most other grasses in partial shade, and it owes its common name to this characteristic. It is a good pasture grass, as it starts growth early in the spring, endures drought well and continues growth late in the fall. However, it is not as palatable to stock as is timothy or bluegrass. Therefore care must be taken to stock the pasture heavily enough so that the grass will be grazed down before it becomes tall and woody.

In most districts it is not wise to include orchard grass in pasture mixtures for seeding a large acreage of pasture. There may then be much difficulty in getting it grazed down in the spring before it becomes woody and unpalatable. On the other hand, orchard grass is excellent in a mixture for a pasture of limited size that is to be used for heavy early grazing.

While late-cut orchard grass makes harsh, woody hay, that cut in early to full bloom is equal to the best of the grass hays. Orchard grass furnishes more second growth than any other hay grass adapted to temperate conditions. It is also richer than most grasses in phosphorus and calcium.[3]

454. Other northern grasses.—*Canada bluegrass (Poa compressa)* will yield fair pasturage on poor or thin soil where Kentucky bluegrass fails. It withstands close grazing and is considered excellent for fattening cattle. This grass is important on the poorer soils in New England, Ontario, and New York and is also common in Pennsylvania, the Virginias, and Maryland.

Fowl meadow grass (Poa palustris), a close relative of Kentucky bluegrass, thrives in the northeastern states on wet land subject to overflow, where even red top and alsike clover are killed out. On such wet meadows in Vermont yields of 1.2 to 2.5 tons per acre have been reported of hay which was as well relished by stock as upland hay.[4]

Rhode Island bent (Agrostis vulgaris or *tenuis)* is the most common pasture grass in New England and eastern New York, and is found southward to Virginia and westward to the Pacific slope. It thrives on soils too low in lime or too poor in fertility for bluegrass. Like bluegrass, it is a pasture grass, rather than a hay grass.

Bromegrass (Bromus inermis) is of much importance in that part of the great plains region from South Dakota and Montana northward to Saskatchewan, for it is drought resistant and hardy. It furnishes good crops of hay, fully equal to timothy in feeding value, for 3 or 4 years after seeding. By that time it usually becomes sod-bound and should be renewed by disking or shallow plowing. Bromegrass has never succeeded as well in the eastern states as in the West.

Brome is one of the most palatable of pasture grasses, and it starts into growth early in the spring and endures heavy grazing. It is usually cut for hay just after full bloom, at the stage known as "the purple," but still makes good hay at somewhat later stages. Under favorable conditions two cuttings may be secured, and the average annual yield per acre is about 1.5 tons. Though it is the most drought resistant of the common cultivated grasses, brome is usually less productive than the native prairie grasses in the drier parts of the great plains.

Tall meadow oat-grass (Arrhenatherum elatius), or tall oat-grass, is one of the common grasses of continental Europe, but it has never become important in this country. This is perhaps on account of the high cost of the seed. It is adapted to about the same climatic conditions as orchard grass, but will not endure shade. It is primarily a hay grass and is usually grown in mixtures with other grasses and clovers.

Meadow fescue (Festuca elatior), a tufted, long-lived perennial grass, is adapted to practically the same area as timothy, which excels it for hay. Though it thrives best on rich moist land, the largest acreage in this country has been grown in eastern Kansas, chiefly for seed to be exported to Europe. It is best as a pasture grass, starting growth early in the season and continuing till late in the fall. As the seed is high-priced, it is usually sown in mixture with other grasses for permanent pastures.

Italian rye-grass (Lolium multiflorum) and *English rye-grass (Lolium perenne)* are short-lived, rapid-growing perennials. Though of great importance in Europe they are not grown extensively in this country, except in the humid region of western Washington and Oregon, where they are among the best pasture grasses.

Reed canary grass (Phalaris arundinacea), a native of temperate sections of North America, Europe, and Asia, is especially well adapted to wet soils which are subject to overflow for periods which would kill other grasses. It has proved the best crop for wet peat lands in certain sections of Minnesota and western Oregon. It is a hardy, vigorous grass which grows 4 to 6 feet tall and provides good pasture and heavy yields of hay higher in protein than timothy.[5]

Slender wheat-grass (Agropyron tenerum), known in Canada as western rye grass, is a native North American grass which has proved valuable under cultivation. It is an excellent grass for the northern plains district, as it is markedly drought resistant.

Quack grass (Agropyron repens), also called "witch" or "couch" grass, is one of the most widely distributed and destructive weeds of the North Temperate Zone. Though quack grass is known chiefly for its bad habits as a weed, when cut in early bloom it makes hay that is said to be equal to timothy, and it furnishes satisfactory pasture.[6] It often forms a considerable part of the "timothy" hay on the market, especially in New England. In permanent pastures it tends to become root bound in 3 to 4 years and often nearly disappears. On account of the great difficulty of eradicating quack grass, it should never be purposely introduced on clean land.

455. The small grains for forage.—All the small grains are suitable for hay, for pasture, and for soiling crops. The acreage of small grains grown for hay, not including that for other purposes, was 4,354,000 acres in 1935, according to estimates made by the United States Department of Agriculture, and the yield of hay was 5,009,000 tons, or 1.15 tons per acre.

The small grains are especially important as hay crops in the Pacific Coast states, surpassing alfalfa in acreage and forming nearly one-third of all the tame hay. Here barley and wheat are the chief grains used for this purpose. In the Pacific-Coast district wild-oat hay is also important, making satisfactory hay for stock.[7] The small grains are also valuable hay crops in North Dakota and Montana.

Except for horses, oats and wheat make better hay in the humid districts when cut in the milk stage than if cut later.[8] For horses, cutting in the soft-dough stage is preferred by many. In the case of barley hay there may be less tendency for the beards to cause sore mouths in stock if the hay is cut after the milk stage, when the beards have become brittle. Rye should be cut in the blossom stage for all stock, as it soon becomes straw-like. Cereals cut in the milk stage cure rather slowly, and therefore care is necessary to get the hay sufficiently dry to prevent heating or molding after it is stored.

In the semi-arid districts of the northwestern United States and western Canada, oats make excellent dry forage when cut in the dough stage or even later. Oats are extensively harvested with a binder when in the dough stage in the plains areas of western Canada, and cured as "sheaf oats" for feeding to cattle and other stock. In such climates the leaves and stems are apparently more palatable at late stages of maturity than in humid sections. In experiments at the Washington Station oat hay, from oats that were nearly ripe, was more palatable than that cut when immature.[9] Also, because of the grain it contained, the late-cut hay was lower in fiber and more nutritious.

In the district from Virginia to Georgia and westward to Kentucky,

BEEF CATTLE FATTENING ON BLUEGRASS PASTURE

In the northeastern United States, Kentucky bluegrass is by far the most important pasture grass.

CUTTING A FINE FIELD OF TIMOTHY

On most farms where timothy is now extensively grown, greater use should be made of the legumes. The latter not only yield more hay, and hay of higher feeding value for most stock, but also increase the fertility of the land.

THE CEREALS FURNISH GOOD FALL AND SPRING PASTURE

In some sections the cereals are widely grown as hay and pasture crops. In the North rye is the most commonly used for pasture.

SUDAN GRASS AND SOYBEANS MAKE A GOOD EMERGENCY CROP

Where Sudan grass thrives, it furnishes good yields of hay which is superior to millet. Sudan grass may be grown with soybeans or cowpeas to increase the richness of the hay in protein. (From Wisconsin Station.)

Tennessee, and Louisiana, and also in some of the New England States, the greater part of the oats raised for grain is not threshed, but is fed unthreshed. The use of sheaf or bundle oats for feeding horses has also increased in other states during recent years.

In the northern states, except on the Pacific Coast, oats or other small grains for hay are usually seeded with field peas. This combination produces a larger yield and also provides more palatable and nutritious hay. In the South, combinations of oats, wheat, hairy vetch, and crimson clover are often used. The use of such combinations has been discussed in Chapter XIII.

Well-cured cereal hay resembles good timothy hay in composition and feeding value and may be used similarly in stock feeding.[10] It is satisfactory as the only roughage for mature horses and for wintering beef breeding cows. For dairy cattle, for growing or fattening cattle, or for sheep, it should be fed, if possible, as only part of the roughage, along with legume hay or silage. A sufficient amount of protein supplement should be used to balance the ration, for cereal hay is low in protein.

In the North fall-sown rye or wheat furnishes excellent late-fall and early-spring pasture, while spring-sown oats or barley provide green forage in early summer. In the winter-wheat belt it is often possible to graze a regular seeding of wheat for 3 or 4 weeks in early spring without diminishing the yield of grain. In the South fall-sown grains may be pastured moderately through the winter, and will still yield considerable hay or grain. Green rye may give a marked flavor to milk unless the cows are pastured on it for only 2 or 3 hours after milking. A combination of wheat and rye furnishes pasture over a longer season than either grain alone.

While cereals cut for hay at the usual stage of maturity are relatively low in protein, such forages are rich in protein at the early stages of growth. For example, green rye, wheat, or oats 5 inches high will contain 20 to 25 per cent of protein, if dried to the same moisture content as hay.

A field sown to rye, wheat, oats, or barley for temporary pasture may be changed to a permanent one by sowing clover and grass seed thereon early in spring. The grass and clover plants will then begin growth under shelter of the young grain. Stock may graze on the cereal plants regardless of the young grasses and clovers but should be kept off the fields after rains, and the pasture should not be grazed too closely. After the cereal plants are grazed off, the grasses and clovers spread until they form a permanent sod.

If ensiled when the kernels are just past the milk stage or slightly earlier, the cereals make fair to good silage. The crop should be run through a silage cutter and unusual care taken in tramping down the mass to force the air out of the hollow stems.

456. Wild or native grasses; prairie grass and hay.—The value of wild or native grasses for pasture or hay varies widely in different regions, depending on the climate, the character of the soil, and the species of grasses.[11] The grasses on the western mountain meadows and on the upland prairies are generally highly nutritious and palatable when actively growing. They then furnish excellent pasturage and also provide hay about equal to timothy, when the growth is tall enough to be cut. Prominent among the species of valuable prairie grasses are the grama grasses, the wheat grasses, bluestem, and buffalo grass.

It has already been pointed out in Chapter XI that grass which has matured may have a very low feeding value, due to weathering and leaching. (304) Therefore such pasturage may be poor and may even produce nutritional trouble, due to lack of protein, vitamins, or minerals. When there is little or no rain after the grass reaches full development, much less loss through weathering will occur, and the dried mature grass may furnish satisfactory feed, except that it will be low in vitamin A content. (186)

Prairie hay cut when still green is similar to timothy hay in composition and feeding value, although usually somewhat higher in protein. It is satisfactory as the only roughage for mature horses and mules and for wintering beef breeding cows, which do not need much protein. For dairy cattle, for young beef cattle, and for sheep it produces much better results when used as only part of the roughage. It should be fed to such stock, if possible, with some legume hay or else with silage and a sufficient amount of protein supplement to balance the ration. Unless the hay is grown on soil well supplied with calcium, it may be necessary to add a calcium supplement to the ration.

For dairy cows prairie hay is satisfactory as part of the roughage, but it is distinctly inferior to good legume hay and only about equal to timothy hay of the usual kind.[12] In Wyoming trials prairie hay was satisfactory as the only feed for wintering beef yearlings, but not for wintering beef calves, which need more protein.[13] In Oklahoma experiments it was fed successfully as the only roughage to fattening calves when it was supplemented with ground limestone and cottonseed meal. However, it was worth only one-half to three-fourths as much per ton as alfalfa hay.[14]

Marsh hay is usually decidedly inferior in value to hay from upland meadows, though bluejoint *(Calamagrotis Canadensis)*, cut before maturity, nearly equals timothy in value. Marsh hay may often be used satisfactorily for horses and mules, especially those which are idle or not working hard. It is not well suited to dairy cattle or sheep. The marsh hay of the western mountain districts, though consisting largely of sedges and rushes, is usually of higher value than such hay in the eastern states.[15]

457. Sudan grass.—Sudan grass *(Sorghum vulgare sudanese,* or *Andropogon sorghum sudanensis)* is the most important annual hay grass in the United States. It is a near relative of the sorghums and of Johnson grass and resembles the latter closely in leaf, stem and seed, though it is taller and the leaves are broader and more numerous. However, it is distinctly an annual and entirely lacks the underground stems or rootstocks which make Johnson grass a serious pest in the South.

Sudan grass grows 4 to 8 feet high in cultivated rows, and 3 to 5 feet when sown broadcast. For so rank a grass, the stems are fine, being seldom larger than a lead pencil, and the leaves are soft in texture. It is adapted to the same conditions as the sorghums and is equally drought resistant, but it is earlier and may be grown farther north. However, it is decidedly a warm-weather grass and is not as resistant as corn to cold in the early stages of growth. Therefore it does not do well in the northern limits of corn culture. It yields best on fertile, well-drained soil, but it will grow better on poor or sandy soil than most hay or pasture crops. It does not thrive along the Gulf Coast.

Where alfalfa, clover, and timothy flourish, the chief use of Sudan grass is as an emergency hay crop or as a supplementary pasture crop. It surpasses the millets in yield as well as in value of forage, and it has therefore largely displaced them where it thrives. On account of its drought resistance, it is one of the most valuable crops for the western part of the plains region, from central South Dakota to Texas.

Mixtures of Sudan grass and either soybeans or cowpeas are often grown, especially for hay. In humid districts the combinations usually yield more than the legume alone and also cure more readily. In addition, the hay is more nutritious than Sudan grass hay. In Illinois the combination of soybeans and Sudan grass was the best emergency forage crop for late summer use, with oats and peas excelling for early summer.[16]

Because Sudan grass crosses readily with the sorghums and the seed closely resembles that of Johnson grass, unusual care is necessary to ensure its purity.

458. Sudan grass for hay.—Sudan grass makes good hay when cut from the time it begins to head until the seed are in the dough stage. If cut when heading out or in early bloom, the hay is richer in protein and of higher value per ton.[17] In addition, two cuttings can often be then secured, even in the northern states. However, if cut at this stage the grass is more difficult to cure. In the southern states Sudan grass yields 2 or 3 cuttings of hay.

Yields of 2 to 4 tons of hay are secured per acre on good soil when the rainfall is ample. In the semi-arid districts the yield is considerably less, but in the irrigated districts of the Southwest, Sudan grass sometimes yields as much as 8 to 10 tons of hay per acre.[18]

Sudan grass hay compares favorably with hay from the other grasses in feeding value, but is of considerably lower value than that from alfalfa or clover.[19] It is slightly laxative in nature. Sudan grass hay is satisfactory as the only roughage for horses and mules. For dairy and beef cattle, and especially for sheep, it gives much better results when fed with some legume hay or with silage, than when it is fed as the only roughage. It has given poor results as the only roughage for fattening lambs, even when chopped and supplemented with a protein supplement.[20]

459. Sudan grass for pasture, soilage, and silage.—Sudan grass is one of the best annual pasture crops, especially to provide feed for the mid-summer period when permanent pastures are usually short.[21] It is therefore particularly valuable for dairy cows, as it provides a large amount of palatable succulent feed just when often needed to prevent a serious shrinkage in yield of milk. In a good season Sudan grass pasture should furnish pasturage for about one cow per acre from July for a period of 2 to 3 months. It should not be grazed until it is 15 to 18 inches high, but it may be ready in about a month after it is sown.

With Sudan grass there is much less danger from prussic acid poisoning than in the case of the sorghums.[22] (**501**) However, it is wise to use caution when the crop has been stunted by drought. Also, after the grass has been injured by severe frost, it is not safe to graze it until it has dried and cured thoroughly on the ground.

Sudan grass also provides very satisfactory pasture for horses, beef cattle, and sheep. For swine, alfalfa, red clover, or rape are preferable, where they thrive, for these crops are more palatable to swine and also furnish forage over a longer period.[23] Even for swine, however, Sudan grass is one of the best pasture crops in the drier portions of the plains states.[24]

Sudan grass is well suited for use as a late summer soiling crop and it makes satisfactory silage. In a California trial Sudan grass silage was considered worth 10 per cent less than corn silage for dairy cows.[25]

460. The millets.—The millets are rapid-growing, hot-weather annuals of many races and varieties. Of these, the *foxtail millets (Setaria Italica,* spp.) are the type most grown for forage in the United States. In this group are *common millet,* the earliest and most drought-resistant; the less drought-resistant, shorter-stemmed *Hungarian millet,* the seeds of which are mostly purplish; and *German millet,* late-maturing and with nodding heads, which yields more hay but not of quite such good quality.

The foxtail millets are especially valuable as hay crops on dry-farms in the northern plains region. In the more humid regions they are grown chiefly as catch crops, for they may be seeded later than other crops and still make a crop of hay. Millet may be made into silage satisfactorily, but the feeding value of such silage per ton is considerably less than that from corn or the sorghums.

In the humid regions millet should be considered merely an emergency crop, for Sudan grass surpasses it in yield and feeding value, and soybeans or oats-and-peas produce hay of much greater feeding value. Millet should be seeded thickly for hay and should be cut just after blooming, or even before this stage. The hay is usually less palatable and inferior in feeding value to timothy hay or even bright, fine corn or sorghum fodder. It may sometimes cause scouring. Since millet hay is sometimes injurious to horses, it should be fed sparingly to them.

Japanese millet (Echlinochloa frumentacea), a cultivated, rank-growing variety of common barnyard grass, will grow better in cool regions and on wetter soils than the foxtail millets or Sudan grass. It is taller and coarser than the foxtail millets and may be used as a soiling crop, as hay, or as silage. Japanese millet hay does not apparently have the injurious effect on horses that foxtail millet hay sometimes does. This millet has been extravagantly advertised as "billion-dollar grass" or "million-dollar grass."

Proso, or *broom corn millet,* described in Chapter XVII, is grown chiefly for seed production, as the yield of forage is low and the stems woody. *Pearl millet (Pennisetum glaucum),* also called pencillaria or cat-tail millet, is adapted to the same conditions as the sorghums, but they have proven more valuable and have largely displaced it in both the semi-arid regions and the South. As a soiling crop, it should be cut when 3 to 4 feet high, before the stems become hard.

461. Bermuda grass.—This low-growing, creeping grass *(Cynodon dactylon)* is the most important pasture grass in the southern states. It is likewise the chief lawn grass of the South and is an important hay grass on the more fertile soils. It is most commonly propagated by planting small pieces of sod, but it may also be raised from seed.

Bermuda grass forms a dense soil-binding sod but does not provide pasturage over as long a season as carpet grass or Dallis grass. It is late in starting in the spring and ceases growth with the first frost in the fall. It provides the best pasturage when closely grazed, as otherwise it becomes tough and wiry. Because of its aggressiveness, it drives most other grasses out in summer, but lespedeza and white clover will flourish in spots among this grass and improve the pasture. For winter pasture when Bermuda is dormant, Bermuda sod may be seeded to bur clover, hairy vetch, or Italian rye grass.

According to Piper, good Bermuda pastures will carry one cow to the acre during the summer and the best mixed Bermuda-and-lespedeza pastures have an even greater carrying capacity.[26] The yield of forage is increased when the pasture is subdivided and the stock are rotated on the plots.

Though primarily a pasture grass, on rich soil Bermuda gives good yields of hay which is about equal to timothy in feeding value. The average yield does not exceed 1 ton per acre, though as high as 3 to 4 tons have been reported under unusually favorable conditions. The stout rootstocks when plowed up are readily eaten by hogs, and in the tropics, when the top growth is scanty, are often pulled up and fed to horses.

462. Carpet grass.—Carpet grass *(Axonopus compressus)* is a perennial, creeping grass that probably ranks next to Bermuda as a pasture grass for the southern half of the cotton belt, being especially useful on moist, sandy lowlands. It endures close grazing well and does not become troublesome as a weed in the United States. It is only fairly nutritious, however, and forms such a dense turf that it is difficult to keep legumes in it.

463. Dallis grass.—Dallis grass *(Paspalum dilatatum)* is a perennial southern grass that grows in clumps or bunches 2 to 4 feet high. It is becoming increasingly important in the South, for it is more drought resistant than Bermuda grass or Johnson grass and furnishes pasture over a much longer season than Bermuda grass, often remaining green during the winter. Owing to its tendency to lodge, it is better for pasture than for hay. A fungus somewhat similar to ergot often severely attacks the seed heads and may cause poisoning of cattle. To avoid this the grass should be grazed so heavily that it does not head out, or it should be mowed.

464. Johnson grass.—Johnson grass *(Sorghum halepense* or *Andropogon halepensis)* is a perennial southern grass which is a close relative of the sorghums and of Sudan grass. It is perhaps the most striking example in this country of a plant that was purposely introduced as a useful plant, but which has become a serious pest. Johnson grass is the worst weed of the cotton planter, and yet it is the best meadow grass for some sections of the South. Its vigorous creeping rootstocks make it very difficult to eradicate when once established, and therefore it should never be sown on clean fields.

When cut not later than early bloom, Johnson grass makes hay which is similar to timothy in feeding value. Where it is firmly established, many farmers prefer to use it for forage, instead of fighting it as a pest. Often a winter crop of oats or oats and vetch is grown after a field is plowed, and then two or three crops of Johnson grass are cut for hay. If a field is not plowed each year or two, the yield of hay becomes small. It is not very well suited for pasture on account of its coarse growth, but it may be cut once a month during the summer as a soiling crop. Sometimes a field of Johnson grass is plowed in the winter so hogs can forage on the rootstocks, of which they are fond.

465. Japanese cane; sugar cane; sugar-cane bagasse.—Because of its heavy yields, *Japanese cane*, a slender-stemmed variety of the common sugar cane *(Saccharum officinarum)* is one of the cheapest forage crops that can be grown in the Gulf states, and possibly in southern California. In Florida it furnishes good pasture for cattle and hogs from November to March, but is killed by grazing after growth starts in the spring. It may be fed in the fall as a soiling crop or may be kept for winter by shocking it in the field. The stalks remain juicy, while the leaves dry out. This crop also makes good silage. Yields of 12 to 25 tons of green forage per acre are not unusual.

The tops and leaves of common *sugar cane*, removed on harvesting the cane, also make satisfactory forage for livestock.[27] Much feed is wasted when this by-product is not utilized by feeding it to stock, for the amount of leaves and tops ranges from 4 to 8 tons per acre. This waste is usually left in the field until early spring and then burned.

Sugar cane bagasse, left at the sugar factories after as much as possible of the juice has been pressed out of the crushed stalks, is extensively used as fuel in the factories. Sometimes the bagasse is dried and the more fibrous parts are used in the manufacture of insulating board. The smaller and more pithy fragments screened out are called *sugar cane pulp.* This or the entire dried bagasse may be mixed with cane molasses, with or without other feeds in addition, for feeding to horses, mules, or cattle.

According to reports from plantations in this country and Hawaii, work stock have been kept in good condition on such a mixture as sugar cane pulp or bagasse, cane molasses, and soybean oil meal. The dried bagasse and the dried pulp contain somewhat more fiber than straw from the small grains and supply only about one-half as much protein and one-fourth to one-third as much fat.

466. Other southern grasses.—*Rhodes grass (Chloris gayana),* a native of South Africa, is adapted as a perennial only to Florida and a narrow strip in this country along the Gulf Coast to southern Texas and westward to southern California. With irrigation it has succeeded on soil too alkaline for other crops, and it has also given good results in southern Texas, due to its drought resistance. It produces good hay and in central and southern Florida as many as 6 or 7 cuttings may be made in a single season. In tropical countries it is said to be the best hay grass.

Napier grass (Pennisetum purpureum) is a giant tropical grass that grows 12 to 18 feet tall in clumps consisting of 20 to 200 stalks about an inch in diameter. It is adapted to about the same area in this country as Japanese sugar cane. It is an excellent soiling crop for dairy cows and can be cut every 3 to 4 weeks during the growing season. It also makes good silage.[28]

Para grass (Panicum barbinode) is a perennial tropical grass with long creeping stems, which is now commonly grown in most tropical countries. It is usually fed green and is often sold in bundles on the market. Para grass is adapted only to the extreme southern part of the United States. If wanted for hay, the grass should be cut when 3 to 4 feet high. The hay is coarse but of excellent quality if cut before the stems become woody.

Guinea grass (Panicum maximum), perhaps the most famous of tropical grasses, is adapted in this country only to a narrow strip from Florida to southern California. In the Tropics guinea grass is used chiefly for pasture, but it is often fed as a green soiling crop. In the Gulf region 4 to 6 cuttings a season can be made.

Rescue grass (Bromus willdenowii), a short-lived perennial which usually behaves as a winter annual in the South, is probably the best grass for temporary winter pastures on rich land in the southern states. It may also be cut for hay.

Natal grass (Tricholaena rosea), when once seeded in the Gulf section, volunteers from year to year, coming after early crops and producing good late summer and fall grazing and good hay.[29] It is well adapted to poor sandy soils.

Bahia grass (Paspalum notatum), the most common grass of western Cuba, is hardy throughout Florida and along the Gulf Coast. Close grazing or frequent cutting does not injure the stand or reduce the yield.[30] It succeeds even on sand-hill soil, the chief handicap to its culture being the poor germination of the seed.

Teosinte (Euchlaena Mexicana), a relative of Indian corn, requires a rich, moist soil and is too tropical to have value north of the southern portion of the Gulf states. Teosinte has never become important in the United States, because on moderately fertile soils it yields less than sorghum, and on rich land less than Japanese cane.

II. STRAW AND CHAFF

467. Composition of straw.—As the small grains and other plants mature, the nutrients which have been built up in the green parts are in large part transferred and stored in the ripening seed. Thus the straw, consisting of the mature stems and leaves, is left with but relatively little protein, starch, or fat, while the content of fiber or cellulose is high. The straw is also low in calcium and phosphorus and in vitamins, especially vitamin A. The nutritive value of straw is therefore very much lower than that of hay made from the same plants before they have matured.

The feeding value of each kind of straw may differ widely, depending on the stage at which the crop was cut, the care with which it was cured, the soil and climate, and the amount of more nutritious grasses and weeds present. The value of straw from the legumes has been discussed in Chapter XIII. (**418**)

468. Straw and chaff of the cereals.—Straw from the small grains is high in fiber and supplies less digestible nutrients and much less net energy than good hay. Also, it is very low in digestible protein, the nutritive ratio being 1:40 or wider.

Straw is satisfactory as a considerable part of the roughage for idle horses and mules and those at light work, or for wintering beef breeding cows. These animals need relatively little protein and vitamins and their requirements for net energy are not high. However, they need considerable heat to keep their bodies warm, and this is furnished by the heat liberated in the mastication and digestion of the straw. (**86-88**)

On the other hand, straw should not, under usual conditions, form any large part of the roughage for dairy cows, for growing or fattening cattle or sheep, or for horses or mules at hard work. When there is a shortage of better roughage on account of drought, considerable straw can be fed to these classes of stock with fair results, if care is taken to use sufficient amounts of protein supplements, to feed more concentrates than usual, and to add a calcium or phosphorus supplement when necessary. Also, a deficiency of vitamin A must be guarded against. Beef cattle fed a limited amount of better roughage will eat more straw during cold weather when they have need for more heat-producing feeds than in mild weather.[31]

In Canada and Europe pulped roots and meal are often mixed with cut or chaffed oat straw, and the moist mass allowed to soften. It is then readily consumed by cattle and sheep. In many districts of Europe horses are fed cut straw mixed with their concentrate allowance, small amounts being thus utilized even for horses that are at hard work.

The use of cereal straw for the various classes of stock is discussed further in the respective chapters of Part III.

Oat straw with its soft, pliable stems is the most nutritious, followed by *barley straw*. *Wheat straw*, being coarse and stiff, is not so readily eaten, and *rye straw*, which is harsh and woody, had better be used for bedding. The *chaff* of wheat and oats contains more protein than does the straw and is a useful roughage when not loaded with dust, rust, or mold. *Rice straw,* if well cured, may be fed in the same manner as straw from the other cereals.[32]

469. Straw from other plants.—When timothy, red top, or other grasses are raised for seed, the threshed *grass straw* can often be used for feeding in the same manner as cereal straw.

Flax straw is about equal to oat straw, when of good quality. South Dakota experiments show that it can be used satisfactorily as the only roughage for wintering beef breeding cows or yearling steers.[33] The statement, sometimes made, that the stringy fiber of flax forms indigestible balls in the stomach, is unwarranted, since it is digested the same as other fibrous material.

Flax straw that has considerable green, immature flaxseed must, however, be fed with great caution, as it may contain poisonous amounts of prussic acid.[34] (**501**) Volunteer flax which sometimes springs up in the fall is very unsafe for pasturing.

Buckwheat straw is of low value and may cause digestive disturbances if fed in large amounts.[35]

QUESTIONS

1. Why should a mixture of grasses and legumes be commonly used for permanent pasture or meadows, instead of merely one variety of grass?
2. Why is timothy the great hay grass of the northern United States, and in what respects is it inferior to legumes? When should it be cut for hay?
3. What are the advantages of seeding a mixture of timothy and clover or timothy and alfalfa in comparison with seeding timothy alone for hay?
4. Why does Kentucky bluegrass rank first as a pasture grass in most of the northern half of the United States?
5. Under what conditions is red top chiefly grown?
6. Discuss the characteristics and value of orchard grass.
7. Of what importance are the small grains for forage in your district; in other sections of the United States?
8. Discuss the use and value of wild or native grasses; of prairie hay.
9. What are the characteristics of Sudan grass? Discuss its value for hay; for pasture; for soilage; for silage.
10. Name 3 types of millets. Of what importance are the millets in your district?
11. Discuss the importance and use of Bermuda grass; of carpet grass.
12. State the characteristics and value of 4 other grasses which are of importance in your district.
13. Discuss the composition of straw and state how it may be best used in stock feeding.

REFERENCES

1. Ritzman and Benedict, N. H. Bul. 270; Prince, Blood, and Percival, N. H. Cir. 41; Pieters, Evans, Salter, Welton, Willard, et al., Ohio Sta., mineo, rpt.; Waters and Schweitzer, Mo. Res. Buls. 19, 20.
2. Hughes, Wilkins, and Cannon, Iowa Rpt. 1933; Beaumont and Gaskill, Mass. Bul. 280.
3. Archibald and Bennett, Mass. Bul. 293.
4. Hills, Vt. Bul. 137.
5. Id. Bul. 197; Hughes, Wilkins, and Cannon, Iowa Rpts. 1932, 1933; Arny, Hodgson, and Nesom, Minn. Buls. 252, 263; Stoa, N. D. Bul. 256; Hodgson et al., Wash. Buls. 275, 291; Holden and Albert, Wis. Cir. 264; Schoth, U. S. Dept. Agr., Farmers' Bul. 1602.
6. Kephart, U. S. Dept. Agr., Farmers' Bul. 1307.
7. Guilbert, Cal. Bul. 481.
8. Hendry, Cal. Bul. 394; Thatcher, Ohio Bul. 543; Sotola, Wash. Bul. 275.
9. Sotola, Wash. Bul. 291.

10. Sackville and Bowstead, Alberta, Canada, Col. of Agr. Bul. 13; Bowstead and Sackville, Alberta, Canada, Col. of Agr. Bul. 19 and mimeo. rpt.; Woll, Cal. Bul. 394; Miller, Cal. Rpt. 1928; Jones, Dickson, Black, and Jones, Tex. Sta., mimeo. rpt.; Hackedorn and McCall, Wash. Buls. 275, 291.
11. Willard, Wyo. Bul. 199.
12. Haecker, Minn. Buls. 35, 67; Dice and Jensen, N. D. Bul. 217; Willard, Wyo. Bul. 145.
13. Hays, Wyo. Bul. 128, Wyo. Rpt. 1922.
14. Blizzard, Okla. Rpt. 1930-32.
15. Knight, Hepner, and Morton, Wyo. Bul. 78.
16. Pieper, Ill. Rpt. 1929.
17. Dawson, Graves, and Van Horn, U. S. Dept. Agr., Tech. Bul. 352; Karper, Quinby, and Jones, Tex. Bul. 396.
18. Piper, U. S. Dept. Agr., Farmers' Bul. 1254.
19. Cunningham and Davis, Ariz. Rpt. 1921; Kan., Fort Hays Branch Station, Livestock Investigations, Rpts. 1923, 1924, 1925.
20. Miller, Cal. Rpt. 1931; Darlow, Okla. Bul. 213; see also: Reed and Marston, Kan. Rpt. 1922-24.
21. Fitch, Kan. Rpts. 1928-30, 1930-32; Dorrance, Mich. Spec. Bul. 240; Monroe, Hayden, Bell, and Thatcher, Ohio Bul. 532; Willham, Okla., Panhandle Sta. Bul. 15; Olsen and Robinson, S. D. Bul. 265; Neel, Tenn. Cir. 44; Karper, Quinby, and Jones, Tex. Bul. 254; Dawson, Graves, and Van Horn, U. S. Dept. Agr. Tech. Bul. 352.
22. Menaul and Dowell, Jour. Agr. Res., 18, 1920, pp. 447-450; Swanson, Jour. Agr. Res., 22, 1921, pp. 125-138.
23. Dvorachek, Ark. Bul. 221; Evvard and Culbertson, Iowa Sta., mimeo. rpt.; Snyder, Nebr. Rpt. 1924; Loeffel, Nebr. Rpt. 1925.
24. Bell, Winchester, and Marston, Kan. Cir. 98; Loeffel, Nebr. Rpt. 1924.
25. Woll, Cal. Bul. 282.
26. Forage Plants, rev. ed., p. 268.
27. Brandes, Sherwood, and Belcher, U. S. Dept. Agr. Cir. 284.
28. Shealy, Fla. Bul. 260; Neal, Becker, and Dix Arnold, Fla. Bul. 279; Piper, U. S. Dept. Agr., Farmers' Bul. 1254; Wilsie and Takahashi, Hawaii Bul. 72.
29. Piper, U. S. Dept. Agr., Farmers' Bul. 1433.
30. Leukel and Coleman, Fla. Bul. 219.
31. Black, U. S. Dept. Agr., Farmers' Bul. 1382.
32. Nelson, Ark. Bul. 98; Martin, Ark. Sta., information to the author.
33. Wilson, Wright, and Fenn, S. D. Cir. 3 and mimeo. rpt.; see also: Laude and Grimes, Kan. Cir. 133.
34. Ince, N. D. Bul. 106; Stevens, N. D. Bul. 265.
35. Pott, Ernähr. u. Futtermittel, II, p. 329.

CHAPTER XVI

ROOTS, TUBERS, AND MISCELLANEOUS FORAGES

I. ROOTS AND TUBERS

470. Unimportant for livestock in the United States.—In northern Europe and eastern Canada root crops are extensively grown for stock, but in this country they have never been widely used. The acreage has now declined to an insignificant amount in comparison with other forage crops. According to the Census, in 1929 only 14,752 acres of roots were raised for forage in the entire United States, in comparison with 88,333 acres in 1919. Of the total acreage in 1929, nearly one-half was in the three Pacific States—California, Oregon, and Washington. In comparison with this very small acreage of roots, in 1929 the acreage of corn grown for silage in the United States was 4,005,539 acres; of corn cut for fodder, 6,263,881 acres; and of sorghums grown for forage, 4,355,919 acres.

The great difference in the importance of roots for livestock feeding in this country and in northern Europe is due chiefly to the difference in climate. Northern Europe with its cool summers is well suited to growing roots but not to the culture of corn. In most parts of our country the summers are hot and corn or the sorghums thrive, furnishing in the form of silage palatable succulent feed which is much cheaper than roots. Also root crops require much more hand labor than corn or the sorghums, and labor is cheap in Europe in comparison with this country.

In the United States, the growing of roots for livestock is advisable only under the following special conditions: (1) In those districts where the summers are too cool for corn; (2) on farms in the corn belt where too few animals are kept to use silage economically; (3) to serve as a relish for show animals or dairy cows on official test; or (4) for poultry feeding.

While the acreage of root crops grown for stock feeding in the United States is very small, the production of sugar beets for sugar manufacture is of importance in certain sections, particularly in Colorado and the other western Mountain States. During the 10-year period, 1924-33, an average of 743,000 acres of sugar beets was harvested for sugar production, with an average yield of 11.0 tons per acre. The by-products from the beet-sugar industry—beet pulp, beet molasses, and beet tops—are used for stock feeding. Also, cull and surplus potatoes and sweet potatoes are important by-product feeds in certain sections.

471. Composition and value of roots and tubers.—All root and tuber crops are exceedingly watery and low in dry matter. Especially so are mangels with an average of only 9.4 per cent dry matter, turnips with 9.5 per cent, and rutabagas with 11.1 per cent. This is much less than half the percentage of dry matter in good corn silage. The dry

308

matter that roots and tubers do contain is low in fiber and highly digestible, and it is therefore relatively high in net energy per pound. Roots and tubers should therefore be regarded, not as roughages, but as watery or diluted concentrates.

The chief nutrients in roots and tubers are carbohydrates—largely cane sugar in beets and mangels and starch in potatoes. Roots and tubers are low to fair in protein content, are low in calcium, and only fair in phosphorus. Also, they contain but little vitamin D and, with the exception of carrots and yellow sweet potatoes, are low in vitamin A value. In general, roots are therefore in decided contrast to legume hay, which is rich in protein, in calcium, and in vitamins A and D.

Because their dry matter is highly digestible and rich in net energy, roots can be used as a substitute for a considerable part of the grain usually fed to dairy cows or to fattening cattle and lambs. This is usually not an economical practice in the United States, but is common in northern Europe. In most of the trials with dairy cows a pound of dry matter in such roots as mangels, sugar beets, or rutabagas has been equal to a pound of dry matter in grain, such as corn, wheat, or barley, or at least to equal a pound of such grain.[1] Hansson values roots slightly lower in comparison with grain for dairy cows, rating 1.1 lbs. of dry matter in roots equal to 1 lb. of corn or barley.[2]

Because such roots as mangels, rutabagas, and turnips contain less than half as much dry matter as corn silage, they are worth much less per ton for stock feeding. The experiments reviewed in Part III show that for dairy cows 100 lbs. of corn silage are worth more than 200 lbs. of such roots. For fattening lambs it has required, on the average, 145 lbs. of roots to replace 100 lbs. of corn silage.

In addition to the nutrients they furnish, roots and other succulent feeds have a beneficial tonic effect upon animals and are highly esteemed for keeping breeding cattle and sheep in thrifty condition. Many successful stockmen recommend roots for animals being fitted for show and for dairy cows crowded to maximum production on official tests.

In this country the daily allowance of roots per 1,000 lbs. live weight is usually 25 to 50 lbs. or less. Throughout Great Britain fattening cattle and sheep are often fed 100 lbs. of roots, or even more, per 1,000 lbs. live weight daily with satisfactory results. Sheep are sometimes fattened on concentrates and roots alone but better results are secured when some dry roughage is fed.

Roots are usually chopped or sliced before feeding to avoid any danger of stock choking on them, and the grain or concentrate mixture is often sprinkled over them. Any undue amount of dirt should be removed before the roots are chopped. Cooking or steaming roots or tubers, except potatoes for swine, is a waste of labor and money. In Canada and England, roots for fattening cattle are often pulped and spread in layers some inches thick, alternating with other layers of cut or chaffed hay or straw. After being shoveled over, the mass is allowed to stand several hours before feeding, to moisten and soften the chaffed straw or hay. In this manner considerable straw may be successfully utilized.

For winter feeding in the northern states roots must be stored in well-ventilated pits or cellars, but in mild climates they may remain in the field until fed. In experiments in Ireland, mangels lost about 27 per cent of their dry matter during 5 months' storage, due to the respiration which is continuously taking place.[3] In West Virginia tests mangels and rutabagas stored for 3 months had dried out to such an extent that the *percentage* of dry matter was about one-third greater than when harvested, though there had undoubtedly been some loss in *total amount* of dry matter during storage.[4]

The use and value of roots for the various classes of stock are discussed in the respective chapters in Part III.

472. Economy of roots vs. corn silage.—To grow, harvest, and store an acre of roots costs considerably more than to grow an acre of corn and ensile it, because root crops require more thorough preparation of the soil and far more hand labor in cultivation, harvesting, and storage. Moreover, experiments show that where corn thrives it has yielded on the average 68 to 92 per cent more dry matter per acre than mangels, sugar beets, or rutabagas.[5] The total yield of such roots as mangels or rutabagas may be much larger than that of corn forage, but these roots contain less than half as much dry matter per ton as corn silage furnishes.

The estimated average yield of corn grown for silage in the United States was 7.0 tons per acre for the 7-year period, 1927 to 1933.[6] According to the United States Census, the estimated average yields of root crops grown for stock feeding were 6.62 tons per acre in 1919 and 9.73 tons per acre in 1929. The average yield of roots in Canada for a 10-year period was 9 tons per acre, and the yield for a 4-year period at eight experiment stations in eastern Canada was 19.5 tons per acre in comparison with 14.5 tons for corn silage.[7]

The cost of growing and harvesting roots at these Canadian stations was estimated under 1927 conditions at $3.22 per ton and of growing and ensiling corn at $3.45 per ton. These very low costs per ton were made possible only by the high yields per acre. The root crops required about twice as many hours of man labor per acre as did corn. In the extreme northern part of Wisconsin, where only very early varieties of corn can be grown, the cost for corn silage was $5.35 per ton and for rutabagas $4.06 per ton.[8]

Due to the low content of dry matter in roots and the high cost per acre of growing root crops, in good corn-growing sections corn silage will furnish dry matter and digestible nutrients at half the cost of roots. Under such conditions corn silage is much more economical than roots as a succulent feed for dairy cattle, beef cattle, or sheep.

The relative yields of the various root crops vary widely in different districts, depending on the soil and climate.[9] Under especially favorable conditions as much as 20 to 30 tons per acre, or even more, are sometimes produced by mangels, sugar mangels, rutabagas, or turnips.

473. Mangels.—Mangels, or mangel wurzels *(Beta vulgaris,* var.), are the most watery of roots, containing only 9.4 per cent dry matter. Yet due to the enormous yields—20 to 30 tons per acre on good soil and under favorable conditions—they produce a large amount of dry matter per acre. Because they stand well out of the ground, mangels are much more easily harvested than sugar beets, and they also keep better in winter storage than sugar beets, rutabagas, or turnips. They likewise withstand drought and hot weather better than rutabagas or turnips. Mangels should not be fed until after they have been stored for a few weeks, as the freshly-harvested roots may cause scouring. Half-sugar mangels, which are crosses between sugar beets and mangels, are richer in dry matter and sugar than are mangels.

Mangels are a very satisfactory feed for dairy cows, beef cattle, or sheep, with the following exception. It is pointed out in Chapter XXXIII that rams or wethers are possibly more apt to be affected with dangerous urinary calculi, or stones, when fed mangels or sugar beets for long periods, than on other rations. In feeding dairy cows, mangels and sugar beets have an advantage over rutabagas and turnips, because there is no danger of tainting the milk.

474. Sugar beets.—The sugar beet *(Beta vulgaris,* var.) has been so developed for sugar production that some strains now contain 16 per cent or more of cane sugar. The yields are smaller than those of mangels, but due to the higher sugar content sugar beets generally produce about as much dry matter per acre. However, they require more labor in cultivating and harvesting than mangels, as they set deep in the ground. They are well liked by stock and are often fed to dairy cows on test. As in the case of mangels, it is not wise to feed sugar beets to rams or wethers for long periods, on account of the possibility of the formation of urinary calculi, or stones.

The composition and value of beet pulp and beet molasses are discussed in Chapter XIX.

475. Beet tops.—In harvesting sugar beets for sugar production, the crowns are cut off, because they contain salts which interfere with the recovery of sugar from the juice. When gathered without undue waste, the tops, which include the crowns and the leaves, will weigh about one-half as much per acre as the marketed beets. The green weight of the tops in proportion to the weight of the beets will, however, range all the way from 30 to 70 per cent or even more, depending on the percentage of dry matter in the tops and the leafiness of the crop. Often the tops are purchased on the basis, not of actual weight of tops, but of the amount of tops from each ton of marketed beets.

To utilize the tops three different methods are followed: Cattle or sheep may be turned into the field to graze on them. The tops may be put into small piles (the size of an inverted wash tub), allowed to cure out more or less, and then hauled to the feeding yards. Sometimes the tops are ensiled. In Europe the tops are sometimes dried artificially for sale as a stock feed. If a crop is infested with nematodes, the tops should be pastured, or ensiled, to avoid spreading infestation. Otherwise, grazing the tops is not usually the best practice from the standpoint of securing the greatest value. Also, in wet weather the trampling of the stock may injure the texture of the soil and make it cloddy.

Beet tops are decidedly laxative and should therefore be fed in moderation. The silage is less laxative than the fresh tops, but it is best not to feed more than 30 lbs. per head daily to cattle or more than 3 lbs. to sheep.[10] Beet leaves contain considerable oxalic acid, which is poisonous if animals receive too large amounts.

The tops may be fed in larger amounts to cattle and sheep in proportion to their live weight, than to horses and swine. This is because the fermentations in the paunch of ruminants destroy some of the oxalic acid. If it is desired to feed the maximum amounts of tops, it is well to add 1 ounce of finely-ground limestone or chalk to each 50 lbs. of tops, as calcium changes the oxalic acid to insoluble calcium oxalate. If considerable dirt is adhering to the tops, as much of it as possible should be removed before feeding the tops or ensiling them.[11] Otherwise digestive disturbances may result.

Beet tops make satisfactory silage if allowed to dry out somewhat before ensiling them, for the fresh tops usually contain too much water. Beet-top silage tends to spoil quickly on exposure to the air, especially in warm weather. Running the tops through a silage cutter is the most convenient method of elevating them into an ordinary silo, but, when they are put into a trench or pit silo, it is not necessary to cut them. In silos of the latter types, the tops are often ensiled in alternate layers with straw. When this is done, the mass must be packed especially well, and the tops ensiled before they dry out. Beet tops make good silage when run through a silage cutter with an equal weight of dry corn fodder, enough water being added so the mass will pack well.

When fed with grain and legume or other hay, beet tops and beet-top silage are satisfactory for fattening cattle and sheep or lambs, and also for dairy cows.[12] They are too laxative to be used as the only roughage. In 15 Nebraska experiments the beet tops from each ton of sugar beets saved, on the average, 24 lbs. concentrates plus 102 lbs. alfalfa hay in fattening lambs, and slightly more rapid gains were secured when beet tops were added to the ration of grain and alfalfa hay.[13] Similar results were secured in Colorado trials.[14]

In Nebraska experiments beet-top-silage was worth 60 per cent more than the tops fed without ensiling.[15] When the silage was added to the excellent ration of corn, cottonseed cake, and alfalfa hay for fattening lambs, the gains were slightly increased, and 1 ton of silage saved 83 lbs. of concentrates and 329 lbs. of alfalfa hay. In Montana trials beet tops had an even higher value for fattening lambs.[16]

476. Rutabagas.—The rutabaga, or swede *(Brassica campestris)*, which is grown extensively in Great Britain and Canada, ranks next to the mangel in ease of cultivation. Sheep prefer it to all other roots. Rutabagas and turnips do not require such fertile soil as mangels, but do best where the climate is cool. In the central part of the corn belt and southward much of the growing season is too hot for them and they are apt to grow large necks, instead of developing good-sized roots. Like other turnips, rutabagas are apt to taint the milk of cows, unless fed only immediately after milking.

477. Turnips.—Turnips *(Brassica rapa)* are more watery than rutabagas and do not keep so well. Hybrid turnips, crosses between the turnip and the rutabaga, keep better than ordinary turnips. Maturing early, large yields of turnips are often secured without cultivation. Though used mainly for sheep, they can also be fed to cattle.

478. Carrots.—Carrots *(Daucus carota)* usually yield much less than the root crops previously discussed; they are more particular in their soil and climate requirements; and the cost of growing the crop is higher. They are therefore of little importance for stock feeding in this country.

As horses are especially fond of carrots, the crop is occasionally grown for them. Hard-worked or driving horses should not be fed large allowances of carrots, and some advise feeding no carrots to brood mares for a few weeks before and after they foal. Yellow carrots are an excellent root crop for poultry, as they are rich in vitamin A value (carotene).

479. Parsnips.—The parsnip *(Pastinaca sativa)* is the favorite root crop with dairymen on the islands of Jersey and Guernsey. Parsnips contain about as much dry matter as sugar beets, but as the yield in this country is relatively low and the roots are difficult to harvest, they are rarely grown here for stock feeding.

480. Potatoes.—In Europe heavy-yielding varieties of large-sized potatoes *(Solanum tuberosum)* are extensively raised for stock. In the United States other crops excel potatoes for feed production, and therefore only cull potatoes are generally fed to stock, unless potatoes are unusually low in price.

Potatoes contain more dry matter than most root crops, having 21.2 per cent. However, they are more watery than many realize, and contain less dry matter and total digestible nutrients per 100 lbs. than corn silage. They are rich in starch, on the dry basis, but are very low in protein, having the nutritive ratio of 1:14.7. Care should therefore be taken to include plenty of protein-rich feeds in the ration, when a heavy allowance of potatoes is fed. Potatoes do not contain any significant amounts of vitamins A or D. This lack should be supplied by feeding them with well-cured legume hay or good mixed hay.

From the standpoint of total digestible nutrients, it takes about 400 to 450 lbs.

of potatoes to equal 100 lbs. of grain, and when potatoes are properly fed, this measures their general value for stock. Stated in another way, 100 lbs. of potatoes are worth about 22 to 25 per cent as much as 100 lbs. of grain. For swine, potatoes, fed after cooking, have a somewhat higher value, as is stated later.

Potatoes are satisfactory for feeding to dairy cows, beef cattle, sheep, horses, and swine in limited amounts as a substitute for grain or other feed. They should be cooked for swine, but this it not necessary or profitable for other stock. Potatoes should be sliced or chopped before feeding to cattle or sheep, to make them more palatable and to avoid choking. Stock should be accustomed to potatoes gradually, as they are often not very palatable. Feeding too large amounts of raw potatoes may cause scours.

Unripe potatoes and especially the sprouts of stored potatoes contain small amounts of solanin, a poisonous compound. It has, therefore, been advised that in feeding badly-sprouted potatoes the sprouts be removed. In trials at the North Dakota Station, however, when dairy cows were fed for considerable periods on reasonable quantities of sprouted, sunburned, or decomposed potatoes, and even on potato sprouts, along with other feeds, there was no injurious effect.[17] However, on account of reports of stock being injured by excessive amounts of potatoes, it is not wise to let them have access to an unlimited amount of either good or poor-quality potatoes.

For dairy cows potatoes were a good substitute for corn silage in North Dakota trials, when fed at the rate of 24 to 40 lbs. per head daily.[18] However, the potatoes were not quite so palatable as the silage and the cows seemed to lose their appetites for potatoes after several months. Fed in such quantities, potatoes did not affect the flavor of the milk or the odor of the milk or butter, but milk or cream exposed to an atmosphere heavy with potato odor readily took it up. Potatoes should therefore be fed immediately after milking and not before. When a large allowance of potatoes was fed to cows in Vermont tests, the potatoes were not equal to the same weight of dry matter in corn silage, and the butter was soft.[19] If potatoes are fed in a properly-balanced ration they do not dry up cows, as is sometimes believed.

Cull potatoes are often fed to fattening lambs in the potato-growing districts of the West. In 11 comparisons with fattening lambs the addition of cull potatoes to a ration of grain and legume hay, with or without a protein-rich supplement, has usually increased slightly the gains of the lambs.[20] In these trials one ton of potatoes was equal in feeding value, on the average, to 185 lbs. grain plus 12 lbs. cottonseed meal and 430 lbs. alfalfa hay. With hay valued at half the price of grain per ton, cull potatoes would be worth 21 per cent as much per ton as grain.

Cull potatoes have been used satisfactorily in place of corn silage for feeding fattening beef cattle and beef breeding cows.[21] When fed with alfalfa hay they have been worth, on the average, about 80 per cent as much per ton as corn silage. When fattening steers were fed equal weights of dry matter in potatoes and in rutabagas, in a Scotch trial, the gains were a trifle more rapid on the potatoes.[22] As potatoes contain more than twice as much dry matter as rutabagas, their value per ton was correspondingly greater. Potatoes may be fed to horses in amounts up to 15 to 20 lbs. per head daily, either raw or cooked.

For swine, potatoes give very good results when used as a partial substitute for grain, provided that they are thoroughly cooked, that the ration furnishes sufficient protein and also protein of good quality, and that it provides enough vitamins A and D. In the case of swine not on pasture, care should be taken to use one of the efficient protein supplements recommended in Chapter XXXVI for dry-lot feeding.

For the best results the proportion of potatoes for swine should not be greater than 4 lbs. of potatoes to each pound of concentrates. It is best to add salt to the water in which the potatoes are cooked, to increase the palatability. The potatoes should be cooked thoroughly, and the water in which they are cooked should be discarded, as it is not palatable. Raw potatoes generally produce poor results when fed to swine.[23]

When cooked potatoes have been fed to pigs as a partial substitute for grain in properly-balanced rations, it has required only 351 lbs. of potatoes (weighed before cooking) to equal 100 lbs. of grain and other concentrates.[24]   In earlier trials, where cooked potatoes were fed in less efficient rations, it required 400 to 442 lbs. of potatoes to equal 100 lbs. of grain.[25]

In Germany potatoes are sometimes dried and fed to stock in the form of dried potato flakes. These are nearly equal to grain in value.

481. Potato silage.—Potato silage may be made by chopping potatoes and mixing them with 2 per cent by weight of ground corn to inoculate the mass with lactic acid bacteria, so the material will undergo the proper fermentation. (Ground corn normally contains an abundance of these bacteria.)

After dairy cows became used to it, such silage was a satisfactory substitute for corn silage in trials by the United States Department of Agriculture.[26]   It was also satisfactory for fattening lambs in a Colorado test.[27]   However, for pigs potato silage was not a satisfactory substitute for cooked potatoes in a trial at the Wisconsin Station.[28]

Cull potatoes may also be successfully ensiled by mixing them with dry corn or sorghum fodder. In Colorado tests satisfactory silage was produced by running a mixture of about four-fifths cull potatoes and one-fifth dry corn fodder, by weight, through a silage cutter.[29]   When fed with alfalfa hay as the roughage for fattening cattle, such potato-corn fodder silage was worth nearly as much as corn silage.

482. Sweet potatoes.—Sweet potatoes *(Ipomea batatas)* are a southern crop that may be grown as far north as New Jersey and Illinois. Like potatoes, the crop is generally grown in this country for human food and not primarily for stock feeding. However, several million bushels of cull or unmarketable sweet potatoes are available each year for feeding in the South, and they can usually be utilized best for swine. They may also be fed to cattle or sheep or substituted for half the grain in the rations of work horses or mules.

In case there is a surplus of sweet potatoes, swine can be used to harvest some of the crop, thus saving the cost of digging. Swine can also be used to clean up sweet potato fields after the potatoes are dug for market. Marketable potatoes, after they are dug, are almost always worth more for sale than for stock feeding.

Since the cost per acre of growing sweet potatoes is considerably greater than that of corn, the latter crop commonly furnishes cheaper feed for stock, except possibly on soil that is very poor and sandy. The average yield for the 10-year period, 1925-34, was 89.0 bushels per acre, and it requires 4 to 5 bushels of sweet potatoes to equal 1 bushel of corn in feeding value.

Sweet potatoes are high in dry matter for a root crop, averaging 31 per cent, and are rich in starch, but they are extremely low in protein, having the unusually wide nutritive ratio of 1:33.4. They are also low in calcium and phosphorus. In feeding swine on sweet potatoes it is therefore important to furnish sufficient high-quality protein supplement and also to provide the lacking minerals.

When pigs are grazed on sweet potatoes or are fed the harvested tubers, the best results are secured when they are fed one-third to one-half the usual grain allowance, in addition to protein and mineral supplements. Only good-sized pigs or older hogs should be grazed on the crop, as sweet potatoes are too bulky for small pigs. Sweet potatoes

SUGAR BEETS IN A WESTERN IRRIGATED DISTRICT

While but relatively few acres of sugar beets are grown for stock feeding in this country, the raising of sugar beets for the beet sugar factories is an important industry in certain sections, especially in some of the irrigated districts of the West. (From U. S. Reclamation Service.)

RAPE EXCELS AS AN ANNUAL FORAGE CROP IN THE NORTH

At small expense rape furnishes excellent forage for sheep, swine, or cattle from early summer to late fall.

SOAP WEED (YUCCA ELATA) IN THE SOUTHWEST

Several species of Yucca and Sotol furnish valuable emergency feed for range cattle in the Southwest in time of drought. See Page 319. (From U. S. Department of Agriculture.)

SINGEING PRICKLY PEAR WITH A GASOLINE TORCH

After the spines have been singed off cattle can feed on prickly pear without harm. Another method is to cut the cacti and run them thru machines which chop them, rendering the spines comparatively harmless. (From U. S. Department of Agriculture.)

produce hard pork, but pigs heavily fed on the crop tend to be paunchy and have a low dressing percentage.

In extensive Louisiana tests it required 4.3 lbs. of sweet potatoes to equal 1 lb. of grain and other concentrates, when sweet potatoes were fed in dry lot; and 4.9 lbs. of the potatoes (but not including the vines eaten) to equal 1 lb. of corn when the crop was hogged-down.[30] The value was much lower when proper supplements were not provided. Similar results have been secured in other trials.[31]

Since sweet potatoes supply about one-third as much total digestible nutrients as corn, these values are somewhat lower than would be expected from the chemical composition.

483. Jerusalem artichoke.—The tubers of this hardy perennial *(Helianthus tuberosus)* are sometimes grown for human food or for feeding livestock. They resemble the potato in composition, except that the chief carbohydrate is inulin, instead of starch. This crop has often been recommended enthusiastically for livestock, but has not proved to be as economical or useful as more common crops. For this reason they have never been used to any appreciable extent for stock feeding in this country. In various tests the yield of tubers has ranged from 6 to 15 tons per acre, or even more.

The forage may be cut and used for silage or as a green soiling crop, yielding from 5 to 9 tons of green fodder per acre, but the yield of tubers is greatly reduced by cutting the tops at the silage stage.[32] In an Illinois test artichoke silage was not very satisfactory for beef cattle.[33] It is apparent that artichokes do not compare favorably with corn and other common silage crops.

The tubers are difficult to harvest and do not keep well in storage. They live over winter in the ground, and, even when they are dug in the fall, enough are usually left to make the next crop. Due to this, the plant may sometimes become a weed. Pigs may be turned in to harvest the tubers, but should be fed grain in addition, as they will make but little gain on the artichokes alone. For swine feeding, artichokes have proven less valuable than corn grown for hogging down, or than other forage crops.[34]

484. Chufa.—The chufa sedge *(Cyperus esculentus)*, frequently a weed in damp fields on southern farms, produces small, chaffy tubers, that remain in the ground uninjured over winter. In certain sections of the South chufas are often used for fattening swine, which are turned in to harvest the crop.[35]

Chufas grow best on sandy soils, yielding from 100 to 150 bushels of 44 lbs. each per acre. As they are very low in protein, they should be supplemented by protein-rich feeds. Good crops of chufas have produced 307 to 592 lbs. of pork per acre, after making allowance for the other feed consumed by the pigs. However, they produce a soft carcass which can be hardened only by prolonged feeding of other such feeds as corn.

485. Cassava.—*Cassava (Manihot utilissima)*, a bushy plant from 4 to 10 feet high with fleshy roots like those of the sweet potato, grows in Florida and along the Gulf Coast. Some tropical varieties contain much prussic acid and must be heated or dried before feeding to drive off this poison. The varieties grown in this country are not poisonous.

From 5 to 6 tons of roots, containing 25 to 30 per cent of starch, are produced per acre. They are used for the manufacture of starch or for feeding cattle and swine. However, the culture of cassava in the United States has declined, due to the fact that other crops give larger yields of feed at less expense. In experiments at the Hawaii Station when cassava roots supplied half the dry matter for dairy cows and pigs, scours resulted. When cassava formed not over one-third the dry matter in the ration of pigs, satisfactory results were secured.[36]

The value of *dried cassava meal*, or manihot meal, the by-product from cassava-starch factories, is discussed in Chapter XIX.

II. Miscellaneous Succulent Feeds

486. Rape.—*Dwarf Essex rape (Brassica napus)*, a member of the turnip and cabbage family, is widely grown throughout the United States as a temporary pasture crop or as a soiling crop. It stores its nutrients in the numerous leaves and stems. Bird-seed rape is worthless for forage. While rape may be used as a soiling crop, it is best to let stock graze the crop. The plants should never be grazed so closely that only the bare stalks remain, or the yield of new leaves will be greatly reduced. Rape is not satisfactory for silage.

The seed, which is inexpensive, may be sown from early spring to August in the North and even later in the South, either broadcast or in drills and cultivated. It may also be sown in corn previous to the last cultivation. In 6 to 12 weeks after seeding the crop is large enough for use. As it endures rather severe frosts, rape is excellent for late autumn feed. Rape requires a rich soil and plenty of moisture, and does not thrive on poor sandy land. In Ontario, Canada, an average yield of 19.2 tons per acre of rape forage was secured on test plots over a period of 15 years.[37]

Rape is chiefly used as a pasture crop for swine and sheep and ranks high for this purpose, as is pointed out in Chapters XXXVI and XXXIII. It is also satisfactory for cattle, but dairy cows should be fed rape or grazed on the crop only immediately after milking, to avoid tainting the milk. Access to clover or bluegrass pasture when on rape is advantageous for cattle and sheep, as it reduces the danger from bloat. Animals on rape should be freely supplied with salt, as this tends to check any undue laxative effect. Sometimes stock must be accustomed to rape, but later they become fond of it.

A large-growing variety of rape, called "giant rape," or "broad-leaved rape," is often grown in Great Britain but is not common in the United States. In New York tests this variety furnished slightly more grazing for sheep than Dwarf Essex rape.[38]

487. Cabbage.—On rich ground cabbage *(Brassica oleracea)* gives as large returns of palatable forage as do root crops, but because more labor is required in its cultivation, it is but little grown for stock feeding. Cabbage is prized by shepherds when preparing stock for exhibition, and is also used for feeding milk cows. Like other plants of the mustard family, it should be fed after milking, to avoid tainting the milk. When cabbage is raised for market, the small heads and the leaves may be fed to stock unless the leaves carry too much poisonous spray residue.

488. Kohlrabi.—Kohlrabi *(Brassica caulorapa)*, another member of the cabbage family, can be grown wherever rutabagas thrive. Under favorable conditions for rutabagas, kohlrabi yields less, but in hot weather it does better than rutabagas. Since the thickened, turnip-like stems stand well above the ground, the crop is readily pastured by sheep, which also relish the leaves. Kohlrabi apparently does not taint the milk when fed to dairy cows.

489. Kale; marrow-stem kale.—*Kale (Brassica oleracea, var. acephala)*, a cabbage-like plant that does not form heads, is grown extensively for stock feeding in this country only in the northern Pacific-coast district. A large-growing variety, "thousand-headed kale," is there considered the best fall and winter soiling crop for dairy cows and is also used for sheep and swine. In that district kale will usually remain green most of the winter.

The average yield of kale in tests in the Willamette valley, Oregon, was 18.1 tons per acre, costing $3.78 per ton, in comparison with 5.7 tons per acre for corn silage, costing $7.40 per ton.[39]   For dairy cows 131 lbs. of kale equalled 100 lbs. of corn silage in Oregon tests, and on the acre basis 1 acre of kale was worth 2 acres of corn silage.[40]   Kale, like others of the mustard family, should be fed after milking to avoid tainting the milk.

Marrow-stem kale, a kind with enlarged, fleshy stems, is used to some extent in England as a soiling crop, especially for sheep.

490. Sunflowers as a forage crop.—Where the season is too short and cool for corn, Mammoth Russian sunflowers *(Helianthus annus)* are sometimes used for silage and to feed as a green soiling crop.   Sunflowers are not affected by cool weather or injured by light frosts so much as is corn.   They will therefore produce a good crop under conditions where corn would be a failure.   The crop is used chiefly for silage, but it also makes a satisfactory soiling crop for late summer and fall feeding.

In such districts as the higher-altitude areas of the Mountain States and the most northern parts of the United States, sunflowers will commonly produce twice as much forage per acre as corn.   Even in good corn areas, the yields of green forage and of dry matter per acre may be higher from sunflowers, returns of 15 to 20 tons of green forage per acre not being rare.

However, sunflowers cannot be recommended in place of corn for silage where the latter thrives, for the silage is decidedly less palatable and usually considerably lower in feeding value than corn silage.   Average sunflower silage supplies only 12.6 lbs. total digestible nutrients per 100 lbs., in comparison with 18.7 lbs. for well-matured corn silage and 13.3 lbs. for silage from immature corn, such as is often produced where the growing season is very short.

When stock are accustomed to good corn silage, it is sometimes difficult to get them to take sunflower silage, but they can usually be induced to eat it, if it is mixed with more palatable feed.   Sunflower silage is sometimes rather constipating and had best be fed with laxative feeds, such as legume hay.

For dairy cows good sunflower silage has usually been worth decidedly less per ton than good corn silage or sorghum silage, and it has been more similar in value to silage from oats-and-peas or oats-vetch-and-peas.[41]

Similar results have usually been secured in the experiments in which sunflower silage has been fed to beef cattle.[42]   The value of sunflower silage has been especially low per ton in comparison with that of well-matured corn silage, in tests where pigs have followed the cattle to utilize the unmasticated corn kernels in the manure.   For sheep sunflower silage has also generally been much inferior in value per ton to good corn or sorghum silage, or even to that from peas-and-oats or peas-and-barley.[43]   For the various classes of stock sunflower silage is therefore worth decidedly less per ton than good corn or sorghum silage.

Sunflowers are sometimes grown in combination with corn for silage, with the hope of securing a larger yield or a surer crop than from corn alone, and obtaining a more palatable silage than from sunflowers alone.   This practice seems of rather doubtful value.   If a large enough proportion of sunflowers is planted to increase the yield materially, the corn plants will be shaded so that the proportion of corn fodder will be insignificant. It would probably be better to grow the two crops separately and mix them when ensiled.[44]

Recommendations concerning the best stage to harvest sunflowers for silage vary considerably, ranging all the way from the one-sixth-bloom stage to the dough stage. Most of those who have experimented with the crop prefer to ensile the crop by the time half to two-thirds of the heads are in bloom. When too immature, the plants are so watery that much juice runs out of the silo. If the harvesting is delayed too long, the bottom leaves dry up and are lost, and the stems become so woody that the silage is not palatable.

Occasionally sunflower silage will not keep properly, because too little fermentable sugar is present to form sufficient acid to prevent undesirable changes. For example, sunflowers did not make good silage at the Huntley, Montana, Experiment Farm unless molasses, corn forage, or sugar beets were added to supply more sugar.[45]

Sunflower silage is much heavier per cubic foot than corn or sorghum silage, weighing from 1.5 to 3.0 times as much as corn silage.[46] A silo must therefore be strongly built to resist the pressure.

491. Pumpkins, squashes, and melons.—The *pumpkin (Curcubito pepo)* is often planted in cornfields and the fruits used as a relish for horses, cattle, and pigs. Pumpkins contain only 10.4 per cent dry matter and their feeding value per ton is therefore low. One ton of pumpkins, including seeds, equals in feeding value for dairy cows about 333 to 400 lbs. mixed hay or 800 lbs. corn silage.[47]

In early experiments summarized by Rommel, pigs required 376 lbs. of pumpkins plus 273 lbs. of grain for 100 lbs. gain.[48] In a Washington experiment well-grown pigs fed pumpkins alone gained only 0.55 lb. a head daily and required 5,719 lbs. pumpkins per 100 lbs. gain.[49] In two experiments pigs fed grain and pumpkins gained 1.38 lbs. daily, on the average, and required 400 lbs. grain and 1,396 lbs. pumpkins per 100 lbs. gain.

From these trials we may conclude that it would take 10 tons or over of pumpkins to equal 1 ton of grain for pigs. Cooking pumpkins for swine is not beneficial. There is a common opinion that pumpkin seeds are harmful to stock, but this is not true.[50] Feeding the seeds alone, however, is apt to cause indigestion on account of the high fat content.

In Colorado hogs have been fattened exclusively on raw *squashes (Cucurbita,* spp.). The meat had a good flavor, but the fat had an undesirable yellow color.[51]

Melons, especially pie melons, or citrons, are occasionally fed to stock.[52]

492. Apples and other fruits.—Windfall and surplus apples and other fruit can sometimes be fed advantageously to stock. Apples, peaches, plums, and even pears contain somewhat more dry matter than do such roots as mangels and ruta-bagas. The chief nutrients are sugars, and fruits are extremely low in protein.

In Vermont tests it was concluded that apples were worth about 40 per cent as much per ton as corn silage for dairy cows.[53] In a Washington test in which 1.5 lbs. per head daily of apples were fed to fattening lambs, along with alfalfa hay and corn grain, as good results were secured as when the same weight of corn silage was fed in place of the apples.[54] When a larger allowance of apples was fed, the results were less satisfactory. When apples were used to replace part of the grain for pigs in Utah trials, it required 9 to 15 lbs. of apples to equal 1 lb. of grain.[55] In an Arizona test lambs fed ripe olives and alfalfa hay made satisfactory gains.[56]

The value and use of dried apple pomace, wet apple pomace, apple pomace silage, and other fruit by-products are discussed in Chapter XIX.

493. Spurrey.—Spurrey *(Spergula sativa)*, which requires a cool, moist growing season, is sometimes used as a catch crop for feeding green to stock on sandy land in northern Europe. It has proved of little value in this country, not being adapted to our hot summers.

494. Prickly comfrey.—Prickly comfrey *(Symphytum asperrimum)*, which is occasionally exploited by advertisers, is inferior to the standard forage plants. When carefully cultivated, it gives fair yields of forage which is at first not relished by cattle.

495. Tree leaves and twigs.—The leaves and small branches of trees are sometimes fed to farm animals in certain countries when better feed is scarce. In some of the mountain range areas of this country the leaves and twigs of shrubs form no small part of the forage eaten by stock.

Tree leaves are more digestible than twigs, and the better kinds compare favorably with ordinary hay in feeding value. Leaves of the ash, birch, linden, and elder are valued in the order given. They are eaten with relish, especially by goats and sheep. These statements apply only to leaves gathered at the right stage and cured like hay. Leaves which turn brown and drop from the trees in autumn are worthless for feeding farm animals. Brush feed, consisting of ground and crushed twigs, stems, and leaves, has occasionally been used in certain mixed feeds as an absorbent for molasses.

496. Hydrolyzed straw; hydrolyzed sawdust.—In numerous German experiments it was found some years ago that the digestibility and nutritive value of straw could be increased considerably by heating it under pressure with dilute alkali or dilute acid. The cost of such treatment is so high, however, that the method is not of practical value except when there is an extreme shortage of feed for stock.

By heating sawdust with dilute acid under pressure, the digestibility can likewise be increased. In the process a portion of the crude fiber is converted into more soluble compounds, including certain sugars. Cattle will not usually eat the hydrolyzed sawdust unless mixed with well-liked feeds. However, dairy cows have been successfully fed concentrate mixtures containing one-quarter to one-third of the hydrolyzed sawdust. When thus used the feeding value of hydrolyzed sawdust made from either pine or fir has differed greatly in the limited tests made with it.[57] The value has ranged from only one-fourteenth as much as grain to about one-half as much as grain. Due to the expense of producing the hydrolyzed sawdust, the method would be of practical importance only during a prolonged period of serious feed shortage.

III. Plants of the Arid Districts

497. Sagebrush, saltbush, and the greasewoods.—Many species of sagebrush *(Artemesia,* spp.), saltbush *(Atriplex,* spp.), and greasewood *(Sarcobatus,* spp.) flourish in the arid portions of the West where drought, alkali, and common salt make conditions unfavorable for most of the ordinary forage crops. On many ranges they furnish much of the feed consumed by stock.[58] The Australian saltbush, introduced into certain sections of the West, has proved of much less value than was first expected. It is less drought resistant than the native saltbushes and is rather unpalatable on account of its high salt content. Its chief value, where it thrives, is to furnish green feed late in summer when most other plants have become entirely dry. It makes a fair soiling crop but has little value for hay.[59]

498. Yucca and sotol.—It has been found that various species of yucca *(Yucca,* spp.), including soapweed and the Spanish bayonet, and also sotol *(Dasylirion,* spp.), a near relative of the yuccas, furnish valuable emergency feed for range cattle in the Southwest. Usually the dry leaves are first burned off and then the plants are cut with an axe and hauled to a central location. Here they are finely chopped or shredded by special machines and fed to the cattle. The prepared forage may also be ensiled. The compact heads of sotol are used similarly. Cattle may be maintained on either of these emergency feeds alone through long droughts when they would otherwise starve.[60]

499. Russian thistle.—The Russian thistle *(Salsola kali,* var. *tragus),* now growing over great areas of the western plains, is used to some extent for pasture, hay, or silage, especially in times of drought.[61]   The mature plants are woody and loaded with alkali. Russian thistles should be cut when in bloom, before the spines form and harden and the stems become too harsh and prickly. The hay is often very laxative. If the plants are too mature when cut for hay, the hay should be sprinkled with water several hours before feeding, so that the spines will soften. Russian thistles may also be ensiled. If too immature, they should be allowed to wilt somewhat, before putting them in the silo.

500. Cacti.—During periods of drought the cacti, especially prickly pears *(Opuntia,* spp.) are a boon to stockmen on the southwestern ranges.[62] Because of their peculiar structure and habits, cacti can survive long droughts, though they make little growth at such times. The prickly pear cacti, which grow wild on the ranges, may be fed where they stand by first singeing off the spines with a gasoline torch, or they may be gathered and run through machines which chop them in such a manner that the spines are comparatively harmless. Cacti grow but slowly on the range, and can usually be harvested but once in 5 years, even under favorable conditions.

Prickly pear cacti contain about 16.6 per cent dry matter, being less watery than roots, and cane cacti *(Cholla* spp.) contain somewhat more dry matter. Since they are low in protein, all the cacti should be fed with a protein-rich concentrate or roughage. Cacti alone will not maintain stock. Though desert cattle sometimes subsist on them for three months of the year, they become very emaciated. Fed in large amounts with no dry feed, cacti tend to produce scours.

Spineless cacti, long known but sometimes exploited as a novelty, have only limited usefulness for stock feeding, both because they do not survive where the temperature falls below 20 degrees F. and because on the open range cattle will graze and destroy them.[63] Moreover, they must be enclosed by rabbit-proof fences.

The chief importance of cacti is undoubtedly to furnish emergency forage for stock in the semi-arid regions in case of drought, for these plants are able to utilize most efficiently small and irregular supplies of moisture. For this purpose plantations of the spiny cacti may be established on the open range, where they will be able to grow and hold their own until drawn upon in time of serious drought, for cattle will not graze them when other feed is reasonably abundant.

IV. Poisonous Plants and Poisonous Feeds

Any detailed discussion of poisonous plants and other poisonous feeds is outside the scope of this volume, and only the briefest mention can be made of some of the most important facts concerning them. One in trouble should consult a competent veterinarian or his state agricultural college or experiment station.

501. Prussic acid, or hydrocyanic acid, poisoning.—It is well known that some plants may, under certain conditions, cause the death of stock from prussic acid, or hydrocyanic acid, poisoning.[64] Of the several species of plants which may cause such poisoning the most important are chokecherry, black cherry, the sorghums, Johnson grass, arrow grass, velvet grass, Christmasberry, and Sudan grass.

When the plants are poisonous, the poison is usually not present in appreciable amounts as free prussic acid, but in the form of complex compounds, called glucosides. These must be broken down and the free prussic acid liberated before poisoning occurs. However, the glucosides are readily broken down by an enzyme usually present in the plant. The poison may be set free in the digestive tract of an animal eating the dangerous plants, and it may also be set free in the plants on wilting or being bruised. Cattle and sheep may be affected by the poison, but horses and swine are apparently not injured, or only very rarely.

The poisonous property usually develops in dangerous amounts only when the normal growth of the plants is checked or stopped by drought, frost, trampling, mowing, or wilting. Young plants may contain much more of the poison than when growth is well advanced. It is therefore not advisable to pasture cattle or sheep on young or second-growth sorghum.

Plants on poor soil contain less prussic acid than those on rich soil, especially that high in nitrogen. Cases of poisoning by the sorghums have been largely confined to the western plains states, which are especially subject to protracted droughts. In the South but few cases have been reported. When sorghum or other forage is thoroughly cured as hay or dry fodder, the poisonous property is usually destroyed, and silage is ordinarily safe. Sudan grass is much less apt to cause poisoning than the sorghums and is therefore safer to use for pasture or for a soiling crop.

Stock affected by the poison often die in a few minutes after eating only a small amount of the dangerous forage, perhaps only a few mouthfuls. Therefore there is usually no time for treatment. In pasturing sorghums the only safe way is to turn an animal of little value into the field first. If no poisonous effects are observed, the rest of the stock may then be allowed to graze the crop.

Glucose in the paunch checks the rate of formation of the prussic acid, and it has been found that it is wise to give cattle or sheep a starchy feed, such as corn or the grain sorghums, before allowing them to graze on or in the vicinity of plants that may be dangerous. The starch in the grain forms glucose in the digestive tract and thus aids in preventing trouble. It has recently been found by the United States Department of Agriculture that combination injections of solutions of sodium nitrite and sodium thiosulfate will save the lives of many animals, if administered in time.[65]

502. Ergot.—The seeds of rye and many grasses are sometimes attacked by a fungus which produces enlarged black, sooty masses, known as ergot. Occasionally rye grain containing ergot, or hay or straw bearing the fungus, injures stock which are continuously fed thereon. The poor results often secured when rye grain forms a large part of the ration for pigs may be due in some degree to ergot present in the grain. Animals showing symptoms of this trouble should have their feed changed to remove the cause, and be warmly housed and liberally supplied with nourishing food.

503. Scabbed barley.—Sometimes barley is seriously affected by the fungus which causes scabbed kernels. Experiments have shown that such scabbed barley has no injurious effect on cattle, sheep, or poultry, and it gives approximately the same results as normal barley.[66] On the other hand, horses refuse barley that is very scabby. Pigs also will not eat much badly scabbed grain and are made sick if more than about 10 per cent of the ration consists of scabbed barley kernels.

504. Smut on corn and other grain.—Corn forage or corn ears affected by smut are apparently harmless to stock, though animals may possibly be injured if fed large amounts of smut separated from such corn.[67] There is no need of removing the masses of smut from corn forage as it is being fed or ensiled or of removing smut from dry fodder. Grain sorghum smuts are also not injurious to stock,[68] and wheat damaged by stinking smut did not injure poultry in a Maryland test.[69]

505. Spoiled or moldy feed; forage poisoning; botulism.—Many cases have been reported in which the death of stock, especially horses, has apparently been caused by the eating of spoiled feed. From time to time serious losses of livestock have occurred, especially in the Mississippi valley, from so-called "forage poisoning" or "blind staggers." Such trouble occurs most frequently in animals fed spoiled corn forage or corn silage. For example, many horses were killed in the fall of 1934 in some sections of the corn belt, apparently from eating spoiled ear corn or corn forage.

With the exception of deaths from botulism and from the sweet-clover disease, which is discussed in Chapter XIII, but few of the cases have been conclusively proved to have been caused by the feed. However, it seems probable that such trouble may be caused by spoiled feed, just as food which has spoiled may cause the poisoning of humans.

The common molds are not poisonous in themselves, and moldy feed may not be at all injurious to stock.[70] However, the presence of mold indicates that other changes may have taken place which may produce poisons, as in the case of damaged sweet clover hay or silage. Horses are most susceptible to injury from spoiled feed, and sheep are also affected more often than cattle. Therefore great care should be taken not to feed spoiled silage or other feed to these two classes of stock. Hay which is slightly moldy (except sweet clover) is not ordinarily dangerous, however, though it tends to cause trouble from heaves in horses.

Cattle are rarely affected by feed that is slightly moldy or spoiled, and usually they may be fed silage with traces of mold without danger. Any large masses of spoiled silage should be discarded, and should be placed where horses or sheep cannot eat it. Swine are not usually affected by moderately moldy feed, though they are injured by scabbed barley, as has been pointed out previously in this chapter. Also, the feeding of damaged corn to young pigs caused inflammation of the vulva and vagina in young pigs in Illinois experiments.[71]

It has been proved by Graham and associates that some cases of forage poisoning are caused by feed contaminated with the bacteria which cause botulism in humans *(Clostridium botulinum)*.[72] He isolated these bacteria from samples of spoiled silage, corn fodder, oat hay, wheat bran, wheat screenings, rice meal, and oats which had poisoned stock. While the dangerous feed is often spoiled or moldy, in some cases it is wholesome in appearance. Animals on pasture which have been forced to drink stagnant surface water have been affected with forage poisoning, doubtless due to the water having passed through moldy vegetation. Suspected samples of feed should never be tasted by persons, as mere traces of the poison may prove fatal.

In cases of suspected botulism or other forage poisoning the feed should be changed and a competent veterinarian consulted. The use of antitoxin is beneficial in cases that are not too far advanced.

506. Various poisonous plants.—A considerable list of plants are definitely poisonous to stock, and particularly on the western ranges serious losses of stock sometimes occur from poisoning. Some plants are dangerous only at certain stages of growth, and some affect one class of stock but not others.

Stock seldom eat poisonous plants by choice, but only when induced or compelled by the scarcity of other feed.[73] When the grazing is short, animals should therefore be kept away from spots definitely known to be infested with such plants. In moving herds or flocks on the range special precautions should be taken when it is necessary to pass over a trail that has been used by many others, for all good feed will have been consumed, and the stock will eat whatever is left.

Among the plants that may cause serious trouble on the western ranges are larkspurs, loco weeds, lupines (from the time the pods appear), death camas, bitterweed, greasewood (early in spring), certain milk weeds, water hemlock (tubers and young shoots), woody aster, and some vetches.

It has been found that certain shale soils in an area of considerable size, located in South Dakota, Montana, and Wyoming, contain appreciable amounts of selenium and other rare mineral elements which are poisonous to animals. Some plants, including woody aster, certain vetches, and Nuttall's saltbush, accumulate in their tissues the selenium and perhaps other toxic minerals, and are poisonous only when growing on these soils. When these plants die and decay, other plants, even the grasses or cultivated crops, may take up these poisonous minerals and become toxic. The poisoning known as "alkali disease," or "blind staggers," in certain northern range areas may be largely due to this cause. A method of treatment has recently been developed by the Wyoming Station.[74]

Other important plants which may cause poisoning are the common brake fern or bracken, mountain and sheep laurel, certain nightshades, cocklebur (young plants before the leaves are developed, and also the seeds), corn cockle, and potato tops. White snakeroot and rayless goldenrod not only cause a poisoning of stock, called "trembles," but also the milk produced by affected animals may cause the same poisoning in humans or suckling animals.

Mustard seed and rape seed contain glucosides that may produce poisonous volatile oils when the seed is eaten. Therefore these seeds may be dangerous and also mustard-seed or rape-seed oil cake from which the dangerous property has not been removed. Castor beans and castor-bean oil meal are also dangerous to stock.

QUESTIONS

1. Why are roots unimportant for stock feeding in the United States? Under what special conditions may the use of roots for feeding be advisable in this country?
2. Discuss the composition and feeding value of roots.
3. Compare the economy of roots and corn silage for stock feeding.
4. State which of the following are of importance for stock feeding in your district and tell how the crop is used: (a) Mangels; (b) sugar beets; (c) sugar beet tops; (d) rutabagas; (e) turnips; (f) carrots; (g) parsnips.
5. Discuss the composition and the use of potatoes for stock feeding.
6. Discuss the value and use for stock feeding of any of the following that may be of importance in your section: (a) Sweet potatoes; (b) Jerusalem artichokes; (c) chufas; (d) cassava; (e) cabbage; (f) kohlrabi; (g) kale; (h) pumpkins, squashes, or melons; (i) waste fruit.
7. State the characteristics of rape and discuss its use in stock feeding.
8. Under what conditions might you use sunflowers as a silage crop?
9. If the following are of importance in your section, tell how they may be used in stock feeding: (a) Sagebrush, saltbush, and the greasewoods; (b) yucca and sotol; (c) Russian thistle; (d) cacti.
10. Tell the main facts concerning the following: (a) Prussic acid poisoning of stock; (b) ergot; (c) scabbed barley; (d) smut on grain; (e) spoiled or moldy feed; (f) botulism.
11. What general precautions should be taken to avoid injury to stock from poisonous plants?

REFERENCES

1. Haecker, Minn. Rpt. 1913; Wing and Savage, N. Y. (Cornell) Bul. 268; Fries, Denmark, abstracted in Expt. Sta. Rec., 14, 1903, p. 801.
2. Hansson, Meddel. Central anst. Försöksv. Jordbruksområdet (Sweden), No. 268, 1924.
3. Pyne, Irish Free State, Dept. Lands and Agr. Jour., 27, 1927, pp. 33-35.
4. Morrow, Dustman, and Henderson, Jour. Agr. Res., 43, 1931, pp. 919-930.
5. Penn. Rpt. 1898; Woll, Book on Silage; Ontario, Canada, Dept. Agr. Bul. 288; Westover and Schoth, U. S. Dept. Agr., Tech. Bul. 416.
6. U. S. Dept. of Agr. Yearbooks.
7. Hopkins, Canada Dept. of Agr., Bul. 94.
8. Delwiche, Wis. Bul. 330.
9. Moore and Wheeler, Mich. Spec. Bul. 216; Westover, Schoth, and Semple, U. S. Dept. Agr., Farmers' Bul. 1699; Westover and Schoth, U. S. Dept. Agr., Tech. Bul. 416; Piper, Forage Plants and Their Culture, p. 587; Ontario, Canada, Dept. of Agr. Bul. 228.
10. Jones, U. S. Dept. Agr., Farmers' Bul. 1095.
11. Niedig, Jour. Agr. Res., 20, 1921, pp. 537-542; Id. Bul. 122.
12. Maynard and Osland, Colo. Press Buls. 65, 70; Maynard and Fairbanks, Colo. Exten. Bul. 269 a; Maynard, Morton, and Osland, Colo. Bul. 379; Eckles, Minn. Spec. Bul. 129; Vinke and Hansen, Mont. Exten. Cir. 26; Holden, Nebr. Buls. 194, 216, 268; Holden, U. S. Dept. Agr. Cir. 289; Skuderna and Sheets, U. S. Dept. Agr., Farmers' Bul. 1718; Woodman and Bee, Jour. Agr. Sci., England, 17, 1927, pp. 477-488; Johnson, Jour. Royal Agr. Soc., England, 90, 1929, pp. 182-194.
13. Holden, Nebr. Buls. 194, 216, 268, and mimeo. rpt.
14. Maynard, Morton, and Osland, Colo. Bul. 379.
15. Holden, Nebr. Bul. 216.
16. Vinke and Hansen, Mont. Exten. Cir. 26 and mimeo. rpt.
17. Dice, N. D. Buls. 233, 249.
18. Dice, N. D. Buls. 233, 249; see also: Huffman and Baltzer, Mich. Exten. Bul. 73.
19. Hills, Vt. Rpt. 1896.
20. Maynard, Morton, and Osland, Colo. Bul. 379; Morton, Maynard, and Fairbanks, Colo. Press Bul. 76; Rinehart, Hickman, and Johnson, Id. Bul. 194; Holden, Nebr. Bul. 216; Hackedorn, Sotola, and Singleton, Wash. Bul. 258.
21. Morton, Maynard, and Osland, Colo. Press Buls. 74, 77; Maynard, Colo. Exten. Bul. 276 a; Hickman, Rinehart, and Johnson, Id. Bul. 209; Hackedorn, Sotola, and Bean, Wash. Bul. 229.
22. Paterson, Highl. and Agr. Soc., Scotland, Trans. 5 ser., 43, 1931, pp. 86-89.
23. Grisdale, Ottawa, Canada, Expt. Farms Bul. 57; Potter, Breeder's Gazette, 63,

1913, p. 896; Wilson and Kuhlman, S. D. Bul. 210; Ireland Dept. Agr. and
Tech. Instr. Jour., 20, 1920, pp. 190-193; Edwards-Ker and Hannaford, Seale-
Hayne Agr. Col., England, Pamphlet 9.
24. Wilson and Kuhlman, S. D. Bul. 209; Swier, Wash. Bul. 291; see also: Vaughan,
Mont. Rpt. 1929.
25. Henry, Wis. Rpt. 1890; Fjord, Copenhagen, Denmark, Rpt. 1890; Fjeldsted and
Potter, Ore. Bul. 165.
26. Gore, U. S. Dept. Agr., information to the author.
27. Maynard, Morton, and Osland, Colo. Bul. 379.
28. Morrison and Bohstedt, Wis. Sta., unpublished data.
29. Morton, Maynard, and Fairbanks, Colo. Press Bul. 76; Maynard, Colo. Exten.
Bul. 276 a.
30. Bray and Francioni, La. Bul. 236.
31. Edwards and Massey, Ga. Bul. 181; Hostetler et al., N. C. Rpt. 1923; see also:
Duggar, Ala. Buls. 93, 122; Shealy and Sheely, Fla. Bul. 236; Patterson, Md.
Bul. 63; Newman and Pickett, S. C. Bul. 52; S. C. Rpt. 1922; Nobles, Va.
Bul. 246.
32. Cormany, Mich. Quar. Bul. 10, 1928, No. 4; Schoth, Ore. Cir. 89; Pittman, Utah
Bul. 209; Anderson and Kiesselbach, Jour. Am. Soc. Agron., 21, 1929, pp.
1001-1006.
33. Rusk, Ill. Rpt. 1932.
34. Evvard and Culbertson, Iowa mimeo. rpt.; French, Ore. Bul. 54; Campbell,
Reading Univ. (England), Bul. 35.
35. Shealy and Sheely, Fla. Bul. 236; Edwards, Ga. Rpt. 1927.
36. Hawaii Sta., Rpt. 1920.
37. Zavitz, Ont. Dept. Agr. Bul. 228.
38. Willman, N. Y. (Cornell) Rpt. 1934 and unpublished data.
39. Selby, Ore. Bul. 251.
40. Jones and Brandt, Ore. Bul. 272, Bien. Rpt. 1928-30.
41. Woll et al., Cal. Rpts. 1922, 1923; Morton, Colo. Rpt. 1920; Ga. Rpt. 1922; Idaho
Bul. 131; Nevens, Ill. Bul. 253; Ind. Rpt. 1923; Mich. Quar. Bul., 2, 1920,
No. 4; Tretsven, Mont. Bul. 282; Quesenberry, Cunningham, and Foster, N.
Mex. Bul. 126; N. D. Bul. 159; Jones, Ore. Bul. 194; Bechdel, Penn. Bul. 172;
Woodward, Wash. Bul. 158; Henderson and Gifford, West Va. Bul. 210; Holden
et al., Wis. Buls. 319, 323; Quayle, Wyo. State Farms Bul. 3, 1922; Moseley,
Stuart, and Graves, U. S. D. A. Tech. Bul. 116; Bowstead and Sackville,
Univ. of Alberta, Canada, mimeo. rpt.; Canada Expt. Farms, An. Husb.
Div., Interim Rpt. 1922; Canada Expt. Farms, Agassiz (B.C.) Farm, Rpt.
Supt., 1923; Canada Expt. Farms, Fredericton (N.B.) Sta., Rpt. Supt., 1923.
42. Ariz. Rpt., 1922; Osland, Colo. Bul. 380; Buchanan, Miss. Bul. 278; Arnett, Mont.
Rpt., 1923; Quesenberry, Cunningham, and Foster, New Mex. Bul. 126; Chris-
tensen, N. D. Buls. 174, 217; Blizzard, Okla. Buls. 134, 139, 147; Wilson and
Kuhlman, S. D. Bul. 199; Hackedorn, Wash. Bul. 175; Hackedorn, Sotola, and
Bean, Wash. Bul. 186; Fuller and Morrison, Wis. Bul. 352; Hays, Wyo. Bul.
128; Sackville and Bowstead, Alberta, Canada, Agr. Col. Bul. 8; Rothwell,
Canada Expt. Farms, An. Husb. Div. Rpt. 1922.
43. Maynard, Morton, and Osland, Colo. Bul. 379; Joseph, Mont. Bul. 164; Darlow,
Okla. Buls. 136, 142; Potter and Dean, Ore. Bul. 198; Hackedorn, Wash. Bul.
158; Hays, Wyo. Bul. 130; Fairfield, Canada Expt. Farms, Lethbridge (Alberta)
Sta. Rpts. Supt., 1922, 1923.
44. Delwiche, Wis. Exten. Cir. 220.
45. Hansen, U.S.D.A., Dept. Cir. 275; Blish, Mont. Bul. 163.
46. Murdock, Mont. Bul. 191.
47. Hills, Vt. Rpt. 1908; Lindsey, Mass. Bul. 174.
48. Rommel, U. S. Dept. Agr., Bur. Anim. Indus., Bul. 47.
49. Sotola, Amer. Soc. Anim. Prod., Proc. 1927, pp. 107-9.
50. Masurovsky, Jour. Agr. Res., 21, 1921, pp. 523-539; 27, 1924, pp. 39-42.
51. Cottrell, Colo. Bul. 146.
52. S. C. Rpt. 1931.
53. Hills, Vt. Rpt. 1901.
54. Hackedorn, Singleton, and Sotola, Wash. Bul. 291.
55. Clark, Utah, Bul. 101.
56. Ariz. Rpt. 19.
57. Archibald, Mass. Bul. 230; Morrison, Humphrey, and Hulce, Wis. Bul. 323;
Woodward et al., U. S. Dept. Agr. Bul. 1272; Sherrard and Blanco, Jour.
Indus. and Engin. Chem., 13, 1921, pp. 61-65.
58. Bidwell and Wooton, U. S. Dept. Agr. Bul. 1345; Foster, Lantow, and Wilson,
New Mex. Bul. 125; Brown, New Mex. Bul. 135.
59. McKee, U. S. Dept. Agr. Bul. 617; see also: Headden, Colo. Bul. 345.
60. Forsling, U. S. Dept. Agr., Farmers' Bul. 1428; Foster and Humble, New Mex.
Bul. 114; Brown, New Mex. Bul. 133.
61. Morton, Osland, and Brandon, Colo. Press Bul. 80; Christensen, N. D. Exten.
Cir. 125.
62. Vinson, Ariz. Bul. 67; Ariz. Rpt. 21; U. S. Dept. Agr., Bur. Anim. Indus., Bul. 91.
63. Griffiths, U. S. Dept. Agr., Farmers' Buls. 483, 1072; Dameron, Tex. Rpt. 1932.
64. Couch, U. S. Dept. Agr. Leaflet 88.
65. Bunyea, Couch, and Clawson, Jour. Wash. Acad. Sci., 24, 1934, pp. 528-532; 25,
1935, pp. 57-59.
66. Roche, Bohstedt, et al., Wis. Buls. 410, 425; Rusk and Snapp, Ill. Rpt. 1929.
67. Henry, Univ. of Wis., Rpt. of Board of Trustees, 1881; Smith, Mich. Bul. 137;
Wilson and Kuhlman, S. D. Bul. 199; U. S. Dept. Agr. Bur. Anim. Indus.,
Bul. 10.

68. Heller, Caskey, and Penquite, Jour. Agr. Res., 40, 1930, pp. 347-351.
69. Quigley and Waite, Md. Bul. 325.
70. Eckles, Fitch, and Seal, Jour. Agr. Res., 64, 1924, pp. 716-722; Minn. Rpts. 1921, 1922, 1924; Church and Buckley, North Amer. Vet., 4, 1923, pp. 7-12.
71. Graham, Tunnicliff, and McCulloch, Ill. Rpts. 1928, 1929.
72. Graham, Brueckner, and Pontius, Ky. Buls. 207, 208; Graham, Ill. Exten. Cir. 38.
73. Marsh, U. S. Dept. Agr., Farmers' Buls. 536, 720; Marsh, U. S. Dept. Agr. Bul. 1245; Durrell and Glover, Colo. Bul. 316; Hansen, Ind. Cir. 175; Gates, Kan. Tech. Bul. 25; Stevens, N. D. Bul. 265; Lawrence, Ore. Bul. 187; Beath, Draize, and Gilbert, Wyo. Bul. 200.
74. Beath, Draize, and Gilbert, Wyo. Bul. 200.

CHAPTER XVII

THE CEREALS AND THEIR BY-PRODUCTS

I. The Characteristics of the Cereals as Stock Feeds

507. Importance of the cereal grains in stock feeding.—In the previous chapters emphasis has been placed on the basic importance for livestock of good roughage, including pasture, hay, dry fodder, and silage. However, farm animals cannot usually produce milk, meat, or labor efficiently unless they are provided with concentrates in addition to high-quality roughage. This is because forage alone is too low in digestible nutrients and net energy to meet the needs of stock fed for large production.

To secure a profitable yield of milk from dairy cows it is generally necessary to furnish them a liberal supply of concentrates in addition to a bountiful amount of good roughage. Likewise, in order to produce the quality of meat desired by consumers, fattening cattle and lambs must usually receive considerable quantities of rich concentrates. Horses or mules cannot perform much work on roughage alone, even if it is of excellent quality. Swine and poultry must be fed chiefly on concentrates, because their digestive systems can make only limited use of forage.

The cereal grains and their by-products form by far the greater part of all the concentrates used for livestock in this country. Indeed, over much of the United States all classes of stock are frequently fed only farm-raised roughage and cereal grains, with the relatively small amounts of protein supplements in addition that may be needed to balance their rations. The by-products obtained in the milling of the cereals for human use are also among the most important stock feeds.

The cereals and their by-products therefore merit first consideration among all the concentrates.

508. Nutritive characteristics of the cereals.—The cereal grains are all rich in starch and either low or relatively low in fiber. They therefore rank high in content of total digestible nutrients and net energy. In addition, the cereals as a class are highly palatable to stock, a factor that is of much importance with animals being fed for production. Rye is the only one of the common cereals that is sometimes not well liked by farm animals.

Corn and wheat lead in amount of total digestible nutrients and net energy, being closely followed by the grain sorghums, and by rye and barley. Oats, with their thick hulls, are higher in fiber and therefore lower in digestible nutrients. This bulkiness gives oats especial usefulness for horses, but makes this grain less valuable in general for meat production.

Corn and rice are low in protein, and the other cereals are relatively low in this nutrient. In addition to this lack in amount of protein, the proteins furnished by all the cereal grains are unbalanced in composition. In other words, the proteins contain but small amounts of certain of the essential amino acids. Therefore the grains do not produce efficient results in stock feeding unless this lack is corrected by proteins from other sources. (**148**)

It is fortunate indeed that for those classes of stock which can consume considerable roughage, legume hay can fully make good this deficiency in the quality of the cereal proteins. (**154**) In feeding swine and poultry, however, it is necessary to supplement the grains with concentrates that furnish high-quality protein, such as animal by-products, soybean oil meal, or peanut oil meal.

The cereals are not rich in phosphorus, but are slightly higher in this mineral nutrient than are all the common hay crops, including both the legumes and grasses. Corn and the grain sorghums are lower in phosphorus than oats, wheat, barley, or rye. Certain of the cereal by-products, especially wheat bran and wheat middlings, are rich in phosphorus. On the other hand, corn gluten meal and brewers' grains do not contain much more phosphorus than the grains themselves. (**160**)

All the cereals are very low in calcium, and this fact must be borne in mind in livestock feeding. (**161**) Corn is especially deficient in this respect.

None of the cereals contains an appreciable amount of vitamin D. (**192**) With the exception of yellow corn, none of the cereals supplies any significant amount of vitamin A. (**188**) The cereals are rich in vitamins B and E, but have little vitamin G. However, these vitamins, as has been stated previously, are not usually deficient in the rations commonly fed farm animals, except that poultry rations may often lack vitamin G. (**195-200**)

It is very fortunate that the deficiencies of the cereal grains in amount and quality of protein, in calcium, and in vitamins A and D are all corrected by well-cured legume hay or by pasture rich in legumes. Therefore, except for a possible lack of phosphorus where the soil is deficient in phosphorus, excellent rations for dairy cattle, beef cattle, and sheep are provided by home-grown cereal grain and legume roughage.

II. Indian Corn and Its By-products

509. Importance of Indian corn for grain.—The prime importance of Indian corn *(Zea mays)*, or maize, as a grain crop in the United States is shown by the fact that in acreage, in total yield, and in value, it far exceeds any other cereal. This is because corn surpasses all the other cereals in yield of both grain and forage, wherever it thrives.

During the ten-year period, 1924-1933, the average acreage of corn grown for all purposes in this country was 101,564,000 acres, and the average yield was 25.2 bushels per acre. The total value of the corn crop for this period averaged $1,686,976,000. Of the entire crop, 84 per cent was harvested for grain. (The data for 1934 are not included in the average yields given in this chapter for corn and the other cereals, because the yields for that year were exceptionally low because of the severe and unusual drought over wide areas. As a result of the drought, the average yield of corn, for example, was only 15.8 bushels per acre for the entire country.)

The general requirements for the growth of corn and its use and value as a forage crop have already been discussed in Chapter XIV.

510. Composition and nutritive value of corn.—The corn grain is particularly rich in starch, containing about 70 per cent of nitrogen-free extract, nearly all of which is starch. Corn is also higher than any of the other cereals except oats in fat, having about 4 per cent of this energy-rich nutrient. It contains only 2.3 per cent fiber and it is highly digestible. Because of these facts, corn ranks high in content of total digestible nutrients and net energy, being equalled only by wheat among the cereals.

Being so rich in starch, corn is naturally low in protein. Moreover, as has been shown previously, the protein in corn is unbalanced in composition. (**142**) The chief protein, called zein, entirely lacks two of the amino acids which are necessary for animal life. Corn is also unusually low in mineral matter, especially calcium. Indeed, corn has but 0.01 per cent of calcium. This means that there is only 0.2 lb. of calcium in an entire ton of the grain. Corn is also lower in phosphorus than oats, wheat, barley, or rye, having only 0.28 per cent phosphorus.

In the development of the present high-yielding varieties of corn, there has apparently been an appreciable lowering of the fat content, a slight lowering of the protein, and slight increases in starch and fiber. For example, in the compilation, made under the supervision of the author, of analyses of American feeding stuffs reported previous to 1915, well-dried dent corn had the following average composition: Protein, 10.1 per cent; fat, 5.0 per cent; fiber, 2.0 per cent; and nitrogen-free extract, 70.9 per cent. (See the fifteenth to nineteenth editions of Feeds and Feeding.) On the other hand, the average of recent analyses, given in Appendix Table I of this volume, shows the following averages: Protein, 9.7 per cent; fat, 4.0 per cent; fiber, 2.3 per cent; and nitrogen-free extract 71.1 per cent.

Plant breeders have developed by long-continued selection strains of corn in which the grain is much higher than normal in protein or fat.[1] However, these strains are not yet of practical importance, because the yields are very low.

511. Yellow corn rich in vitamin A.—Yellow varieties of corn and varieties with yellow endosperm (the inner starchy part of the kernel) are good sources of vitamin A.[2] On the other hand, white corn or other corn with white endosperm has practically no vitamin A. Experiments have shown that the vitamin content of red varieties or varieties with hulls of other colors will depend entirely on whether the endosperm is yellow or white. The deeper the shade of yellow, the greater will be the amount of vitamin. The gluten from yellow corn is considerably richer than the rest of the kernel in the vitamin. Therefore corn gluten feed and gluten meal from yellow corn are good sources of vitamin A.

The vitamin A value of yellow corn is due to small amounts of carotene and a closely-related compound. (**187**) Though yellow corn is a good source of vitamin A, it contains considerably less per pound of dry matter than do green plants or even green-colored hay, as has been shown in Chapter VI.

Yellow corn or corn with yellow endosperm is much more valuable than white corn for continuous feeding to animals not otherwise receiving sufficient vitamin A. On the other hand, white corn is equal to yellow corn for all stock on green, actively-growing pasture, and also for dairy cattle, beef cattle, horses, or sheep that are fed a reasonable amount of well-cured hay. For pigs or poultry that do not get plenty of fresh green forage, the difference in vitamin A value of yellow and white corn may make all the difference between profit and disaster. Therefore, if they are fed white corn, care should be taken to provide green-colored legume hay or some other source of the vitamin. (188)

Previous to the discovery in 1920 that yellow corn has a high vitamin A value, only about one-half of the corn sold under Federal inspection on the large markets of this country was yellow.[1a] The remainder was either white corn or mixed corn. In 1933-34 80 per cent of the corn on these markets was yellow, and only 14 per cent white and 6 per cent mixed.

Like the other cereals, both white and yellow corn lack vitamin D.

512. Corn as a feed.—Corn grain is one of the best feeds for all classes of stock, when it is so fed as to take advantage of its great virtues and to correct its deficiencies. On account of the importance of corn in animal husbandry, its use for each class of stock and the best form in which to feed the grain are discussed in considerable detail in Part III.

Corn is one of the most widely-used concentrates for dairy cattle, and it is the chief basis for the production of pork, beef, and mutton over much of the United States. It is also satisfactory for work horses and mules when fed in suitable rations. Corn is probably the most palatable of the cereals to farm animals. A possible explanation for this is the high fat content, and the fact that on mastication the kernels break into nutty particles which are more palatable than meal from wheat, for example.

As is pointed out in later chapters, ear corn, shelled corn, ground corn, and corn-and-cob meal (ground corn and cob) are all used for stock feeding. The relative value of the various forms of corn for any class of stock depends primarily on how thoroughly they chew their grain. When corn is ground for stock, medium-fine grinding is much preferable to fine grinding, for such ground corn is more palatable, and also much less labor and power are required for the grinding. It is pointed out later in this chapter that ground corn keeps much more poorly in storage than shelled corn or ear corn.

Seventy pounds of dry dent ear corn of good varieties yield 1 bushel, or 56 lbs., of shelled corn, but in early fall buyers frequently demand 75 to 80 lbs. or more, according to the estimated water content. Flint varieties have a somewhat smaller shelling percentage than dent corn.

There are three important types of corn—dent, flint, and sweet. In *dent corn* the starch is partly hornlike and partly floury, rendering the kernel easy of mastication. In *flint corn* the starch is mostly hornlike and flinty, making the kernel harder for the animal to crush. There is but little difference in the composition of dent and flint corn. They also have the same feeding value, except that there may be somewhat more advantage in grinding flint corn for stock than in the case of dent corn.

In *sweet corn* the starch is hornlike and tough. Before hardening, the milky kernels of this race carry much glucose, which is changed to starch as they mature into the shrunken grain. Sweet corn has somewhat more protein, much more fat, and correspondingly less carbohydrates than the other races. The grain is rarely fed to stock.

513. Corn-and-cob meal; corn cobs. — *Corn-and-cob meal* is the usual term for ground ear corn, including the cobs. Sometimes this is called *ear corn chops*. When the entire corn ears in the husks, or shucks, are ground, the product is called *ear corn chops with husks*. Because of the rubber-like consistency of corn cobs, more power is required to grind ear corn to corn-and-cob meal than to grind shelled corn. Also, if the cob particles are not reasonably fine, often stock will not eat them.

Corn cobs have 32 per cent fiber and furnish but little more digestible nutrients than oat straw. Therefore any benefit from including the cobs in grinding is not due chiefly to the nutrients they furnish, but to the fact that they make the meal more bulky. This causes it to lie loosely in the stomach, thus sometimes aiding in digestion.

If the cost of grinding ear corn to corn-and-cob meal is no more, or not appreciably more, than shelling the corn and grinding the shelled corn, the use of corn-and-cob meal may be economical for dairy cows. It is much less commonly fed to horses, beef cattle, or sheep, and it is not as satisfactory as other forms of corn for swine. Manifestly, it is not economical to buy corn cobs in low-grade mixed feeds at a price that would buy good grain.

514. Storage and shrinkage of corn. — When husked in the fall, well-matured ear corn should not contain more than 20 to 25 per cent of water. This is about the upper limit of moisture for safe storage in the usual types of corn cribs. Corn that is not thoroughly ripe may contain 35 per cent of moisture or more. Twisting the ears will indicate approximately the moisture content. Loose-grained, "sappy" ears carry too much moisture to be stored safely in cribs without special ventilation.

Shelled corn may spoil when stored, if it contains more than about 14 to 15 per cent water. In cool weather it can usually be shipped without great risk of heating when it contains 16 to 18 per cent moisture, but such corn cannot be stored safely in elevators.[3]

Ground corn is especially apt to mold or turn rancid in storage and should not be stored for any considerable period if it contains more than about 12 per cent water.[4] Even then it may gradually become sour, because of rancidity of the oil in the germs and also the development of acid-producing bacteria. On the farm shelled corn should therefore not be ground a long period in advance of use.

As ear corn dries out the weight shrinks, due chiefly to the evaporation of water, but also due in small part to the slow respiration of the grain, in which some of the nutrients are oxidized. The rate of shrinkage depends not only on the dryness of the corn when husked, but also on the humidity of the air. When the water content of the corn falls to 12 per cent, shrinkage practically ceases.

Corn is stored mostly on the husked ear in the North, but in the South the husks are left on to protect the ears from weevils. As corn keeps better in the ear than when shelled, it should be held in this form as long as possible.

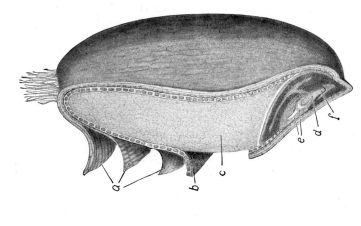

DIAGRAM OF A KERNEL OF DENT CORN

A, hull; b, hornlike gluten; c, floury starch; d, horny starch; e, embryo, or germ; f, embryo stem; g, embryo root; h, tip cap.

DIAGRAM OF WHEAT KERNEL

A, the bran coats; b, aleurone layer; c, cells filled with starch grains; d, embryo, or germ; e, embryo leaves; f, embryo root. (Partially after Neumann.)

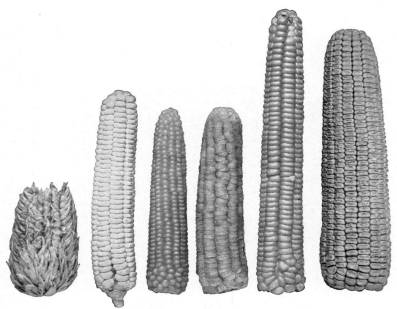

EARS OF DIFFERENT TYPES OF CORN

From left to right: Pod corn, a primitive type; soft corn, an unimproved type having no horny starch; pop corn; sweet corn; flint corn; dent corn. (From Wisconsin Station.)

PROFITABLE CROPS CAN BE EXPECTED ONLY FROM WELL-BRED SEED

By skillful and patient work plant breeders have developed high yielding pedigree varieties of grains particularly adapted to various sections. The view shows the grain-breeding plots at the Wisconsin Station.

515. Grades of shelled corn.—The Federal corn grades, by which shelled corn is sold on the large markets, are based on the percentage of water and also on the percentage of unsound kernels and foreign material. It is obvious that the value per ton of corn for any purpose will depend, first of all, on the water content. Therefore in Appendix Table I separate averages are given for corn of the various grades.

According to the Federal grades, the percentage of water in corn must not exceed 14 per cent for Number 1; 15.5 per cent for Number 2; 17.5 per cent for Number 3; 20.0 per cent for Number 4; and 23.0 per cent for Number 5. Corn containing more than 23 per cent water, or which does not come up to the standards in other respects, must be sold as "Sample grade."

516. Soft corn.—When corn is frosted before the grain matures, the ears contain too much water for storage in ordinary cribs. Such soft corn can best be utilized for stock feeding. The entire crop may be ensiled; it may be put in small, well-built shocks in the field until it is fed; or silage may be made from the snapped ear corn.[5] Soft corn should be used up during the cold weather, as it will spoil when the weather becomes warm. If soft corn is cribbed, the cribs must be ventilated by special devices, or it will not keep. Some sprinkle 0.5 to 1.0 lb. of salt over each 100 lbs. of ear corn, but the value of this practice may be doubtful.

Snapped ear corn makes very satisfactory silage which may be fed as a substitute for other forms of corn grain, especially to fattening cattle or sheep. The snapped corn must be chopped finely by running it through a silage cutter and should be tramped well in the silo. If the corn is past the milk stage, it is well to add approximately 40 gallons of water to each ton of ears. When the ears are in the milk, it will not be necessary to add water. Chopped straw or corn stover, well wet down, should be used to cover the ear corn at the top of the silo, to prevent the waste of the more valuable feed.

Soft corn, if not moldy, may be fed to all classes of stock. Moldy corn is especially dangerous to horses and sheep, but does not usually injure cattle. Swine can generally be allowed to eat all they want. As is shown in Part III, soft corn and soft-ear-corn silage have given satisfactory results in fattening cattle, and soft corn is also efficiently used by pigs. Each 100 lbs. of dry matter in the grain of soft corn are nearly equal in feeding value to the same weight of dry matter in sound corn.

517. Composition of the corn kernel.—Before discussing the value of the various corn by-products resulting from the manufacture of human food, it will be helpful to consider the composition of the different parts of the corn kernel.[6] The flinty, or horny endosperm (or horny starch) at the sides and back of the kernel of dent corn forms nearly half the total weight. About 88 per cent of this portion is starch, with but 10 per cent protein, less than 1 per cent fiber, and but a trace of fat and minerals. The floury endosperm (or floury starch) at the tip of the kernel and partially surrounding the germ forms about one-fourth of the kernel. It is even higher in starch than the flinty endosperm, but carries only 7.8 per cent protein.

The hulls and tip caps, which make up 7 per cent of the kernel, are also composed largely of carbohydrates, though containing less starch and about 15 per cent fiber. The hornlike gluten layer (8 per cent of the kernel), just under the hull, contains about 22 per cent protein; and the germ (12 per cent of the kernel) carries nearly as much protein and about 35 per cent fat or oil.

518. Ground corn; corn meal; corn chop; corn feed meal.—In this book the term *ground corn* is commonly used for the entire ground corn grain from which the hulls or germs have not been removed. Ground corn is also called *corn meal (feeding)* and *corn chop*. Especially for poultry feeds, the fine siftings are often removed from cracked corn or coarsely-ground corn and the product is then called *screened ground corn* or *screened cracked corn*. The fine siftings that are removed, with or without the light fragments of the hulls, etc., are known as *corn feed meal*. This has about the same composition and feeding value as ground corn, except that it is slightly higher in fat, but also higher in fiber.

In the usual method of manufacturing corn meal for human use, and also in making hominy and hominy grits, the kiln-dried corn is first cleaned and tempered with a slight amount of water. In the milling process the germs and hulls are removed from the corn meal, along with fine siftings from the endosperm, or starchy portion, of the kernels. The corn meal thus produced has a more attractive appearance than the entire ground grain and also keeps much better in storage. However, it contains less protein and fat and therefore is of slightly lower value for stock feeding. Sometimes degermed cracked corn is used for poultry feed. This is much lower in vitamin B than ground corn.

The by-product obtained in the manufacture of corn meal by this degerming process, and also in the manufacture of hominy and hominy grits, is *hominy feed*. *Hominy grits* or *corn grits* consist of the fine or medium-sized, hard, flinty portions of corn grain, containing little or none of the bran or germ.

519. Hominy feed, hominy meal, or hominy chop.—These terms are all applied to the mixture of corn bran, corn germ (with or without the extraction of part of the oil), and a part of the starchy portion of the corn kernels, which is obtained in the manufacture of corn meal, hominy grits, and hominy by the degerming process. Hominy feed has 6.9 per cent fat, on the average, and should not contain less than 5 per cent fat. If the fat content is lower than this, it means that most of the oil has been removed from the germs, or that a considerable portion of the germs, after the extraction of oil, has been marketed separately as corn germ meal or cake.

Hominy feed resembles ground corn in composition, but it is usually slightly higher in protein and also it contains more fiber and therefore is somewhat more bulky. Unless part of the fat has been extracted from the germs, it will be considerably richer than corn in fat and will furnish slightly more digestible nutrients than well-dried corn.

Since hominy feed is kiln-dried, it is almost invariably sweet and it keeps better in storage than ground corn. In general, it is about equal to ground corn in feeding value for the various classes of stock, as is pointed out in Part III. Since it is a bulkier feed than ground corn, it is preferred by many for dairy cows.

520. Corn bran.—Corn bran is the outer coating of the corn kernels, including the hull and the tip cap, with little or none of the starchy part of the germ. Very little corn bran now comes upon the market as such, but it is usually mixed with other by-products. Corn bran does not resemble wheat bran in composition, for it does not contain appreciably more protein than corn grain. It has nearly as much fiber as oats and furnishes slightly more total digestible nutrients.

521. Starch and glucose by-products.—In the manufacture of commercial starch and glucose from corn by the so-called "wet-milling process," the grain is cleaned and then softened by soaking in warm water, slightly acidified with sulfurous acid. Next the corn kernels are torn apart in special mills, so as to liberate the germs. The material is then mixed with water and passed into tanks. Here the germs, which are lighter on account of the large amount of oil they carry, rise to the surface and are removed. After washing, the residue is finely ground, and the coarser part (the bran) separated by bolting cloth sieves.

The remainder, called "starch liquor," contains the starch, the gluten, and very fine particles of fiber. The starch is separated by either one of two processes. In a process which has recently been developed, the starch liquor is passed through centrifugal separators, somewhat like the cream separators used for milk. These machines separate the starch very completely from the gluten.

In the older process the starch liquor is passed slowly over starch tables. These are long, shallow, slightly-inclined troughs in which the starch settles like wet lime, while the gluten, being lighter, is carried off in the current of water. The gluten is then removed from the water by filter presses and dried. The starch is dried for sale as starch or is treated with weakly-acidulated water under pressure to convert the starch into sugar, in making corn syrup and similar products. The steep water in which the corn is soaked is usually evaporated to recover the soluble nutrients removed from the grain in the soaking process. This residue is called "corn solubles."

In this process the following by-products are thus obtained: (1) The germs, from which most of the oil is later expressed; (2) the bran; (3) the gluten; and (4) the corn solubles.

The corn bran is not usually marketed as such, but goes into the gluten feed, as mentioned later. The corn solubles may go into the gluten feed or may be used for other purposes, as in the production of yeast.

522. Corn oil meal; corn oil cake.—After the germs are dried, they are crushed, cooked, and run through oil expellers which express most of the oil or fat. The corn oil is used for the production of refined oil for human food and for technical purposes. The *corn oil meal* which remains is sold as such, or it goes into corn gluten feed, or sometimes into gluten meal, when there is a better market for these products than for the corn oil meal. Formerly hydraulic presses were used to express the oil, and *corn oil cake* was produced, which was ground later. Sometimes the oil is removed by the solvent process.

Corn oil meal is slightly lower in protein than corn gluten feed. Unless the oil is removed by the solvent process, it will be considerably higher in fat than gluten feed, and it will furnish slightly more total digestible nutrients. The protein is also of somewhat better quality than the protein of corn gluten feed or corn gluten meal. Most of the corn oil meal that is marketed separately is used for feeding swine or poultry, being especially popular as an ingredient in mixtures for the commercial fattening of poultry, on account of its high water-absorbing capacity. However, it is also satisfactory as a part of the concentrate mixture for dairy cattle, beef cattle, sheep, and horses.

523. Corn gluten feed.—Corn gluten feed, usually called simply "gluten feed," consists of corn gluten meal and corn bran, and also may contain more or less of the corn solubles. In addition, it sometimes includes part of the corn oil meal. Some manufacturers standardize the protein content of corn gluten feed at 25 per cent or at some other percentage, and then sell separately the corn gluten meal in excess of the amount needed to produce the standardized corn gluten feed. Others include all the gluten meal in their gluten feed, which may therefore have a higher protein content than the standardized product.

Gluten feed of average composition contains 26.4 per cent protein, 7.1 per cent fiber, 48.4 per cent nitrogen-free extract, and 2.5 per cent fat. It supplies about three-fourths as much digestible protein as linseed meal, and is about equal to linseed meal, cottonseed meal, and barley in content of total digestible nutrients.

The amount of phosphorus in corn gluten feed will depend on whether or not the corn solubles have been included in it. The average phosphorus content is 0.55 per cent, but it will be considerably lower if none of the corn solubles are present, and somewhat higher if the gluten feed contains all the corn solubles. Due largely to lime used in neutralizing the corn solubles, gluten feed usually contains much more calcium than corn or the other grains.

The total amount of mineral matter averages about 6 per cent, but shows considerable variation in various lots, ranging from 4 per cent to 7 per cent or more.

Most of the corn used in the wet-milling process is yellow corn. Since the gluten of yellow corn is richer than other parts in vitamin A, gluten feed therefore usually contains considerably more of this vitamin than yellow corn. The color of the gluten feed will indicate whether yellow or white corn has been used chiefly in its production.

On account of the importance of gluten feed, its use for the various classes of stock is discussed in detail in later chapters. It is chiefly fed to dairy cattle and is one of the most common protein supplements in rations for dairy cows. It gives excellent results when properly combined, as it usually is, with other feeds that supply proteins which make good the deficiencies of those in corn. It should not be fed as the only protein supplement when there is little or no legume roughage in the ration.

Gluten feed is not quite so palatable as corn, oats, wheat bran, etc. It should therefore usually be mixed with such well-liked feeds as these. However, stock soon get used to its taste, and when gluten feed is cheap in price it has even been fed with satisfactory results to dairy cows as the only or the chief concentrate. Judging from the very limited data available, in the case of fattening cattle or sheep it is best to use gluten feed in combination with other protein supplements. It is not commonly fed to horses or swine, but may be an economical feed for them when cheap in price, if it is fed in proper combination.

524. Corn gluten meal.—Corn gluten meal, often called merely "gluten meal," consists chiefly of the corn gluten separated in the wet-milling process of starch manufacture, with little or practically none of the hull fragments. It may or may not include corn solubles and may perhaps occasionally contain some of the corn oil meal.

Gluten meal usually has more than 40 per cent protein, averaging 42.9 per cent. It commonly contains less fat than corn grain and is low in fiber. Gluten meal supplies as much digestible protein as 43-per-cent-protein cottonseed meal and is slightly higher in total digestible nutrients than cottonseed meal.

When made chiefly from yellow corn, as is generally the case, gluten meal is even richer than gluten feed in vitamin A, but it is much lower in calcium and phosphorus.

Just as in the case of gluten feed, gluten meal should be used with other feeds that make good the deficiencies in quality of the corn proteins. When thus fed, it is an excellent high-protein concentrate, being especially popular in dairy rations. Gluten meal is also a satisfactory protein supplement for beef cattle or sheep when fed in combination with such supplements as linseed meal, cottonseed meal, soybean oil meal, or soybeans, or with legume hay. It is a heavy feed and is not especially palatable. It should therefore be mixed with better-liked feeds, just as in the case of gluten feed.

525. Corn germ meal; corn germ cake.—As has been mentioned previously, these by-products are sometimes produced in the dry milling of corn for corn meal, hominy grits, etc. They are similar to corn oil meal in composition and feeding value, but are slightly lower in protein and higher in nitrogen-free extract, because in this process the germs cannot be separated as completely from the starchy part of the kernels.

III. Oats and Their By-products

526. Importance of oats.—Oats (*Avena sativa*) rank third in acreage among the cereals in the United States and are next in importance to corn for livestock feeding. In the 10-year period, 1924-1933 inclusive, an average of 40,528,000 acres of oats were grown for grain in this country, with a yield per acre of 29.2 bushels of 32 lbs. each. About three-fourths of the acreage of oats is in the North Central States, but oats are an important grain crop in nearly all the states. They are not commonly grown so far north or at such high altitudes as barley, and they do not endure drought so well. On the other hand, oats yield better than barley on poor soil.

In the South about one-half the acreage of oats is seeded in the fall, and this practice is also common in some localities of the Pacific Coast region. Winter oats are less hardy than rye or wheat, and the yield of grain is reduced much more by pasturing the crop.

From the South Atlantic States west to the Mississippi River, the greater proportion of the oat crop is fed unthreshed to stock. A considerable part of the oats in New England, Missouri, and Arkansas is also fed in this form. The use of unthreshed or sheaf oats has already been discussed in Chapter XV.

Where barley thrives, oats are frequently grown in combination with it for stock feeding, the mixture often producing a greater weight of grain than either crop alone.

527. Composition and nutritive value.—Oats contain nearly as much protein as does wheat, averaging 12.0 per cent for all sections of the country except the Pacific Coast States. There oats average only 9.0 per cent in protein content. Oats contain even more fat than does corn, averaging 4.7 per cent. Due to their hulls, they have 10.6 per cent fiber and supply only 71.5 lbs. total digestible nutrients per 100 lbs., in comparison with more than 80 lbs. for corn or wheat that is well dried.

Oats have the same nutritional deficiencies as the other cereals, which have been pointed out at the beginning of this chapter.[7] The proteins are not of high quality but contain low amounts of certain of the essential amino acids. Oats also lack vitamin D, like all cereals, and contain but little vitamin A, like white corn.

The percentage of fiber in oats and the weight per bushel vary considerably, depending on the proportion of hull to meat. On the average, oats contain about 30 per cent hulls, and the usual weight per bushel of high-quality oats is 32 lbs. or more. Light-weight oats with poorly-developed kernels may be over one-half hulls, while there may be only 24 per cent of hulls in very plump, heavy oats. Oats that are high in hulls are obviously low in digestible nutrients and therefore inferior in feeding value. The Red Rust Proof oats and certain other varieties grown extensively in the South and on the Pacific Coast have heavy, coarse hulls and also the kernels bear awns. This causes the weight per bushel to be low.

Clipped oats have been run through an oat clipper, which clips off the pointed ends of the hulls, thereby increasing the weight per bushel and lowering the fiber content.

Bleached oats have been bleached by the use of sulfur or other chemicals to whiten the grain and improve the appearance. This of course does not increase their feeding value and may even be deleterious.[8]

Hull-less oats, varieties from which the hulls are removed from the kernels by the threshing process, are grown but little in this country, as the ordinary sorts with hulls yield much more. Hull-less oats are similar to wheat in fiber content.

528. Oats as a feed.—Because of the importance of oats for all classes of stock, their use and value are discussed in Part III under each kind of livestock. Due to the hulls, oats are the safest of all common grains for horse feeding, and hence are widely used for this purpose. They are also one of the most popular dairy feeds, but often other grains supply digestible nutrients more cheaply. Oats are useful, because of their bulk, in starting fattening cattle or sheep on feed, but more concentrated grain is usually substituted for all or most of the oats as fattening progresses. Oats are highly esteemed as part of the concentrates for ewes, young lambs, brood sows, and young pigs. They are too bulky to serve well as the chief grain for fattening pigs.

Oats should be ground for swine and for cattle, except calves up to 6 to 8 months of age. For feeding pigs and young calves, oats are sometimes run through a hulling machine, which grinds the grain and removes most of the hulls.

529. Oatmeal manufacture and by-products.—In the manufacture of oatmeal the light-weight oats and foreign material are first removed from high-grade oats. The oats are then dried in large heated pans with constant stirring, to make the hulls brittle, so they can be removed more readily from the kernels, or groats. Next, after the oats are graded according to size, the hulls are removed in hulling machines, which also polish the groats. In this process the fuzzy material covering the kernels (called *oat shorts* or *oat dust*) is removed and also fragments from the groats themselves (these fragments being called *oat middlings*). The oat groats are then steamed to make them less brittle, and finally rolled, cut, or ground to make rolled oats, cut oats, or oatmeal.

Usually the entire mill-run of oat hulls, oat middlings, and oat shorts is combined and sold as *oat mill feed,* which is often called simply *oat feed.* Sometimes a higher grade of oat mill feed is sold, which contains a larger proportion of the oat middlings and oat shorts, and less of the hulls. The remainder of the hulls are then sold as *oat hulls* for litter for poultry or for feed, or they are used for fuel or for the manufacture of the chemical called furfural. Molasses is added to some of the oat mill feed to make *sugared* or *sweetened oat mill feed.*

530. Oat mill feed.—Oat mill feed, or oat feed, as it is often called, usually contains 5 to 6 per cent protein, 27 to 30 per cent fiber, and about 2 per cent fat. Approximately 80 per cent of it is oat hulls and 20 per cent consists of the more valuable oat middlings and oat shorts. The higher-grade oat mill feed, mentioned previously, usually has 11 to 14 per cent protein and not over 20 per cent fiber.

Oat mill feed of the common grade is similar in composition to grass hay, having about the same amounts of protein and fiber as average timothy hay and slightly less fat. It furnishes somewhat less digestible nutrients than such hay, but it has about equalled hay of this kind, pound for pound, in feeding experiments. Oat mill feed is generally finely ground.

Extensive experiments have been conducted by the Wisconsin Station to determine the value of ordinary oat mill feed for the various classes of stock.[9] In these trials, which have covered more than 8 years, thousands of animals have been fed experimentally in order to secure conclusive results. These experiments show that oat mill feed is palatable to stock and that it is not only a satisfactory substitute for hay, but that it can also be successfully used to replace part of the grain.

Since oat mill feed is high in fiber and relatively low in digestible nutrients and net energy, it obviously will not have nearly so high a feeding value per ton as grain. Also, because it is lower than grain in protein, it is necessary to include a larger amount of protein supplements in the ration when oat mill feed is fed as a grain substitute.

In these experiments fattening cattle and lambs made good gains when oat mill feed formed not over 30 per cent of the concentrate mixture. Taking into consideration the greater amount of protein supplement required, the oat mill feed was actually worth about one-half as much per ton as corn or hominy feed. In trials with dairy cows oat mill feed was worth about 70 per cent as much as wheat bran, when forming not more than 25 per cent of the concentrate mixture.

Even though oat mill feed is high in fiber, the gains of pigs were not decreased when as much as 16 per cent was included in the excellent ration of ground corn or hominy feed, supplemented by tankage, linseed meal, and alfalfa meal. Thus fed, the oat mill feed was worth about one-half as much per ton as corn or hominy feed.

Oat mill feed was successfully used in the Wisconsin trials as a substitute for one-half or for all of the timothy hay in feeding work horses for periods of some months. In one test 1,650-lb. horses at light to medium work were even successfully fed nothing but oat mill feed, salt, and water for extended periods, the horses consuming 40 to 45 lbs. of the feed a day.[10] In feeding fattening cattle and sheep it was also a satisfactory substitute for part of the hay. As is pointed out in Part III, oat mill feed is useful to mix with corn or other grain in self-feeding fattening lambs.

In the Wisconsin investigations and in Massachusetts and South Dakota experiments oat mill feed was satisfactory as a substitute for timothy or other grass hay for dairy cows.[11] In the Wisconsin and South Dakota tests corn silage was fed in addition, and in the Massachusetts test the oat mill feed was substituted for not more than 40 per cent of the hay. Used in this manner oat mill feed was about equal in value per ton to ordinary grass hay. In Michigan tests 25 per cent of either oat mill feed or finely-chopped oat straw was included in the concentrate mixture for dairy cows which were fed in addition alfalfa hay and corn silage or beet pulp.[12] Thus fed, oat mill feed did not produce appreciably better results than the chopped straw.

In using oat mill feed as a hay substitute, at least for other stock than mature work horses or mules, care should be taken to include in the ration a sufficient amount of protein supplements, and enough high-quality legume hay or mixed hay or else good silage to furnish plenty of vitamin A and vitamin D. Also, it may be advisable to add a calcium supplement, unless the ration contains considerable legume hay.

531. Oat hulls; clipped oat by-product.—*Oat hulls,* from which most of the oat middlings and oat shorts have been removed, are obviously higher in fiber and lower in protein and nitrogen-free extract than is oat mill feed. Oat hulls have 30 per cent or more of fiber and only 3 to 4 per cent of protein. They furnish only 38.3 lbs. total digestible nutrients per 100 lbs., in comparison with 44.1 lbs. for oat straw. Judging from the analyses reported by feed inspection officials, oat hulls are sometimes improperly sold under the names of oat mill feed or oat feed.

Clipped oat by-product (often called "oat clippings") is the by-product obtained in the manufacture of clipped oats. It may contain, according to the definition of the Association of American Feed Control

Officials, the light chaffy material broken from the ends of the hulls, and also empty hulls, light immature oats, and dust.[13] It must not contain an excessive amount of hulls. This by-product usually contains 8 per cent or more of protein and 24 to 28 per cent of fiber. It is therefore worth somewhat more than oat mill feed of the usual grade. Clipped oat by-product is chiefly used as an ingredient in certain mixed feeds.

532. Oat meal; hulled oats.—The oat groats, with hulls removed, are highly nutritious, as they have less fiber than corn grain, contain even more fat, and carry 16 to 17 per cent protein. Therefore oat meal and also ground oats with most of the hulls sifted out have a high value for such stock as young pigs or calves, though often rather high in price.

533. Sprouted oats.—For a time, sprouted oats were used to a considerable extent in the winter feeding of poultry to furnish a green and succulent feed. With the recent advances in the knowledge concerning the importance of vitamins and other factors in poultry nutrition, efficient rations have been developed that have made the labor and expense of sprouting oats unnecessary. Therefore the practice has been largely discontinued.

Certain instances have been reported by the Bureau of Dairy Industry of the United States Department of Agriculture in which it was thought that the feeding of sprouted oats aided in overcoming sterility in dairy cows and heifers that had failed to conceive from repeated services.[14] The results in the few other studies that have been reported on this question have differed widely and no definite conclusions concerning the effectiveness of the remedy seem warranted as yet.[15]

534. Corn-and-oat feed.—This feed, variously called corn-and-oat feed, corn-and-oat chop, ground corn and oats, ground feed, and provender, is extensively used in the eastern and southern states for feeding dairy cows and especially horses. In composition it ranges from a mixture of various proportions of good-grade corn and oats to one containing a large proportion of low-grade materials, such as oat hulls, ground corn cobs, and other refuse.

The best guide to the purity of this feed is the fiber content. As corn contains only 2.3 per cent fiber and oats 10.6 per cent, when ground corn and oats contains over 7 to 8 per cent fiber, it has either been adulterated or was made from poor quality oats. Where more than 9 per cent fiber is present, the feed is definitely of low grade. Corn-and-oat feed should be purchased only on guarantee and from reliable dealers.

IV. Wheat and Its By-products

535. Importance of wheat.—Wheat *(Triticum sativum)* is second only to corn in importance as a cereal in the United States, an average of 56,835,000 acres having been grown in the 10-year period, 1924-1933 inclusive, with a yield of 14.1 bushels of 60 lbs. each. The farm value of the wheat crop of the country averaged $745,000,000 during this period.

Most of the wheat in the United States is raised for the manufacture of flour or other human foods, and under usual conditions relatively little is fed to stock. In practically every section of the United States grain for stock feeding is provided at lower cost by some other cereal—corn, oats, barley, or the grain sorghums, as the case may be. However, wheat is satisfactory for all classes of farm animals when properly fed, and it has been extensively used for stock feeding when unusually low in price. Also, for livestock low-grade wheat that is not suitable for milling is often nearly equal in feeding value to grain of high milling quality.

Though wheat itself is not commonly fed to farm animals in this country, the wheat bran and middlings secured in milling wheat for flour are by far our most important by-product stock feeds. The outstanding importance of these wheat mill feeds in this country is shown by the fact that in 1929, according to the Census, 4,681,802 tons of bran and middlings (nearly all from wheat) were produced, valued at over $140,000,000. This does not include the amounts or value of screenings and certain other by-products of the milling industry.

536. Composition and nutritive value of wheat.—Wheat resembles the other cereals in the general nutritive characteristics that have been discussed previously in this chapter. It has 13.1 per cent protein, on the average, which is slightly more than oats have and considerably more than corn contains. However, as has been pointed out in Chapter IV, the protein content of wheat is markedly affected by the climate and to a less extent by other factors. As is shown in Appendix Table I, wheat from the northern plains states averages 13.5 per cent in protein, while that from the Pacific Coast has but 9.9 per cent, or only about as much as corn.

When grown under the same conditions, spring wheat is usually slightly richer in protein than winter wheat, but is also higher in fiber. Durum wheat, grown extensively in the western part of the northern plains area, has about the same composition and feeding value as other wheat grown under the same environment.

The amount of protein in wheat is highly important from the milling standpoint, as it indicates the amount of gluten. Since gluten gives wheat dough the tenacity required in bread making, a high gluten content is desired. Therefore much wheat is now sold at the central markets on the basis of certified protein content.

As shown in Chapter VI, the protein of the bran layers and the germ is of better quality than that of the endosperm. (**148**) Wheat bran and wheat middlings therefore furnish protein which is superior to that supplied by flour or by the entire grain. However, the protein in the wheat by-products is decidedly inferior to that from such animal sources as milk, meat scraps, tankage, or fish meal.

Wheat equals corn in percentage of nitrogen-free extract (which is nearly all starch) and does not contain much more fiber than does corn. It has only about 2 per cent of fat in comparison with 4 per cent for corn. Wheat is as high as corn in digestibility, and it has a trifle larger percentage of total digestible nutrients than does corn of the same dry matter content.

Wheat is low in calcium, containing only 0.03 per cent. This is but one-third as much as in oats, but is more than in corn. In phosphorus, wheat is the highest of the cereals, having 0.43 per cent.

Wheat is lacking in vitamin D, the same as the other grains, and it supplies no appreciable amount of vitamin A.

537. Wheat as a feed.—The numerous experiments with the various classes of stock, which are reviewed in the chapters of Part III, show conclusively that wheat is a satisfactory feed for all farm animals when it is fed in suitable rations. Wheat is usually well liked by stock and is frequently fed as the only grain to swine and to fattening cattle and sheep. There is occasionally a tendency for fattening cattle or sheep to go "off feed" when heavily fed on wheat, or to have digestive disturbances. For this reason, wheat sometimes gives the best results when mixed with other feeds, such as corn, oats, barley, or bran.

Since the kernels of wheat are rather hard and small, wheat should be ground or crushed for all classes of stock, except sheep and possibly pigs when they are self-fed. The grain should be ground to only a medium degree of fineness, for wheat ground to a fine, floury meal is less palatable and more apt to form a pasty mass in the mouth.

When forming one-third to one-half the concentrate mixture for dairy cows, ground wheat is about equal to ground corn. In experiments with fattening cattle and with pigs ground wheat has also been equal to corn, as far as amount of feed required to produce 100 lbs. gain is concerned. However, the gains may not be quite so rapid on wheat, when fed as the only grain or the chief part of the grain mixture. For fattening lambs wheat has been about equal to barley in several experiments, but worth somewhat less per 100 lbs. than corn. Ground wheat can be fed successfully to horses and mules when mixed with some bulky feed, so as to avoid digestive trouble.

In using wheat as a stock feed, the fact that it is higher than corn in protein should be borne definitely in mind. This means that less protein supplement will be needed to balance a ration when wheat is the chief grain, than in the case of corn. This fact has even been overlooked in several experiments conducted to study the feeding value of wheat. When this advantage is not recognized, wheat cannot have its maximum value as a feed.

538. Flour manufacture and the milling by-products.—The wheat kernel is covered with a brownish bran coating in which four layers can be distinguished under the microscope. The bran is richer in protein and minerals and also much higher in fiber than the entire grain. Under the bran is the brownish aleurone layer, also rich in protein. The germ, which is at the base of the kernel, is rich in oil, protein, and minerals. The remainder of the kernel consists of thin-walled cells packed with starch grains. Among the starch grains are the particles of gluten that give wheat dough its tenacity.

In producing flour the miller desires to secure all the starch and gluten possible from the wheat grains, while avoiding the germ and bran. He leaves out the germs because they make a sticky dough and also soon turn dark and rancid, giving the flour a specked appearance. Nor does he use the aleurone layer, as it gives a brownish tint to the flour.

In modern milling, the wheat is first cleaned and moistened to toughen the bran. Then it passes between pairs of steel rollers, the first pairs of which are corrugated. These rollers gradually break the kernels into pieces, flatten out the bran, and separate the flour from it. After passing through each "break," or pair of rollers, the flour is removed by sieves and bolting cloth. Later in the process the various by-products are separated, all possible flour being recovered at each step in the reduction of the kernels.

The terms used to designate the various by-products differ somewhat in various parts of the country, and also the names of certain of the winter wheat by-products differ from those of the spring wheat by-products. The term *wheat bran* (often called merely "bran") is used for the coarsest by-product, which consists chiefly of the bran layers. For the finer by-products from spring wheat the terms commonly used are *standard middlings, flour middlings,* and *wheat red dog flour.* In the case of the by-products from winter wheat, the common names are *brown shorts, gray shorts,* and *white middlings.*

In the manufacture of white flour, approximately 72 to 75 per cent of the weight of the cleaned wheat usually goes into the flour and the remainder into the by-products.[16] Bran and standard middlings (or brown shorts) each form about 11 per cent of the weight of the original grain, and red dog flour (or white middlings) about 5 per cent.

539. Wheat bran.—Wheat bran, which consists almost entirely of the coarse outer coatings of the wheat kernel, is one of the most useful and important stock feeds. It averages 15.8 per cent in protein and 5.0 per cent in fat, and does not usually contain more than about 10 per cent fiber. Wheat bran supplies 70.2 lbs. total digestible nutrients per 100 lbs., which is a trifle less than oats furnish.

The protein of bran is of considerably better quality than that of white flour, but nevertheless it is not so well-balanced in composition as the protein in such feeds as milk, meat by-products, and fish by-products.

In phosphorus content bran is one of the richest of all common feeds, but it is low in calcium. It has 1.32 per cent of phosphorus, but only 0.12 per cent of calcium. This lack of calcium in bran and also in the grains should be borne in mind when they form the chief concentrates for stock.

Bran is one of the most palatable of stock feeds and it has a mild laxative effect. Also, it is twice as bulky as oats. Its popularity is due in no small part to these characteristics. The laxative effect has been attributed by some to its high content of phytin (an organic phosphorus compound) and by others to its content of fiber and pentosans.[17] Recent investigations indicate that the latter are the primary cause of this effect.

540. Wheat bran with screenings; spring wheat bran.—The best grades of bran have large clean flakes, and contain no screenings. Such bran is often called "pure wheat bran." When bran contains screenings, most states require that the fact be indicated on the feed tags. **(548)** "Standard bran," or bran containing screenings, usually sells at 50 cents to $1.00 a ton less than pure bran. Since wheat screenings have much the same chemical composition as wheat bran, there is often no significant difference in composition between bran without screenings and standard bran.

Unless bran contains more screenings than usual or unless the weed seeds are of a kind that give it a bitter taste, the difference in price between the two grades probably represents the approximate difference in actual value. It must be borne in mind, however, that there is somewhat more danger of introducing noxious weeds on the farm when screenings are fed. This is because they are not usually ground finely enough to destroy the smallest seeds.

Hard spring wheat bran contains slightly more fiber than winter wheat bran, but it also averages appreciably higher in fat and slightly higher in protein. In content of total digestible nutrients it is slightly higher than winter wheat bran.

541. Country mill bran and middlings.—Bran and middlings from small mills that lack machinery for perfect separation of the flour from the bran coats contain more flour and are therefore a little higher in nitrogen-free extract and lower in fiber than the bran from large mills. However, such bran and middlings are also slightly lower in protein. The terms "country mill bran" and "country mill middlings" are often used for such feeds, and they frequently sell at a slightly higher price. Sometimes, however, these terms are used in a misleading manner for any bran or middlings that does not come from a mill in one of the large milling centers.

542. Wheat bran as a feed.—Because of the importance of wheat bran, its value and use for each class of stock are discussed in detail in Part III. The palatability, the bulky nature, and the mild laxative effect of bran make it an especially good feed for dairy cattle, and it is one of the most common ingredients in their rations. When the cost of total digestible nutrients in bran is considerably higher than in grain or other concentrates, the amount of bran in the dairy ration should be kept at a minimum, or bran should be entirely replaced by other suitable feeds. Though bran is excellent for dairy cows, it should be borne in mind that it is not indispensable.

Bran is a very useful feed for horses, especially as a laxative or to mix with heavy concentrates that might otherwise cause digestive trouble. It is one of the most popular ingredients in mixtures for breeding ewes and growing lambs. Bran is useful for mixing with heavy grains in starting fattening cattle or lambs on feed, but later it is usually replaced by grain, or the amount greatly reduced. While bran is a useful feed for brood sows, middlings are much preferable for pigs of all ages, as bran is too bulky for them.

543. Wheat standard middlings; brown shorts.—*Wheat standard middlings*, usually called merely "standard middlings" (sometimes "standard shorts") are the by-product from spring wheat that consists mostly of fine particles of bran and germ, with very little of the red dog flour. The similar by-product from winter wheat milling is called *wheat brown shorts*, or sometimes "red shorts." These feeds have about the same composition, except that standard middlings are slightly higher in fiber and also higher in fat than brown shorts. According to the definitions of the Association of American Feed Control Officials, standard middlings must not contain more than 9.5 per cent fiber and brown shorts not more than 7.5 per cent.[13]

Standard middlings are slightly richer in protein and fat than wheat bran and contain more nitrogen-free extract. They average 17.4 per cent in protein, 6.8 per cent in fiber, and 5.5 per cent in fat. They are appreciably more digestible than wheat bran and furnish, on the average, 78.4 lbs. of total digestible nutrients per 100 lbs., in comparison with 70.2 lbs. for bran. Standard middlings thus supply about 12 per cent more total digestible nutrients. They therefore have a correspondingly higher value as a feed, except when the more bulky nature and greater laxative effect of bran are desired. Standard middlings are rich in phosphorus, containing 0.94 per cent, but they are low in calcium, like bran and other wheat by-products.

The value of standard middlings for the different classes of stock is discussed in the chapters of Part III. They are used chiefly for swine, calves, and poultry, but may also be fed to other stock in place of bran. Standard middlings and other types of middlings are excellent swine feeds when part of the protein in the ration comes from such feeds as tankage, fish meal, skimmilk, etc. On the other hand, if middlings are fed as the only supplement to the cereal grains, even to pigs on pasture, the results are usually unsatisfactory. This is due primarily to deficiencies in the quality of the protein.

When fed as a part of a suitable concentrate mixture, wheat middlings are satisfactory for dairy cows. Middlings alone should never be fed to horses, since they are too heavy in character and are liable to produce colic.

544. Wheat red dog flour; wheat white shorts.—*Wheat red dog flour,* also called "red dog flour" or "wheat red dog," is the by-product from spring wheat that consists chiefly of the aleurone, with small quantities of flour and fine bran particles. The similar by-product from winter wheat is *wheat white shorts,* also called "white middlings."

Red dog flour is slightly higher in fiber and also in fat than white middlings, but otherwise there is little difference in composition between the two by-products. According to the definitions of the Association of American Feed Control Officials, wheat red dog flour must not contain more than 4.0 per cent of fiber and wheat white shorts not more than 3.5 per cent.[13]

These by-products contain slightly less protein and fat than standard middlings or brown shorts, but they are considerably lower in fiber and higher in nitrogen-free extract. Both are highly digestible, and they are even richer than the entire wheat grain in total digestible nutrients. They are fed chiefly to swine, especially young pigs, but are also often used as an ingredient in calf meals, on account of their high digestibility.

545. Wheat flour middlings; wheat gray shorts.—*Wheat flour middlings* consist of standard middlings and red dog flour combined in the proportions obtained in the usual process of milling spring wheat. The similar by-product from winter wheat is *wheat gray shorts* (also called "gray middlings" or "total shorts"). Neither flour middlings nor gray shorts should contain more than 6 per cent fiber. The average fiber content for flour middlings is 4.4 per cent and for gray shorts 5.6 per cent.

Flour middlings and gray shorts are used in general much like standard middlings, but are especially well suited to young pigs on account of their low fiber content and richness in nitrogen-free extract. They are slightly higher in total digestible nutrients than standard middlings or brown shorts.

546. Wheat mixed feed.—Wheat mixed feed consists of the wheat bran and the flour middlings or gray shorts, combined in the proportions obtained in the usual process of commercial milling. Wheat mixed feed from hard spring wheat should not contain more than 9.5 per cent fiber and from winter wheat not more than 8.5 per cent. The name "wheat mixed feed" is sometimes loosely used for various mixtures of bran and middlings.

Since wheat mixed feed of good quality contains all the middlings, it is somewhat lower than wheat bran in fiber and it is about 5 per cent higher than bran in total digestible nutrients. This will represent about the usual difference in feeding value, unless bran is desired for greater bulk.

547. Wheat germ.—Certain of the larger mills separate some of the wheat germ more or less completely from the middlings and sell this product as "wheat germ meal" or "pure wheat germ." This feed, which contains 25 to 30 per cent protein or more, is used as an ingredient in certain mixed poultry feeds and calf meals.

548. Screenings.—When wheat and the other small grains come from the threshing machine, they contain various amounts of screenings. These must be removed as completely as possible before the grain is milled for human food. The screenings consist of small, broken, or shrunken kernels of grain, wild oats and wild buckwheat, smaller weed seeds, and more or less chaff and broken pieces of stem. It is estimated that there were over 18,580,000 bushels of screenings a year in the wheat and rye crop in only four states—North Dakota, South Dakota, Minnesota, and Montana—during the period, 1923 to 1930.[18]

When farmers market their wheat or other grain before first cleaning it thoroughly, they not only lose the feeding value of the screenings, but they also have to take an appreciably lower price for the grain. The increase in price will much more than cover the cost of cleaning the grain, and in addition the screenings will be saved for feeding on the farm.

Screenings vary so widely in composition and feeding value that no very definite statements can be made concerning them. The best grades, consisting chiefly of broken and shrunken kernels of grain, with wild oats and other palatable weed seeds, resemble oats in composition. Such screenings, when ground, may closely approach grain in feeding value. Light, chaffy screenings are, of course, much higher in fiber and consequently lower in value. Some screenings even resemble straw more than grain in composition and value.

If the screenings contain too large a proportion of "black seeds," consisting of mustard seed, lambs' quarter, and pig weed, the value will be low. In case there is much mustard seed present, the screenings may be very unpalatable to stock. Poisonous seeds, such as corn cockle, are rarely present in sufficient amounts to cause ill effects. Flax screenings are usually considerably higher in fat than wheat screenings, due to immature or broken flax seeds. However, they are also generally higher in fiber.

Especially in Canada, screenings are often separated at the mills into three classes: *Recleaned elevator screenings* (consisting chiefly of wild buckwheat, broken or shrunken wheat, and wild oats, with not over 3 per cent of small weed seeds); *oat scalpings,* or "mill oats" (consisting of wild oats, tame oats, and other grain) ; and *refuse screenings* (consisting of small weed seeds, chaff, dust, and dirt).

Unless the weed seeds in screenings are killed by fine grinding, many will pass through stock uninjured and be carried to the fields in the manure. Therefore screenings should be finely ground, even for sheep. The experiments that have been conducted to determine the value of screenings for stock feeding show that the best heavy-weight screenings, high in grain and in wild oats and wild buckwheat, are practically equal to grain in feeding value.[19] On the other hand, chaffy screenings or those high in pigeon grass seed have been of much less value.

In Idaho tests, well-cleaned alfalfa-seed screenings were superior to barley for fattening lambs.[20] On the other hand, in one trial uncleaned screenings were unpalatable on account of the strong taste of some of the weed seeds, and the lambs would eat only 0.2 lb. per head daily. Screenings containing a large proportion of certain weed seeds may even cause an objectionable flavor in the meat of animals heavily fed on them.[21]

Ground screenings of good quality can be used satisfactorily as one-fourth or somewhat more of the concentrate mixture for dairy cows, beef cattle, or swine. The best results are secured when screenings are fed with considerable legume hay. It is pointed out in Chapter XXXIII that screenings are fed extensively to fattening lambs, especially in the wheat-growing areas of the West. Often they are used as the only concentrate. At the start light-weight, chaffy screenings are fed, and when the lambs are safely on full feed, heavier screenings, richer in grain, are substituted. Various proportions of screenings are used in certain of the lower-grade mixed feeds, especially those for dairy cows. (**665**)

The composition and value of alfalfa-seed screenings and sweet-clover-seed screenings are discussed in the following chapter. (**606**)

V. Barley and Its By-products

549. Importance of barley.—Barley, which ranks fourth in importance as a grain crop in the United States, is the most widely cultivated of the cereals throughout the world. The crop is adapted to a wide range of climatic conditions. For instance, barley grows in Alaska and flourishes beside orange groves in California. Once the chief bread grain of many ancient nations, barley is now used almost wholly for brewing, for stock feeding, and to a much less extent for making pearled barley. (Most of the six-row varieties of barley are classed by botanists as *Hordeum vulgare* and most of the two-row barleys as *Hordeum distichon.*)

Throughout the northern range of states, except on the lighter soils, barley commonly yields more pounds of grain per acre than do oats. Since the feeding value of barley is as high or even higher than that of oats, pound for pound, the acreage of the improved, high-yielding pedigreed varieties of barley has been greatly increased during recent years, and the grain has been used in place of oats for feeding stock. According to the Census, the acreage of barley in the United States increased from 6,472,888 acres in 1919 to 12,890,772 acres in 1929. The average yield of barley in this country for the 10-year period, 1924 to 1933 inclusive, was 22.0 bushels of 48 lbs. each, per acre.

The large increase in barley acreage may have been partly because of the recent development of smooth-awned varieties by the experiment stations. These have removed from harvesting barley much of the disagreeableness caused by the barbed beards of ordinary varieties.

Barley is especially suited to sections with rather scanty rainfall and short growing seasons. It holds first rank among the cereals in North Dakota and California, and it is of much importance in the entire district from Michigan westward to Montana, Wyoming, and Colorado.

In growing barley one should be sure that he has a variety that is well adapted to his locality, for the results from any variety differ widely in various sections. Where barley stripe is serious, it is important to have a variety resistant to the disease. The hull-less varieties of barley, in which the hulls do not adhere to the kernels when the grain is threshed, yield considerably less than the common varieties in nearly all sections.

Often a combination of barley and oats will produce a greater weight of grain per acre than either crop grown alone. The combination is therefore extensively raised in some localities, when the grain is intended for stock feeding and not for market.

550. Composition and nutritive value.—The average protein content of barley for all sections of the United States except the Pacific Coast States is 11.8 per cent. This is nearly as high as the protein content of oats, which averages 12.0 per cent. However, barley varies considerably in protein content, depending on the climate, just as in the case of wheat. It will be noted in Appendix Table I that barley from the Pacific Coast averages only 8.7 per cent in protein.

The hulls form about 15 per cent of the usual types of barley, the best grades of which weigh 46 lbs. or more per bushel. (The legal weight of barley per bushel in most states is 48 lbs.) Due to the hulls, common barley averages 5.7 per cent in fiber content. It supplies about one-tenth more total digestible nutrients per 100 lbs. than oats and 5 per cent less than corn of Federal grade No. 1.

Some of the barley varieties grown in the West, such as Coast barley, have thicker hulls, and weigh only 45 lbs. per bushel. Such barley is somewhat lower in digestible nutrients and feeding value than the ordinary varieties. Hull-less barley resembles wheat or rye in composition, as the hulls do not adhere to the kernels of the threshed grain.

Barley has the same nutritive deficiencies as the other cereals, which have been discussed at the beginning of this chapter. It is low in vitamin A, though apparently containing somewhat more than white corn.[22]

551. Barley as a feed.—As is pointed out in the various chapters of Part III, barley is a satisfactory feed for all classes of stock. For dairy cows ground barley is about equal to ground corn. For horses a given weight of barley will replace more than the same weight of oats, but greater care is necessary in feeding, or it may cause colic. For swine, for fattening cattle, and for fattening lambs or sheep, barley is an excellent feed, but it is worth somewhat less per ton than corn. Barley should be ground or crushed for all these classes of stock, except sheep.

Occasionally cattle bloat when fed barley as the only or the chief grain, especially when the roughage is alfalfa hay. However, the trouble from this source is ordinarily not serious. The use of scabbed barley has been discussed in Chapter XVI.

552. Brewing and brewery by-products.—The first step in the production of beer is the making of malt from barley. After being cleaned of foreign material, the barley is steeped in warm water for 48 to 70 hours and then removed from the water and kept at the proper temperature for germination. The amount of diastase, an enzyme which converts starch into malt sugar, increases greatly, and some of the starch in the grain is changed by the diastase. When the action has gone far enough, the grain is dried. The small, shriveled roots, or "sprouts," are then separated from the grains. These form the feed known as *malt sprouts.*

In the manufacture of beer, the malt, after being crushed, is "mashed" with water held at the proper temperature for diastatic action. Often there is added to the mash some corn grits, rice grits, or other grain, which has been cooked to gelatinize the starch. During the mashing process most of the starch in the malt and in any added grain is converted into malt sugar. The sugar and other soluble material is next extracted from the mash to form "wort." This is boiled with hops, and then filtered. Finally, yeast is added and the fermentation proceeds.

The residue left after the wort is extracted constitutes *wet brewers' grains.* These are usually dried and sold as *brewers' dried grains* or *dried brewers' grains.* The spent hops, after drying, are sometimes used in mixed feeds, but have little feeding value.

The yeast that develops in the fermentation process is sometimes recovered, dried, and sold as *brewers' yeast.* The value of this by-product is discussed in Chapter XIX.

553. Malted barley.—It was once believed that the malting of barley increased its general value for stock feeding. This practice has, however, been practically discontinued, except that malted barley is sometimes used in calf meals. For young calves, before their ability to digest grain has been well developed, it may possibly possess some slight advantage over ground barley.

Early experiments showed that for dairy cows and fattening animals a given weight of barley is worth more than the amount of malt and malt sprouts that can be made from it.[23] This is because there is a loss of 5 to 7 per cent of the dry matter in the steep water and in the oxidation of nutrients during the germinating process. Malt is, however, very palatable to stock and is occasionally used as an appetizer in fitting stock for show.

554. Brewers' dried grains.—Brewers' dried grains contain an average of 25.6 per cent protein, 6.7 per cent fat, 14.8 per cent fiber, and 42.0 per cent nitrogen-free extract. The nitrogen-free extract is largely pentosans, for most of the starch is removed in the malting and mashing processes. Brewers' grains do not rank high in total digestible nutrients, having only 65.3 per cent on the average, in comparison with 70.2 per cent for wheat bran and 77.4 per cent for corn gluten feed. They also contain slightly less digestible protein than does corn gluten feed, for they have only 20.7 per cent, on the average, in comparison with 22.7 per cent for corn gluten feed. Brewers' dried grains are nearly as bulky as wheat bran, and they keep fairly well in storage. They are not very palatable to stock and should therefore be mixed with better-liked feeds, if possible.

Brewers' dried grains are used chiefly for dairy cattle, especially dairy cows. It is pointed out in Chapter XXV that they are entirely satisfactory for this purpose when forming not over one-third of a concentrate mixture which consists chiefly of well-liked feeds. They may also be fed similarly to beef cattle and sheep. When cheap in price, they may be used economically as a substitute for half of the oats in feeding work horses, equalling oats, pound for pound, in feeding value.[24] They are said to be somewhat constipating for horses.[25] On account of their bulkiness, brewers' dried grains are not usually fed to swine, but they may be used as a substitute for oats in feeding brood sows.

555. Wet brewers' grains.—Because of their watery nature and perishable character, wet brewers' grains are usually fed near the brewery. They are commonly sold by the bushel, as the water content and therefore the value per ton varies widely, depending on how well the water has drained out. A bushel of wet grains is usually equal to about 11 to 13 lbs. of the dried grains. If the water has thoroughly drained out, the wet grains will still contain about 75 to 80 per cent water and it will take nearly 4 lbs. to equal 1 lb. of the dry grains.

The wet grains should be hauled to the farm in as fresh a condition as possible. To avoid spoilage it may be necessary to haul them every day or two in summer and twice a week when cooler. They may be kept longer by storing them in tight barrels or tanks, or if they are well compacted, with a small quantity of salt sprinkled throughout the mass.[26]

In feeding the wet grains, care should be taken to keep the mangers and containers clean and free from any spoiled material. The mangers should be of concrete or so constructed that there are no crevices that can become filled with decomposed grains. This is especially important in feeding dairy cows. Because the wet grains have sometimes been fed carelessly to cows in the past, some boards of health now regulate or prohibit their use in the production of market milk.

Wet brewers' grains may be fed to dairy cows at the rate of 20 to 30 lbs. per head daily to replace an equal weight of silage, or as a substitute for part of the concentrates (at the rate of 4 lbs. of the wet grains for 1 lb. of the concentrate mixture). When properly used, they will not produce any undesirable flavor or odor in the milk. To avoid any tainting of the milk, they should be fed after milking, rather than before, and they should not be stored in the stable.

The wet grains may also be fed to other classes of stock, just as in the case of the dried product. On account of the "washy" nature of the wet grains, horses should not be fed more than about 20 lbs. per head daily, and pigs not over 2.5 lbs. per 100 lbs. live weight.

556. Dried malt grains.—Dried malt grains are similar in nature to dried brewers' grains, and are a by-product in the manufacture of malt syrup. They are solely a barley by-product and other grains are not added in the manufacturing process.

557. Malt sprouts.—In the malting of barley, only about 3 lbs. of malt sprouts are produced for each 100 lbs. of barley malted. Sometimes the malt sprouts are mixed with the brewers' dried grains and the mixture sold under that name. In the proportions produced, the malt sprouts form only one-tenth of such a mixture.

Malt sprouts are similar in chemical composition to brewers' dried grains, containing about the same amount of crude protein (about one-third of which is amids), much less fat, and slightly more total digestible nutrients. They are also about as bulky as brewers' dried grains, and they have a great absorptive capacity for water. Due to this they sometimes absorb moisture and become moldy unless stored in a dry place. On account of this absorptive power, they are a good carrier of molasses in mixed feeds.

Malt sprouts are somewhat bitter and therefore unpalatable if fed alone. Doubtless for this reason, they are mostly used by feed manufacturers as an ingredient in mixed feeds, especially for dairy cattle. They are entirely satisfactory for this purpose when used in moderate amounts and are often an economical source of protein and total digestible nutrients.

Due to this lack of palatability, it is preferable not to include more than about 10 to 15 per cent of malt sprouts in a concentrate mixture for dairy cows or other stock. However, stock will usually eat a mixture containing a somewhat greater proportion if the other feeds in it are well liked. In a Massachusetts trial 2 lbs. of malt sprouts were about equal to 1.5 lbs. of gluten feed for dairy cows.[27] Feeding too large an amount to dairy cows is said to impart a bitter taste to the milk.

In Europe horses are fed as much as 6 lbs. per head daily with good results; cattle, 3 lbs.; and sheep, 0.75 lb. Since malt sprouts swell greatly when they absorb water, they may cause digestive disturbances if fed dry in too great quantities. Therefore large allowances should be soaked for several hours before feeding. When not over 1 to 2 lbs. per head are fed to cattle, soaking is unnecessary, but moistening to lay the dust may be advisable.

558. Spent hops.—The spent hops, left after the wort has been boiled with the hops and filtered, are sometimes dried and used for feed or for fertilizer. They contain not only the hop residue, but also some protein precipitated from the wort in the boiling process. Though they have 20 per cent of protein or more, the digestibility of the material is so low that the product is of doubtful value as a feed.[28] Also, the spent hops are bitter and unpalatable to stock and therefore only a small proportion can be included in a mixture of better-liked feeds.

559. Barley feed; barley mixed feed; barley hulls.—In the manufacture of pearled barley for human food, *barley feed* is secured as a by-product. This consists of the hulls and the outer coats of the kernels. A by-product called *barley mixed feed*, which has about the same composition, is secured when barley flour is manufactured. This should contain not only the hulls but also all the middlings from the kernels.

Usually there is but a small amount of these feeds available in this country, but during the World War, when large quantities of barley were milled for flour, considerable barley feed was available. A good grade of barley feed, containing 11 per cent fiber, was worth nearly as much as wheat bran for dairy cows in a Wisconsin trial.[29] For fattening pigs, barley feed was worth 17 per cent less per ton than ground barley.

Barley bran is erroneously named, as it consists almost entirely of barley hulls, with only a small amount of the outer coat of the kernel proper. Barley bran containing 27 per cent fiber was worth only two-thirds as much per ton for dairy cows as wheat bran in another Wisconsin trial.

VI.   RYE AND ITS BY-PRODUCTS

560. Importance of rye in the United States.—Rye *(Secale cereale)* is one of the principal cereals of North Europe but is not extensively grown in America. During the 10-year period, 1924-1933 inclusive, an average of only 3,345,000 acres of rye were grown for grain in the United States, in comparison with 56,835,000 acres of wheat. The largest acreage is in North Dakota, but rye is also an important crop in Minnesota, South Dakota, Nebraska, Wisconsin, Michigan, and Pennsylvania.

Though it repays good treatment, rye thrives better than the other cereals on poor or very sandy land. Practically all the rye in this country is winter rye, which is even hardier than wheat. In tests in·certain sections of the northernmost states rye has led the cereals in average weight of grain produced per acre, even on good soil.

As a winter cover and pasture crop, rye is grown widely in certain sections of the South and to a lesser extent in other districts. Its value for pasture during the fall, winter, and early spring has been discussed in Chapter XV. (455)

561. Rye for stock feeding.—Rye grain is raised chiefly for bread-making in Europe and is also used largely for this purpose in this country. However, a considerable part of the crop is often fed to livestock here. Considering only its chemical composition, we should expect rye to equal wheat in feeding value, for the composition of these grains is very similar. However, even when rye is not appreciably contaminated with ergot, it is usually less palatable to stock than the other grains. Also, when fed as the only concentrate or in too large amounts, it is more apt to cause digestive disturbances.

Rye should therefore be fed with due care and preferably as only part of the concentrates. The best methods of using rye for each class of stock are discussed in Part III. It is there pointed out that rye has given particularly good results in experiments with fattening lambs, even when fed as the only grain. It is also satisfactory for dairy cattle and beef cattle when fed as part of the concentrate mixture. On the other hand, the results in swine feeding have been extremely variable. In some trials rye has been successfully fed as the only grain, while in others, especially with younger pigs, rye has produced poor results when forming any large part of the ration.

Rye which is appreciably contaminated with ergot is unpalatable to stock and may even be dangerous, if it contains too much of this poisonous substance. (502)

562. Rye feed; rye middlings.—Usually all the by-products that are obtained in the milling of rye for flour are combined and sold as *rye feed* or *rye middlings*, instead of being marketed separately as bran, middlings, and red dog flour.

Rye feed, as defined by the Association of American Feed Control Officials, should consist of the entire by-product obtained in the milling of rye, except the rye red dog.[13] However, there is practically no rye red dog on the market, and therefore most rye feed as now produced apparently also contains this finer by-product.

The term *rye middlings* is defined as the combination of rye feed and rye red dog in the proportions obtained in the usual process of milling rye flour. When screenings are present, this should be indicated in the name.

There now seems to be no particular difference in the composition of the feeds sold as rye feed and as rye middlings. Both are a little lower in protein than standard wheat middlings but usually have less fiber. These rye by-products furnish slightly less total digestible nutrients than standard wheat middlings and somewhat more than wheat bran. The rye by-products are, however, less palatable than the wheat by-products, and therefore the best results are secured when they are fed as only part of a good concentrate or grain mixture, along with well-liked feeds.

For dairy cows, beef cattle, or sheep these rye by-products may be used satisfactorily as a substitute for wheat bran to a limited extent. Under usual conditions, the amount had best be limited to 15 to 25 per cent of the concentrate mixture, though a larger proportion could possibly be fed successfully with good legume hay and corn silage.

Rye feed and rye middlings have not been used extensively for swine feeding, but can probably be fed in limited amounts with satisfactory results. Since rye grain sometimes does not give good results in feeding swine when forming too large a part of the ration, it would also seem wise not to include over 15 to 25 per cent of these rye by-products in the ration. To this extent they can be substituted for wheat middlings.

VII. THE SORGHUMS

563. Sorghums important grain crops in areas of low rainfall.— It has already been pointed out in Chapter XIV that in the plains states from southern Nebraska to Texas, New Mexico, and Arizona on the south, the sorghums *(Andropogon sorghum,* or *Sorghum vulgare,* vars.)* are of great value for grain and also for forage. In the portions of this great area where the rainfall is scanty, they largely take the place of corn, due to the fact that they are much more drought resistant. The various types of the sorghums, both the grain sorghums and the sweet sorghums, have been previously described, and the special advantages of these types for grain or for forage pointed out.

564. Grain sorghums.—The grain sorghums include *milo, kafir, feterita, kaoliang,* and the less important *hegari, durra,* and *shallu.* In this class are also certain hybrids between the grain sorghums and the sweet sorghums, such as *darso, shrock,* and *sagrain. Atlas sorghum,* another hybrid, is more commonly classed with the sweet sorghums, though it is used for grain as well as for forage.

By careful breeding and selection, varieties of grain sorghum have been developed which are suited to the various climatic conditions. Of especial importance in the drier districts are dwarf strains which have erect heads that may be harvested with a grain header or a combine harvester, and which are early maturing, thus escaping late summer droughts. Also, through the development of early varieties the sorghums are being carried farther north.

Throughout the western portion of the sorghum belt, the grain sorghums are much surer crops than corn, due to their drought-resistant qualities. Here they usually give decidedly higher yields than corn. For example, the average yield of 5 varieties of kafir over an 8-year period in trials at Hays, Kansas, was 38 bushels per acre, in comparison with only 24 bushels for corn.[30] In central and eastern Kansas and Oklahoma, the sorghums are superior to corn on poor, thin uplands. Even on the better land in the eastern part of the grain-sorghum belt, it is advisable to use the sorghums as a partial substitute for corn as an insurance against loss from drought.

The average yield of the grain sorghums in the United States has ranged from more than 20 bushels per acre to less than 10 bushels, depending on the rainfall. Yields of 50 bushels or more per acre are sometimes secured under very favorable conditions.

The customary basis for selling the seed of the grain sorghums is by the 56-lb. bushel, but the usual weight is about 54 lbs. Grain sorghum heads commonly yield from 70 to 75 per cent of grain on threshing, and it requires 75 to 80 lbs. of sorghum heads to make a bushel of threshed grain. Although the percentage of grain in the entire crop varies widely with the season and the thickness of the stand, about 30 per cent of the weight of well-cured grain sorghum plants will be grain, on the average.[31]

When cut for grain, grain sorghum should not be harvested until the seeds are well matured. Because the hard-coated seeds when apparently dry may contain much moisture, the grain sorghums are especially apt to heat in the bin unless the grain is well cured before it is threshed.

565. Grain sorghums as feeds.—The grain sorghums resemble corn grain in composition and in feeding value. Like corn, they contain about 70 per cent nitrogen-free extract, which is nearly all starch, and they are very low in fiber. Most of the grain sorghums are higher than corn in protein but they contain considerably less fat.

The grain sorghums have the same general nutritive virtues and deficiencies as the other cereals, which have been discussed in detail earlier in this chapter.[32] As in the case of the other cereals, the proteins of sorghum grain are unbalanced in nature. Sorghum grain is also nearly as deficient in calcium as corn grain, and, like corn, is somewhat lower in phosphorus than wheat, barley, or oats.

All the varieties of sorghum grain, even those which are yellow in color, are apparently low in vitamin A, resembling white corn and the small grains in this respect. In the yellow-seeded grain sorghums the color is confined to the hull, and the endosperm is not colored, as in yellow corn. Sorghum grain is deficient in vitamin D, the same as the other cereals.

When properly supplemented with feeds rich in protein, calcium, and vitamins A and D, the grain sorghums are excellent for all classes of stock. The experiments reviewed in the respective chapters of Part III show that for dairy cows and sheep the grain sorghums are about equal in value to corn, pound for pound. For fattening cattle and for swine their value has been somewhat lower than that of corn. There is apparently no important difference in the value for stock feeding of the grain from the various types and varieties of grain sorghums. The grain of the sweet sorghums is of lower value, as is stated later.

The grain sorghums are well liked by stock, though they are sometimes slightly less palatable than corn. The seeds of darso, shrock, and sagrain, which are hybrids between grain sorghums and sweet sorghums, are somewhat bitter, due to a high content of tannin. Nevertheless, they give good results when fed to stock.

For horses, fattening cattle, and dairy cows, sorghums are ordinarily ground, being then usually called "chop." Grinding for sheep is not necessary, and there is but a small saving in grinding grain sorghum for swine when the grain is fed in a self-feeder on a suitable platform. Often the unthreshed heads are fed, or the forage carrying the heads is supplied, especially to idle horses, colts, and young stock. The product obtained by grinding the entire heads, called "head chop," resembles corn-and-cob meal in composition.

566. Sweet sorghum seed.—The seed of the sweet sorghums, or sorgos, contains considerable tannin, which makes it bitter and astringent. Its feeding value is only about two-thirds as much per pound as seed from the grain sorghums. For grain production sweet sorghum is surpassed by corn in the humid regions and by the grain sorghums in the plains districts.

567. Broom corn.—In harvesting broom corn the heads are cut before the seed has fully matured, and the seed is removed from the brush before it is thoroughly dry. This seed has considerable feeding value and may be saved by drying or ensiling.

VIII. Rice and Its By-products

568. Rice.—Rice is one of the most important cereal crops of the world and forms a large part of the food of the Oriental peoples. The production in the United States is but about 1 per cent of the world production, an average of only 910,000 acres being grown in this country during the 10-year period, 1924-1933 inclusive. Over half the acreage is in the coastal section of Louisiana, and practically all the remainder in Arkansas, Texas, and California. Most of the rice grown in this and other countries is of the lowland type, which requires flooding with water after the plants have well started.

Like wheat, rice is used almost entirely for human food, the grain being fed to stock only when off-grade or unusually low in price. The rice kernel is very hard and is enclosed in a hard hull, which has small ridges with sharp, tooth-like projections. The threshed grain, called *rough rice*, or *paddy rice*, is nearly as high as oats in fiber and is the lowest of the cereals in protein, averaging only 8.3 per cent. It has the common merits of the cereals as a feed and also the same general nutritive deficiencies, including a lack of vitamin A.

When available at an economical price, rough rice may be used as a substitute for corn or other grain in feeding the various classes of stock. It should be ground for all stock, on account of the hardness of the kernels. In trials with work horses and mules and with dairy cows ground rough rice has been about equal to ground corn.[33] In a Missouri trial with fattening steers it was worth only three-fourths as much as corn.[34]

For swine we should expect that the value of ground rough rice would be somewhat lower than that of ground corn or barley, and more similar to that of oats, on account of the higher fiber content. The value of ground rough rice for swine in comparison with these grains has varied considerably in the few trials in which they have been compared.[35]

Red rice, a pest in the rice fields, probably equals the cultivated grain in feeding value.

569. Rice milling and rice by-products.—In milling rice to produce polished rice for human food, first the hull is removed, and next the germ and all the layers of bran except a part of the last layer. The germs and the bran, with only such quantities of hull fragments as are unavoidable in the regular milling process, form the by-product called *rice bran*. The starchy part of the kernel is left, surrounded by part of the last bran coat. The rice is now nearly white but the grains are rather rough. It is therefore "polished" by being treated in revolving cylinders, padded with leather. In this process the remnants of the last brown bran layer are removed and also fine polishings from the starchy part. These form *rice polish*.

The very small pieces of broken grains that are removed in the milling process are separated and marketed as *brewers' rice*.

In the milling of rice approximately 65 per cent of milled rice is obtained, 19 per cent of hulls, 8 per cent of rice bran, 3 per cent of rice polish, and 2 per cent of brewers' rice, with about 3 per cent of screenings and waste.[36] The amount of rice by-products produced in the United States is small, according to the Census amounting in 1929 to only 111,700 tons for rice bran, rice polish, and brewers' rice, combined.

570. Rice bran.—Rice bran of good quality has been defined previously in the description of the milling process. Such rice bran averages 12.8 per cent in protein and 13.4 per cent in fat, with 13.0 per cent fiber. It should be borne in mind that rice bran is not a protein-rich feed, for it is similar to oats or wheat in protein content, and considerably lower than wheat bran or middlings.

Rice bran varies decidedly in fiber content, depending on the proportion of hulls present, and sometimes is intentionally adulterated with hulls. It is fairly palatable to stock when fresh, but often turns rancid in storage, on account of the high content of rice oil. Thorough heating and drying at the mill improve the keeping quality. In purchasing rice bran it is safest to buy it only under strict guarantee of composition and also from a sample which has been examined for rancidity.

Rice bran is fed chiefly to dairy cattle. When forming not more than about one-third the concentrate mixture for dairy cows, it has been worth 75 to 80 per cent as much as ground corn or milo grain, and has been about equal to wheat bran.[37] Rice bran that is not rancid does not injure the flavor of milk, but too large a proportion may cause soft butter. It may also be used in place of part of the grain

Heads of Different Types of Wheat

From left to right: 1, bearded winter wheat (Turkey Red); 2, beardless spring wheat (Blue Stem); 3, bearded spring wheat (Velvet Chaff); 4, Durum, or macaroni wheat; 5, club wheat.

Heads of Oats, Emmer, and Spelt

From left to right: 1, variety of oats with open or spreading panicle; 2, side oats; 3, emmer; 4, spelt.

HEADS OF DIFFERENT VARIETIES OF BARLEY AND OF RYE

From left to right: 1, two-rowed barley; 2, common six-rowed barley, or so-called four-rowed barley; 3, true six-rowed barley; 4, California feed barley; 5, beardless barley; 6, rye.

HEADS OF DIFFERENT TYPES OF GRAIN SORGHUMS

From left to right: 1 and 2, yellow milo; 3, white kaoliang; 4, brown kaoliang; 5, feterita; 6, red kafir; 7, pink kafir; 8, black-hulled kafir. (From *Breeder's Gazette*.)

for beef cattle or sheep, its value being usually three-fourths that of corn or even higher.[38]

Several experiments have shown conclusively that rice bran has very decided limitations as a feed for swine.[39] It is satisfactory as part of the ration for brood sows and their litters when used as wheat bran would be fed. On the other hand, it contains so much fiber that it does not give the best results if it forms too large a part of the ration for growing and fattening pigs. It also produces soft pork. In addition, too large a proportion of rice bran is apt to cause serious scouring of pigs under 75 to 85 lbs. in weight, especially if they are on rye pasture.

For older pigs, fairly satisfactory gains are produced by rice bran or about equal parts of rice bran and ground corn or other grain, properly supplemented with a feed like tankage. The gains will, however, usually be less rapid than on grain and the supplement. Thus fed, rice bran has been worth 75 to 90 per cent as much as ground corn.

571. Rice polish.—Rice polish is the finely powdered material obtained in polishing the rice kernels, after the hulls and bran have been removed. It contains approximately as much protein and nearly as much fat as rice bran, and has only 3 per cent fiber. Because of its higher fat content, it supplies slightly more total digestible nutrients than corn. Rice polish tends to become rancid in storage, like rice bran, and should therefore be fed when as fresh as possible.

It is satisfactory as part of the concentrate mixture for dairy cattle, beef cattle, and sheep. In Arkansas trials it was equal to ground corn for dairy cows when forming one-fourth of the concentrate mixture, but when as much as this was fed it produced soft butter.[40] It has given good results when fed to fattening cattle in Louisiana and Texas experiments.[41]

For swine feeding rice polish has much the same limitations as rice bran, except that it is much lower in fiber.[42] It tends to produce soft pork, especially when it forms more than one-half of the ration for fattening pigs. It is also apt to cause serious scours if too much is fed to pigs under about 75 to 80 lbs. in weight. For pigs over this weight it is fully equal to, or even superior to, ground corn or barley, so far as the amount of feed required per 100 lbs. gain is concerned. Rice polish is entirely satisfactory as part of the ration for brood sows and litters. If the pigs are then grown and finished on non-softening feeds, their carcasses will not be soft.

572. Brewers' rice; rice meal.—*Brewers' rice*, which has previously been defined, is a very satisfactory substitute for corn or other grain in stock feeding. Though it is lower than corn in protein and fat, it contains more starch. It furnishes about as much total digestible nutrients per 100 lbs. as the grain sorghums or barley. Since brewers' rice may be less palatable than grain, it is best to mix it with well-liked feeds. Opposite in effect to rice bran and rice polish, it produces firm, hard pork.[43]

Rice meal, according to the definition of the Association of American Feed Control Officials, should be ground brown rice (ground rice after the hull has been removed).[13] The term is, however, used sometimes for entire ground rice, including the hulls. Rice meal is nearly equal to corn for stock feeding.[44]

573. Rice hulls.—Rice hulls are tasteless, tough, and woody. They are heavily charged with silica, have sharp, roughened edges, and are said to be irritating and dangerous to the walls of the stomach and intestines. In any event, they are digested to only a small extent by animals and furnish but about one-third as much digestible nutrients as wheat straw. They should therefore never be fed to stock. Yet they are still occasionally used by unscrupulous persons for adulterating stock feeds.

IX. EMMER; SPELT; MILLET

574. Emmer and spelt.—Emmer *(Triticum sativum, dicoccum)* and spelt *(Triticum sativum, spelta)* are close relatives of wheat, but the grain resembles barley in appearance, for the hulls are not usually removed from the kernels in threshing. These grains have never become of any importance in the United States, because the other cereals are more productive in most sections.[45]

In 1929 only 344,324 acres of emmer and spelt (mostly emmer) were grown in the United States, with an average yield of 18.1 bushels per acre. Three-fourths of the total acreage was in North Dakota and South Dakota. Though the acreage in these states had increased considerably during the previous 10-year period, these grains were of minor importance in comparison with wheat, oats, or barley. Emmer is often incorrectly called "speltz" or "spelt." Spelt is grown but little in this country and has been largely displaced by other grains where once raised in Europe.

Emmer and spelt closely resemble oats in composition. They may be used in the same manner as oats in feeding the various classes of stock and have about the same value as oats per 100 lbs.[46] The weight of these grains per bushel varies considerably, a common weight being 40 lbs. per bushel.

When a large proportion of the hulls is removed in threshing, emmer will resemble barley more than oats in composition and feeding value.[47]

575. Hog millet, or proso.—The only kind of millet grown in this country as a grain crop is hog millet *(Panicum milaceum)*, or proso, also called broom-corn millet. It is the ordinary millet of the Old World, which has been raised since prehistoric times as an important grain crop for human food. The forage types of millet have been discussed in Chapter XV.

Hog millet has spreading or panicled heads, wide, hairy leaves, and large seeds. It is not raised for grain to any extent in this country, except in the northern plains district, where the growing season is too short for the grain sorghums. Here it is often grown as a late-sown catch crop, for other cereals will usually outyield it if seeded at the normal time. The yields usually range from 10 to 30 bushels per acre.

Hog millet seed is a satisfactory feed for stock when it is ground, as it should always be. In trials with fattening cattle and lambs ground hog millet seed has been worth 75 to 90 per cent as much as corn per 100 lbs.[48] In Colorado experiments it has been nearly as valuable as corn for fattening pigs.[49]

X. BUCKWHEAT AND ITS BY-PRODUCTS

576. Buckwheat.—Buckwheat *(Fagopyrum esculentum)* is not really a cereal, but belongs to an entirely different family of plants. However, it is discussed in this chapter because the seed has much the same general nutritive characteristics as the cereal grains. Also, like wheat and rye, buckwheat is used chiefly for flour manufacture. Other food products (buckwheat farina and buckwheat groats) are made from buckwheat, and buckwheat is used for stock feeding when the grain is low in price.

Buckwheat often does better than the small grains on poor or very acid soil. It is also grown as a late-sown catch crop, because of its short growing season. An average of 622,200 acres were raised in the United States during the 10-year period, 1924-1933 inclusive, with a yield per acre of 15.7 bushels of about 45 to 48 lbs. each.

The woody hulls of buckwheat form about 18 to 20 per cent or more of the seed, and buckwheat grain has 10.3 per cent fiber, which is about as much as in oats. Buckwheat has about as much protein as oats, but it contains only 2.4 per cent fat. It supplies 64.4 lbs. total digestible nutrients per 100 lbs., which is one-tenth less than oats. The protein of buckwheat is not of high quality, and the grain and its by-products are deficient in calcium and in vitamins A and D.[50]

Buckwheat is not as palatable as most of the grains. It should therefore be mixed with such grain as corn, oats, or barley, the buckwheat preferably not forming over one-third the mixture. It should be ground for all classes of stock except poultry. Fed in a suitable mixture, it is a satisfactory substitute for grain in feeding dairy cows and other stock, probably being worth 10 to 15 per cent less than oats. In Canadian trials buckwheat was somewhat inferior to wheat or wheat middlings for fattening pigs.[51] When buckwheat forms too large a part of the ration, it tends to produce soft pork.[52]

Occasionally buckwheat grain and also the green fodder or straw cause peculiar eruptions and intense itching of the skin. This affects only white or light-colored portions of the hide, and animals are usually thus injured only when exposed to light.

Tartary buckwheat (Fagopyrum tataricum), also called "India wheat" or "rye buckwheat," is higher in hull and lower in milling quality and in feeding value than ordinary buckwheat. However, it does better on very poor soil and matures in an even shorter time.

577. Buckwheat by-products.—*Buckwheat hulls* are woody and higher in fiber than most straw. They therefore have little feeding value and should be used for fuel, bedding, or packing, rather than for feed.

Buckwheat middlings (also called *buckwheat shorts)* are the portions of the buckwheat grain immediately inside the hull, which are separated from the flour in the milling process. They contain on the average 29.7 per cent crude protein, 7.3 per cent fat, and 7.4 per cent fiber. They are therefore a rich, concentrated feed and have a high feeding value. The composition of this feed varies considerably, depending on the milling processes.

Sometimes the miller, desiring to dispose of as much of the hulls as possible, mixes them with the middlings to form *buckwheat feed* (sometimes called "buckwheat bran"). From the guaranteed composition of any lot and the average composition of buckwheat middlings and buckwheat hulls, one can estimate quite closely how much hulls have been included. For example, if the product has 20 per cent fiber, it will be about one-third hulls.

Buckwheat middlings are used most commonly for dairy cows, and are a satisfactory protein supplement when not forming over one-third the concentrate mixture. In New Jersey and Pennsylvania trials a good grade of buckwheat middlings was, on the average, nearly equal to gluten feed.[53] In a Pennsylvania test buckwheat middlings were about equal to brewers' dried grains for dairy cows.[54]

Buckwheat middlings are not satisfactory as the only protein supplement for pigs, thus resembling wheat middlings and linseed meal.[55] However, they proved superior to standard wheat middlings in trials at the West Virginia Station[56] when fed in combination with yellow corn and tankage. They were also used satisfactorily to replace linseed meal in the efficient "trio" supplemental mixture, consisting of tankage, linseed meal, and alfalfa hay.

QUESTIONS

1. Discuss the general nutritive characteristics of the cereal grains, considering amount and quality of protein, amounts of calcium and phosphorus, and content of the various vitamins.
2. Discuss the composition and the special nutritive characteristics of corn grain.
3. Under what conditions and for what classes of stock would you use corn-and-cob meal in place of shelled corn or ground shelled corn?
4. What is the approximate upper limit of moisture for safe storage of ear corn in a crib; for safe storage of shelled corn in a bin?
5. How may soft corn be utilized?
6. Discuss the composition of the different parts of the corn kernel.
7. Distinguish between *ground corn* and *corn feed meal.*
8. What is hominy feed? Compare the composition and feeding value of hominy feed and corn.
9. State the origin and composition of corn bran.
10. Describe the manufacture of starch from corn and name the by-products resulting.
11. Of what is corn oil meal composed and what is its general composition?
12. Discuss the composition and feeding value of corn gluten feed; corn gluten meal.
13. How does corn germ meal differ from corn oil meal?
14. Discuss the composition of oats in comparison with that of corn, and state the classes of livestock to which oats are most commonly fed in your district.

15. What is the chief by-product secured in the manufacture of oat meal? Discuss its composition and feeding value.
16. For what classes of stock are oat meal or hulled oats sometimes used?
17. How could you tell from the guaranteed composition whether a particular lot of corn-and-oat feed was of good grade?
18. Compare the composition and feeding value of wheat and corn.
19. Describe the manufacture of flour from wheat, and state the by-products secured in the milling process.
20. Discuss the composition and uses of: (a) Wheat bran; (b) standard wheat middlings, or brown shorts; (c) red dog flour, or white shorts; (d) flour wheat middlings, or gray shorts; (e) wheat mixed feed; and (f) wheat screenings.
21. Compare the composition of barley and corn, and their values for horses, dairy cows, fattening cattle, fattening lambs, and swine.
22. Describe the malting process, and discuss the composition and feeding value of brewers' dried grains; of malt sprouts.
23. What limitations has rye as a feed for livestock?
24. What are the chief rye by-products? Compare their composition with those of the corresponding wheat by-products.
25. Discuss the composition and feeding value of the grain sorghums, in comparison with corn.
26. If any of the following are of importance in your district, summarize briefly the information concerning their composition and feeding value: (a) Rough rice; (b) rice bran; (c) rice polish; (d) rice hulls; (e) emmer; (f) hog millet; (g) buckwheat; (h) buckwheat middlings.

REFERENCES

1. Woodworth and Mumm, Ill. Rpt. 1933; Fowlds, S. D. Rpt. 1930.
1a. Grain Div., Bur. Agr. Econ., U. S. Dept. Agr., mimeo. rpts. and information to the author.
2. Steenbock, Wis. Bul. 319; Steenbock and Boutwell, Jour. Biol. Chem., 41, 1920, pp. 81-96; Hetler and Meyer, Ill. Rpt. 1929; Hauge and Trost, Ind. Rpts. 1929, 1930, Jour. Biol. Chem. 86, 1930, pp. 161-172; Fraps, Tex. Bul. 422.
3. U. S. Dept. Agr., Misc. Pub. 173.
4. McHargue, Jour. Indus. and Engin. Chem., 12, 1920, pp. 257-262; Bailey and Thom, Oper. Miller, 25, 1920, pp. 368-371.
5. Rusk and Snapp, Ill. Bul. 313; Ill. Cir. 293; Evvard, Lamb, and Maynard, Iowa Bul. 216; Richey, U. S. Dept. Agr. Cir. 333.
6. Hopkins, Ill. Bul. 87.
7. Mitchell and Smuts, Jour. Biol. Chem., 95, 1932, pp. 263-281; Hetler and Meyer, Ill. Rpt. 1929; Ohio Bul. 373.
8. Smith, U. S. Dept. Agr., Bur. Plant Indus., Bul. 74.
9. Bohstedt, Lathrop, Sell, and Wolberg, Wis. Buls. 405, 410, 420, 421; Amer. Soc. Anim. Prod., Proc. 1928.
10. Lathrop and Bohstedt, Amer. Soc. Anim. Prod., Proc. 1932.
11. Lindsey and Beals, Mass. Bul. 200; Olson. S. D. Bul. 281; see also: Berry, Md. Bul. 332; Watson, Muir, Davidson, and Dore, Sci. Agr., Canada, 13, 1933, pp. 382-394.
12. Taylor and Anthony, Mich. Quar. Bul., 17, 1934, No. 1.
13. Assoc. of Amer. Feed Control Officials, Official Publication, 1935.
14. Winters, Hoard's Dairyman, 71, 1926, p. 776; Graves and Miller, Jersey Bulletin, 46, 1927, p. 1251; Moseley, Stuart, and Graves, U. S. Dept. Agr., Tech. Bul. 116; Miller and Graves, U. S. Dept. Agr., Tech. Bul. 321.
15. Cunningham, Ariz. Rpt. 1932; Moore, Miss. Rpt. 1927.
16. Bailey, The Chemistry of Wheat Flour, p. 122.
17. Jordan, Hart, and Patten, N. Y. (Geneva) Tech. Bul. 1; Williams, Amer. Jour. Physiol., 83, 1927, pp. 1-14; Falcon-Lesses, Jour. Nutr., 2, 1930, pp. 295-310; Cowgill and Anderson, Jour. Amer. Med. Assoc., 98, 1932, pp. 1866-1875; Rose et al., Jour. Amer. Dietet. Assoc., 8, 1932, pp. 133-156.
18. Sheets and Boerner, U. S. Dept. Agr., Misc. Rpt., 1931.
19. Selvig, Minn. Sta., Crookston Substa. Rpt. 1924; Linfield, Mont. Buls. 47, 59; Griswold, N. D. Bul. 274; Foster and Merrill, Utah Bul. 78; Dunsmore, Canada Dept. of Agr., Pamphlet 87.
20. Hickman, Rinehart, and Johnson, Id. Buls. 142, 194; Id. Cir. 40.
21. Vaughan, Joseph, and Vinke, Mont. Rpt. 1927.
22. Hughes, Cal. Sta., Jour. Agr. Res., 47, 1933, pp. 487-494.
23. Lawes and Gilbert, Rothamsted Memoirs, Vol. IV.
24. Halnan, Minister of Agri. Jour., Great Britain, 30, 1924, p. 960; Voorhees, N. J. Rpt. 1892.
25. Hooper and Anderson, Ky. Bul. 176.
26. Sheets and Shepherd, U. S. Dept. Agr., mimeo. rpt.
27. Lindsey, Mass. Bul. 94; see also: Hills. Vt. Rpt. 1902.

28. Davies and Sullivan, Jour. Agr. Sci., England, 17, 1927, pp. 380-387; Mangold, Handb. Ernähr. und Stoffwechsels, Vol. I.
29. Morrison, Humphrey, and Bohstedt, Wis. Bul. 302.
30. Swanson and Laude, Kan. Bul. 266.
31. Jones and Dickson, Tex. Bul. 379.
32. Smith, Jour. Agr. Res., 40, 1930, pp. 1129-1145; Menaul, Okla. Bul. 152; Okla. Rpt. 1922; Bidwell, Bopst, and Bowling, U. S. Dept. Agr. Bul. 1129.
33. Dvorachek, Ark. Bul. 203; Dalrymple, La. Bul. 122; Calloway, La. Rpt. 1921.
34. Trowbridge, Mo. Bul. 310 and mimeo. rpt.
35. Bray, La. Rice Expt. Sta. Rpt. 1929-31; Weaver, Mo. Bul. 310; Hale, Tex. Rpt. 1931.
36. Sheets and Semple, U. S. Dept. Agri., Misc. Pub. 132.
37. Dvorachek, Ark. Bul. 215; Lush and Hale, Tex. Bul. 352.
38. Miller, Cal. Sta., mimeo. rpts.; Craig and Marshall, Tex. Bul. 76; Burns, Tex. Bul. 182; Knox, J. H. Jones, Black, and J. M. Jones, Tex. Rpt. 1933; Quesenberry, U. S. Dept. Agr. Cir. 65.
39. Dvorachek, Ark. Bul. 128; Dvorachek and Sandhouse, Ark. Bul. 142; Martin, Ark. Bul. 303; Hughes, Cal. Bul. 420; Bray, La. Bul. 242; Templeton, Miss. Rpt. 1924; Burk, Tex. Bul. 224; Williams and McConnell, Tex. Bul. 286; Warren and Williams, Tex. Bul. 313; Sheets and Semple, U. S. Dept. Agr., Misc. Pub. 132; Tirol, Philippine Agriculturist, 21, 1933, pp. 628-638.
40. Dvorachek, Ark. Buls. 221, 257.
41. Quesenberry, U. S. Dept. Agr. Cir. 65; Craig and Marshall, Tex. Bul. 76.
42. Dvorachek, Ark. Bul. 128; Martin, Ark. Bul. 303; Hughes, Cal. Bul. 420; La. Planter, 69, 1922, pp. 59-61; Bray, La. Bul. 242; Barnett and Goodell, Miss. Bul. 218; Templeton, Miss. Rpt. 1924; Williams and Warren, Tex. Bul. 313; Sheets and Semple, U. S. Dept. Agr., Misc. Pub. 132.
43. Martin, Ark. Bul. 303; Bray, La. Bul. 242; Barnett and Goodell, Miss. Bul. 218; Hankins and Ellis, U. S. Dept. Agr. Buls. 1407, 1492; Quesenberry, U. S. Dept. Agr. Cir. 65.
44. Starkey and Salmon, S. C. Bul. 214; Barton, Ness, and Crampton, MacDonald Col., Canada, Tech. Bul. 4.
45. Martin and Leighty, U. S. Dept. Agr., Farmers' Bul. 1429; U. S. Dept. Agr. Bul. 1197.
46. Buffum and Griffin, Colo. Bul. 75; Wilson and Skinner, S. D. Buls. 80, 81, 86, 97; Wilson, S. D. Bul. 160; Hackedorn, Sotola, and Singleton, Wash. Bul. 258; Faville, Wyo. Buls. 81, 85.
47. Olson, S. D. Bul. 264.
48. Osland, Maynard, Morton, and Brandon, Colo. Bul. 395, Press Bul. 80; Wilson and Skinner, S. D. Buls. 83, 86, 97; Wilson, S. D. Bul. 160.
49. Maynard and Brandon, Colo. Press. Bul. 69.
50. Longwell, Amer. Soc. Anim. Prod., Proc. 1928; Palladin, Biochem. Ztschr., 136, 1923, pp. 346-352; Coe, U. S. Dept. Agr. Cir. 190.
51. Ottawa, Canada, Expt. Farms, Rpts. 1894, 1901.
52. Grisdale, Ottawa, Canada, Expt. Farms, Bul. 51.
53. N. J. Rpt. 1931; Penn. Bul. 170; see also: Hills, Vt. Rpt. 1902.
54. Hayward and Weld, Penn. Bul. 41.
55. Robison, Ohio Bul. 349.
56. Livesay and Stillwell, West Va. Bul. 213; see also: Penn. Bul. 170.

CHAPTER XVIII

OTHER SEEDS AND THEIR BY-PRODUCTS

I. Cottonseed and Cottonseed By-products

578. Importance of the cotton crop.—Cotton *(Gossypium hirsutum)* ranks next to corn in importance and value in the United States, and is by far the most important southern crop. During the 10-year period, 1925-34 inclusive, there were produced in this country an average of 14,315,000 bales of cotton lint, having a gross weight of 500 lbs. each and a net weight of 478 lbs.; and, in addition, 6,362,000 tons of cottonseed. The total average farm value of the cotton crop for this period was slightly over one billion dollars a year. In 1934 only 9,731,000 bales of lint cotton and 4,324,000 tons of cottonseed were produced, due to the Federal crop-reduction program.

The cottonseed meal and cake which are secured in the manufacture of oil from cottonseed rank next in importance to the wheat by-products in value and importance among all the by-product concentrates used for stock feeding in this country. Indeed, the tonnage of cottonseed meal and cake has exceeded the total tonnage of all other oil meals and cakes combined, plus the tonnages of the corn-starch by-products, the oat by-products, the brewing and distilling by-products, and the meat and fish by-products. In addition, cottonseed hulls are one of the most important roughages for stock in the South.

From 1924-25 to 1932-33 there were produced in the United States an average of 2,314,000 tons of cottonseed meal and cake, and 1,437,000 tons of cottonseed hulls. From each ton of cottonseed there are secured approximately the following: Cottonseed cake or meal, 915 lbs.; crude oil, 299 lbs.; hulls, 579 lbs.; and linters, or short fiber, 69 lbs.; with a loss of 138 lbs.[1]

In spite of the high value of cottonseed meal for stock feeding, 8 to 9 per cent of that produced is often used for fertilizer. This is on account of the high content of both nitrogen and phosphorus in the meal.

579. Manufacture of cottonseed meal and cake.—At the oil mills, after the cottonseed has been cleaned and more or less of the short lint covering the seed has been removed by machinery, the leathery hulls of the seed are cut by machines, called hullers, so the kernels can drop out. The kernels are separated more or less completely from the hulls by shakers and beaters, containing metal screens. They are then crushed into thin flakes, cooked by steam, put between cloths, and placed in hydraulic presses. Here as much as possible of the oil is expressed. The residue is cottonseed cake, in the form of hard slabs about one-half inch thick, 14 inches wide, and 32 inches long.

In a few oil mills the oil is expressed from the cottonseed kernels by machines called "expellers," and the residue is then in flake form, instead of cake. The expeller-process cottonseed meal has the same composition and value as the hydraulic-process product. In the Southwest the oil is sometimes expressed from the whole seed by expellers, without hulling. *Whole-pressed cottonseed,* which is discussed later in this chapter, is the by-product from this method.

For sale in the eastern and central states and for feeding to dairy cattle the cottonseed cake is generally ground to a fine meal. For sale in the western states, especially for use on the ranges, it is frequently broken into pieces of pea or nut size, and for export it is often left whole. For feeding out of doors, the broken cake is preferable to the meal, as it is not scattered by the wind. Since the great majority of the product is fed in this country as cottonseed meal and also since the meal and cake have the same general value, the term cottonseed meal will be generally used in this volume in referring to both cottonseed meal and cottonseed cake.

In addition to cottonseed meal, the following sizes of cottonseed cake are made in this country: *Nut-size cake,* consisting of pieces from three-fourths to 1.5 inches in diameter; *sheep-size cake,* from five-eighths to seven-eighths inch; *pea-size cake,* from three-eighths to five-eighths inch; and *pebble-size cake,* under three-eighths inch in diameter.

580. Grades of cottonseed meal or cake.—Because cottonseed meal and cake are used chiefly as protein supplements, they are graded and sold on the basis of the guaranteed protein content, in addition to the general quality of the product. According to the definitions adopted by the Association of American Feed Control Officials, "cottonseed meal is a product of cottonseed only, composed principally of the kernel, with such portion of the hull as is necessary in the manufacture of oil; provided that nothing shall be recognized as cottonseed meal that does not conform to the foregoing definition and that does not contain at least 36 per cent of protein."[2]

In the definitions cottonseed meal is classed either as *prime quality* or *off quality.* "*Cottonseed meal, prime quality* must be finely ground, not necessarily bolted, of sweet odor, reasonably bright in color, yellowish, not brown or reddish, free from excessive lint, and shall contain not less than 36 per cent of protein. It must be designated and sold according to its protein content." For example, prime-quality cottonseed meal guaranteed to contain 43 per cent protein must be designated as "43 per cent protein cottonseed meal, prime quality."

Cottonseed meal not fulfilling the above requirements as to color, odor, and texture must be designated as "cottonseed meal, off quality," the guaranteed protein content also being stated.

On account of the considerable variation in the composition of the various grades of cottonseed meal, it should always be purchased on definite guarantees not only of protein content, but also of fat and fiber. It is shown in Appendix Table I that grades of meal with lower protein content not only supply less protein, but are also higher in fiber. This is because the hulls are usually removed less completely in the production of meal of medium protein content. Such meal therefore furnishes less total digestible nutrients than that which has 41 per cent or more of protein.

The cottonseed raised in certain sections of the Southwest, especially in Texas, is higher in protein than the seed produced in the other cotton-growing districts. For this reason, to be sold as cottonseed meal in Texas, a state law requires that the product contain at least 43 per cent protein. If lower than this, it must be sold as cottonseed feed. The 41 per cent protein product from Texas seed will usually contain more hulls and therefore be slightly higher in fiber and lower in feeding value than cottonseed meal containing 41 per cent protein from the districts where the cottonseed has a lower protein content. (See Appendix Table I.) The same is true for the Texas products containing lower percentages of protein.

581. Composition and nutritive properties.—Cottonseed meal of the best grades has 41 per cent or more of protein, therefore being appreciably richer in protein than linseed meal and supplying about the same amount as corn gluten meal. The most common protein guarantee for cottonseed meal is 41 per cent, but considerable is sold with a guarantee of 43 per cent, and some of the Texas product is guaranteed to contain 45 per cent. The average composition of the various grades is shown in Appendix Table I.

The protein of cottonseed meal is of good quality to supplement the cereal grains in feeding cattle, sheep, or horses. For swine and poultry much better results are secured when cottonseed meal is used as only part of the protein supplement, the rest of the protein being furnished by such feeds as tankage, meat scraps, fish meal, or milk products.

High-grade cottonseed meal supplies slightly less total digestible nutrients than linseed meal, the 43-per-cent-protein grade of cottonseed meal containing 75.5 per cent total digestible nutrients, and the 41-per-cent grade, 73.6 per cent.

Cottonseed meal is one of the richest feeds in phosphorus, containing an average of 1.19 per cent for the 41-per-cent-protein grade. It is fair in calcium for a seed by-product, having about 0.20 per cent. Like other seed products, cottonseed meal lacks vitamin D, and it also has little or no vitamin A.

These lacks can readily be made good by including in the ration a sufficient amount of well-cured legume hay or mixed hay high in legumes. If grass hay, such as timothy or prairie hay, is of excellent quality, it will supply these necessary nutritive factors, except that it may not furnish enough calcium, unless grown on soil rich in lime.

Cottonseed meal tends to produce hard body fat and also milk fat of a high melting point. Therefore it helps to overcome the tendency of peanuts and soybeans to produce soft pork. If dairy cows are fed large amounts of cottonseed meal, the butter may be tallowy and undesirably hard. If too much cottonseed meal is fed to poultry, it will tend to cause the yolks to turn dark when the eggs are kept in storage. While cottonseed meal has been often considered slightly constipating in its effect, there was no such tendency in Michigan tests in which it was fed with legume hay.[3]

582. Effects of cottonseed meal when improperly fed.—It is generally known that cottonseed contains appreciable amounts of a substance called *gossypol,* the quantity varying considerably with various climatic and soil factors.[4] Cottonseed from Oklahoma and Texas apparently contains less gossypol than that from the southeastern states.

Investigations have shown that gossypol is definitely poisonous to certain species of animals if consumed in too large amounts, and that the tolerance of various species varies widely. Cattle are not affected by considerable amounts of gossypol, while swine are seriously injured by similar amounts. Care should also be taken that too much cottonseed meal is not fed to calves, at least up to about 3 or 4 months of age. Horses and sheep are probably affected by smaller amounts of gossypol than are cattle, but they will tolerate larger proportions than swine.

Fortunately, in the ordinary cooking of cottonseed kernels in the process of oil manufacture, most of the gossypol is converted into a substance (called d-gossypol, or bound gossypol) which has much less toxic properties. The same change is produced by the heating that occurs in the expeller-process of production of oil from cottonseed. By special heating of dampened cottonseed meal under steam pressure, the gossypol can be destroyed so completely that the product can be safely fed to swine in considerable amounts.[5]

On account of the great importance of cottonseed meal and cake for livestock feeding in this country, the use for each class of stock is discussed fully in Part III. The numerous experiments are there summarized that have been conducted to determine the value of cottonseed meal in comparison with the other common protein supplements.

583. Cattle may safely be fed much cottonseed meal.—Extensive investigations by the Michigan, North Carolina, Oklahoma, Pennsylvania, and Texas Stations and by the United States Department of Agriculture have shown conclusively that cattle over 3 or 4 months of age may safely be fed large amounts of cottonseed meal continuously for long periods, if care is taken to provide sufficient high-quality hay or good pasturage.[6] Such roughage makes good the lack of vitamins (especially vitamin A) and of calcium in the cottonseed meal and in the other concentrates usually fed.

These investigations have proved that in the case of cattle these deficiencies are the cause of the so-called "cottonseed-meal poisoning" which often results when stock are heavily fed on cottonseed meal combined with roughage low in vitamins and calcium. Cattle are not affected by the amount of gossypol usually present in cottonseed meal, or even in cottonseed. They remain healthy when suitable roughage is used, even if much larger amounts of cottonseed meal are fed than were formerly considered safe.

In these trials dairy cows which were fed large amounts of cottonseed meal for long periods have maintained good milk production and produced healthy calves, if they were given plenty of well-cured legume hay or prairie hay or if they were on good pasture. Similar results have been secured with beef cattle. On the other hand, failure resulted when cottonseed meal was fed with feeds low in vitamin A, such as cottonseed hulls, grain straw, corn stover, sorghum fodder or dried beet pulp. The results were somewhat better when cottonseed meal was fed as the only concentrate with corn or sorghum silage than when the meal was fed with cottonseed hulls, but silage apparently does not always furnish sufficient vitamin A to protect cattle entirely from injury.

Symptoms similar to the so-called "cottonseed-meal poisoning" were produced in some of these experiments when cattle were fed rations low in vitamin A, but which included no cottonseed products whatsoever. Provided the injury on such a ration as cottonseed meal and hulls had not progressed too far, the animals could be cured rather rapidly by feeding cod-liver oil, good legume hay, or fresh green forage.

In these experiments very large amounts of cottonseed meal have been fed to dairy cows with entire success when they have had plenty of good roughage. For example, in the Oklahoma trials cows have been fed continuously for three consecutive lactation periods in dry lot, without pasture, on only cottonseed meal and good-quality prairie hay, with satisfactory production and without any symptoms of injury. The cows consumed an average of 10.3 lbs. cottonseed meal per head daily over this extended period. When dried beet pulp, which is low in vitamin A and calcium, was substituted for the prairie hay, the animals developed the symptoms of "cottonseed-meal injury."

In the Michigan experiments calves were raised from 90 days of age on a ration of cottonseed meal (fed as the only protein supplement), corn grain, high-quality timothy hay, and corn silage. This ration was fed for several years and the offspring of the original heifers were continued on the same ration. No bad effects were produced and the milk yield was normal, though large amounts of cottonseed meal were fed. Up to 150 days of age the calves received 0.5 lb. cottonseed meal per head daily, and the heifers received about 2.3 lbs. a head daily from 6 months of age to first calving. During milk production certain cows were fed as much as 9 lbs. of cottonseed meal on the average for the entire lactation period, and as much as 17 lbs. a day were fed to a high-producing cow for several months.

Some believe that the heavy feeding of cottonseed meal tends to cause mastitis or other udder trouble in dairy cows. In these experiments, however, no such effect was observed.

These results, which show that with good roughage cottonseed meal can be safely fed to dairy cows and other cattle, except young calves, in large amounts and even as the only concentrate, are of especial importance in the southern states. There cottonseed meal is often the cheapest source not only of protein but also of digestible nutrients. Under these conditions it is often economical to feed cottonseed meal as the only concentrate to dairy cows and beef cattle, or at least in considerably larger amounts than are needed to balance the ration in protein content.

584. Cottonseed meal should be limited for other stock. — For other stock than cattle over 3 to 4 months of age, care must be taken to limit the amount to that which has been proven definitely to be safe for the particular class of animal. Recommendations are given in the respective chapters of Part III for each class of stock. When it is thus fed, cottonseed meal is an excellent supplement for sheep, for horses and mules, and even for calves and swine. Swine should not receive more than 9 per cent of cottonseed meal in their rations. Horses and mules may be fed 1 to 2 lbs. of cottonseed meal per head daily with good-quality roughage. Sheep may be fed as much cottonseed meal as is needed to balance their rations, but should not be fed large amounts for extended periods.

585. Cottonseed feed.—In the production of cottonseed oil a certain proportion of hulls must be included with the kernels in order to secure the maximum yield of oil. Occasionally a considerable proportion of hulls is left with the kernels. As has been stated before, the term *cottonseed feed* should be used instead of cottonseed meal when the protein content of the product is reduced below 36 per cent (for sale in Texas below 43 per cent).

As is shown in Appendix Table I, cottonseed feed is not only lower in protein than high-grade cottonseed meal, but it is also higher in fiber and lower in total digestible nutrients. Cottonseed feed is sometimes sold for but a few dollars a ton less than the best grades of cottonseed meal. It is therefore important to note the fiber guarantee for any lot of cottonseed meal or cottonseed feed.

One can determine approximately the proportion of additional hulls in a sample of cottonseed feed by comparing its fiber guarantee with the average fiber figures shown in Appendix Table I for high-grade cottonseed meal and for cottonseed hulls. By appearance alone it is impossible to distinguish good cottonseed meal from finely ground cottonseed feed. Cottonseed feed may be an entirely legitimate product, for it is sometimes impossible to separate thoroughly the hulls of certain kinds of cottonseed from the kernels. However, such feed should be bought at a price corresponding to its actual value.

In case of doubt as to purity, the following simple test will show the approximate amount of hulls present in cottonseed meal:[7]

Place a teaspoonful of the meal (do not use more) in a tumbler and pour over it from 1.5 to 2 ounces of hot water. Stir the mass till it is thoroughly wet and all the particles are floating. Allow it to settle for 5 to 10 seconds and pour off the liquid. If there has settled out in this time a large amount of fine, brown sediment which is noticeably darker than the fine yellow meal and which keeps settling out on repeated treatments with hot water, the product is low grade. All meals contain small quantities of hulls and will show dark specks when thus tested, but the results are striking when pure meal is compared with cottonseed feed.

586. Whole-pressed cottonseed.—At some oil mills the hulls are not removed from the cottonseed, but the whole seeds are processed in expeller machines. The by-product in this method is called *whole-pressed cottonseed*, or sometimes "cold-pressed cottonseed cake," or "caddo cake." It is marketed in flake form, or is ground and sold as *ground whole-pressed cottonseed*.

Since this feed contains all the cottonseed hulls, it is much lower in protein and higher in fiber than cottonseed meal, and has a correspondingly lower feeding value per ton. It is usually guaranteed to contain 25 or 28 per cent protein and generally has 23 to 25 per cent fiber.

Whole-pressed cottonseed may be fed to stock in the same manner as cottonseed meal.[8] A safe basis for valuing this feed in comparison with cottonseed meal, when the guaranteed protein content of each is known, is to estimate the amount of cottonseed meal and of cottonseed hulls a ton of the whole-pressed cottonseed contains, and add to the value of this amount of meal the value of the hulls as roughage. Thus, a ton of whole-pressed cottonseed having 28 per cent protein will be about equal to 1,200 lbs. of 43 per cent protein cottonseed meal and 800 lbs. of cottonseed hulls.

587. Cottonseed.—Commonly but little cottonseed is fed to stock, but instead farmers sell the seed to the oil mills and buy cottonseed meal. This is both on account of the value of the oil and because cottonseed meal usually gives better results as a stock feed. However, when the price for cottonseed is unusually low in comparison with that of cottonseed meal, it is an economical feed.

Animals fed too large amounts of cottonseed may scour badly, on account of the large amount of oil. In trials with dairy cows it has required 171 to 206 lbs. of cottonseed to equal 100 lbs. of high-grade cottonseed meal. It is sometimes difficult to get cows to eat the seed, unless a more palatable feed, such as ground corn or wheat bran, is mixed with it.[9] There is no advantage in grinding cottonseed for cattle, and this is a difficult task in certain types of mills, due to the high oil content. Cottonseed has an even more marked hardening effect than cottonseed meal on the character of butter.

Excellent results have been secured in recent Texas trials in which whole cottonseed has been used in place of cottonseed meal as a supplement for fattening beef cattle.[10] When only enough cottonseed was fed to balance the ration, it required 140 lbs. or less of cottonseed to equal 100 lbs. of cottonseed meal in value. The cottonseed replaced not only the cottonseed meal in the ration, but also, on account of its richness in oil, it replaced part of the grain. In earlier trials in which larger amounts of cottonseed were fed to fattening cattle, it had a lower value in comparison with cottonseed meal.[11] Not over 4 lbs. of cottonseed per head daily should be fed to fattening calves, due to the high oil content.

Though cottonseed is rarely fed to sheep, fattening lambs made satisfactory gains in a Texas trial on a ration of 0.8 lb. milo grain, 0.4 lb. whole cottonseed, and 1.4 lbs. alfalfa hay.[12] The results were unsatisfactory on a ration of whole cottonseed and cottonseed hulls, due to the lack of vitamins and calcium. When 0.6 lb. of whole cottonseed per head daily was substituted for the cottonseed cake and part of the sorghum grain in a ration for fattening lambs of sorghum heads, cottonseed cake, and alfalfa hay, each 100 lbs. of cottonseed was equal to 27 lbs. of cottonseed cake and 80 lbs. of sorghum heads. Even better results were secured in another trial when cottonseed was substituted for part of the sorghum grain in a ration of sorghum grain, cottonseed meal, and alfalfa hay.

Immature cottonseed, or bolly cottonseed, is much lower in protein and fat than mature seed. Its feeding value is correspondingly less.

588. Cottonseed hulls.—Cottonseed hulls are one of the important roughages in the South, especially for cattle, to which they are chiefly fed. Cottonseed hulls supply 43.7 per cent of total digestible nutrients, which is about as much as is furnished by late-cut grass hay or by oat straw. The hulls are very low in protein and practically none of it is digestible. As a result, they have only 0.1 per cent of digestible protein. The hulls are also low in calcium and phosphorus and are lacking in vitamins.

To secure good results in feeding cottonseed hulls they must be fed so as to correct their deficiencies. The use of cottonseed hulls for dairy cattle, beef cattle, and sheep is discussed in detail in the chapters of Part III. For cattle they are about equal to fair-quality grass hay and are worth more per ton than corn stover, sorghum stover, straw, or poor hay, if they are properly fed.

Cottonseed hulls should be fed with protein-rich feeds and as only part of the roughage, along with good-quality legume hay or other forage that will supply the vitamins and the minerals in which they are deficient. Unless they are fed with considerable legume hay, a calcium supplement should be used, such as ground limestone or oyster shells. Also, a phosphorus supplement should be added, unless sufficient of this mineral is furnished by a phosphorus-rich protein supplement, such as cottonseed meal.

Cottonseed hulls are usually fuzzy, due to short lint which remains on the seed. Sometimes this lint is removed from the seed at the oil-mills for paper making and other purposes and the hulls from such seed are ground, being then called *cottonseed hull bran*. Though finely ground, the value of the product is not appreciably greater than that of ordinary hulls.

II. FLAXSEED; LINSEED MEAL AND CAKE; OTHER FLAX BY-PRODUCTS

589. Flaxseed.—Flax *(Linum usitatissimum)* is grown in this country almost entirely as a cash crop for the production of linseed oil from the seed. During the 10-year period, 1924-1933 inclusive, an average of 2,712,000 acres of flaxseed were raised, with a yield per acre of 6.6 bushels, weighing 56 lbs. each. Over 90 per cent of the crop was produced in the four leading hard-spring-wheat states — North Dakota, Minnesota, South Dakota, and Montana. Practically no flax is grown for fiber in the United States. Our flax fiber is imported from countries where the cost of labor is lower, for much hand labor is required in the retting of flax and the preparation of the fiber.

But little flaxseed is used directly for feeding, on account of the value of the seed for oil production. However, ground flaxseed is entirely satisfactory as a protein supplement in place of linseed meal. Though it contains only two-thirds as much protein as linseed meal, it is one of the richest of feeds in total digestible nutrients. On account of its high oil content (which averages 36.4 per cent), it supplies more than 100 lbs. total digestible nutrients per 100 lbs. (including digestible fat multiplied by 2.25).

In feeding experiments with fattening cattle, fattening lambs, and pigs ground flaxseed has usually been equal or slightly superior to linseed meal in feeding value.[13] If too much flaxseed is fed to pigs, soft pork may be produced. Ground flaxseed is sometimes used as an ingredient in calf meals.

It is of interest to note that the reserve food stored in flaxseed is largely oil and pentosans, no starch grains being found in well-matured seed. Very rarely flaxseed may contain a compound which, when acted upon by an enzyme in the seeds, yields the poison prussic acid. This enzyme is destroyed by the heat to which the ground flaxseed is ordinarily subjected in oil extraction. In making gruel or mash from untreated flaxseed, it is advisable to use boiling water and keep the mass hot an hour or two, to destroy any prussic-acid-forming enzyme in the seed.

590. Production of linseed oil and linseed meal or cake.—In the production of linseed oil, the carefully-cleaned flaxseed is coarsely ground, heated, and then pressed in hydraulic presses, as in the "old process" of cottonseed oil production. The *linseed cake* thus produced is commonly ground to various degrees of fineness to form *linseed meal* or nut-size or pea-size linseed cake.

The "new process" of oil extraction, in which the oil is extracted by means of gasoline, has never been used to any considerable extent in this country. This was because farmers preferred the old-process linseed meal, for the new-process meal is not so palatable and has less of a beneficial laxative effect. None of the linseed meal now made in the United States is produced by the "new process," and therefore when "linseed meal" or "linseed oil meal" is mentioned in this volume, the old-process product is meant.

This feed is variously called *linseed meal* or *linseed cake,* and sometimes merely *oil meal* or *oil cake.* Ground flaxseed is not called "linseed meal" in this country. The terms *oil meal* and *oil cake* should always mean the linseed product, unless the term is prefaced by some other name, as *soybean* oil meal, for example.

Linseed meal or cake is sold primarily on the basis of its protein content, and the percentage of protein should be stated definitely in the trade name of the meal. For example, linseed meal guaranteed to contain 34 per cent protein is called "34-per-cent-protein linseed meal."

Flaxseed grown in this country and Canada is higher in protein than the kind produced in Argentina, from which country much is imported into the United States. Linseed meal or cake from North American flaxseed usually contains at least 34 per cent protein and often more than 36 per cent, while that from well-cleaned Argentine seed may not have over 30 to 31 per cent. Separate averages are given in Appendix Table I for the various grades of linseed meal.

591. Linseed meal and linseed cake as feeds.—In this country most of the linseed cake is ground to form linseed meal, and therefore this term will be used generally for both forms of the feed. Linseed meal is one of the most popular protein supplements for dairy cattle, beef cattle, horses, sheep, and swine. Its value and use for each of these classes of stock are treated in detail in the chapters of Part III. The importance of linseed meal and cake in the United States is shown by the fact that on the average over 300,000 tons are fed annually to our livestock.

The popularity of linseed meal is due not only to its richness in protein, but even more to its palatability and to its slightly laxative and conditioning effects, which aid in keeping stock thrifty. Linseed meal produces excellent results when used as the only protein supplement in feeding dairy cattle, beef cattle, sheep, and horses. In the case of swine and poultry linseed meal should be used in combination with another protein supplement which provides protein of better quality, such as meat scraps, tankage, fish meal, or dairy by-products. (151)

On account of its laxative effect, linseed meal is of especial value for cattle, sheep, or horses when they have little or no legume hay and the roughage they are fed is of rather poor quality. For dairy cattle linseed meal is in high regard as a protein supplement, and it is one of the most common ingredients in dairy rations throughout most of the country, except in the cotton belt. When cows have plenty of good roughage, cottonseed meal or gluten meal may be worth more per ton as protein supplements, on account of their higher protein content.

For fattening cattle linseed meal, when used as the only protein supplement, has proven in numerous experiments to have a considerably higher value than cottonseed meal, ton for ton, even when fed with excellent roughage. However, a combination of half linseed meal and half cottonseed meal produces just as good results as does linseed meal alone and generally at lower cost. Differing to a surprising degree from the results with cattle, linseed meal has not been of higher value than cottonseed meal for fattening lambs, when either has been fed as the only supplement. With the exception of wheat bran, linseed meal is the most common protein supplement in horse feeding.

On account of the wide demand for linseed meal, it is often not such a cheap source of protein as some of the other protein supplements. It should then not be fed as the only protein supplement, but should be combined with the cheaper sources of protein and used on account of its particular regulating and conditioning effects.

592. Other flax by-products.—*Screenings oil feed* is the ground product obtained after extraction of part of the oil by either the "old process" or the "new process" from the smaller, imperfect flaxseed, weed seeds, and other foreign materials having feeding value, separated in cleaning flaxseed. The composition and feeding value of this feed and also of flaxseed screenings differ quite widely. (548)

Unscreened flaxseed oil feed cake is the product obtained by extraction of part of the oil from unscreened flaxseed. Depending on the proportion of screenings present, its value will be correspondingly lower than that of linseed meal.

Flax plant by-product is that portion of the flax plant remaining after the separation of the seed, the bast fiber, and a portion of the shives (the stems after the fiber is removed). It consists of flax shives, flax pods, broken and immature flax seeds, and the cortical tissues (bark and outer portions) of the stems. It is a by-product secured in the manufacture of flax fiber for rugmaking, etc., from flax straw. This low-grade product is used in certain cheap mixed feeds. Smith of the Massachusetts Station concluded that such material was not worth to the Massachusetts farmer even the cost of the freight from the states where it is produced.[14]

593. Linseed-meal-and-screenings-oil-feed.—Sometimes the screenings are not removed thoroughly from the flaxseed before it is processed, or screenings oil feed is added to the linseed meal. Such a product should be sold definitely as *linseed-meal-and-screenings-oil-feed*, and not as linseed meal. According to the definition of the Association of American Feed Control Officials, linseed meal must contain less than 6 per cent of weed seeds and other foreign materials and no portion of the stated 6 per cent shall be deliberately added.[2]

The percentage of protein or even of fiber in the linseed meal may not be a reliable indication that screenings or screenings oil feed have not been added. This is because some screenings contain no more fiber than pure linseed meal. If the linseed meal that is being produced contains 37 per cent or more of protein, as meal from North American flaxseed sometimes does, a limited amount of screenings can be added without reducing the protein content below 32 to 34 per cent or without increasing the fiber content appreciably.

In purchasing linseed meal one should read carefully the name on the tag or sack. In the past linseed-meal-and-screenings-oil-feed has occasionally been branded in large letters "old-process linseed meal," with some such statement below in much smaller letters as "and screenings oil feed." These inferior products are sometimes sold for substantially as high a price as pure linseed meal. In certain cases they may contain such a large amount of bitter-tasting weed seeds that they are decidedly unpalatable to stock and may even produce a flavor in the milk of cows.

III. Legume Seeds and Their By-products

594. Soybeans.—The great and increasing importance of soybeans in the United States has already been pointed out in Chapter XIII, and their use as a forage crop is there discussed in detail. The acreage of soybeans harvested for seed has increased tremendously in the past few years. In 1935 there were grown 2,681,000 acres of soybeans, not including the large acreage which was raised for hay. Of this amount, the seed was harvested on 2,379,000 acres, the rest being used for pasture, for hogging down, for silage, or as a soiling crop. The average yield of seed per acre for the 4-year-period, 1932-1935 inclusive, was 15.4 bushels of 60 lbs. each. A large part of the seed produced is used for the making of soybean oil and soybean oil meal.

The seeds of the soybean are the richest in protein of all the common seeds used for feed, averaging 36.9 per cent. Moreover, soybean protein is of excellent quality to supplement the proteins of the cereal grains. Indeed, soybeans and peanuts provide proteins of distinctly better quality than other common seeds or the by-products from the seeds. They are excelled in quality of protein only by feeds of animal origin, such as milk products, tankage, meat scrap, and fish meal.

In addition to their richness in excellent protein, soybeans contain 17.2 per cent fat and are low in fiber. Therefore they furnish considerably more total digestible nutrients than the grains and other common concentrates, having 86.2 per cent. Soybeans are rather low in calcium, having only 0.20 per cent, and they contain 0.60 per cent phosphorus, being decidedly lower in phosphorus than the wheat by-products, cottonseed meal, or linseed meal. Also, like other seeds, they are lacking in vitamin D, and they supply no appreciable amount of vitamin A. Because of the high fat content of soybeans, stock sometimes tire of them if they are fed considerable amounts for an extended period.

On account of the importance of soybeans, their use and value for the various classes of stock are discussed in detail in Part III. It is there shown that soybeans are in general as satisfactory and valuable a protein supplement as cottonseed meal for dairy cattle, beef cattle, sheep, and horses.

Unfortunately, as is discussed in detail in Chapter XXXV, when fattening pigs are fed a considerable amount of soybeans for any extended period, the lard becomes so soft that the quality of the carcass is injured. Soybean oil meal does not have a marked effect on the carcass when it is fed in such amounts as are necessary to balance the ration, because most of the oil has been removed. As stated previously, soybeans do not have any appreciable effect on the carcasses of ruminants, including cattle, sheep, and goats. (**222**)

It is shown in Part III that for cattle, sheep, and horses raw soybeans are very satisfactory as a protein supplement. On the other hand, the value of soybeans for swine is greatly increased by cooking.[15] This does not, however, counteract the softening effect of soybeans on the carcass of swine. Cooking soybeans for swine not only increases the palatability, but also improves the digestibility and the utilization of the protein.

Recent Wisconsin and New York experiments show that the nutritive value of the proteins in well-cooked soybean oil meal is much greater for swine or poultry than that of raw soybeans or of soybean oil meal that has not been thoroughly cooked in the manufacturing process.[16] The Wisconsin investigations indicate that this increase in nutritive value of the soybean protein through cooking is due, at least in part, to the heat making available cystine compounds in the soybeans. While uncooked soybeans furnished an inadequate amount of cystine to laboratory animals, cooked soybeans apparently provided an ample amount of this sulfur-containing amino acid.

PICKING A GOOD CROP OF COTTON

Cotton is by far the most important southern crop. The cottonseed meal
and cake which are secured in the manufacture of oil from cottonseed rank
next in importance to the wheat by-products in value and importance among
all the by-product concentrates used for stock feeding in this country. (Copyright photograph by Underwood and Underwood.)

A Forty-acre Field of Soybeans in the Corn Belt

The culture of soybeans is increasing rapidly in the United States. This crop not only furnishes excellent protein-rich hay and pasture, but it also produces the largest yield of seed of any legume suited to temperate climates.

Spanish Type of Peanuts

In the South the peanut has become of great importance for stock feeding during recent years. Spanish peanuts, a small-podded variety, are grown more commonly for "hogging-down" than the large-podded types. (From U. S. Department of Agriculture.)

It is shown in Chapter XXXVI that well-grown pigs make fairly good gains on yellow corn supplemented with raw soybeans and a mineral mixture. On the other hand, for young pigs, much better results are generally secured when soybeans are used as only part of the supplement, and a small amount of some supplement of animal origin is fed in addition. As shown in Chapter XXXVI, if brood sows eat too great an amount of soybeans during the latter part of the gestation period, injurious effects may apparently sometimes be produced on the litters.

Soybeans should be ground for dairy cattle, but this is unnecessary for horses and sheep, and also for beef cattle if pigs follow the cattle to utilize the unmasticated grain and beans in the droppings. It is sometimes difficult to grind soybeans alone in the ordinary feed meal, on account of their high fat content. However, a mixture of grain and not over one-half soybeans is readily ground. The ground beans are apt to turn rancid in warm weather, and therefore should not be ground too long before they are fed.

595. Soybean oil meal or cake.—The use of soybeans for the production of soybean oil and soybean oil meal or cake has increased rapidly in this country during the past few years, and this excellent protein supplement has become increasingly popular with American farmers. It is estimated that in 1934-35 about 218,000 tons of soybean oil meal were produced in the United States. In this country nearly all the product is used in the form of soybean oil meal, and not as the oil cake.

Three different methods are employed in processing soybeans. The first is the hydraulic method, or so-called "old process," which is commonly used for flaxseed and cottonseed. In this method the crushed seed is first cooked and then pressed in hydraulic presses to remove as much of the oil as possible. The second is the expeller method, in which the crushed seed is subjected to great pressure in machines called "expellers," which express most of the oil. In this process considerable heat develops, on account of the friction as the material passes through the machine under the tremendous pressure. This cooks the meal. In the third process, which is the solvent process, the crushed seed is extracted by low-boiling-point gasoline. This removes the oil much more completely than the first two processes. Later the gasoline is thoroughly removed by treatment with steam, which also cooks the feed. The solvent-process product is ground to form soybean oil meal or is sold in flake form.

Soybean oil meal is especially rich in protein, and the protein is also of excellent quality. The soybean oil meal made in the corn belt usually contains 41 to 45 per cent protein, while that from seed grown in the southeastern states is higher in protein, often having 48 per cent or more. Therefore separate averages are given in Appendix Table I for the meal of three grades, according to percentage of protein, as well as for solvent-process soybean oil meal.

Soybean oil meal produced either by the old process or the expeller process usually contains 5 to 7 per cent of fat or oil, while solvent-process soybean oil meal may contain less than 1 per cent fat, though sometimes having 3 per cent.

Soybean oil meal is lower in fiber than cottonseed meal or linseed meal, containing an average of only 5.6 per cent. On account of its high digestibility, it supplies 82.2 lbs. total digestible nutrients per 100 lbs., which is somewhat more than is furnished by linseed meal or cottonseed meal. Solvent-process soybean oil meal is slightly higher in protein, but is lower in fat and therefore in total digestible nutrients than oil meal made by the other methods from seed of the same composition.

Just as is the case with soybeans, soybean oil meal does not supply vitamins A and D, and it is rather low in calcium and not very rich in phosphorus. On the average, soybean oil meal has 0.31 per cent calcium and 0.66 per cent phosphorus. Minerals are added to soybean oil meal by one manufacturer to supply additional calcium and phosphorus, and the product sold under a trade name. However, the same results can readily be obtained with the regular soybean oil meal, if the recommendations with reference to mineral supplements are followed that have previously been given in Chapter VI of this volume. (**181**)

For swine or poultry soybean oil meal that has been thoroughly cooked in the manufacturing process is much better than that which has not been heated sufficiently. (**594**) The results secured in swine feeding with well-cooked soybean oil meal and with that which has been insufficiently cooked are summarized in Chapter XXXVI. In using soybean oil meal for cattle, sheep, and horses there is apparently no difference in value between well-cooked soybean oil meal and that which is raw-tasting. As has been stated previously, raw soybean seed is an excellent protein supplement for these animals.

The taste of the product indicates in a general way whether it has been heated sufficiently to make it suitable for swine or poultry. If the soybean oil meal has a raw, "beany" taste, it has not been heated sufficiently for efficient use in feeding these classes of stock. Well-cooked hydraulic-process or expeller-process soybean oil meal has a pleasant nut-like taste and a light brownish or tan color. Solvent-process soybean oil meal may be decidedly lighter in color and not have any pronounced nut-like taste, even though it has been thoroughly cooked in the manufacturing process. However, such soybean oil meal will not have a raw, "beany" taste, if it has been well cooked.

Soybean oil meal is an excellent protein supplement for all classes of stock. For dairy cows and sheep it is fully equal to linseed meal or cottonseed meal. For use as the only supplement in fattening cattle it is equal to cottonseed meal and is only excelled by linseed meal. For swine feeding thoroughly-cooked soybean oil meal is excellent when properly fed. On account of the importance of soybean oil meal, its value and use for each class of stock are discussed at length in the respective chapters of Part III.

596. Other soybean by-products.—With the increasing use of soybean products for human food, it is probable that there will come on the market soybean by-products of various kinds which contain varying proportions of the soybean hulls (the outside coat of the seed). The fiber guarantee of any such product will indicate whether it resembles soybeans or soybean oil meal in composition, or whether it is largely composed of hulls. This is because the whole seed is low in fiber, having an average of only 4.5 per cent.

A by-product called "soya grits" which, according to the statement of the manufacturers, has over 20 per cent fiber, has recently come to the attention of the author. Judging from the fiber content and from the appearance of the feed, this by-product contains a large proportion of soybean hulls, and is therefore considerably lower in feeding value than soybeans or soybean oil meal.

597. Peanuts.—The peanut, or earth nut *(Arachis hypogaea)*, sometimes called "goober" in the South, is one of the important southern crops. Peanuts are grown chiefly for human consumption as peanuts, peanut butter, or peanut oil. However, a considerable part is hogged down by swine, as is discussed in Chapter XXXVI. After a crop of nuts has been harvested, pigs are also often turned in to clean up any nuts left in the ground, or which have shattered from the vines. When used for hogging down, the peanuts are often grown in combination with corn.

During the 10-year period, 1925-34, an average of 1,939,900 acres of peanuts were grown in the United States (including those raised in corn, reduced to their equivalent solid acreage of peanuts). Of this total, an average of 1,260,500 acres were harvested, and the remainder were hogged down. The average yield for this period was 664 lbs. of nuts per acre. Of the harvested nuts, only the small proportion of cull nuts is generally fed to stock. The use and value of the "peanut hay," which remains after the nuts are picked from the cured vines, have been discussed in Chapter XIII.

Peanuts, including the shells, contain an average of 24.9 per cent protein, 36.2 per cent fat or oil, and 17.5 per cent fiber. Though they are high in fiber, they furnish the high amount of 103.5 lbs. of total digestible nutrients per 100 lbs., on account of the large amount of fat. (**73**) When available, ground peanuts may be used as a protein supplement for the various classes of stock. As is pointed out in Chapter XXXVI, peanuts produce soft pork when they form any considerable part of the ration of pigs. It is somewhat surprising that recent Georgia experiments have shown that they do not have any appreciable effect upon the character of fat in beef cattle. (**222**)

Peanuts furnish a good quality of protein, but they are deficient in vitamins A and D, are low in calcium, and are not very rich in phosphorus. In North Carolina experiments pigs in dry lot made good gains when fed only shelled peanuts, with alfalfa hay and a mineral mixture to supply the lacking vitamins and calcium.[17] On exposure to the air, shelled peanuts soon become rancid.

598. Peanut oil meal or cake; unhulled peanut oil feed.—In the production of oil from peanuts the nuts may be first shelled, or hulled, or the entire peanuts may be ground and the oil expressed or extracted.

The terms *peanut oil meal* and *peanut oil cake* should be used only for the products from well-hulled kernels. According to the definitions adopted by the American Association of Feed Control Officials, the term *unhulled peanut oil feed* should be used for the ground residue obtained after the extraction of part of the oil from whole peanuts (including the shells), and the ingredients must be designated as peanut oil meal and peanut hulls.[2] This product is often called "whole-pressed peanuts."

Only a relatively small amount of peanut oil meal is produced in the United States, as no large proportion of the peanut crop is used for the production of oil. According to the Census, in 1929 only 11,618 tons of peanut oil meal and cake were produced in this country.

Peanut oil meal of the best grade contains 45 per cent or more of protein and an average of 8.6 per cent fat, with only 9.2 per cent fiber. Such peanut oil meal has 83.5 lbs. total digestible nutrients per 100 lbs., thus slightly excelling the best grade of cottonseed meal in content of both protein and total digestible nutrients. Peanut oil meal made by the solvent process is lower in fat and total digestible nutrients and higher in protein than when a pressure process is used.

Unhulled peanut oil feed has an average of 33.2 per cent protein, 8.7 per cent fat, and 17.7 per cent fiber, and supplies 73.1 lbs. total digestible nutrients per 100 lbs. It therefore has 73 per cent as much protein and 88 per cent as much total digestible nutrients as the best grade of peanut oil meal. The value of peanut oil meal made from peanuts that are only partially hulled will depend on the proportion of hulls present. This can be estimated from the fiber content.

Peanut oil meal is one of the best protein supplements for livestock feeding. This is not only due to its richness in protein and total digestible nutrients, but also because it is well liked by stock and because the protein is of especially high quality. (150) Peanut oil meal from well-hulled nuts is fully equal to linseed meal, cottonseed meal, or soybean oil meal in feeding value for the various classes of stock. It is most commonly fed to dairy cattle and is a very popular feed for milk cows in sections where it is available.[18] Peanut oil meal is somewhat laxative and if high in fat even may be undesirably so, when forming more than one-fourth of the concentrate mixture. It furnishes protein of excellent quality for milk production, even slightly excelling cottonseed meal or soybean oil meal in this respect in Virginia experiments.[19]

Peanut oil feed from partially hulled nuts, containing 38 per cent crude protein and 11 per cent fiber, was not quite so valuable as cottonseed meal containing 42 per cent protein in a Texas trial with dairy cows.[20]

Peanut oil meal and unhulled peanut oil feed are likewise excellent protein supplements for beef cattle and sheep. In Texas trials with fattening cattle peanut oil meal containing 52 per cent protein was slightly superior in feeding value to cottonseed meal containing 45 per cent protein.[21] On the other hand, unhulled peanut oil feed having 36 per cent protein and 22 per cent fiber was slightly less valuable than whole-pressed cottonseed. For fattening lambs peanut oil meal has been similar to linseed meal or cottonseed meal in value.[22]

Peanut oil meal from well-hulled nuts is one of the best protein supplements of plant origin for swine feeding, being approximately equal to soybean oil meal. Because it lacks vitamins A and D and is low in calcium, care should be taken to include in the ration other supplements that will make good these lacks.

Well-grown pigs or pigs on pasture will make good gains when fed corn supplemented by only peanut oil meal or unhulled peanut oil feed, with ground limestone or some other calcium supplement in addition. South Carolina experiments show that for young pigs in dry lot it is best to combine the peanut products with tankage, meat scraps, or fish meal, in order to furnish protein of optimum quality.[23] In these tests pigs weighing 75 lbs. or less at the start gained an average of only 1.28 lbs. per head daily when fed yellow corn, peanut oil feed, and a mineral mixture in dry lots. Others fed fish meal in place of peanut oil feed gained 1.87 lbs. per head daily and required less feed per 100 lbs. gain. A mixture of one-half peanut oil feed and one-half fish meal produced practically as rapid gains as fish meal alone. When fed in this combination, the peanut oil feed, which contained 32 to 40 per cent protein and 13 to 15 per cent fiber, was worth 78 per cent as much as fish meal.

In 4 trials at the Arkansas, Iowa, Ohio, and Texas Stations pigs fed peanut oil meal and corn gained as much as others fed tankage and corn.[24] They required 343 lbs. corn and 68 lbs. peanut oil meal for 100 lbs. gain, while the pigs fed tankage required 391 lbs. corn and 35 lbs. tankage. Good results were secured in dry lot feeding of well-grown pigs as well as with pigs on pasture, and both in self-feeding and in hand-feeding. In these trials 100 lbs. peanut meal was equal in feeding value to 71 lbs. grain plus 52 lbs. tankage.

The value of peanut oil feed, made from unhulled peanuts or partially hulled nuts, will depend chiefly on the amount of crude protein it contains in comparison with peanut oil meal from hulled nuts. In 3 trials at the Kansas, Mississippi, and Texas Stations in which peanut oil feed has been compared with tankage as a supplement to corn or milo, 100 lbs. of peanut oil feed has been worth as much as 46 lbs. grain plus 37 lbs. tankage.[25] As will be noted, this is much lower than the value of peanut oil meal from hulled nuts, given in the preceding paragraph.

599. Peanut hulls.—Peanut hulls, or shells, are a by-product at the factories making peanut butter, shelled peanuts, or peanut oil from shelled nuts. Commercial peanut hulls usually contain fragments of kernels and therefore have a little more protein and fat than the pure hulls. However, even such hulls are too low in nutrients to warrant their use for stock feeding. They are over one-half fiber and are much less nutritious than straw. Occasionally they are ground and used as an adulterant in low-grade mixed feeds.

600. Peanut skins.—Peanut skins are the by-product consisting of the thin red-brown covering of the kernels, together with more or less of the germs and broken bits of the kernels. Peanut skins have an average of 15.9 per cent protein, 22.4 per cent fat, and 10.6 per cent fiber. They are used chiefly in certain mixed feeds. They are rather bitter in taste and are therefore mixed in small proportions with better-liked feeds.

601. Peas *(Pisum arvense)*.—Field peas and also varieties of peas grown for human food are raised chiefly in the northern-most states, in Canada, and in certain sections of the West where the climate is cool. They do not thrive unless the spring and summer temperatures are moderate. Field peas do not usually yield over 15 to 20 bushels of 60 lbs. each per acre. Because of this low yield, field peas are not commonly raised to produce seed for stock feeding, but they are grown chiefly for forage or for seed peas.

As has been pointed out in Chapter XIII, peas are often grown with oats or barley for hay, pasture, or silage. Also field peas are raised extensively in certain mountain valleys of the West and the entire crop harvested by lambs or hogs which are grazed on it. Sometimes a combination of barley, oats, and field peas is grown for grain in the northern states.

Field peas are relished by stock and are an excellent feed, when they are not too high in price. Cull peas that are not satisfactory for seed or for human consumption may be nearly equal to good-quality peas in feeding value. Peas have nearly as much protein as corn gluten feed and furnish slightly more total digestible nutrients. The seed of green varieties equals yellow corn in content of vitamin A, and even yellow varieties have an appreciable amount. Peas are lacking in vitamin D, and they are low in calcium. Also, their protein does not apparently supplement very effectively the protein of the grains in swine feeding.

Experienced shepherds esteem field peas for fattening sheep for shows, because they produce firm flesh. Of several concentrate mixtures tested at the Wisconsin Station for fitting yearling wethers for shows, the best results in finish of lambs and firmness of flesh were

secured with a mixture of peas, oats, and bran.[26]   In 2 Idaho trials
fattening lambs fed a mixture of 20 lbs. cull field peas and 80 lbs.
barley with alfalfa hay gained slightly more than others fed only barley
and hay, and 100 lbs. of peas were equal in value to 69 lbs. barley plus
103 lbs. hay.[27]   Ground cull peas had a still higher value for fattening
cattle in Montana trials, when forming 20 per cent of the concentrate
mixture.[28]

Peas are satisfactory as the only protein supplement for pigs on
good pasture,[29] but they should not be thus used for swine not on
pasture.   In experiments by the Idaho, Montana, and Washington Stations pigs not on pasture made more rapid gains and remained more
thrifty when they were fed alfalfa hay in addition to grain and peas.[30]
However, the results are still better when an efficient protein supplement, like tankage or fishmeal, is also fed.   Unsatisfactory litters resulted when brood sows were fed peas alone during the winter in an
Idaho trial, but thrifty litters were produced by sows fed grain, peas,
and plenty of alfalfa hay.[31]   Pigs fed only peas or peas and grain for
extended periods when not on pasture are apt to suffer severely from
rickets.[32]

602. Pea feed.—Pea feed is the by-product from the manufacture of split peas
for human food.   It consists chiefly of shrunken, broken, or otherwise damaged peas,
together with the pea hulls (or bran) and meal made up of the germs and broken
particles from the seed.   Pea feed varies considerably in composition and often contains 25 per cent fiber.   However, the fiber seems to be highly digestible and therefore the content of total digestible nutrients is greater than would be expected from
the chemical composition.[33]   When fed to dairy cows as part of a suitable concentrate
mixture, pea feed was worth about one-half as much per ton as linseed meal in Idaho
tests.[34]   In a similar Washington trial 100 lbs. of pea feed was worth as much as
80 lbs. of wheat bran plus 20 lbs. linseed meal.[35]

603. Cowpeas.—The use of the cowpea *(Vigna sinensis)* for forage has already
been discussed in Chapter XIII.   The seeds of cowpeas ripen unevenly, and therefore
when the crop is grown for seed it is necessary to pick the pods by hand as they
ripen, or else the plants are cut when about three-fourths of the pods are ripe, and
before the first ones are shattered or damaged.   For this reason cowpeas are used
mostly for forage or for the production of seed for human food.

In composition, cowpea seed is similar to field-pea seed.   Cowpeas furnish protein of fair quality to supplement the cereal grains and they are richer than the
common grains, except yellow corn, in vitamin A.   Cowpea seed may be used satisfactorily as a protein supplement in feeding cattle, sheep, horses, or swine.   However,
for swine feeding they had best be fed in combination with some other supplement
which furnishes better-quality protein.[36] **(150)**

604. Field and other beans; cull beans.—Several varieties of beans *(Phaseolus,*
spp.) are raised in this country for human food.   These include the ordinary field or
navy beans, the lima beans, the kidney beans, and the pinto beans and tepary beans
of the Southwest.   All of these varieties have the same general composition and
feeding value.

In amount of total protein and other nutrients these beans closely resemble field
peas.   However, their feeding value is much lower.   These beans are not very palatable to stock; their digestibility is not high when they are fed raw, especially to
swine; and their proteins are not of good quality. **(150)**   Due to these facts, their
feeding value is less than would be expected from the chemical analysis.

The *cull beans* which are sorted out from the first-quality dry beans can be used
satisfactorily for stock feeding, if due attention is paid to their limitations.   Such
cull beans include not only discolored and shrunken beans and broken beans, but also

more or less of such waste as broken bits of stems, small stones, and dirt. Sheep are well suited to disposing of cull beans, for they will sort out the beans from the trash. If the cull beans do not contain too large a proportion of such waste material, they can also be fed in limited amounts to other stock.

Ground cull beans can be fed to dairy cows as a substitute for other protein supplements, when forming not over about one-fifth of the concentrate mixture. However, in Michigan trials, unless they were mixed with very palatable feeds, such as ground corn, ground oats, and linseed meal, there was difficulty in getting cows to clean up the feed.[37] When thus used, the ground cull beans were worth about one-half as much per ton as cottonseed meal. Larger amounts of cooked beans can be fed to cows, but cooking involves considerable expense.

In an Idaho trial with fattening steers satisfactory results were secured when cull beans formed 16 per cent of the grain mixture, but in a Montana trial poor results were secured when 26 per cent of beans were included in the grain mixture for fattening steers.[38]

Whole cull beans are satisfactory for fattening lambs, if they form not more than 20 to 25 per cent of the grain mixture. A larger amount is apt to cause serious scouring and may be unpalatable. In 9 trials fattening lambs fed such a mixture of cull beans and barley with alfalfa hay for roughage gained about as rapidly as others fed barley and alfalfa hay, but they required somewhat more concentrates and hay per 100 lbs. gain.[39] On the average, 100 lbs. of cull beans equalled in value 88 lbs. barley minus 12 lbs. alfalfa hay. With grain at twice as high a price per ton as hay, cull beans were worth 82 per cent as much as barley.

In 4 trials lambs fed cull beans as the only concentrate gained only 0.25 lb. daily on the average, in comparison with 0.29 lb. for others fed corn or barley, and required considerably more concentrates and hay per 100 lbs. gain.[40] In these trials cull beans were worth only 74 per cent as much as grain, without considering the less rapid gain.

Cull beans are satisfactory for swine when thoroughly cooked and fed with grain, and preferably with an efficient protein supplement. It has been shown in Michigan experiments that much better results are secured when pigs are fed tankage, fishmeal, or some other efficient protein supplement in addition to beans and grain.[41] Pigs fed 2 parts of cull beans, cooked before feeding, and 1 part corn, by weight, along with tankage, alfalfa hay, and a mineral mixture, gained 1.4 lbs. per head daily. Others fed corn and the same supplements gained 1.7 lbs. per head daily. The cull beans were worth 89 per cent as much per 100 lbs. as corn, not considering the difference in rate of gain.

605. Velvet beans; ground velvet bean and pod.—Since the usefulness of velvet beans *(Stizolobium* spp.) in the South is chiefly for forage, the general discussion of the crop is given in Chapter XIII. Commonly velvet beans are grown with corn to support the vines, and most of the ears of corn and some of the beans are gathered by hand. Stock is then turned in to graze the field.

Velvet beans are usually fed in the pod, either in whole form or ground to make *ground velvet bean and pod,* also called *velvet bean feed.* The former term is preferred by the Association of American Feed Control Officials.[2] The name *velvet bean meal,* sometimes used for this product, should be given only to the ground velvet bean seed, containing only an unavoidable trace of pods.

Velvet beans in the pod contain 18.1 per cent protein and 13.0 per cent fiber, thus being slightly higher in protein but also higher in fiber than wheat bran. They supply slightly less than one-half as much protein as the best grades of cottonseed meal, but furnish nearly as much total digestible nutrients.

Though velvet beans in the pod or the ground beans and pods are not very palatable, they can be used satisfactorily for dairy cows, beef cattle, or sheep when not forming too large a part of the ration. When too much is fed, they may be unduly laxative. The dry beans in the pod are satisfactory for fattening cattle, and it does not pay to soak or grind them.[42] However, for dairy cows the value is increased considerably by grinding.[43] If this cannot be done, the beans and pods should be soaked for 24 hours before feeding, to soften them.

Velvet beans in the pod have been satisfactory for fattening cattle, when used as a protein supplement or when fed as the entire concentrate, along with suitable roughage.[44] In the latter case the gains are usually somewhat less than on a combination of corn and cottonseed meal. For fattening cattle velvet beans in the pod are worth one-half or nearly one-half as much per ton as cottonseed meal. In an Iowa trial velvet bean feed (ground velvet beans and pods), containing 17 per cent crude protein and 14 per cent fiber, was worth 60 per cent as much per ton as linseed meal.[45]

With dairy cows the best results are secured when ground velvet beans and pods do not form more than 40 per cent of the concentrate mixture, the rest consisting of better-liked feeds. Thus fed, this feed, on the average, has been about equal to wheat bran and has been worth about one-half as much as cottonseed meal.[46] Ground velvet bean meal (without the pods) has a somewhat greater value, as it is higher in protein and total digestible nutrients.[47]

While velvet beans usually give good results with cattle and sheep, even when fed in considerable amounts, they are generally very unsatisfactory for swine (either brood sows or growing and fattening pigs) when forming any considerable part of the ration.[48] This has been the case, no matter whether the beans have been fed shelled, ground, or as ground velvet bean and pods. The velvet beans even cause severe vomiting and diarrhea.

The poor results seem to be caused largely by a substance that is poisonous to swine, and also by the poor quality of the protein in the beans.[49] The toxicity is lessened by cooking and the beans are made more digestible, but this does not generally make them satisfactory for swine. Pigs will not do well when following steers heavily fed on velvet beans, unless the pigs get considerable other feed. When velvet beans do not form more than one-fourth the ration for swine and an efficient protein supplement like tankage or fish meal is included, fair results may be secured.[50] Even velvet bean pasture cannot be recommended for swine.

It is of interest to note that the same condition is true with velvet beans, cottonseed meal, and scabby barley. These feeds can all be fed in large amounts to cattle or sheep, but they are poisonous to swine when forming any large part of the ration. Possibly the toxic substances are largely destroyed in the case of the ruminants by the fermentations in the paunch.

606. Other legume seeds.—The *horse bean (Vicia faba)* is used in England for feeding stock, especially horses. This legume grows fairly well in some parts of Canada, but has never proved a success in the United States, except in the central coast district of California.[51] Horse bean seeds are similar in composition to field peas.

Alfalfa seed screenings consist chiefly of the shriveled or light-weight alfalfa seeds removed in cleaning alfalfa seed, along with varying amounts of weed seeds, bits of alfalfa leaves and stems, etc. Screenings that contain but little low-grade material have an average of 31.1 per cent protein, 9.9 per cent fat, and 11.1 per cent fiber.

The screenings should be finely ground before feeding, to make them more digestible and to prevent infestation of the land with weeds. They are not very palatable to stock, but a limited amount can be satisfactorily included in a mixture of better-liked feeds. When forming one-quarter of the concentrate mixture for dairy cows in Idaho trials, each 100 lbs. of ground alfalfa-seed screenings replaced 57 lbs. of linseed meal and 42 lbs. of barley and wheat bran.[52]

Sweet-clover screenings are generally lower in protein and higher in fiber than alfalfa-seed screenings, and vary rather widely in composition. North Dakota tests show that the ground screenings may be used as part of the concentrates for stock in the same manner as alfalfa-seed screenings, a good grade being equal or superior to wheat bran in feeding value.[53]

Red-clover-seed screenings closely resemble alfalfa-seed screenings in composition.

Carob beans (Ceratonia siliqua), or St. John's bread, are produced by a legume tree grown chiefly in Mediterranean districts. The seeds are imbedded in a thick, fleshy pod, rich in sugars, which forms about 89 per cent of the fruit.[54] The ground pods and seeds form *carob-bean meal,* which is used chiefly in certain mixed feeds, especially calf meals. It contains only 5.5 per cent protein, thus differing from most legume seeds. In a California test crushed carob beans and pods were equal to ground barley as part of the ration for dairy calves.[55]

The *mesquite* and *tornillo* are large leguminous shrubs or small trees common in certain sections of the southwestern states. Often these produce abundant crops of pods which are eaten by stock when they fall to the ground. The seeds are so small and hard that they largely escape digestion, unless the pods and seeds are ground finely. This is difficult, due to the high sugar content of the pods.

In New Mexico trials with sheep and pigs the value of mesquite and tornillo pods and beans varied widely, but on the average they were worth only about 40 per cent as much as grain.[56]

Chick peas (Cicer arietinum), also called gram, are grown over an extensive area from India to southern Europe and northern Africa for human food and also for stock feeding. Chick peas resemble field peas in composition, but are slightly lower in protein and somewhat higher in fat.

The *pigeon pea (Cajanus indicus),* a perennial legume of tropical and subtropical countries, has been an important food plant in India for centuries and is widely grown in other countries. The seed is commonly used for human food, but the straw left after the seed is threshed is fed to stock. In Hawaii pigeon peas become shrubs 5 to 10 feet tall and make excellent pasture and also the young growth is used as a soiling crop.[57]

IV. Miscellaneous Seeds and Their By-products

607. Coconut oil meal or cake; coconuts.—Coconut oil meal or cake (also called "copra oil meal") is the by-product from the production of coconut oil from copra, the dried meats from the nuts of the coconut palm *(Cocos nucifera).* Coconut oil meal is usually made by the hydraulic process (the so-called "old process") or by the expeller process. Such meal contains an average of 8.2 per cent fat, while meal from the solvent process has only 2.4 per cent fat.

Coconut oil meal of a good grade should be whitish or very light brown in color. Too high a temperature in the process of expressing the oil will result in a dark oil meal, which has a lower value. Thus, in such coconut oil meal the digestibility of the protein is considerably decreased. Trouble was formerly experienced from coconut oil meal turning rancid in warm weather, but it now usually has a sufficiently low moisture content to keep satisfactorily in storage.

Coconut oil meal contains somewhat more protein than wheat bran and somewhat less than corn gluten feed, the old-process oil meal having 20.8 per cent protein on the average. The protein is of better quality than that in corn or corn gluten feed, but is not of such high quality as that of soybeans or peanuts. Therefore coconut oil meal should not be fed as the only protein supplement to grain for swine not on pasture or for poultry. Some such protein supplement as meat scrap, tankage, or fish meal should be fed in addition.

In the United States coconut oil meal is fed mostly to dairy cows, for which purpose it gives excellent results. In a Massachusetts experiment it was about equal to corn gluten feed for milk production.[58]

Coconut oil meal supplies nearly as much digestible protein as a mixture of one-half grain and one-half linseed meal or cottonseed meal, and it was fully equal to such a mixture in an Ohio trial, when forming 30 per cent of the concentrate mixture.[59]

Claims are made that coconut oil meal will increase the percentage of fat in the milk of dairy cows. This question is of especial interest, since coconut fat resembles butter fat in containing appreciable amounts of certain of the simpler fatty acids. It is shown in Chapter XXIV, where the influence of feeds upon the fat content of milk is discussed in detail, that a feed such as old-process coconut oil meal, which contains considerable fat, often causes a temporary increase in the percentage of fat in milk. Sometimes the feeding of coconut oil meal may cause a very slight increase in the fat content of milk over a considerable period. (832)

A limited amount of coconut oil meal produces firm butter of excellent quality, but when more than 3 or 4 lbs. of pressure-process coconut oil meal are fed, the butter may be too hard.

In California experiments coconut oil meal was found to be a desirable protein supplement for fattening lambs which were fed barley and alfalfa hay.[60] It was also satisfactory as a protein supplement for fattening cattle, or as a substitute for part of the grain, being worth about as much as barley for the latter purpose.[61] It was used successfully in an experiment by the Guam Station as a substitute for one-third to one-half the oats ordinarily fed work horses.[62]

For swine feeding, coconut oil meal may be used in place of such feeds as wheat middlings or linseed meal, but, like these feeds, it does not generally produce good results when fed to young pigs not on pasture as the only supplement for grain.[63] On the other hand, it produced satisfactory results in a California test when fed with barley to pigs on good pasture.[64] Also, in a Delaware trial pigs weighing 150 lbs. at the start made good gains when fed only corn and coconut meal.[65]

If coconut oil meal is cheaper in price than grain, it may be used as a substitute for part of the grain in swine feeding, being worth about as much per 100 lbs. as ground barley when fed in limited amounts.[66] The ration may be too laxative if pigs on alfalfa pasture are fed more than 1 lb. of coconut oil meal to each 3 or 4 lbs. of barley.

Coconuts were used successfully in Guam tests for feeding growing pigs and brood sows on pasture.[67] As the coconut meats contain 60 to 70 per cent fat, on the dry basis, the energy value is correspondingly high.

608. Palm-kernel oil cake or meal.—Palm-kernel oil cake or meal is the by-product from the production of oil from the seed kernels of certain oil palms (*Elaeis,* spp.). It varies considerably in composition, especially in fiber content. Palm-kernel oil meal of the best grade contains slightly more protein than wheat bran and is also higher in fat, if made by the "old process." Though it is somewhat higher than bran in fiber, it supplies slightly more total digestible nutrients, due to the greater fat content. Solvent-process palm-kernel oil meal usually has less than 4 per cent fat.

Palm-kernel oil cake and meal are well-liked by stock and keep well in storage, and as a result they are popular feeds in Europe, where most of the product is used. Palm-kernel oil meal and cake are fed chiefly to dairy cows. It is shown in Chapter XXIV that although these feeds may cause a temporary increase in the fat content of milk, there is generally no important permanent effect upon the richness of milk when they are added to a good dairy ration. (832)

In a Kentucky trial solvent-process palm-kernel oil meal was about equal to wheat bran for feeding dairy cows, when used as a partial substitute for bran.[68] Palm-kernel oil meal tends to produce hard fat when fed to stock, and thus makes firm butter and pork of good quality. It is not very palatable to pigs and should not form more than one-fifth of their ration.[69]

609. Sesame oil meal or cake.—This protein-rich oil meal or cake is the by-product in the production of oil from sesame seed *(Sesamum,* spp.), which is raised in India and other tropical countries. Sesame oil meal contains nearly as much protein as high-grade cottonseed meal, averaging 39.6 per cent. It is also high in calcium and phosphorus and supplies protein of good quality.

This oil meal is well-liked by stock, keeps well in storage, and is highly regarded in Europe. It is satisfactory for all classes of stock, but too large amounts produce soft pork and butter. In a California test sesame oil meal was an excellent protein supplement for fattening lambs fed barley and Sudan-grass hay.[70]

610. Sunflower seed; sunflower-seed oil cake.—A considerable acreage of sunflowers *(Helianthus annus)* is raised in certain sections of Russia for seed. This is used chiefly for human food, either as sunflower-seed oil or in the form of the hulled seeds. As has been pointed out in Chapter XVI, sunflowers are grown to a limited extent in this country for silage or as a green soiling crop in localities where the climate is too cool for corn.

Only a very small acreage is raised here for seed, a part of which is used in poultry and bird feeds. Other crops produce much larger yields of feed per acre.

The *sunflower-seed oil cake,* resulting from expressing oil from the seed, contains nearly as much protein as linseed meal and somewhat more fat, if made from well-hulled seed, but it is higher in fiber. This oil cake is well-liked by stock and keeps well in storage. It is a popular feed in Europe for all classes of stock, especially dairy cows.[71] It is said to resemble linseed meal in its favorable effect on stock. Due to the character of the oil it contains, sunflower-seed cake tends to produce soft pork, and it also makes the butter soft, if fed in large amounts to dairy cows.

611. Rubber seed meal.—This by-product (also called *Para rubber meal)* from the manufacture of oil from the seed of the Para rubber tree *(Hevea brasiliensis)* is occasionally found on the United States markets. Rubber seed meal is a dry, rather powdery meal which is not very palatable when fed alone. It should therefore be mixed with well-liked feeds. In a Virginia trial cows were fed 5 lbs. per head daily of either rubber seed meal or linseed meal, with alfalfa hay and corn silage.[72] The rubber seed meal gave as good results as the linseed meal in this ration, which supplied somewhat more protein than was required by the cows. In tests in England it was fed satisfactorily to milk cows and fattening cattle, but a few sheep refused to eat it, even when mixed with other feeds.[73]

612. Cocoa meal; cocoa shells.—In the manufacture of chocolate and cocoa from the beans of the cacao tree *(Theobroma cacao),* the beans are first roasted and the cocoa shells, which form about 12 per cent of the weight, are removed. The beans are then ground very finely, and a portion of the semi-liquid mass is pressed to remove part of the fat, which is called cocoa butter. The residue, after hardening and grinding, forms the cocoa that is used as a beverage. Chocolate is made by enriching the ground beans with a certain percentage of cocoa butter.

On account of the large demand for chocolate in confections and other food, more cocoa must often be produced than can be sold for human use. This may then be offered for sale as a stock feed under the name of *cocoa meal,* but it has an exceedingly low value for feeding.

Experiments by the Vermont Station show definitely that cocoa meal not only has a very low digestibility, but also it tends to depress the digestibility of the other feeds in a ration.[74] A concentrate mixture containing only 15 per cent of cocoa meal was unpalatable to dairy calves, heifers, and cows, and also to swine.

Such a mixture tended to produce scours in calves, and cows in milk would not consume enough of the mixture to meet their needs. In addition the cocoa meal decreased the milk yield of cows, though slightly increasing the fat percentage. These effects are apparently due to the alkaloids (theobromine and caffein) which the cocoa meal contains. In view of these results, cocoa meal is not an economical feed, even when seemingly cheap in price.

Cocoa shells consist of the hard outside coating of the cocoa bean. These shells, which are dark brown and brittle, are used in a few mixed feeds. Only 11 per cent of the crude protein in this material is digestible, on the average. In studies at the Massachusetts Station cocoa shells were considered to be worth not more than half as much as corn meal.[75]

613. Vegetable ivory meal.—Ivory nuts, or vegetable ivory, the nuts of the ivory palm *(Phytelephas macrocarpa)*, are manufactured into buttons and the residue is ground finely to form ivory-nut meal. This consists chiefly of mannan, one of the less common carbohydrates. In studies at the Massachusetts Station this material was found to be fairly digestible.[76] It supplies about as much total digestible nutrients as barley grain, but contains only 0.8 per cent digestible protein.

614. Rape-seed oil meal.—Rape-seed oil meal, or colza oil meal, is the by-product resulting in the production of oil from various kinds of rape seed *(Brassica, spp.)*. It contains an average of 34.8 per cent protein, 5.1 per cent fat, and 11.7 per cent fiber. Experience in feeding rape-seed oil meal in Germany, where it has long been used for stock, shows that it must be very carefully fed to avoid injurious results.

Rape-seed oil meal contains varying amounts of glucosides, from which mustard oils may be formed in the digestive tracts of animals under certain conditions. The mustard oils are irritating to the digestive system and produce serious results when present in appreciable amounts. Though as much as 5 lbs. per head daily have been fed to cattle without injury, in other cases 3 lbs. have produced bad results. It is therefore safer to feed no more than 2 lbs. per head daily to cattle and corresponding amounts to other stock. Caution is especially necessary in feeding rape-seed meal to young animals or to those which are pregnant.

On account of its sharp, bitter taste rape-seed oil meal is often not liked by stock, especially at first. It should therefore be mixed with better-liked feeds.

615. Hemp-seed oil meal.—Hemp-seed oil meal is the by-product in producing oil from the seed of hemp *(Cannabis sativa)*. It contains 31 per cent protein, but it is high in fiber and it furnishes less total digestible nutrients than good legume hay. Recent California experiments show that hemp-seed oil meal is not palatable to stock.[77] It should therefore be mixed with better-liked feeds.

German authorities state that hemp-seed oil meal may contain narcotic substances which may have injurious effects on stock when any large amount is fed. They recommend that dairy cows not be fed more than 1.1 lbs. of hemp-seed oil meal per head daily; horses and beef cattle not more than 3 lbs. per head daily; and sheep not more than 0.25 lb. per head daily.

QUESTIONS

1. Describe the process of expressing oil from cottonseed and state what by-products are usually obtained.

2. Distinguish between cottonseed meal, cottonseed feed, and whole-pressed cottonseed.

3. Discuss the composition and nutritive properties of cottonseed meal.

4. Discuss the use of cottonseed meal for cattle, sheep, horses, and swine. State specifically the precautions that must be taken in feeding cottonseed meal to any of these classes of stock.

5. Describe a simple test for distinguishing between high-grade cottonseed meal and cottonseed feed.

6. If the following are important in your district, discuss their composition and feeding value: (a) Whole-pressed cottonseed; (b) cottonseed.

7. Discuss the value of cottonseed hulls as a feed.

8. Discuss the composition and use of linseed meal. What is the difference in composition between linseed meal made from Argentine flaxseed and that from North American flaxseed?

9. Define: (a) Screenings oil feed; (b) unscreened flaxseed oil feed cake; (c) flax-plant by-product; (d) linseed-meal-and-screenings-oil-feed.

10. Discuss the composition of soybeans and their use for dairy cattle, beef cattle, horses, sheep, and swine.

11. Why is soybean oil meal a popular stock feed? What precaution would you take when purchasing soybean oil meal for feeding to swine or poultry?

12. In what manner are peanuts used for stock feeding?

13. Discuss the composition and value of peanut oil meal; of peanut oil feed. Why are peanut hulls unsuitable for use as a feed?

14. Discuss the composition and feeding value of pea seed. Why are peas not more commonly used for stock feeding?

15. Discuss the composition and use of any of the following that are of importance as feeds in your district: (a) Pea feed; (b) cowpeas; (c) cull beans; (d) velvet beans; (e) alfalfa-seed screenings; (f) mesquite beans and pods.

16. Compare the composition and feeding value of coconut oil meal and corn gluten feed.

17. Discuss the composition and use of any of the following that are sold on the feed markets in your section: (a) Palm-kernel oil meal; (b) sesame oil meal; (c) sunflower-seed oil cake; (d) rubber seed meal; (e) cocoa meal; (f) cocoa shells; (g) vegetable ivory meal; (h) rape-seed oil meal; (i) hemp-seed oil meal.

REFERENCES

1. Fraps, Tex. Bul. 189.
2. Assoc. of Amer. Feed Control Officials, Official Pub., 1935.
3. Huffman and Moore, Jour. Dairy Sci., 12, 1929, pp. 410-418.
4. For a more detailed summary and references to the numerous publications on this subject see: Halverson and Sherwood, N. C. Tech. Bul. 39. For more recent work see: Hunt, Ohio Bimo. Bul. 158; Gallup, Okla. Rpt. 1930-32; Gallup, Jour. Biol. Chem., 91, 1931, pp. 387-394; 93, 1931, pp. 381-405; 94, 1931, pp. 221-231.
5. Dowell and Menaul, Jour. Agr. Res., 26, 1923, pp. 9-10; Gallup, Jour. Dairy Sci., 10, 1927, pp. 519-526; Robison, Ohio Bul. 534.
6. Reed, Huffman, and Addington, Jour. Dairy Sci., 11, 1928, pp. 488-515; Huffman and Moore, Jour. Dairy Sci., 12, 1929, pp. 410-418; 13, 1930, pp. 478-494; Halverson and Sherwood, N. C. Tech. Bul. 39; Kuhlman, Weaver, and Gallup, Okla. Rpts. 1930-32, 1932-34; Bechdel and Williams, Penn. Bul. 279; Bechdel, Williams, and Skaggs, Penn. Bul. 308; Copeland and Fraps, Tex. Bul. 473; Woodward, Shepherd, and Graves, U. S. Dept. Agr., Misc. Pub. 130; Hotis and Woodward, U. S. Dept. Agr., Tech. Bul. 473; see also: Cunningham and Addington, New Mex. Bul. 226.
7. Hills, Jones, and Hollister, Vt. Bul. 101.
8. Stanley and Scott, Ariz. Bul. 109; Guilbert, Cal. Bul. 418; Lee and Woodward, La. Bul. 110; Moore, Miss. Bul. 174; Gramlich and Savin, Nebr. Bul. 173.
9. Lush and Gelpi, La. Bul. 227; Moore, Miss. Bul. 60; Cunningham, N. Mex. Rpts. 1926, 1927.
10. J. M. Jones, J. H. Jones, Black, Dickson, and Bayles, Tex. Rpt. 1933; see also: Scott and Stanley, Ariz. Sta., mimeo. rpt.
11. Stanley, Ariz. Bul. 93; Burns, Tex. Buls. 110, 159.
12. Jones et al., Tex. Bul. 379, Tex. Rpt. 1933.
13. Morton, Fairbanks, and Osland, Colo. Press Buls. 78, 79, 80; Robison and Thatcher, Ohio Sp. Cir. 17; Wilson and Wright, S. D. Bul. 293.
14. Smith, Mass. Bul. 136.
15. Shrewsbury, Vestal, and Hauge, Jour. Agr. Res., 1932, pp. 267-274; Vestal and Shrewsbury, Ind. Bul. 400; Robison, Ohio Bul. 452.
16. Bohstedt, Fargo, and Hayward, Wis. Bul. 430 and information to the author; Norris and Wilgus, N. Y. (Cornell) Sta., mimeo. rpt.
17. Halverson, Hostetler, and Sherwood, N. C. Tech. Bul. 41.
18. McCandlish, Jour. Dairy Sci., 5, 1922, pp. 27-38; Tomhave, Del. Bul. 148.
19. Holdaway, Ellett, and Harris, Va. Tech. Bul. 28.
20. Ewing, Ridgeway, and Doubt, Tex. Bul. 238; see also: Woodward et al., U. S. Dept. Agr. Bul. 1272.

21. Burns, Tex. Bul. 263.
22. Dunn and Evvard, Iowa Bul. 185; Miller, Amer. Soc. Anim. Prod., Proc. 1931.
23. Godbey and Durant, S. C. Bul. 234.
24. Dvorachek and Sandhouse, Ark. Cir. 45; Evvard, Iowa Sta., mimeo. rpt.; Robison, Ohio Bul. 349; Burk, Tex. Bul. 201.
25. McCampbell, Kan. Cir. 78; Barnett and Goodell, Miss. Bul. 218; Burk, Tex. Bul. 201; see also: Burk, Tex. Bul. 228.
26. Humphrey and Kleinheinz, Wis. Rpt. 1905, Bul. 232.
27. Rinehart, Hickman, and Johnson, Id. Bul. 194.
28. Vinke and Pearson, Mont. Bul. 251.
29. Churchill, Mich. Cir. Bul. 145.
30. Nordby, Id. Cir. 50, Id. Buls. 129, 131, 133, 135, 149; Vaughan, Joseph, and Vinke, Mont. Rpt. 1927; Corbin, Wash. Bul. 260.
31. Nordby and Snyder, Id. Cir. 48.
32. Nordby and Gildow, Id. Exten. Bul. 89.
33. Knott, Tretsven, and Hodgson, Wash. Bul. 287.
34. Id. Buls. 179, 192.
35. Knott, Tretsven, and Hodgson, Wash. Bul. 287.
36. Duggar, Ala. Bul. 82; Gray, Duggar, and Ridgeway, Ala. Bul. 147; Willson, Tenn. Bul. 114.
37. Reed and Burnett, Mich. Quar. Bul., 6, 1923, No. 2; 7, 1924, No. 1; Huffman and Baltzer, Mich. Exten. Bul. 73.
38. Hickman, Rinehart, and Johnson, Id. Bul. 209; Vinke and Pearson, Mont. Bul. 251.
39. Rinehart, Hickman, and Johnson, Id. Bul. 194; Quayle, Wyo. Bul. 191.
40. Miller, Cal. Bul. 431 and mimeo. rpt.; Maynard, Morton, and Osland, Colo. Bul. 379; Wilson and Lantow, N. Mex. Bul. 155.
41. Edwards and Brown, Mich. Quar. Bul. 11, 1928, No. 2; see also: Thompson and Voorhies, Cal. Bul. 342; Shaw and Anderson, Mich. Bul. 243; Wilson and Lantow, N. Mex. Bul. 155.
42. Greene and Semple, U. S. Dept. Agr. Bul. 1333.
43. LaMaster and Jones, S. C. Bul. 216; Ewing, Ridgway, and Doubt, Tex. Bul. 238.
44. Templeton, Ferguson, and Gibbens, Ala. Buls. 192, 198, Cir. 40; Scott, Fla. Bul. 102; Ga. Rpts. 1928, 1930; Miss. Rpts. 1922, 1924; Starkey and Salmon, S. C. Bul. 214, Rpts. 1924, 1925; Greene and Semple, U. S. Dept. Agr. Bul. 1333.
45. Dunn and Evvard, Iowa Bul. 185.
46. Templeton, Ferguson, and Gibbens, Ala. Bul. 198; Jarnagin, Ga. State Col. of Agr. Bul. 159; Hooper, Ky. Cir. 23; Lindsey and Beals, Mass. Bul. 197; Moore, Miss. Rpt. 1922; see also: Hunt, Va. Bul. 225.
47. Woodward et al., U. S. Dept. Agr. Bul. 1272.
48. Templeton et al., Ala. Buls. 198, 213; Miller, Grimes, and Salmon, Ala. Rpts. 1924, 1925, 1926, 1927; Dvorachek, Ark. Cir. 45; Scott, Fla. Bul. 141; Edwards, Ga. Cir. 84, Rpts. 1928, 1929, 1930; Good and Mann, Ky. Cir. 20; Norton, Mich. Rpt. 1918; Barnett and Goodell, Miss. Bul. 218; S. C. Rpts. 1922, 1923, 1925.
49. Miller, Jour. Biol. Chem., 44, 1920, p. 481; Finks and Johns, Amer. Jour. Physiol., 57, 1921, p. 61; Waterman and Jones, Jour. Biol. Chem., 47, 1921, pp. 285-295; Jones, Finks, and Waterman, Jour. Biol. Chem., 52, 1922, p. 209; Sure, Jour. Biol. Chem., 50, 1922, pp. 103-111; Read and Sure, Jour. Agr. Res., 24, 1923, pp. 433-440.
50. Lindsey, Mass. Bul. 197; U. S. Dept. Agr., Rpt. Bur. Anim. Indus. 1919.
51. Kennedy, Cal. Cir. 257.
52. Atkeson, Warren, and Johnson, Id. Bul. 206.
53. Dice, N. D. Buls. 217, 233; Hopper, N. D. Bul. 256, Griswold, N. D. Bul. 274.
54. Condit, Jaffa, and Albro, Cal. Bul. 309.
55. Woll and Voorhies, Cal. Bul. 271.
56. Wilson and Lantow, New Mex. Bul. 155.
57. Krauss, Hawaii Bul. 64.
58. Lindsey, Mass. Bul. 155.
59. Perkins, Bachtell, and Weaver, Ohio Bul. 497; see also: Woll, Cal. Bul. 335.
60. Guilbert, Cal. Bul. 418.
61. Cal. Rpt. 1919.
62. Edwards, Guam Sta., Rpt. 1924.
63. Hughes and Feldmiller, Cal. Exten. Cir. 15; Robison, Ohio Bul. 349; Fjeldsted and Potter, Ore. Bul. 165; Hackedorn and Sotola, Wash. Bul. 169.
64. Thompson and Voorhies, Cal. Bul. 342.
65. Hays, Del. Bul. 124.
66. Thompson and Voorhies, Cal. Bul. 335; Headley, Nev. Rpt. 1934 and information to the author.
67. Edwards, Guam Sta. Rpt. 1926.
68. Hooper and Nutter, Ky. Cir. 23.
69. Stewart, Min. of Agr. Jour., Great Britain, 30, 1923, pp. 631-632.
70. Miller, Cal. Rpt. 1931.
71. Mangold, Handb. Ernähr. und Stoffwechsels, Vol. I, pp. 471-472; Halnan, Minister of Agr. Jour., Great Britain, 30, 1924, p. 1166.
72. Ellett, Holdaway, Eheart, and Lasting, Va. Tech. Bul. 41.
73. Spring and Day, Agr. Bul. of Federated Malay States, Vol. VI, No. 5, 1918.
74. Ellenberger and Newlander, Vt. Bul. 243; Ellenberger and Aplin, Vt. Buls. 272, 284; Aplin, Vt. Bul. 271; see also: Lund and Hansen, Ber. K. Vet. og. Landbohöjskoles Lab. Landökonom Forsog, Copenhagen, 89, 1915; Bünger and Lamprecht, Milchw. Forsch., 3, 1926, pp. 3-20.
75. Lindsey and Smith, Mass. Bul. 158.
76. Beals and Lindsey, Jour. Agr. Res., 7, 1916, pp. 301-320.
77. Guilbert and Regan, Cal. Sta., information to the author.

CHAPTER XIX

MISCELLANEOUS CONCENTRATES

I. Cow's Milk and Milk By-products

616. Nutritive value of milk.—It has been emphasized in Chapters VII and VIII that whole milk is nearly a perfect food for young mammals. Milk from which the fat has not been removed has the following nutritive virtues: (1) It contains an abundance of protein of exceptionally high quality, which effectively makes good the deficiencies in the proteins of the cereal grains; (2) it is high in calcium and phosphorus; (3) it provides an ample supply of energy in the milk sugar and fat; (4) it is rich in vitamin A value, if produced by animals fed good rations; (5) it is one of the best sources of vitamin G; (6) it is fair in vitamin B content; and (7) it is almost wholly digestible, and therefore has an exceedingly high value, considering the amount of dry matter it actually contains.

Recent investigations have shown, as has been pointed out previously, that milk is not a perfect food for exclusive feeding to animals over long periods. (**137**) It has but little iron; the content of vitamin D is low; and it is not rich in vitamin C. The lack of iron is of importance in livestock feeding only in the case of young pigs which are not on pasture. (**174**) The relatively low content of vitamin D can readily be made good by allowing the animals access to sunlight, or by including in the ration well-cured legume hay or some other source of vitamin D. (**191-192**) The fact that milk contains but little vitamin C is not of importance in feeding farm animals, so far as is known.

The effects of various factors, including the kind of feeds in the ration, upon the composition and nutritive value of milk are discussed in detail in Chapters VIII and XXIV.

617. Whole milk.—Whole cow's milk is too valuable for human food to be used in stock feeding under usual conditions, except for feeding to young dairy calves until they become old enough to live on other feeds. The use of whole milk for this purpose is treated fully in Chapter XXVIII. The experiments there reviewed show conclusively that it is not necessary to continue the feeding of whole milk to calves longer than 3 to 6 weeks, when a plentiful supply of skimmilk is available, or when reconstituted skimmilk (made from dried skimmilk) is fed. If other methods of raising calves are followed, it is then necessary to feed whole milk for a longer period.

One should not hesitate to use whole milk when needed in rearing an orphan foal or lamb, and young stock being fitted for show can be forced ahead rapidly by its judicious use.

Whole milk usually contains from 2 to 3 per cent of casein, 0.4 to 0.9 per cent albumin, and traces of other proteins. It carries from 4 to 5 per cent of milk sugar, which is only slightly sweet, is much less

soluble than cane sugar, and has about the same feeding value as starch.
When milk sours, some of the sugar is changed to lactic acid, which
curdles the casein. This fermentation ceases when about 0.8 per cent of
acid has developed, so that in sour milk usually most of the sugar is
still unchanged.

It is shown in Chapter XXIV that the percentage of fat varies
widely, depending on individuality, breed of cow, and the portion of
the milk drawn, the strippings sometimes containing 10 times as much
fat as the first-drawn milk.

618. Skimmilk.—Skimmilk has all the nutritive virtues of whole
milk, except for the removal of nearly all of the fat. It is even richer
than whole milk in protein, milk sugar, and minerals, due to the absence
of the fat. Skimmilk from properly-adjusted centrifugal separators
contains about 3.7 per cent protein, 5.0 per cent milk sugar (shown
in feeding stuff analyses as nitrogen-free extract), and only 0.03 to
0.10 per cent fat.

Due to the low fat content, skimmilk supplies but little vitamin A,
for nearly all of the vitamin A in whole milk is contained in the fat.
Skimmilk also furnishes considerably less energy than whole milk,
because most of the fat has been removed.

In feeding skimmilk, it should be borne in mind that it is exceedingly rich in protein, on the dry-matter basis. While the nutritive ratio
of whole milk is 1:3.9, that of skimmilk is only 1:1.5. Due to this high
proportion of protein, there is no need of using other protein supplements in the ration when sufficient skimmilk is available. Instead, it
should be fed with the cereal grains or other concentrates low in protein. When full advantage is not taken of this richness of skimmilk
in protein, the value secured from it is correspondingly decreased.
Skimmilk is at its best for feeding, especially to young calves, when
it comes fresh and yet warm from the farm separator.

Skimmilk is used chiefly for dairy calves, pigs, and poultry, and
it has an especially high value for them. When it is fed in suitable
amounts to these classes of stock, it has a considerably higher value
per 100 lbs. than an equal amount of protein and other nutrients in
the feeds from other animal sources, such as tankage, meat scraps, or
fish meal. Due to the lack of vitamin A in skimmilk, it is highly
important that the ration include other feeds which furnish an ample
amount of the vitamin.

Full information on the use of skimmilk in raising dairy calves
is given in Chapter XXVIII. The experiments there reviewed have
proven that just as thrifty calves can be raised when they are changed
from whole milk to skimmilk, by 4 to 6 weeks of age, as when whole
milk is continued longer.

The numerous experiments which have shown the high value of
skimmilk for pigs are discussed in Chapter XXXVI. Specific information is there given on the amounts of skimmilk needed to balance the
rations of pigs of various ages and when fed various combinations of
feed. Though skimmilk is an ideal protein supplement for swine of
all ages, including brood sows, it has its highest value for young pigs
before weaning and especially immediately after weaning. Skimmilk
and other milk by-products in general have a particularly high value

SKIM MILK IS AN EXCELLENT FEED FOR PIGS AND CALVES

Rich in protein of the highest quality and high in calcium and phosphorus, skim milk is a superior feed for young animals. These young pigs are being fed skim milk and a suitable concentrate mixture inside the "creep," where the sows can not enter. (From Wisconsin Station.)

A PORTION OF THE UNION STOCK YARDS AT CHICAGO

The Chicago Union Stock Yards occupy an area of 500 acres, and have 25 miles of streets and 300 miles of railway tracks. The yards would hold at one time 75,000 cattle, 125,000 sheep, 300,000 hogs, and 6,000 horses and mules. Some of the large packing plants may be seen in the background at the right.

FATTENING STEERS ON BEET PULP IN THE WEST

In the vicinity of the beet sugar factories thousands of cattle are fattened on wet beet pulp and other feeds. In the feed lots shown in this view the beet pulp is brought from the beet sugar factory on the tramway.

BEET TOPS ARE OFTEN ENSILED IN TRENCH SILOS

Especially in the western states, trench silos have become popular during recent years. The loss of nutrients is higher than in silos of the ordinary types, but this is offset more or less by the small cost.

for poultry feeding, because these milk by-products are exceedingly rich in vitamin G, which is required in unusually large amounts by poultry.

When more skimmilk is available than is needed by calves, pigs, or poultry, it may be fed to dairy cows and heifers. Only a few cows will drink skimmilk, but the allowance may be poured on the grain in a pail, and this mixture then fed on top of the silage. In Minnesota trials 8 lbs. of skimmilk replaced 1 lb. of linseed meal when dairy cows were thus fed 2 lbs. of skimmilk per pound of grain mixture.[1] Likewise, in experiments with dairy heifers 8 lbs. of skimmilk were equal to 1 lb. of linseed meal as a protein supplement to corn grain and timothy hay. In Montana tests 4 cows were taught to drink skimmilk, then taking an average of 19 lbs. a day.[2] Fed in this manner, each 5.9 lbs. of skimmilk replaced 1 lb. of the grain mixture.

619. Buttermilk.—Unless wash water from the churn has been added to it, buttermilk has practically the same composition as skimmilk, except that it usually contains 0.4 per cent fat or more. Also, in buttermilk from sour cream a part of the sugar has been changed to lactic acid. Buttermilk of good quality is a satisfactory substitute for skimmilk in feeding calves and pigs, as is pointed out in Chapters XXVIII and XXXVI. It is also an excellent feed for poultry. When properly fed, undiluted buttermilk is worth about as much per 100 lbs. as skimmilk.

Since buttermilk often has a more laxative effect than skimmilk, calves should not be changed to buttermilk quite as early as in the case of skimmilk. Buttermilk that is allowed to ferment and putrefy in dirty tanks is a dangerous feed.

620. Whey.—In the manufacture of cheese practically all the casein and most of the fat go into the cheese, leaving in the whey the milk sugar, the albumin, and a large part of the ash. Whey is more watery in composition than skimmilk, containing only about 6.6 per cent dry matter. Whey from the manufacture of Cheddar and most other types of cheese contains about 5.0 per cent milk sugar and 0.3 per cent fat, with only 0.9 per cent protein, the nutritive ratio being 1:6.1, which is much wider than that of skimmilk. Whey from Swiss cheese contains 0.8 to 1.0 per cent fat. To save the fat for butter manufacture, whey, especially from Swiss cheese, is often skimmed at the factories. Skimmed whey is worth slightly less than unskimmed whey.

In feeding whey it is very necessary to bear in mind the fact that most of the protein has been removed, and that whey is not a protein-rich feed, like skimmilk and buttermilk. The milk albumin it does contain is, however, of high efficiency in making good the deficiencies in the proteins of the cereal grains.

Whey is chiefly fed to swine, and its value for this purpose is discussed fully in Chapter XXXVI. For swine feeding, whey is worth about one-half as much per 100 lbs. as skimmilk. Whey can also be used satisfactorily for raising dairy calves, as is pointed out in Chapter XXVIII, when it is fed with a suitable concentrate mixture, rich in protein. It is an excellent feed for poultry, as it is just as rich in vitamin G as is skimmilk.

621. Importance of pasteurizing factory by-products.—Since milk from different farms is mixed at the creamery and cheese factory, bovine tuberculosis, Bang's disease, and other diseases may be widely spread from a diseased herd through the skimmilk, buttermilk, or whey.

Since disease-producing bacteria are killed by heating the milk or whey to a temperature of 180° F., this simple precaution will remove danger from this source. The pasteurized product also keeps better and is less likely to cause scours. This practice is likewise advantageous to the factories, for the milk cans may be more readily kept in good condition and the quality of the milk delivered at the factory will thereby be improved. Careful farmers should therefore insist that skimmilk, buttermilk, and whey be thoroughly pasteurized at the factory before they take it back to their farms for feeding.

622. Dried skimmilk; dried buttermilk.—Considerable quantities of skimmilk and buttermilk are now dried at the factories to produce *dried skimmilk* (also called "dry skimmilk") and *dried buttermilk*. In addition to their use in human foods, these products are employed widely for poultry feeding and also for feeding dairy calves. One pound of either of these feeds has practically the same composition and feeding value as 10 lbs. of the liquid skimmilk or buttermilk, respectively. Dried skimmilk contains an average of 34.8 per cent protein, 50.1 per cent milk sugar, 8.0 per cent minerals, and 0.9 per cent fat. Dried buttermilk is a little lower in protein, but has an average of 5.6 per cent fat. The fat content varies widely, however, ranging from less than 1 per cent to 8 per cent or more. The products low in fat are probably from soured skimmilk, instead of buttermilk.

Due to the alkalies used in partially neutralizing very sour cream, dried buttermilk is higher in minerals, or ash, than dried skimmilk. Occasionally some lots are excessively high, containing 15 to 18 per cent of ash, with correspondingly less protein and sugar.

On account of their richness in vitamin G and the high quality of milk proteins, these products are of especial value in poultry feeding. They are also often used as substitutes for milk in raising dairy calves in market milk and condensery districts. As is described in Chapter XXVIII, 9 lbs. of water may be added to each pound of the dried skimmilk or dried buttermilk to make reconstituted skimmilk or buttermilk; or the dried milk products can be included in a calf meal, or "calf starter."

When expense is not considered, dried skimmilk and dried buttermilk are excellent protein supplements for swine, especially young pigs. It is pointed out in Chapter XXXVI, however, that they are usually too expensive for this purpose, since excellent results can be secured on cheaper rations.

623. Condensed or evaporated buttermilk.—Condensed or evaporated buttermilk, also called "concentrated buttermilk" and "semi-solid buttermilk," is made by evaporating buttermilk until it is reduced to about one-third the original weight. According to the definition adopted by the Association of American Feed Control Officials, this product should contain not less than 27 per cent of total solids, not less than 2 per cent of fat, and not more than 0.14 per cent of ash for each per cent of solids.[3]

Though condensed buttermilk is semi-solid, it generally contains over 60 per cent water, and about 3 lbs. are required to equal 1 lb. of dried buttermilk or dried skimmilk in amount of milk solids. On account of its nature, condensed buttermilk must be shipped in barrels or other water-tight containers. Due to this and also the high cost of transporting the watery product, the price is usually higher than the cost of an equivalent amount of dried buttermilk or dried skimmilk.

It is pointed out in Chapters XXVIII and XXXVI that other protein supplements are usually more economical than condensed buttermilk for dairy calves or pigs. This product is used chiefly for feeding poultry.

624. Dried whey, or milk-sugar feed; cheese meal.—*Dried whey,* or milk-sugar feed, is obtained by drying whey from cheese manufacture or from the manufacture of casein from skimmilk. It has an average of 12.5 per cent protein and 72 per cent milk sugar. Because of the richness of dried whey in vitamin G, it is used chiefly as an ingredient in poultry feeds. One pound of dried whey is about equal to 14 lbs. of liquid whey in value. Dried whey may also be used for pigs, but its value for this purpose is lower than for poultry.[4]

Cheese meal, a by-product from the manufacture of processed cheese, is composed of the cheese trimmings, from which most of the fat has been removed. It contains about 60 per cent protein and 7 per cent fat, thus resembling the best grades of tankage in composition. In Wisconsin tests cheese meal was an excellent protein supplement for pigs, being worth even more than tankage.[5]

II. Packing-plant and Fishery By-products

625. The packing-plant by-products.—The various packing-house by-products used for stock feeding include digester tankage, or meat meal; dry-rendered tankage, or meat scraps; meat-and-bone meal, or meat-and-bone scraps; dried blood; steamed bone meal; and raw bone meal. The tankages and meat and bone meals and scraps are high in protein that is of an excellent quality to correct the deficiencies of the proteins in the cereal grains. These by-products are also rich in calcium and phosphorus. They are therefore of especially high value for swine and poultry, but are also efficient protein supplements for other classes of stock. The bone meals, which have been discussed in Chapter VI, are the most common phosphorus supplements used in stock feeding. (**167-168**)

In the production of the tankages, meat meals, and meat scraps two different processes are employed. The method which has been used in this country for the most part until the past few years is the digester method, also called the "wet-rendering method." Recently, the dry-rendering method has rapidly come into more common use.

626. Digester tankage.—In the digester method the fresh meat scraps, fat trimmings, and scrap bones are thoroughly cooked for 6 to 8 hours by steam under pressure in large vertical tanks.[6] After the cooking is completed, the fat is skimmed off the top, the soupy liquid is drained off, and the solid residue pressed in hydraulic presses to remove as much of the fat and water as possible.

The liquid is evaporated down to a gluey consistency, then being called "stick." This stick is next added to the solid meat residue, and the mixture is dried in steam-jacketed dryers. The dry material is at last ground, after being passed over powerful magnets to remove any pieces of metal. This product is *digester tankage,* which is also called meat meal, or feeding tankage. The best grade is usually guaranteed to contain 60 per cent protein. As shown in Appendix Table I, it contains an average of 61.3 per cent protein, 19.2 per cent mineral matter, and 8.8 per cent fat. In producing this grade of digester tankage, partly-dried blood is often added to the meat residue and the stick, to bring the protein content up to the desired percentage.

Some digester tankages are guaranteed to contain 55 per cent protein, and meat-and-bone products may contain only 40 to 50 per cent protein. The differences in protein content are due primarily to the proportions of bone in the product. The value of any grade will depend primarily on the protein content, unless the additional amount of bone is actually needed in the ration.

627. Meat scraps, or dry-rendered tankage.—The more efficient dry-rendering method of processing meat or meat-and-bone residue is rapidly replacing the older wet-rendering method. In the dry-rendering process the raw material is cooked in a fat-melter, which is an open steam-jacketed vessel, with paddles to agitate the mass.[6]

The moisture is driven off, the excess fat drained off, and the solid matter is next pressed in a screw press to remove as much of the fat as possible. The dry residue is then granulated or is ground into a meal.

The dry-rendered product does not have as strong an odor as digester tankage, and it is lighter in color. Though usually containing only 50 to 55 per cent protein, dry-rendered tankage or meat scraps has proven to be equal to high-grade digester tankage containing 60 per cent protein. (See Chapter XXXVI.) This is probably because the protein is more digestible and has a higher nutritive value in the dry-rendered product. Sometimes dried blood is added to dry-rendered tankage to increase the protein content to 60 per cent.

The terms *meat scraps* and *meat and bone scraps* are generally used for the dry-rendered products, though sometimes they are called dry-rendered tankage, or meat meal, or meat and bone meal.

628. Meat and bone products.—According to the definitions of the Association of American Feed Control Officials, digester tankage, meat scraps, or meat meal should not include hoof, horn, manure, and stomach contents, except in such cases as might occur unavoidably in good factory practices and must not contain more than 10 per cent of phosphoric acid (4.4 per cent of phosphorus).[3] If the phosphorus content is higher than this, the product must be called *digester tankage with bone,* or *meat and bone digester tankage,* or *meat and bone meal,* or *meat and bone scraps.*

629. Use of tankage and meat scraps.—Tankage, meat meal, and meat scraps are used chiefly as protein supplements for swine and poultry. Their richness in protein of excellent quality and also their high content of calcium and phosphorus make them especially valuable for these classes of stock. These meat by-products are also satisfactory for feeding dairy cattle, beef cattle, sheep, and horses. While these animals may at first not like the feeds, generally they will soon eat a mixture of concentrates which contains the small proportion of a meat by-product that is needed to balance the ration. Occasionally, a certain lot of tankage or meat scraps may prove unpalatable to cattle.

Due to the high protein content of tankage, meat scraps, and meat meal, care should be taken to feed correspondingly less than would be required of such supplements as linseed meal, cottonseed meal, or soybean oil meal. Otherwise full advantage will not be gained from the richness in protein.

On account of the importance of these meat by-products, their use for each class of stock is considered in detail in Part III. It is of interest to note that a protein supplemental mixture called an "all-purpose protein supplement," which is very satisfactory for feeding to several classes of stock, has been developed by the Ohio Station. In these tests a mixture of 30 lbs. meat scraps, 30 lbs. soybean oil meal, 20 lbs. cottonseed meal, 15 lbs. linseed meal, and 5 lbs. minerals (equal parts of steamed bone meal, ground limestone, and salt) has been very satisfactory for dairy cattle, beef cattle, sheep, swine, and poultry.[7] Modifications can readily be made in the mixture to adapt it to varying feed prices.

630. Rendering-plant tankage, or reduction tankage.—The small rendering plants which render scrap meat and bones from butcher shops, dead animals, etc., for soap grease, produce tankage of various qualities. This rendering-plant or reduction tankage is used chiefly for fertilizer, but some is fed to stock. The use of this tankage for swine feeding is discussed in Chapter XXXVI. There is no danger of infecting animals with disease in using such tankage, if due care is taken in its production, for the high temperature thoroughly sterilizes it. However, some of the raw material may have begun to decompose before it is processed, and therefore tankage of this kind may not be of sufficiently good quality for feeding purposes.

631. Adulteration of tankage.—The tankages and meat meals or meat scraps produced by the large packing plants with established reputations are practically always good products, made under careful control and from suitable raw materials. Occasionally, products are found on the market which are adulterated with such materials as hoof meal, hair, leather meal, paunch or intestinal contents, etc.[8] Some carry an unduly large proportion of dried blood to bring up the protein content of a low-protein product.

Certain tankages and meat scraps are also made too largely of waste that is high in gristle and connective tissue, the proteins of which are of low value.[9] Also, some tankages contain too large a proportion of "stick," which supplies protein of poor quality.[10]

These poor-quality tankages may contain as much protein and fat as high-grade tankages, but they have a lower feeding value. As it is impossible for the usual purchaser to detect the poor quality of such products by ordinary inspection, it is wise to buy only tankage made by establishments of known reputation for high-quality products.

632. Blood meal.—The blood is collected at packing plants and heated in large vats until it is thoroughly coagulated. The excess water is drained off and more moisture removed in a hydraulic press. The solid residue is then dried and ground to form blood meal, or dried blood.

Blood meal is the richest in protein of all packing-plant by-products, containing over 80 per cent. It is low in calcium and phosphorus, thus differing greatly from tankage or meat scraps. Blood meal is used chiefly for feeding calves, and its value for this purpose is discussed in Chapter XXVIII. Blood meal has been fed successfully to horses, especially to those that were thin and run-down; it is occasionally fed to young pigs, but tankage is usually cheaper and better for this purpose.[11]

On account of the temperature employed in the usual method of drying blood, the protein is not highly digestible. Therefore, special methods are sometimes used to produce a more soluble and more digestible product, called "soluble blood meal or flour." This has a higher value in calf feeding than the ordinary grade.

633. Gelatin.—The protein in gelatin has a low nutritive value, and therefore gelatin is not satisfactory as a substitute for tankage in stock feeding.[12] A by-product composed chiefly of gelatin, called "alba blood," made from discarded printers' rolls, is sometimes used as an adulterant in tankage.[13]

634. Production of fish meal.—Because of the experiments which have shown conclusively the high feeding value of fish meal for swine and poultry, the production of this feed has increased considerably during recent years. Some years ago the fishery wastes were either used to produce fish meal for fertilizer or were not utilized at all, but dumped in the sea. Even now the total production of fish meal in the United States is relatively small in comparison with the amounts of tankage and meat scraps.

Several types of fish meal are made, differing not only in the raw material used but also in the method of drying. Menhaden fish meal, which is the most common kind in the eastern states, is produced by processing the entire menhaden herrings for fish oil and fish meal. These are a fat fish, not suited for food, which are caught in large quantities off the Atlantic coast.

White fish meal is made chiefly from the waste from the cod and haddock industry, not including the entrails, which, with the exception of the livers, are usually dumped at sea. The proportions of scrap meat, heads, and bones may vary considerably in the product. If the proportion of heads is large, the value of the fish meal is decreased.

Fish meal is also made at sardine canning plants from the heads and the broken and damaged fish. On the North Atlantic coast small herring are canned for sardines and on the Pacific coast pilchard are chiefly used. Some fish meal is also made on the Pacific coast from the waste of the salmon and tuna canning factories. Small amounts of other fish wastes are also made into fish meal.

Formerly, the menhaden fish product was dried in so-called "flame driers," in which the material was exposed to a heat of 500° to 600° F. or more for several minutes. This method is still used to a large extent in the production of menhaden fish meal and also other fish meals. However, it is being replaced by the method of drying in steam-jacketed drums under partial vacuum, to lower the temperature of the process.

In the case of oily fish waste, most of the oil is expressed or extracted from the product.

635. Nutritive value of fish meals.—Fish meals differ somewhat in nutritive value, depending on the type of raw material used, the method of drying, and the care taken in the process. But few direct comparisons have been made of the various kinds of fish meal, and therefore only general statements can as yet be given concerning their relative feeding value.

In general, a fish meal carefully made from sound, undecomposed material is an excellent protein supplement, especially for swine and poultry. Indeed, good fish meal is superior to high-grade tankage or meat scraps in value per ton for these classes of stock.

Fish meal usually contains from 50 to 60 per cent of protein and 15 to 25 per cent of mineral matter, which is chiefly fish bones. Therefore fish meal is rich in calcium and protein. The protein of fish meal is of high nutritive value, tending to be even more efficient as a supplement to the grains than the protein in tankage or meat scraps. **(149)**

Due to the lower temperature during the drying process, vacuumdried fish meal is superior to a flame-dried fish meal made from the same raw material.[14] The protein is more digestible and it has a higher nutritive value. Also the content of vitamins A, D, and G is much greater. Indeed, some fish meals dried at high temperatures contain practically no vitamins.

It must be borne in mind, however, that vacuum drying is no guarantee in itself that the product is always of high quality. Occasionally the raw material may have been unsuitable for feeding purposes or the process improperly carried out. For example, in New York experiments with pigs excellent results were generally secured from a certain brand of vacuum-dried fish meal, which was supposedly of excellent quality. However, on two different occasions pigs fed this fish meal became very unthrifty, apparently due to its poor quality, though this was not evident from an inspection of the fish meal.[15] At the same time excellent gains were made by similar pigs fed alongside on flame-dried menhaden fish meal or on digester tankage. Obviously, much more care must be taken to prevent decomposition or injury of the product in the production of fish meal for stock feeding than in the making of fish meal for fertilizer. Certain fish waste is too high in salt to be used for fish meal for stock feeding, unless the salt is removed from the product.

Some have hesitated to use fish meal for stock feeding, fearing that it might cause a fishy flavor in the milk of cows or in the meat of swine, cattle, or sheep. In the numerous feeding experiments with fish meal no injurious effect whatsoever has been produced when good fish meal, not unduly high in fat, has been fed in such amounts as were needed to balance the ration. If a larger allowance of fish meal is fed, there may be some danger of such an effect.

636. Use of fish meal.—As has been stated previously, fish meal has an especially high value for swine and poultry, on account of the excellent quality of its protein. The use of fish meal for swine feeding is discussed in detail in Chapter XXXVI.

Fish meal can also be used economically as a protein supplement for cattle and sheep, when it is a cheap source of protein. However, for these classes of stock, fish meal usually has no higher value per pound of digestible protein than protein supplements of plant origin, such as linseed meal or cottonseed meal. Also, it is often not palatable to cattle. Usually they will soon become accustomed to a concentrate mixture containing 10 to 15 per cent of fish meal, but occasionally animals will refuse to eat such a combination.

In most of the experiments in which fish meal has been fed to dairy cows the yields of milk and fat have been satisfactory, but in some instances the fish meal has slightly decreased the percentage of fat in the milk.[16] The same effect is produced by cod-liver oil and certain other fish oils. Often the mixture containing fish meal has been less palatable to cows than the usual type of dairy concentrate mixture.

It is pointed out in Chapter XXVIII that fish meal can be used as a partial substitute for milk in raising dairy calves. Fish meal of good quality has produced satisfactory results when used as a protein supplement for fattening lambs and fattening steers.[17] It is also sometimes fed to horses.

637. Shrimp meal.—Shrimp meal, also called "shrimp bran," consists of the dried waste of the shrimp industry, including the heads and hulls (or shells). Shrimp meal does not keep well when stored for any long time. It contains about 42 per cent protein and was equal or superior to high-grade tankage as a protein supplement for swine in Louisiana trials.[18] Still better results were secured from a combination of half shrimp meal and half cottonseed meal. For pigs not on pasture especially good results were obtained when a combination of 50 lbs. shrimp meal, 30 lbs. cottonseed meal, and 20 lbs. ground alfalfa or clover hay was fed as a supplement to grain.

In Louisiana tests shrimp meal was also satisfactory for dairy cows when 10 to 19 per cent was included in the concentrate mixture as a substitute for cottonseed meal.[19] Likewise, steam-dried shrimp meal was a good supplement in poultry rations, but air-dried shrimp meal was less desirable, on account of the high salt content.

638. Whale meal.—Whale meal that is suitable for stock feeding is made from the clean, dried, undecomposed flesh of the whale, after part of the oil has been extracted. It resembles tankage in composition, having about 50 per cent protein. Sometimes whale meal is not of satisfactory quality for feeding purposes. In North Carolina tests with pigs whale meal did not give good results when fed as the only supplement to corn.[20]

III. SUGAR-FACTORY BY-PRODUCTS

639. Beet sugar production and by-products.—Approximately six million tons of sugar, made from sugar cane and from sugar beets, are consumed annually in the United States. During the five years, 1930-34 inclusive, about 1,305,000 tons of this total has been beet sugar produced in this country; 199,000 tons, cane sugar produced in Louisiana; and the remainder, sugar imported from our insular possessions and from other countries, chiefly Cuba.

In the manufacture of beet sugar, the sugar beets are first washed and then cut into thin strips. The juice is thoroughly extracted from these strips by means of warm water, leaving the by-product known as *wet beet pulp*. The juice is next clarified and purified with lime and carbon dioxide and in some cases also with sulfur dioxide. After filtration, the clear juice is evaporated under a partial vacuum until the sugar crystallizes. The grains of sugar are then separated from the residual sirup by a centrifuge. This sirup is commonly reboiled and the process repeated once more, or even twice, to secure as large a yield of sugar as possible.

The residual sirup, called *beet molasses,* still contains a large amount of sugar, along with mineral salts and other impurities.

This molasses is used for stock feeding, or it may be treated further in the Steffen's process or in both the Steffen's process and the barium process, to recover still more sugar. The residual molasses remaining from these processes contains as much nutrients as the ordinary beet molasses and has as high a feeding value.[21]

The beet tops which are removed from the beet roots before they are sent to the sugar factory form another important by-product for livestock feeding. The use of beet tops has already been discussed in Chapter XVI.

640. Production of sugar from cane; by-products.—In the production of sugar from sugar cane, the cane stalks are cut close to the ground, the tops and leaves removed, and the stalks sent to the sugar factory. Here they are crushed in three or more mills between sets of powerful rollers to remove the juice. To increase the recovery of sugar, water is sprayed upon the partially-extracted cane, as it passes from one mill to the next.

The sugar is produced from the juice in much the same manner as in the manufacture of sugar from sugar beets. The molasses resulting from the process is called *cane molasses,* or *blackstrap.* The sugar-cane tops and also the bagasse (the stalk residue, after the juice is expressed) are sometimes used for stock feeding, as has been pointed out in Chapter XV.

641. Cane molasses.—In addition to the limited amount of *cane molasses,* or *blackstrap,* made in the continental United States, a large amount is imported. From 50,000,000 to 100,000,000 gallons are used annually for stock feeding in this country, and still more is used for the production of alcohol, yeast, and other fermentation products. In 1933-34, about 70 per cent of the amount for feed was used by central feed manufacturers in mixed feeds and 20 per cent by retail feed mixers. Only about 10 per cent of the total was purchased as molasses by stockmen.

Cane molasses is very palatable and is much relished by stock. It also has a mild laxative effect that is beneficial when the other feeds in the ration are constipating. The molasses of the usual grade contains 55 per cent or more of sugars, which are the only important organic nutrients. Cane molasses has only 2.8 per cent protein, on the average, and this consists largely of compounds having low nutritive value. When large amounts of molasses are fed, it is therefore especially important that sufficient protein be furnished by the rest of the ration.

Cane molasses contains an average of 25.9 per cent water and supplies only 56.6 lbs. of total digestible nutrients per 100 lbs., which is only about 70 per cent as much as is furnished by corn grain. Cane molasses weighs about 11.7 lbs. per gallon, and therefore approximately **171** gallons make a ton.

Molasses has its highest value per pound when its palatable **nature** is utilized to induce stock to eat roughage with less waste of the stems and coarser parts than there would be otherwise. It is often diluted with 1 to 2 parts of water and sprinkled over poor-quality hay or other roughage of rather low palatability. The animals will then consume a greater amount of such roughage and there will be less waste. When thus fed, molasses may be worth fully as much or even more than corn or other grain.

Cane molasses is used as an ingredient in many of the mixed feeds, especially those for cattle and horses. It not only increases the palatability of these feeds, but is often one of the cheapest sources of carbohydrates for the feed manufacturer, who can use it in tank-car lots. When molasses must be shipped in barrels, the cost is much greater than in tank cars. Therefore it is frequently expensive for the individual farmer, when it may be cheap at a central feed-mixing plant.

Farmers who desire to secure molasses as cheaply as possible should co-operate in arranging with their local feed dealer or other agency to order a tank car of molasses. It can readily be hauled direct from the car to the farms in whatever containers may be available, such as well-cleaned, second-hand oil drums. In cold weather it may be necessary to warm the molasses by passing steam through the coils in the tank car, so the molasses will flow satisfactorily.

The experiments summarized in Part III show that when molasses is added to a ration made up of feeds that are otherwise palatable, the production of milk or meat is very satisfactory and may even be slightly increased. However, when molasses is thus fed, it is generally worth considerably less per 100 lbs. than corn or other grain. This would be expected from the fact that it supplies a decidedly smaller amount of digestible nutrients than does grain.

Cane molasses is fed most commonly to dairy cows, beef cattle, sheep, and horses, but may be also fed in limited amounts to swine and poultry. For fattening cattle, molasses is sometimes fed in a trough, where the animals help themselves. Some farmers put a barrel of molasses, with bung open, in a tight grain bunk. The molasses then runs out until it reaches the level of the bung, and flows out as it is eaten by the cattle. When animals are fed considerable molasses, they drink more water than usual.

642. Beet molasses.—Beet molasses resembles cane molasses in content of nutrients and has fully as high a feeding value per ton when properly used. However, it is much more laxative than cane molasses, on account of the high content of certain alkaline salts and other laxative substances. Therefore, stock should be accustomed to beet molasses gradually, and the amounts fed should be strictly limited.

The maximum amounts of beet molasses advised by various authorities for animals used to the feed are as follows, per 1,000 lbs. live weight daily: Driving horses, 2.5 lbs.; up to 4 lbs. or even more for draft horses; dairy cows, 2.5 to 3 lbs.; fattening cattle, 4 to 8 lbs.; fattening sheep, 3 to 5 lbs.; and fattening swine, 5 to 10 lbs. Breeding animals should be fed less than those being fattened, and the amount should be materially reduced 6 weeks before the young are born.

The use of beet molasses for the various classes of stock is discussed later in the chapters of Part III. As in the case of cane molasses, beet molasses is used in various mixed feeds, especially in alfalfa-molasses feeds.

643. Wet beet pulp.—At the beet-sugar factories the wet beet pulp is dried to produce dried beet pulp or dried molasses-beet pulp, or it is dumped in huge open silos, which are merely paved areas with strong walls. Here the wet pulp undergoes an acid fermentation similar to that which occurs in corn silage.

Sometimes the fresh pulp is hauled to the farms and stored in ordinary silos or else in pit or trench silos. The fresh pulp may be pressed at the factory to remove some of the water, but even the pressed pulp contains only about 14 per cent dry matter. Ensiled pulp keeps much better than fresh pulp exposed to the air, and it is therefore preferred for feeding. Due both to the draining away of water and to the loss of nutrients in the fermentation, there will be a shrinkage in weight of the pulp when ensiled, ranging from 20 to 40 per cent or more.[22]

Though carrying only 1 to 2 per cent of sugar, wet beet pulp contains considerable of other easily-digested carbohydrates, and the dry matter is equal to that of roots in feeding value. The pulp is low in protein and it is especially low in phosphorus. Therefore, when heavy allowances are fed to stock, it is necessary to see that these nutrients are otherwise supplied.

Fortunately, in the West wet beet pulp is commonly fed with alfalfa hay, which is rich in protein and fair in phosphorus content. However, Utah experiments have shown that there may be a serious lack of phosphorus in rations consisting only of alfalfa hay and wet beet pulp or other beet by-products, with or without cereal grain.[23] Therefore steamed bone meal or some other safe source of phosphorus should be added to such rations.

Wet beet pulp is extensively fed to fattening cattle and lambs or sheep in the western beet-sugar districts. It is also a good feed for dairy cattle and in limited amounts is satisfactory for idle horses. The results of experiments in which its value for cattle and sheep has been determined, are presented in Part III.

644. Dried beet pulp; dried molasses-beet pulp.—The greater part of the wet beet pulp produced in the United States is now dried alone to form *dried beet pulp,* or is combined with beet molasses and dried to form *dried molasses-beet pulp.* These products are palatable, bulky, slightly laxative, and keep well in storage. Their use for the various classes of stock is discussed in detail in Part III.

Dried beet pulp contains an average of 9.0 per cent protein, 59.9 per cent nitrogen-free extract, 0.8 per cent fat, and 18.8 per cent fiber. Though dried beet pulp contains a large amount of fiber for a concentrate, the fiber is highly digestible, and therefore the feed supplies 71.8 lbs. total digestible nutrients per 100 lbs., which is about as much as oats furnish.

It is shown in Part III that when rather small amounts of dried beet pulp are used to increase the palatability of the ration for dairy cows or for fattening cattle or sheep, it may be worth as much as corn, pound for pound. However, when larger amounts are fed as a substitute for grain, the value per pound will be somewhat lower.

Largely on account of its bulky nature and its palatability, dried beet pulp is a very popular feed for dairy cattle, and most of it is fed to dairy cows. It is also used extensively in the sugar-beet districts as a substitute for part of the grain in the fattening of cattle or sheep, and may also replace one-fourth to one-third of the grain in feeding work horses.

Dried molasses-beet pulp does not differ markedly from dried beet pulp in content of nutrients or in feeding value, and it may be used in the same manner. Very recently the production of dried molasses-beet pulp has exceeded that of dried beet pulp in the United States, which is an indication of its popularity.

645. Sugar.—Though the nutritive value of sugar is no greater than that of an equal weight of starch, the great fondness for it shown by stock makes it helpful in some cases for stimulating the appetite. For this reason, a small allowance is often used in fitting animals for show. In a Hawaiian trial, the addition of 5 per cent of sugar to the ration for pigs increased the feed consumption and resulted in slightly more rapid gains.[24]

646. Molasses feeds.—It has been stated previously that cane molasses or beet molasses is used as an ingredient in many of the mixed feeds on the market. These range in character from superior feeds, made entirely from high-grade ingredients, to cheap feeds which contain a large proportion of lower-grade ingredients, such as grain screenings and oat hulls. From the list of guaranteed ingredients and the guarantees for protein, fat, and fiber, one can usually determine approximately the relative value of any particular feed.

Molasses is added to high-grade mixed feeds on account of its palatability and also because it is often one of the cheapest sources of readily-digested carbohydrates. Many experienced dairymen prefer a high-grade mixture containing molasses to one made of the same ingredients, except without molasses.

In lower-grade mixed feeds, molasses has a special value, as it aids in making a mixture palatable that might otherwise not be liked by stock. Unfortunately, molasses also tends to mask the presence of low-grade ingredients, and therefore may make a trashy feed appear much more valuable than is actually the case.

Molassine meal is sometimes made in Europe by mixing molasses with peat or sphagnum moss, and occasionally the product has been imported into the United States. Peat has no nutritive value for stock and the moss is also of very low worth, though arctic animals live on it to some extent. Practically the only nutrient in molassine meal is in the molasses it contains, and at the prices usually asked it is a very uneconomical purchase.[25]

647. Alfalfa-molasses feeds.—In the western alfalfa districts a considerable amount of alfalfa-molasses feeds is manufactured. These consist of combinations of alfalfa meal with various percentages of beet or cane molasses. Usually such feeds contain between 20 and 40 per cent of molasses.

Alfalfa-molasses feeds are palatable to stock and can be used to replace a limited amount of the grain in the ration of dairy cows, beef cattle, and sheep. It must be borne in mind, however, that such feeds are more of the nature of a roughage than of a concentrate. Therefore, as is shown in Part III, when any considerable amount has been fed to fattening cattle or sheep, the alfalfa-molasses feed has been worth decidedly less per ton than corn or barley.

Sometimes alfalfa-molasses feeds are unwisely used as a substitute for such protein supplements as linseed meal or cottonseed meal. It must be remembered that they are not high in protein, and therefore should be used as a substitute for grain, and not as a protein supplement.

IV. Other Miscellaneous Concentrates

648. Distillers' corn dried grains; distillers' rye dried grains.— These by-products are produced in the manufacture of distilled liquors and alcohol from cereals. The grain—corn, rye, barley, etc.—is ground and mixed with barley malt and warm water. The mixture, called the mash, is held at the proper temperature for the diastase in the malt to convert the starch in the mixture into sugar. In the next stage of the process the sugar in the watery mash is converted into alcohol by the action of yeast. After the fermentation is completed, the alcohol is distilled off, leaving a watery residue, called *distillery slop*.

The solid matter is usually strained out of this slop and dried to form *distillers' dried grains*. This consists of the portions of the grains and malt which are not acted on during the fermentation process; i.e., the protein, fat, and also the pentosans in the nitrogen-free extract. In addition it includes much of the yeast formed in the fermentation.

Since distillers' dried grains which are produced chiefly from corn differ markedly in composition and feeding value from those chiefly from rye, the grains should be called either *distillers' corn dried grains* or *distillers' rye dried grains,* depending on the grain which predominates.

Distillers' corn dried grains are considerably higher in value than the rye grains, and usually have 28 per cent or more of protein, averaging 30.6 per cent. In addition, they are rich in fat, usually containing 9 to 11 per cent or even more, and they have only 10.8 per cent of fiber, on the average. Distillers' corn grains are about as bulky as wheat bran, but they rank high in amount of total digestible nutrients. They furnish 85.0 lbs. of total digestible nutrients per 100 lbs., which is even more than is supplied by such feeds as corn grain, corn gluten feed, linseed meal, and cottonseed meal. Some of the distillers' grains sold as distillers' corn dried grains are of distinctly lower value than the usual grade, being lower in both protein and fat.

Distillers' corn grains are deservedly a popular feed for dairy cattle, and are chiefly used for this purpose. The high opinion dairymen have of them is due not only to the richness in nutrients, but also to the bulky nature. Though they are not especially well liked by stock when fed alone, there is no difficulty from this when they are fed in suitable mixtures. Indeed, distillers' corn grains are a common ingredient in mixtures for feeding dairy cows on official test. As is pointed out in Chapter XXV, distillers' corn grains are slightly superior to corn gluten feed for dairy cows. This would be expected from their composition and content of digestible nutrients.

They may also be used satisfactorily as a protein supplement for beef cattle and sheep. If they are cheaper per ton than corn, distillers' corn grains may be used in larger amounts than necessary to balance the ration, being then used as a substitute for part of the grain. In a New York test, fattening lambs made good gains on a mixture of one-half corn and one-half distillers' corn grains,[26] However, when the animals were fed the distillers' corn grains as the only concentrate, the gains were very poor.

A large allowance of distillers' corn grains is not relished by horses, but they may form one-fourth of the concentrate mixture.[27] On account of the bulkiness, they should not comprise more than 15 to 20 per cent of the ration for pigs, but may be fed in larger proportions to brood sows, if cheaper in price than grain.

Distillers' rye dried grains contain an average of only 18.1 per cent protein and 6.9 per cent fat, and they are much higher than distillers' corn grains in fiber, averaging 17.0 per cent. They rank decidedly below distillers' corn grains in digestibility, furnishing but 62.9 lbs. total digestible nutrients per 100 lbs., which is less than in wheat bran. Considering the wide difference in composition and digestibility, the rye distillers' grains are probably not worth more than about two-thirds as much per ton as the usual grade of distillers' corn grains, though no direct comparisons of these feeds have apparently been made by the experiment stations.

649. Distillery slop.—The distillery slop left after the alcohol is distilled from the fermented mash is sometimes fed to fattening cattle near the distillery. The whole slop contains only about 6 to 7 per cent dry matter, and the strained slop, after the wet distillers' grains are removed, 5 per cent or less.

Cattle fattened on distillery slop are allowed to drink all of the slop they will take. However, the slop is too watery to make good gains when fed only with hay or other roughage. To produce satisfactory gains the cattle should be fed what hay or other dry roughage they care for, and at least one-third of the usual allowance of grain. No protein supplement is needed, as the slop is rich in protein, on the dry basis. The slop sometimes has an unduly laxative effect, and therefore the roughages should be such as will tend to counteract this action. Hay from the grasses, straw, cottonseed hulls, oat hulls, or oat mill feed are good for the purpose.

A method has recently been developed of drying the whole, unstrained distillery slop. Dried rye slop of this kind contains about 30 per cent protein, 3 per cent fat, and only 8 per cent fiber. Judging from the chemical composition, its value is considerably higher than that of ordinary distillers' rye dried grains.

650. Yeast dried grains; vinegar dried grains.—*Yeast dried grains* and *vinegar dried grains* are by-products from the manufacture of yeast and of malt vinegar from the cereals and other products. As is shown in Appendix Table I, they are similar to distillers' rye dried grains in composition, and they probably have about the same feeding value.

651. Industrial alcohol by-product feed.—When alcohol is made from cane molasses, a dried by-product can be made from the residue which has about 31 per cent protein, 9 per cent fat, and 9 per cent fiber. In Maryland tests it was found that this feed was not palatable when fed alone, and that the protein was not of good quality when used as the only source of protein.[28]

For these reasons this by-product should be mixed with well-liked feeds and used along with protein supplements of better quality. Very good gains were produced when pigs were fed a combination of one-half of this feed and one-half of fish meal as a supplement to corn.

652. Brewers' dried yeast.—In Europe the yeast growth which is filtered from beer after the fermentation is completed is often dried for stock feeding. Sometimes the yeast is included in the brewers' dried grains.

Brewers' dried yeast contains 40 per cent or more of protein, and it has been used for a considerable time in Europe as a protein supplement for the various classes of stock. It is not only high in protein, but the protein is of good quality. Also, it is very rich in vitamins B and G, which gives it a special value in poultry feeding.

In Canadian experiments brewers' dried yeast was equal to linseed meal for dairy cows when fed as a supplement to a ration of grain, silage, and hay.[29] Both on account of its richness in protein and its rather bitter taste, dried yeast should not ordinarily form more than 10 per cent of the concentrate mixture for stock.[30] However, in Germany dairy cows are fed as much as 2 to 4 lbs. per head daily; horses, 1 to 2 lbs. or more; and swine, 0.3 to 1.3 lbs.[31] The yeast should be heated sufficiently high in the drying process to kill the yeast cells, as otherwise marked fermentations may be produced in the digestive tract when much is fed, resulting in indigestion.

The use of yeast as a vitamin supplement has been discussed in Chapter VI. (198)

653. Apple pomace; apple pectin pulp.—The *wet apple pomace* which remains when the juice is expressed from apples for cider or for vinegar averages 21 per cent in dry matter, in comparison with 28 per cent for silage from well-matured corn. Apple pomace has only one-third as much digestible protein as such corn silage and is also slightly lower in total digestible nutrients. Apple pomace may be fed fresh, it may be ensiled, and it is sometimes dried to make *dried apple pomace*.

Though apple pomace silage is lower in nutrients than corn silage, it has proven to be a good substitute for corn silage in feeding dairy cows, being approximately equal to corn silage in value per ton.[32] It should be fed after milking, to avoid tainting the milk.

Dried apple pomace may be used in the same manner as dried beet pulp, and it has given very satisfactory results. In experiments where dried apple pomace has been substituted for an equal weight of dried beet pulp in a dairy ration, the cows have usually produced slightly less milk and fat.[33] Considering the amount of feed required per 100 lbs. of milk, dried apple pomace has been worth 75 per cent or more of the price of dried beet pulp.

Apple-pectin pulp is the residue left when the pectin is extracted from apple pomace for jelly making. *Dried apple-pectin pulp* was not as palatable to dairy cows as dried beet pulp in a test by the United States Department of Agriculture, when both were fed after soaking with water.[34] This difficulty can be avoided by mixing the apple-pectin pulp with well-liked concentrates.

654. Pineapple bran or pulp.—A considerable amount of pineapple bran, also called "dried pineapple pulp," is produced at the canning factories in Hawaii. This is used in Hawaii for stock feeding and a considerable proportion is shipped to the Pacific-Coast states. Pineapple bran consists principally of the outer shells of the pineapples, and also sometimes the cores. The material may or may not be pressed to extract juice before it is dried, and cane molasses is sometimes added to the product.

Pineapple bran resembles dried beet pulp in composition, except that it contains only 4 per cent protein. In Hawaiian experiments good results were secured when it formed one-third to two-thirds of the concentrate mixture for dairy cows.[35] It was also satisfactory for work mules when forming 53 per cent of the concentrates, and for pigs when used as 30 to 50 per cent of the concentrates.

Pineapple bran is fed extensively to horses and mules on Hawaiian plantations as a substitute for grain, forming as much as one-half of the concentrate mixture. California dairymen consider pineapple bran a good substitute for dried beet pulp. Sometimes it is soaked before feeding and used as a substitute for silage. In digestion trials by the California Station pineapple bran was not digested as completely by sheep as would be expected from the results that have been secured in the feeding tests with the product.[36]

655. Citrus by-products.—At the citrus-fruit canning factories, which make citrus fruit juices, canned fruit, and other products, a considerable amount of waste remains. This consists of the peel, the "rag" (residue of the inside portion), the seeds, and more or less cull fruits. Sometimes the citrus-peel oil is removed from the orange and lemon peel for flavoring extracts. The citrus by-products may be fed in fresh form near the canneries, or they may be dried. The dried orange and lemon by-products are often not palatable to stock and therefore should be mixed with better-liked feeds.

Dried orange pulp is lower in fiber and richer in nitrogen-free extract than dried beet pulp and supplies slightly more total digestible nutrients per 100 lbs. In a California test dried orange pulp was approximately equal to dried beet pulp for dairy cows, when fed as part of a suitable concentrate mixture.[37] The fresh orange pulp was more palatable than the dried pulp. *Dried orange waste*, consisting chiefly of the peel, was palatable to cattle in a Florida test and had a moderate laxative effect.[38]

Dried grapefruit refuse is fully equal to dried beet pulp in content of total digestible nutrients, as shown by Florida experiments.[39] Cattle would soon eat it without mixture with other feeds. The grapefruit refuse seemed to have a good effect on the thrift of the cattle, for it was mildly laxative and tended to produce a sleek, oily condition of the hair. Dairy cows fed dried grapefruit refuse gave good yields of milk.

Dried lemon pulp, a by-product in the manufacture of citric acid from lemons, consists of the extracted peel, pulp, and seeds. On account of the bitter taste, it is not palatable to stock and must be mixed with better-liked feeds. In California tests it was equal to dried beet pulp in content of total digestible nutrients.[36]

656. Cull raisins; raisin and grape by-products.—When available, *cull raisins* may be used for stock feeding as a partial substitute for grain. In California trials they were worth 82 per cent as much as barley for fattening lambs, when approximately 1 lb. of cull raisins was fed to each 2 lbs. of barley, along with alfalfa hay.[40] In tests with pigs, satisfactory gains were produced when cull raisins replaced one-third to one-half the barley in a ration of barley with skimmilk or tankage as the supplement.[41] However, the relative value of the cull raisins per 100 lbs. was not so high as for lambs.

Raisin pulp is a by-product from the production of seeded raisins or of the manufacture of syrup from raisins. It is of much lower value than cull raisins, as it is higher in fiber and the raisin seeds have little value for stock. In California trials with fattening lambs raisin pulp was worth only 59 per cent as much as barley, when fed as a substitute for part of the grain in a ration composed of barley and alfalfa hay.[42]

Grape pomace, or *grape-seed meal*, which consists chiefly of the seeds and skins left in the production of grape juice or wine, is of such low value that it should not be used for feeding. In a New York trial ground grape pomace had no value whatsoever for pigs, when used as a partial substitute for grain.[43]

657. Olive pulp.—Dried olive pulp, consisting of whole olives, minus the oil, was found to be practically valueless as a feed in California tests, even though finely ground.[36] Nearly 40 per cent of the product consisted of the pits. To be of value for feeding, the pits should be removed from the by-product.

658. Tomato pomace.—This by-product in the manufacture of tomato juice or tomato catsup consists chiefly of the skins and seeds. It is sometimes dried to form *dried tomato pomace*, which contains 20 per cent or more of protein and 12 per cent or more of fat, but which has about 30 per cent fiber.

Dried tomato pomace was satisfactory for dairy cows in Delaware trials, when forming 15 per cent of the concentrate mixture.[44] In another test, when wet tomato waste was added to a ration of hominy feed and tankage for pigs, the gains were increased.[45] On account of the richness of *dried tomato pomace* in vitamin A, it is sometimes used in poultry rations as a vitamin-A supplement.

659. Cassava or manihot meal.—This by-product is produced in the manufacture of starch from the roots of the tropical cassava. (485) It is rich in nitrogen-free extract and low in fiber, but it has an unusually small amount of protein and fat. It may be used as a substitute for part of the grain in feeding dairy cows and other stock, being approximately equal to grain in value, except for its lowness in protein.[46]

660. Acorns.—In some portions of the South and in California, acorns, the nuts of the oak (Quercus, spp.), are of importance in swine feeding, the pigs usually being allowed to forage upon the scattered nuts. Acorns may be used for other stock in limited amounts. Poisoning has been reported where stock ate damaged acorns or too large amounts.

661. Stale bread; bakery waste.—Sometimes stale bread or other bakery waste can be secured at a price that makes it an economical stock feed. Such waste can be used in place of part of the grain usually fed. Bread, though apparently a dry feed, usually contains over 30 per cent water. Therefore its feeding value will be only about three-fourths that of an equal weight of corn or other grain.

Kiln-dried bakery waste is similar to grain in composition, except that it is lower in fiber and may be higher in fat. In Pennsylvania trials kiln-dried stale bread, fed after being moistened with water, was about equal to corn for pigs on pasture, but was constipating unless fed with some laxative feed.[47] Stale crackers were somewhat less valuable.

662. Miscellaneous feeds.—*Palmo middlings*, or "palmo midds," is a by-product in the making of tin plate. In preparing the tin plate for the market the excess of palm oil on the plate is removed by scouring it with wheat middlings (often containing some ground wheat screenings). This mixture of middlings with a small amount of oil is sold as palmo middlings. Occasionally the feed is adulterated with finely ground peanut hulls.

This by-product usually contains 7 to 10 per cent of fat or oil and is slightly lower in protein than standard wheat middlings. It should be used in the same manner as wheat middlings in stock feeding and is chiefly fed to swine. On account of the rather high oil content it had best not form more than 20 to 25 per cent of the concentrate mixture. In experiments in which it has been compared with standard wheat middlings as a feed for pigs, palmo middlings has, on the average, been worth slightly less per ton than the standard middlings.[48]

In addition to the oil meals previously discussed in Chapter XVIII the following are of minor importance:

Babassu oil meal is produced from the hard-shelled seed of a Brazilian palm (*Orbignya speciosa*). It is similar in composition to coconut oil meal, averaging a trifle higher in protein. It is palatable to stock and in a Danish trial was about equal to coconut oil meal for dairy cows.[48a] Like palm-kernel oil meal, it seems to cause a slight increase in the fat percentage in milk.

Tucum-nut oil meal is produced from the seed of tucum palms (*Astrocaryum*, spp.).

Poppy-seed oil meal or cake is the by-product from the production of oil from the seed of the opium poppy (*Papaver sommiferum*). It contains about 36 per cent protein. Since it has weak narcotic properties, due to the presence of opium alkaloids, it is not generally fed to young animals or to breeding stock. The amount for dairy cows should be limited to 2 or 3 lbs. per head daily, since a greater amount is said to decrease the fat percentage of the milk.

Perilla oil meal is the by-product from the production of oil from the seed of perilla plants (*Perilla*, spp.), Chinese plants which are members of the mint family. This oil meal contains 37 to 38 per cent protein, but is high in fiber, having over 21 per cent. In digestion trials at the California Station perilla oil meal was palatable to sheep. The protein and fat were well digested, but the digestion coefficients for the fiber and the nitrogen-free extract were low.[48b]

Kapok oil meal is the by-product from the manufacture of oil from the seed of the kapok tree *(Ceiba kentandra)*. Kapok fiber adheres to the seed of this tree in a manner somewhat similar to that found in the cotton plant. Kapok oil meal was so unpalatable to sheep in a California trial that the digestibility of the feed could not be determined.[48b]

663. Garbage.—Until the discovery of methods of vaccination against hog cholera, most attempts to feed swine household garbage on a large scale were unsuccessful, due to heavy losses from this disease. Now, however, the garbage from a large number of cities is fed to swine. In most cases the garbage is fed by contractors who purchase the collected garbage from the cities or else collect it themselves under rigid rules.

Garbage varies greatly in composition and feeding value, but on an average and allowing for normal losses of hogs by death, a ton of municipal garbage may be expected to produce 40 lbs. of marketable live weight of hog. Garbage of excellent quality, such as that from large hotels and restaurants, may be worth twice as much, or even more.[49]

The garbage must be collected with reasonable frequency and be free from tin cans, soap, broken glass, and other undesirable or injurious foreign articles. The public should be kept informed that the garbage is being fed, so they will not put in such material. Usually it is best for the cities to make the collections and then dispose of the garbage to individuals or corporations on a contract basis, unless the city operates its own hog-feeding farm. Long-time contracts are likely to be most satisfactory, for they tend toward a better class of equipment and more sanitary conditions.

The pigs to be fed may be bought as feeders or may be raised. Methods of feeding, handling, housing, and care may differ considerably, so long as the essentials of sanitation and hog comfort are observed. Equipment for feeding should be adapted to the type of garbage available and to local conditions, climate, and transportation.

Raw garbage generally is better for hogs than cooked garbage. Frozen garbage, however, should be thawed before feeding. As a rule, the use of grain as a supplementary feed is not an economical practice, but grain may be used to advantage when the supply of garbage is temporarily short. Thorough immunization against hog cholera is very important, because of raw pork scraps frequently deposited in garbage cans. Garbage-fed hogs show no greater susceptibility to other diseases than grain-fed animals. The pork is as good in quality as that produced on other feeds, and average garbage-fed hogs sell at practically the same prices as average grain-fed animals.

664. Processed garbage, or table scrap meal.—Sometimes city garbage is processed and dried, with the production of processed garbage (also called "table scrap meal," or "garbage tankage") and the recovery of some fat for industrial uses. The dried processed garbage is a product much different in composition and value from digester tankage or meat scraps, and usually contains only 14 to 18 per cent protein.

It can be used to replace part of the tankage or fish meal in swine rations, but should not be used as the only supplement to grain for young pigs, even when they are on good pasture. In 6 comparisons at the Indiana and Missouri Stations young pigs fattened to market weight on corn, processed garbage, and good pasture gained only 1.17 lbs. per head daily in comparison with 1.50 lbs. for others fed corn and digester tankage on good pasture.[50] Not considering the difference in rate of gain, each 100 lbs. of the digester tankage was equal to 111 lbs. processed garbage plus 114 lbs. corn in feeding value.

When pigs on pasture were fed a supplemental mixture of one-half processed garbage and one-half digester tankage, the gains were satisfactory, and the processed garbage had a considerably higher value. Likewise, in a trial at the Indiana Station with fattening lambs, a mixture of one-half garbage tankage and one-half meat scraps was satisfactory as a protein supplement. However, garbage tankage as the only supplement was inferior to cottonseed meal or meat scraps.[50a]

665. Commercial mixed feeds.—The manufacture of commercial mixed feeds has become a very important industry in the United States. In 1929 there were, according to the Census, 750 establishments manufacturing prepared feeds for animals and fowls, and the total value of the feeds produced was about $300,000,000 in 1927 and $400,000,000 in 1929. Much larger tonnages of mixed feeds are manufactured for dairy cattle and for poultry than for other classes of stock.

Most of the commercial mixed feeds on the market are intelligently and honestly made of good ingredients, and such feeds produce very satisfactory results. In purchasing mixed feeds one should consider the general reputation of the manufacturers of the various brands of feed available. Particularly, he should determine whether any given manufacturer has in the past been fully meeting his guarantees of composition and of declared ingredients.

As has been pointed out in Chapter IV, nearly all the states in this country now have laws governing the manufacture and sale of commercial feeds and publish reports on the guarantees for the various brands of feed on sale in the state, and also of the actual chemical analyses and ingredients, as found through the feed inspection service. From these reports one can readily determine whether or not any particular manufacturer is living up to his guarantees.

In the opinion of the author there is no one best formula for a feed mixture for any class of stock, in spite of claims sometimes made to the contrary. Many formulas can be recommended that will produce excellent results, and the choice between them will depend solely on the prices of the various individual ingredients at any particular time.

It has been emphasized in Chapter X that it is decidedly uneconomical to adhere to the same formula, month after month and year after year, without regard to the relative cost of the various individual ingredients that are available. Feed manufacturers can obviously study the changes in the prices of various feeds much more closely than most farmers. They are therefore in a position to make such changes in their formulas as are necessary to furnish efficient mixed feeds to their customers at the minimum price.

Suitable concentrate mixtures and complete rations are recommended in Part III and in Appendix Table VII for each class of stock. It is believed that these mixtures and rations will all produce excellent results, when made up of good-quality feeds, and fed intelligently. It is hoped that these recommendations may be helpful both to farmers and to those manufacturing mixed feeds.

In deciding whether to buy a commercial mixed feed, or to mix a suitable feed himself, one should base his decision on the cost of the mixed feed and the cost of the home mixture, including the labor involved in the home mixing. The factor of convenience must also be taken into consideration. In the comparisons summarized in Part III that have been made by the experiment stations of commercial mixed feeds and of home-mixed rations, the latter have generally proven fully as efficient, and in some cases have been superior.

It will often be found that a high-grade mixed feed can be pur-

chased at a price little or no higher than it would cost to mix a feed
of the same actual value on the farm. The wise manufacturer secures
his profits by building up a large volume of sales through selling his
feed on a narrow margin of profit. He uses his ability to purchase
ingredients in large quantities and his knowledge of the prices and
values of the various available ingredients to put on the market feeds
that furnish nutrients at as low a cost as possible.

Especially in using molasses, the feed manufacturer has a great
advantage over the individual farmer. When bought by the feed manufacturer in tank cars, molasses is often the cheapest source of carbohydrates in many parts of the country. Yet, when purchased by a
farmer in barrels, molasses may be more expensive than grain.

666. Lower-grade feeds.—A large proportion of the commercial
mixed feeds are made of only high-grade ingredients. Others, especially
some of those for cattle, contain more or less of cheaper products, such
as grain screenings, oat hulls, and oat mill feed. These materials have
a definite feeding value and can be used best when intelligently combined in reasonable proportions with feeds of higher value. In particular, molasses adds to the palatability and usefulness of a mixture
containing considerable grain screenings.

Mixed feeds of this character are therefore entirely legitimate when
honestly sold for what they actually are. In purchasing such feeds one
should use proper discrimination and not pay more than the product is
really worth, as shown by the chemical analysis and the guaranteed
ingredients.

667. Open formulas vs. closed formulas.—There has been considerable discussion during recent years concerning the advantages and disadvantages of ''open formulas'' and ''closed formulas'' for commercial
mixed feeds.[51] In open-formula feeds, not only are the ingredients
declared and the usual guarantees made as to content of protein, fat and
fiber, but also the number of pounds of each ingredient in a ton of the
mixture is stated. In the case of closed-formula feeds, the ingredients
are usually stated, for this is required under the feeding stuff laws in
most states, but the amount of each of the ingredients is not specified.

Thus far, the open-formula method has been used chiefly by co-
operative organizations of farmers manufacturing mixed feeds, and the
method has distinct advantages when used by such organizations. The
exact amount of each ingredient is known at a glance, and one can
readily compare the cost of the feed with the cost of making the same
or a similar mixture on his own farm.

The amounts of digestible protein and of total digestible nutrients
in the mixture can readily be computed, and the computations can be
checked by anyone from such tables as Appendix Table I of this volume.
The amounts of digestible protein and of total digestible nutrients are
usually stated on the feed tag, along with the open formula. These
figures are necessary if one desires to compute a balanced ration accurately in accordance with the feeding standards.

Such data are not commonly given by manufacturers of closed-formula feeds, and, if given, the accuracy of the figures cannot be checked,
because the amounts of the various ingredients are not known by the
purchaser.

Unfortunately, there is no method by which the exact amount of any feeding stuff in a mixed feed can be determined with accuracy. The best that can be done by a skilled microscopist is to ascertain whether any particular ingredient is present and to estimate approximately the proportion in which it occurs. The laws can be enforced that require the ingredients in a commercial feed to be declared, for the microscopist can testify definitely on the witness stand that he has or has not identified any particular ingredient in the feed.

On the other hand, a law requiring that the manufacturer guarantee the amount of each ingredient in a mixed feed could not be enforced. This is because the amounts of the various individual ingredients could not be determined with sufficient accuracy to serve as a basis for prosecution when the law was violated.

One of the reasons why nearly all private manufacturers of mixed feeds have been unwilling to adopt the open-formula plan, is that this might make possible unfair competition from unscrupulous competitors. Such competitors could print the same formulas on their feed bags, but cheapen the actual composition of their feeds by making certain changes in the proportions of various ingredients. Nevertheless, they could meet the same guarantees of ingredients and of content of protein, fat, and fiber. Therefore they could not be prosecuted under any feeding stuff law. Such an unscrupulous manufacturer could sell his cheaper feeds at a lower price than the first concern could sell the feeds which had been made according to the published formulas. Yet he might claim that his feeds were the very same products as those made by the honest manufacturer.

In addition, if a feed manufacturer believes that through knowledge and experience he has developed formulas that are particularly efficient, he may naturally hesitate to give this information to his competitors by using the open-formula plan.

668. Mixing feed on the farm.—Statements are sometimes made that it is difficult to mix on the farm several ingredients into a mixture that is sufficiently uniform to produce the best results in stock feeding. As a matter of fact, it is a relatively simple task to mix a suitable concentrate mixture. All that is needed is a smooth, tight barn floor, a scoop shovel, and someone to use it with willingness and average intelligence.

One should first decide on the exact amount of each ingredient to be put in each ton, or perhaps each 1,000 lbs. of the mixture, and write down this formula, so it can be followed exactly. Then the floor should be swept, and the ingredients assembled. Scales should be at hand to weigh the feed, if full 100-pound sacks of each ingredient are not to be used.

Some of the ground grain, if it is the chief ingredient, should be spread on the floor to a depth of a few inches. Then a layer of each of the other ingredients should be distributed over the grain, and the process repeated until a long pile has been made two or three feet deep. If only a small amount of some ingredient is used, as in the case of salt or another mineral supplement, this had best be distributed evenly over the top of the pile.

Now, starting at one end, the feed is shoveled into a new pile of the same shape, a convenient distance from the first pile. Shoveling the mixture over three times will usually make it sufficiently uniform. Where a large amount of feed is mixed on a farm each year, it is advantageous to use one of the small feed mixers that have been developed for farm use.

669. Stock foods; condition powders; tonics.—In spite of the advice of the experiment stations to the contrary, American farmers continue to spend millions of dollars each year for various proprietary products called "stock foods," "condition powders," "tonics," etc.

The better class of stock foods are composed largely of such feeds as linseed meal or wheat middlings, while the cheaper ones contain ground screenings, low-grade milling by-products, etc. To this "filling" are added various percentages of such materials as common salt, charcoal, copperas (iron sulfate), pepper, Epsom salts, Glauber's salts, fenugreek, gentian, etc., with or without such materials as turmeric or iron oxide, for coloring.

The stockman is told that a tablespoonful of the compound with each feed will cause his stock to grow faster, fatten more rapidly, give richer milk, etc., etc. Yet this amount will supply only an insignificant part of the dose of these drugs which is prescribed for animals by competent veterinarians. Tests of many stock foods and tonics by the experiment stations in general show clearly that there is no advantage in their use. Farm animals managed with reasonable care have appetites which do not need stimulating. Sick animals or those out of condition should receive specific treatment rather than be given some cure-all. A good stockman has no use for high-priced stock foods or condition powders, and a poor manager will never have fine stock by employing them.

The flattering testimonials which the stock-food companies advertise are explained without granting any special virtue to their "food." The stock foods are usually accompanied by directions which advocate liberal feeding and good care for the animals to be fed, in order to "secure the benefits from the tonic." Under this guidance the farmer feeds and cares for his stock better than ever before and secures better results, due not to the stock food but to following the directions which accompanied it. Rather than purchase advice with costly condimental foods, the wise feeder will secure it in standard agricultural papers and books, or from the experiment stations and the United States Department of Agriculture.

In rare cases some conditioner may be helpful to stimulate the appetite or otherwise improve the general thrift of the animal. A formula recommended by Doctor Hadley of the Wisconsin Station[52] is: Common salt, 280 lbs.; dried iron sulfate, 16 lbs.; powdered wood charcoal, 12 lbs.; and flowers of sulfur, 8 lbs. These materials should be well mixed or ground together to make a powder. This mixture, which, it will be noted, consists chiefly of common salt, should be kept in suitable boxes so that the animals may have free access to it.

Artificial Carlsbad salt is used among veterinarians, as a conditioner, especially for horses. The formula for this is as follows:[53] Dried sodium sulfate, 40 parts by weight; sodium bicarbonate, 35 parts; common salt, 15 parts; potassium sulfate, 2 parts. The ingredients should be mixed and powdered. For mature horses 1 to 2 heaping tablespoonfuls, and for mature cattle 1.5 to 3 heaping tablespoonfuls should be given 2 or 3 times daily on the feed. The dose for swine or sheep is one-fifth as much as for horses. Half-grown animals should be given half as much as mature animals; younger ones one-eighth to one-fourth the full dose; and sucklings one-sixteenth the full dose.

670. Mineral mixtures; vitamin preparations.—Many mineral mixtures have been extensively advertised during recent years, since the importance of minerals in stock feeding has been realized. Some of these are honest efforts to supply at a reasonable price the minerals which may be lacking in certain rations. Others are sold at excessively high prices or are even of poor quality.

In the discussion of the mineral requirements of livestock presented in Chapter VI, it is shown that it is the belief of most animal husbandry scientists that there is no benefit from using complex mineral mixtures for stock. (**182**) In their opinion simple mineral mixtures, such as are there recommended, will produce just as good results as those which contain a large number of ingredients.

Before purchasing a mineral supplement or a mineral mixture, one should determine, if possible, what particular minerals may actually be lacking in the ration he is feeding. Information on this problem is presented in Chapter VI and in the discussions in Part III of the nutrient requirements of the various classes of stock.

A simple commercial mineral mixture of good quality has the advantage of convenience, in comparison with the home-mixing of a suitable mineral mixture. However, it is not ordinarily necessary to include in a mineral mixture more than 3 or 4 simple ingredients. One cannot, therefore, afford to pay any large premium for a commercial mineral mixture, over the cost of the ingredients. The stockman should always view with suspicion those brands of mineral mixtures for which extravagant claims are made.

The vitamin requirements of farm animals have been considered in detail in Chapter VI. It has there been shown that, for all livestock except poultry, an ample supply of the necessary vitamins can readily be provided in rations made up of common feeds, without the use of special vitamin supplements.

In spite of claims that are sometimes made to the contrary, there is no scientific evidence that any mineral mixture or vitamin supplement will prevent or cure Bang's disease (contagious abortion) in cattle. This disease must be clearly distinguished from the rare cases of abortion that may be produced by a serious lack of vitamins and minerals.

671. Kelp; manamar.—Dried *kelp* (the giant seaweed from the seacoast of southern California) has been widely advertised during recent years as a supplement for livestock feeding, and also *manamar* (a proprietary combination said to consist entirely or chiefly of dried kelp, fish meal, and ground oyster shells).

It has been claimed that the use of these products would benefit livestock in a very striking manner. However, as is shown in later chapters, in most of the tests conducted by the experiment stations with kelp or manamar there has been no appreciable benefit, or no benefit at all, from adding them to well-balanced rations. When there is a lack of minerals or vitamins in the rations for livestock, in the opinion of the author these deficiencies can be remedied more cheaply by following the simple recommendations made in this volume than by the use of these products.

QUESTIONS

1. State 7 merits of milk as a food for young mammals. What limitations does milk have as an exclusive food for long periods?
2. What is the composition of cow's milk? To what extent is whole cow's milk used in stock feeding?
3. Compare the composition and nutritive value of skimmilk and whole milk.
4. Discuss the composition and value of buttermilk; of whey.
5. Why should dairy by-products be pasteurized or sterilized before being hauled from a creamery or cheese factory to the farm for stock feeding?
6. For what purposes are the following used in stock feeding and what is the relative value of each: (a) Dried skimmilk; (b) dried buttermilk; (c) condensed buttermilk; (d) dried whey; (e) cheese meal?
7. Describe the two processes used in producing tankage.
8. What is the approximate protein content of the most important grades of digester tankage and of meat scraps?
9. Discuss the use of tankage and meat scraps in stock feeding.
10. What is rendering-plant tankage, or reduction tankage?
11. For what purpose is blood meal chiefly used in stock feeding?
12. Tell about the production of fish meal and discuss the nutritive value of fish meal.
13. For what classes of stock is fish meal chiefly used? Why is this so?
14. What by-products are obtained in the manufacture of sugar from sugar beets; from sugar cane?
15. Discuss the composition, value, and use of cane molasses for feeding.
16. In what respects does beet molasses differ from cane molasses?
17. Discuss the composition and value of: (a) Wet beet pulp; (b) dried beet pulp; (c) dried molasses-beet pulp; (d) molasses feeds; (e) alfalfa-molasses feeds.
18. Compare the composition and value of distillers' corn dried grains and distillers' rye dried grains.
19. Discuss the composition and value of any of the following that are available on your local feed markets: (a) Yeast dried grains; (b) vinegar dried grains; (c) industrial alcohol by-product feed; (d) brewers' dried yeast; (e) apple pomace; (f) pineapple bran; (g) citrus by-products; (h) raisin by-products; (i) tomato pomace; (j) cassava meal; (k) stale bread or other bakery waste; (l) palmo middlings.
20. What use can be made of garbage in stock feeding? What are some of the essentials in feeding garbage?
21. How should a farmer decide whether to buy a commercial mixed feed or to prepare a suitable mixture on the farm?
22. What is meant by open formulas and closed formulas for mixed feeds? What are the advantages of each?
23. Tell how you would prepare a concentrate mixture on the farm.
24. Discuss the use of stock feeds, condition powders, and tonics.
25. What is your opinion concerning the use of complex mineral mixtures for livestock?

REFERENCES

1. Eckles and Shultz, Jour. Dairy Sci., 4, 1931, pp. 189-197; see also: Beach and Clark, Conn. (Storrs) Rpt. 1904.
2. Tretsven, Mont. Bul. 282; see also: Arnett, Mont. Rpt. 1921.
3. Assoc. of Amer. Feed Control Officials, Official Pub., 1935.
4. N. J. Rpt. 1931; Orr and Crichton, Scot. Jour. Agr., 6, 1923, pp. 63-67.

5. Bohstedt and Fargo, Wis. Bul. 430.
6. Clemen, By-products of the Packing Industry; Moulton, Meat Through the Microscope.
7. Gerlaugh, Salisbury, Robison, Bell, and Kennard, Ohio Bul. 532.
8. Culbertson and Evvard, Amer. Soc. Anim. Prod., Proc. 1924.
9. Hoagland and Snider, Jour. Agr. Res., 33, 1926, pp. 829-843; Mitchell, Beadles, and Kruger, Jour. Biol. Chem., 73, 1927, pp. 767-774.
10. Curtis, Hauge, and Kraybill, Jour. Nutr., 5, 1932, pp. 503-517.
11. Burkett, N. C. Bul. 189; Pott, Ernähr. u. Futtermittel, III, 1909, p. 515; Quick, Va. Bul. 176.
12. N. J. Rpt. 1928.
13. Ind. Rpt. 1926.
14. Dove, Maine Bul. 369; Cleveland, Mass. Bul. 305; Maynard, Bender, and McCay, Jour. Agr. Res., 44, 1932, pp. 591-603; Schneider, Jour. Agr. Res., 44, 1932, pp. 723-732; Norris, N. Y. (Cornell) Station, mimeo. rpt.; Record, Bethke, Wilder, and Kennard, Ohio Bul. 532; Mangold, Das Fischmehl als Futtermittel.
15. Morrison and Willman, N. Y. (Cornell) Sta., unpublished data.
16. Scott, Fla. Rpt. 1922; Corbett and Hall, Maine Sta., information to the author; Ingham, Md. Bul. 342; Bartlett, N. J. Rpt. 1929; Monroe, Krauss, and Hayden, Ohio Buls. 497, 532; Campbell, Vt. Bul. 333; Ellington and Knott, Wash. Bul. 229; Woodward et al., U. S. Dept. Agr. Bul. 1272; Archibald, Dominion Expt. Farms, Canada, Pamphlet 17; De Lisle, Fisheries Dept., British Columbia, Canada, Rpt. on Edible Fishmeal, 1930.
17. Miller, Cal. Rpt. 1930; Paterson, West of Scot. Agr. Bul. 97.
18. Bray, Francioni, and Gregory, La. Bul. 228, La. Rpt. 1931-1933; see also: Barnett and Goodell, Miss. Bul. 218.
19. Lush and Upp, La. Bul. 262; La. Rpt. 1931-1933.
20. Hostetler, N. C. Rpts. 1928, 1929.
21. Maynard, Morton, and Osland, Colo. Bul. 379.
22. Maynard and Osland, Colo. Press Buls. 65, 70, and mimeo. rpt.
23. Maynard and Greaves, Utah Bul. 250.
24. Henke, Hawaii Sta., information to the author.
25. Lindsey and Smith, Mass. Bul. 158; Hills, Vt. Bul. 171.
26. Morrison and Willman, N. Y. (Cornell) Sta., unpublished data.
27. Plumb, Ind. Bul. 97; Lindsey, Mass. Bul. 99.
28. Broughton, Frey, and Carmichael, Md. Bul. 349.
29. Barton, Ness, and Crampton, Macdonald Col., McGill Univ., Canada, Tech. Bul. 3.
30. Halnan, Great Britain, Min. of Agr. Jour., 30, 1924, p. 962.
31. Mangold, Handb. Ernähr. und Stoffwechsels, Vol. I.
32. Atkeson and Anderson, Id. Bul. 150; Lindsey, Mass. Rpt. 1905; Hills, Vt. Rpt. 1903.
33. Lindsey, Beals, and Archibald, Mass. Bul. 205; Holdaway, Va. Bul. 243; Knott, Hodgson, and Ellington, Wash. Bul. 270; see also: Walton and Bidwell, U. S. Dept. Agr. Bul. 1166.
34. Woodward et al., U. S. Dept. Agr. Bul. 1272; see also: Walton and Bidwell, U. S. Dept. Agr. Bul. 1166.
35. Henke, Hawaii Cir. 2 and mimeo. rpts.; see also: Ellington and Knott, Wash. Bul. 196.
36. Mead and Guilbert, Cal. Bul. 439.
37. Mead and Guilbert, Cal. Bul. 409; Regan and Mead, Cal. Bul. 427.
38. Neal, Becker, and Dix-Arnold, Fla. Bul. 275.
39. Neal, Becker, and Dix-Arnold, Fla. Bul. 275, Press Bul. 466; Scott, Fla. Rpt. 1926.
40. Miller, Cal. Bul. 431.
41. Hughes, Cal. Countryman, 10, 1924, pp. 9, 16.
42. Miller, Cal. Bul. 431.
43. Morrison and Willman, N. Y. (Cornell) Station, unpublished data.
44. Tomhave, Del. Buls. 172, 179.
45. Hays, Del. Bul. 124.
46. Henke, Hawaii Bul. 6.
47. Grimes, Penn. Buls. 215, 230.
48. Skinner and Starr, Ind. Bul. 219; Grimes, Penn. Buls. 196, 215, 230.
48a. Frederiksen, Meddelelse fra Forsogslaboratoriets Husdyrbrugsafdeling, Denmark, 1923, No. 1: Honcamp and Peterman, Zeit. Tierzucht., 15, 1929, pp. 359-374.
48b. Folger, Cal. Sta., information to the author.
49. Ashbrook and Wilson, U. S. Dept. Agr., Farmers' Bul. 1133; Williams and Cunningham, Ariz. Rpts. 1918, 1919, 1922, 1923; Thompson, Voorhies, and Vestal, Cal. Rpt. 1919; Ky. Rpt. 1918; Allen, Md. Bul. 227; Miss. Bul. 218; Thompson, Okla. Rpt. 1919; Hultz and Reeve, Wyo. Bul. 135.
50. Vestal, Ind. Sta., mimeo. rpt.; Weaver, Mo. Bul. 247; see also: Evvard, Culbertson, et al., Iowa Leaflet 6.
50a. Harper, Ind. Sta., mimeo. rpt.
51. Savage and Maynard, Better Dairy Farming, pp. 67-69; Strowd, Commercial Feeds, pp. 175-189.
52. Principles of Veterinary Science, p. 217.
53. Winslow, Veterinary Materia Medica and Therapeutics, p. 113.

CHAPTER XX

MANURIAL VALUE OF FEEDING STUFFS

672. Importance of manure in maintaining fertility.—On livestock farms it is highly important that efficient use be made of the farm manure, so as to maintain and build up the fertility of the fields at minimum expense. Unless the plant food removed from the soil by the growth of crops is returned in some form, the land will sooner or later be so reduced in fertility that profitable crops cannot be grown.

Already the soil in many once-productive areas of this country has been ''mined'' to such an extent that good crops are possible only when commercial fertilizers are liberally applied. While the purchase of commercial fertilizers is wise when they are needed, they should be used on stock farms as supplements to farm manure.

673. Farm manure as a fertilizer.—Farm manure, like commercial fertilizers, is valued chiefly on the basis of the amounts of nitrogen, phosphorus, and potassium it contains. These fertilizing constituents and calcium are the only plant foods which ordinarily need to be replaced of those that are removed from the soil by crops. The necessary nitrogen may, as we have seen, be indirectly obtained from the air by growing legumes, but in practice much is purchased in commercial fertilizers, along with phosphorus and potassium.

Not only does farm manure supply plant food but also the organic matter helps to increase the productivity of the soil. As this organic matter gradually breaks down in the soil, the acid products help dissolve and make available to plants some of the otherwise insoluble plant food in the soil. Furthermore, the humus formed from the organic matter of manure helps retain moisture in the soil, improves its texture, and renders it more resistant to wind action. The value of adding organic matter to the soil is shown by the fact that green manuring crops are often grown and turned under, solely to increase the humus content.

Manure also has a beneficial effect, due to the great numbers of various kinds of bacteria that it contains. These cause chemical changes not only in the manure but also in the soil itself, converting insoluble plant food into forms available for crop growth.

Experiments have shown that the fertilizing constituents present in manure when it is applied to the land have as high a value as those in high-grade commercial fertilizers. The cost of nitrogen, phosphorus, and potassium in commercial fertilizers at any time varies considerably, depending on the type of fertilizer and the section of the country. In this chapter the following prices are used in computing the fertilizing values of feeding stuffs and of farm manures: Nitrogen, 11 cents per pound; phosphoric acid, 5 cents per pound; and potash, 5 cents per pound.

The amount of phosphorus in a commercial fertilizer is commonly

412

expressed in terms of *phosphoric acid* (P_2O_5), instead of *phosphorus* (P). On the other hand, in animal nutrition and livestock feeding, the amount of the mineral is now more generally expressed as *phosphorus*. Similiarly, the amount of potassium in fertilizers is usually expressed in terms of *potash* (K_2O), instead of potassium (K).

The preceding prices for phosphoric acid and potash are equivalent to 11.4 cents per pound for phosphorus and 6.0 cents per pound for potassium.

674. Fertilizing constituents recovered in manure.—The fertilizing constituents in manure come entirely from the feed consumed, for an animal creates no fertility value. It merely voids in the feces and urine a greater or less percentage of the nitrogen, phosphorus, and potassium that is contained in the feed it consumes. The value of the manure therefore depends, first of all, on the kind of feed the animal gets. Only feeds rich in these fertilizing constituents make rich manure.

The proportion which is recovered in the manure of the total fertilizing constituents supplied in the feed, depends on the age and kind of animal. A mature animal which is not gaining in weight and which is not pregnant or producing milk will excrete in feces and urine all the fertilizing constituents in its feed, with the exception of the nitrogen used in the growth of hair or wool and the small amounts of the fertilizing constituents contained in the sweat. Thus, a mature work horse which is not gaining in weight and which is not pregnant or nursing a foal, will excrete in feces and urine practically all the nitrogen, phosphorus, and potassium in its ration.

On the other hand, a young, growing animal will store in its body a considerable part of these constituents in its daily feed. For example, a young calf or lamb a few weeks old may store in its body two-thirds or more of the nitrogen and mineral matter that is supplied by the milk and other feed it consumes. Such an animal will therefore void in its excrement only one-third or less of the fertilizing constituents in its ration. **(204)**

As an animal grows older, the proportion of nitrogen and mineral matter stored in growth rapidly decreases, and calves or lambs 5 months old or more will usually store only 20 to 30 per cent of the nitrogen in their ration, excreting the rest. In Illinois experiments 2-year-old fattening steers fed a liberal ration excreted in feces and urine 87 per cent of the nitrogen and phosphorus they consumed.[1] Fattening pigs excrete about 85 per cent of the nitrogen and 96 per cent of the minerals contained in their ration.[2]

On account of the richness of milk in nitrogen and in phosphorus, well-fed dairy cows producing a good yield of milk, which are fed the usual types of well-balanced rations, will excrete in feces and urine only 60 to 70 per cent of the nitrogen in their ration and 40 to 60 per cent of the phosphorus.[3] The proportion of potassium will be somewhat higher, ranging usually from 60 to 80 per cent.

Considering the proportion of the various classes and ages of animals on the average general farm, probably about 80 per cent of the fertilizing value of the feed is excreted in the feces and urine. On dairy farms, where most of the animals are cows in milk, the percentage will be somewhat lower.

675. Fertility and manurial value of feeds.—In buying or selling feeds, far too few farmers consider their value as fertilizers as well as their feeding value. The amounts of fertilizing constituents in the important feeds are given in Appendix Table I. To bring out certain points, there are presented in the following table these data for a few typical feeds and also data for certain animal products. The fertility value of each has been computed at the rates for nitrogen, phosphorus, and potassium previously given.

The last column gives the average manurial value of the various feeds. This has been computed on the assumption that when proper care is taken of the manure, there can be recovered in the manure for application on the land an average of 70 per cent of the phosphorus and potassium and 50 per cent of the nitrogen contained in the feed. These estimates take into consideration the fact that some losses of fertilizing constituents, especially of nitrogen, occur in the storage and application of manure, even when the precautions are taken which are mentioned later. Obviously, these manurial values hold good only when the manure is handled properly.

Fertilizing constituents in feeds and in animal products

	Fertilizing constituents			Fertility value per ton	Manurial value per ton
	Nitrogen	Phosphorus	Potassium		
	Per cent	Per cent	Per cent	Dollars	Dollars
Concentrates					
Corn, dent, No. 2..................	1.50	0.27	0.31	4.29	2.34
Oats	1.92	0.33	0.40	5.46	2.97
Wheat	2.10	0.43	0.44	6.13	3.37
Wheat bran	2.53	1.32	1.24	10.06	5.93
Soybeans	5.90	0.60	1.91	16.64	9.05
Linseed meal	5.63	0.86	1.27	15.87	8.63
Cottonseed meal, 43% protein grade.	6.91	1.11	1.36	19.36	10.51
Tankage, 60% protein grade........	9.81	6.21	0.16	35.93	20.84
Roughages					
Timothy hay	0.99	0.14	1.36	4.13	2.45
Red clover hay...................	1.89	0.18	1.58	6.46	3.69
Alfalfa hay	2.35	0.21	2.02	8.07	4.62
Oat straw	0.64	0.13	1.66	3.70	2.31
Corn silage	0.37	0.06	0.30	1.31	0.75
Animal products					
Fat steer	2.56	0.59	0.14	7.15	....
Fat pig	2.32	0.37	0.13	6.10	....
Milk	0.56	0.09	0.14	1.61	....
Butter	0.14	0.02	0.01	0.37	....

The table shows that the fertility value of corn grain is $4.29 per ton. This means that the nitrogen, phosphorus, and potassium removed from the soil in each ton of corn would cost about $4.29 if bought in commercial fertilizers. The manurial value of corn grain is $2.34 per ton, which means that the manure resulting from feeding a ton of the grain to stock will, on the average, supply about $2.34 worth of fertilizing constituents, if proper care is taken of the manure.

The fertility values and the manurial values are somewhat higher for oats and wheat than for corn, because these grains contain more nitrogen, phosphorus, and potassium than does corn. The values for the protein-rich feeds, such as soybeans, linseed meal, cottonseed meal, and tankage, are high, due to their richness in nitrogen and also in minerals. If legume crops, such as soybeans, are properly inoculated, the amount of fertility removed from the soil is much less than indicated by the fertility value of the crop. This is because most of the nitrogen will have been secured from the air, instead of from the soil.

When such protein-rich feeds as cottonseed meal, linseed meal, and tankage are purchased and fed to stock and proper care is taken of the manure produced, a double return is secured. The first return comes from the high feeding value of these protein supplements, and the second comes from the fertility added to the soil.

The fertility value of legume hay is much greater than that of grass hay, because of its richness in protein. It is important to note that when legume hay is fed to stock and proper care is taken of the manure, each ton of red clover hay will add $3.69 worth of plant food to the soil and each ton of alfalfa hay, $4.62.

676. Selling fertility.—The preceding table further shows that those who sell such crops as hay, corn, and wheat, part with more fertility for a given sum than do those who sell animals or their products. The farmer who sells 1,000 lbs. of clover hay, worth $6 to $10, parts with about as much fertility as if he had sold 1,000 lbs. of fat cattle or pigs, worth ten times as much, or even more. Based on the selling price, milk carries considerable fertility from the farm, and butter practically none.

Farm crops may be regarded as raw products, while farm animals, milk, wool, butter, etc., represent manufactured products. A large amount of raw material in the form of grass, hay, corn, etc., is put into animals, and the heavy waste or by-product resulting in the form of manure conserves most of the fertility, when carried back to the fields. The farmer who feeds his crops to livestock is a manufacturer as well as a producer, with two possible profits instead of one, while his farm should lose little of its fertility.

The farmer who grows and sells grain, hay, and straw is selling a large amount of fertility, the need of which will surely be apparent as time goes on and his fields give smaller and smaller returns. Such a farmer is slowly but surely mining phosphorus and potassium from his soil, which can be replaced only by some purchased material.

Virgin soils as a rule contain great quantities of available fertility, and the pioneer farmers in America, drawing upon Nature's store, gave little consideration to how their crops were fed and did not realize that they were steadily and often wastefully drawing on the fertility which was their principal capital.

The western farmer, when marketing corn or wheat, considers he is selling labor and rent of land. Rarely does he realize that he is also selling fertility, to replace which would cost a considerable part of all the crop brings. Rather than to reckon the value of his crop at the market price, he should recognize that its true value when sold from the farm is really the market price minus the value of the fertility which the crop removes from the soil.

In Great Britain, where many of the farmers are long-period tenants, the manurial value of feeding stuffs is recognized by law. When a tenant vacates his leasehold he is paid for the manurial value of feeds which he has recently purchased and fed on the farm, and, under certain conditions, for the manurial value of grain produced on the farm and fed to stock. Similar provisions should be drafted into farm leases in this country.

677. Buying fertility in purchased feeds.—Even in livestock farming where little or no grain or roughage is sold and when proper care is taken of the manure, not all of the fertility in the crops is returned in the manure. The growth of legumes will aid in maintaining the nitrogen supply in the soil, but under actual conditions on most farms, supplying additional nitrogen in manure or fertilizer will increase crop yields.

Sooner or later in practically all cases it is necessary to replace the small but steady loss of phosphorus and potassium, even when most of the crops are fed to stock and the manure is handled properly. Therefore, in purchasing feeding stuffs, one should always consider not only their feeding value but also their worth as fertilizers. By a wise selection of purchased concentrates the livestock farmer can build up the fertility of his farm without the use of any commercial fertilizers, except lime to correct soil acidity and probably phosphate to balance the farm manure, which is ordinarily much richer in nitrogen than in phosphorus. To determine which feeds are the cheapest when consideration is given to the manurial value, one should deduct the manurial value per ton from the gross price.

For instance, in an example given in Chapter X of the method for determining which feeds are the cheapest sources of total digestible nutrients and of digestible protein, it was assumed that a dairyman had ground corn available on the farm at a price of $22.00 per ton. (**285**) Among the protein supplements he could purchase on his local market was cottonseed meal (43 per cent protein grade) at $34.00 per ton.

If we deduct the manurial value of cottonseed meal per ton (which is $10.51) from the purchase price, the net cost per ton would be only $23.49 per ton. Similarly deducting the manurial value of corn ($2.34 per ton) from the price, the net cost would be $19.66 per ton. Thus, at these prices the net cost of cottonseed meal is only $3.83 more per ton than that of corn, if proper credit is given for the difference in the manurial values of the two feeds.

678. Composition and value of fresh manure.—The value of farm manure produced by animals of the same kind varies rather widely, depending primarily on the nature of the feed supplied. However, it is desirable to have an approximate idea of its general composition.

Mixed fresh farm manure, including bedding, contains, on the average, about 12 lbs. of nitrogen, 5 lbs. of phosphoric acid (equivalent to 2.2 lbs. of phosphorus), and 12 lbs. of potash (equivalent to 10.0 lbs. of potassium) per ton. With these fertilizing constituents at the prices stated previously, average farm manure has a value of $2.17 per ton.

The average composition of fresh manure (including bedding,

except in the case of hen manure) for the various classes of farm stock is about as follows.[4] The last column of the table shows the average value per ton of the various kinds of manure.

Composition of average manure from farm animals

	Percentage composition				Pounds per ton			Value per ton
	Water	Nitrogen	Phosphorus	Potassium	Nitrogen	Phosphorus	Potassium	
	Per cent	Per cent	Per cent	Per cent	Lbs.	Lbs.	Lbs.	Dollars
Horses	59	0.70	0.11	0.64	14.0	2.2	12.8	2.56
Dairy cattle	79	0.57	0.10	0.52	11.4	2.0	10.4	2.11
Fattening cattle ..	78	0.73	0.21	0.46	14.6	4.2	9.2	2.64
Sheep	64	1.44	0.22	1.01	28.8	4.4	20.2	4.88
Swine	74	0.49	0.15	0.39	9.8	3.0	7.8	1.89
Hens (without litter)	55	1.00	0.35	0.33	20.0	7.0	6.6	3.39

The manure from horses, sheep, and hens is much drier than that from cattle or swine, and therefore is especially apt to heat unduly in storage, on account of rapid fermentation. These manures are often called "hot manures," in contrast to manures from cattle and swine, which are termed "cold manures."

679. Manure and fertilizing constituents produced yearly.—The amount of manure (including bedding) and the amounts of fertilizing constituents produced yearly by any class of stock will vary considerably, depending chiefly on the liberality of feeding and the amount and kind of bedding. According to Van Slyke, approximately the following amounts of manure, including bedding, are produced per 1,000 lbs. live weight annually by the various classes of stock, if it is all saved throughout the entire year: Horses, 12.0 tons; dairy cows, 15.0 tons; fattening cattle, 9.0 tons; sheep, 9.8 tons; swine, 18.2 tons; and hens (not including litter) 4.2 tons.[5]

Under usual farm conditions much of the manure is not voided in the stable. That which is excreted by stock on pasture or by horses working in the fields is commonly well utilized, but a considerable loss occurs through the amounts voided in exercise paddocks or by horses on the road.

In Ohio studies it was estimated that the following amounts of manure, ready for field application, were produced *per head* by farm animals in a year, excluding that voided while the animals were in the yards or at work: Horses, 6.0 tons; fattening cattle, 7.8 tons; sheep, 0.75 ton; and hogs, 1.7 tons.[6] In studies on Illinois dairy farms it was found that 6.6 loads of manure (including bedding) were actually recovered annually per mature cattle unit.[7] For work horses and mules the amount actually hauled to the fields was 5.45 loads per head annually.

680. Importance of saving urine.—In preventing losses of fertilizing value in farm manure, one of the most important points is to use sufficient bedding to absorb the urine. In the case of cattle and sheep, the urine may contain more than one-half of the total nitrogen in the excrement and more than two-thirds of the potassium.[8] Even for horses and swine, one-third of the nitrogen and two-fifths of the potassium are in the urine. Practically all the phosphorus and calcium is in the feces, except in the case of swine, which excrete about 12 per cent of the phosphorus in the urine.

Pound for pound, the urine has a greater fertilizing value than the feces, except with swine, whose urine is large in quantity, and watery. The fertilizing constituents in the urine are also in solution and hence much more readily available to plants than those in the feces. The feces consist chiefly of food residues that were too insoluble to be digested.

It is obvious that much fertility is lost if the urine drains away from the stable, because of insufficient bedding and gutters that are not water-tight. Also, there is usually a heavy loss of fertility in exercise paddocks.

681. Bedding.—Where considerable small grain is grown on the farm, *straw* is commonly the chief bedding material. Straw that is not too coarse will absorb 2 to 3 times its weight of water, or even more.[9] Unless the straw is very coarse, as is the case with rye straw, cutting does not increase its absorptive power materially. For dairy cows, it may require a larger quantity of cut straw than of uncut straw, as the latter stays in place better.[10] In New Jersey tests flax straw had an especially high water-absorbing capacity.[11]

From 4 to 8 lbs. of straw per head daily are usually sufficient for dairy cows in stanchions, if the platforms are of the proper length. In Illinois tests 4 to 5 lbs. per head daily of straw were needed for 1,000-lb. fattening steers which were fed in open sheds that were cleaned once a month.[12] Twice as much was needed when cattle were kept in single stalls that were well-bedded and cleaned once a day.

When stock are fed *shredded* or *cut dry corn* or *sorghum stover* or *fodder,* the coarser parts that are refused make satisfactory bedding. If not needed for feed, finely-shredded stover makes excellent bedding, nearly equalling straw in water-absorbing capacity.

When these farm-produced bedding materials are not available, either *wood shavings* or *sawdust* are used most commonly as the substitute. These wood by-products often have a somewhat lower absorptive capacity per pound than straw, especially in the case of hardwood by-products. Shavings and sawdust add less fertility to the manure than does straw, and they do not decompose readily in the soil. In Rhode Island tests the effect produced on crops by shavings or sawdust used as bedding for stock was compared with that of straw.[13] No detrimental effect on the land resulted from the use of shavings or sawdust. The crop yield was slightly higher when straw was used, but it was concluded that this was due to the greater amount of fertilizing constituents contained in the straw.

Dry *peat moss* absorbs 5 to 10 times its weight in water, is a good deodorant, and is excellent for bedding, but it is usually expensive.[14] It is especially good for calf pens. Cows may become stained if the same peat moss is used in the stall too long. The statement is sometimes made that flies will not develop in peat-manure, but in tests by the United States Department of Agriculture peat had no inhibiting effect on the development of flies in the manure.[14a]

Cocoa shells are sometimes used for bedding and have about the same absorbing capacity as straw.[15] They are a good deodorant, or

Such Losses of Fertility Occur on Many Farms

When manure is loosely piled under the eaves, heavy losses of fertility occur thru fermentation and leaching. Note that every hard rain will leach fertility from the manure pile to the ditch in the foreground. (From Wisconsin Station.)

The Result of Allowing Manure to Waste Away

When manure is allowed to waste away as in the preceding illustration, not only is much of the weight of the manure lost, but that which remains contains much less fertility per ton than fresh manure. The pile of corn at the left was grown on a plot fertilized with manure which had been exposed to the weather over winter. The large pile at the right was grown on a plot fertilized with the same amount of fresh manure. (From Wisconsin Station.)

SAVING THE FERTILITY IN FEEDING STUFFS

If possible, the manure should be drawn directly to the fields and spread each day. However, this is not advisable on sloping land in winter when there is deep snow on the fields.

A CHEAP BUT EFFICIENT MANURE PIT

When manure is piled solidly in a pit like this with concrete walls and floor, there is but little loss from fermentation and none from leaching.

masker of odors, but are difficult to keep in place in dairy stables, and they pack hard.

Peanut hulls, or shells, are sometimes used for bedding. The unground hulls have about the same water-absorbing capacity as sawdust or shavings. However, peanut hulls are said to be less economical than shavings for bedding in dairy stables, for they do not stay under the cows so well.[15a] They are also inclined to stick to the hair of the cows about the udder. Therefore in the production of sanitary milk cows bedded with peanut hulls may require more brushing than those bedded with straw or shavings. It is reported that in the summer time peanut hulls attract flies, because of small amounts of fragments of the oily peanut kernels still left in the hulls.

Buckwheat hulls have about the same absorptive capacity as shavings, but they are rather hard to keep in place for dairy-cow bedding.[16] They sometimes lodge between the toes of cattle, causing infection. It is not safe to bed calves with buckwheat hulls, for they often eat them, which causes indigestion. *Oat hulls* may likewise be used for bedding, but they have the same disadvantages as buckwheat hulls and are dusty for use in dairy stables. They are excellent, however, as poultry litter.

682. Reducing the losses in farm manure.—In spite of the value of farm manure, many farmers who freely purchase commercial fertilizers allow much of the worth of the manure produced by their livestock to be wasted. It is important to realize that manure is a perishable product, and that unless proper care is taken over half its value may be lost. The losses of plant food from manure occur through: (1) Loss of urine; (2) loss by leaching; and (3) loss of nitrogen by fermentation.

A manure pile against the side of the barn and under the eaves, or manure lying for months in an open barn yard, is a sight all too common on American farms. When manure is thus exposed to the leaching action of rains, the losses are great, even amounting to half of the total value in periods of 2 to 5 months. Unfortunately, the loss falls on the constituents which are most soluble and therefore most quickly available to plants.

Farm manure contains myriads of bacteria, molds, and yeasts, the numbers often running into billions for each gram of manure. These organisms break down the complex compounds of the manure into simpler ones, which are soluble. Some of these changes are advantageous, as they make the plant food more available to crops, but under improper conditions of storage much of the nitrogen in the manure may be lost through these fermentations.

When the manure is dry or loosely packed, the bacteria which thrive in the presence of air develop profusely, causing "hot" fermentation. In this process there is a rapid formation of ammonia from the nitrogenous compounds of the manure, and much of this ammonia passes as gas into the air. The strong smell which every farmer has noticed in close horse stables is due to this escaping ammonia gas, produced by the breaking down of nitrogenous compounds in the urine. In still other changes which may take place, free nitrogen gas may be formed, which is likewise lost into the air.

When the pile of manure is well packed and is kept damp, these changes cannot go on, but only the decompositions which render the plant food more available and produce what is termed "well-rotted manure." If the manure is very loose and dry, "fire fanging" may occur, the manure becoming grayish or dusty in appearance. This change, which is brought about by certain fungi or molds, seriously injures the value of the manure. Phosphorus and potassium are not lost through fermentation, but heavy losses of these minerals may occur through leaching.

To reduce the losses of fertility in manure to the minimum, first of all, the urine should be saved by having tight gutters and using plenty of bedding. If possible, the manure should be drawn directly to the fields and spread each day. This is not advisable, however, in winter on very sloping land when covered by deep snow, as much fertility may wash down the hill in the spring. Even when the fresh manure is spread daily on the fields, a heavy loss of nitrogen may occur if it is not plowed under or disked under as soon as possible. In Wisconsin tests as much as 60 per cent of the nitrogen was lost from fresh manure which was spread on the field and allowed to dry 4 days before it was turned under.[17]

Adding acid phosphate (superphosphate) to the manure greatly decreases the losses of nitrogen, no matter whether it is spread at once or whether it is properly stored. Also, since manure is much richer in nitrogen than in phosphorus, this reinforcement of manure with phosphorus usually increases crop yields considerably.[18] Hydrated lime increases the loss of nitrogen from manure, as the alkaline action tends to drive off ammonia.

When manure cannot be spread at once on the land, it should be stored under cover, if possible, and in well-packed piles which are kept moist to prevent hot fermentation. The shed or pit should preferably have a concrete floor, to prevent any draining away of liquid. If hogs have access to the shed, they aid in firming the mass. It is an excellent plan to mix the manure from horses, sheep, or poultry, which is drier, with the cattle or pig manure, which contains more water.

When it is necessary to leave manure outdoors, the pile should be built with the sides perpendicular and the top sloping slightly toward the center, so that all rain will soak into the pile instead of draining off as from a stack of hay. It is impossible to prevent all waste when manure is stored, but under proper management not over 25 to 30 per cent of the nitrogen and practically none of the phosphorus and potassium will be lost.

QUESTIONS

1. How are the fertilizing values of feeding stuffs and of farm manures computed?
2. What beneficial effects does farm manure produce in the soil in addition to the plant food it supplies?
3. About what percentage of the fertilizing constituents in their feeds do mature work horses (not pregnant or nursing foals) void in the manure; young calves; dairy cows?
4. Give examples of feeds which are high and of others which are low in fertility value?
5. How is the manurial value of a feed computed?
6. A farmer who intends to fatten some steers has on his farm shelled corn, corn silage, and clover hay. To provide a well-balanced ration, he sells 10 tons

of corn and buys as much cottonseed meal as he can with the proceeds. Using local market prices and assuming that the feeding value of the cottonseed meal is enough greater than that of the corn to pay for hauling, find the gain or loss in manurial value from the exchange.

7. Compare the fertility lost in selling a ton of corn; a ton of fat pigs; a ton of butter.
8. What are the average amounts of fertilizing constituents in a ton of mixed fresh farm manure?
9. Discuss the differences in composition and value of manure from horses, dairy cows, fattening cattle, sheep, swine, and poultry.
10. What are "hot manures" and "cold manures"?
11. About how much manure, including bedding, is produced per head annually by horses; by dairy cows; by sheep; by hogs?
12. Why is it important that the urine be saved?
13. What kinds of bedding are used for stock in your district?
14. Discuss the losses that occur in farm manure and tell how it should be handled to reduce the losses to a minimum.

REFERENCES

1. Grindley, Mumford, Emmett, and Bull, Ill. Bul. 209.
2. Warington, Chemistry of the Farm, p. 214.
3. Forbes et al., Ohio Buls. 295, 308, 330, 363; Wells and Dunbar, Jour. Agr. Res., 30, 1925, pp. 985-998.
4. Ames and Gaither, Ohio Bul. 246; Van Slyke, Fertilizers and Crop Production, pp. 218, 225.
5. Van Slyke, Fertilizers and Crop Production, p. 225.
6. Ames and Gaither, Ohio Bul. 246.
7. Ross, Ill. Bul. 240.
8. Van Slyke, Fertilizers and Crop Production, p. 221; Forbes et al., Ohio Buls. 295, 308, 330, 365; Ames and Gaither, Ohio Bul. 246.
9. Doane, Md. Bul. 104; Ames and Gaither, Ohio Bul. 246; Vt. Bul. 360; Whisenand, Jour. Agr. Res. 14, 1918, pp. 187-190.
10. Savage and Albrectsen, N. Y. (Cornell) Rpt. 1931.
11. Sprague, N. J. Cir. 295.
12. Snapp, Beef Cattle, p. 89.
13. Odland and Knoblauch, R. I. Bul. 251.
14. N. J. Rpt. 1929; Vt. Bul. 360.
14a. Woodward, Shepherd, and Graves, U. S. Dept. Agr., Misc. Pub. 179.
15. Vt. Bul. 360.
15a. Bartlett, N. J. Sta., information to the author.
16. Bartlett, N. J. Rpt. 1925.
17. Heck, Musbach, and Whitson, Wis. Bul. 410.
18. Collison and Conn. N. Y. (Geneva) Bul. 494; Carter and Millar, Mich. Quar. Bul. 16, 1934, No. 3.

PART III

FEEDING FARM ANIMALS

CHAPTER XXI

GENERAL PROBLEMS IN HORSE HUSBANDRY

I. FACTORS INFLUENCING THE WORK DONE BY HORSES

683. The horse and mule situation.—The large decrease in the number of horses and mules in the United States since 1920 has had grave and far-reaching effects, not only upon farmers but also upon the rest of our population as well. In 1920 there were 20,092,000 horses and 5,656,000 mules on farms and about 2,000,000 horses and mules in the cities in this country.

Due to replacement by tractors, trucks, and automobiles, by 1936 the number of horses on farms had decreased to 11,637,000 and of mules to 4,685,000. Automobiles and trucks had displaced all but a few hundred thousand of the horses and mules in cities. Thus a total decrease of more than 10,000,000 horses and mules had occurred during this period. It will be noted that there was a much greater decrease in the number of horses during this period than in the number of mules.

It has been estimated that 30,000,000 acres to 45,000,000 acres of crop land that had previously produced feed for these 10,000,000 horses were turned during this period to the growing of crops for other purposes.[1] In addition, much pasture land was released for other classes of stock.

Unfortunately these changes took place at the same time when a considerable decline in our exports of agricultural products occurred. These conditions, in combination with other factors, brought about large surpluses of many agricultural products, including not only crops like wheat, corn, cotton, and tobacco, but also such animal products as pork, beef, and dairy products. These surpluses depressed the prices of these products to ruinous levels, and this greatly reduced the purchasing power of farmers. In turn, the depression in agriculture was an important factor in industrial unemployment. Also, the substitution of tractor power for horse power on farms tended to reduce the number of farm laborers required, thus adding to the unemployment in the nation.

Finally, in 1933 the Federal Government embarked on a definite program of restricting the production of certain important crops, in an endeavor to adjust the production to the probable consumptive demand at price levels that would bring fair returns to farmers.

In comparing the relative advantages of horse and tractor power on their farms, farmers should consider not only the cost per hour of horse labor and of tractor labor, but also the other important factors.

They should bear in mind that horses effectively dispose of home-raised agricultural crops and convert them into power. On the other hand, the substitution of tractors for horses adds to a surplus of the products a farmer has for sale. Also, the cash costs of horse-power farming are usually much less than those of tractor farming. The important farm question of "horses vs. the tractor" is discussed in greater detail later in this chapter. (718)

During this period of rapid decline in numbers of horses and mules, the number of colts raised each year dropped to about one-third the former number. For example, 1,587,515 horse and mule colts were raised in 1919, in comparison with only 576,138 in 1929. As a result of this decline in the raising of work stock, the ages of the horses and mules on farms in 1935 undoubtedly averaged much older than in 1920. Therefore the rate of mortality was correspondingly increased.

On account of the impending serious shortage of horses and mules, interest in the raising of colts has now become more general. Increasing numbers of farmers realize that when they have abundant supplies of cheap home-grown feed available, it is a wise plan to raise at least the necessary replacements for their work stock. Raising colts for sale is also a profitable side-line on many farms.

684. Importance of economical feeding and care.—Many people fail to realize the magnitude of our horse and mule industry. Even after the great decline in numbers of horses and mules, the 16,322,000 head on farms on January 1, 1936, had an estimated total value of $1,690,586,000, a sum greater than that of any other class of livestock, even dairy cattle.

To feed and care for these horses and mules means a total expense of over a billion dollars a year. In spite of the magnitude of the industry, less attention is given to the economical feeding of this class of livestock than to any other farm animals. Many a farmer, for instance, will carefully determine which of the feeds available for his dairy herd will furnish a well-balanced ration most cheaply. Yet he may forget that similar principles apply to the feeding of his work animals. An average of 2.6 horses or mules are kept on each farm in the United States. It is often possible through economy in feeding to save 10 to 20 per cent or more of the usual feed bill, with no injury and in some cases even a benefit to the animals. It is therefore evident that a careful consideration of the principles governing the feeding of horses will pay every owner in dollars and cents. Furthermore, it is just as essential to care for work animals in a manner to ensure their maximum efficiency as it is to care for and lubricate properly the vehicles and machinery they draw.

Before studying in detail the feeds for horses and the methods of feeding and caring for them, it is necessary to consider briefly the principles determining the value of the different classes of feeds for the production of work and the various factors which influence the amount of labor animals can perform.

Most of the discussions which follow treat of the horse particularly, since about 70 per cent of our work animals are horses, and nearly all of the scientific trials have been conducted with them. The same feeds may be used for mules, however, and the same principles of feeding

and care apply to these animals. Special hints on the feed and care of
the mule are given later in this chapter. (**719**)

685. Work done by horses.—In measuring the rate of work done
by horses or other forms of motive power, the common unit of measurement is the *horse power*. This is the performance of 33,000 foot pounds
of work in a minute.* Horse power is computed by multiplying the
force which is acting, expressed in pounds, by the distance in feet
through which it moves in one minute, and dividing the product (the
foot pounds of work) by 33,000. For example, if a horse exerts a pull
of 150 lbs. while traveling at a speed of 2.5 miles per hour (220 feet per
minute), it will do 150 times 220 foot pounds of work a minute, or 33,000
foot pounds. This is exactly one horse power.

The work which horses can do depends on their weight, muscular
development, and endurance. At steady and continuous work for 10
hours a day, the pull (or draft) for a horse should not be more than
one-eighth to one-tenth its weight. On the average, the 1,000-lb. horse
working steadily 10 hours a day can develop about 0.67 to 0.83 horse
power. A 1,600-lb. horse will produce 1.06 to 1.33 horse power.

An ox can draw about as heavy a load as can a horse of the same
weight, but ordinarily at only two-thirds the speed. The work a man
can do is usually from one-tenth to one-sixth of a horse power, but for
a minute or two he can exert a full horse power or even more. It was
found in Iowa trials that horses weighing 1,500 to 1,900 lbs. could pull,
day after day, a load requiring one horse power of work, over a course
of 20 miles a day.[2]

For a brief interval a well-trained horse can develop 10 times the
normal rate of work and can exert a pull nearly as great as his weight.
A few can momentarily exert a pull even greater than their weights.
The horse greatly excels all types of engines and motors in this capacity
for overload. This reserve power of a good team is of great importance
in their ordinary work. For example, it may require more than 10 times
as great a pull to start a loaded wagon as it will take to pull it on
a level pavement, after it is once in motion. Also, this reserve power
is essential in drawing loads over uneven roads and up steep grades, or
under other conditions where great effort is needed for relatively short
periods.

Recent investigations by Ritzman at the New Hampshire Station
indicate that horses when well fed store much greater amounts of glycogen in their muscles and other tissues than other farm animals.[3] This
reserve store, which can serve as an immediately available source of
energy, explains the well-deserved reputation of the horse for muscular
endurance. Horses were also found to have a much higher rate of
metabolism per unit of weight when idle than other farm animals, and
about double that of man. Ritzman points out that this high rate of
metabolism of the horse is "that of a tensely nervous animal that does
not easily lay on flesh and . . . is in full keeping with its muscular
power and the capacity of almost explosive activity."

686. Horse-pulling contests and champion pull.—The horse-pulling
contests, sponsored by the Horse and Mule Association of America and

*A foot pound is the amount of work done in lifting one pound one foot against
the force of gravity. A foot ton is 2,000 foot pounds.

conducted under the auspices of the various agricultural colleges in this country, have done much to call to the attention of farmers and others the great power possessed by good horses and to emphasize the factors that influence the work they can perform. In these contests specially constructed dynamometers are used, in which the power required to pull the dynamometer can be adjusted at various amounts. At first the apparatus is set at a moderate pull and this is then gradually increased during the contest. As the tractive power required is increased, any team that is unable to exert a given pull for the entire distance of 27.5 feet is eliminated. Finally the winner is the team that can exert the greatest tractive power for the required distance.

In 1935 Rock and Tom, an Ohio team, weighing a total of 4,450 lbs., pulled the dynamometer the full distance when set at a pull (or tractive resistance) of 3,900 lbs., establishing a new world's record. In 1934 this same team won the title of World Champions at the Century of Progress Exposition, Chicago, with a pull of 3,350 lbs. This latter record was made on a soft clay footing, which is not favorable to a maximum pull. In the 1934 record, the team exerted 30 horse power during their pull. The champion pull of 3,900 lbs. would be equivalent to starting a load of more than 25 tons for 20 consecutive times on a good pavement.

687. Factors determining work done by horses.—The horse-pulling contests have shown that weight is the most important single factor which determines the amount of pull a draft horse can exert, but as the weight of draft horses increases, their pull per 100 lbs. live weight decreases somewhat.[4]

For the best work, horses should have energetic but calm dispositions, and they must be well trained and be driven skillfully and steadily. The nervous, excitable driver cannot get the utmost effort from his team. Among horses of equal weight, those with the greater heart girth and compact, muscular build are able to exert the greater pull. Horses must also be in good flesh to do their best.

The careful fitting of the harness is important, especially the correct fitting of collars.

Proper care of the horses' shoulders is essential if maximum service is to be obtained. When horses must be worked hard during rainy weather, hame housing should be provided to keep the collars and shoulders as dry as possible. An excessive amount of moisture under the collar is apt to cause sore shoulders, which greatly reduce the horses' efficiency. Humid days in summer are harder on horses than dry, hot days. When properly shod, horses are able to pull more than when unshod.

688. Effect of character of roadbed.—The character of the roadbed is a most important factor in determining how heavy a load a horse can draw. While only 25 to 50 lbs. of draft are required, after the load is started, to haul a load of a ton (including weight of wagon) on a level pavement made of concrete, granite blocks, or brick, the draft on a common earth road is 75 to 225 lbs. or more per ton.[5]

On a soft surface, the height of wheel and the width of tire are important, as they affect the amount that the wheels will cut into the ground. However, on a hard roadbed, such as a concrete highway, there is very little difference in draft required with different kinds of wheel equipment.[6]

689. Nutrients required in various types of work.—It is evident that the horse at work must receive a larger supply of nutrients than when idle, and that the amount needed will depend on the severity of the work done. Let us then consider what types of work the horse performs. His work usually consists of a more or less complex combination of the following simple kinds: (1) Locomotion, or traveling along a level course without a load; (2) raising the body, with or without a load, against the force of gravity in ascending a grade; (3) carrying a load; (4) draft, or hauling a load.

A horse drawing a load up a hill combines all of these types. He is (1) advancing and at the same time (2) raising his body. Likewise, he is (3) carrying the harness and (4) hauling the load. In descending the hill the horse will be called upon to perform even a fifth type of labor, bracing himself to prevent too rapid a descent.

The amounts of nutrients required in each of these types of work were determined many years ago in painstaking and extensive experiments of Wolff, Grandeau, LeClerc, and Zuntz and his associates. Wolff's experiments were with a sweep-power constructed so that the amount of work performed could be measured. Zuntz, in conjunction with Lehmann and Hagemann, conducted hundreds of tests with horses working on a tread-power so built that the distance traveled and the work performed were measured.[7] The animals breathed through a tube inserted in the windpipe, by which means the oxygen inhaled and the carbon dioxide exhaled were accurately determined. To such gaseous intake and outgo was added that which passed through the skin and rectum, as determined by placing the animal in a respiration apparatus. Recently, somewhat similar experiments have been conducted by Brody and associates at the Missouri Station.[8]

The results of these investigations are chiefly of theoretical importance, rather than of practical value in the computation of rations for horses. This is because the work of most horses varies greatly from day to day and is usually of a complex nature, difficult to separate into the different simple types. All that can commonly be done is to estimate whether the horse is performing light, medium, or heavy work, and then compute a ration which meets the standard for this degree of labor.

690. Locomotion and carrying a load.—Considerable energy is expended by the horse in merely moving his body along a horizontal road, since he must lift his body at each step and propel it forward. Yet in this work of locomotion, no useful work is accomplished in the mechanical sense.

Zuntz found that when walking at a speed of 2.5 miles per hour, the 1,100-lb. horse, carrying a 44-lb. harness, required, for each mile he traveled on a level road, 0.240 therm of net energy in addition to the maintenance requirements when idle. When the horse carried a load of 220 lbs. on his back, the amount of net energy expended was increased 24 per cent above the amount required for the same distance and at the same speed without a load. Brody and associates found that when walking at a speed of 2.2 miles per hour, horses expended 77 to 144 per cent more energy than when standing idle.

691. Work of draft.—When the horse pulls a load and thus accomplishes useful mechanical work, obviously he will expend more energy than when merely moving his own body along a level road. Zuntz found that in performing each 1,000 foot tons of work of draft (which is about an hour's work for a horse weighing 1,400 lbs.) the horse expends 2.078 therms of net energy in addition to the maintenance requirements. Such a horse would be performing about one horse power of work. In the experiments by Brody and associates horses expended about 1.87 therms of energy in addition to their maintenance requirements, for each horse power of draft accomplished.

692. Influence of speed.—The horse is most efficient in doing a day's work when working at a speed of 2 to 2.5 miles per hour. Walking somewhat more rapidly than this may not reduce the efficiency of the labor over a short period of time, according to the Missouri experiments. For example, work was performed as efficiently by horses walking 3.1 miles per hour as when they walked at a speed of 2.2 miles an hour. However, if horses are forced to walk too rapidly for a considerable time when performing hard work, they will become over-heated and tired, and then will be less efficient. In the experiments by Zuntz 26 per cent more energy was required when a horse traveled one mile on a level road at a speed of 3.5 miles an hour than when the same distance was covered at a speed of 2.5 miles an hour.

When the speed is increased to a trot, nearly twice as much energy is required per mile of travel as at a walk. The efficiency continues to become less as the speed increases, until when worked at a speed of 11.25 miles an hour, a horse can accomplish less than one-tenth of the amount of work he can perform at a moderate pace.

Among the reasons why more energy is required to do a certain amount of work at a fast pace are: (1) In trotting or galloping the rise and fall of the body are much greater than in walking. Energy is wasted in these movements, and hence a smaller amount is available for onward movement. (2) At a rapid pace the work of the heart is increased, the temperature rises, and much heat is lost through the evaporation of water from the skin and lungs in the effort to keep the body temperature normal. The proportion of the food which produces heat is thus increased, while less can be converted into work.

On account of the speed at which they traveled, mail-coach horses in early days could often be worked but one hour a day, covering only eight miles, even on good roads. While a pound of additional load makes but little difference to a draft horse, with running horses the requirement of speed makes it necessary that the weight carried (rider and saddle) be as small as possible. An ounce of additional loading may make a difference of a yard or more in half a mile of running.

693. Influence of grade.—In going up a grade, the horse must not only propel his body and the load over the ground but must also raise them against the force of gravity. In ascending a grade of 10.7 ft. in 100 ft., the horse expends three times as much energy per mile as when traveling on a level road. The steeper the grade, the greater the energy required.

On the other hand, in going down a gentle incline, owing to the force of gravity less energy is required than on a level road. However, if the grade is steeper than 10 ft. in 100, the horse must expend energy in bracing himself and the load against too-rapid a descent, and hence he uses as much energy as when traveling on the level. On a still steeper downward slope more energy is expended than on a level course. Obviously, a considerable saving of feed may be effected by a proper use of wagon brakes in a hilly country.

694. Influence of size of horse and rate of work.—If large and small horses do amounts of work which are in proportion to their live weights, their efficiencies in the actual performance of labor will be equal, according to Missouri experiments.[9] On the other hand, if a large horse is not worked in such a manner as to perform an amount of labor which is proportional to his size, his efficiency will be lowered.

What is the best size of horses or mules for any particular farm will depend on several factors. On level farms with large fields, heavier work animals are desirable than on hilly farms where the land is cut up into small fields by the rough topography. On heavy soil where the draft of tillage implements is great, large size in work animals is advantageous. However, on sandy soil most farmers favor animals which are not too heavy.

During recent years there has been a pronounced tendency among farmers, even in the corn belt, to prefer draft horses which are not extremely large. Work horses weighing 1,800 lbs. and over are less popular than some years ago. Lighter horses that can be maintained more cheaply are usually more active and will perform just as much of many kinds of farm work as extremely heavy horses. For the tillage operations which require much power, such as plowing with gang plows, the necessary power can be secured by using moderate-weight draft horses in teams of 3 to 5 animals, or even more. (**717**)

695. Efficiency of the horse as a motor.—Such a large part of the mechanical power used on farms is furnished by horses that it is of much interest to determine the efficiency with which they actually convert into useful work the nutrients in the feed they consume. Zuntz found that horses converted into the actual work of draft about 31 per cent of the energy they expended, beyond the amounts they used for the maintenance and locomotion of their bodies. Similar results were secured in recent Missouri investigations, the average efficiency on this same basis being about 34 per cent.[9] When horses worked at the usual rates, they converted into actual work about 16 to 20 per cent of the total energy expended, not deducting the amounts used for maintenance and for the locomotion of their bodies.

To gain a true idea of the efficiency of the horse as a source of power, we must compute his over-all efficiency for the entire day. This is the percentage of the total energy in the feed he eats during a day, which he is able to convert into useful work. The approximate over-all efficiency may be found as follows: A 1,500-lb. horse should readily haul a load having a draft of 150 lbs. at a speed of 2.5 miles per hour for 8 hours a day. In doing this the horse will perform 7,920 foot tons of useful work, not including the work of moving his own body along the roadway. Expressed in therms, this amount of work is equal to 5.1 therms per day.

For such a horse a ration of 15.0 lbs. timothy hay, 8.0 lbs. corn, and 9.5 lbs. oats will be satisfactory. This ration will furnish about 57.2 therms of gross energy. Dividing 5.1 therms (the useful work accomplished) by 57.2 therms (the gross energy of the feed) gives an over-all efficiency of 8.9 per cent for this horse.

However, farm horses do not work every day, though they must eat every day. Therefore the over-all efficiency for the entire year is much lower than for a 24-hour period in which the horse does a good day's work. On the average, the yearly over-all efficiency of farm horses, which usually work only about 800 to 1,000 hours a year, is about 2 to 3 per cent. Obviously, any factor which increases the number of hours of work a horse does during the year increases his over-all efficiency and reduces the actual cost of his labor per hour, since less of his feed will then go for maintaining him when idle.

It is of interest to compare the efficiency of horses in the conversion of the energy of their feed into draft, with the efficiency of farm tractors in converting the energy of the gasoline or other fuel into draft. In recent tests of farm tractors by the University of Nebraska, gasoline tractors converted 13.0 per cent, on the average, of the energy of the gasoline into the work of draft.[10] This is probably higher than the efficiency of the average tractor, for these tractors were handled by experts and were in ideal mechanical condition for the tests.

In comparing this efficiency of 13.0 per cent for tractors with the efficiency of 8.9 per cent for horses in converting the energy of their feed into draft when working a full day, we must consider the following: The horse is supplied with feed in crude form, and a considerable part of it is indigestible and therefore of no value in the production of work. The gasoline or kerosene tractor, however, is not supplied with crude fuel, but with highly-refined fuel from which the waste portions have been removed. Moreover, the horse repairs his body continuously, while the tractor cannot replace the daily wear of its parts.

II. Nutrient Requirements of Horses

696. Digestibility of feeds by horses.—Too few digestion trials have been conducted with horses to warrant the computation for horse feeding of separate tables of digestible nutrients. Therefore, in computing rations for horses, such figures as are given in Appendix Table I are commonly used. These are based upon digestion trials with ruminants, chiefly with sheep.

Horses digest their feed somewhat less completely than do ruminants, as has been shown previously. However, the difference is not marked except in the case of low-grade roughage, such as straw or poor-quality hay.[11] There is generally a greater difference in the digestibility of fiber, nitrogen-free extract, and fat than in the case of protein. The difference in the digestibility of fat is probably because there is a greater excretion in the feces of fat-soluble excretory products in the case of horses, rather than there being an actual difference in the digestibility of fat by horses and by ruminants.

The Morrison feeding standards for horses, which are presented in Appendix Table III, are specifically designed for use with the digestible nutrient values in Appendix Table I. Therefore, rations will be satisfactory under practical conditions, which are computed according to these standards and according to the rules for feeding concentrates and roughages that are given in Appendix Table III, immediately previous to the Morrison feeding standards.

Investigations showed many years ago that moderate work, even immediately after a horse had eaten, tends to increase the digestion and absorption of nutrients.[12] Severe labor may, however, retard digestion. Contrary to some statements, reasonable exercise does not hasten the passage of food from the stomach into the small intestine.

697. Net energy values vs. total digestible nutrients.—It has been pointed out in Chapters III and VIII that only the net energy supplied by a feed can be used to produce such external work as propelling the body, carrying a burden, or pulling a load. Theoretically, the most correct method of comparing the value of various feeds for the production of work would be upon the basis of the net energy furnished by each. There are, however, insufficient data on the actual net energy values of different feeds for horses to permit the computation for horse feeding of reliable tables of net energy values.

The few net energy values of feeds for horses that have been determined differ quite widely from the values for ruminants. For example, according to Armsby the net energy value of dent corn for ruminants was 85.50 therms per 100 lbs., while the net energy value of corn for horses has been 113 to 117 therms.[13] In Massachusetts trials, the net energy value of oats for horses was even higher than that of corn, while practical feeding experiments show that to keep a hard-worked horse in condition it will take decidedly more pounds of oats than of corn.[14]

The data secured in net energy investigations with horses have been of much importance in emphasizing the great difference in value for the production of work between the concentrates, such as grains, and the feeds very high in fiber, such as straw or poor-quality hay. Thus, for horses wheat straw has a negative energy value of 20.9 therms per 100 lbs. for the production of work. This means that the work of masticating and assimilating wheat straw uses up more energy than the straw furnishes. This feed is therefore worse than worthless for feeding a hard-worked horse.

On the other hand, straw is of value for maintaining idle horses and may be used advantageously as part of the ration for this purpose. This is because the chief need of idle animals is not for net energy but for heat to maintain the body temperature. As has been shown in Chapter III, the energy used in mastication, digestion, and assimilation is all transformed into heat and thus aids in warming the body. (86-88)

698. Maintenance requirements of horses.—In maintaining horses when they are idle, it is important to know the amount of nutrients they need for mere maintenance of the body. Mature, idle horses have been maintained for considerable periods in careful experiments on 6.4 to 7.0 lbs. of digestible nutrients daily per 1,000 lbs. live weight, supplying 11.9 to 13.1 therms of metabolizable energy (available energy).[15] Due to their more nervous disposition, under practical conditions where horses are allowed to move about considerably, horses have a somewhat higher maintenance requirement in proportion to their size than do cattle or other farm animals.[16]

In certain of the maintenance experiments horses were maintained successfully for 4 or 5 months on meadow hay alone, which furnished only 0.54 lb. digestible protein daily per 1,000 lbs. live weight. Most authorities believe that the health of animals is improved when they are fed slightly more than the theoretical minimum amount of nutrients for maintenance. This is a matter of particular importance with horses, for they should be fed so as to be kept efficient for a long period of years. Therefore in the Morrison feeding standards 0.6 to 0.8 lb. digestible protein and 7.0 to 9.0 lbs. total digestible nutrients are recommended daily for idle 1,000-lb. horses (Appendix Table III). If exposed to extremely cold weather, idle horses will probably require more total digestible nutrients than these amounts to prevent loss of weight.

In a maintenance ration for an idle mature horse, about two-thirds of the nutrients are required merely to maintain the body temperature. Only the remaining one-third is needed in the form of net energy to cover the requirements for the internal work of the body and the repair of body tissues. Therefore, idle horses can be maintained chiefly on such feeds as hay, corn stover, and straw, which furnish relatively little net energy but produce a large amount of heat in the body as the result of mastication and digestion. As roughages are usually cheaper sources of digestible nutrients than the concentrates, maintaining idle horses on such feeds is obviously economical. If the roughages are of sufficiently good quality, horses may be maintained on such feeds alone. Several suitable rations for maintaining idle horses are given in Appendix Table VII.

Horses are sometimes wintered on nothing but straw, which makes a ration exceedingly low in protein and also deficient in total digestible nutrients and in calcium and phosphorus. The folly of this practice is shown by investigations at the South Dakota Station.[17] Mature horses wintered on straw alone became emaciated and digested their feed poorly. They also tended to become lame, and post mortem examination showed that the joints had become eroded, on account of the deficiencies in the ration.

699. Excess of roughage injurious.—Through mistaken kindness or through carelessness horses are often fed too much hay or other roughage. Cattle and sheep should ordinarily be given all the roughage they will eat, even if it is very palatable, but this is not a wise plan with horses. If allowed to eat all the good hay they will consume, horses often eat too much, with labored breathing and quick tiring as the result. This difference between horses and ruminants is doubtless due chiefly to the relatively small size of the simple stomach of the horse, in comparison with the four-fold stomach of a ruminant. Also, when the digestive tract of a work horse is unduly distended with much roughage, he will be at a disadvantage in hard labor, and digestive disturbances may result.

Therefore, instead of keeping the mangers filled, there should be a definite, limited daily allowance of hay, fed mostly at night when there is ample time for its mastication and digestion. Not only does this save feed, but it is much better for the horses.[18] Limiting the amount of hay is especially important when very palatable hay is fed, such as alfalfa, clover, or early-cut timothy.

700. Proportion of roughages and concentrates for horses.—The allowance of hay for work horses should generally not be over 1.0 to 1.5 lbs. daily per 100 lbs. live weight, the amount depending on the severity of the work. Horses at hard work require a large proportion of concentrates in their ration, and can make less use of hay than those which are idle or at lighter work. As is pointed out in Chapter XXIII, it is imperative that the concentrate allowance of hard-worked horses be reduced on days when they are idle, or azoturia may result.

In spite of the importance of the problem, little information is available concerning the actual relative value per pound of hay and of grain for producing work, and the results of the few experiments have differed widely.[19] The net energy value of a feed for horses measures its value for the production of work, while the amount of total digestible nutrients is a better measure of its value for maintaining idle horses, whose chief need is heat for the maintenance of the body temperature. On the basis of the determinations of net energy values of feeds for horses, it would take 3.0 lbs. of hay or more to equal 1.0 lb. of corn or oats for the production of work, while it would take only 1.5 to 2.0 lbs. of hay to equal 1.0 lb. of grain in value for maintaining an idle horse. From experiments in Sweden with farm horses, 2.5 lbs. of meadow hay were considered equal to 1.0 lb. of barley or corn grain for the production of work.[20]

These approximate values may be used in determining the relative economy of various rations for horses under local conditions, but it must be borne in mind that horses at hard work cannot utilize an undue amount of hay. Hence, their need for energy must be met by supplying sufficient concentrates, even when hay is cheap.

When hay is relatively high in price, compared with grain, it is important to know the minimum amount of hay that is needed for work horses to maintain their health. While horses will not thrive on grain alone, without hay, they need less hay than is generally thought. Hard-worked horses weighing 1,200 to 1,300 lbs. were kept in good condition in Connecticut trials for more than 8 months on only 8 lbs. of hay per head daily, plus a sufficient allowance of grain.[21]

701. Protein required by work horses.—It has been pointed out in Chapter VIII that normally the carbohydrates and fats furnish the energy needed in producing work, and little or no more protein is broken down during work than during rest. Therefore, the rations of work horses can consist chiefly of carbohydrates and fat, with only sufficient protein for the maintenance of the body and to ensure complete digestion of the ration.

It is not necessary and is generally not economical to feed work horses as much digestible protein as was recommended in the older feeding standards, such as the Wolff-Lehmann or the Armsby standards. Mature horses at hard work have even been fed for considerable periods without harm on rations having nutritive ratios as wide as 1:28.0.[22] However, the digestibility of the ration is decreased when the proportion of protein is too low, as has been pointed out in Chapter IV.

In trials at the New York (Cornell) Station Harper secured just as satisfactory results with mature farm horses at medium to hard work on a ration having a nutritive ratio of approximately 1:11.0, as on a ration richer in protein which had a nutritive ratio of about 1:8.0.[23] The low-protein ration consisted of a mixture of 900 lbs. cracked corn and 100 lbs. rolled oats, fed with timothy hay cut reasonably early. The horses on the other ration were fed the same weight of a mixture of 400 lbs. corn, 500 lbs. oats, and 100 lbs. linseed meal, and received the same amount of the hay. If the hay had been late-cut timothy hay, low in protein, the results probably would have been much less satisfactory on the combination of corn and timothy hay with the small amount of oats. It should be pointed out that young, growing horses or pregnant mares or those with foals should be fed more protein than was furnished by this ration.

702. Morrison feeding standards for horses.—In the Morrison feeding standards, which are presented in Appendix Table III, recommendations are made which, it is believed, will meet adequately the nutrient requirements of the various classes of horses. It will be noted that the standards are stated in terms of dry matter, digestible protein, and total digestible nutrients required daily by horses of various live weights and performing various degrees of labor. To indicate readily the proportion of digestible protein advised for each class of horses, the nutritive ratios of the rations are also given.

In these standards the allowance of total digestible nutrients advised for the horse at hard work is about double that for the idle horse, while the amount of dry matter is increased to a much less extent. This means that the ration must consist more largely of concentrates as the work becomes harder. Horses probably differ more in temperament and in individual feed requirements than do other classes of stock. Therefore a feeding standard can serve only as a general guide as to the amount of grain any particular horse will need to keep him in proper condition.

It will be noted that these standards recommend sufficient protein to provide rations having nutritive ratios no wider than 1:10.0 to 1:12.0 for idle horses, and no wider than 1:9.0 to 1:11.0 for those at work. It is believed that with feeds of average quality and average digestibility these standards will furnish ample amounts of protein. When protein-rich feeds are unusually expensive, undoubtedly mature idle horses or work horses can be fed for considerable periods on even less protein than is recommended in these standards. However, for continued feeding over a long time, the author would not advise less protein than is recommended in the standards. In this connection it should be mentioned that in the revised Morrison standards presented in this volume less protein is advised than in the standards for horses given in the fifteenth to nineteenth editions of this book.

When protein-rich feeds are lower in price than those low in protein, it will be economical to feed considerably larger amounts of protein than advised in the standards, which are the minimum amounts recommended. (**288**) It should be borne in mind that, as pointed out in a preceding paragraph, these feeding standards are specifically designed for use with the values for digestible nutrients in the various feeds that are given in Appendix Table I.

The practical feeding of horses is discussed further in Chapter XXIII. Also, in Appendix Table VII many different rations are suggested for idle horses and for those at light, medium, and hard work, respectively. Most farm horses actually work but 1,000 hours a year, or less, the average time worked per day being but 3 to 4 hours throughout the year. However, during the rush seasons farm horses usually work long hours and should then be classed as at hard work.

703. Mineral requirements of horses.—The mineral requirements of horses have been investigated but little. However, practical experience and our general knowledge of nutrition indicate that mature work horses, with the possible exception of brood mares, do not require the addition of any minerals, except common salt, to ordinary rations which contain a normal amount of good hay. This is because their needs for calcium and phosphorus are but little higher than for mere body maintenance. In Iowa tests with work horses, the addition of a mineral mixture (supplying calcium, phosphorus, and iron) to a ration of oats, corn, timothy hay and common salt did not save feed or make a marked difference in the condition of the horses.[24]

It is important that growing colts have an ample supply of calcium and phosphorus and also sufficient vitamin D to enable them to develop strong, sound bones. Likewise, pregnant mares and mares nursing foals require much more calcium and phosphorus than do other mature horses. Well-cured legume hay or mixed hay high in legumes is therefore the best roughage for colts and brood mares during the winter season.

Whenever horses must be fed rations that are deficient in either calcium or phosphorus, care should be taken to supply a suitable mineral supplement. Such a mineral mixture as is recommended in Chapter VI may be placed where the horses have access to it, or a single mineral supplement may be fed. (**181**) If calcium is the only mineral lacking, 1 ounce per head daily of ground limestone or other calcium supplement will correct the deficiency. If phosphorus is lacking, 1 ounce per head daily of steamed bone meal or some other safe source of phosphorus should be used. (**165-171**)

The feeding of rations unusually low in calcium or phosphorus to horses, even to those which are mature, may cause serious bone disease. For example, in a German experiment a horse fed oats alone, without roughage, lost calcium from its body and soon became lame and sore.[25] When stallions were fed rations very low in calcium and phosphorus in California investigations, there seemed to be a decided decrease in the number of spermatozoa and in their vigor.[26]

In areas where there is a deficiency of iodine, brood mares should be fed iodized salt during at least the latter half of pregnancy, to avoid danger of goiter in the new-born foals. It has been mentioned in Chapter VI that in certain tests navel-ill and weakness of foals have apparently been lessened when doses of potassium iodide have been fed to brood mares during pregnancy. (**172**)

704. Salt requirements of horses.—Horses show great fondness for salt, and thrive best when regularly supplied with it. Horses at hard work require more salt than those laboring less severely, for a considerable amount is excreted in the sweat. Since horses differ quite widely in the amount of salt they desire, it is a good plan to supply salt where they can take what they wish, either flake salt from a suitable box, or block salt.

Well-Bred Draft Horses Working in Big-Team Hitches

By means of the improved multiple hitches, which have been brought to public attention largely through the work of the Horse Association of America and of the agricultural colleges, a team of 5 or even more horses can readily be driven by one man.

Speed Decreases the Work that Can Be Performed

A pound of additional load makes but little difference to a draft horse, but with the race horse the load must be made as light as possible.

REDUCING THE COST OF HORSE LABOR BY RAISING FOALS

A team of such brood mares would bring added profits to many farms where no foals are now raised. They will not only produce profitable foals, but will also do no small part of the farm work. (From Illinois Station.)

HORSES AND MULES COMPETE SUCCESSFULLY WITH TRACTORS

Under present conditions, tractors will usually supplement, rather than replace horse or mule labor on most farms. With feed low in price, the horse or mule performs draft more cheaply than the tractor.

An allowance of 1.75 to 2.00 ounces of salt per head daily is ample for horses, and many will take less than this. Horses having free access to flake salt in a Michigan experiment consumed 1.8 ounces a day, on the average.[27] However, the consumption of individual horses varied widely, the range being from 3.26 ounces daily to a minimum of 0.27 ounce. Mules used for heavy farm work at the Mississippi Station consumed an average of 0.4 ounce of brick salt per 1,000 lbs. live weight daily.[28]

705. Vitamin requirements of horses.—No especial attention need be given to the vitamin supply of mature work horses, except perhaps brood mares, because the requirements of such horses for vitamins A and D are apparently low, and there seem to be no deficiencies in ordinary rations.

Foals, on the other hand, sometimes develop rickets, due to a lack either of vitamin D or of calcium or phosphorus. If a foal shows symptoms of rickets, it should be given an ounce of cod-liver oil a day, or preferably an equivalent amount of a vitamin D concentrate. (**194**) It should also be allowed access to bone meal or a suitable mineral mixture, in addition to receiving plenty of good legume hay or good pasture. When a foal is on well-fertilized pasture or when it is fed plenty of good legume hay, there will be no deficiency of vitamin A, vitamin D, or calcium, all of which are needed in liberal amounts for thrifty growth. The vitamin requirements of brood mares will be met if they are fed good legume hay or mixed hay.

706. Watering horses.—An ample amount of water of good quality is essential for horses. About 10 to 12 gallons, or 80 to 100 lbs., of water should be provided daily for each horse. In warm weather and when at hard work, horses will drink more water than at other times, owing to the greater evaporation of water from the body. The nature of the feed also affects the quantity of water drunk, more being needed when legume hay is fed than when the roughage is hay from the grasses.

Extensive tests have shown that horses may be watered before, after, or during a meal without interfering with the digestion or absorption of the food eaten.[29] Therefore, individual circumstances and convenience should determine the time of watering, but when a system is once adopted it should be adhered to, for a change from one system to another lessens the appetite. A horse long deprived of water or having undergone severe exertion should be watered before being fed, but it is dangerous to allow a horse much water when very warm. A moderate drink taken slowly will refresh him and do no harm.

During hot weather horses should be watered every hour or so while at hard work, for they need a frequent drink of water nearly as much as does a man under similar conditions. Taking a can or barrel of water along to the field, so the horses can be thus watered, will aid greatly in preventing injury from over-heating.

707. Variations in body weight.—During exercise and work, a loss in body weight occurs, because of the greater oxidation, or breaking down, of the nutrients in the body and the largely increased evaporation of water. Grandeau and LeClerc[30] found that 2 horses lost on the average 2.3 lbs. each when walked for 148 minutes without drawing a load, while on hauling a load at a trot for 79 minutes each lost 9.3 lbs. A horse performing a certain amount of work at a trot gave off 20.6 lbs.

of water vapor, nearly twice as much as when doing the same amount of work at a walk, and over 3 times as much as when at rest. When horses which have been idle for a period and consequently have soft muscles are put at hard work, they will often lose 50 to 100 lbs. in weight, especially if they are not gradually accustomed to the work. Because of the large capacity of their digestive tracts, the weights of horses or cattle on consecutive days, taken at a uniform hour and under similar conditions of feed and care, may vary 15 to 30 lbs. or even more. This shows the necessity of conducting feeding experiments for considerable periods of time and with several animals in order to lessen the errors which are introduced into the calculations through accidental variations in the weights of the animals studied.

III. PREPARATION OF FEED; GENERAL PROBLEMS

708. Grinding or crushing grain.—It is pointed out in the following chapter that the value of oats for horses with good teeth is increased only about 5 per cent by grinding or crushing. Whether or not this preparation will pay, will depend on the cost under one's local conditions, compared with the price of oats. (**722**)

Throughout the corn belt, corn is usually fed on the cob or as shelled corn. (**726**) The danger from colic is least in feeding ear corn, and shelled corn is slightly safer than ground corn in this respect.

The effect of crushing a mixture of one-half oats and one-half shelled corn, fed with mixed alfalfa and timothy hay to work horses, was studied in 3 Michigan trials.[31] Equal weights of the whole grain and of the crushed grain were fed to the respective lots of horses, but the horses receiving the crushed grain ate 0.9 lb. less hay per head daily on the average and maintained their weights slightly better. However, with the whole grain at $21.67 a ton and a charge of $2.33 a ton for crushing, the feed cost per head daily was 2.4 cents higher for the horses fed the crushed grain.

Barley, wheat, rye, and the grain sorghums should be ground or crushed for horses. On account of the small size of the kernels, these grains are chewed less thoroughly than corn or oats, and hence there is a much greater saving through grinding or crushing them.

709. Cutting or grinding hay and other roughage.—Cutting or chopping good-quality hay for work horses does not increase its value sufficiently to justify the expense. In 3 Wisconsin experiments a ration of whole timothy hay and grain was compared with a ration consisting of the same weight of cut hay and 10 per cent less grain than in the first ration.[32] It was estimated that a saving of about 10 per cent of the grain would be required to make the cutting of the hay economical. On the whole-hay ration the horses gained an average of 6.8 lbs. during 8 weeks, while they lost 19.2 lbs. on the cut-hay ration. Taking into consideration the loss in weight on this ration, the cutting of the hay was not economical.

Horses maintained their weights slightly better on cut timothy hay and grain in a New York trial than they did on approximately the same weights of whole hay and grain, but it was concluded that the difference was not sufficient to justify the expense of cutting the hay.[33] Colts fed cut alfalfa and timothy hay made slightly more rapid gains in Iowa trials than those fed uncut hay.[34]

If horses are fed poor-quality hay, chopping it may reduce the wastage sufficiently to be worth while. A common practice in Europe is to mix chopped straw with chopped hay, more straw thus being eaten than would otherwise be the case.

Horses usually waste a considerable portion of such coarse dry forage as corn or sorghum fodder or stover. Therefore it will usually pay to cut or shred such roughage.[35]

Grinding hay into a meal cannot be recommended for horses.[36] This requires much more power than to chop it, and the ground hay is dusty, tending to irritate the air passages of the horses. While the dust may be laid by wetting the ground hay, this requires considerable labor.

710. Soaking or cooking grain; fermenting feed.—When such grains as wheat and barley cannot conveniently be rolled or ground, they should be soaked before feeding, to soften the kernels. Ear corn that is so dry and flinty as to injure the horses' mouths should also be soaked or ground.

The custom of cooking even a small portion of the feed given to horses has almost ceased, since it has been found that uncooked feed gives just as good results. (**102**)

"Predigesting," or fermenting, grain or hay for horses does not increase the value and is an uneconomical practice. (**104**)

711. Self-feeding; stall vs. lot feeding of mules.—Though the self-feeding of grain or mixtures of cut hay and grain is satisfactory, under certain conditions, for fattening cattle and sheep, the self-feeding method is not adapted to horses. Even if a mixture of cut hay and grain were fed, it would be impossible to adjust the amounts of grain for the various horses, so that the easy keepers would not be overfed while the hard keepers received too little grain.

However, Mississippi experiments show that mules can be satisfactorily self-fed grain or a mixture of grain and cottonseed meal, with hay fed separately in a rack.[37] Also, a mixture of grain and chopped or ground hay can be self-fed as the entire ration. When self-fed on grain, the mules did not gorge on it, as horses would have done, and there was no trouble from digestive disturbances. However, mules usually eat more grain and less hay under this system than when hand-fed.

Where large numbers of mules are fed in the South on plantations, in lumber camps, etc., a common practice is to provide grain and hay separately in a lot where all the mules may eat what they want. In trials during 3 years at the Mississippi Station[38] this system was compared with separate feeding in stalls. The stall-fed mules were given 13.7 lbs. ear corn and 12.0 lbs. Johnson grass hay on the average, while the lot-fed mules ate 15.2 lbs. ear corn and 11.3 lbs. hay, making the feed cost 19 per cent more for the lot-fed animals.

712. Hints on caring for horses.—There is great truth in the Arab saying, "Rest and fat are the greatest enemies of the horse." Regular exercise or work is necessary for health and a long period of usefulness. Wherever possible, idle horses should be turned out so they can exercise at will. Growing colts need opportunity for plenty of exercise. Whenever a horse is not working, the grain should be reduced, to two-thirds or even one-half the usual amount, to avoid digestive troubles, as is pointed out in Chapter XXIII.

To perform work efficiently, the horse must have a properly fitting harness. The collar needs special attention, for the capacity of many a horse is decreased because he wears an ill-fitting collar. It is important that his feet be well cared for, so that the weight and strain are evenly distributed on the joints of the ankle. The other mechanical principles which determine the efficiency of work, such as the correct use of eveners, the proper adjustment of traces and of line of draft, the distribution of the load on the wagon, and the influence of size of wheel, width of tires, and character of roadbed should all be given due consideration.

In starting the day, the horse should be gradually warmed to his work, so that his muscles will be in proper trim, his bowels relieved, and breathing and heart action quickened before he is put to extreme exertion. It is likewise well to cool him off gradually at the end of a trip or of the day's work before returning to the stable. That he may rest in comfort, his stall should be well bedded.

A good horseman is careful to make any decided change in the ration gradually, in order to avoid colic. A quick change from oats to corn may bring on colic, but changing from corn to oats or other bulky feeds is not dangerous. Horses are especially susceptible to poisoning from eating spoiled grain, hay, or silage.

In stables where many horses are maintained, a group or row of animals should remain in the care of the same attendant, the whole establishment being under the watchful supervision of the superintendent. While we can estimate quite closely the amount of food to be given a number of horses, one horse may need more than the regulation allowance, and the next possibly a little less, the object being to keep each in the desired condition. It is often not a wise plan to leave the feeding of horses to their own driver, for he may have likes and dislikes, and the favorite is apt to receive more than his proper allowance of grain, while another may suffer. A watchful superintendent must ever be on the alert to see that each animal secures his due share of feed.

713. The stable.—To keep them in good health, horses should be housed in well-ventilated quarters and be protected from drafts. Cool quarters with good ventilation are far preferable to warm, close stables. Poorly-ventilated stables that are damp or too warm may cause serious troubles from respiratory diseases.

714. Blanketing and clipping.—Horses at work prove more efficient and last longer when reasonably protected against sudden changes in temperature and cold rains. It is important to blanket the horse in cold weather, whenever his work ceases and he is forced to stand in the cold for even a short time. Stable blankets keep the coat in better condition, but when they are used it is especially necessary to protect the horse when standing idle out of doors in inclement weather.

The heavy coat which the horse grows for winter protection has certain disadvantages. The horse with a long coat sweats unduly at work, rendering him especially subject to colds. It may often be advisable to clip him early enough in the fall to permit the growth of a lighter coat for protection before severe weather begins. However, he should not be fall-clipped unless he is carefully protected from cold at all times when not working. Horses are often clipped in the spring after the shedding process has begun, but before the new coat has started. This avoids the nuisance of the shedding coat, especially disagreeable in the case of white or gray horses.

715. Grooming.—The horse at severe labor gives off several pounds of perspiration daily. When this evaporates, considerable solid waste material is left on the animal's coat. Thorough and careful grooming is necessary to remove such body waste, so as to keep the pores open and the skin healthy. Aside from the better appearance which results, proper grooming pays in the greater efficiency of the hard-worked animal. It is best to groom the work horse at night after a severe day's work, so that he may rest more comfortably. As idle horses running at pasture sweat little and have abundant opportunity to roll, grooming them is unnecessary. While grooming should be thorough, a dull curry-comb is preferable to a sharp one, and a brush should be used on the tender head and legs.

716. Care of teeth.—The teeth of horses often wear irregularly, especially those of old horses, leaving sharp points and jagged edges that cause pain, prevent proper mastication of food, and result in unthriftiness. The teeth should therefore be examined frequently and the irregularities removed by a float or guarded rasp. The first, or milk teeth, may remain too long in the young horse's mouth, causing crooked permanent teeth. In such cases the milk teeth should be removed with forceps.

717. Reducing the cost of horse labor.—On most farms horse labor makes up a considerable part of the operating expenses. Moreover, it is, above all other items of expense, the one which can be profitably reduced by good methods of farm organization. Hence, a clear understanding of the following ways in which this expense can be lessened is of prime importance:[39]

1. By economical feeding, care, and management. Farm management surveys have shown that it costs some farmers nearly twice as much to feed their horses as it costs their neighbors, though the horses may do but little more work. Through economical feeding the cost of horse labor may be greatly reduced.

To reduce the cost of feed to a minimum, idle horses and those at light work must be wintered economically, largely on cheap feeds, such as straw, corn fodder or stover, or waste feed from stubble fields, stalk fields, and meadow aftermath. The efficient use of good pasture, including night pasture for farm work horses, will also reduce the cost of horse labor. (**758**) Horses that are pastured together usually handle better in big teams than when not accustomed to each other.

Improper shoeing or a poorly-fitting collar may reduce the capacity of a horse for work just as much as feeding an inadequate ration.

2. By raising good colts. Even though the direct profits to be made in raising colts may not be large, successful farmers, at least in the corn belt and westward, find it wise to raise well-bred colts to replace the older horses worn out or sold.

3. By reducing depreciation charges. Many farmers largely avoid the depreciation in the value of horses due to their becoming old, by raising good colts, starting them to work when 3 years old, and selling them after working 4 or 5 years, when they are yet in their prime and bring good prices.

4. By having the farm of adequate size. When a farm is too small, neither horse nor man labor can be utilized most efficiently.

5. By securing an even distribution of horse labor. The crop rotation should be so planned that the horse labor will be distributed as evenly as possible throughout the year. When the rotation is poorly planned, the peak load of horse labor that is needed will be much greater than under a wise rotation. This will necessitate the keeping of extra horses, merely for this peak load. An important advantage of livestock farming is that it provides productive labor for horses, as well as for men, during the winter.

6. By efficient use of horses. The good farm manager will see that his fields are so laid out, and buildings, yards, paddocks, and lanes so arranged that just as much labor as possible is saved, both of men and horses. Furthermore, he will save much man labor by having gang plows, and harrows, drills, cultivators, etc., of large size, so that teams of 3 horses or more can be used. By means of the improved multiple hitches, which have been brought to public attention largely through the work of Dinsmore of the Horse Association of America and of the agricultural colleges, a team of 5 or even more horses can be readily driven by one man.[40]

As Robbins well states, a good slogan is: "More horses to the plow and fewer in the pasture."[41] He points out that in the past many corn-belt farmers have worked only four horses to a plow or other tillage implement, and have had to rest the team much of the time, while in the pasture were idle horses. If the implement pulls so hard that the horses must be rested very frequently, it usually pays well to add more horses to the team.

A farmer who is a good manager will also be foresighted in his work and will not allow tasks which can be done just as well at some other time to interfere with the peak loads of planting, cultivating, and harvesting the crops, all of which cannot be delayed without serious loss. For instance, by doing considerable plowing in the fall, the peak load in the spring can be reduced and often one or more horses dispensed with. Last, but not least, he will keep no more than the minimum number of work horses necessary to meet efficiently the peak load of horse labor during the year.

7. By controlling internal parasites. Many horses and mules are badly rundown in condition and even unfit for work as a result of severe infestation with internal parasites. Demonstrations recently conducted on more than 8,600 farms in Illinois show the great improvement that results from the eradication and control of internal parasites, especially bots, round worms (ascarids), and palisade worms (strongyles).[42]

Proper treatment with suitable vermifuges produced striking improvement in the condition of horses seriously affected with parasites and greatly reduced the trouble from colic. Many horses that were unfit for work were restored to usefulness. The results also showed clearly that when horses are badly infested with parasites, much feed is wasted, due to the drain on them by the parasites. Since there is more danger to horses in administering doses of a vermifuge than in the case of other stock, the treatment had best be given by a veterinarian.

718. The horse vs. the tractor.—Whether or not it will be economical to purchase a tractor to replace some of the work horses on their farms, is a problem that has perplexed many farmers. Though each farm is an individual problem, the numerous economic studies of this question have shown the general principles which should be considered in making a decision.[43]

Before buying a tractor, a farmer should be sure that the purchase will be a profitable investment under his own conditions. If his capital is limited, even if he thinks that using a tractor will be economical, he should consider whether a tractor will increase his net income over a term of years as much as might some other purchase. Thus, for a dairyman, perhaps a bred-for-production, purebred dairy bull would be a wiser investment.

It should be borne in mind that horses use feed which is produced for the most part on the farm, and that horse labor requires very little cash expenditure. Horses can easily be reproduced on the farm, and the average useful life of a horse is greater than that of a tractor. Horses are able to develop great reserve power for emergencies and temporary overloads, are adapted to all the types of draft work, and do not require constant attention in guiding them. They are usually handled much more successfully by hired help than is a tractor.

One of the chief advantages of a tractor is its ability to do heavy work, such as plowing and the preparation of land, in a shorter time than it can be done with horses, thus permitting the planting of crops at just the right time. This advantage can, however, be largely gained with horses by using teams of three or more animals with suitable plows and other implements.

Perhaps the chief advantage in the use of a tractor comes in the actual displacement of horses. It also relieves the horses which cannot be displaced of some of the heaviest work during the rush seasons, so that they may need a little less feed. In nearly all the surveys conducted in various parts of the United States the actual reduction in numbers of horses on farms due to the use of a tractor has been found to be less than often supposed. The reduction in horses has usually been only from 1.5 to 2.5 animals per farm. The farms included in these surveys have commonly been large units of 200 acres or more. The "general purpose" tractor, which may be used for cultivation and other work for which the older types were not adapted, makes possible a somewhat greater displacement of horses.

Generally a tractor will save some hired labor, but the amount of this saving will depend on whether the peak load of man labor comes at the same time as the peak load of horse or tractor labor. Commonly claims are made that a tractor will increase crop yields through deeper plowing, more thorough preparation of the seed bed, and planting of the crop at the right time. In some of the surveys the farmers have reported a slight increase in yields, but in others no such increase has been apparent. In a few cases decreases in yields were mentioned, due to the tractor packing the soil when too damp.

On the average, farm tractors are used only about 30 to 50 days in a year, including both draft and belt work. Since depreciation and interest are large items, the cost per hour of tractor work is high when the amount of use is low. The entire yearly cost of using a farm tractor will vary widely, depending on many factors, especially on the initial price of the tractor, its durability, and the price of gasoline or kerosene. In recent surveys the yearly cost of using a two-plow tractor, including the expense for fuel, lubricants, repairs, depreciation, and interest on the investment has averaged about $230 to $300, not including the wages of the operator.

When the cost of feed and the price of horses are relatively low in comparison with the cost of tractors and their operation, farmers will rely entirely on horses on farms where they might otherwise find the use of a tractor economical. The cash expenses are less for farms operated with horses than for farms on which tractors are used. In a period when farm incomes and purchasing power are low, this is an important matter.

719. Mules.—The hardiness of mules and their ability to perform satisfactory service under adverse conditions have been leading factors in causing an increase in proportion of mules to horses in this country. **(683)** As is mentioned elsewhere, it is possible that mules also require less feed than horses to do a given amount of work. **(781)** Mules are generally more sensible in eating and less likely to gorge themselves than horses and hence are less subject to colic or founder. Indeed, mules are often fed at troughs, like cattle, and allowed to eat all they desire. Mules are not fastidious in their taste and will consume roughages which horses will refuse. They also endure hot weather better, and because of the peculiar shape of the foot and its thick strong wall and sole, are less subject than horses to foot lameness.

Mules have peculiarities of disposition, however. As Williams states: "The mule is an animal with possibly more eccentricities and undeniable virtues than any other domestic animal. The difficulty is to know how to handle the mule in order to keep the desirable qualities of his maternal ancestry in the foreground and to keep subservient the latent donkey characteristics. To treat consistently a conglomeration of stubbornness and willingness, temper and sullenness, contentment and restlessness, slyness and docility, faithfulness and waywardness, with no knowledge of which virtue or vice is going to assert itself next, is a problem which may well tax the qualities of the best horseman."[44]

Though mules will endure more neglect than horses, good care and feed will prove profitable. For feeding mules the same feeds may be used as in the case of horses, and the same principles apply in suiting the feed to the size of the animal and the severity of the work performed.

QUESTIONS

1. Discuss the present horse and mule situation in the United States.
2. Define *horse power*. How heavy a horse does it take to perform 1.0 horse power of work at steady labor?
3. What factors determine the amount of work a horse can do?
4. State the various types of work horses perform.
5. Discuss the influence of speed upon the efficiency with which horses perform work; the influence of grade.
6. What is the relative efficiency of large and small horses in doing work?
7. Discuss the efficiency of the horse as a motor.

8. Compare the digestibility of feeds by horses and by ruminants.
9. What is the net energy value of wheat straw for a work horse?
10. Discuss the maintenance requirements of horses. What may the result be when horses are maintained for long periods on nothing but straw?
11. Should horses be allowed to eat all the good-quality hay they will consume?
12. Approximately what is the relative value per pound of grain and hay for the production of work?
13. Discuss the nutrient requirements of horses under the following headings: (a) Protein; (b) salt; (c) other minerals; (d) vitamins; (e) water.
14. Are the following methods of preparing feed for horses advisable: (a) Grinding or crushing oats; (b) grinding corn; (c) grinding barley, wheat, or grain sorghum; (d) chopping hay; (e) grinding hay; (f) cooking feed; (g) fermenting feed?
15. Discuss the use of self-feeders in feeding horses and in feeding mules.
16. Mention some important points to be observed in caring for horses.
17. In what 7 ways may the cost of horse labor be reduced?
18. What general principles should be considered in deciding whether it is economical to buy a tractor to replace some of the work horses on a farm?
19. What advantages and disadvantages do mules have in comparison with horses?

REFERENCES

1. Pettet, U. S. Dept. of Commerce, Bureau of the Census, "The Farm Horse," 1933; Dinsmore, Horse and Mule Assoc. of America, "It Strikes You," 1933.
2. Collins and Caine, Iowa Bul. 240.
3. Ritzman, N. H. Buls. 262, 270.
4. Edmonds, Robbins, and Crawford, Ill. Rpts. 1928, 1929; Robbins and Crawford, Ill. Rpt. 1933; Collins and Caine Iowa Bul. 240; Rhoad, Amer. Soc. Anim. Prod., Proc. 1928.
5. Agg, Construction of Roads and Pavements, p. 343; Collins and Caine, Iowa Bul. 240; Wooley and Jones, Mo. Bul. 237.
6. Wooley and Jones, Mo. Bul. 237.
7. Zuntz, Landw. Jahrb., 27, 1898, Sup. III.
8. Hall and Brody, Mo. Res. Bul. 208; Procter, Brody, Jones and Chittenden, Mo. Res. Bul. 209.
9. Procter, Brody, Jones, and Chittenden, Mo. Res. Bul. 209.
10. Brackett, et al., Nebr. Bul. 277.
11. Lindsey and Archibald, Mass. Bul. 230; Armsby, The Nutrition of Farm Animals, pp. 604-606.
12. Grandeau and Le Clerc, Ann. Sci. Agron., 1884, II, p. 235; Colin, Traite Physiol. Comp. Anim. 1886, p. 822; Tangl, Pflüger's Arch. Physiol., 63, 1896, p. 545; Scheunert, Pflügers Arch. Physiol., 109, 1905, pp. 145-198.
13. Armsby, Nutrition of Farm Animals, p. 721.
14. Lindsey and Archibald, Mass. Bul. 230.
15. Grandeau and Le Clerc, L'alimentation du Cheval de Trait, 1883, III; Zuntz, Landw. Jahrb., 27, 1898, Sup. III.
16. Ritzman, N. H. Bul. 262.
17. Dunbar, S. D. Bul. 212.
18. Simms and Williams, Conn. (Storrs) Buls. 132, 173; Clark, Mont. Bul. 95.
19. Harper, N. Y. (Cornell) Bul. 437; Rpt. 1930; Simms and Williams, Conn. (Storrs) Bul. 173.
20. Hansson, Meddel. Centralanst. Försöksv. Jordbruk. (Sweden), No. 253, 1924.
21. Simms and Williams, Conn. (Storrs) Bul. 173; see also: Harvey, Amer. Soc. Anim. Prod., Proc. 1934.
22. Grandeau and Alekan, Ann. Sci. Agron., 1901, II, p. 38.
23. Harper, N. Y. (Cornell) Rpts. 1933, 1934, and information to the author.
24. Caine, Iowa Cir. 130, Iowa Rpt. 1929.
25. Scheunert, Schattke, and Weise, Biochem. Ztschr., 139, 1923, pp. 1-9; see also: Bang, K. Vet. og. Land., Denmark, Aarsskr. 1925; Niimi, Aoki, and Kato, Jour. Japan Soc. Vet. Sci., 6, 1927, Nos. 3, 4; 7, 1928, No. 3.
26. Cal. Rpt. 1928.
27. Hudson, Mich. Quar. Bul., 8, 1926, No. 3.
28. Templeton, Miss. Rpt. 1928.
29. Tangl., Landw. Vers. Stat., 57, 1902, p. 329.
30. Grandeau and LeClerc, Ann. Sci. Agron., 188, II, p. 276.
31. Hudson, Michigan. Quar. Bul. 16, 1933, No. 1.
32. Morrison, Fuller, Arneson, and Roche, Wis. Buls. 388, 396; Fuller and Roche, Wis. Bul. 405; Roche, Fuller, and Bohstedt, Wis. Res. Bul. 102; see also: Kuykendall, Miss. Bul. 305.
33. Harper, N. Y. (Cornell) Bul. 437.
34. Caine, Iowa Rpts. 1931, 1932.
35. Hudson, Mich. Quar. Buls. 15, 1933, No. 4; 16, 1934, No. 4; Kuykendall, Miss. Bul. 305.

36. McCampbell, Kan. Bul. 186.
37. Kuykendall, Miss. Bul. 305; Templeton, Miss. Bul. 270.
38. Templeton, Miss. Bul. 270.
39. Handschin, Andrews, and Rauchenstein, Ill. Bul. 231.
40. Dinsmore, Horses-Mules-Power-Profit, Horse Assoc. of America, Chicago, Ill.; Robbins, Ill., Cir. 355; Snyder and Collins, Iowa Exten. Bul. 140; Torrance and Harvey, Minn. Spec. Bul. 162; Wilson and Hallman, Mont. Exten. Pub. 70; Hauser, S. D. Exten. Cir. 271; Fuller, Wis. Cir. 244.
41. Robbins, Ill. Cir. 355.
42. Graham et al., Ill. Rpt. 1933; see also: Snell and Taggart, La Bul. 1932, La. Rpt. 1933.
43. Dargan, Ark. Bul. 280; Fletcher and Kinsman, Cal. Bul. 415; Fain et al., Ga. Agr. Col. Bul. 434; Johnston and Wills, Ill. Bul. 395; Ross, Shawl, and Andrews, Ill. Rpts. 1926, 1927; Lloyd and Hobson, Ind. Bul. 332; Ind. Rpt. 1930; Hopkins, Iowa Bul. 264; Saville and Reuss, La. Bul. 218; Cavert, Minn. Bul. 262; Schwantes and Pond, Minn. Bul. 280; Smith and Jones, Mo. Res. Bul. 197; Gilbert, N. Y. (Cornell) Bul. 506; Gross and Waller, N. J. Bul. 386; Morison, Ohio Bul. 383; Dowler, Ohio Bul. 481; Stephens, Okla. Bul. 208; Reynoldson and Tolley, U. S. Dept. Agr., Farmers' Buls. 1295, 1296, 1297, 1299, 1300; Tolley and Humphries, U. S. Dept. Agr. Bul. 1202; Washburn and Scudder, U. S. Dept. Agr. Bul. 1447; Reynoldson et al., U. S. Dept. Agr., Tech. Bul. 384.
44. Williams, U. S. Dept. Agr., Farmers' Bul. 1341.

CHAPTER XXII

FEEDS FOR HORSES AND MULES

I. Grains and Other Carbonaceous Concentrates

720. Many feeds suitable for horse and mule feeding.—In most localities the usual ration for horses and mules consists of only one or two kinds of grain, with no more variety in the roughages. Due to custom and prejudice, many persons insist that these particular feeds are by far the most economical and satisfactory. Yet, in traveling from one district or country to another, we find a large number of feeds successfully used for horses.

In the northern Mississippi Valley the ration generally consists of oats and corn with timothy hay or mixed hay for roughage, while in the South corn is the chief concentrate, fed with dried corn fodder, legume hay, and other roughages. A common ration on the Pacific Coast consists of crushed barley and hay from the cereals. In Europe various oil cakes and beans are often fed. In Arabia, Persia, and Egypt barley is the only grain, while in sections of India a kind of pea, called gram, is often fed. In some districts horses are fed such unusual feeds as the leaves of limes and grapevines, the seeds of the carob tree, bamboo leaves, and dried fish.

Since many feeds are well suited to horses and mules, careful attention should be given to the prices of the feeds that are available locally. A ration should be selected that will be as cheap as possible, yet entirely satisfactory for keeping the animals thrifty and efficient over a long period of usefulness.

It is more important for horses than with other classes of livestock that the feeds be of sound quality and not moldy, spoiled, or extremely dusty. This is because horses are especially apt to be injured by damaged feeds, and dusty hay or other forage greatly increases the trouble from heaves.

The composition and nutritive value of the many feeds that may be fed to horses and mules are discussed in detail in the respective chapters of Part II. In this chapter information is given on the special value and usefulness for horse and mule feeding of the concentrates and roughages most commonly used for this purpose. The grinding or crushing of the various grains and the cutting or grinding of hay are discussed in the preceding chapter.

It will be noted that most of the experiments reviewed in this chapter have been with horses, rather than with mules. However, the various feeds have the same general values for mules as for horses. Also, the same general principles apply in feeding them, as is pointed out in the preceding chapter. (**719**)

721. Oats, the standard grain for horses.—Oats are such an excellent grain for horses that they are the standard with which other concentrates are compared. (**528**) Due to the bulky hulls, oats are the safest of all grains for the horse. They form a loose mass in the stomach that can be easily digested, while such heavy feeds as corn, wheat, or barley tend to pack, sometimes causing colic. Even if a horse gains access to the grain bin and gorges on oats, there is much less danger of serious digestive trouble than in the case of the heavier grains.

Oats contain sufficient protein so that merely oats and grass hay make a well-balanced ration for mature work horses, without the addition of any protein supplement. Oats are rather low in total digestible nutrients and net energy, because of the hulls. Therefore, to keep work horses in condition, a somewhat greater weight of oats is required than of corn, hominy feed, or ground barley. For horses at very hard work, a mixture of oats with these more concentrated feeds is better than oats as the only grain.[1]

New or musty oats should be avoided in horse feeding. Some horses are inclined to eat their oats too rapidly, without thorough chewing. To prevent this, a little chopped hay may be mixed with the oats or some whole corn cobs or a few smooth stones can be placed in the feed box with the oats.

722. Grinding or crushing oats.—Whether or not it pays to grind or crush oats for horses is a question often discussed. In trials during two summers at the Wisconsin Station crushing oats for horses at hard work increased the value of the grain only about 5 per cent.[2] In other trials work horses have maintained their weights slightly better when fed ground oats than when receiving the same weight of whole oats.[3] We may conclude that for horses with good teeth the value of oats will be increased about 5 per cent by crushing or grinding. For horses with poor teeth and for foals up to 7 or 8 months of age, grinding or crushing oats is advisable.

When whole oats are mixed with cut hay or straw, the percentage of unmasticated kernels which pass through the digestive tract is smaller than when the oats are fed separately. Lavalard concluded from his extensive trials with cab, omnibus, and army horses in France that grinding oats did not pay when the oats were mixed with such cut roughage.[4]

723. Sheaf oats.—Sheaf oats (unthreshed oats in the bundle) are often an economical feed for horses, since the cost of threshing is saved and much of the straw is utilized.[5] If they are bright and well-cured, sheaf oats are surprisingly palatable to horses. Care should be taken not to feed musty sheaves. The amount of grain in the feed may be estimated from the fact that in a good crop of early northern-grown oats, the weights of grain and straw are usually about equal. To lessen the damage from mice, the sheaves should be stacked in the mow away from hay and from the sides of the building.

724. Oat feed.—This by-product of oat-meal manufacture may be used as a substitute for part of the hay or even for part of the grain in feeding work horses. Its use and value are discussed in Chapter XVII. (530)

725. Substitutes for oats.—Because of the popularity of oats, they are often higher in price, considering their actual feeding value, than other grains available for horse feeding. Fortunately, both science and practice show that other single grains, and also combinations of grains and other concentrates, may be substituted for oats without injury to the condition, the wind, the endurance, or even the spirit of horses.

The Arab horse, so renowned for mettle and endurance, is fed no oats, but chiefly barley. After experiments covering 35 years with over 30,000 horses, Lavalard, the great French authority on the feeding of horses, concluded that other feeds could often be substituted for oats with a great saving in cost of feed and without lowering the efficiency of the horses.[4]

The entire success attained with grain mixtures containing no oats, but which are properly balanced in nutrients and have the requisite bulk, shows that in making up rations for horses, just as with other animals, the prices of the different available feeds should always be considered. The various grains and by-products which may be used in place of oats are discussed in the following paragraphs. From the data there given one can easily determine what feeds are most economical for him to use, considering the local prices. In replacing oats with other feeds that are lower in protein, due care must be taken to add a protein supplement, if necessary to balance the ration.

726. Indian corn.—Next to oats, Indian corn is the grain most commonly used for horses and mules in America. On thousands of farms they are fed corn as the chief or the only grain, many scarcely knowing the taste of oats. Because corn usually costs less and has a higher feeding value than oats per 100 lbs., it is extensively used where large numbers of horses must be fed economically. (**512**)

As corn is a heavy, highly-concentrated feed, care must be taken to limit the amount to the needs of the animal. It will require about 15 per cent less corn than oats to keep work horses in condition, when the ration is properly balanced in protein content. When corn is fed as the chief grain, with hay from the grasses as the only roughage, a small amount of protein supplement should usually be added to balance the ration, unless the hay is early-cut and therefore higher than usual in protein. On the other hand, the experiments reviewed later show that corn, fed with legume hay or with mixed hay containing at least one-third legumes, makes a well-balanced, economical ration for work horses. In all cases changes from oats to corn should be made gradually. The objections often raised that horses fed corn are sluggish, sweat easily, and wear out earlier are probably due to neglect of these principles of feeding.

In the corn belt, corn is usually fed to horses on the cob or as shelled corn. No experiments have apparently been reported in which the exact saving through grinding ear corn or shelled corn for horses has been determined. In a trial with mules at the Mississippi Station grinding ear corn or grinding shelled corn increased the value about 10 per cent.[6] From the results of the experiments on grinding oats for horses, we should expect that the saving through grinding shelled corn for horses would not be greater than 5 per cent.

Ear corn is safer to feed than shelled corn, for it keeps better and horses eat it more slowly and chew it more thoroughly. If corn is ground for horses with poor teeth or those working long hours, it should be cracked or ground coarsely, for fine meal forms a mass in the stomach which is difficult to digest and may even cause colic.

Feeding corn in the form of corn-and-cob meal is preferable to using ground corn, for the cobs supply bulk, making the feed more like oats in physical nature. In a Minnesota test with work horses corn-and-cob meal was not so palatable as whole oats, but the weights of the horses were maintained on a slightly smaller amount of corn-and-cob meal than of oats.[7]

727. Corn and legume hay.—Many experienced horsemen have a decided prejudice against feeding corn as the only grain. However, experiments have shown definitely that it is satisfactory as the only concentrate for work horses and mules, if fed with legume hay so as to correct the deficiencies in protein and calcium. It may also be used successfully as the only concentrate with mixed hay, if there is at least one-third and preferably more of legumes in the hay.

One mule in each of two farm teams was fed shelled corn in a trial at the Missouri Station and the other one oats for 364 days, all receiving mixed clover-and-timothy hay.[8] The rations were then reversed and the feeding continued for another 364-day period. The mules fed corn maintained their weights slightly better than those fed oats, though each received 145 lbs. less grain and 75 lbs. less hay in a year than their oat-fed team mates. With oats at 40 cents and shelled corn at 50 cents a bushel, there was a saving of 21 per cent in the cost of feed for the corn-fed horses.

In a similar trial at the Ohio Station with farm horses fed either ear corn or oats with mixed clover-and-timothy hay, the corn-fed horses maintained their weights nearly as well as those fed oats, though they received only the same weight of ear corn, including cobs, as the others did of oats.[9] With corn at a price one-third higher than that of oats per bushel, feeding the ear corn in place of oats saved over one-fourth in the cost of feed. In both these trials the corn-fed animals endured hard work during hot weather as well as those fed oats and showed just as good health and vigor.

Excellent results were also secured at the Illinois and North Carolina Stations when corn was fed as the only grain with alfalfa or other legume hay, and at the Illinois Station when a combination of two-thirds ear corn and one-third oats was fed with mixed hay.[10]

Especially when the corn is fed as ground corn, instead of as ear corn or shelled corn, such a mixture as half corn and half oats may be more satisfactory than corn alone. There is more tendency for the horses to go off feed when they are fed ground corn as the only concentrate or as too large a part of the concentrates.[11]

728. Supplement needed with corn and grass hay.—A ration composed only of corn and such protein-poor roughage as timothy or prairie hay cut at the usual stage of maturity is rather too low in protein, even for work animals. While such a ration may be adequate for a limited time, it will generally pay to add a small amount of a protein supplement to balance the ration properly. For example, in a Kansas trial artillery horses, performing more severe labor than ordinary farm horses, lost weight during warm weather on a ration of 12 lbs. shelled corn and 14 lbs. prairie hay.[12] Others maintained their weights satisfactorily on 12 lbs. oats and 14 lbs. prairie hay. The results were also entirely satisfactory with a third group which was fed the same amount of hay and 6 lbs. corn, 3 lbs. wheat bran, and 1 lb. linseed meal. These horses received 2 lbs. less concentrates per head daily than those in the other groups.

A ration of only corn and grass hay may keep work animals in satisfactory condition and spirit, but more feed will usually be required than on a ration richer in protein. For example, in a trial at the Mississippi Station work mules fed only ear corn and Johnson grass hay maintained their weights fully as well and showed as good endurance as others fed ear corn with cottonseed meal or cottonseed meal and oats.[13] However, the mules on the ration of corn and grass hay, which had a nutritive ratio of 1:12, ate 7 per cent more concentrates and 8 per cent more hay than their team mates fed the better-balanced ration.

Mules fed corn with timothy and oat hay at the Kentucky Station did not show as thrifty an appearance as others fed a well-balanced mixture of 3 parts corn, 1 part wheat bran, and 1 part linseed meal, with the same kind of hay.[14] Similar results were secured by Lavalard in France with 17,000 army horses and 10,000 cab horses.[4] Feeding corn exclusively with hay from the grasses was found to depress the spirits of the horses, but a mixture of one-third corn and two-thirds oats was satisfactory.

As has been shown in the previous chapter, a mixture of 900 lbs. corn and only 100 lbs. oats was satisfactory for work horses in New York trials, when fed with good-quality timothy hay that had been cut reasonably early and therefore contained more protein than much of the timothy hay fed to horses. (701)

729. Hominy feed.—Hominy feed is about equal to shelled corn for horse feeding. It is somewhat more bulky than ground corn and keeps better in storage. A mixture of half hominy feed and half ground oats was slightly superior to half ground corn and half ground oats in New York trials.[1] (519)

730. Barley.—On the Pacific Coast and in Europe, Africa, and many parts of the Orient, barley is extensively fed to horses. (550-551) It should be crushed or ground (not too finely) for horses, as the grains are hard and small. Crushed barley was worth 10 per cent more than crushed oats per 100 lbs. in trials at the Wisconsin Station with farm horses at hard work.[15] On the other hand, whole barley is not worth so much per pound as whole oats, because horses do not masticate the grain completely.[16]

Since barley is not so bulky as oats, there may be more trouble from colic when it is fed as the only grain. This can be prevented by mixing with the barley some bulky feed, such as 15 per cent or more of wheat bran or cut hay or 25 per cent of ground oats.[17]

731. Wheat.—Although the price of sound wheat usually prohibits its use as a horse feed, that which has been frosted or otherwise damaged, if not moldy, may be fed with economy. Wheat should be ground coarsely or preferably crushed, and it should be fed only in moderate amounts and mixed with a bulky concentrate, such as oats or wheat bran, or with chopped hay to avoid digestive troubles. (537)

732. Rye.—Rye is not especially palatable to horses, and it is apt to produce digestive troubles if fed as the only grain or if the change to rye is made abruptly. (561) It is satisfactory when fed as only part of the concentrate mixture along with better-liked feed, and preferably with oats or some other bulky concentrate. As rye kernels are small and hard, they should be ground coarsely or preferably crushed. Most of the trouble experienced in feeding rye has doubtless been due to over-feeding or feeding it as the only concentrate.

733. Grain sorghums.—In the regions where they flourish, the various grain sorghums are extensively employed for feeding horses and are only slightly less valuable than corn.[18] (**565**) Being small and hard, they should be ground or crushed and if possible mixed with bran or middlings, for they tend to produce constipation. These grains may also be fed unthreshed in the heads or along with the forage.

734. Cane molasses.—Cane molasses, or blackstrap, is well-liked by horses, and even when molasses is higher in price than grain a quart or so a day is often fed as an appetizer or a conditioner.[19] (**641**) If one is forced to feed rather coarse and unpalatable hay or other forage, sprinkling diluted molasses over it will induce the horses to clean it up much better, thus cutting down the wastage.

Throughout the sugar-cane districts cane molasses is often the most economical source of carbohydrates for work animals. The molasses is usually mixed with cut hay or with ground grain or other concentrates, but it is sometimes fed in troughs or poured on uncut roughage. Mules were fed as much as 9 lbs. per head daily of cane molasses with satisfactory results in Louisiana trials.[20] However, the feeding of as heavy an allowance of molasses as this tended to increase sweating and "winding" of the mules, especially in hot weather. The molasses was mixed with cut hay and a reduced allowance of corn was fed in addition. When thus fed as a partial substitute for grain, the molasses was equal to corn, pound for pound, in feeding value. The use of molasses in this manner reduced the feed cost by 31 per cent. When mules were fed only molasses and chopped hay, without grain, they were not able to do heavy work in hot weather.

735. Beet molasses.—Because of its laxative properties, beet molasses must be fed only in limited amounts. (**642**) When not given in excess, it is satisfactory and is well liked by horses. The maximum amounts that should be fed daily, per 1,000 lbs. live weight, are about 4 or 6 lbs. for work horses and about 2.5 lbs. for driving horses. The molasses may be thinned with warm water and mixed with cut fodder or fed in such mixtures as molasses-beet pulp, or alfalfa-molasses meal. In trials with 130 hard-worked horses of a Budapest transportation company, good results were obtained with a ration, per 1,000 lbs. live weight, of 4.1 lbs. beet molasses mixed with 5.6 lbs. wheat bran and fed with 5.7 lbs. corn and an unlimited allowance of hay.[21] One pound of molasses replaced 0.78 lb. of corn.

736. Molasses feeds.—Various molasses feeds, especially those containing some alfalfa meal, are extensively used in feeding horses in some sections of the eastern and southern states. Good-quality feeds of this character are satisfactory when economical in price, for they are palatable to horses, have sufficient bulk to prevent trouble from colic, and are usually slightly laxative. (**646**)

In a Michigan test, two brands of commercial molasses feeds consisting chiefly of cane molasses, crushed oats, cracked corn, and alfalfa

FARM HORSES USED IN FEEDING TRIALS AT WISCONSIN

Experiments during two years with these horses proved that crushing oats makes a saving of only about 5 per ct. Some of the buildings of the College of Agriculture are shown in the background.

BARLEY IS A SATISFACTORY FEED FOR WORK HORSES

Other trials at the Wisconsin Station showed that crushed barley is worth more than crushed oats per pound for horses.

CORN IS THE CHIEF GRAIN FOR MANY CORN-BELT HORSES

Because of its lower cost and its higher feeding value per pound, corn is widely fed to horses in the corn belt.

OATS ARE UNEXCELLED FOR CARRIAGE OR SADDLE HORSES

While oats excel any other single grain or concentrate for such horses, a proper combination of other concentrates will give just as satisfactory results.

FILLIES EATING GRAIN ON PASTURE

It is important to keep foals growing properly by supplying enough concentrates. These may be chiefly the farm grains.

meal, had no appreciable advantage over a mixture of crushed oats and cracked corn, and the latter was cheaper.[22] The molasses feeds sometimes became sour or caked in the sacks.

737. Dried beet pulp.—Dried beet pulp is often refused by horses when fed alone, but when mixed with other concentrates it may be used as a portion of the ration, if not too high in price compared with its feeding value. (644) Allowances of 5 to 6.6 lbs. per head daily have given good results in Europe. •

738. Sugar.—Small amounts of sugar have occasionally been recommended for horses. When 0.5 lb. of sugar was substituted for 2.0 lbs. of oats in a ration of oats and prairie hay in a Kansas trial, the horses fed sugar showed a greater tendency to sweat, although having good appetites and excellent coats of hair.[12] It was concluded that while a small amount of sugar may be fed occasionally as a conditioner, it is not an economical substitute for the various grains ordinarily available.

739. Other concentrates low in protein.—In addition to the cereals and other low-protein concentrates that have been discussed in this chapter, several other feeds of this nature are satisfactory for horses and mules. These include emmer, ground millet seed, ground rough rice, brewers' rice, and ground buckwheat. For information on these the reader is referred to Part II of this volume.

II. Protein-rich Concentrates

740. Wheat bran.—Wheat bran is one of the most useful feeds for horses, because of its bulky nature and mild laxative properties. (542) If not more freely provided, its use once a week is desirable. When horses are fed grain as the only concentrate on work days, it is a good plan to feed them on Sundays and other idle days a mixture of one-third bran with two-thirds oats or other grain.

Bran is excellent as a part of the ration for brood mares, foals, and stallions. In case of constipation, a wet bran mash may be used, which has a more pronounced laxative effect than dry bran fed in mixture with other feed. A wet bran mash is often prepared by pouring hot water over the bran and letting it stand for a half hour or more before feeding. As the immediate effect of a bran mash may be somewhat weakening, it should be given at night and preferably before a day of rest.

When bran is cheap, it may be an economical substitute for part of the grain in the ration. Fed with timothy hay, a mixture of equal weights of bran and corn was found equal to one of half oats and half corn in a New Hampshire test.[23] When bran is fed in large amounts, it should be borne in mind that it is very low in calcium, although it is high in phosphorus. Legume hay will make good this calcium deficiency.

741. Wheat middlings; wheat shorts.—Though furnishing more nutrients than bran, wheat middlings or shorts are not so desirable for horses, because of their heavier character. (543) When fed to horses, they should be mixed with bulky feeds and should not form over one-fourth the concentrates, as they may tend to produce colic if fed in too large amounts.

742. Linseed meal.—Linseed meal, rich in protein and having tonic and somewhat laxative properties, is an excellent supplement for rations low in protein. (591) Not over 1 to 1.5 lbs. per head daily are needed to balance such a ration as corn and timothy hay for work horses. Linseed meal is useful for bringing into condition run-down horses with rough coats, and it gives bloom and finish in fitting horses for show or sale.

In a trial with 1,170-lb. artillery horses at the Kansas Station, excellent results were secured with a ration of 1 lb. linseed meal, 4 lbs. oats, 6 lbs. corn, and 12 lbs. prairie hay.[12] As less was needed to balance the ration, linseed meal was considerably more economical as a supplement than wheat bran. In a trial at the Iowa Station with 3 teams of farm horses a mixture of 1 part oil meal and 10 parts shelled corn, fed with timothy hay, was too laxative for horses at hard work in summer.[24] A mixture of 1 part oil meal, 4 parts oats, and 12 parts corn proved as satisfactory as one of 6 parts oats and 4 parts corn, and it was cheaper than the latter mixture.

743. Cottonseed meal.—Cottonseed meal is often used, especially in the South, as a protein supplement in rations for horses and mules. **(581-584)** In several experiments satisfactory results have been secured when it has been thus fed.[25] A rule sometimes followed is to feed not over 1 lb. of cottonseed meal daily per 1,000 lbs. live weight. However, horses and mules were fed as much as 2 lbs. per head daily for long periods with entire success in Texas trials with a total of more than 90 animals.[26] Work stock and also growing colts and brood mares were included in the experiments. In these trials pasture was provided during a considerable part of the year, and a mineral supplement supplying calcium was included in the rations. In Mississippi trials, 3 lbs. of cottonseed meal daily per 1,000 lbs. live weight were fed to work mules with satisfactory results.[27]

When cottonseed meal is added to a ration low in protein, it is worth considerably more per pound than corn or other grain. Such balancing of the ration improves the condition and appearance of the horses or mules. Using cottonseed meal as a large part of the concentrates is not safe, as it may cause serious digestive disturbances because of its heavy nature. Also, it may be poisonous when fed in too large amounts. Only bright, high-grade meal should be fed to horses or mules.

As cottonseed meal is not particularly relished by horses, it should be mixed with better-liked feeds. If more than 1.0 to 1.5 lbs. daily are fed, it is a good plan to mix it with a bulky feed, such as oats, bran, or corn-and-cob meal. It is best to feed not over one-fourth pound per head daily at first and gradually increase the allowance as the horses become accustomed to it.

744. Legume seeds.—Soybeans, field peas, cowpeas, and horse beans may all be used in limited amounts as protein supplements for horses. All these legume seeds should be ground. They should not form over one-third the concentrate mixture, else they may cause digestive trouble, owing to their heavy nature. Farmers have reported that feeding a small amount of soybeans to horses in the spring seems to have the same effect as linseed meal, in making their hair smooth and sleek.[28] In Europe horse beans and other varieties of beans are extensively used in horse feeding.

745. Miscellaneous protein-rich concentrates.—*Gluten feed* is most commonly used for dairy cattle, but it may be fed to horses in limited amounts, mixed with better-liked feeds, as a protein supplement to balance the ration. (523)

Gluten meal was used successfully as a supplement to corn meal in a trial at the Iowa Station, but it proved rather unpalatable to horses.[24] (524)

Brewers' dried grains, though most commonly fed to dairy cattle, are sometimes an economical substitute for oats in horse feeding. A good quality of brewers' dried grains is equal, pound for pound, to oats in feeding value. (554)

Distillers' dried grains have given satisfactory results when fed as not over one-fourth of the concentrate allowance to horses. (648)

Coconut meal is a safe, though rather unpalatable, feed for horses. It may replace oats to the extent of one-fourth to one-half the concentrates when economy justifies the measure. (607)

Peanut meal can be fed very satisfactorily to horses as a protein supplement. High-grade peanut meal is as rich in protein as is cottonseed meal, so not more than 1 to 1.5 lbs. per head daily will be needed to balance a ration low in protein. (598)

Oil cakes and meals from sunflower seed, rape seed, sesame seed, etc. are fed to horses in Europe in quantities of 2.2 to 4.4 lbs. per horse daily with good results.

Tankage and *blood meal* may be useful for run-down, thin horses, 1 to 2 lbs. of tankage or 1 lb. of blood meal per head daily being used. As such animal by-products are unpalatable to horses, they must be mixed with well-liked feeds. (629, 632)

Velvet bean feed was found satisfactory for horses at the Massachusetts Station when forming about one-sixth of the concentrate mixture.[29] (605)

III. Hay and Other Dry Roughages

746. Proportion and amount of roughage.—The injurious effects of feeding too much hay or other roughage to horses are pointed out in the preceding chapter. (699) Information is also there given on the relative value of hay and of concentrates for the production of work.

It is not advisable to feed new hay to horses until it has passed through the sweat in the mow or the stack, and has cooled off.

747. Timothy hay.—Timothy is the standard hay for horses over a large part of the northern states and in eastern Canada. (449) Its popularity and wide use for horses are due to the ease of its culture and the readiness with which it can be cured into bright hay, free from dust or mold. Experiments have shown that for work horses, legume hay or mixed hay is usually more economical than pure timothy. This is because the allowance of grain can be reduced somewhat when these hays are fed, for they are higher than timothy in digestible nutrients.

The actual nutritive value of timothy hay much more nearly approaches that of legume hay for feeding work horses than it does for any other class of stock. The low percentage of protein in timothy hay is of less importance in feeding work horses, because they require relatively little of this nutrient. For this same reason, timothy hay is a better feed for work horses than it is for colts or brood mares, which need an abundance of protein.

While timothy cut too early makes "washy" hay for work horses, it should not be allowed to stand after full bloom, or it will become woody and indigestible. Much more timothy hay is cut too late than too early.

748. Cereal hay.—On the Pacific Coast the cereal hays—barley, wild oats, wheat, etc.—are extensively used for horses, and in the Rocky Mountain region oat hay is of considerable importance. (455) Hay from cereals can often be advantageously employed in many other sections of the country, as it is about equal to timothy for horses. When cereal hay contains much grain, the amount of concentrates fed should be reduced accordingly.

The use of sheaf oats for horses has been discussed earlier in this chapter.

749. Other grass hays.—*Prairie hay* from the wild grasses is an excellent roughage for horses throughout the western states, being but slightly less valuable than timothy.[12] (456)

Brome hay, a common roughage in the northern plains region, is about equal to timothy.[30] (454)

Millet hay from Hungarian grass, Japanese millet, etc., is satisfactory for horses, if cut before it is mature and if fed as only half the roughage. (460) When fed as the only roughage to horses for long periods, millet hay has produced serious lameness and swelling of the joints and has increased the action of the kidneys.[31] The latter was perhaps due to a considerable amount of millet seed in the hay, as it is claimed that these have a harmful effect on the kidneys.[32]

Sudan grass hay is palatable to horses and makes a satisfactory roughage for them, much superior to millet hay. (458)

Bermuda grass hay and *Johnson grass hay* are southern hay crops which are excellent for work horses and mules, being about equal to timothy hay in value.[33] (461, 464)

750. Corn fodder and corn stover.—Properly-cured corn fodder (especially that grown thickly for fodder) or even bright corn stover is a satisfactory substitute for timothy hay in feeding idle horses or those at moderate work, and for brood mares, stallions, and growing colts. When well cured and not damaged by weathering, these feeds are palatable and usually quite free from dust. To reduce the waste, it is best to cut or shred fodder or stover. The portion of good corn fodder or stover that is actually eaten is about equal to timothy hay in feeding value. There will usually be considerable refuse in feeding fodder or stover, however, even when it is cut or shredded. This refuse may be used for bedding.

An excellent and economical roughage combination for wintering farm horses is half corn fodder or stover and half legume hay.[34] For idle horses, no grain will be needed in addition, except for a few weeks before the spring work begins.

751. Sorghum fodder or hay.—Forage from the sweet sorghums, when properly cured, is superior to corn forage for horses. It usually deteriorates rapidly in value after midwinter unless well cured and kept dry. Moldy, decayed sorghum forage is especially dangerous to horses. Forage from the grain sorghums, though not so palatable as that from the sweet sorghums, is extensively used in the southwestern states.

752. Straw.—Because of its high content of fiber and consequent low value for the production of work, but little straw should be fed to hard-worked horses. On the other hand, horses doing little or no work and having ample time for chewing and digesting their feed may be wintered largely on bright straw, instead of more-expensive hay.

The saving that can be made through the use of straw and other cheap roughage in wintering horses is well shown in a trial at the Michigan Station.[35] The cost of feed was reduced more than 40 per cent and the horses maintained their weights better, when a ration of oat straw and shredded corn stover, fed with roots and a suitable concentrate mixture consisting largely of ear corn, was substituted for a ration of timothy hay and oats. Farm horses working 5.5 hours a day on the average were kept in satisfactory condition during the winter in a Missouri trial on 14.3 lbs. oat straw per head daily as the only roughage, fed with 14.8 lbs. corn-and-cob meal and 1.7 lbs. linseed meal.[36] Adding a little legume hay to such a ration would be advisable, to supply more calcium and vitamins.

Horses should not be wintered on straw or stover only, for such feeds are too low in protein, in calcium and phosphorus, and even in digestible nutrients to form the sole feed, even of idle horses. Such a ration may injure the health of the horses, as is pointed out in the preceding chapter. (**698**)

753. Legume hay.—Well-cured legume hay is entirely satisfactory for horses if it is properly fed. The common prejudice against legume hay for horse feeding is due to the use of poor-quality hay or to feeding an excessive amount. Horses are especially fond of good legume hay, and therefore they must not be allowed to eat all they desire. The amount fed should be limited strictly to their requirements, as has been pointed out in the previous chapter. (**699**) Since alfalfa and clover hay are higher in digestible nutrients than timothy hay, less is needed to replace a given amount of timothy.

It is important that legume hay for horses be bright and well cured, for that which is loaded with mold or dust and otherwise injured in quality may cause heaves. Dampening dusty hay before feeding helps somewhat, but it is far better to prevent the mold and dust by proper curing.

754. Red clover hay.—Because red clover hay is often carelessly made and dusty, it is disliked by many horsemen, particularly for feeding roadsters. This objection does not apply to clean properly-cured clover hay. For driving horses, clover hay can be fed with timothy hay or bright straw, while for horses at ordinary farm work it may form the only roughage. (**382**)

The value of this hay for farm horses is shown by an Illinois trial in which one horse in each of 6 teams received clover hay and the other an equal amount of timothy.[37] The horses in each group were fed the same amount of a mixture of corn, oats, wheat bran, and linseed meal, so the timothy-hay ration was well balanced in protein content. After 28 weeks the rations were reversed and the trial continued for 20 weeks.

The horses maintained their weights better on the clover-hay ration than on the timothy-hay ration. Also, although most of the teamsters were prejudiced in favor of timothy hay at the beginning, they later reported that they could observe no difference in the spirit of the horses or in their ability to endure hot weather. The horses fed clover hay had glossier coats and their bowels were looser, but not objectionably so for doing hard work.

Second-crop clover hay may cause slobbering, for some unknown reason.

755. Alfalfa hay.—Experience on thousands of farms in the western part of the United States, where alfalfa hay has been fed for many years as the only roughage to horses, shows that it is economical and entirely satisfactory when properly fed. With the spread of alfalfa growing into the eastern states, its use for horses is increasing there. (373)

Alfalfa hay for horses should be free from dust or mold and should not be cut until about full bloom, as hay cut earlier may be too laxative for horses. Alfalfa is very palatable to horses, and therefore the amount fed must be strictly limited, or they will eat too much. (699) Not over 1.0 to 1.1 lbs. daily per 100 lbs. live weight should be fed work horses. Although alfalfa hay can be fed with entire success to work horses as the only roughage, some prefer to use it for but one-third to one-half the daily allowance of hay, the remainder being hay from the grasses.[38]

The good results which can be secured when alfalfa hay is used as the only hay for work horses are well shown in a trial at the Michigan Station which covered an entire year.[39] One horse in each of 8 teams doing farm work was fed first-cutting alfalfa hay and ear corn, and their teammates were fed timothy hay, oats, and ear corn. The rations were reversed at the end of 13 weeks and the experiment was then continued for the rest of the year. The results on each ration are shown in the table:

Alfalfa versus timothy hay for work horses

Average ration		Av. gain or loss per head Lbs.	Daily cost of feed per head Cents
Alfalfa-fed horses			
Alfalfa hay, 17.9 lbs.	Ear corn, 12.2 lbs.....	21	31.0
Timothy-fed horses			
Timothy hay, 19.6 lbs.	Oats, 6.2 lbs		
	Ear corn, 8.0 lbs......	—17	36.5

The alfalfa-fed horses gained 21 lbs. on the average during the year, while the timothy-fed horses lost 17 lbs., though they were fed 1.7 lbs. more hay and 2.0 lbs. more grain a day. The daily cost of feed for the timothy-fed horses was 5.5 cents more than for those fed alfalfa, and the value of the timothy hay for the horses was only 67 per cent as much per ton as that of the alfalfa hay. Similar favorable results with alfalfa hay for farm horses have been secured in several other experiments.[40]

That alfalfa hay may be used successfully even for horses doing hard work at a rapid pace, is shown in a trial with artillery horses conducted by the Kansas Station.[12] These horses performed a considerable part of their work at the trot and no small part at a gallop. One lot of horses, fed an average of 10 lbs. alfalfa hay, 8 lbs. shelled corn, and 2 lbs. oats, gained 25.6 lbs. per head during 140 days, while others, fed 14 lbs. timothy hay with 4 lbs. corn and 8 lbs. oats, lost an average of 7.7 lbs. The cost of the alfalfa ration was only about two-thirds that of the timothy ration, and the alfalfa-fed horses showed no shortness of wind, softness, or lack of endurance. First-quality alfalfa hay, bright and free from dust, is now even fed to race horses at some stables.

A common ration for idle horses in the West is alfalfa hay fed with no grain, but often with what straw the animals will eat.

756. Miscellaneous legume hays.—Hay from soybeans, cowpeas, field peas, sweet clover, lespedeza, and other legumes may be used with good results in feeding horses and mules, if it is well-cured and if no more is fed than is actually needed by the animals.

Soybean hay was worth 9 per cent more a ton than Johnson grass hay in 3 experiments at the Mississippi Station.[41] In these tests the mules in 5 or 6 teams were fed either soybean or Johnson grass hay with ear corn for 150 days, and then the rations were reversed and the experiment continued for a second period of the same length. (**398**)

Cowpea hay and corn-and-cob meal made a satisfactory work ration in a trial at the North Carolina Station.[42] (**401**)

Lespedeza hay was decidedly superior to timothy for growing mules at the Louisiana Station.[43] (**405**)

757. Mixed legume and grass hay.—Excellent hay for horses is furnished by well-cured mixed clover-and-timothy, mixed alfalfa-and-timothy hay, or similar combinations. Such hay possesses much of the good qualities for horses of both timothy hay and legume hay. If one has various lots of mixed hay containing differing proportions of legumes, it is wise to use for work horses the hay which contains less legumes, and to feed the hay higher in legumes and therefore richer in protein to colts, brood mares, dairy cattle, beef cattle, or sheep. This is because these other classes of stock need much more protein than do work horses.

IV. Pasture and Other Succulent Feeds

758. Pasture.—Good pasture is exceedingly important for colts and brood mares. Also, through the well-planned use of pasture the cost of keeping farm work horses can usually be considerably reduced. For early spring and for fall pasture, bluegrass or other permanent pasture is excellent. Mixed pasture that contains a considerable proportion of white clover or other legumes is even better than grass alone.

The use of pastures grown in the regular crop rotation, instead of parasite-infested permanent pasture, will help greatly to reduce infestation with internal parasites. Since horses are much less subject to bloat than are cattle or sheep, legume pasture is excellent for them. Alfalfa, red clover, or sweet clover pasture is very satisfactory for horses. In an Illinois test weanling foals on sweet clover pasture seemed to crave some dry carbonaceous feed, however, and sheaf oats were used both for this purpose and to supply some grain.[44]

Alsike clover may sometimes apparently be the cause of a serious disease known as "big liver," or "liver disease," in horses, if it forms the chief part of the pasturage.[45]

Whenever farm work horses are idle during the pasture season, they should be turned to pasture, thus reducing the labor and expense to a minimum. Even when horses are worked regularly, it is economy to turn them out at night, after they have eaten their grain, into a nearby pasture which has been fertilized so that there is plenty of grass. This practice not only reduces the cost of feed but also helps to keep the horses thrifty and to lessen the trouble from swollen legs. During hot weather, horses are much more comfortable at night when turned out to pasture than when confined in stalls. Pasturing work horses at night may increase the tendency to sweat while at work, but this is not of great importance when the benefits are considered.

In the spring, work horses should not be turned on pasture too early in the season, as the grass is then too "washy" and laxative. Also, it is best to accustom work horses to pasture gradually, and the pasturing should be regular, and not intermittent. To avoid too laxative a condition when work horses are pastured, the other feeds should not be of a laxative nature.

After the harvest is over in the fall, horses not needed for work should be turned to pasture. They should have access to an enclosed shed and should have some good-quality dry roughage, fed in a rack, to supplement such feed as they can secure from stalk and stubble fields and meadows. Where there is little snow in winter, idle horses can get no small part of their winter feed by cleaning up such fields.

Colts and also brood mares which are not at work should be on good pasture throughout the growing season, care being taken that they actually have enough feed to keep them thrifty. City horses are often turned on pasture so that their feet may recover from the ill effects of hard pavements.

759. Corn silage.—While silage is fed to horses much less frequently than to cattle or sheep, many farmers have had success in using it. (**426**) Only silage of high quality, free from decay or mold, should ever be fed to horses, for they are much more susceptible to poisoning from spoiled silage than are cattle or even sheep. Trouble from this source seems to be more common during warm spells in early spring, probably due to spoilage through carelessness in handling the silage.[46]

Silage should not be the only roughage for horses, but it may replace one-third to one-half the hay usually fed. The animals should be accustomed to it gradually, and certain horses may not take to it readily at first. Some advise feeding no more than 10 to 15 lbs. per head daily, although much larger allowances have been fed satisfactorily.[47]

Because of its bulky nature, horses at hard work cannot consume much silage, but it is well suited to idle horses, brood mares, and growing colts. If the silage contains much corn, the amount of grain that is fed should be reduced accordingly. In trials at the Missouri Station idle brood mares averaging 1,593 lbs. in weight were wintered with economy on such rations as 16.8 lbs. corn silage and 8.0 lbs. of mixed hay per head daily.[48] A ration of 22.0 lbs. corn silage, 10.4 lbs. timothy hay, 8.4 lbs. oats, and 2.1 lbs. wheat bran was very satisfactory for wintering draft foals in a Wisconsin test.[49] Using the silage to replace part of the grain and hay commonly fed, made a saving of 20 per cent in the cost of feed and slightly increased the gains.

760. Wet beet pulp.—Wet beet pulp is unsuited for work horses, according to Pott, although it may be fed to idle horses at the rate of 22 to 44 lbs. per head daily.[50] (**643**) Larger quantities are said to be injurious. Colts were allowed constant access to pulp at a sugar-beet factory for several years without trouble arising.[51]

761. Roots; tubers; fruits; etc.—The only importance of roots for horse feeding in most sections of this country is as an aid to digestion, for the cereals generally furnish nutrients at a lower cost.

Carrots, especially relished by horses, are great favorites with horsemen when cost of keep is not considered. They may be fed whole or sliced, but if sliced, the pieces must be small enough so the horses will not choke on them. Though containing only half as much dry matter as corn silage, carrots were worth more than corn silage, pound for pound, for idle horses in a trial at the Michigan Station.[52] As has been stated previously, some advise feeding no carrots to brood mares for a few weeks before and after they foal. (478)

Potatoes may be fed, cooked or raw, in amounts up to 15 or 20 lbs. per head daily. (480)

Fresh fruit may sometimes be profitably fed in moderate amounts when there is no market for it, and dried fruits, slightly injured and therefore unsalable, have been successfully used for horses. (492)

QUESTIONS

1. Why are oats the standard grain for horse feeding?
2. Discuss the use for horses of corn with legume hay; of corn with non-legume roughage.
3. What is the value of hominy feed for horses in comparison with that of corn?
4. State the manner in which each of the following can be used satisfactorily in horse feeding: (a) Barley; (b) wheat; (c) rye; (d) grain sorghums.
5. Discuss the value and use of the following for horses and mules: (a) Cane molasses; (b) beet molasses; (c) molasses feeds; (d) dried beet pulp; (e) sugar.
6. How should wheat bran be used in horse feeding?
7. Why is linseed meal popular as a protein supplement for horses?
8. Discuss the use of cottonseed meal for horses and mules.
9. What other protein supplements are used for feeding horses or mules in your district?
10. Why is timothy hay so popular for horse feeding?
11. Discuss the value of any of the following that are of importance for horses or mules in your locality: (a) Cereal hay; (b) prairie hay; (c) brome hay; (d) millet hay; (e) Sudan grass hay; (f) Bermuda grass hay; (g) Johnson grass hay.
12. Discuss the use of corn fodder and corn stover; of sorghum fodder or hay.
13. How can straw be economically used in horse feeding?
14. What are the merits and the limitations of legume hay for horses and mules?
15. Discuss the value of red clover hay for horses.
16. What have experiments shown concerning the value of alfalfa hay for horses?
17. If any of the following are used for horses or mules in your region, state their value for this purpose: (a) Soybean hay; (b) cowpea hay; (c) lespedeza hay.
18. Suppose a dairy farmer has one mow of mixed hay containing over one-half clover and another mow of mixed hay containing only one-third clover. Which hay should he feed to his cows and which to his work horses?
19. Discuss the importance and use of pasture for horses.
20. What limitations does corn silage have as a feed for horses or mules?

REFERENCES

1. Harper, N. Y. (Cornell) Bul. 437.
2. Morrison, Fuller, and Bohstedt, Wis. Bul. 302.
3. Harper, N. Y. (Cornell) Bul. 437; Tinline, Canada Expt. Farms, Scott, Saskatchewan, Sta., Rpt. Supt. 1922.
4. Lavalard, Expt. Sta. Rec., 12, 1900, p. 12.
5. Edmonds and Crawford, Ill. Cir. 424.
6. Templeton, Miss. Bul. 270.
7. Harvey, Amer. Soc. Anim. Prod., Proc. 1934.
8. Trowbridge, Mo. Cir. 125.
9. Carmichael, Ohio, Bul. 195.
10. Edmonds and Kammlade, Ill. Bul. 238; Gray and Hostetler, N. C. Dept. Agr. Bul., Sept., 1922.

11. Edmonds and Kammlade, Ill. Bul. 238; Harper, N. Y. (Cornell) Bul. 437.
12. McCampbell, Kan. Bul. 186.
13. Templeton, Miss. Bul. 244.
14. Hooper and Anderson, Ky. Bul. 176.
15. Morrison, Fuller, and Bohstedt, Wis. Bul. 319, pp. 68-9.
16. Shepperd, N. D. Bul. 45; Lavalard, Expt. Sta. Rec., 12, 1900, p. 14.
17. Harper, N. Y. (Cornell) Rpt. 1931, p. 32.
18. Kuykendall, Miss. Bul. 305.
19. Simms, Conn. (Storrs) Bul. 132.
20. Snell and Taggart, La. Bul. 230; see also; Gramlich, U. S. Dept. Agr., mimeo.
    rpt.; Dalrymple, La. Bul. 86.
21. Weiser and Zaitschek, Landw. Jahrb., 37, 1908, pp. 138-149.
22. Hudson, Mich. Quar. Bul. 16, 1933, No. 1.
23. Burkett, N. H. Bul. 82.
24. Kennedy, Robbins, and Kildee, Iowa Bul. 109.
25. Kennedy, Robbins, and Kildee, Iowa Bul. 109; Templeton, Miss. Bul. 244; Godbey,
    S. C. Rpts. 1929, 1930; Sheets and Thompson, U. S. Dept. Agr., Farmers'
    Bul. 1179.
26. Williams, J. M. Jones, and J. H. Jones, Tex. Bul. 492.
27. Means, Miss. Rpt. 1932; Leveck, Miss. Sta., mimeo. rpt.
28. Edmonds and Crawford, Ill. Cir. 369.
29. Lindsey, Mass. Bul. 188.
30. Shepperd, N. D. Bul. 45.
31. Hinebauch, N. D. Bul. 26.
32. Bell and Williams, U. S. D. A., Farmers' Bul. 1030.
33. Grimes and Taylor, Ala. Cir. 54; Lloyd, Miss. Station, information to the author.
34. Hudson, Mich. Quar. Bul., Vol. 10, No. 1, 1927.
35. Norton, Mich. Bul. 254.
36. Trowbridge, Mo. Buls. 163, 179.
37. Obrecht, Ill. Bul. 150.
38. Edmonds and Crawford, Ill. Cir. 424.
39. Hudson, Mich. Cir. Bul. 65.
40. Edmonds and Kammlade, Ill. Bul. 238; Obrecht, Ill. Bul. 150; Caine, Iowa Cir.
    130; Gramlich, Nebr. Exten. Bul. 28; Carroll, Utah Cir. 43; Faville, Wyo.
    Bul. 98.
41. Templeton, Miss. Bul. 270.
42. Burkett, N. C. Bul. 189.
43. Lloyd, La. Sta., information to the author.
44. Edmonds and Crawford, Ill. Bul. 292.
45. Schofield, Ontario, Canada, Veterinary College, Cir. 52.
46. Hadley, Wis. Bul. 352.
47. Ariz. Rpt. 1918.
48. Trowbridge and Chittenden, Mo. Bul. 210.
49. Fuller, Roche, and Bohstedt, Wis. Bul. 420.
50. Pott, Handb. Ernährung und Futtermittel, Vol. III, 1909, p. 299.
51. Clark, Utah Bul. 101.
52. Hudson, Mich. Rpt. 1926.

CHAPTER XXIII

FEEDING AND CARING FOR HORSES

I. Feeding Work Horses; Fattening and Fitting Horses

762. Importance of skill and good judgment.—Skill and good judgment enter into the success or failure of feeding and caring for horses even more than with other classes of stock. Under similar conditions, two men may secure widely different results. In one case the team has an action and style which at once show it to be in the best of condition. In the other, the lagging step, dull eye, and rough coat show better than words the lack of judgment in feeding and management. The unsatisfactory condition has not necessarily been brought about by any saving at the feed bin and hay mow. Indeed, the good horseman will usually feed his team the more economically.

The principles of successful horse feeding are, however, simple and easily understood. If the few necessary rules and precautions are observed, coupled with good judgment at all times, there should be no difficulty in maintaining horses in condition to work most efficiently.

763. Work horses.—The nutrient requirements of work horses and the general principles of feeding and caring for them have been discussed in Chapter XXI. If these principles are understood, it is relatively easy to feed horses efficiently. (**698-706**)

The amount of feed necessary for a work horse will depend on the size of the animal, on the severity of the work, and also on whether he is an easy or a hard keeper. As a general average, the total allowance of concentrates and hay should be from 2.0 to 2.5 lbs. daily per 100 lbs. live weight. The amounts of concentrates (including grain and any other concentrates) and of hay daily per 100 lbs. live weight for various degrees of work should be about as follows:

Hard work, 1.00 to 1.40 lbs. of concentrates and about 1 lb. of hay.
Medium work, 0.75 to 1.00 lb. of concentrates and 1.00 to 1.25 lbs. of hay.
Light work, 0.40 to 0.75 lb. of concentrates and 1.25 to 1.50 lbs. of hay.

A horse that is a hard keeper will need considerably more grain than an easy keeper when doing the same amount of work. Young horses that are still growing and also mares that are in the last half of pregnancy or those suckling foals will need more grain than other work horses.

Usually the amount of grain or other concentrates is divided equally into 3 feeds, and given at morning, noon, and night. It is best to feed only a small amount of hay in the morning, for a digestive tract distended with hay is a hindrance in hard work. A common plan is to feed about one-fourth the daily allowance of hay in the morning, one-fourth at noon, and one-half at night. Some omit the noon feeding and give one-third the hay in the morning and the remainder at night, when the horses have plenty of time to eat it.

The importance of pasture in reducing the cost of feeding farm work horses has been discussed in the preceding chapter. (**758**)

Horses that are inclined to bolt their grain, or eat it too rapidly, can be made to eat more slowly by placing several smooth stones about 3 inches in diameter or a few whole corn cobs in the feed box. Another method is to feed the grain well spread out in a large, flat feed box, or else to mix it with bran or chopped hay.

To avoid digestive troubles and possible deaths from azoturia, it is imperative that the allowance of grain for horses at hard work be reduced on idle days to 50 to 70 per cent of the amount usually fed. It is best to feed on such days in place of only grain, a mixture of two-thirds grain and one-third bran. Some feed a small allowance of grain at noon on idle days, with only a bran mash both morning and night. Others feed only a bran mash on Saturday night, and on Sundays and other idle days omit the noon feed of grain entirely.

On coming to the stable at noon, the work horse should have a drink of water, care being taken, if he is warm, that he does not drink too much. Before going to work, he should be watered again. If possible, an hour should be allowed for the mid-day meal, and many good horsemen remove the harness so the horse can eat his meal in comfort and rest easily. When the horse comes in after the day's labor, he should be given a drink, unharnessed at once, and when the sweat has dried, brushed well. Horses will also appreciate a drink in the evening after they have eaten most of their hay.

The same general principles apply in feeding and caring for mules as in the case of horses. (**719**)

764. Rations for work horses.—As a guide in working out economical rations adapted to local conditions, several example rations are given in Appendix Table VII for 1,200-pound horses which are at hard, medium, and light work and for horses which are idle. All these rations meet the requirements according to the Morrison feeding standards and should prove satisfactory in practice. With horses of other weights, the rations should be increased or decreased by approximately one-twelfth the amounts of feed shown, for each 100 lbs. the live weight differs from 1,200 lbs.

The following will illustrate the substitutions which may be made in these rations. Still others are discussed in the preceding chapter, which treats in detail the various feeds that are used for horses. Hay from other grasses may be substituted for timothy hay, usually pound for pound. The legume hay may be alfalfa, red clover, sweet clover, soybean, cowpea, lespedeza, etc. Fodder and stover from the sorghums may replace corn fodder and stover. For horses at work, straw had best be chopped and mixed with the concentrates.

Crushed or ground barley may be substituted for oats, one-tenth less being fed. If barley is fed as the only grain, it is best to add 15 per cent or more of bran or chopped hay to make the mixture more bulky, so as to prevent colic. Crushed or ground wheat or rye may be substituted for oats or corn, but these grains should not form more than one-third the grain mixture, on account of their heavy, pasty nature.

Cottonseed meal may replace linseed meal, not over about 2 lbs.

per head daily being fed. Wheat bran, gluten feed, peanut meal, and other protein-rich feeds may be substituted for linseed meal, the amount being increased proportionally in the case of bran, gluten feed, or other supplements which are lower than linseed meal in protein.

765. Wintering farm horses.—To reduce the cost, farm horses when idle during the winter should be maintained on roughages, with grain or other concentrates added only when necessary to balance the ration or to keep them from running down in condition. The roughages used for this purpose can often be those that are unsalable and not adapted to other stock. For example, there may be thus used the refuse stems from clover or alfalfa hay that has been fed to dairy cattle or to fattening cattle or sheep.

Idle horses can also get much of their feed in fall and early winter by grazing the aftermath in meadows or by cleaning up stalk and stubble fields. Straw or stover from corn or the sorghums can also form a considerable part of their ration, but care should be taken to supply some feeds higher in protein, minerals, and vitamins, or bad results may follow. (698) If not provided more liberally, it is wise to feed 5 lbs. per head of legume hay at least 3 times a week. Light grain feeding should begin a few weeks before spring work starts, to get the horses into such condition that they can do the hard work required at that time of the year.

Idle horses should be turned out daily for exercise in a lot, protected from the wind. If they have the run of fields during the winter, they should have access to a dry shed for shelter.

766. Fitting horses for the market; fitting for shows.—Many farmers do not realize that horses which are fattened or fitted before sale usually bring a sufficiently higher price to make this profitable. Horses that are thin and have unkempt, shaggy coats do not present an appearance that attracts most buyers, though they may actually be excellent animals. The market for horses is seasonal, and various types and weights of horses often sell best at different seasons. A farmer with horses to sell should therefore post himself as to when they will probably bring the highest price, and then fit them for sale at that time.

Some men have made a practice of buying horses in the fall after farm work is over and fattening them for market. The horses are gradually accustomed to a heavy grain ration, getting all they will clean up when on full feed. At this time some of the heaviest feeders will consume nearly twice as much as when at hard work, or about 2 lbs. of grain for every 100 lbs. live weight. Due to the forced feeding, surprising gains are often secured. Instances are reported where horses have gained 4 lbs. or even more per head daily for periods of about 2 months. While horses thus fattened often bring the best prices, such rapid and excessive fattening is of little benefit and may be injurious. When put to hard work, the horse quickly loses much of the soft flesh gained by such forcing.

The chief concentrates used in fattening horses are corn and oats, often with moderate allowances of such protein-rich feeds as wheat bran, linseed meal, or cottonseed meal added to balance the ration. Clover or alfalfa hay is commonly fed, for these hays are much superior to timothy hay for this purpose. In addition, silage of good quality may be advantageously fed.   At the Illinois Station[1] a ration of 8.6 lbs. corn, 8.6 lbs. oats, 2.4 lbs. wheat bran, 0.4 lb. linseed meal, and 13.7 lbs. clover hay gave excellent results in fattening horses.   A most successful ration for fattening 1,450-lb. horses at the Pennsylvania Station[2] was 12.3 lbs. shelled corn, 1.4 lbs. cottonseed meal, 16.9 lbs. corn silage, and 10.5 lbs. mixed hay.   Horses thus fattened require about the same amount of feed as fattening cattle for 100 lbs. gain in weight.

Horses which are being fattened should be allowed to run in paddocks for exercise, to avoid digestive troubles and to keep their legs from becoming stocked.   There is more risk in fattening horses than in fattening cattle, even without considering fluctuations in market price.   Heavily-fed horses kept in idleness are apt to become blemished or injured through playfulness, and the risk of sickness is greater than with other classes of stock.

All show horses should be in good flesh, draft classes especially. The advice above given for fattening horses will apply to fitting draft horses for show, except that they must be exercised daily to keep their muscles in good trim.   All show horses should be carefully fed, groomed, and exercised to bring them into proper "bloom."   Training also counts for much in the show ring.

II. FEED AND CARE OF THE LIGHT HORSE

767. Feed and care of carriage and saddle horses.—Style and action are of the greatest importance with these horses, economy of feeding standing second.   Many horsemen in this country still assert that the oat-fed horse exhibits mettle as from no other feed.   Though oats easily excel any other single grain or concentrate, there are numerous instances in which a properly-combined concentrate mixture has given just as good results.   From 8 to 10 lbs. of oats or their equivalent, divided into 3 feeds, should suffice for concentrates, the evening meal being the largest.   In case the horse is at all constipated, bran should be fed, dry or as a mash.

The hay is usually fed long, for the carriage or saddle horse has ample time for his meals.   From 10 to 12 lbs. of hay are a liberal allowance, bringing the total ration within 18 to 22 lbs.   The light horse must be trim in body and so cannot consume too much bulky feed, yet some roughage is always necessary.   With this class of horses the horseman must also guard against feeding too large amounts of such laxative feeds as clover and alfalfa hay or bran.

Light horses are usually overfed and exercised irregularly or too little, and mainly for these reasons their period of satisfactory service is often brief.   On days when they are not driven or ridden, the usual amount of roughage may be fed but the amount of grain should be reduced.

768. Feed and care of race horses.—The single requisite of speed makes the carrying of every pound of useless body weight, and more especially of feed, a serious matter in the management of the race horse. There is also to be considered the effect of the food on the character of the muscles formed from it, and especially on the nerve and mettle of the horse. Most horsemen agree in regarding oats as the one grain suitable for horses where speed is sought regardless of cost of food. While this opinion prevails in this country, we should remember that the Arab horse usually subsists upon barley.

For information on feeding the trotter we can draw from no better source than Woodruff, whose advice is here condensed.[3]

After weaning, trotting-bred colts should be fed about 2 lbs. of oats per day, with an unlimited allowance of hay. As the colt grows older the amount of oats should be increased to 4 lbs. for the yearling, 6 lbs. for the 2-year-old before training, and 8 to 12 lbs. for the colt 2 to 3 years old in training, an unlimited allowance of hay being given all this time.

When going into winter quarters, the feed of the trotter should be reduced fully one-half in order to prevent fattening. A few carrots may be given and a bran mash occasionally, with good clean, sweet hay. Horses whose legs must undergo blistering or firing should have more cooling feed, as mashes and carrots, with less oats, in order to reduce the tendency to feverish, inflammatory symptoms. Care must be taken not to permit the animal to get flabby or washy by too much soft food while undergoing treatment.

Horses turned out in the field should be fed oats twice a day, for the exposure increases the need of heat-giving food. In the spring when animals are shedding, bran mashes are in order to keep the bowels open.

With the beginning of the training season the feed should be increased to 8 or 10 lbs. of oats daily, in which case the horse wants less hay, but may still have all he will clean up unless he is a glutton. It is necessary to muzzle some greedy horses to prevent their eating the bedding long before the time for the race. No carrots or corn should now be given, unless it is necessary to induce a light feeder to eat his oats by mixing a handful of corn with them.

During the jogging and after preparation, a bran mash about once a week, depending on the condition of the horse's bowels, will be proper. The trainer must never relax his vigilant observation, or let his judgment sleep. During the fast work, preparatory to the coming trial, the horse will be put upon his largest allowance of strong food. Some will not eat more than 8 or 10 lbs. of oats a day; and it is necessary that such light feeders be not over worked. A good feeder ought to have about 12 to 13 lbs. of oats with a fair amount, say 6 to 8 lbs., of hay. Some will eat 16 lbs. of oats a day.

III.   RAISING HORSES

769. Feed and care of brood mares.—Many farmers who raise no colts would find it profitable to keep a good team of brood mares to do part of the farm work and also to raise colts each year. The brood mare must, however, have proper feed, care, and management. It is estimated that only 60 per cent of the brood mares that are bred each year produce living foals. This enormous loss is largely due to neglect and carelessness. Control of breeding diseases is also necessary to secure a high percentage of foals.

Idleness must be avoided in the case of brood mares. Those which work regularly are more certain to bring good foals than idle ones, yet judgment must always be used in working them. Pulling too hard, backing heavy loads, wading through deep snow or mud, or other over-exertion is dangerous. When not worked, the mare should be turned out daily for exercise. As foaling time approaches, the work should be lightened, and preferably discontinued 3 days to a week before foaling. When laid off, the mare should still be allowed exercise. Mares heavy in foal are apt to be cross and quarrelsome, but they should always be handled gently.

Feeding a brood mare that is worked, is simpler than feeding an idle one. The essential is a well-balanced ration of good-quality feeds, containing a liberal supply of protein, calcium, and phosphorus, which are needed for the growth of the fetus. An abundance of these nutrients is especially needed by pregnant mares that have not yet finished their own growth and by mares that are suckling foals.

To supply sufficient protein, minerals, and vitamins, it is desirable that at least half the roughage for brood mares during the winter be legume hay. The rest may be grass hay, corn stover, corn silage, or even good straw. Brood mares which are idle during the winter will need but little concentrates, if they have plenty of good roughage. Sufficient grain or other concentrates should be fed, if needed, to keep the mares in thrifty condition, but they should not be allowed to become fat. It is important to keep their bowels active through the use of such feeds as bran and linseed meal.

It does not take very much more feed to maintain through the year a work mare that raises a colt, than it does to maintain another horse doing an equal amount of work. For example, Percheron mares which raised foals were worked in a Missouri trial throughout a year in teams with similar mares that were not bred.[4] Both groups of mares did the same amount of work, averaging 4.8 hours daily for the year. The former ate 5,905 lbs. grain and 7,561 lbs. hay per head during the year, which was only 794 lbs. more grain and 119 lbs. more hay than eaten by the mares that did not raise foals.

770. Gestation period and foaling time.—The average period of gestation for the mare is about 11 months, or 340 days, though it may vary quite widely. Shortly before foaling, the grain allowance should be decreased and laxative feeds more freely used. When wax forms on the mare's teats, the foal may nearly always be expected within 3 days. To avoid infection which may cause navel ill and joint disease, the mare should foal in a roomy box stall, unless she can foal at pasture. The stall should be disinfected, and bedded with dry straw that is as free as possible from chaff and dirt. It should be kept well cleaned.

As foaling time approaches, the mare should be watched so assistance can be rendered, if necessary. Yet she must not know that anyone is on guard, for often a mare will not give birth to her foal when persons are present, if she can delay it. If it is seen that the mare is in difficulty, an experienced veterinarian should be secured.

The mare should be given a half bucket of lukewarm water before foaling, and when on her feet again she will need another drink of water. A light feed of bran is suitable for the first meal, and this may be followed by oats, or by such a mixture as oats and bran. After foaling the mare should be confined for a few days, her ration not being too abundant. With favorable conditions, after 4 or 5 days she may be turned to pasture, and in 10 days, if work is urgent and the mare has fully recovered, she may go back to light work, for a part of the day at least.

Although the natural and customary foaling time is in the spring, where the mare must do a hard season's work or when she does not get

WELL-BRED MARES AND FOALS ON A CORN-BELT FARM

Only about 60 per ct. of the mares that are bred each year produce living foals. The greater part of this enormous loss can be prevented by proper feed, care, and management.

PURE-BRED PERCHERON FILLIES AT THE ILLINOIS STATION

These fillies were fed equal parts of corn and oats with pasture in summer and with alfalfa hay and a little oat straw in winter. The total cost of feed per head from weaning to 2 years old was $103.59.

THREE-YEAR-OLD COLTS AT NEW YORK (CORNELL) STATION

The cost of raising these pure-bred colts to 3 years of age was only $158.34 a head, without allowing any credit for the manure.

A Creep for Feeding Foals on Pasture

For foals on pasture with their dams, a creep should be provided, such as this, where the foals can have access to a separate supply of grain or other concentrates.

Mules at Work on a Corn-belt Farm

The mule is the chief work animal on southern farms and is increasing in popularity in the corn belt.

in foal from spring service, she may be bred to foal in the fall. If one has a warm barn with a roomy box stall, mares may be bred to foal in January or February, at a time when they are not usually needed for work.

Only the quick-maturing draft filly should be bred as a 2-year-old; all others when 3 years or past. If the desire is to improve the strain of horses, one should not breed even the draft filly at 2 years of age. When market draft horses are raised it may prove economical to breed fillies at 2 years of age. This will not injure them to any noticeable degree if they are well-grown for their age and are properly fed and cared for.

771. Mare's milk.—Mare's milk is white or bluish in color with an aromatic, sweetish, slightly bitter taste. As is shown in Appendix Table I, it is much lower in fat, protein, and mineral matter than is cow's milk, but it is somewhat richer in milk sugar. The milk yield of good brood mares is greater than is often supposed. In German tests the daily milk yield of draft brood mares suckling foals was 26 to 77 lbs.[5] It was found in English studies that in the case of foals which were not thriving the milk of the dam was usually abnormal in composition, and often unduly high in fat.[6]

772. The foal.—A thrifty, well-fed foal should make approximately half its entire growth during its first year. If stunted during this time, rarely will it reach full size. It is therefore of the greatest importance that the foal start life full of vigor and that it be kept growing thriftily. Soon after birth, the foal should get the colostrum, or first milk, of its dam, because this increases the resistance of the digestive tract to bacterial infection. If the fecal matter is not voided in a few hours and the foal has a listless appearance, a dose of castor oil or a rectal injection is necessary. On account of the great danger from navel or joint disease, the stump of the navel cord should be carefully disinfected.

If the dam does not supply the proper amount of milk, feed should be given her which will stimulate the milk flow. Good pasture grass is, of course, the best, but in its absence a liberal allowance of grain should be fed. On the other hand, an oversupply of milk or milk too rich in fat may cause indigestion in the foal. The dam's ration should then be reduced and some of her milk drawn, the foal being allowed the first portion, which is the poorest in fat.

773. Weights and gains of foals.—To determine the rate of growth of liberally-fed draft colts, Crampton of Macdonald College, Canada, secured data on 409 draft colts.[7] The average weight of the sires of these colts was 2,050 lbs. and of their dams, 1,760 lbs. At birth the average weight of the colts was 120 lbs. Their average weights at various ages were as follows: 6 months old, 730 lbs.; 1 year, 1,020 lbs.; 18 months, 1,350 lbs.; 2 years, 1,480 lbs.; 3 years, 1,790 lbs.; and 4 years, 1,980 lbs.

During the first 6 months the colts gained an average of 3.4 lbs. a day; from 6 months of age to a year of age, 1.6 lbs. a day; from a year of age to 18 months of age, 1.8 lbs. a day; during the next 6 months, 0.7 lb. a day; during the third year, 0.9 lb. a day; and during the fourth year, 0.5 lb. a day. It will be noted that the average daily gain from 6 months to 1 year of age was slightly less than during the following 6-month period. This slower rate of gain was due to the effect of weaning during the former period.

Allen found that 1,071 trotting-bred foals averaged 110 lbs. at birth.[8] Their average gain was 534 lbs. for the first year, 264 lbs. for the second, 118 lbs. for the third, and 76 lbs. for the fourth, making their average weight 1,102 lbs. at 4 years of age.

Hooper found that Thoroughbred fillies which were foaled from the latter part of February to the end of April averaged 760 lbs. in weight and 14 hands 2 inches in height on April 1 of the next year.[9] Colts averaged 780 lbs. at the same age.

774. Feeding the foals.—Foals should learn to eat grain as early as possible, so as to keep gaining rapidly. Also, if the mares are working, the foals will then fret less for their dams. By placing the feed box low, the foal will begin nibbling from the mother's supply at 3 or 4 weeks of age. Crushed or ground oats or wheat bran are excellent feeds for young foals, and also such a mixture as 4 parts by weight of cracked or ground corn, 3 of bran, and 1 of linseed meal. By the time they are to be weaned they should be eating 2 to 3 lbs. of concentrates a day. They should also be given good legume hay as soon as they will eat it, and they should have access to a supply of good water.

If the dam has insufficient milk, the foal may be fed cow's milk, preferably milk low in fat. Watchfulness should always detect the first appearance of such ailments as constipation or diarrhea. Adding a little linseed meal to the ration will help relieve constipation. In case of diarrhea, the feed for both dam and foal should at once be lessened.

If the mares and foals are on pasture, a small enclosure, called a "creep," should be made at a spot where the horses are inclined to loiter, with a gate and also with an opening of such size that the foals can enter, while the mares are kept out. Here a suitable grain mixture should be supplied in a feed trough. To accustom the foals to eating inside the creep, the gate should be left open for a few days, so the mares will enter and eat the grain mixture. After the mares are shut out, a salt block or a large lump of rock salt can be kept nearby, so the mares will loiter near the creep.

When the mares are worked, it is usually best not to have the foals follow them while at work. A small pasture paddock should be provided, with a shed for shelter. Burlap sacks hung from such a shed will brush flies off the foals as they pass under them. The mare should be brought to suckle the foal in the middle of the forenoon and afternoon for the first 2 or 3 weeks. Before turning her with the foal, she should be allowed to cool off, and perhaps some of the milk drawn from her udder. If the foal is housed in the barn during the day, it is well to turn both dam and foal to pasture at night. Brood mares at work and nursing strong foals should be heavily fed to sustain a good milk flow.

775. Weaning.—At from 4 to 6 months of age, the foal should be weaned. When the mare is bred soon after foaling, or if for any reason the dam or foal is not doing well, it is best to wean comparatively early. On the other hand, if the mother has a good flow of milk and her services are not needed, the foal may be allowed to suckle for 6 months. If the foal has become accustomed to eating grain before weaning time, weaning will cause little, if any, setback. To wean the foal it should be separated from its dam and never be allowed with her again until they have forgotten each other. The grain ration of the mare should be reduced till she is dried off, and her udder partly milked out when necessary.

The education of the colt should not be postponed until it is time to "break" him for work. The breaking process will be much easier and the colt will usually make a better-behaved horse if the training starts early. As a foal he should be taught to lead at the halter, stand tied in the stall, and display proper stable manners.

776. After weaning.—Foals should be kept growing thriftily after weaning by providing them with ample feed which supplies plenty of protein and also sufficient vitamins and minerals, especially calcium and phosphorus. The nutrient requirements of foals, according to the Morrison feeding standards, are shown in Appendix Table III. It will be noted that rations having nutritive ratios no wider than 1:6 to 1:7 are advised for foals from weaning to 1 year of age, and no wider than 1:7 to 1:8 for colts over 2 years of age.

During the pasture season foals should have first class grazing. Alfalfa, red clover, or sweet clover pasture is excellent for them. For roughage during the winter, legume hay or mixed legume-and-grass hay is the best, but it should be of good quality and as free from mold and dust as possible. Where there is not an abundance of such hay on the farm, at least one feed of it should be provided daily. The rest of the roughage can then be hay from the grasses, well-cured corn or sorghum fodder, or corn or sorghum silage.

Several different concentrate mixtures have given good results for raising foals in trials at various stations.[10] With good legume hay for roughage, excellent results will be secured from oats as the only concentrate or from such mixtures as the following: (1) Equal parts by weight of oats and either corn or barley; (2) a mixture of 3 or 4 parts oats by weight and 1 part wheat bran; (3) a mixture of 3 parts corn and 1 part wheat bran; (4) a mixture of 2 parts corn, 2 parts oats, and 1 part wheat bran.

When the roughage is chiefly grass hay or other forages low in protein, the ration should be balanced by feeding about 1 lb. per head daily of a protein supplement, such as linseed meal, soybeans, soybean oil meal, gluten feed, gluten meal, peanut oil meal, or cottonseed meal. For example, satisfactory mixtures for use with such roughage are: (1) A mixture of 3 parts oats by weight, 3 parts corn, 3 parts bran, and 1 part linseed meal or other protein-rich supplement; (2) a mixture of 3 parts corn, 3 parts bran, and 1 part protein-rich supplement.

Many expert horsemen believe that foals develop better quality of bone when the concentrate mixture is made up largely of oats instead of corn, but corn is satisfactory, providing care is taken to supply plenty of protein and minerals in the ration, preferably by feeding legume hay.[11]

Trials at the Illinois Station show that for foals during the first and later winters, unthreshed sheaf oats, fed uncut, are excellent as part of the ration, along with a limited amount of concentrates and some legume hay.[12] Sheaf oats provide both grain and roughage, and the expense of threshing is saved.

Though most farmers do not break draft colts to work until they are about 3 years old or more, others break well-grown colts when 2 years old and use them for limited work. By following this method, the cost of raising them can be reduced materially. Male colts intended for work animals should be castrated between one and two years of age.

777. Raising an orphan foal.—If the mare dies, the foal may, with proper care, be raised on cow's milk. As mare's milk contains much less fat but more sugar than cow's milk, the milk should be modified for a very young foal. Choose milk from a cow in the first part of the lactation period and one giving milk low in fat, if possible. Put 4 tablespoonfuls of lime water and 2 teaspoonfuls of ordinary cane sugar in a pint jar and then fill it with fresh milk. Feed about one-fourth pint about every hour for the first day or so, warming the milk to 100° F. and using an ordinary nursing bottle with a large nipple. This must be carefully cleansed and sterilized.

If the foal is doing well, the amount of milk may be gradually increased and the period between feedings lengthened, until the foal is fed only 4 times a day. After a few days unmodified whole milk may be substituted and the foal taught to drink from a pail. In 5 to 6 weeks sweet skimmilk may gradually replace the whole milk and after 3 months the foal may be given all it will drink 3 times a day. As soon as possible, the foal should be fed solid food, such as crushed or ground oats, bran, a little linseed meal, and legume hay, and it should have the run of a paddock where there is good grazing.

778. Amount of feed required to raise colts.—The amount of feed required to raise a colt will vary widely, depending on the size it reaches. This is governed by heredity and by the liberality with which it is fed while growing. It is important that well-bred draft foals be given sufficient feed so they will develop into draft horses of good size, for this is the kind that can do the greatest amount of work and that commands the best prices on the market.

The amount of grain and other concentrates required will depend to a considerable extent on the quality of roughage fed during the winter and the kind of pasture available during the growing season. When colts have plenty of good legume hay or mixed hay in winter and excellent pasturage in summer, the amount of concentrates can be reduced considerably without interfering materially with their growth. It is, however, especially important that they be fed sufficient concentrates during the first year to keep them growing well.

In the trials mentioned previously, in which well-bred draft foals have been fed at several experiment stations so as to grow into heavy draft horses, the foals received during the first winter a total of 13.5 to 20 lbs. or more of concentrates and hay or other dry roughage a day and gained 1.3 to 1.8 lbs. per head daily.[11] The daily concentrate allowance ranged from 5 to 11 lbs. or even more, and the consumption of hay or other roughage from 12 lbs. to 6 lbs. or less, the foals which were heavily fed on concentrates, of course, eating a smaller amount of hay. Foals of smaller size or those less well fed would naturally have consumed much less feed.

The second summer, the amount of concentrates needed will vary widely, depending on the amount and kind of pasturage. In these trials the foals received 3 to 6 lbs. or more of concentrates per head daily, with hay or other roughage when the pasture was short, and they gained 1.1 to 1.6 lbs. per head daily.

The second winter, the colts ate 22 to 27 lbs. total dry feed per head daily, consisting of 6 to 12 lbs. concentrates and 17 to 13 lbs. hay or other dry roughage, and gained 0.7 to 1.3 lbs. per head daily.

The third summer, no grain is needed if the pasture is excellent, unless it is desired to force the colts to make maximum growth. With reasonably good pasture, not over 4 to 5 lbs. of concentrates per head daily should be required in any event. The third winter, the total amount of feed will be about the same as the second, but the colts will take somewhat more roughage, eating as much as 20 lbs. a day, with 5.5 to 11 lbs. concentrates.

779. Raising colts on limited amount of grain.—Liberal amounts of grain are necessary if colts are to reach maximum size as 3-year-olds. Therefore it usually pays to feed them well if they are to be sold at this age. However, except when grain is unusually low in price, colts can be raised more cheaply when the amount of grain is decidedly limited. In an experiment at the Michigan Station one group of draft colts (Lot I) was raised from weaning to 3 years of age on a very liberal amount of grain with what hay they would eat and good pasture in summer.[13] Lot II was raised on 55 per cent as much grain and 81 per cent as much hay as Lot I, but the colts in this lot were allowed all the oat straw they would eat. Those in Lot I were also offered straw, but they consumed practically none. Lot III was fed only one-third as much grain as Lot I, with straw in abundance and a limited amount of hay.

At slightly less than 3 years of age the colts in Lot I averaged 1,574 lbs. in weight and 63.8 inches in height. They had received from weaning time to that age an average of 7,360 lbs. of concentrates (nearly all oats and ear corn, with a little linseed meal and wheat bran), 7,960 lbs. hay, and 240 lbs. straw, in addition to pasture. (The weight of ear corn has been reduced to the shelled-corn equivalent). Lot II averaged 1,479 lbs. in weight and 63.6 inches in height, and had received 4,226 lbs. of concentrates, 6,460 lbs. hay, and 3,400 lbs. straw, plus pasture during the summers. Lot III averaged 1,347 lbs. in weight and 63.0 inches in height, and had received only 2,380 lbs. concentrates and 6,400 lbs. hay, with 3,720 lbs. straw and pasture as in the case of the other lots.

At the end of the experiment the colts in Lot I were very fat; those in Lot II, in good thrifty condition; and those in Lot III, thin but showing good size. At five years of age, after all the colts had been put to work and had been fed similarly, there would undoubtedly have been much less difference than this in their weights, for the colts in Lots II and III would have continued to grow more than those which had previously been liberally fed.

The average feed cost for the colts in the 3 lots to the end of the experiment was $118.05 for those in Lot I, $87.99 for those in Lot II, and $69.56 for those in Lot III. The colts in Lots I and II were sufficiently developed so that they could have been put to work as 2-year-olds. If this had been done, they would have paid for their feed after that time.

This would have reduced the average cost of feed to $78.45 for the colts in Lot I and $52.42 for those in Lot II.

Percheron colts were raised on a limited amount of concentrates with good hay in winter and good pasture in summer at the Missouri Station, in comparison with others fed concentrates liberally.[14] At 3 years of age the limited-fed colts weighed 1,411 lbs., on the average and were 64.3 inches high at the withers. From birth they had eaten an average of 4,238 lbs. concentrates and 5,724 lbs. hay, plus pasture. The liberally-fed colts averaged 1,517 lbs. in weight and 64.5 inches in height. There was thus a difference of only 106 lbs. in weight between the colts in the two groups and practically no difference in height. To three years of age the liberally-fed colts had eaten an average of 7,638 lbs. concentrates and 4,665 lbs. hay, on the average, plus pasture.

The colts in both groups were put to work the spring they were 3 years old and were then fed and handled alike. Those which had been raised on the limited ration continued to gain somewhat, while the others did not increase in weight. At five years of age the horses which had been raised on the limited amount of concentrates averaged only 8 lbs. less in weight than those in the other group.

If plenty of good legume hay is available in winter and good pasture during the growing season, colts will make fair gains when fed no concentrates after the first winter. However, they will not make as large horses as they would otherwise. In a Nebraska trial, colts averaging 589 lbs. on January 1st of their first year, were fed 4 lbs. of grain per head daily the first winter and none thereafter, but had an abundance of alfalfa hay in winter and good alfalfa pasture in summer.[15] They gained 678 lbs. on the average during a period of three years, and then averaged 1,268 lbs. in weight. Another group fed prairie and sorghum hay during the winter, with native pasture during the summer, averaged only 1,158 lbs. in weight, though they were fed some grain during the second winter.

780. Feed and care of the stallion.—In the care of the stallion nothing that is so vital to his well-being is so commonly neglected as proper exercise. The best exercise is actual work, and there is no better advertisement of a stallion than letting him be seen at work. Even during the breeding season a half day's work each day is beneficial. When real work is impossible, the stallion should be exercised daily by being turned into a roomy paddock, or should be exercised on the road for a mile, or preferably considerably more. Exercising a stallion daily by driving or leading him is a burdensome task, and less apt to be done regularly than turning him out into a suitable paddock.

The ration of the stallion should consist of first-class, wholesome feeds, supplying ample protein, mineral matter, and vitamins for thrift and vigor. The choice of feeding stuffs will depend on the particular locality. Legume hay is excellent for the stallion, providing it is not dusty. Care must also be taken not to feed more of such palatable hay than the stallion actually needs.

The nature of the concentrates should depend on the kind of hay that is fed. The following mixtures are well suited for use with timothy hay or other non-legume roughage: (1) Oats 4 parts by weight and wheat bran 1 part; (2) oats 4 parts, corn 6 parts, and wheat bran 3 parts; (3) oats 4 parts, corn 4 parts, and linseed meal 1 part. For mature stallions oats can be used as the only concentrate, even when no legume hay is fed.

If a considerable proportion of the roughage fed a stallion is legume hay, a mixture of grain alone is satisfactory, even for young stallions. It may, however, be desirable to include a little wheat bran in the mixture, merely for its laxative effect. Even with legume hay as the only roughage, most horsemen prefer not to include more than one-half corn in the grain mixture for stallions.

No specific directions as to the total amount of feed required can be given, since this depends on the exercise the animal gets and whether he is a "hard" or "easy" keeper. A safe rule is to keep the stallion in good flesh, but not "hog fat," for this will injure his breeding powers. Most horsemen advise that in the breeding season he be kept gaining just a bit, rather than be allowed to run down in flesh.

It is important that the stallion be kept in vigorous, thrifty condition, so that he may be more sure in getting foals. The stallion should have a roomy clean box stall, well lighted and well ventilated. As a horse likes companionship, it is well to have his stall near those of other horses. He should be regularly and thoroughly groomed, and frequent attention should be given his feet.

The idea that drugs or stock tonics are necessary for stallions is nonsense. The most successful grooms secure their good results by good feed and intelligent care. It is important to conserve the energies of the stallion by regulation of the number of services.

IV. Cost of Horse Labor; Cost of Raising Horses

781. Cost of keeping farm horses.—The most extensive recent information on the cost of keeping farm horses is furnished in studies made on 736 corn-belt farms in Indiana, Iowa, Michigan, and Missouri by the United States Department of Agriculture, in co-operation with the experiment stations in these states.[16] The data covered the year 1929, but the costs were also computed on the basis of prices prevailing in 1931-32.

The table on page 474 summarizes the costs of horses on three of the classes of farms included in these studies. These are: (1) Farms on which the horses were worked in teams of no more than 3 animals and on which there was no tractor; (2) non-tractor farms on which the horses were worked to some extent in big-team hitches of 4 or more animals; and (3) farms on which a general-purpose tractor was used for part of the work.

It will be noted that the crop acreage was the largest for the big-team-hitch farms and smallest for the farms on which the horses were worked in ordinary teams. On these corn-belt farms the horses were worked for a somewhat smaller number of hours a year than would often be the case where the farming was more diversified. This rather small amount of work per year reduces the annual cost of keeping horses, but makes the cost per hour of horse labor higher than where the horses do more work a year.

On these farms more than half of the grain fed was corn, and a large proportion of the hay was legume hay or mixed legume-and-grass hay. On farms where the chief hay was legume, more use was generally made of straw and stover. On these farms the horses were on pasture more than half of the year, thus considerably reducing the cost of feed. (**758**)

Average yearly cost of keeping horses on corn-belt farms

	Horses worked in ordinary teams	Big-team-hitch farms	General-purpose-tractor farms
Crop acreage per farm, acres..............	137	252	196
Number of horses per farm...............	6	11	4
Hours of work per horse.................	691	746	704
Feed per horse:			
Oats, lbs.	1,565	1,682	1,345
Corn, lbs.	1,730	1,509	1,633
Other concentrates, lbs.................	18	2	32
Legume and mixed hay, lbs.............	2,260	2,360	2,080
Non-legume hay, lbs....................	1,060	780	1,540
Straw and stover, lbs..................	1,640	2,240	1,480
Grass pasture, months.................	4.4	4.2	4.8
Corn stalk and stubble field pasture, months	1.7	2.5	1.7
Costs at 1929 prices			
Feed	$77.68	$76.80	$81.67
Chore labor	15.23	11.19	17.65
Bedding	3.99	4.02	4.36
Shoeing	0.56	0.09	0.47
Veterinary and medicine...............	0.63	0.71	0.77
Harness charge	2.21	1.48	2.77
Interest	5.90	6.88	6.41
Depreciation	2.06	0.16	0.21
Total gross cost.....................	$108.26	$101.33	$114.31
Credits			
Manure	10.62	9.37	10.51
Colts	1.64	3.85	2.26
Total credits	$12.26	$13.22	$12.77
Net cost per year, 1929 prices.............	$96.00	$88.11	$101.54
Net cost per hour labor, 1929 prices........	$ 0.14	$ 0.12	$ 0.14
Net cost per year, 1931-32 prices...........	$52.08	$47.76	$ 54.52
Net cost per hour labor, 1931-32 prices....	0.08	0.06	0.08

With costs based upon 1929 prices, the average total gross cost of keeping a horse on these farms ranged from $101.33 for the big-team-hitch farms to $114.31 for the general-purpose-tractor farms. Deducting credits for the value of the manure produced and for colts raised on some of the farms, the annual net cost ranged from $88.11 per horse for the big-team-hitch farms to $101.54 for the general-purpose-tractor farms. The net cost per hour of horse labor at 1929 prices ranged from 12 cents to 14 cents for these types of farms.

On account of the great decline in price levels between 1929 and 1931-32, the costs were much less when computed at the prices during the latter period. At 1931-32 prices the cost per hour of horse labor was only 6 cents per hour for the big-team-hitch farms and 8 cents for the other groups.

The cost of horse labor on farms in various districts will vary widely, depending chiefly on the prices for feeds and on the number of hours the horses are worked each year. The various ways in which the cost can be reduced have been discussed in detail in Chapter XXI. (717)

In studies conducted by the Missouri Station it was found that the feed cost per hour of actual work performed was 5.0 cents on the farms where mules were the chief work animals, 5.6 cents where geldings were mainly used, and 6.0 cents where most of the work animals were mares.[17] Though the cost of labor per hour may be slightly higher with mares, this does not mean that on many farms it is not profitable to keep high-grade mares as work animals and raise foals from them.

782. Cost of raising horses.—The cost of raising horses will vary widely in different parts of the United States, depending chiefly on prices for feed, which is the largest item of expense.

The average total cost of raising colts on farms to the age of 3 years, according to estimates received from over 10,000 farmers in various sections of the United States by the Bureau of Statistics, United States Department of Agriculture, was $104.06, under conditions prior to the World War.[18] If we deduct the value of the work done by the average colt before his third year, the net cost without giving any credit for the manure produced was $96.54, or 70.9 per cent of the estimated selling price, which was $136.17. The cost in different states varied from $69.50 for New Mexico and $71.59 for Wyoming, to $149.98 for Connecticut and $156.60 for Rhode Island. The average cost was distributed as follows:

Cost of raising colts to 3 years of age under pre-war conditions

	First year Dollars	Second year Dollars	Third year Dollars	Total cost Dollars
Service fee	12.95	....	....	12.95
Time lost by brood mare	10.06	....	....	10.06
Breaking to halter	2.22	....	....	2.22
Care and shelter	4.98	5.36	6.35	16.69
Cost of grain fed	4.98	7.14	9.56	21.68
Cost of hay fed	4.14	6.61	8.48	19.23
Cost of pasture	2.56	5.41	6.21	14.18
Veterinary and miscellaneous	....	....	....	7.05

$104.06

The cost of raising heavy draft colts will be somewhat greater than shown in these estimates, because of the larger amount of feed needed. The cost of the feed consumed by such colts up to 3 years of age can be readily estimated at local prices, from the data presented previously. (778-779) To the feed cost must be added the other items of expense shown in the previous table.

The method of estimating the total cost under local conditions is shown by the following averages for 66 colts (chiefly purebred and high-grade Percherons) raised at the New York (Cornell) Station from 1909 to 1918.[19] Up to weaning time these colts consumed the total of 180 lbs. grain and other concentrates on the average; from that time to 1 year of age, 1,214 lbs. concentrates and 1,594 lbs. hay; during the second year 1,507 lbs. concentrates and 2,525 lbs. hay; and during the third year 1,898 lbs. concentrates and 2,790 lbs. hay; making a total of 4,746 lbs. concentrates and 6,804 lbs. of hay eaten per head up to 3 years of age. The average birth weight of the colts was 116 lbs. and their average weight when 3 years old was 1,270 lbs.

The average cost of raising these colts to 3 years of age was as follows: Feed, $123.64, with concentrates at $28 a ton and hay at $12 a ton (cost of concentrates, $67.18; hay, $41.46; pasture, $15.00); care and shelter, $20.00; service fee, $15.00; inconvenience, and time lost by mare, $10.00; mortality risk and insurance, $16.85; veterinary service and supplies, $2.00; total gross cost, $187.49.

There should be deducted from this gross cost a credit for the value of the manure produced. This should amount to $25.00, if proper care is taken of the manure. Also, colts can readily earn their keep at two and a half years of age, and therefore half of the cost for the third year (or $29.15) can be deducted. This would reduce the net cost of a 3-year-old colt under these conditions to $133.34.

QUESTIONS

1. State some of the most important points in feeding work horses. About how great an amount of concentrates and roughages combined should be fed daily to work horses per 100 lbs. live weight?
2. What sort of rations should be used for wintering idle farm horses?
3. Discuss the fitting of draft horses for the market.
4. State a satisfactory ration for a carriage or saddle horse.
5. Discuss the feed and care of brood mares, (a) previous to foaling; (b) at foaling time.
6. In what respects does mare's milk differ from cow's milk?
7. Discuss the feed and care of foals, (a) before weaning; (b) at weaning time; (c) after weaning.
8. Approximately how much total concentrates and how much roughage does it take to raise a draft colt to 3 years of age, (a) when it is fed a liberal amount of grain; (b) when only enough grain is fed to produce satisfactory growth?
9. Discuss the feed and care of the stallion.
10. Discuss the cost of keeping farm horses, stating the chief items of expense and their approximate size. What credits should be deducted from the gross cost?
11. What was the approximate cost per hour of horse labor on corn-belt farms in 1929; under conditions in 1931-32?
12. What items must be considered in estimating the cost of raising horses? About how much did it cost to raise horses on farms in this country under conditions prior to the World War?

REFERENCES

1. Obrect, Ill. Bul. 141.
2. Cochel, Penn. Bul. 117.
3. Woodruff, The Trotting Horse in America, pp. 90-105.
4. Trowbridge and Chittenden, Mo. Bul. 197.
5. Blechschmidt, Landw. Jahrb., 77, 1933, pp. 463-560.
6. Linton, Jour. Agr. Sci., England, 21, 1931, pp. 669-688.
7. Crampton, Macdonald College, Canada, information to the author; see also: Fuller, Wis. Cir. 244; Breeder's Gazette, 59, 1911, p. 1223.
8. Allen Farm Catalog, 1905.
9. Hooper, The Thoroughbred Record, July 9, 1921.

10. Edmonds and Kammlade, Ill. Buls. 192, 235; Edmonds and Crawford, Ill. Buls. 262, 292; McCampbell, Kan. Cir. 57; Trowbridge and Chittenden, Mo. Buls. 179, 189, 210, 228, 236, 244; Mont. Rpt. 1931; Harper, N. Y. (Cornell) Bul. 403; Cochel and Severson, Penn. Bul. 122; Fuller, Wis. Cir. 244.
11. McCampbell, Kan. Cir. 57.
12. Edmonds and Crawford, Ill. Buls. 262, 292.
13. Hudson, Mich. Spec. Bul. 253.
14. Trowbridge and Chittenden, Mo. Bul. 316.
15. Snyder, Nebr. Bul. 130.
16. Reynoldson, Humphries, Speelman, McComas, and Youngman, U. S. Dept. Agr., Tech. Bul. 384; see also: Adams, Cal. Bul. 401; Johnston and Wills, Ill. Bul. 395; Hopkins, Iowa Bul. 264; Smith and Jones, Mo. Res. Bul. 197; Morison, Ohio Bul. 470; Stephens, Okla. Bul. 308; Selby, Rodenwold, and Scudder, Ore. Bul. 250; Maxton, Kifer, and Vernon, Va. Bul. 272; McNall, Wis. Bul. 388; Cooper and Williams, U. S. Dept. Agr., Farmers' Bul. 1298.
17. Johnson and Green, Mo. Bul. 152.
18. Gay, Productive Horse Husbandry.
19. Harper, N. Y. (Cornell) Bul. 403.

CHAPTER XXIV

GENERAL PROBLEMS IN DAIRY HUSBANDRY

I. Factors Determining the Efficiency of Dairy Cows

783. Economy of dairy cows.—Among all the animals of the farm, dairy cows of good productive capacity are unequalled as producers of human food. They convert the products of the fields, many of which are in large part inedible for man, into food for humans with greater efficiency than do any other class of farm animals. Even more important than this economic superiority, however, is the fact that the food which they produce is of inestimable value to us. It has been previously emphasized that milk is in a class by itself as a food. (**207, 616**) Because of the efficiency with which she makes this unrivalled food, the dairy cow has well earned the title, "the foster mother of the human race," which was apparently first bestowed on her by W. D. Hoard of Wisconsin. It has been shown previously that good dairy cows yield in their milk, per acre of crops eaten, 711.8 therms of energy and 72.3 lbs. of digestible protein. This is over 5 times as much energy and nearly 4 times as much protein as is contained in the beef made by steers from the same amount of feed. (**231, 236**) The efficiency in the production of human food is still more striking in the case of cows of extremely high productive capacity.

In experiments at the Minnesota Station Haecker found that well-fed dairy cows of average size, producing about 1 lb. of fat daily, actually yielded in their milk about 29 per cent of the digestible nutrients in their feed.[1] They used approximately 47 per cent of their food for body maintenance and 24 per cent in the work of converting food nutrients into milk.

Forbes and Voris found in metabolism trials at the Pennsylvania Institute of Animal Nutrition that Holstein cows, averaging 11,783 lbs. in yield of milk and 1,146 lbs. in live weight, returned in their milk 21.0 per cent of the gross energy of the feed they ate during their lactation periods, which averaged 313 days. For the entire calendar year, they transformed 18.7 per cent of the gross energy of their feed, including that which they ate when dry, into energy in their milk.[2]

784. Dairy vs. beef type.—When in full flow of milk, a high-producing dairy cow is generally spare and shows an angular, wedge-shaped form, a roomy barrel, and a capacious udder. This conformation is in strong contrast to that of the low-set, blocky, beef animal, with its compact, rectangular form, and broad, well-fleshed back. Even greater than the difference in external characteristics is the difference in structure of the udder of dairy and beef cows. In good dairy cows the udder is made up almost entirely of gland tissue, while in beef cows there is but a small quantity of gland tissue, surrounded by a heavy layer of fat.[3]

These two types of cattle are the result of careful breeding with opposite objects in view. The beef animal has been developed to store in its carcass the largest possible amount of meat. On the other hand, for generations the dairy cow has been bred for the primary object of producing large yields of milk and butter fat. As a result, though a good dairy cow will put on flesh when she is dry, the impulse to milk production is so strong when she is in milk that even under liberal feeding she shows little or no tendency to fatten. Instead, she uses all the surplus feed above maintenance for the manufacture of milk.

In view of the widely differing nature of milk and flesh production, it is not surprising that both cannot be developed to the highest degree in the same animal. As a rule, the most perfect beef cows are not economical milkers, and the best dairy cows are not satisfactory beef makers. In a trial at the Minnesota Station cows of the beef type required 47 per cent more feed per pound of butter fat produced than those of good dairy type.[4] Shallow-bodied cows which are neither of the dairy type nor of the beef type are not generally economical producers, for they cannot consume enough feed to make a large yield of milk possible.

785. High producers are economical producers.—Cows which produce a large amount of milk and fat naturally must eat much more feed than those yielding less, just as hard-worked horses require more feed than those at light work. However, the yield of the high-producing cows is so much greater that it more than offsets the higher cost of their feed. They therefore under usual conditions produce milk and fat much more cheaply than do low-yielding cows.

Practically all studies of production and feed costs in dairy herds show this fundamental fact—that high producers are usually economical producers. A good example is the table on page 480, compiled by McDowell of the Bureau of Dairy Industry, United States Department of Agriculture.[5] In this table the records of production, feed costs, and net returns over feed cost of the cows which completed records in the United States dairy herd-improvement associations during 1934 are grouped according to production of butter fat.

The table shows that as the production of the cows became greater there was a steady increase in the cost of feed, the increase in the cost of concentrates being much greater than in the cost of roughage, including pasture. While the yearly cost of feed per head was only $38 for the cows averaging 2,650 lbs. of milk and 106 lbs. of fat, the feed cost was $123 per cow for the small group averaging 21,432 lbs. of milk and 874 lbs. of fat. However, the value of the product increased much more rapidly as the yield rose than did the cost of feed.

The most important fact presented by the table is that the return over feed cost steadily became greater as the yield of milk and fat increased. This was true even at the extremely high levels of production Thus, for the group of cows averaging 7,573 lbs. milk and 300 lbs. fat, the value of product was $135 per head; the feed cost, $59; and the net return, $76. The feed cost for the highest-producing group averaged $123, or about twice as much as for the former group. However, the average value of their product was $442, and the net return per head over feed cost was $319, or more than four times as much as for the cows that yielded 300 lbs. of fat a year.

Yearly production and returns from cows in dairy herd-improvement associations*

No. of cows	Average yield of milk	Average yield of fat	Value of product	Cost of roughage including pasture	Cost of concentrates	Total cost of feed	Return over feed cost	Return for $1 spent for feed	Feed cost of 100 lbs. milk
	Lbs.	Lbs.	Dollars	Dollars	Dollars	Dollars	Dollars	Dollars	Dollars
1,383	2,650	106	50	26	12	38	12	1.32	1.43
5,485	3,981	155	71	28	15	43	28	1.65	1.08
16,151	5,233	203	92	30	19	49	43	1.88	.94
29,642	6,425	251	114	32	22	54	60	2.11	.84
36,721	7,573	300	135	33	26	59	76	2.29	.78
31,655	8,666	348	157	34	30	64	93	2.45	.74
20,067	9,739	397	177	35	33	68	109	2.60	.70
10,440	10,906	446	202	36	37	73	129	2.77	.67
4,582	12,111	496	225	37	41	78	147	2.88	.64
1,736	13,379	545	250	40	45	85	165	2.94	.64
781	14,749	596	268	41	48	89	179	3.01	.60
259	16,343	646	296	43	53	96	200	3.08	.59
97	18,062	696	350	49	58	107	243	3.27	.59
47	19,078	743	365	51	57	108	257	3.38	.57
26	19,859	796	387	47	65	112	275	3.46	.56
14	21,432	874	442	49	74	123	319	3.60	.57
Average	7,904	316	143	33	27	60	83	2.38	.76

*The two lowest-producing groups of cows are omitted from this table, as most of the records probably do not represent full lactation periods. Also, the California records are not included in the tabulation, because data on value of product and cost of feed were not reported. Including the California records, the average production per cow for 1934 of all cows in the associations was 8,0˙˙⁵ lbs. of milk containing 322 lbs. of butter fat.

This table effectively controverts the statement, sometimes made, that greater net returns are secured from moderate rates of production than from the high levels of production reached by excellent cows fed in accordance with their nutrient requirements.

786. Why cows differ in efficiency of production.—Individual cows differ widely in the efficiency with which they convert their feed into milk, and therefore in the cost of feed per 100 lbs. of milk produced.[6] While there may be differences in efficiency between cows that yield the same amounts of milk and fat, the chief difference is between low producers and high producers. On account of the importance of the problem, investigations were conducted at the Missouri Station to determine just why high-producing cows are more efficient than low producers in converting feed into milk.[7]

It was found in these studies that high-producing cows require as much feed for maintenance as do low producers. Also, there is probably little difference in the efficiency with which they digest their feed, providing they are healthy. Neither do high producers and low producers differ materially in the amount of milk or fat they are able to produce from each 100 lbs. of feed they eat beyond the amounts they need merely to maintain their bodies.

The reasons for the efficiency of the high producers are these: They have great inherited capacities for milk production and strong constitutions as well. On account of this inherited stimulus to high production, they secrete an abundance of milk. Due to the great amount of nutrients they put into their milk, they have keen appetites and if liberally fed, will eat much more feed than the low producers. They therefore have available for the actual production of milk a decidedly greater proportion of the total feed they consume, and hence produce milk at a much lower cost per 100 lbs.

787. Feed good cows liberally, but not poor cows.—Unless cows of high productive capacity are fed with sufficient liberality to provide them with the nutrients they need for the production of a large amount of milk and fat, their yield will soon decline to the level permitted by the supply of nutrients they receive. Many cows which are potentially large producers and efficient producers are thus forced into the inefficient and unprofitable class, because their owners do not appreciate these basic facts of nutrition.

It has been shown in Chapter IV that farm animals digest and utilize their food somewhat more completely when given a scanty ration than when fed liberally. (**113**) It might be concluded from this that it would be most profitable to feed good cows rather meagerly, so that they would digest their feed with maximum efficiency. However, as has been there explained, other factors generally much more than offset the increased digestibility and percentage utilization of a scanty ration.

It has been stated previously in this chapter that a well-fed dairy cow producing about 1 lb. of butter fat a day requires 47 per cent of the feed she eats for the maintenance of her body. (**783**) She therefore has available for milk production only about one-half of her feed. If such a cow is fed only two-thirds as much feed, she will digest the scanty ration a trifle better, but she will still need nearly as much feed as before to maintain her body. As a result of the scanty feeding, she will probably have available for milk production only 30 per cent or less of the total feed she eats. This great reduction in the amount of feed that is left after her maintenance requirements have been met, will much more than offset the slightly greater digestibility of the limited ration. Also, as has been pointed out in Chapter IV, the overhead expenses in stock feeding are greater when an animal is producing at a low rate.

It is just as unwise to overfeed a poor cow as it is to be stingy with a good producer. A cow lacking in productive capacity that is fed a liberal ration cannot increase her milk production beyond her inherited capacity. All she can do is to store the excess nutrients in the form of body fat, instead of turning them into milk. The best plan is to get rid of such a cow, for she will not pay for her keep. If she is retained, it is important that she be fed according to her actual production of milk, instead of being given as much grain as the efficient animals in the herd.

Except when grain and other concentrates are very expensive in comparison with hay, pasture, and other roughage, cows of large productive capacity produce the greatest net income over cost of feed and also the largest profit, when they are fed concentrates with sufficient liberality to meet the recommendations of modern feeding standards. The amount of concentrates to feed dairy cows is considered in detail later in this chapter. (**804-807**)

788. Purebreds vs. grades.—"Do purebred dairy cows produce more milk and fat than good grade cows with the same feed and care?" is a question often discussed by dairymen. Analyzing the data secured in United States dairy herd-improvement associations, McDowell found that in 1931 the average production for 63,739 registered purebred dairy cows was 8,443 lbs. of milk and 325 lbs. of fat, while the average for 107,309 grade cows was 7,623 lbs. of milk and 298 lbs. of fat.[8] The purebred cows therefore produced, on the average, 820 lbs. more milk and 27 lbs. more fat a year. The average cost of feed for the purebreds was $83, and for the grades only $67, but the production of the purebreds was so much larger that the average net income over cost of feed was $20 more per cow for the purebreds. The purebreds therefore decidedly surpassed the grades in dairy capacity; that is, in ability to consume a large amount of feed and convert it economically into milk.

It is possible by the use of excellent purebred sires in a grade herd for many years, combined with careful culling, to develop a herd that probably cannot be distinguished in appearance or production from a herd of purebreds. However, it must be borne in mind that the merits of high grades are due to their purebred ancestors, and not to the trace of scrub blood they still possess.

789. Weed out low-producing, unprofitable cows.—Although the average production of the dairy cows in the United States has been increased considerably as better feeding and breeding practices have been adopted by dairymen, the production is still relatively low. In 1934 it was only 4,030 lbs. of milk and 158 lbs. of fat per cow (not including milk sucked by calves and that which was wasted).[9] Even with average prices for dairy products, probably one-fourth or more of the dairy cows fail to pay for their feed and care. When dairy prices are low, the condition is even more serious.

The chief reason why such a condition is found now, when the principles of successful selection, feeding, and care of dairy cattle have long been known, is that the owners do not know which of their cows fail to yield enough milk to pay for their feed and care. They do not realize that though the gross income from their herd would be reduced by weeding out the "boarders," their profits would be decidedly increased.

On comparing the results from the highest-producing cows and the lowest-producing cows in the dairy herd-improvement association herds in this country, McDowell found that the highest-producing cow in each herd returned more net profit, on the average, than the 7 lowest producers.[10] Yet, the low producers in such herds are much better cows than the low-yielding cows in average herds. When there is a surplus of dairy products on the market, which demoralizes prices, it is important to realize that these 7 lowest producers placed 4 times as much milk and fat on the market as the single high producer. As McDowell concludes, "Here again we have an example of low-producing cows flooding the market with milk produced at a loss."

Even experts are often unable to tell from the appearance of a cow whether or not she will be a profitable producer. The only reliable way of finding this out is from records of the actual amount of milk and fat she yields. Fortunately, such records may be easily secured by the use of the milk scales and the Babcock fat test. Knowing the production of each cow and the approximate amount of feed she has consumed in a given period, the dairyman can discard the unprofitable animals, and gradually build up a herd of high producers at small expense by using a bred-for-production sire and saving the heifer calves from the best cows.

The Cow-tester Finds the "Boarder" Cow

Most dairy herds contain some cows that are not paying for their keep. The tester in a cow testing association soon discovers these robbers.

E.R. McINTYRE

The Dairy Cow Before the Jury

Even a skilled judge often makes mistakes in predicting the production of a cow from her appearance alone. However, this jury—the milk scales, the Babcock test, the milk record, and the feed book—never err in determining her actual profitableness. (From Wisconsin Station.)

A Scrub Cow Used in the Iowa Experiments

The average annual production of this scrub cow was only 3,312 lbs. of milk and 178 lbs. of butter fat. (From Iowa Station.)

Half-blood Holstein from Scrub Cow and Pure-bred Bull

This cow, a daughter of the scrub above, averaged 6,385 lbs. milk and 305 lbs. fat a year, a remarkable increase over the yield of her scrub dam. (From Iowa Station.)

Grand-daughter of Original Scrub

This heifer, out of the half-blood Holstein cow and a pure-bred Holstein bull, not only shows marked dairy conformation and temperament, but also the characteristic color markings of the breed. (From Iowa Station.)

By this means the average yield of fat for the herd can be gradually increased year by year, until it is raised to 300 lbs., later to 350 lbs., and then even higher. As good cows sometimes have "off years" in production, animals should not be discarded after a single year's trial, if there is good reason to believe they will do better in the future. It has been found, however, that usually the production of a cow for one lactation period under normal conditions is an excellent index to what her production will be in following years.[11]

790. Keeping records of production.—The most accurate way of finding the value of each cow is to weigh and record each milking from every animal. This does not require much work, if a convenient spring balance and handy milk sheets for entry of the records are provided. Such daily individual records make possible the feeding of each cow with the greatest economy, enable the herdsman to detect sickness quickly by the decline in milk flow, and aid in judging the efficiency of the different milkers. Where the weight of each milking is recorded, it is sufficient to take a sample for fat testing one day each week, or else a sample once a month for one or preferably two consecutive days.

Those who feel that they cannot spend the time necessary to weigh each milking can obtain reasonably accurate records by weighing and sampling the milk regularly for one day each month. This is the method followed in the dairy herd-improvement associations (cow testing associations) and the dairy record clubs in this country.

Dairymen who have these organized testing services available to them will usually find that membership in one of these organizations is the best way of securing information on the production of each of their cows. This service is relatively inexpensive, and the advice furnished concerning the feeding and management of the herd is of much value.

Tests covering only a week or even a month of the year are far less reliable than tests covering the entire year, for cows differ widely in persistence of milk yield. A cow which gives a good flow of milk for a time but goes dry relatively soon may be much less profitable than a persistent milker that never yields as much fat in any one week as does the first cow.

Also, if a short-time test is made early in the lactation period, particularly in the case of a cow which has been fattened before freshening, the fat test of the milk in such a test may be much higher than for the rest of the year. (**829**) For these reasons none of the dairy cattle breed associations in this country now sponsor brief tests.

791. Cow testing associations and dairy record clubs.—In all the countries where cow testing associations have been extensively developed, they have caused great improvement in the dairy industry. In the United States the number of cows under test in cow testing associations, or dairy herd-improvement associations, as they are called in this country, increased steadily during recent years, until 510,714 were under test in 1930. A decline then occurred, due to the economic conditions.

The average production of association cows in 1934 was 8,015 lbs. of milk and 322 lbs. of fat, in comparison with the average of only 4,030 lbs. of milk and 158 lbs. of fat for all cows in the country. The great opportunity for further improvement in dairy efficiency is shown by this difference in average production, and by the further fact that less than 1.5

per cent of the dairy cows in the United States were under test in associations in 1935.

The improvement wrought by these associations in Denmark, where they were first developed, is truly remarkable. In this small country more cows were under test in these associations during 1930 than in the whole United States, about 48 per cent of all the cows in that country being in the "control societies," or testing associations. Largely due to the work of the associations, the average yield of all the cows in Denmark increased from 3,530 lbs. of milk and 111 lbs. of fat in 1881 to 7,300 lbs. of milk and 272 lbs. of fat in 1930.[12]

In dairy herd-improvement associations in the United States a trained tester is employed who spends one day every month with each of the herds in the association. Arriving on the farm in the afternoon, he weighs and samples the milk from each cow at milking time and also weighs the feed. The following morning this is repeated, after which the samples of milk are tested for butter fat. From this day's record he computes the milk and fat production and the cost of feed for each cow for the current month. While such records are not as exact as if every milking were weighed, careful studies have shown the results to be within 3 per cent of the actual production of the cow. The tester also studies the local feed market and aids the dairyman in working out economical rations.

In the dairy record clubs, or "mail-order" type of cow testing, which have been developed more recently in this country, the dairyman weighs and samples carefully the milk from every cow for one day each month and then mails the samples and the record of weights to a central testing laboratory, usually conducted by the state college of agriculture. Here the samples are tested, the amount of fat is computed, and the records mailed back to the dairyman. The dairy-record-club plan is especially convenient for farmers who have only a few cows or who live in localities where no dairy herd-improvement association is available. Since less service is rendered in this type of testing, the cost can be very low.

792. Advanced registry of dairy cows.—The advanced registries, or registers of merit, conducted by the various breed associations, have been exceedingly important in the development of dairy cattle breeding in this country. A cow is entitled to advanced registry only when her yield in a test supervised by the state experiment station has reached a standard set by the breed association. These records increase the money value, not only of the given cow, but also of her relatives, for progressive breeders in buying animals now rely more and more on records of production instead of merely show-ring successes.

The herd-test type of official testing is conducted in a dairy herd-improvement association, with certain additional requirements and with supervision by the state experiment station. The feeding and care of cows on advanced registry test are discussed in Chapter XXVII.

793. Building a profitable herd.—The farmer who has a herd of low-producing, unprofitable cows cannot hope for any real success in dairying until he has secured a herd of good producers. He should therefore at once take steps to accomplish this result. Even if he starts with scrub or with beef-type cows he can in 5 to 6 years make considerable improvement in his herd by using a carefully selected, purebred dairy bull, with a bred-for-production pedigree. However, it is usually best to make more rapid progress by selling the poorest producers in the herd, replacing them with a few high-producing grade or even purebred cows of the breed desired. If a good purebred dairy bull is then always used in the herd, and the lowest yielders are culled out each year, in a relatively short time he should have a herd of efficient producers.

The striking improvement which is made in one to three generations by using good purebred dairy bulls on scrub cows or on beef-type cows is shown in experiments by the Iowa, Minnesota, Oklahoma, and South Dakota Stations and the Canadian Department of Agriculture.[13] In the Iowa experiment scrub mature cows, heifers, and a bull were purchased in a district where no purebred bulls had ever been used and where no attention had been paid to the proper feeding of dairy cattle. These animals and their progeny were brought to the Station farm and fed and cared for the same as the animals in the purebred dairy herd.

The average yearly production of the original scrub cows with good feed and care at the Station was only 4,110 lbs. of milk, containing 192 lbs. fat. The daughters of these scrubs, sired by purebred bulls, averaged 5,815 lbs. of milk and 267 lbs. of fat, an increase of 41 per cent in milk yield and 39 per cent in yield of fat. The grand-daughters of the scrub cows, carrying three-fourths of dairy blood, averaged 8,056 lbs. milk and 363 lbs. of fat, an increase of 96 per cent in yield of milk and 89 per cent in yield of fat over the scrubs. The much greater production of the grades was due not only to a larger yield when in milk but also to the fact that they were much more persistent milkers than the scrubs, whose lactation periods were short.

Even more important than the greater yield of milk is the fact that the cost of feed for 100 lbs. milk was 13 per cent less for the three-quarter bloods, even though they were only heifers, than for their scrub grand-dams. Not only was the production rapidly improved by grading up, but also just as striking improvements were made in the conformation of the animals, especially in their udders. The grades, especially of the second cross, were stamped plainly with the breed characteristics of the purebred sires.

Scrub heifers were also raised at the station out of the scrub cows and the scrub bull. They produced 10 per cent more milk and 13 per cent more fat a year than their scrub dams. This small increase, which is strikingly inferior to that produced by the use of purebred sires, is due to the fact that the heifers were so fed and cared for as to develop fully what little tendency they did have for milk production. Scrubs which came to the station as heifers produced on the average 27 per cent more milk than cows that were mature when they first received good feed and care. The scrubs which were 4 years old when purchased showed less response to good feeding than did the heifers. These facts emphasize the necessity of feeding heifers so that they will develop properly.

In these trials the offspring from one of the purebred sires used on the scrub cows fell much below the others in productivity. This illustrates the well-known fact that to build up a herd a sire must not only be a purebred but also must be prepotent in transmitting high production.

II. Nutrient Requirements of Dairy Cows

794. Nutrients required by dairy cows.—It has been shown in Chapter VIII that the nutrient requirements of animals producing a large amount of milk differ greatly from the requirements of animals being fattened or of those doing muscular work. (**236-240**)

For efficient milk production it is essential that dairy cows receive: (1) A liberal amount of total digestible nutrients or net energy; (2) a relatively large amount of protein of the proper quality; (3) at least a certain minimum amount of fat; (4) sufficient phosphorus, calcium, common salt, and other essential minerals; and (5) an ample supply of vitamins A and D. These requirements are discussed in the paragraphs that follow.

The amounts of nutrients required by any particular milk cow will depend, first of all, on her size, since the maintenance requirements are proportional to body size. (**124**) Her requirements will also depend on the amount of milk she is producing, and on its richness in fat. If she is a heifer, she will need additional nutrients for the growth of her body. When she is pregnant, there will be a still further need of nutrients for the development of the fetus. (**217**) This latter requirement will be insignificant in amount during the first part of the gestation period, and will not be large even during the latter part.

In order to keep the recommendations in feeding standards relatively simple, they are usually based merely on (1) the size of cows and (2) on the amounts and the richness in fat of the milk they are producing. It must therefore be understood that during the last half of the gestation period, and also for heifers, the feed supply should be a little more liberal than is called for by the recommendations in the standards.

795. Feeding standards vs. actual requirements.—In the following discussions concerning the nutrient requirements of dairy cows and the recommendations made in various feeding standards, the purpose and nature of feeding standards must be borne clearly in mind. Feeding standards are intended as practical, convenient guides for the proper feeding of the various classes of stock. They are not intended as statements of the theoretical minimum requirements of nutrients.

It has been shown previously that when animals are fed a liberal ration, they digest a slightly smaller percentage of the food nutrients than when they receive a scanty ration. (**113**) Practically all the experiments to determine the digestibility of various feeds have been conducted, not with amply-fed dairy cows, but with steers or wethers fed rather limited rations. This plan has been followed because it is essential in digestion trials that the animals eat all the feed that is offered them, without leaving any waste whatsoever.

Tables giving the digestible nutrients in various feeds, such as Appendix Table I of this volume, must consequently be computed from these digestion coefficients, since they are the only ones available. It must therefore be borne in mind that liberally-fed dairy cows will really secure from the feeds they eat slightly smaller amounts of nutrients than are shown in Appendix Table I. This fact is, however, fully taken into consideration in the recommendations made in the Morrison feeding standards for the feeding of dairy cows. This has been done by placing the advised amounts of nutrients slightly above the theoretical requirements, to cover the decrease in digestibility when liberal rations are fed.

In certain recent feeding standards for dairy cows no such correction factor has apparently been applied. As a result, dairy cows will be under-fed, if rations are computed according to these standards and using the available figures for the digestible nutrients in various feeds.

796. Requirements for maintenance and pregnancy.—The most extensive investigations on the maintenance requirements of dairy cows are those conducted by Hills and associates at the Vermont Station over a period of 14 years with a total of 81 cows.[14] In these experiments certain cows that were dry and non-pregnant were fed rations just sufficient to maintain their body weights for periods of more than a year. So that a complete record could be secured of all the feed consumed, these cows were not turned to pasture. Other studies were conducted with dry cows that were pregnant, and still others were with cows handled under usual herd conditions and calving at normal intervals.

From these extensive investigations Hills concluded that dry, non-pregnant, mature cows weighing 1,000 lbs. could be maintained satisfactorily on 0.6 lb. of digestible protein and 6.48 lbs. of total digestible nutrients (or 6.0 therms of net energy) per head daily.

He concluded, furthermore, that during the first two-thirds of the gestation period the need of additional nutrients was so small that it was unnecessary to provide an additional supply beyond the combined need for maintenance and milk production. He recommended that during the last third of gestation there should be added to the ration for the growth of the fetus about twice as great an amount of digestible nutrients as is contained in the newborn calf, care being taken to see that this increment contains a sufficient amount of digestible protein.

It is of interest to compare the conclusions of Hills with the amounts of nutrients recommended by others for the maintenance of dairy cows. His conclusions are the same as those reached previously by Armsby and by Eckles, both of whom recommended for the maintenance of the 1,000-lb. cow 6.0 therms of net energy and 0.5 lb. digestible true protein per head daily.[15] (This amount of digestible true protein is equivalent to 0.6 lb. digestible crude protein, which is called merely digestible protein in this volume.)

From his investigations at the Minnesota Station, Haecker had earlier recommended somewhat greater amounts of protein and of total digestible nutrients, advising 0.7 lb. digestible protein and 7.925 lbs. total digestible nutrients daily per 1,000 lbs. live weight.[16]

Forbes and associates found in experiments at the Pennsylvania Institute of Animal Nutrition that when dry dairy cows were fasted for 3 to 9 days they excreted nitrogen equivalent to 0.6 lb. digestible protein daily per 1,000 lbs. live weight.[17] From experiments with dry cows in the respiration calorimeter, Forbes and Kriss concluded that 5.97 lbs. of total digestible nutrients were required daily for the maintenance of the 1,000-lb. cow.[18] Converted to terms of total digestible nutrients, the recommendation of Mollgaard (which is expressed in terms of starch values) is practically the same as this, and the recommendation of Hansson (which is expressed in feed-units) is even lower.[19]

The recommendations made in the revised Morrison feeding standards for the maintenance of dairy cows provide somewhat more total digestible nutrients than have been required in the investigations of Hills and Forbes. Cows in milk which are fed with the liberality necessary to produce a good yield of milk digest and utilize their feed somewhat less efficiently than do dry cows fed only enough to maintain their weights. Therefore their supply of feed for maintenance must probably be more liberal.

In recent studies of the results secured in feeding experiments with dairy cows at various experiment stations, Brody and Procter concluded that a 1,000-lb. cow in milk requires about 8.2 lbs. of total digestible nutrients daily for maintenance, in addition to suitable allowances for milk production and for any gain in body weight.[15a] In the Morrison standards an allowance of 7.93 lbs. of total digestible nutrients is recommended for the maintenance of a 1,000-lb. cow in the column entitled, "For good cows under usual conditions," and a figure of 7.00 lbs. is given in the column entitled, "Minimum allowance advised."

The amounts of nutrients recommended in these standards for the maintenance of cows of other live weights than 1,000 lbs. have been computed on the basis that maintenance requirements are proportional, not to the live weight, but to the 0.87 power of the live weight.

797. Requirements for milk production.—The amounts of nutrients a milk cow requires in addition to her maintenance needs will depend both upon the amount of milk she is producing and on its richness in fat. It was recognized by the early agricultural scientists that the nutrient requirements of dairy cows depended on the amount of milk they yielded. However, Haecker of the Minnesota Station was apparently the first to appreciate that the nutrient requirements also depended on the richness of the milk. He recommended a greater amount of nutrients for the production of each pound of milk rich in fat than for each pound of milk lower in fat content.[16]

Milk that is rich in fat is also considerably higher in protein and usually is a trifle higher in sugar than milk which contains less fat. Therefore, a greater amount of total digestible nutrients and also more protein are required for the production of each pound of it than are needed to make milk lower in fat percentage. The rate of increase in protein for each increase of 1.0 per cent in fat content is fairly regular, the protein increasing about 0.42 per cent for each 1.0 per cent increase in fat. (**821**) It is, therefore, possible in a feeding standard to state accurately the amounts of total digestible nutrients and also of digestible protein required for the production of each pound of milk of various degrees of richness, by giving separate recommendations for milk containing the various percentages of fat.

798. Protein requirements for production.—Because it was known that milk was very rich in protein, it was perhaps natural that the early feeding standards should recommend for milk cows considerably more protein that has been shown by later investigations to be necessary. Thus, the Wolff-Lehmann standards advised 3.5 lbs. digestible protein daily and a nutritive ratio of 1:4.5 for cows yielding 27.5 lbs. of milk. Such a ration would furnish, in addition to the maintenance requirement, nearly 3 times as much digestible protein as is contained in this amount (27.5 lbs.) of milk of average composition.

The first great advance in the knowledge concerning the protein requirements for milk production was made by Haecker, who conducted extensive investigations at the Minnesota Station over a period of several years.[16] He recommended that there be provided, in addition to a maintenance allowance of 0.7 lb. digestible protein daily per 1,000 lbs. live weight, definite amounts of digestible protein per pound of milk of the various fat percentages. These additional amounts of digestible protein were set at 1.75 times the estimated amount of protein contained in the milk. Later investigations have shown that milk of the different fat percentages contains somewhat more protein than was found in Haecker's studies. For this reason, the amounts of digestible protein recommended by him were actually only about 1.5 times the amounts of protein contained in milk of average composition.

Recently much more study has been given to the protein requirements of dairy cows than to those of any other class of stock. Among the studies of especial interest are those at the New York (Cornell) Station,[20] the Ohio Station,[21] the Vermont Station,[14] the Virginia Station,[22] the Wisconsin Station,[23] the Wyoming Station,[24] the Pennsylvania Institute of Animal Nutrition,[25] and the Bureau of Dairy Industry of the United States Department of Agriculture.[26]

The results secured in these experiments are of much importance to dairymen, since protein supplements generally cost more than do the farm grains. It is therefore decidedly uneconomical under usual conditions to feed a greater amount of protein supplements than is actually needed.

In such a volume as this, only the main conclusions reached in the investigations can be presented. These experiments have proved that fairly-good production can be secured when cows receive, in addition to the allowance of protein for maintenance, only about 1.25 times as much digestible protein as there is protein in the milk they produce. However, cows of high productive capacity may yield somewhat more milk and fat when the protein allowance is greater than this, especially during the first part of the lactation period. When more digestible protein is supplied than about 1.60 times as much as is contained in the milk, in addition to the maintenance requirement, the production is not increased appreciably.

In certain of the experiments cows of high productive capacity have yielded a surprising amount of milk when fed even less than 1.25 times as much digestible protein, in addition to maintenance, as their milk contained. Thus, in Ohio experiments Holstein cows fed rations having a nutritive ratio of 1:11 produced as high as 11,013 lbs. of 4 per cent milk a year.[21] However, the yield was much less than from the same cows when fed rations containing an adequate supply of protein. On the protein-poor ration the digestibility of the feed was also considerably decreased. Therefore it was necessary to feed very liberal amounts of concentrates to secure fair production. The cows lost about 200 lbs. in weight during milk production, but regained their original weight during the dry period.

In the Ohio experiments other cows were fed rations extremely rich in protein, having a nutritive ratio of 1:2. There were no marked injurious effects from this great excess of protein, although there was a tendency toward delayed breeding on this ration and a longer period than normal between calvings.

The results of these recent investigations have been fully considered in drawing up the recommendations made in the revised Morrison feeding standards for dairy cows, which are presented in Appendix Table III. It will be noted that a range is given in the amounts of protein recommended. The amounts of digestible protein stated in the column headed "Recommended for good cows under usual conditions" supply about 1.5 times as much digestible protein as there is in milk of the various fat percentages. In the column headed "Minimum allowance advised," amounts of digestible protein are stated which furnish only about 1.25 times as much digestible protein as there is in the milk.

Reasonably satisfactory yields of milk can undoubtedly be secured from good cows that are fed only as much protein as provided by the lower figures. However, under usual conditions, the author believes it is the best plan to feed cows capable of producing 1 lb. or more of butter fat a day, according to the more liberal recommendations. If protein-rich feeds are unusually expensive, it may be most economical, even in the case of good cows, to supply no more than the lower amounts of protein shown in the standards.

799. Investigations on protein requirements.—For those especially interested in the protein requirements of dairy cows, a brief summary is presented of the more important investigations on this subject, since the investigations conducted by Haecker.

From studies at the New York (Cornell) Station, Savage concluded in 1912 that it was advisable to provide somewhat more protein than was recommended in the Haecker standards.[27] In the Savage standards, which are well known, allowances of digestible protein were recommended, in addition to 0.7 lb. digestible protein daily per 1,000 lbs. live weight for maintenance, which were about 1.80 times the amount of protein contained in milk of average composition. From recent investigations, which are summarized later, Savage has now concluded, however, that cows do not require so much protein as this for satisfactory production.[20] **(801)**

From a study of the available data, the author decided in 1915 that good milk production could undoubtedly be secured when cows were fed no more protein than was advised in the Haecker standards, but that the production might be slightly greater when the protein allowance was somewhat more liberal. Therefore in the Morrison standards he included a range in the amounts of digestible protein advised, the lower figures being the amounts recommended by Haecker and the higher figures, those advised by Savage at that time.[28]

The recommendations in the Armsby standards, the Eckles standards, the Mollgaard standards, and the Hansson standards, which are based on digestible true protein, must be converted into digestible crude protein (called digestible protein in this volume) to compare them with the standards previously discussed. When this is done and the amounts of protein recommended for maintenance are added to the amounts for milk production, it will be found that about the same amounts of protein were advised in the Armsby standards as in the Haecker standards.[15] Somewhat greater amounts were recommended in the Hansson standards, the Mollgaard standards, the Eckles standards and also in the standards presented by Ellett, Holdaway, and Harris of the Virginia Station.[29]

Hills and associates conducted extensive investigations on this problem at the Vermont Station continuously for a period of 13 years.[14] In these experiments the cows, chiefly grade Jerseys, produced satisfactorily on rations having a nutritive ratio of 1:8.5 and providing 1.26 to 1.46 times as much digestible protein, in addition to maintenance, as the milk contained. The yield on such rations was nearly as high as when the protein supply was more liberal. However, these cows were not high producers, for they averaged 16 to 19 lbs. of milk and 0.78 to 0.92 lb. fat daily during the lactation period. With such cows the production was not seriously decreased when rations still lower in protein were fed, which supplied, in addition to the maintenance requirements, no more digestible protein than was contained in the milk.

It has been found in metabolism experiments that cows will remain in nitrogen balance (without losing protein from their bodies) when receiving a somewhat smaller amount of digestible protein than is called for by the Haecker standards.[23, 25] Such studies indicate that a supply of protein is sufficient for ordinary production if it furnishes, in addition to maintenance needs, 1.25 times as much digestible protein as is contained in the milk.

In certain of the investigations, the production of milk and fat has apparently been increased when a very liberal amount of protein was supplied. However, in the most extensive trials and in those which have covered the longest periods, there has usually been no very large increase in production when cows have received, in addition to the maintenance requirements, about 1.5 to 1.6 times as much digestible protein as their milk contained.

The inadvisability of feeding dairy cows rations too low in protein is shown in recent investigations by the Bureau of Dairy Industry of the United States Department of Agriculture.[26] Two cows were fed a ration having an abundance of total digestible nutrients, but supplying only 1.25 times as much digestible protein as was contained in the milk, in addition to an allowance of only 0.5 lb. digestible protein daily per 1,000 lbs. live weight for maintenance. On this ration the cows produced 22 to 50 per cent less milk and fat than on a ration containing a liberal amount of protein. (It should be noted that only 0.5 lb. digestible protein daily per 1,000 lbs. live weight was allowed for maintenance in these tests, which is lower than the amount recommended in the revised Morrison standards.)

800. Importance of protein content of roughage.—The percentage of protein that is needed in the concentrate mixture, or so-called "grain mixture," to make a properly-balanced ration will depend on the protein content of the roughage fed. (866) When the only roughage is alfalfa hay, cowpea hay, or soybean hay (all of which are very rich in protein), the amount of protein supplied by the hay will be so large that there will be sufficient protein for a cow of ordinary productive capacity when merely corn grain or a mixture of corn and other grain is fed.

Thus, 24 lbs. of average alfalfa hay and 12 lbs. of corn (No. 2 grade) will furnish 3.39 lbs. of digestible protein. This amount of protein is sufficient for a 1,200-lb. cow producing daily 50 lbs. of milk containing 3.5 per cent fat. For high-producing cows it may be wise to include wheat bran or some other protein-rich concentrate to make the mixture more palatable, even though the additional amount of protein is not actually needed. Also, such a ration may be too low in phosphorus, unless the hay comes from soil well supplied with this mineral.

The amount of protein supplied by the roughage will be somewhat less when red clover hay is fed than with alfalfa hay. For example, 24 lbs. of average red clover hay and 12 lbs. of corn supply only 2.53 lbs. digestible protein. This is less than a high-producing cow needs, and therefore it would be necessary to add a protein supplement to the ration. However, a ration of only good clover hay and corn grain would provide sufficient protein for a cow producing not over 30 lbs. of 3.5 per cent milk daily.

When non-legume roughage, such as corn or sorghum silage, is fed along with legume hay, or when the hay is mixed legume-and-grass hay, considerably less protein will obviously be supplied by the roughage. The concentrate mixture must then be richer in protein than is needed when pure legume hay is the only roughage. However, less protein is needed in the concentrate mixture under such conditions than many dairymen believe essential. When only non-legume roughage is fed, the concentrate mixture must be rich in protein.

It is shown in the following chapter that such a grain mixture as one-half ground corn and one-half ground oats is satisfactory for cows yielding not over 1.25 lbs. butter fat a day, when the animals are full-fed good alfalfa hay and corn silage for roughage. (**865**) For higher-producing cows and when the amount of alfalfa hay is limited, protein supplements should be added to the ration.

Since young, actively-growing pasture plants are even richer than alfalfa hay in protein, on the dry basis, it is unnecessary to use a concentrate mixture high in protein for cows on excellent pasture. This matter is discussed further in Chapter XXVI.

There are given in Appendix Table VII many different concentrate mixtures which are well adapted for use with the various types of roughages. These example formulas will be helpful in deciding what kind of a mixture to feed under one's local conditions.

801. Requirement with mixed hay and corn silage.—In the northern states, especially in the Northeast, a very common roughage combination for dairy cows is mixed clover-and-timothy hay and corn silage. Experiments have been recently conducted by Harrison, Savage, and Work at the New York (Cornell) Station to determine how much protein is needed in a concentrate mixture for feeding with this combination of roughage.[20]

The hay used in these trials was early-cut mixed clover-and-timothy hay of good quality, containing 30 to 50 per cent clover. The cows in each lot were continuously fed the same ration throughout each trial, except in one of the experiments. In this one experiment the rations were reversed at the end of each 5-week period to determine the effect of changing abruptly from a ration low in protein to one high in protein, and vice versa.

In 5 experiments the cows fed a concentrate mixture containing 16 per cent total protein produced a daily average of 33.1 lbs. milk (equated to a basis of 3.5 per cent fat), while those fed a concentrate mixture containing 20 per cent total protein produced 34.4 lbs. milk. After deducting 0.6 lb. digestible protein per head daily for maintenance, the former ration furnished 1.2 to 1.4 times as much digestible protein as was contained in the milk, and the latter ration about 1.6 to 1.7 times as much. Though the average yield of milk was slightly greater on the 20-per-cent-protein mixture, the difference was too small to be statistically significant.

During 3 years a concentrate mixture containing 24 per cent total protein was tested. No more milk or fat was produced on this high-protein mixture than on the mixture containing 20 per cent protein. When a low-protein concentrate mixture which contained only 12 per cent protein was fed, the production of milk was decidedly decreased in each of 2 experiments, the average decrease being 12 per cent. This showed that a 12-per-cent-protein concentrate mixture did not supply sufficient protein for feeding with good-quality mixed clover-and-timothy hay and corn silage. After deducting 0.6 lb. digestible protein daily per 1,000 lbs. live weight for maintenance, this ration did not supply quite as much digestible protein as was contained in the milk. During the height of milk production, the cows fed this ration therefore had to draw on their bodies for some of the protein they put in their milk. Also, it was found in digestion trials that on this low amount of feed-protein the digestibility of the ration was considerably decreased.

In one experiment when the cows were changed abruptly from the 16-per-cent protein mixture to the 24-per-cent protein mixture, there was no effect upon the yield of milk or on the health of the cows. The reverse change also had no effect.

Experiments have also been conducted recently by the Ohio Station to determine the amount of protein needed in a concentrate mixture with good mixed legume-and-grass hay and corn silage.[30] In 2 trials the yield of milk was 6 per cent greater on a concentrate mixture containing 19.0 per cent total protein than on one containing 13.8 per cent. The ration higher in protein content supplied about as much protein as recommended in the Haecker standards. The other ration furnished, above maintenance requirements, about 1.25 times as much digestible protein as was contained in the milk.

These recent investigations are of much importance to northeastern dairymen, for a large proportion of them had previously been feeding concentrate mixtures containing 24 per cent protein, with first-class mixed clover-and-timothy hay and corn silage for roughage. These experiments show that with such roughage just as high production can be secured from a mixture containing 20 per cent protein, or probably from one containing 18 per cent protein. When protein supplements are high in price, a mixture containing only 16 per cent protein will generally be more economical with such roughage than one higher in protein. It must be borne in mind, however, that with mixed hay containing only a small proportion of clover or that which is late-cut, more protein than this should be supplied in the concentrate mixture.

802. Quality of protein.—It has been shown in Chapter VI that when dairy cows are fed considerable well-cured legume hay, the ration will provide protein of good quality for milk production, even if no protein supplements are fed that furnish protein of high quality. (152-155) In the case of ruminants, legume hay amply corrects any deficiencies in the proteins of the cereal grains and their by-products.

When there is little or no legume hay in the ration, it is not wise to balance the ration with only such supplements as corn gluten feed, corn gluten meal, brewers' dried grains, or distillers' dried grains, which have proteins that are low in certain of the essential amino acids. Instead, these supplements should be used in combination with such feeds as linseed meal, cottonseed meal, soybeans, soybean oil meal, and peanut oil meal, all of which provide proteins of better quality.

For dairy cows fed the usual roughages, it has been found that meat meal, tankage, and fish meal are apparently no more efficient sources of protein than are such supplements of plant origin as cottonseed meal, soybeans, linseed meal, etc.[31] These animal by-products therefore have a lower relative value for dairy cows than for swine and poultry. (143) With the exception of the general facts which have been summarized in these paragraphs, the experimental data are too limited to warrant definite conclusions concerning the relative efficiency for milk production of proteins furnished by various rations and protein supplements.[32]

803. Fat requirements.—It has been pointed out in Chapter VIII that the fat in milk can be formed by a lactating animal from other food nutrients than fat, but that the animal can apparently make milk fat more readily from food fat than by synthesizing it from carbohydrates. Therefore, unless the ration for a high-producing cow contains at least a certain minimum amount of food fat, the yield of milk and of fat will be considerably decreased.

There is a tendency for dairy rations to have less fat than formerly, because of changes in the process of oil extraction in which the various oil meals are obtained as by-products. When the solvent process is employed, practically all the fat is removed from the oil meal. It is therefore of much practical importance to determine the minimum amount of fat needed in dairy rations for maximum production.

In some of the earlier experiments on this question the low-fat rations, with which rations higher in fat were compared, still contained so much fat that no increase in production was obtained on the high-fat ration.[33] It was therefore concluded that the percentage of fat in dairy rations was of no practical importance, and that the efficiency of a concentrate mixture depended on the amount of net energy or of total digestible nutrients (including digestible fat multiplied by 2.25) it furnished, and not on the percentage of fat in it.

In experiments by Maynard, McCay, and associates at the New York (Cornell) Station it has been found, however, that the yield of milk and of fat is decidedly decreased when cows receiving such roughage as a combination of corn silage and mixed clover-and-timothy hay, are fed a concentrate mixture containing less than about 4 per cent of fat.[34] On a ration containing 4 per cent fat the feed supplied about 70 per cent as much total fat as was secreted in the milk.

When fed with this combination of roughage, a concentrate mixture containing 6.6 to 7.2 per cent fat did not produce significantly more milk or fat than one which contained about 4 per cent fat, though there was a tendency for the yield to be a trifle higher on the mixture richer in fat. It was concluded that a higher level of fat in the concentrate or grain mixture than 4 per cent is not justified, if it increases the cost of the ration per pound of total digestible nutrients.

On a concentrate mixture containing only 1 per cent of fat, fed with alfalfa hay and dried beet pulp, which are both low in fat, the yield of milk and of fat by cows was decreased considerably, but the percentage of fat in the milk was not reduced. On a concentrate mixture containing only 3 per cent fat, fed with the same roughage, smaller but significant decreases in milk and fat yield occurred. In the case of milk goats a low-fat ration not only decreased the yield of milk, but also tended to reduce the percentage of fat in the milk.

The effects of various feeds on the character of the milk fat and on the percentage of fat in milk are discussed later in this chapter.

804. Total digestible nutrient requirements.—The various modern feeding standards state the amounts of total digestible nutrients (or of net energy) that should be supplied, in addition to the maintenance requirements, for each pound of milk of the various fat percentages. Since feeding standards are intended as guides in the economical feeding of livestock, the amounts of total digestible nutrients recommended are the quantities advised for general herd feeding. Where maximum production is desired, regardless of expenses, somewhat greater amounts must be supplied.

Substantially the same amounts of total digestible nutrients were recommended for the production of milk of various fat percentages in the Savage standards[27] and in the final form of the Haecker standards.[16] The Armsby standards, which were expressed in terms of net energy, supplied about 15 to 20 per cent less nutrients than the Savage and Haecker standards.[15] The Hansson and the Mollgaard standards recommended about the same levels of feeding as the Armsby standards.[29] Except for milk very rich in fat, the standards recently proposed by Forbes and Kriss recommend slightly more total digestible nutrients for production than the Armsby figures.[18] However, the Forbes and Kriss standards are enough lower in the amount of nutrients recommended for maintenance to offset this difference in the case of cows of usual productive capacity.

It was found in an experiment at the Wisconsin Station that when cows were fed according to the Savage standards the milk production was appreciably higher than when they were fed a ration which met the Armsby standards.[35] From 1 to 3 lbs. less grain were required per head daily in the latter rations than in the rations which met the recommendations of the Savage standards. Likewise, it was found in experiments by the Bureau of Dairy Industry of the United States Department of Agriculture that dairy cows fed according to the methods of feeding commonly followed in the eastern states required 15 per cent more nutrients for milk production than were recommended in the Armsby standards.[36]

Even for cows of ordinary productive capacity, the recommendations of the Savage and Haecker standards call for a fairly liberal amount of concentrates, in addition to an abundance of roughage. When hay and other roughages supply nutrients much more cheaply than do concentrates, it is most economical to feed a somewhat smaller amount of concentrates than is needed to balance the ration according to these standards, even though the production is thereby decreased somewhat.

For this reason, in the Morrison feeding standards, which were first presented in 1915, a range was given in the amounts of total digestible nutrients recommended for each pound of milk of the various fat percentages.[28] The higher figures were the averages of the recommendations of Savage and of Haecker. The lower figures were placed 10 per cent below the higher recommendations, for use when roughages were much cheaper sources of nutrients than were concentrates.

These recommendations have been modified somewhat in the revised Morrison standards presented in Appendix Table III. The recommendations for milk containing various percentages of fat have been computed on the basis of the Gaines' formula for estimating the energy content of milk. (822) The higher amounts of total digestible nutrients are recommended for good cows under usual conditions. When roughage is very cheap in comparison with concentrates, it may be more profitable to supply no more total degistible nutrients than called for by the figures in the column entitled, "Minimum allowance advised."

805. Feeding cows chiefly or entirely on roughage.—In order to secure the greatest net returns from dairying, one of the first essentials under usual conditions is to provide the cows with an abundance of good-quality roughage. The importance of first-class hay and silage and of excellent pasturage has been emphasized in Chapters XI and XII. Without a proper supply of excellent roughage, unduly large amounts of grain and purchased concentrates must be fed to secure satisfactory milk production.

With plenty of good roughage available, the question then arises as to what is the most profitable amount of concentrates to feed. The answer will depend on the productive capacity of the cows, on the relative cost of nutrients in roughage and in concentrates, and on the price received for the milk. The feeding of concentrates to cows on pasture is considered in Chapter XXVI.

In the corn belt and eastward it is generally most profitable to supply good cows with enough concentrates, in addition to an abundance of high-quality roughage, to meet the recommendations of the feeding standards. Guides for determining the amount of concentrates to be fed to cows producing various amounts of milk and with various types of roughage are given in Chapter XXVI and in Appendix Table IX.

In such sections as some of the alfalfa districts of the West where good roughage is very cheap in comparison with grain and other concentrates, it is generally most profitable to feed less concentrates than called for by the feeding standards. Under these conditions it may even be most economical to use no concentrates whatsoever, but to feed the cows only hay and other roughage. When milk is high in price, it pays even under such conditions to feed some concentrates, in order to secure a large yield.

When cows are fed all the high-quality hay they will eat during the winter, with excellent irrigated pasture during the summer, relatively good production is often secured with little or no concentrates. Since they have a greater capacity to consume roughage, Holsteins and cows of the other large breeds usually do better on such a ration than smaller animals.

On nothing but roughage, even that of excellent quality, the yield of milk will be decidedly less than when at least a moderate amount of concentrates is supplied. Roughage alone, even choice alfalfa hay, is too bulky and not rich enough in net energy to permit continued high production.

In some districts of the West, cows are fed nothing but alfalfa hay during the entire year, with little or no pasturage, but perhaps with some green alfalfa fed as a soiling crop during the summer. Under such conditions the production is apt to be decidedly less than when good pasture is available during the summer. (870)

In Oregon tests, cows fed solely on alfalfa hay produced an average of only 4,464 lbs. of 4 per cent milk on a mature-equivalent basis during a 305-day lactation period.[37] On alfalfa hay plus 10 lbs. per head daily of a mixture of ground oats and barley, the average yield was 8,416 lbs. The average production on alfalfa hay was therefore only 53 per cent of that on hay plus grain. The low production on alfalfa hay alone in these tests was perhaps due partly to the fact that it was somewhat lower than normal in phosphorus.

Heifers raised on alfalfa hay alone in Kansas experiments and continued on this ration through their second lactation period, produced only 4,124 lbs. of milk and 150 lbs. of fat a year.[38] Others fed alfalfa hay with grain and silage yielded an average of 6,156 lbs. milk and 226 lbs. fat. It was concluded that with grain costing 3 times as much as alfalfa hay per ton, it was profitable to add it to the ration. In a Nevada cow-testing association cows fed nothing but alfalfa hay produced a yearly average of 7,060 lbs. milk, containing 263 lbs. of butter fat.[39]

806. Feeding only alfalfa hay and silage.—When silage from corn or other suitable silage crops is fed during the winter in addition to alfalfa hay, the milk yield is generally much greater than on alfalfa hay alone. The possibilities of milk production from alfalfa hay and corn silage are well shown in the "most-milk-per-acre demonstration" conducted for 6 years by Fraser at the Illinois Station.[40]

A herd of 11 well-selected grade Holstein cows was maintained throughout each year exclusively on the alfalfa hay and the corn crop grown on 20 acres. Most of the corn was made into silage, and during 2 years there was only enough corn forage to provide silage. Consequently, the cows had only alfalfa hay and corn silage, with no grain in addition. During the four other years they had a very limited amount of corn grain. The cows yielded on the average 7,470 lbs. of milk and 262 lbs. of fat a year for the entire six years, producing 3,888 lbs. of milk per acre a year. This was practically three times as much milk per acre as was commonly produced at that time on the average dairy farm in Illinois. During the time that 9 cows were fed on roughage alone they averaged 7,029 lbs. of milk a year.

These results should not be interpreted to mean that under the usual conditions in the corn belt and eastward, cows of good productive capacity should be fed roughage alone. As Fraser points out: "Undoubtedly these cows would have produced more milk and would have done it more economically had they been fed grain when the production was more than 20 lbs. of milk per day. . . . It is strongly recommended that when cows are producing more than 20 lbs. of 3.5 to 4 per cent milk per day, they should be fed grain.''

In Montana experiments well-bred Holstein cows that had excellent irrigated pasturage in summer were fed during the winter chiefly on alfalfa hay and corn silage, with a limited amount of sugar beets and a total of 65 lbs. of dried beet pulp per cow during the year.[41] These cows, which averaged 1,240 lbs. in weight, yielded an average of 13,295 lbs. of milk and 464 lbs. of fat. This exceptionally large production on this roughage ration was due to the high productive capacity of the cows and the excellent quality of the roughage.

During other years the same cows yielded an average of 16,407 lbs. of milk and 576 lbs. of fat when fed, in addition to the roughage, 1 lb. of concentrates for every 6 lbs. of milk produced. Even under Montana conditions, the annual net return over cost of feed was $25.03 more per head on this ration than on the roughage ration.

During other lactation periods these Holstein cows were fed on official test, receiving even more concentrates than required to meet the recommendations of the feeding standards. They were given, in addition to the excellent roughage, 1 lb. of concentrates for each 3 pounds of milk produced. On this test ration the yield of milk was only 6 per cent greater (on the mature-equivalent basis) and the net return over cost of feed much lower than on the smaller allowance of concentrates.

These experiments and also the results of similar investigations show the value of good roughage in milk production, and the importance of adapting the method of feeding to the local conditions.[42]

807. It pays to feed good cows liberally.—Except when concentrates are very high in price in comparison with hay and other roughage, it is most profitable to feed good cows enough concentrates to maintain a high level of milk production. Even when concentrates are so high priced that it is wise to reduce the concentrate allowance below the normal amount, the cows should still get all the good roughage they will eat. Otherwise, their production will be so low that the net income over cost of feed will be seriously reduced.

Demonstrations by the Indiana Station, the New York (Cornell) Station, and the Ohio Station have shown in a striking manner the financial benefits from the proper feeding and care of good cows.[43] In the Indiana demonstrations 5 cows were selected from herds on dairy farms where records of feed and production had been kept the previous year, but where the animals had not been well fed. Cows were chosen that had been low producers, but that were of good dairy type. They were brought to the Station farm, where they were fed and cared for in the same manner as the cows in the Station herd. They received roughage of good quality and were fed concentrates strictly according to their actual yield.

On the Indiana farms these cows had produced an average of 5,064 lbs. milk and 203 lbs. fat for the previous year, at an average feed cost of $43.72. The average value of the milk produced was $121.36, leaving $77.64 as the average net return above feed costs.

In the Station herd the same cows produced an average of 8,662 lbs. milk and 317 lbs. fat, at a feed cost of $72.34. The milk produced was worth $207.38, on the average, leaving $135.04 as the net return

JEWEL

7 DAY RECORD

MILK 483.8 BUTTER 27.54

YEARS RECORD

MILK   19793.5 lbs.
FAT   676.95
BUTTER 846.2

BALANCED RATIONS ARE NECESSARY FOR PROFITS IN DAIRYING

The farmer who does not feed his cows a concentrate mixture that makes a well-balanced ration should not expect a profit. Even well-bred cows can not be expected to give a large yield of milk unless they are furnished the proper raw materials in their feed. (From Wisconsin Station.)

CASEY JONES PRODUCED THREE TUBS OF BUTTER A YEAR

Casey Jones was a good-looking, pure-bred Holstein, but she produced only 3 tubs of butter a year. The cow tester discovered her. (From Wisconsin Station.)

"HANDSOME IS AS HANDSOME DOES"

Vickery Vale Beechwood, another pure-bred Holstein, did not look much better than Casey Jones, but she yielded 20 tubs of butter a year. (From Wisconsin Station.)

above feed cost. Some dairymen would doubtless have thought that the cows were being fed extravagantly, for their average feed cost was $28.62 more than for the previous year. However, this investment in liberal feeding, along with better care, brought an increase of $86.02 per cow in the value of the milk produced, and it added $57.40 per cow to the net income over cost of feed. Just as striking proofs of the benefits from proper feeding and care are furnished by numerous instances in the records of cow-testing associations, where dairymen have greatly increased their net income by adopting improved methods of feeding and care.

808. Restricting the roughage.—Some producers of market milk on high-priced land near the large cities follow the plan of limiting the amount of roughage and feeding an unusually liberal amount of concentrates. They do this because they wish to keep the maximum number of cows on their farms, and they can more readily provide additional feed in the form of purchased concentrates than in the form of purchased roughage.

In experiments at the Massachusetts Station this method of feeding was compared with the use of a maximum amount of roughage and a rather low allowance of concentrates.[44] The cows in the first group were fed only 20 lbs. of corn silage per head daily, with what hay the cows would clean up and 1 lb. of concentrates for every 2.5 lbs. of milk. The cows in the other group received 35 lbs. corn silage, a liberal amount of hay, and only 1 lb. of concentrates to every 4.5 lbs. of milk.

On the low-roughage ration the average yield of milk was 31.7 lbs. daily in comparison with 27.7 lbs. for the ration containing the less liberal amount of concentrates. At the particular time when the experiments were conducted (1928-32), the cost of milk production was practically the same under the two methods of feeding. When concentrates are very cheap in comparison with roughage, it would obviously be more economical to purchase concentrates instead of hay to supplement the feed raised on the farm.

809. Relative value of concentrates and hay.—When there is only a limited amount of roughage available on the dairy farm, the problem always arises as to whether it is more economical to buy hay or to purchase additional concentrates as a substitute for part of the usual roughage allowance. The net energy values of concentrates and of hay provide the best basis for making a decision. Comparisons based on total digestible nutrients will give somewhat too high a value to hay, if there is already available on the farm enough good-quality roughage to supply sufficient bulk and enough vitamins.

A good concentrate mixture, or mixed dairy feed, will contain about 70 to 75 therms of net energy per 100 lbs., while good-quality hay will supply 40 to 45 therms per 100 lbs. On the average, it will take about 1.75 lbs. of good hay to provide as much net energy as is furnished by 1.0 lb. of a good dairy concentrate mixture. On this basis, such a concentrate mixture would be worth 1.75 times as much as good hay as a substitute for part of the roughage usually fed to dairy cows.

810. Self-feeding cows.—While the self-feeding method is widely used in swine feeding and is also often employed in the fattening of cattle and lambs, it is not satisfactory for dairy cows. Experiments at the Illinois and Virginia Stations show that when cows are self-fed grain and other concentrates they will eat a much greater amount than they need, thus making the method decidedly uneconomical.[45] If self-fed different concentrates, free-choice, they will also eat a much larger proportion than necessary of the protein-rich feeds.

811. Mineral requirements.—The general mineral requirements of livestock have been discussed in Chapter VI. It is there shown that in most rations which are otherwise satisfactory for cattle, common salt is the only mineral that is practically always deficient.

Since milk is very rich in calcium and phosphorus, we might suppose that it would be necessary to add calcium and phosphorus supplements to the usual rations for dairy cattle. Fortunately, however, the recent investigations summarized in the following pages have proved that the majority of well-balanced dairy rations supply amounts of these minerals which are adequate for all cows except the highest producers. However, under certain conditions the use of a phosphorus supplement is necessary, and occasionally a calcium supplement is needed.

In addition to calcium, phosphorus, and common salt, which are considered in detail in the paragraphs that follow, iodine and also iron and copper must sometimes be considered in the feeding of dairy cattle. Sufficient amounts of the other essential minerals are supplied by any ordinary rations, so far as is known.

In certain areas, there is a lack of iodine in the feed and water which causes goiter in new-born calves. The method of preventing this trouble has been explained in Chapter VI. Experiments have shown that there is no appreciable benefit from adding iodine to the rations of dairy cows except in the areas where goiter in livestock is prevalent. (172) In spite of some claims made to the contrary, these investigations have shown that the use of iodine supplements will not prevent or cure Bang's disease (infectious abortion) or eradicate other breeding troubles.

As is shown in Chapter VI, in a few localities the soil is so deficient in iron or in both iron and copper that serious anemia of livestock results unless these minerals are supplied. (173)

812. Phosphorus requirements.—It has been shown in Chapter VI that in certain districts stock suffer severely from a lack of phosphorus, because of a deficiency of this mineral in the soil and a consequent low phosphorus content in the forages. In such areas care must be taken that dairy cattle are adequately supplied with phosphorus, or poor results will follow. On the other hand, there will ordinarily be no lack of phosphorus in areas where the soil is well supplied with the mineral and dairy cattle are fed the usual type of rations, including grain and protein-rich concentrates, with plenty of good hay or hay and silage.

From investigations at the Michigan Station Huffman and associates recommend that dairy cows be supplied with 10 grams (0.35 ounce) of phosphorus daily per 1,000 lbs. live weight for maintenance and with 0.75 gram (0.026 ounce) for each pound of milk produced.[46] It is recommended further that not less than 17 grams (0.60 ounce) of phosphorus be fed daily during low production and during the dry period prior to calving.

On the basis of these recommendations the ration of a 1,200-lb. cow producing about 30 lbs. of milk a day should contain, on the air-dry basis, about 0.23 per cent phosphorus, and the ration of a cow yielding 60 lbs. of milk, about 0.26 per cent phosphorus. From the data in Appendix Table I, one can determine the approximate percentage of phosphorus a particular ration will furnish, if the roughages have been grown on soil fairly well supplied with phosphorus. If silage is included in the ration, it should be reduced to an air-dry basis by dividing the weight fed by 3 and multiplying the phosphorus percentage shown in the table by 3. For example, 30 lbs. of well-matured corn silage of average composition, containing 0.06 per cent phosphorus, are approximately equal to 10 lbs. of air-dry silage containing 0.18 per cent phosphorus.

It will be noted in Appendix Table I that even alfalfa hay supplies, on the average, only 0.21 per cent phosphorus, and most other hays have still less. As has been emphasized in Chapter VI, the grains contain more phosphorus than the hays, corn grain (which is the lowest in phosphorus) having about 0.27 per cent. (160)   Most of the protein supplements are still higher in phosphorus content, especially wheat bran, standard wheat middlings, cottonseed meal, and linseed meal. Corn gluten meal, corn gluten feed, distillers' dried grains, and brewers' dried grains are only fair in percentage of phosphorus.

When cows are fed only on roughage, even alfalfa hay and silage, the phosphorus content of the ration will be slightly less than is recommended for good milk production. If the roughage has been grown on soil low in phosphorus, the supply of the mineral will be decidedly deficient. The addition of grain, even of corn, to the ration will increase the phosphorus content somewhat. However, Michigan experiments have proved that the phosphorus supply will be seriously deficient for good cows in a ration made up of corn grain fed with alfalfa hay and corn silage of slightly lower phosphorus content than the average.

Unless the roughage is grown on soil well-supplied with phosphorus, a phosphorus supplement should be added to a ration made up of roughage and farm grain, and especially to a ration of roughage alone, without grain. Where part of the roughage consists of a feed very low in phosphorus, such as cereal straw or cottonseed hulls, this fact must be taken into consideration.

Dairy cows will usually receive sufficient phosphorus if they are fed enough concentrates to meet the recommendations of the feeding standards and the concentrate mixture includes at least 25 per cent of the high-phosphorus protein supplements, such as wheat bran, cottonseed meal and linseed meal. The only exception may be when the roughage is from soil decidedly deficient in phosphorus.

When phosphorus is lacking, it can be provided by allowing the cows access to one of the mineral mixtures previously recommended, or 20 to 40 lbs. of bone meal or other safe phosphorus supplement may be added to each ton of the concentrate mixture. (166-170, 181)   A phosphorus supplement containing a dangerous amount of fluorine should not be used for stock feeding. (171)

813. Calcium requirements.—Milk contains a slightly greater quantity of calcium than of phosphorus. Nevertheless, there is much less apt to be a lack of calcium in rations for dairy cows than a deficiency of phosphorus. Even non-legume roughages generally contain more calcium than phosphorus, and all legume roughages are very rich in calcium. Also, cows can apparently utilize the calcium in their feeds somewhat more efficiently than the phosphorus.

In Wisconsin experiments the milk production of good dairy cows fed a ration containing only 0.2 per cent calcium, on the dry basis, was fully as large as that of other cows which were fed a ration rich in calcium.[47] In these experiments, good-producing cows that had been fed continuously on each ration for 3 lactation periods were slaughtered just before calving. It was found that the skeletons of the cows fed the low-calcium ration were entirely normal, and contained as much calcium as those which had received the calcium-rich ration.

No injurious results were produced in Minnesota experiments when dairy cows were fed a ration containing only 0.12 per cent calcium for long periods. In order to reduce the calcium content to this low level, the only roughage was 6 to 7 lbs. of timothy hay that was low in percentage of this mineral.[48] The cows yielded 6,453 to 8,706 lbs. of milk during lactation periods on this ration and produced normal calves.

For high-producing cows it would seem desirable to use rations containing at least 0.2 per cent calcium, on the dry basis, and preferably somewhat more. When such cows receive no legume hay, the use of a calcium supplement is probably wise as an insurance against a deficiency of the mineral, unless the roughage has been grown on soil well supplied with calcium. When at least one-quarter of the roughage, on the dry basis, is legume hay or legume silage, one can be sure that there is no possible deficiency of calcium.

Where the soil is very deficient in calcium, dairy cows fed non-legume roughage, even of good quality, may suffer seriously from a lack of the mineral, unless a calcium supplement is supplied. This is shown by results secured at the Florida Station.[49] For some years the cows in the Station dairy herd had received corn or sorghum silage as the only roughage during the winter and had been on grass pasture during the summer. They had been liberally fed on a good concentrate mixture which was rich in phosphorus and which included a small percentage of alfalfa meal. Though the cows were in good flesh and some were even excessively fat, a few had suffered broken bones with no apparent cause. The milk yield was also very low, considering the quality of the cows and the liberality of feeding.

When a mineral supplement was added to the ration to provide additional calcium, the average milk yield of the cows, which were Jerseys, was increased from 3,980 lbs. a year to 6,425 lbs. No longer was there any trouble from cows breaking their bones, and fewer of the cows showed a tendency to excessive fatness. It should be noted that the condition of these cows when suffering from the deficiency of calcium was entirely different from that which occurs in phosphorus deficiency. In the latter case cattle are run-down and emaciated, due to a lack of appetite and poor utilization of their feed. (**164**)

If there is any possibility of a lack of calcium in the ration, the mineral may readily be supplied by the use of one of the mineral mixtures suggested in Chapter VI, or by including 20 to 30 lbs. of ground limestone or other calcium supplement in each ton of the concentrate mixture. (165, 181) Unless the deficiency of calcium is serious, it is best to use only 20 lbs. of limestone per ton, instead of more, or the palatability of the concentrate mixture may be lessened.

814. Losses and storage of calcium and phosphorus.—Numerous investigations have been conducted in recent years to study the use of calcium and phosphorus by dairy cows and their requirements for these minerals. On account of a lack of space, only a brief summary can be presented here of some of the most important results secured in these experiments.[50]

Metabolism experiments conducted by Forbes and associates at the Ohio Station previous to 1920 revealed a surprising condition.[51] It was found in these investigations, where the gains or losses of calcium and phosphorus in the bodies of the cows were carefully determined, that high-producing cows fed excellent dairy rations were commonly losing significant quantities of these minerals daily from their bodies. The losses were usually less when a liberal amount of legume hay was fed than when no legume hay was included in the ration. Also, the addition of bone meal or other suitable mineral supplements tended to lessen the losses of phosphorus and calcium, but not to prevent them entirely.

Since these losses continued when high-producing cows were fed ideal dairy rations, it seemed evident that the cows were unable to assimilate sufficient of the calcium and phosphorus for the production of a large amount of milk, even when the ration contained liberal quantities of the minerals. Consequently, they drew on the stores of these minerals in their skeletons in order to maintain a normal mineral content in the milk they yielded.

These investigations at once raised the question as to whether or not such losses of minerals during high production were a cause of the relatively short productive life of many high-yielding cows. Since the use of phosphorus and calcium supplements tended to reduce these losses, it was natural to conclude that it was wise to add mineral supplements to ordinary dairy rations. It was believed that this would be good insurance against injurious effects from a drain on the reserves of calcium and phosphorus in the bodies of such cows.

In later investigations Forbes and others found, however, that during the latter part of the lactation period, when the milk yield was lower, and also during the dry period, cows stored considerable amounts of these minerals in their bodies when fed good dairy rations.[52] It therefore seems to be a normal condition for high-producing cows to draw on the reserves in their skeletons for calcium and phosphorus during the flush of milk production, and then to replace these losses late in lactation and when they are dry.

Continuous metabolism experiments over entire lactation periods have recently been conducted with good dairy cows by Ellenberger and associates at the Vermont Station and by Forbes and colleagues at the Pennsylvania Institute of Animal Nutrition.[52a] In these studies the amounts of calcium and phosphorus that each animal gained or lost during the entire year or the complete lactation period were determined. In the Vermont investigations certain animals were continued on the experiments for 5 or more consecutive years.

These high-producing cows, which yielded 9,000 to 15,000 lbs. of milk a year, lost calcium and phosphorus during the first part of the lactation period, when their yields were largest. However, in nearly all cases they stored sufficient of these minerals later so that by the next calving time the losses were more than replaced. This was true even when the cows were fed no legume hay, but only good timothy hay and corn silage as the roughages. The addition of bone meal, ground limestone, or a mixture of the two mineral supplements tended to lessen the losses of minerals during the early part of the lactation period and to result in a greater storage for the entire year. There was, however, no proof that the addition of these supplements improved the health or the production of the cows.

815. Adding calcium or phosphorus to good rations.—Experiments have been conducted by several stations to determine whether or not there would be any benefit from adding a phosphorus and calcium supplement to good dairy rations.[53] In these experiments one group of cows has been fed a well-balanced ration, including the usual amount of a concentrate mixture of the common type and plenty of good roughage, but with no mineral supplement except common salt. Another group has received the same ration, except that a mineral supplement, such as bone meal, has been added to supply additional phosphorus and calcium. In some cases a mineral mixture has been used, containing such mineral supplements as bone meal and ground limestone.

With the exception of the experiments mentioned previously, in which the roughage was unusually low in phosphorus or in calcium, there has been no decided benefit from the use of these mineral supplements. This has been true even when little or no legume hay or other legume roughage has been fed. These experiments have definitely proved that the use of phosphorus or calcium supplements for milk cows is advisable only under the special conditions stated in the previous paragraphs.

816. Salt.—The experiments reviewed in Chapter VI show clearly that dairy cows must have salt to thrive. If they are allowed to consume as much salt as they wish, they will take 1 to 4 ounces per head daily when fed usual dairy rations.[54] The amount of salt needed depends on the live weight and on the amount of milk produced. An allowance of 0.75 ounce daily per 1,000 lbs. live weight, with 0.3 ounce in addition for every 10 lbs. of milk, is generally sufficient.[55]

Cows may be allowed free access to salt; they may be fed salt daily or at regular intervals of two or three days; or it may be mixed with their feed. Probably the best plan in the case of cows being fed the usual amount of a concentrate or "grain" mixture is to mix 1.0 lb. of salt with each 100 lbs. of concentrates, and then in addition provide salt in a salt box or by the use of salt blocks, so the cows can have access to it and take all they wish. Mixing some salt with the concentrate mixture tends to make it more palatable and also insures that the cows get salt each day.

817. Vitamin requirements.—The vitamin requirements of the various classes of stock have been discussed in detail in Chapter VI. It has there been shown that vitamin A and vitamin D are the only vitamins that may be lacking in the usual rations fed cattle. Dairy cows have a rather high requirement for vitamin A and also need more vitamin D than do mature animals not producing milk. As has been shown, the vitamin A content of the milk depends strictly on the supply in the feed. (189)

Among the concentrates of plant origin, yellow corn and by-products from it (corn gluten feed, corn gluten meal, and hominy feed) are the only common ones that have any appreciable amount of vitamin A. Even yellow corn has much less vitamin A value than well-cured hay. Likewise, none of the concentrates of plant origin supplies any significant amount of vitamin D. Therefore dairy cows secure most of their vitamin A supply from the roughage they consume, and meet their vitamin D requirement through the supply of this vitamin in their roughage and through the anti-rachitic effect of sunlight.

There is apparently much more apt to be a deficiency of vitamin A in dairy rations than of vitamin D. This is doubtless due to the beneficial effect of sunlight and also because the vitamin A value (carotene content) of hay is largely destroyed when hay is cured poorly and becomes bleached and weathered. Though such hay contains but little carotene, it apparently still supplies appreciable amounts of vitamin D. The investigations of the Bureau of Dairy Industry of the United States Department of Agriculture are mentioned elsewhere; in these it has been shown that disaster results when cows are fed for a long period on poor-quality grass hay (deficient in carotene) as the only roughage. (882) On such a ration the cows abort or the calves are born weak and often blind. Also, the milk produced is nearly devoid of vitamin A.

The injurious results produced when cows are continuously fed only poor roughage have likewise been shown in a striking manner by the experiments, previously summarized, in which the effect of feeding large amounts of cottonseed meal to cows has been studied. (583) When cattle are fed only on cottonseed meal and roughage deficient in vitamin A, such as cottonseed hulls or poor hay, trouble follows. On the other hand, dairy cows have been fed only cottonseed meal and good-quality hay for years with satisfactory results and with no indication of the so-called ''cottonseed meal injury.''

That straw is unsatisfactory as the only roughage for dairy cows over long periods was shown in extensive investigations at the Wisconsin Station.[56] In these experiments cows fed wheat straw or oat straw as the sole roughage were unable to reproduce normally, and the cows themselves became unthrifty. Some of the calves were dead at birth and the others were usually very weak and often blind. On the other hand, the results were satisfactory when well-cured corn fodder was used as the only roughage. The disastrous results on straw as the sole roughage were due to the deficiency of vitamin A and probably also to the low calcium content of the rations. When a vitamin A supplement and also a calcium supplement were added in later experiments, reproduction was normal.

The vitamin A and D requirements of dairy cows will be amply met when they are fed the usual amount of roughage of good quality, including a reasonable amount of well-cured hay. Hay that has a green color is always rich in vitamin A value (carotene), while that which is bleached has but little. As has been stated previously, the vitamin A value of corn silage will depend on the stage of maturity at which the crop is cut. (**188**) This is also true of sorghum silage. In Texas trials a liberal amount of sorghum silage, fed with cottonseed hulls and cottonseed meal, did not provide sufficient carotene for good health of the cows and a high vitamin A content in the milk.[57] When the cows were also supplied with good pasture, the butter fat contained 9 times as much vitamin A as previously.

Cod-liver oil should not be added to dairy rations, because it lowers the fat content of the milk and also because of the possible toxic effect of cod-liver oil on ruminants. (**194**)

So far as is known, there is no lack of vitamins B and G in any ordinary dairy ration. In a Minnesota experiment there was no advantage in adding yeast, which is rich in both these vitamins, to a normal dairy ration.[58] (**196–198**) There is no lack of vitamin E in the rations commonly fed to dairy cows. (**200**)

818. Supplements do not prevent breeding troubles.—Claims are sometimes made that the addition of various mineral and vitamin supplements to dairy rations will prevent and cure Bang's disease (infectious abortion) and lessen other breeding troubles. (**670**) An extensive experiment was conducted at the Wisconsin Station to study this important problem.[59] Two groups, each of 22 heifers, were selected for the experiment from farms known to be free from Bang's disease.

One group was raised on a ration that was considered ideal from the nutritive standpoint, and then the cattle were continued on the same ration after they came into milk production. This ration consisted of good-quality alfalfa hay and corn silage with a concentrate mixture which supplied ample protein and which was also rich in phosphorus. During the summer the cattle were on legume pasture. Iodized salt, steamed bone meal, and cod-liver oil were included in the concentrate mixture to ensure a liberal supply of iodine, phosphorus, calcium, and vitamins A and D. This ration was also rich in vitamin E.

The cattle in the other group received timothy hay and corn silage, with common salt and with a concentrate mixture that supplied sufficient protein, but was low in phosphorus. In summer the cattle were on grass pasture. This ration was not rich in calcium, phosphorus, and iodine, and also was lower than the first ration in vitamins A, D, and E.

After the first year of milk production on these rations, the cattle in both groups were exposed similarly to infection with Bang's disease. The cows fed the "good" ration, which contained the mineral and vitamin supplements, showed no more resistance to the disease than those fed the other ration. The fat production was slightly less on the "good" ration than on the ration which had been thought to be poorer, because of the effect of cod-liver oil in decreasing the percentage of fat in milk. (**194, 832**)

In experiments by the Ohio Station with dairy heifers there has been little or no benefit from adding manamar to ordinary rations.[60] (**671**) This widely-advertised product did not prevent abortion from Bang's disease in an infected herd, and it did not appreciably increase the growth of heifers or the milk production of cows.

819. Water.—Often the production of cows is lessened merely because they can not conveniently get plenty of good water.[61] There is no greater folly in dairying than this, for feed and labor are expensive, while water is practically always cheap and abundant.

Of all farm animals, dairy cows in milk require the largest amount of water in proportion to their size, because water forms about 87 per cent of the milk they yield. The amount of water they will drink depends on their size, on the yield of milk, on the air temperature, and on the amount of water in the feed they eat.[62] Depending on the size of the cows, from 100 lbs., or 12.5 gallons, up to 120 lbs., or 15 gallons, of water per cow daily may be considered an average amount for a herd, including both cows in milk and dry cows. Cows producing 100 lbs. of milk a day may drink 300 lbs. of water a day or even more. Dry cows will vary widely in water consumption, large cows drinking up to about 100 lbs. a day on dry feed.

Including both the water in their feed and the water they drink, cows usually consume 4.0 to 5.5 lbs. of water for each pound of milk they yield. On a ration of silage, hay, and concentrates, they will drink in ordinary weather 2.3 to 4.4 lbs. of water per pound of milk produced, in addition to the water in their feed.

In hot weather cows may drink 80 per cent more than in moderate weather. In weather down to freezing temperature, they drink about the same amounts as in moderate weather, if the water is not too cold and is comfortably accessible. The feeding of a ration very high in protein considerably increases the water consumption. Adding any succulent feed to a dry ration decreases the water drunk, but not the total intake of water. If roots are fed in place of silage, cows drink less water, but the total water intake in feed and water drunk is greater on the root rations.

Providing water by means of automatic, individual drinking bowls or cups, so cows can drink whenever they wish, increases the milk production, saves labor, and aids in providing a more sanitary supply of water. In trials by the United States Department of Agriculture and the Iowa and Connecticut (Storrs) Stations good cows watered with drinking bowls produced 3.5 to 4.0 per cent more milk than those allowed to drink all the water they wished twice a day, and 6 to 11 per cent more than those watered once a day.[63] In the case of low producers, there was less benefit from the use of drinking bowls. Cows watered with water bowls drank an average of about 10 times each 24 hours, and about one-third of the water was drunk during the night, from 5 p. m. to 5 a. m.

Where drinking bowls are not used, high-producing cows should always be watered at least twice a day, and in severe weather they should be watered indoors, if possible. When cows drink from an outdoor tank, it is probably wise to warm the water during very cold winter weather, so they will drink sufficient for their needs. However, in a Washington test the production was not increased when water was warmed for one group of cows, in comparison with another group receiving water which had a temperature of about 32° F. most of the time.[64]

Care should be taken to keep drinking bowls and tanks in a sanitary condition by frequent cleaning. This is an important point that is often overlooked.

820. Preparation of feed.—The various grains should be ground or crushed for dairy cows and heifers, as a considerable percentage otherwise escapes mastication and digestion. The only exception is when grain is unusually cheap in price, in comparison with the cost of grinding. Most grain need not be ground for calves up to 6 to 8 months of age. Grinding to medium fineness is preferable to grinding to a fine, floury meal, as such grinding is much less expensive in power and time required than fine grinding, and grain ground medium-fine is also more palatable.

Numerous experiments have been conducted to determine whether or not it pays to chop or grind hay for dairy cows.[65] The experiments all show conclusively that when cows are fed the usual amounts of concentrates, it does not pay to chop or grind hay of such quality that it will be cleaned up reasonably well when fed uncut. (**100**) Cows fed chopped or ground hay in such tests have produced no more milk or only slightly more than on uncut hay, and in no case has there been sufficient saving in chopping or grinding good-quality hay to justify the expense. The chopping or grinding of good hay produces little or no increase in its digestibility and fine grinding may even lower the digestibility.[66] Oregon experiments indicate that when cows are fed only alfalfa hay, without any concentrates, it may be profitable to chop or grind the hay.[67]

In the case of hay which is unpalatable or coarse and stemmy, such as coarse soybean hay, there may be enough saving through chopping to warrant it, if it can be done cheaply. However, the waste stems of legume hay can often be fed advantageously to idle horses, which will clean up much of such refuse. Chopping soybean hay for dairy cows has increased its value in some trials by 19 per cent, while in others, where better hay was probably fed, there has been little increase in value through chopping or grinding. Chopping or shredding corn or sorghum fodder or stover is advisable to lessen the waste, and to facilitate handling the manure.

Where it seems desirable to prepare hay for dairy cows, chopping it by means of a silage cutter or other chopping machine is preferable to grinding it. Ground hay is often disagreeably dusty and may be unpalatable to the cows.

Some have advocated that the concentrate mixture be mixed with chopped or ground hay for dairy cows, claiming that such mixtures will be digested better than when the concentrates and hay are fed separately. However, in Ohio and South Dakota trials such mixing was not advantageous.[68]

There is no advantage in soaking or cooking ordinary feeds for dairy cows. In some cases for feeding cows on advanced registry test the concentrate mixture is moistened before feeding, in order to get a cow to eat a larger quantity than she might if it were fed dry. Also, dried beet pulp is sometimes soaked and fed as a substitute for silage. Fermenting, or "pre-digesting," chopped or ground hay or mixtures of such hay and concentrates does not increase the value and is a waste of time and money. That such methods of preparing feed are not profitable has been clearly shown by the experiments which have previously been summarized in Chapter IV. (**104**)

III. Factors Influencing the Composition and Yield of Milk

821. Composition of milk.—The milk of the purebred or high-grade cows of any dairy breed has certain general characteristics, particularly in fat content and in color, although the milk of various individuals may differ considerably from the breed average in percentage of fat and total solids. While the fat content of cow's milk may range from less than 3 per cent to 6 per cent or over, there is much less range in the other constituents. The average composition of milk from purebred cows of the different breeds is shown in the following table:[69]

Composition of milk of purebred cows of various breeds

	Total solids Per cent	Fat Per cent	Protein Per cent	Lactose Per cent	Mineral matter Per cent
Ayrshire	12.97	3.97	3.51	4.81	0.68
Brown Swiss	13.04	4.01	...	...	...
Guernsey	14.52	4.91	3.90	4.97	0.74
Holstein-Friesian	12.29	3.42	3.30	4.89	0.68
Jersey	14.78	5.29	3.79	5.00	0.70
Shorthorn	12.57	3.63	3.32	4.89	0.73

Jersey and Guernsey milk is the richest in fat, and that of Holsteins the lowest in fat among the common dairy breeds in this country. However, the breeds which give milk high in fat usually yield a correspondingly smaller quantity.

As the fat content of milk increases, the percentage of protein rises less rapidly. The Ohio Station reports, from a study of the relationship between the fat content and the protein content in many hundreds of samples of milk, that there is an increase of about 0.42 per cent in protein content for each 1 per cent increase in fat.[70] Casein is the chief protein of milk, there being about 3.0 per cent or more of casein. Milk also has approximately 0.50 per cent lactalbumin (or milk albumin), 0.05 per cent of lactoglobulin, and traces of other proteins. The percentages of lactalbumin and lactoglobulin do not differ much in milk of various fat percentages, but the chief difference in the total protein content is due to a greater or smaller percentage of casein.

The percentage of casein in milk is of great importance in cheese making, since the yield of cheese depends not only upon the percentage of fat but also upon the percentage of casein. A milk testing 6 per cent of fat will not make twice as much cheese as one testing 3 per cent. Therefore, at cheese factories where the milk from different herds differs considerably in fat content, it should be paid for, not on the basis of the fat content alone, but by some method which gives credit for both fat and casein.

Certain investigations, especially those by Hill of the Utah Station, have shown that the hardness of the curd formed from the milk of various cows differs widely.[71] Among normal samples of milk, the percentage of casein is the chief factor affecting the character of the curd, the curd becoming harder as the casein content increases. Milk from cows badly affected with mastitis also may have softer curd than normal.

Since normal soft-curd milk is more readily digested than hard-curd milk, there has been considerable interest in its use for delicate infants. Not only does the milk from various cows differ in character of curd, but also the hardness of curd can be greatly decreased by certain methods of treating the milk.

It is well known that the fat in milk is in the form of minute globules or droplets, which are distributed through the milk in the form of an emulsion. The fat globules range in size from less than 1 micron to 10 microns or even more in diameter.[72] (A micron is one one-thousandth of a millimeter or about 4 one-hundred-thousandths of an inch.) The minute size of the fat globules is shown by the fact that a quart of normal milk contains 4.5 to 9.0 trillion fat globules.

The fat globules of Jersey and Guernsey milk are larger than those in Holstein and Ayrshire milk, while the globules in Shorthorn milk are of medium size. Regardless of breed, there is a tendency for the fat globules to be larger at the beginning than at the end of lactation.

822. Equating milk yield to uniform fat percentage.—Milk of the various fat percentages differs widely in energy content per pound. Therefore to compare the actual energy values of milk differing in richness, the yields must be equated, or changed, to a uniform energy basis. This can be done by converting the various actual yields to equivalent amounts of milk of the same fat percentage, and therefore of the same energy content.

When it is desired to compare yields of milk on an equal energy basis, they are commonly converted to amounts of "4 per cent fat-corrected milk" by the formula which Gaines developed through studies at the Illinois Station.[73] This is done by multiplying the actual milk yield by 0.4 and then adding to this product the actual fat yield multiplied by 15. In condensed form, the formula is:

F. C. M. (4 per cent fat-corrected milk) $= 0.4 \times$ milk $+ 15 \times$ fat.

This method of equating milk yields to a uniform energy basis is now commonly used in investigations with dairy cows, to compare, for example, the yields of milk produced on various experimental rations. If desired, the milk yields can be converted to some other uniform fat percentage than 4 per cent, by the use of a different formula.

823. Factors affecting yield and composition of milk.—In addition to the influence of breed on the composition of milk, the yield and composition are affected by various other factors. These are discussed in the paragraphs which follow.

The amount of milk a cow produces is affected much more readily and to a greater degree than is its composition. The chief factors affecting the yearly yield of milk by any cow are her inherited productive ability, her thrift, her age, and the manner in which she is fed and cared for. The daily yield usually reaches a maximum the second month after calving and then decreases gradually as lactation progresses. Such factors as pregnancy, temperature and humidity, exercise, and turning to pasture may have an appreciable effect on the milk yield.

Of all the milk constituents, the fat percentage is the most variable. While the average percentage of fat in the milk of an individual cow does not usually change much from year to year, the fat content may vary greatly from one milking to another, and often without any apparent cause. In general, whenever the yield of milk rises or falls considerably, the fat percentage is apt to change in the opposite direction.

The variations in fat content from milking to milking, and from day to day, are much greater than generally realized. In milkings made at the same time on successive days, variations of 0.5 per cent in fat are common and of 1.0 per cent not unusual.[74] The variations in the percentage of fat in successive milkings are often greater than this, as the time of day may have an influence on the fat content of the milk.

Due to the variations which occur in the fat percentage, testing the milk from only one milking is often a poor indication of the richness of the milk a cow is producing. Also, on account of the variations in composition of milk, a dairyman who is retailing milk should be sure to mix the milk from various cows thoroughly before bottling it. Otherwise some of the milk may fall below the legal standards for fat or solids-not-fat, even though the average composition is satisfactory.

The fat content of milk is affected somewhat by the stage of lactation, tending to increase gradually after the second month. It is also affected to a slight extent by temperature and season of the year, by interval of time between milkings, by age, and by certain other factors. It may sometimes be increased temporarily by adding to the ration certain fat-rich feeds or fats, but the kind of feed does not exert any large continued effect upon the fat percentage over a long period of time. Cows calving in fat condition may yield milk abnormally high in fat for some weeks after calving, and pronounced underfeeding of a good cow for a few days may cause a temporary increase in the percentage of fat. The character of the fat may be greatly changed by the particular feeds supplied.

The various factors which affect the yield and composition of milk are discussed in detail in the following pages.

824. First and last drawn milk; thorough milking.—Under usual conditions the first milk drawn from the udder is very poor in fat and each successive portion increases in richness. While the first portion may contain less than 1 per cent of fat, the strippings from the same cow may have 6 to 10 per cent of fat.[75] There are various opinions as to the cause of this difference in fat content. It may be due to a holding back of the fat globules in the alevoli and small ducts of the udder tissue. Also, there may be some tendency for the fat to rise in the milk that is contained, previous to milking, in the milk cistern and large ducts of the udder.

If the udder is massaged before milking starts, or if the cow has just had considerable exercise, the difference is much less than if she has been standing quietly in the stable.[76] It also tends to be less in low-producing cows than in high producers. The percentages of other constituents than fat vary but little in the successive portions of milk drawn from the udder. Since the strippings are so much richer in fat, the yield of fat and the richness of the milk are appreciably decreased when cows are not milked thoroughly with care to get all the milk from the udder.

Foremilking, or discarding the first few streams of milk from each quarter of the udder, is sometimes done to increase the fat content of market milk. The discarded milk is then used for feeding calves or other stock. Tests at the New York (Cornell) Station show that a considerable part of the milk must be discarded to make any very marked increase in the richness of the remaining milk.[77] Discarding the first 20 streams from each quarter increased the fat content of the rest of the milk only 0.17 per cent. Yet, to obtain this increase nearly 10.5 per cent of the entire milking was discarded.

To secure an accurate index of a cow's production on an official test, it is important that she be milked clean at the milking before the test period starts. Incomplete milking before a test period begins will usually slightly increase the yield of milk, the percentage of fat, and the yield of fat during the test period.[78]

825. Length of period between milkings; night and day.[79]—When the intervals of time between milkings are unequal, cows generally yield a smaller amount of milk after the shorter period, but this milk is usually slightly richer in fat and total solids. With cows milked twice a day, a difference of 4 hours in the two periods may make a difference of 0.5 to 1.0 per cent in fat content.

If cows are milked twice a day with equal intervals between milkings, the evening milking, according to most investigations, tends to be slightly richer in fat than the morning milking. This may be due to the effect of the exercise during the day. When cows are milked three or four times a day, the milkings during the middle of the day tend to be slightly higher in fat.

826. Frequency of milking.—Milking cows of ordinary productive capacity more than twice a day does not markedly increase their production, and is generally not economical. However, Holsteins milked twice a day will not usually yield much more than 50 to 60 lbs. of milk a day, and Jerseys or Guernseys 35 to 45 lbs. If cows capable of greater production than this are milked three times a day, it will usually increase their production markedly and will often be decidedly profitable.

In experiments with good cows where the same cows were milked three times daily in comparison with twice daily, the yield of milk has been increased from 6 to 20 per cent or more.[80] Those milked four times a day have yielded 6 or 7 per cent more than when they were milked thrice daily. To secure these increases, cows milked more than twice a day must have their concentrate allowance increased in proportion to the milk they are actually producing. Milking cows of high productive capacity more than twice daily tends to increase their persistency in production throughout the lactation and may increase the fat test slightly.

827. Effect of age.[81]—The annual yield of both milk and fat by a cow normally increases from the first lactation until she is mature. Numerous investigations have shown that the maximum yield is usually reached at 7 to 9 years of age, but the increase is only slight after 5 years. Most cows are removed from the herd on account of failure to breed, or due to udder trouble or other causes before their yield is much reduced by old age. Usually there is no marked decline until 12 years of age, if the cow is in good health.

The fat percentage is affected but little by age, though there is usually a very slight tendency for it to decrease as a cow grows older.

In culling cows it is important to bear in mind that while a heifer will ordinarily increase in milk yield with age, the richness of her milk will tend to decrease.

The various breed associations take the effect of age on milk yield into consideration in their requirements for advanced registry of cows of various ages. According to data secured in the United States dairy herd-improvement associations, cows 2 years old when calving will give 77 per cent of their mature production on the average; cows 3 years old, 87 per cent; cows 4 years old, 94 per cent; and those 5 years old, 98 per cent of their yield when mature. The estimated "mature equivalent yield" may be computed by multiplying the yields at the various ages by the following factors: 2 years old at calving, 1.294; 3 years old, 1.149; 4 years old, 1.064; and 5 years old, 1.020.[82] Various investigators have recommended slightly different factors, based on their particular studies.

Heifers are usually more persistent producers in their first lactation than in later lactations. In other words, their decrease in production from month to month is less rapid. This is probably because a heifer is growing in body, and the amount of secreting glandular tissue in her udder is also increasing.

828. Size of cow.—There has been considerable discussion as to whether large or small cows of the same breed are, on the average, more efficient producers of milk and butter fat. To settle this question conclusively would require experiments with a large number of cows, in which accurate records were kept of feed consumed and of production. This would be necessary because cows of the same size differ so greatly in productive capacity.

Studies of the records of cows in dairy herd-improvement associations and also studies of advanced registry records show clearly that within a given breed the large cows give higher average yields of milk and fat than those small in size.[83] This is but natural, for a 1,600-lb. cow, for example, is able to consume much more feed than a 1,000-lb. cow.

Because of the larger average yields of milk, the yearly return per cow over cost of feed averages higher for the large cows of a breed than for those which are small in size. However, studies by Gaines of the Illinois Station indicate that in the percentage-efficiency with which they convert feed into milk, the small cows may excel the larger ones.[84]

In developing a high-producing herd, one should base his selection primarily on productive capacity rather than giving undue attention to size. If a large cow and a cow of moderate size produce equal amounts of milk, the cow of moderate size will be more profitable. This is because she will require somewhat less feed to maintain her body than the large cow.

829. Condition of flesh at calving.—The milk yield of a cow, especially during the first part of the lactation period, depends considerably on having her in thrifty, vigorous condition at time of calving. The fat content of the milk is usually not affected greatly by the condition of flesh at calving, except in the case of cows which are so fed that they are really fat at calving, as is often done with cows on advanced registry test.

When a cow of high productive capacity calves in a fat condition, she may yield milk containing a considerably higher percentage of fat than normal, losing markedly in body weight meanwhile.[85] This is due to her strong dairy temperament, which impels her to withdraw fat from her body and put it into her milk. In the case of Holstein-Friesian cows the increase in fat percentage during this period may be as great as 1 to 2 per cent. Any increase in the case of Guernseys and Jerseys is usually much less marked and often there is none at all.

It is evident that when a cow calves in fat condition, a seven-day record of fat production secured shortly after calving may not be a reliable index to her yearly yield. For this reason, brief official advanced registry tests are no longer sponsored by any of the dairy breed associations in this country.

The total yearly yield of fat can be increased by having cows calve in fat condition, and breeders feeding cows on advanced registry test usually take advantage of this fact.

830. Influence of underfeeding and overfeeding.—It has been pointed out previously in this chapter that the yearly milk and fat yields of many good dairy cows, and the net returns to their owners as well, are seriously reduced because they are underfed. They cannot be expected to produce efficiently unless they are supplied with the proper amount and kind of nutrients.

If good dairy cows are underfed in the first part of the lactation period, they will sometimes maintain their milk flow at a nearly constant level for a short time under the most adverse conditions, drawing on their bodies for nutrients and losing in weight rapidly. In Missouri experiments one cow kept up a normal flow of milk for a month when given only as much feed as would have been required to maintain her weight when dry.[86] When the lactation period has reached a certain stage, however, even moderate underfeeding causes a large decline in milk flow.

Underfeeding following a period of liberal feeding may cause a marked increase in the percentage of fat in the milk, especially when the cow has a surplus store of fat in her body. Underfeeding may also produce marked effects on the chemical and physical properties of the butter fat. These may or may not change the melting point. It was found in Missouri experiments that when the ration of cows during the first half of the lactation period was reduced one-half, the percentage of fat was temporarily increased, the high point occurring either the second or third day after the reduction was made.[87] As soon as the cows were put back on full feed the fat content of the milk fell and went even below normal. The amount of milk varied almost directly with the amount of feed given.

Starvation for a few days greatly decreases the amount of milk and increases the percentage of fat and other constituents, except sugar, which is decreased.[88]

In Missouri experiments to determine the effect of overfeeding dairy cows it was found that the most pronounced effect of overfeeding (feeding a more liberal ration than is required for the production of a normal yield of milk) was that it caused the cow to gain in weight.[89] Only to a limited extent was the excess food used for the production of milk. Even under the most favorable conditions, a cow seemed unable to increase her milk flow beyond the fixed maximum she had inherited. Liberal feeding will sometimes cause a recovery of the milk flow lost because of previous poor nutrition, but this recovery is only partial even under the best conditions.

831. Effect of advancing lactation[90] and of pregnancy.[91]—After calving, the milk yield of cows usually increases until it reaches a maximum during the second month of lactation. It then gradually decreases as lactation advances, the average monthly decrease in well-bred herds being about 6 to 7 per cent from the second to the seventh month. The monthly rate of decrease varies considerably in individual cows, ranging from only 4 per cent or less to 9 per cent or more, depending on their persistency of production. After the seventh month the rate of decrease is considerably more rapid in cows bred to calve with the usual frequency. Cows of the dual-purpose breeds are usually less persistent milkers than cows of the special dairy breeds, and their monthly rate of decline is more rapid.

Pregnancy does not materially affect the milk yield until after about 5 months, after which it considerably hastens the decline. For this reason, separate classifications are provided in the advanced registry requirements of some dairy breeds for cows which meet definite calving requirements.

Particularly in the case of cows which are in good flesh at calving time, the fat percentage is apt to decline slightly for the first month or two after calving. This decrease is apparently most marked in the case of Holsteins and Ayrshires. After the second or third month the fat content usually increases slightly during the remainder of lactation, especially toward the end. Under usual farm conditions there is no marked change in richness until toward the end of lactation, when the decline in milk yield becomes rapid.

832. Influence of feed on richness of milk.—If a cow receives sufficient nutrients to maintain her body weight and if her ration contains at least a certain minimum amount of food fat, the percentage of fat in her milk cannot be increased very markedly over a long period of time by greater or less liberality of feeding or by supplying any particular kind of feed. Decided changes in the ration may sometimes cause a decided temporary change in the fat content.[92] This effect usually lasts only a few days, and sometimes there is no increase in the percentage of fat, or even a decrease.

A temporary increase in the fat content of milk is especially apt to result from adding to the ration a considerable amount of certain feeds high in fat, such as flaxseed, soybeans, or peanuts, or from feeding 1 lb. or more per head daily of certain oils, such as linseed oil, cottonseed oil, or corn oil. Linseed meal, cottonseed meal, or soybean oil meal are less apt to produce such an increase, probably because most of the fat has been removed. Feeding a considerable amount of whole milk to cows that will take it also usually increases both the yield of milk and the fat percentage temporarily.[93]

Coconut meal and palm-kernel meal in some tests have apparently caused a very slight increase in fat content for a considerable period, but in other cases the richness of the milk has not been increased.[94] In a recent New York experiment the effect of substituting 10 per cent of coconut oil meal and 10 per cent of palm-kernel oil meal for part of the more common feeds in a concentrate mixture for dairy cows was tested.[95] Mixed clover-and-timothy hay and corn silage were fed as the roughages in both rations. The feeding of coconut oil meal and palm-kernel oil meal produced a very slight increase in the percentage of fat in the milk over 5-week periods, but the increase was too small to be of much practical importance.

On the average, the use of these feeds increased the fat percentage in the milk only 0.08 per cent and also produced a slight increase in the total yield of fat.

In a series of 7 experiments at the Indiana Station rations containing soybeans were compared with rations that did not contain soybeans.[96] The fat percentage of the milk was 0.25 per cent higher on the rations containing soybeans in these trials.

In Ohio experiments in which rations very rich in protein were compared with rations extremely poor in protein, there was no appreciable change in the composition of the milk, except a slight increase in non-protein nitrogen on the ration very high in protein.[97]

Cod-liver oil causes a distinct decrease in the fat content of milk when as much as 4 ounces per head daily are fed to cows, and menhaden fish oil has had a similar effect.[98] Feeding a considerable amount of prickly pear cactus to cows also seems to lower the fat content.[99]

833. Changes in the character of fat.—While the kind of feed does not greatly change the percentage of fat in the milk, in some cases the character or nature of the fat is decidedly changed by the feed, and this may noticeably affect the hardness of butter.[100] Milk fat is made up of several different kinds of pure fats. Some of these, as stearin and palmitin, are solid at ordinary temperatures, while others, as olein and butyrin, are liquid. Especially if cows are fed a considerable amount of a feed rich in fat, some of this food fat may pass without great change into the milk, thus altering the character of the milk fat in a manner similar to the change produced in lard when hogs are fattened on certain feeds. **(222)**

Feeds rich in vegetable oils (which contain a large amount of olein) usually produce milk fat high in olein. This usually tends to make the butter softer, for olein is a liquid fat, but in some instances this tendency is offset by still other changes in the composition of the fat.

For instance, though the feeding of cottonseed meal, cottonseed, or cottonseed oil increases the amount of olein in the butter fat, yet it raises the melting point and makes the butter harder. This effect is probably due to a decrease in the amount of volatile fatty acids in the butter fat, which more than counterbalances the effect of the increase in the amount of olein. This effect of the heavy feeding of cottonseed meal or cottonseed on butter is of much practical importance in the southern states, for it is a cause of hard, crumbly butter. Coconut oil meal also increases the hardness of butter.

The feeding of cows exclusively on alfalfa hay may cause sticky or crumbly butter, which can be remedied by adding corn silage to the ration. Soybeans and rice polish make the butter soft, if they form too large a part of the concentrate mixture fed cows. A change from dry feed to pasture generally produces milk fat higher in olein and hence causes softer butter. Jerseys seem to produce harder butter than Ayrshires when fed the same rations.

834. Weather and season of year.—The *temperature* of the air has even a more pronounced effect on the fat content of milk than the stage of lactation.[101] The tendency is for cows of all breeds to give richer milk when the temperature falls, and poorer as it rises, at least up to 70° F. The fat content may increase as much as 0.08 to 0.15 per cent for each drop of 10° F. in temperature.

Because of the effect of temperature, perhaps combined with the effect of humidity, the tendency is for cows to give richer milk in winter and poorer milk in summer. In any particular cow this effect may be modified by the usual rise in fat percentage which occurs during the latter part of lactation.

If the weather is too hot for the comfort of the cows, it may cause a decided reduction in yield of milk, with an increase in the fat content and other changes in composition. California experiments show that such an effect is produced when cows are kept in an air temperature above 85° F. (without the cooling effect of a breeze) for more than 48 hours.[102] It was found that during very hot weather the temperature of the air in a field of green alfalfa was 10° F. lower than in a dry, open corral, because of the cooling effect produced by the evaporation of water from the growing plants. Cows kept in this field were much more comfortable during a hot spell than when confined to the dry corral, and their body temperature was appreciably lowered. This shows the importance of pasture for cows in hot weather. Shade should be provided in such pastures, if possible.

Cooling cows during periods of very hot weather by covering them with light muslin cloths kept moist to cause cooling by evaporation, overcame the depressing effect of the heat in a Georgia test, with no bad effect on health.[103]

High humidity of the air may cause a drop in milk yield, high-producing cows being affected more than low producers.[104] It also apparently decreases the fat content of milk.

Exposure to cold rains or other severe weather may cause a serious shrinkage in milk flow and a decrease in the fat content.

The effects upon cows of various stable temperatures and of differences in humidity are discussed further in Chapter XXVI.

835. Season of freshening.—Under the climatic conditions in the chief dairy districts of the United States, cows that freshen in fall or early winter, if properly fed and cared for, yield more milk and fat than those that calve in spring or summer. Fall-fresh cows give a large flow of milk in winter and then flush again with the stimulus of pasture in spring. In a study of dairy herd-improvement association records in this country it was found that cows freshening in fall or early winter yielded, on the average, 11 per cent more milk and fat and returned 11 per cent more income over cost of feed than those freshening in spring or summer.[105] However, the relative profitableness of "winter dairying" and "summer dairying" will depend on the prices received for milk at various seasons of the year and the relative cost of concentrates in comparison with pasture. In the intensive market-milk regions near the large cities, winter dairying is most general, while in the less intensive districts far from market, it may be more profitable to produce most of the milk on pasture.

When cows freshen in the fall, more of the work of milking comes in the winter when farm work is slack. More time can be given to the raising of the calves, and less trouble will be experienced from scours than during the summer. Fall-dropped calves are large enough by spring to make good use of pasture and better able to stand the hot weather. Under this system, moreover, on farms where the milk is separated on the farm, a larger supply of skimmilk is available for the pigs in winter when it has especial value.

836. Miscellaneous factors.—Moderate *exercise* tends to increase slightly the percentage of fat in milk and also the yield of fat.[106] For this reason and also to provide fresh air and sunshine, it is a sound plan in winter to turn cows out of the stable for exercise a part of each day when the weather is suitable. Too much exercise, or hard work, such as milk cows are often used for in Europe, lowers the yield and may decrease the fat content.

Turning cows to pasture from winter stabling usually increases both the yield of milk and its richness, but after 2 to 4 weeks the percentage of fat falls to normal. Especially when the grass is soft and lush, cows lose in weight for a short time when first turned to pasture. The temporary increase in percentage of fat may be due to the fact that such early spring pasture may be so watery that the cows cannot secure from it sufficient nutrients to meet the needs for their production and hence are forced to draw on their bodies. Such underfeeding, as has been pointed out, usually increases the fat content of the milk, if the cows are in a good state of nutrition.

When *abortion* occurs instead of normal calving, there is usually a considerably lower milk yield than normal. The difference is especially great in the case of abortions that occur a considerable time before the end of the normal gestation period. Experiments have demonstrated that the eradication of contagious abortion, or Bang's disease, from a herd by the use of the blood test decidedly increases the milk yield and, of course, results in a much larger number of normal calves. It therefore causes a considerable increase in net return.[107]

The *period of heat*, or œstrum, contrary to considerable popular opinion, does not generally have any marked effect on the yield of milk or fat. In studies on this question, cows were found, on the average, to give 0.6 lb. to 1.5 lbs. less milk on the day of most evident heat, but some cows showed no decrease at all.[108] A few nervous cows are affected more markedly.

Grooming cows is, of course, necessary in the production of high-quality milk with a low number of bacteria, but it may not increase the yield of milk. Grooming cows each day did not increase the yield of milk in Vermont trials in which the ungroomed cows were not allowed to become filthy, while in German trials grooming increased the yield 4 to 8 per cent.[109] Grooming cows with a mechanical, vacuum-cleaner type of grooming machine caused no increase in yield over hand grooming in a Connecticut test.[110]

Dehorning cows causes a small temporary decrease in milk flow but is repaid a hundred-fold in commercial dairy herds in the greater comfort of the cows thereafter and the lessening of injuries. From the standpoint of dairy efficiency, it is unfortunate that in the case of certain breeds, animals without horns are discriminated against in the show ring.

The *tuberculin testing* of cows has practically no effect on the yield of milk or fat.

Infestation with ticks may cause a serious decrease in yield, even when cows are immune to tick fever.[111] Therefore in tick-infested districts cattle should be sprayed or dipped with an arsenical solution, at least when heavily infested. Such dipping causes only a very small temporary decrease in milk yield.[112]

Condimental stock foods or tonics are unnecessary in the efficient feeding of dairy cattle. In two Michigan trials there was no benefit whatsoever from the addition of a widely-used stock tonic to a simple ration of legume hay, corn silage, and a mixture of corn, barley, oats, linseed meal and cottonseed meal.[113] In fact, the feeding of the stock tonic according to the directions of the manufacturers caused some of the cows to go off feed and produced bloating in several cases.

Certain *drugs or hormone extracts* are supposed by some dairymen to increase the yield of milk or fat. Possibly some unscrupulous persons have attempted to increase the yields of cows on official test by these methods. In most of the tests of such products there has been no decided increase in the yield of milk or fat over a 24-hour period.[114] Often, "drugging" a cow has resulted in a decided decrease in yield instead of an increase.

837. Flavor and odor of milk.—On account of the importance of the flavor and odor of milk, numerous studies have been made of the effects of various feeds on the palatability of milk and its products.[115] In the case of most feeds which affect the flavor or odor of milk, the effect, at least in a well-ventilated barn, is produced chiefly by substances carried in the blood from the digestive tract to the udder, and not by odors absorbed from the contaminated stable air by the milk. Generally, any objectionable effect can be entirely prevented or at least greatly lessened by feeding the particular feed only immediately after milking. The substances which cause the objectionable flavor or odor then largely pass off before the next milking.

The most marked injury is produced by garlic, onions, the cruciferæ (including turnips, cabbage, rape, and kale), and certain weeds, including bitterweed (*Helenium tenuifolium*) and French weed or stinkweed (*Thlaspi arvense*). Green alfalfa, green sweet clover, and legume silage may also cause a pronounced flavor if fed within 5 hours before milking. Corn silage, green corn, green rye, or potatoes may produce a less marked effect if fed before milking. Even alfalfa hay may cause a noticeable flavor if fed less than 4 hours before milking. When cows are first turned to pasture, a grass flavor is at once noticed in the milk, but this soon disappears, or else we fail later to notice it.

Heating the milk to 145° F. and aerating it usually removes much of any objectionable feed odor or flavor, and may entirely eliminate slight taints. If a pasture is infested with leeks or wild onions, any pronounced taint may usually be avoided by grazing the cows on the pasture only 2 or 3 hours immediately after milking.

Milk which is high in lactose (milk sugar) and low in chlorides has the most pleasing taste in general, but it is apparently impossible to influence the amount of these constituents by the ration fed.

Sometimes a cow gives milk which is distasteful, being bitter or salty. With few exceptions this occurs only in cows which are far along in lactation and also advanced in pregnancy. It rarely happens when green feed is supplied. Usually the cow is being overfed on concentrates. This trouble, which is due to an enzyme in the milk that acts on the fat, can be prevented by heating the milk, immediately after milking, to the boiling point to destroy the enzyme, and then cooling it as rapidly as convenient. Reducing the concentrate allowance and giving two or three doses of Epsom salts at intervals of 3 days may remove the trouble.[116]

The whole subject of flavors and odors in milk and dairy products is greatly complicated by the fact that there is a wide range in the ability of different individuals to detect and distinguish them. Flavors and odors plainly evident to one person are unnoticed by another. Often odors and flavors charged to feed or cow are due to contamination of the milk in the stable or elsewhere, after it is drawn from the cow.

838. The color of milk and butter fat.—The yellow color of butter fat and of yellow-colored milk is due to the carotene present in it. It has been shown previously that the carotene content of butter fat and of milk depends on the amount of carotene in the ration the cows receive and also on the breed of cow.[117] (**189**) If a ration low in carotene is fed to cows for a long period, the butter fat will have but little yellow color, even in the case of Guernseys and Jerseys. It will also be very low in vitamin A.

The milk and butter fat produced by Guernseys and Jerseys fed a ration rich in carotene will have a pronounced yellow color. This is not because cows of these breeds assimilate more carotene from their feed, but because they change less of it into colorless vitamin A than do cows of the other common breeds.

Milk has the maximum yellowness when the cows are on excellent pasture, for this supplies a great abundance of carotene. During the barn-feeding period the liberal feeding of green-colored hay and of silage high in carotene will aid in maintaining yellowness of color and also a high vitamin A value in the milk. (**188**)

QUESTIONS

1. Compare the efficiency in the production of human food by dairy cows and by beef steers.
2. What do dairy herd-improvement association records show concerning the relative income above feed cost from high-producing cows and from low producers?
3. Why are high producers more efficient than low producers in converting feed into milk?
4. Why does scanty feeding reduce the efficiency of cows of high productive capacity?
5. Discuss the returns from purebreds and from high grades in dairy herd-improvement association herds.
6. Discuss the importance of records of production in the building up of a profitable dairy herd.

7. What are dairy herd-improvement associations; dairy record clubs?

8. Tell about the results that have been secured in experiments in which purebred bulls have been used to develop a good herd from scrubs.

9. State 5 nutrient requirements of dairy cows for efficient production.

10. Why must feeding standards recommend slightly greater amounts of nutrients than dairy cows actually require?

11. How much digestible protein and how much total digestible nutrients should be provided for maintaining a 1,000-lb. dairy cow?

12. Discuss the amount of protein required by dairy cows for milk production.

13. Show by an example how the protein content of the concentrate mixture for dairy cows should depend on the protein content of the roughage.

14. About what percentage of protein should a concentrate mixture contain for feeding with good mixed clover-and-timothy hay and corn silage?

15. Discuss quality of protein in dairy rations.

16. Discuss the fat requirements of dairy cows.

17. Why is a range indicated in the amounts of total digestible nutrients recommended in the Morrison feeding standards for milk production?

18. Discuss the feeding of dairy cows chiefly or entirely on roughage.

19. Tell about the Indiana demonstration which showed that it pays to feed good cows liberally.

20. Under what conditions may it be economical to restrict the amount of roughage fed dairy cows?

21. What is the relative value per pound of good hay and of a good concentrate mixture for milk production?

22. Under what specific conditions should a phosphorus supplement be added to the rations of dairy cows?

23. When would you add a calcium supplement to dairy rations?

24. Discuss the losses and storage of calcium and phosphorus by dairy cows.

25. What results have been secured when calcium and phosphorus supplements have been added to good dairy rations?

26. What are the salt requirements of dairy cows?

27. Discuss the vitamin requirements of dairy cows.

28. Discuss the use of mineral or vitamin supplements to prevent breeding troubles.

29. Discuss the water requirements of dairy cows, considering: (a) amount required; (b) use of drinking bowls.

30. Discuss the grinding of grain for dairy cows; the chopping or grinding of hay.

31. About how much fat, protein, lactose, and mineral matter does cows' milk contain?

32. How does the first-drawn milk differ in composition from that drawn later?

33. What is the effect of an unequal length of time between milkings upon the composition of milk?

34. Discuss the effects of the following upon yield and composition of milk: (a) Age of cow; (b) weight of cow; (c) condition of flesh at calving; (d) under feeding; (e) advancing lactation; (f) pregnancy.

35. Discuss the influence of feed upon the richness of milk; upon character of the fat in milk.

36. Discuss the effect of weather and season of the year on milk composition and yield.

37. What are the advantages of the fall freshening of cows?

38. Discuss the effects on yield or composition of milk of the following: (a) Exercise; (b) turning cows to pasture; (c) abortion; (d) period of heat; (e) grooming; (f) dehorning; (g) infestation with ticks; (h) condimental stock foods or tonics; (i) drugs and hormone extracts.

39. What feeds affect the flavor or odor of milk? How may the trouble be largely avoided?

REFERENCES

1. Haecker, Minn. Bul. 140; see also: Smith and Rice, Guernsey Breeders' Jour., 46, 1934, pp. 176, 177, 227.
2. Forbes and Voris, Jour. Nutr., 5, 1932, pp. 395-401; Forbes et al., Penn. Bul. 319.
3. Swett, Graves, and Miller, Jour. Agr. Res., 37, 1928, pp. 685-717.
4. Haecker, Minn. Bul. 35.
5. McDowell, U. S. Dept. of Agr., information to the author.
6. Headley, Nev. Bul. 119.
7. Eckles and Reed, Mo. Res. Bul. 2.
8. McDowell, U. S. Dept. Agr., Dairy Herd-Improvement Assoc. Letter, Nov., 1932; see also: McDowell, U. S. Dept. Agr. Cir. 26.
9. U. S. Dept. Agr., Yearbook 1935.
10. McDowell, U. S. Dept. Agr., Yearbook 1933, pp. 287-290.
11. Gowen, Me. Buls. 289, 291, 304; Monroe, Ohio Bimo. Bul. 125.
12. Denmark, Volume for 1931, p. 184.
13. Kildee, Weaver, et al., Iowa Buls. 165, 188, 251; Jour. Dairy Sci., 4, 1921, pp. 12-23; Bergh, Minn. Ext. Cir. 15; Kuhlman, McGilliard, and Weaver, Okla. Rpt. 1927-30; Olson, et al., S. D. Buls. 198, 206; Baird, Hilton, and Rothwell, Can. Dept. Agr. Bul. 126.
14. Hills, Beach, Borland, Washburn, Story, and Jones, Vt. Bul. 225.
15. Armsby, The Nutrition of Farm Animals; Eckles, Mo. Res. Bul. 7.
15a. Brody and Procter, Mo. Res. Bul. 222.
16. Haecker, Minn. Buls. 71, 79, 140.
17. Forbes, Fries, and Kriss, Jour. Dairy Sci., 9, 1926, pp. 15-27.
18. Forbes and Kriss, Amer. Soc. Anim. Prod., Proc. 1931, 1932.
19. Kriss, Jour. Nutr., 4, 1931, pp. 141-161.
20. Harrison and Savage, N. Y. (Cornell) Bul. 540; Harrison, Savage, and Work, N. Y. (Cornell) Bul. 578 and unpublished data.
21. Perkins and Monroe, Ohio Bul. 376; Perkins, Ohio Buls. 389, 532; Ohio Spec. Cirs. 29, 43; Perkins, report presented at Annual Meeting of Amer. Dairy Sci. Assoc., 1935.
22. Ellett and Holdaway, Va. Tech. Buls. 12, 20; Ellett, Holdaway, and Harris, Va. Tech. Bul. 23.
23. Hart and Humphrey, Jour. Biol. Chem., 38, 1919, pp. 515-527; 44, 1920, pp. 189-201; 48, 1921, pp. 305-311; Morrison, Hulce, and Humphrey, Wis. Bul. 352; Hart and Humphrey, Wis. Bul. 417.
24. Willard, Wyo. Bul. 182.
25. Forbes and Swift, Jour. Dairy Sci., 8, 1925, pp. 15-27; Fries, Braman, and Kriss, Jour. Dairy Sci., 7, 1924, pp. 11-23; Forbes and Kriss, Amer. Soc. Anim. Prod., Proc. 1931, 1932.
26. Cary and Meigs, Jour. Agr. Res., 29, 1924, p. 603; Cary, Jour. Dairy Sci., 18, 1935, p. 445. In addition to the preceding references, see also: Lindsey, Mass. Rpt. 1911, Part I; Mead and Towles, Md. Rpt. 1919; Buschmann, et al., Landw. Vers. Stat., 101, 1923, pp. 1-216.
27. Savage, N. Y. (Cornell) Bul. 323.
28. Feeds and Feeding, 15th to 19th editions.
29. Hansson, Utfodringslära; Mollgaard, Futtungslehre des Milchviehs; Eckles, Mo. Res. Bul. 7; Ellett, Holdaway, and Harris, Va. Tech. Bul. 23; Kriss, Jour. Nutr., 4, 1931, pp. 141-161.
30. Perkins, Ohio Bimo. Bul. 147 and information to the author.
31. Gerlaugh and Salisbury, Ohio Bul. 532; Morris and Wright, Jour. Dairy Res., England, 4, 1933, pp. 177-196; 5, 1933, pp. 1-14.
32. Huffman and Bowling, Mich. Quar. Bul. 14, 1931, No. 2; Larsen, et al., S. D. Bul. 188; Holdaway, Ellett, and Harris, Va. Tech. Bul. 28.
33. Kellner, et al., Untersuchungeu über die Wirkungs des Nahrungsfett auf die Milchproduktion der Kuhe, 1907.
34. Maynard and McCay, N. Y. (Cornell) Bul. 543; Maynard and McCay, Jour. of Nutr., 2, 1929, pp. 67-81; Maynard, McCay, Williams, and Madsen, N. Y. (Cornell) Bul. 593; Bender and Maynard, Jour. Dairy Sci., 15, 1932, pp. 242-253.
35. Morrison, Humphrey, and Putney, Wis. Bul. 323.
36. Meigs and Converse, Jour. Dairy Sci., 8, 1925, pp. 177-195.
37. Jones, Brandt, and Haag, Ore. Bul. 328.
38. Reed, Fitch, and Cave, Kan. Bul. 233.
39. Headley, Knight, and Cline, U. S. Dept. Agr. Cir. 352; see also: Headley, Nev. Bul. 119; Nev. Rpt. 1934.
40. Fraser, Dairy Farming.
41. Moseley, Stuart, and Graves, U. S. Dept. Agr., Tech. Bul. 116; Dickson and Kopland, Mont. Bul. 293.
42. Woll, Voorhies, and Castle, Cal. Bul. 323; Stephens, Okla. Bul. 208; Willard, Wyo. Bul. 202.
43. Fairchild and Wilbur, Ind. Bul. 277; Hanson and Schaefer, Minn. Spec. Bul. 123; Ohio Bul. 373.
44. Lindsey and Archibald, Mass. Bul. 291.
45. Nevens, Ill. Bul. 289; Hunt, Va. Rpt. 1918.
46. Huffman, Duncan, Robinson, and Lamb, Mich. Tech. Bul. 134.
47. Hart, Keenan, and Humphrey, Wis. Bul. 425; Hart, Hadley, and Humphrey, Wis. Res. Bul. 112.
48. Palmer, Fitch, Gullickson, and Boyd, Cornell Veterinarian, 25, 1935, pp. 229-246.
49. Becker, Neal, and Shealy, Fla. Bul. 262; Jour. Dairy Sci., 17, 1934, pp. 1-10; see also: Lush, La. Cir. 10.
50. For a comprehensive bibliography of the reports of investigations on the calcium and phosphorus requirements of dairy cattle, see: Forbes, et al., Penn. Bul. 319.
51. Forbes, et al., Ohio Buls. 295, 308, 330.
52. Forbes, et al., Ohio Bul. 363; Miller, Yates, Jones, and Brandt, Amer. Jour. Physiol., 72, 1925, pp. 647-654; 75, 1926, pp. 696-703.

52a. Forbes et al., Penn. Bul. 319; Ellenberger, Newlander, and Jones, Vt. Buls. 331, 342, 360, 380.
53. Eaton, Ala. Rpts. 1930, 1931, 1932; Cunningham and Davis, Ariz. Rpts. 1923, 1927; Baker, Del. Bul. 133; Iowa Rpts. 1925, 1927; Lindsey and Archibald, Mass. Buls. 230, 255; Reed and Huffman, Mich. Tech. Bul. 105; Hayden, Monroe, and Crawford, Ohio Bimo. Bul. 145; Ohio Spec. Cir. 29; Hart, Hadley, and Humphrey, Wis. Res. Bul. 112; McCandlish, Scot. Jour. Agr., 8, 1925, No. 1, pp. 55-59.
54. Becker, Neal, and Shealy, Fla. Bul. 231.
55. Babcock and Carlyle, Wis. Rpt. 1905.
56. Hart, McCollum, Steenbock, and Humphrey, Wis. Res. Bul. 17; Hart, Steenbock, and Humphrey, Wis. Res. Bul. 49; Hart, et al., Wis. Buls. 373, 405.
57. Copeland and Fraps, Tex. Bul. 473; Fraps, Copeland and Treichler, Tex. Bul. 495.
58. Eckles and Williams, Jour. Dairy Sci., 8, 1925, pp. 89-93.
59. Hart, Hadley, and Humphrey, Wis. Res. Bul. 112.
60. Monroe and Bachtell, Ohio Bul. 497; Monroe and Krauss, Ohio Bul. 516; Monroe and Mahan, Ohio Bimo. Bul. 155; Monroe, Krauss, and Hayden, Ohio Bimo. Bul. 174.
61. Larsen, et al., S. D. Buls. 132, 147, 175.
62. Armsby, Wis. Rpt. 1886; Collier, N. Y. (Geneva) Rpt. 1893; McCandlish and Gaessler, Jour. Dairy Sci., 2, 1919, pp. 4-8; Eckles, Dairy Cattle and Milk Production, pp. 388-391; Perkins and Monroe, Jour. Dairy Sci., 8, 1925, p. 409-414; Fuller, N. H. Tech. Bul. 35; Moore and Bowling, Mich. Quar. Bul. 13, 1930, No. 1; Woodward and McNulty, U. S. Dept. Agr., Tech. Bul. 278; Cannon, Hansen, and O'Neal, Iowa Bul. 292; Henderson and Morrow, W. Va. Bul. 256; Atkeson, Warren, and Anderson, Jour. Dairy Sci., 17, 1934, pp. 265-277; White and Johnson, Conn. (Storrs) Bul. 198.
63. Woodward and McNulty, U. S. Dept. Agr. Tech. Bul. 278; Cannon, Hansen, and O'Neal, Iowa Bul. 292; White and Johnson, Conn. (Storrs) Bul. 198.
64. Garver and Knott, Wash. Bul. 291.
65. Nevens, Ill. Rpts. 1926, 1927; Wilbur, Hilton, and Mayer, Ind. Rpt. 1927, mimeo. rpt.; Weaver, Ely, and Mathews, Iowa Leaflet 76; Ingham and Meade, Md. Bul. 316; Reed and Burnett, Mich. Quar. Bul. 9, 1926, No. 1; Moore and Cowsert, Miss. Bul. 235; Tretsven, Mont. Bul. 282; Hayden, Monroe, and Perkins, Ohio Bul. 502; Morrow and La Master, S. C. Bul. 255; Olson, S. D. Bul. 252; Morrison, Humphrey, Rupel, et al., Wis. Buls. 388, 396; Rupel, Roche, and Bohstedt, Wis. Res. Bul. 102.
66. Forbes, Fries, and Braman, Jour. Agr. Res., 31, 1925, pp. 987-995; Bechdel, Williams, and Jeffries, Penn. Rpt. 1927; Olson, S. D. Bul. 252.
67. Jones, Brandt, and Haag, Ore. Bul. 328; see also: Tretsven, Mont. Bul. 282; Headley, Nev. Rpt. 1934.
68. Hayden, Monroe, and Perkins, Ohio Bul. 502; Olson, S. D. Bul. 252.
69. Fat percentages for Ayrshire, Guernsey, Holstein, and Jersey milk from dairy herd-improvement association records tabulated by McDowell and associates, Bureau of Dairy Industry, U. S. Dept. Agr., information to the author; other data chiefly from: Overman, Sanmann, and Wright, Ill. Bul. 325; Eckles and Shaw, Bur. Dairy Indus., U. S. Dept. Agr. Bul. 156.
70. Ohio Spec. Cir. 29; see also: Overman, Sanmann, and Wright, Ill. Bul. 325.
71. Hill, Utah Bul. 227, Utah Cir. 101; Doan and Welch, Penn. Bul. 312.
72. Yapp and Campbell, Ill. Rpts. 1931, 1932; Turner and Haskell, Mo. Res. Bul. 130; Campbell, Vt. Bul. 341; Associates of Rogers, Fundamentals of Dairy Science, 2nd edition.
73. Gaines, Ill. Bul. 308; see also: Overman and Sanmann, Ill. Bul. 282; Overman and Gaines, Jour. Agr. Res. 46, 1933, pp. 1109-1120.
74. Eckles, Dairy Cattle and Milk Production, p. 405; Anderson, Mich. Spec. Bul. 71.
75. Van Slyke, Jour. Amer. Chem. Soc., 30, 1908, p. 1166; Eckles, Dairy Cattle and Milk Production, pp. 416-417.
76. Ragsdale, Brody, and Turner, Jour. Dairy Sci., 4, 1921, pp. 448-450; Iowa Rpt. 1929.
77. Ross and Winther, N. Y. (Cornell) Bul. 589.
78. Regan and Mead, Jour. Dairy Sci., 4, 1921, pp. 495-509; Fitch, Becker, and McGilliard, Jour. Dairy Sci., 5, 1922, pp. 259-271; Wylie, Jour. Dairy Sci., 6, 1923, pp. 292-298; Regan, N. J. Rpt. 1921; Penn. Buls. 176, 181.
79. Indermuhl, Jahrber. Landw. Schule Rutti, 1908; Gowen, Jour. Agr. Res., 16, 1919, pp. 79-102; Eckles and Shaw, U. S. Dept. Agr., Bur. Anim. Indus., Bul. 157; Campbell, Jour. Dairy Res., England, 3, 1931, pp. 52-60; 4, 1932, pp. 28-36.
80. Riford, Hoard's Dairyman, 63, 1922, p. 661; Ragsdale, Turner, and Brody, Jour. Dairy Sci., 7, 1924, pp. 249-254; Woodward, U. S. Dept. Agr. Cir. 180; Atkeson, Idaho Bul. 164; Dahlberg, Hoard's Dairyman, 68, 1924, p. 436; Huynen, Proc. World's Dairy Congress, 1923; Woodward, U. S. Dept. Agr., Cir. 180.
81. Gowen, Milk Secretion; Graves and Fohrman, U. S. Dept. Agr. Bul. 1352; White and Judkins, Conn. (Storrs) Bul. 94; McCandlish, Iowa Res. Bul. 73; Headley, Nev. Bul. 131; Turner, Ragsdale, and Brody, Mo. Bul. 221; Brody, Mo. Res. Bul. 105; Clark, Jour. Dairy Sci., 7, 1924, pp. 547-554; Hammond and Sanders, Jour. Agr. Sci., England, 13, 1923, pp. 74-119; White and Drakeley, Jour. Agr. Sci., England, 17, 1927, pp. 420-427; Glen and McCandlish, Jour. Agr. Sci., England, 20, 1930, pp. 45-52; Sanders, Jour. Agr. Sci., England, 20, 1930, pp. 145-185.
82. Kendrick, U. S. D. A., Bur. of Dairy Indus., Mimeo. Cir., 1933.
83. McDowell, U. S. Dept. Agr. Cir. 114; Turner, Mo. Res. Bul. 147; Nevens, Jour. Dairy Sci. 2, 1919, pp. 99-107; Gowen, Jour. Agr. Res. 30, 1925, pp. 865-869.
84. Gaines, Jour. Dairy Sci., 14, 1931, pp. 14-25; see also: Brody and Procter, Mo. Res. Bul. 222; Brody and Ragsdale, Mo. Bul. 351.
85. Eckles, Mo. Bul. 100; Woll, Wis. Rpts. 1902, 1903.
86. Eckles and Palmer, Mo. Res. Bul. 25.
87. Ragsdale and Swett, Mo. Bul. 179.

88. Gowen and Tobey, Me. Bul. 360; Overman and Wright, Jour. Agr. Res., 35, 1927, pp. 637-644.
89. Eckles and Palmer, Mo. Res. Bul. 24.
90. Woll, Cal. Bul. 351; Beach, Conn. (Storrs) Bul. 29; McCandlish, Jour. Dairy Sci., 7, 1924, pp. 255-261; Pearl, Me. Sta., Rpt. of Prog. on Animal Husb. Inves. in 1915; Ragsdale, Turner, and Brody, Mo. Buls. 189, 197; Jour. Dairy Sci., 6, 1923, pp. 527-531; Linfield, Utah Bul. 68; Woll, Wis. Bul. 116; Wis. Res. Bul. 26; Drakeley and White, Jour. Agr. Sci., England, 17, 1927, pp. 118-139; Becker and Dix Arnold, Jour. Dairy Sci., 18, 1935, pp. 389-399.
91. Gaines and Davidson, Ill. Bul. 272; Hooper, Ky. Bul. 248; Ragsdale, Turner, and Brody, Jour. Dairy Sci., 7, 1924, pp. 24-30; Sanders, Jour. Agr. Sci., England, 17, 1927, pp. 502-523.
92. McCandlish, Jour. Dairy Sci., 4, 1921, pp. 301-320; Olson, S. D. Rpt. 1923; Nevens, Alleman, and Peck, Jour. Dairy Sci., 9, 1926, pp. 307-345; Petersen, Jour. Dairy Sci., 10, 1927, pp. 70-82; Bender, N. J. Rpt. 1928; Woods, N. H. Bul. 20; Wing, N. Y. (Cornell) Bul. 92; Lindsey, Mass. Rpt. 1908; Sutton, Brown, and Johnston, Jour. Dairy Sci., 15, 1932, pp. 209-211; Allen, Jour. Dairy Sci., 17, 1934, pp. 379-395.
93. Allen, Jour. Dairy Sci., 15, 1932, pp. 132-141.
94. Frederiksen, Meddelelse fra Forsogslaboratoriets Husdyrbrugsafdeling, Denmark, 1923, 1925, 1927; Woll, Cal. Bul. 335; Perkins, Bachtell, and Weaver, Ohio Bul. 497.
95. Savage, Maynard, and Harrison, N. Y. (Cornell) Station, unpublished data.
96. Hilton, Jour. Dairy Sci., 18, 1935, pp. 443-444.
97. Perkins, Ohio Bul. 515.
98. Channon, Drummond, and Golding, Analyst, 49, 1924, pp. 311-327; Golding and Zilva, Biochem. Jour., 22, 1928, pp. 173-182; Hart, Hadley, and Humphrey, Wis. Res. Bul. 112; Petersen, Jour. Dairy Sci., 15, 1932, pp. 283-286; Brown and Sutton, Jour. Dairy Sci., 14, 1931, pp. 125-135; McCay and Maynard, Jour. Biol. Chem., 109, 1935, pp. 29-37.
99. Woodward, Jour. Dairy Sci., 6, 1923, pp. 466-478.
100. Dvorachek and Lippert, Ark. Buls. 221, 257; Richardson and Abbott, Cal. Rpt. 1930; Hunzicker, et al., Ind. Bul. 159; Lindsey, Mass. Rpt. 1908; Moore, Miss. Rpts. 1930, 1931, 1932; Morse, N. H. Bul. 16; S. C. Rpt. 1929; S. D. Rpt. 1926; Sutton, Brown, and Johnston, Jour. Dairy Sci., 15, 1932, pp. 209-211; Overman and Garrett, Jour. Agr. Res., 45, 1932, pp. 51-58.
101. Brooks, Mass. (Hatch) Rpt. 1895; Hills, Vt. Rpt. 1907; Eckles, Milchw. Zentralblatt, 5, 1909, pp. 488-502; White and Judkins, Conn. (Storrs) Bul. 94; Clothier, Soc. Prom. Agr. Sci., Proc. 39, 1919, pp. 75-112; Ragsdale, Turner, and Brody, Mo. Buls. 189, 197; Woodward, Jour. Dairy Sci., 6, 1923, pp. 466-478; Georgia Rpt. 1925; Brody, Turner, and Hays, Mo. Bul. 236; Davidson, Ill. Rpt. 1926; Weaver and Mathews, Iowa Res. Bul. 107; Brooks, Jour. Dairy Sci., 14, 1931, pp. 483-493; Headley, Nev. Bul. 131; Cal. Rpt. 1932; Houston and Hale, Jour. Dairy Res,. 3, 1932, pp. 294-309; Becker and Dix Arnold, Jour. Dairy Sci., 18, 1935, pp. 389-399.
102. Regan, Richardson, and Kleiber, Amer. Dairy Sci. Assoc., Abstr. of Papers, 29th Annual Meeting, 1934.
103. Georgia Rpt. 1925.
104. Bender, N. J. Rpt. 1928.
105. McDowell, U. S. Dept. Agr., Farmers' Bul. 1604; see also: Cannon, Jour. Dairy Sci., 16, 1933, pp. 11-15; Gaines, Ill. Rpt. 1933.
106. Morgen, Kreuzhage, and Holzle, Landw. Vers. Stat., 51-52, 1898-9, p. 117; Woodward, Jour. Dairy Sci., 6, 1923, pp. 466-478; Kolack, Arch. Tierernähr. u. Tierzucht., 8, 1933, pp. 372-415.
107. White, Johnson, Rettger, and McAlpine, Conn. (Storrs) Bul. 154; Morgan and Davis, Nebr. Res. Bul. 46; Simms and Miller, Jour. Amer. Vet. Med. Assoc., 68, 1926, pp. 455-461; Fritz and Barnes, Jour. Amer. Vet. Med. Assoc., 83, 1933, pp. 680-691.
108. Hooper and Bacon, Ky. Bul. 234; McCandlish, Jour. Dairy Sci., 9, 1926, pp. 65-67; Copeland, Jour. Dairy Sci., 12, 1929, pp. 464-468.
109. Hills, Vt. Rpts. 1899, 1900; Jour. Landw. 41, 1893, p. 332.
110. White, Conn. (Storrs) Bul. 181.
111. Woodward, Turner, and Curtice, U. S. Dept. Agr. Bul. 147.
112. Arnold, Neal, and Becker, Jour. Dairy Sci., 15, 1932, pp. 407-412.
113. Taylor and Anthony, Mich. Quar. Bul., 15, 1932, pp. 118-127.
114. Henderson, Penn. Rpt. 1916; McCandlish, Jour. Dairy Sci., 1, 1917-18, p. 475; Hays and Thomas, Jour. Agr. Res., 19, 1920, p. 123; Jack and Bechdel, Jour. Dairy Sci., 18, 1935, pp. 195-205.
115. Babcock, U. S. Dept. Agr. Buls. 1190, 1208, 1297, 1326, 1342, Tech. Bul. 9, Leaflet 25; Gamble and Kelley, U. S. Dept. Agr. Bul. 1097; Roadhouse, et al., Cal. Rpts. 1929, 1930, 1931; Roadhouse and Henderson, Jour. Dairy Sci., 15, 1932, pp. 299-302; Nevens and Tracy, Ill. Rpt. 1928; Trout, Mich. Quar. Bul. 14, 1932, No. 3; Eckles, Combs, and Derby, Jour. Dairy Sci., 13, 1930, pp. 308-318; N. C. Bul. 247; N. D. Bul. 194; Ore. Rpt. 1926-8; McDonald and Glaser, Tenn. Cir. 26.
116. Eckles, Dairy Cattle and Milk Production, p. 405.
117. Palmer and Eckles, Mo. Res. Buls. 9, 10, 11, 12, Cir. 74; see also: Doane, Jour. Dairy Sci., 7, 1924, pp. 147-153; Yapp and Kuhlman, Ill. Rpts. 1927, 1930.

CHAPTER XXV

FEEDS FOR DAIRY COWS

I. Grains and Other Concentrates Low in Protein

839. Economical rations necessary for profits.—Numerous studies of the cost of milk production, conducted by the experiment stations and other agencies, have shown that on many farms, even where well-bred cows are kept, milk is produced at little or no profit to the owner. Yet, by a wise selection of feeds and intelligent and economical feeding, other dairymen secure good profits from cows no better. This shows emphatically that the feeding of the herd must be given most careful study and the system of farming so planned that a ration well-balanced in nutrients and otherwise satisfactory may be furnished at minimum expense.

To provide an efficient and economical ration for dairy cows, it is necessary to know the advantages and limitations of the various feeds that may be available and their actual relative values for milk cows. This chapter therefore presents detailed information on the feeds commonly used for this purpose. Data are given in Part II on the composition and values of the less common feeding stuffs. In Appendix Table VII many different concentrate mixtures are suggested, which are adapted for feeding with various combinations of roughage and which are suited to the conditions in various parts of this country.

It will be noted in this chapter that there is no one "best ration" for dairy cows. On the other hand it is shown that there is a wide opportunity to substitute one feed for another in a ration, if the substitution is made intelligently. For example, all the grains are satisfactory for dairy cows, when used as advised in this chapter. Also, many different protein supplements can be successfully used to balance the ration, when their specific characteristics are taken into consideration. Likewise, several kinds of legume hay are excellent for dairy cows. If, unfortunately, no legume hay can be provided economically, grass hay can be made a satisfactory roughage, providing it is grown on well-fertilized land, cut early, and cured properly. It is also shown that while silage is an excellent dairy feed, it is not necessary for efficient production, if the cows have an abundance of other high-quality roughage.

On account of this wide choice of satisfactory feeds, a dairyman will find it highly profitable to study his feeding problems carefully and to determine just what combination of feeds will be most efficient and economical under his local conditions. In doing this he should lay aside any prejudices in favor of certain feeds or certain rations. He should be guided solely by the results of the numerous experiments that have been conducted to secure definite and accurate information on the feeding of dairy cattle.

840. Indian corn.—Throughout the corn belt Indian corn is usually the cheapest low-protein concentrate for the dairy herd. Corn is very palatable to dairy cows and can satisfactorily form a large part of the concentrate mixture, for it is rich in digestible carbohydrates and fat, which are needed in large amounts for milk production. In using corn as the chief concentrate, it is important to see that the deficiencies which have been discussed in Chapter XVII are fully corrected. (**508, 512**) Legume hay, especially alfalfa hay, admirably makes good these lacks, except that legume hay is not rich in phosphorus.

Since corn is a heavy feed, most dairymen prefer to feed it as only part of the concentrate or grain mixture, mixing ground corn with such bulkier feeds as wheat bran or ground oats. (**911**)

When cows are fed a reasonable quantity of hay that is cured fairly well, there is probably no difference in the value of white corn and yellow corn, for the hay will furnish an ample amount of vitamin A, which white corn lacks.

841. Corn requires supplement.—The poor results which follow when corn is fed in an unbalanced ration are shown in a trial at the Illinois Station in which one lot of cows was fed for 131 days on corn as the only concentrate, with timothy hay, corn silage, and only a small amount of clover hay as roughage.[1] Another lot was fed a well-balanced ration of clover hay, corn silage, and a mixture of ground corn and gluten feed. The cows fed the balanced ration produced 47 per cent more milk and 39 per cent more fat than those fed the same weight of concentrates and roughages in the unbalanced ration. Also, the cows fed the poor ration frequently went off-feed, which further showed the deficiencies of the ration. This trial and a similar Maryland experiment show the folly of expecting profitable production from unbalanced rations.[2]

842. Preparation of corn.—Experiments have proved conclusively that it pays to grind shelled corn or ear corn for dairy cows.[3] If cows are fed whole shelled corn, as much as 18 to 35 per cent of the grain passes through the digestive tract unchewed and with but little digestion of the nutrients in these whole kernels. The corn should be ground to only a medium degree of fineness, for extremely fine grinding is unnecessary and unduly expensive. Merely cracking it is not sufficient to ensure complete digestion. Cows fed corn ground medium-fine in Indiana trials digested all but 1 to 2 per cent of the grain, in comparison with losses of 5 to 10 per cent for cracked corn and 30 to 35 per cent for whole corn.[4]

Shelled corn is chewed thoroughly by calves up to 6 or 8 months of age and therefore it is unnecessary to grind it for them.[5] Heifers also chew corn much more thoroughly than do cows. In Michigan experiments only 6 per cent of the shelled corn was not masticated by calves and 11 per cent by heifers, in comparison with 23 per cent by cows.[6]

When the concentrate mixture is already reasonably bulky, 100 lbs. of corn grain fed in the form of corn-and-cob meal are apparently worth no more than 100 lbs. of ground corn.[7] On the other hand, when other bulky concentrates are not included in the ration, 100 lbs. of corn-and-cob meal may equal or approach in value an equal weight of ground corn.[8] If the cost of grinding ear corn to corn-and-cob meal is less than the cost of shelling it and then grinding the shelled corn, it is economical to use corn-and-cob meal, even if there are other bulky feeds in the concentrate mixture.

843. Hominy feed.—Hominy feed is similar to corn in composition and is equal or slightly superior to it in feeding value for dairy cows. It is somewhat bulkier than corn, and since it is kiln-dried, it keeps better in storage than does ground corn. (**519**)

844. Oats.—Oats have a higher value for dairy cows in comparison with corn than would be expected from their composition, from the content of digestible nutrients, and from the results of feeding experiments with fattening cattle, sheep, and swine. (**527-528**) Based upon practical experience and feeding trials, the value of oats is rated in the Scandinavian feed-unit system as only 10 per cent less than that of corn, and in a trial at the Massachusetts Station, ground oats, fed as a large part of the concentrate mixture, were equal to the same weight of ground corn.[9]

Ground oats are very palatable to cows, help to give bulk to a concentrate mixture, and are also somewhat higher than corn in protein. Perhaps for these reasons, they are a most popular dairy feed. Experienced dairymen commonly include them as part of the concentrate mixture, unless the price per pound is appreciably higher than that of other grains.

Oats should be ground to a medium fineness or crushed for dairy cows. When whole oats are fed there is nearly as great a loss in unmasticated kernels passing through the digestive tract as there is in the case of shelled corn.[10] It is not necessary to grind oats for calves up to 6 or 8 months of age.

845. Barley.—For many years barley has been a common feed for dairy cows in Europe, where it has a reputation for producing milk and butter of excellent quality. (**550-551**) Recently its use for cows has become more common in the United States. Ground or rolled barley has proved equal to ground corn for dairy cows when forming 40 to 60 per cent of the concentrate mixture in two Wisconsin trials and in Arizona and Michigan experiments.[11]

Some farmers believe that barley tends to dry up cows, but there is no sound basis for this opinion.[12] When cows are fed only rolled or ground barley and alfalfa hay, there may be considerable trouble from bloat, judging from Nevada trials.[13] On a mixture of equal parts rolled barley, corn, and wheat feed, fed with alfalfa hay, there was no bloating.

Barley should be ground to a medium fineness or crushed for dairy cattle. Too fine grinding is undesirable, as finely-ground barley may become pasty in the mouth and consequently unpalatable.[14]

846. Wheat.—Ground wheat is about equal to ground corn for dairy cows and is an entirely satisfactory feed, even over extended periods, if it is fed in a suitable concentrate mixture and in a properly-balanced ration.[15] (**537**) It is considerably higher than corn in protein, but, like corn, it is deficient in calcium. Wheat should be ground, not too finely, or rolled for cows, and, since it is a very heavy feed, it is best to mix it with some bulky concentrate. On account of its rather pasty nature, the best results are probably secured when wheat does not form more than one-third to one-half of the concentrate mixture, although it has been fed successfully as the only concentrate, with plenty of alfalfa hay for roughage.

847. Rye.—Rye is often less palatable than the cereals discussed previously and had best not form more than 40 to 45 per cent of the concentrates for dairy cows. (561) Fed as part of a suitable concentrate mixture, ground rye has been equal or nearly equal to ground barley or ground corn for dairy cows.[16] Large allowances produce a hard, dry butter, but the butter was satisfactory in a Montana trial when rye formed 40 per cent of the concentrate mixture.[17] Rye should be ground, not too finely, or crushed, for dairy cows.

848.—Grain sorghums; sweet sorghums.—The *grain sorghums* are of great importance to dairymen in the semi-arid Southwest, usually being the cheapest concentrates available. (565) They resemble corn in composition but are considerably lower in fat and slightly higher in protein. Sorghum grain should be ground for cattle. Kansas tests show that more than half of the seed may pass through cows unmasticated when the whole grain is fed.[18]

Ground grain sorghum is approximately equal to ground corn for dairy cattle. In Kansas experiments ground milo was equal to ground corn for dairy cows, and ground kafir was equal to ground corn for dairy heifers and worth only 2 to 4 per cent less for dairy cows.[19] Similar results were secured in Arizona and Mississippi tests.[20] Contrary to the belief of some farmers, feeding pregnant heifers exclusively on sorghum grain, silage, and fodder did not cause abortion in the Kansas investigations.

Seed from the sweet sorghums, or sorghos, has been considered somewhat unpalatable for dairy cows and it has been said to have a tendency to dry them up. However, in Kansas trials a mixture of 4 parts ground sorgo seed, 2 parts wheat bran, and 1 part linseed meal was just as palatable and fully as efficient as one containing ground corn in place of the sorgo seed.[21] Ground sorgho seed was also satisfactory for dairy heifers. Ground sorghum heads gave good results when forming two-thirds of the concentrate mixture for dairy cows.[22]

849. Molasses.—Either *cane molasses* or *beet molasses* contains less than 60 lbs. of total digestible nutrients per 100 lbs., in comparison with about 80 lbs. for corn of the usual grades. On account of this lower content of digestible nutrients, when molasses is added to a good dairy ration consisting of palatable feeds, it will be worth somewhat less than corn, pound for pound. For example, in two Wisconsin trials when 10 per cent of cane molasses was incorporated in a mixture of palatable concentrates, the milk production was practically the same as on the concentrate mixture without molasses. In these trials the molasses was worth 89 per cent as much per pound as ground corn.[23]

Molasses may have a decidedly higher value than this when it is used as an appetizer to increase the palatability of other feeds. For example, it is often diluted and sprinkled over rather unpalatable roughage to induce the cows to eat it with less waste. Primarily due to the palatability and appetizing effect of molasses, a considerable proportion of the commercial mixed dairy feeds on the market contain 5 to 10 per cent of molasses or more.

To induce cows on official test to consume more feed, molasses is frequently added to their ration, often being added to water in which dried beet pulp is soaked. In trials by the United States Department of Agriculture with cows heavily fed on official test, molasses thus added to a good ration containing corn silage and legume hay slightly increased the consumption of feed and the production of milk.[24] Except from the standpoint of the value of the increased records, the feeding of molasses was not economical.

Cane molasses and *beet molasses* are equal in value, except that beet molasses should not be fed in too large amounts. (**641, 642**) In sugarcane growing sections cane molasses and in the West beet molasses are often economical substitutes for part of the grain in feeding dairy cows.[25] It was found in Hawaiian experiments covering a period of 7 years that when properly supplemented with protein-rich feeds, cane molasses could be satisfactorily substituted for one-quarter of the concentrates usually fed dairy cows.[26] Though some Hawaiian dairymen believed that the continued feeding of considerable amounts of molasses would impair the breeding efficiency of the cows, there was no such effect.

850. Dried beet pulp; dried molasses-beet pulp.—Because of the bulky nature of *dried beet pulp* and its slightly laxative and conditioning effect, this palatable low-protein feed is popular with dairymen, especially for cows on official test. (**644**) As a source of nutrients for economical production, it is worth no more per ton than ground corn or oats, or even less. However, as a part of the concentrates for cows on official test, or when a limited amount is added to a heavy concentrate mixture to provide bulk, it may be worth more per ton than corn.[27] Cows on official test are often fed 6 to 10 lbs. of dried beet pulp per head daily, well soaked for some hours before feeding with water, to which molasses has perhaps been added.

When silage or other succulent feed is not available, dried beet pulp, soaked before feeding, is sometimes used as a substitute, though it is usually more expensive than silage.[28] Recent trials indicate that for ordinary herd feeding and when cows are provided with water in drinking cups, just as good results are secured when as much as 8 lbs. per head daily of dried beet pulp are fed dry as when it is soaked.[29]

Dried molasses-beet pulp is about equal in feeding value for dairy cows to ordinary dried beet pulp.[30] Both of these feeds are too bulky and too low in total digestible nutrients to serve very efficiently as the only concentrate for good dairy cows. They have a considerably higher value when mixed with more concentrated feeds.[31]

851. Other concentrates low in protein.—In addition to the grains and other concentrates low in protein that have been discussed in this chapter, several other feeds of this kind are suitable for feeding to dairy cows and other dairy cattle. These include ground emmer, ground buckwheat, ground rough rice, rice bran, rice polish, brewers' rice, oat mill feed, and such fruit by-products as apple pomace, apple-pectin pulp, and pineapple bran. All these feeds and still others have been considered in detail in Part II.

II. PROTEIN-RICH CONCENTRATES

852. Wheat bran.—Wheat bran is an excellent feed for dairy cows, for it is palatable, bulky, slightly laxative, higher in protein than the grains, and rich in phosphorus. (**539-541**) Indeed, its value for milk production seems to be somewhat greater than would be estimated from its content of protein and digestible nutrients. Though bran is high in phosphorus, it is very low in calcium.

Bran is usually fed in combination with the grains and with feeds higher in protein, such as the oil meals and gluten feed. It has a higher value when forming not over one-fourth to one-third of the concentrate mixture than when making up a larger part of the ration. On account of its laxative effect and its bulky nature, bran is especially valuable as a part of the concentrates for cows just before and after calving and for those on official test. It is also an excellent feed for dairy calves and heifers. Bran and oats are often substituted for each other in whole or in part in making up concentrate mixtures for dairy cattle.

853. Wheat middlings or shorts; wheat mixed feed.—Though *standard wheat middlings* or *wheat shorts* are less commonly fed to dairy cattle than is bran, they are entirely satisfactory when forming not more than one-third of the concentrate mixture. They are not as bulky as bran and not quite so palatable, but they are slightly higher in protein and furnish 12 per cent more total digestible nutrients per 100 lbs. When standard middlings can be bought for the same price as bran, which is occasionally the case, they can with economy be substituted for part or all of the bran in a concentrate mixture, unless the bulk of bran is desired to lighten up the mixture.

Wheat mixed feed may be used in place of wheat bran in dairy rations and is worth 5 to 10 per cent more a ton for this purpose.[32]

854. Linseed meal.—Without question, old-process linseed meal is one of the most valuable feeds for dairy cows. This high rank is due not only to its richness in protein, but even more to its palatability and its conditioning and slightly laxative effects, which aid in keeping stock thrifty and vigorous. For these reasons, many dairymen include at least 5 to 10 per cent of linseed meal in the concentrate mixture they feed their cows, even when other feeds, such as cottonseed meal and gluten feed, are cheaper sources of protein. Linseed meal is especially valuable, due to its laxative and regulating effect, when no succulent feed is available or when hay from the grasses or dry corn forage must be fed in place of legume hay.

This feed, which is highly palatable to cattle, is greatly esteemed in fitting animals for show or sale, for it aids in producing finish and bloom and in making the hide mellow and the hair silky. It is also widely and successfully used as part of the concentrate mixture for cows on official test and in preparing cows for freshening. For the latter purpose, a popular mixture is equal parts by weight of ground corn or hominy feed, ground oats, wheat bran, and linseed meal. Linseed meal is just as valuable for dairy calves and heifers as it is for milk cows.

Because linseed meal furnishes a little less protein than does cottonseed meal, it was of slightly lower value per ton than the latter as a source of protein when fed with good-quality roughage in trials at the Pennsylvania, Vermont, and North Carolina Stations.[33] With roughage of poor quality, linseed meal would be worth more per ton than cottonseed meal. Linseed meal tends to produce a soft butter, and therefore may sometimes be advantageously fed in rations which would otherwise produce a tallowy product.

855. Cottonseed meal.—Cottonseed meal is one of the most widely-used protein supplements for dairy cows. (**581-583**) It is well suited for this purpose, because it is very rich in protein, the protein is of satisfactory quality for ruminants, and the feed is well liked by cattle. Cottonseed meal is usually the cheapest source of protein in the southern states, and has commonly been one of the most economical protein supplements in the North.

The experiments summarized in Chapter XVIII have proved that when sufficient high-quality hay or good pasturage is provided, cattle over 3 or 4 months of age may safely be fed large amounts of cottonseed meal for long periods. (**583**) Such roughage makes good the lack of vitamins (especially vitamin A) and of calcium in the cottonseed meal and in most other concentrates.

In some of these experiments dairy cows have even been fed an average of 10.3 lbs. of cottonseed meal per head daily as the sole concentrate for 3 years, with good-quality prairie hay as the only roughage. In other tests cows have been fed 9 lbs. of cottonseed meal per head daily, with high-quality timothy hay, corn silage, and corn grain. Some high-producing cows were fed as much as 17 lbs. of cottonseed meal a day for several months, without any injury. Contrary to the opinion sometimes expressed, such heavy feeding of cottonseed meal did not increase the tendency to mastitis in the cows, or make the trouble more severe in the case of cows affected with the disease.

While cottonseed meal is not quite so palatable as linseed meal, it is well liked by cattle. Since cottonseed meal does not have the conditioning effect of linseed meal, many dairymen prefer to use both of these feeds as sources of protein in a concentrate mixture, rather than to use cottonseed meal as the only supplement. Wheat bran is also an excellent feed to use along with cottonseed meal. Even though the cost may be increased by furnishing this greater variety, the practice may be preferable, especially for cows of high productive capacity.

Cottonseed meal has commonly been believed to have a somewhat constipating effect, but when fed with good roughage in Michigan and Texas experiments, it did not have this effect.[34] If cottonseed meal or cottonseed forms too large a part of the concentrates fed cows, the butter is apt to be hard, sticky, and tallowy.[35] Also, an abnormally long time is required for churning. This effect is reduced when the cows have silage or pasture. In Oklahoma experiments the milk from cows fed exclusively on cottonseed meal and prairie hay was slightly lower than normal in percentage of fat and also lower in percentage of solids-not-fat.[36]

In Indiana trials choice cottonseed meal was compared with linseed meal and with gluten feed as a supplement to a ration of ground corn, corn silage, and either alfalfa or soybean hay.[37] The amount of each supplement was adjusted so that all rations furnished the same amount of protein. Relatively small amounts of the supplements were required to balance these rations, which were already fairly high in protein, due to the legume hay. The production of milk and of butter fat was just a trifle higher when the cottonseed meal was fed, but with the different supplements there was no consistent difference in the amount of feed required for 100 lbs. of milk or for 1 lb. of butter fat.

In a Virginia trial it was found that the relative amount of digestible crude protein contained in cottonseed meal and in gluten meal was a fair measure of their feeding value.[38] In a Mississippi trial it was concluded that 1 lb. of cottonseed meal was worth as much as 1.5 lbs. of wheat bran for dairy cows.[39]

856. Corn gluten feed.—Corn gluten feed is one of the most common protein-rich dairy feeds, and it gives excellent results when properly fed. (523) It furnishes only about three-fourths as much digestible protein as does linseed meal, and a correspondingly larger amount is therefore needed to furnish a given amount of protein. Consequently, gluten feed is worth somewhat less per ton than linseed meal or cottonseed meal. Gluten feed is not especially palatable to most cows, and should therefore be mixed with such feeds as ground corn, ground oats, or wheat bran.

Since gluten feed is a corn by-product, the protein is unbalanced in nature, like that of corn. Therefore, gluten feed gives the best results when combined with other protein-rich feeds which supply protein of better quality, such as linseed meal, cottonseed meal, soybeans or soybean oil meal, or wheat bran. If cows are fed an abundance of good legume hay to make good the deficiencies of the corn protein, gluten feed can be used satisfactorily as the chief protein-rich supplement, though more variety of protein-rich feeds is generally preferable. (148)

Gluten feed and linseed meal were compared as the only protein supplements to a ration of ground corn, corn silage, and alfalfa or soybean hay in an Indiana trial, the amounts of gluten feed and linseed meal being adjusted so as to furnish the same quantity of protein.[40] When thus fed with legume hay, there was no appreciable difference in the production on these supplements.

857. Corn gluten meal.—Corn gluten meal supplies slightly more digestible protein than does cottonseed meal of the 43-per-cent-protein grade, and it is a very satisfactory feed for dairy cows, when fed in proper combination. (524) Since it does not contain the corn bran, it is much heavier than gluten feed and hence is usually combined with bulky feeds. Just as in the case of gluten feed, one should remember that the protein of gluten meal is corn protein and of unbalanced nature when forming too large a proportion of the protein in the ration.

858. Soybeans.—Ground soybeans furnish protein of excellent quality to make good the deficiencies in the proteins of the grains, and they are equal to linseed meal as a protein supplement for dairy cows. In trials in which these two feeds have been compared, there has been but little difference in the results, the value of ground soybeans averaging fully as high as that of linseed meal.[41] Ground soybeans have proved slightly superior to cottonseed meal.[42]

Soybeans are well liked by dairy cattle and have a slightly laxative effect when fed in such amounts as are needed to balance ordinary rations. If they form more than one-fourth to one-third of the concentrates, the ration may be too laxative and also less palatable, doubtless due to the high oil content of the soybeans. When only enough soybeans are fed to balance the ration, the quality of the butter is not injured, but if they form more than one-fourth of the concentrates, soft butter may result.[43] Because of the high fat content of soybeans, they may cause a slight increase in the fat percentage of the milk. (**832**)

859. Soybean oil meal or cake.—This palatable feed, containing over 40 per cent of protein of excellent quality, is one of the best protein supplements for dairy cows. (**595**) Its value has averaged fully as high as that of linseed meal, cottonseed meal, or ground soybeans in comparisons which have been made of these feeds.[44] Because most of the oil has been removed from soybean oil meal, it does not affect the hardness of butter.

But little information is available concerning the relative values of soybean oil meal made by the hydraulic process, by the expeller process, and by the solvent process. The latter is very low in fat but is richer in protein than soybean oil meal made by the other methods. When the other feeds in the ration are low in fat, soybean oil meal made by the hydraulic process or by the expeller process is desirable, in order to provide a sufficient amount of fat in the ration to make possible the maximum production of milk and butter fat. (**803**) In tests at the Indiana Station hydraulic process soybean oil meal was slightly more valuable than that made by the solvent process.[45]

860. Brewers' dried grains; brewers' wet grains.—Brewers' dried grains are used chiefly for feeding dairy cattle and are often a very economical protein supplement for them. Though they are about as bulky as wheat bran and supply less total digestible nutrients, they have nearly as much digestible protein as does corn gluten feed. Brewers' dried grains are not very palatable to cattle, but they give very satisfactory results when forming not more than about one-third of a concentrate mixture which consists chiefly of well-liked feeds. Because of their bulk, they are especially useful when the other concentrates are heavy in nature.

Except when protein supplements cost no more than carbohydrate-rich feeds, brewers' dried grains are worth somewhat more than wheat bran, because they are much higher in protein.[46] They are considerably less valuable than corn gluten feed, due to their lower content of total digestible nutrients.

The value of *brewers' wet grains* has been discussed in Chapter XVII. (**555**)

861. Distillers' dried grains.—Distillers' corn dried grains are a popular protein supplement for dairy cows and are a favorite ingredient in concentrate mixtures for cows on official test. (**648**) Though they are nearly as bulky as wheat bran, they rank above corn gluten feed in content of digestible protein and of total digestible nutrients. Since a good grade of distillers' corn grains should have 9 per cent or more fat, they are especially valuable when the other feeds in the ration are rather low in fat.

Distillers' corn dried grains were slightly superior to corn gluten feed in a Massachusetts trial, and they ranked above brewers' dried grains in a Vermont test.[47]

Distillers' rye dried grains are much less valuable than the corn grains, as has been shown in Chapter XIX. (**648**) Some of the distillers' grains sold as distillers' corn grains are, unfortunately, not up to the usual standard for this feed. Distillers' grains should therefore be bought on definite guarantee of composition and only from a reliable manufacturer or dealer.

862. Tankage; meat scraps; fish meal.—*Tankage* and *meat scraps* are not commonly used for dairy cows. However, they are satisfactory for this purpose when they furnish protein fully as economically as do the protein supplements of plant origin. (**626-629**) In a Massachusetts experiment there was no difficulty in getting cows to eat a concentrate mixture containing 17 per cent tankage, and the tankage did not affect the flavor or odor of the milk.[48] Similar results were secured in an Iowa test in which a concentrate mixture containing 8 per cent tankage was used for dairy cows, but in a Minnesota trial a mixture containing a small proportion of meat scraps was not palatable.[49]

It has been mentioned in Chapter XIX that very satisfactory results were secured in Ohio experiments in which an all-purpose protein supplement that included meat scraps has been used for dairy cows. (**629**)

The use of *fish meal* for dairy cows has been discussed in Chapter XIX. (**636**)

863. Other protein-rich feeds.—In addition to the protein-rich feeds most commonly used for dairy cows in this country, which have been discussed in this chapter, many others may be used satisfactorily for this purpose when available at economical prices. Included in this list are buckwheat middlings, rye feed, malt sprouts, corn oil meal, corn germ meal, field peas, cull beans, cowpeas, velvet beans, coconut oil meal, peanut oil meal, palm-kernel oil meal, sesame oil meal, sunflower-seed oil meal, and skimmilk. The composition and uses of these various feeds are discussed in Part II of this volume.

III. LEGUME HAY

864. Value of legume hay for dairy cows.—The outstanding excellencies of legume hay have been pointed out in Chapter XIII. (**358-365**) The nutritive merits of legume hay are of especial value in feeding dairy cows. This is due to their need for liberal amounts of high-quality protein and of calcium to produce a large yield of milk, and to their need for rations rich in vitamins A and D. Legume hay is so important in efficient and economical milk production that usually the dairyman who fails to grow it in abundance seriously reduces his net income.

On most farms in the United States Indian corn or the sorghums provide the cheapest, most abundant, and most palatable carbohydrates the farmer can produce, but they fall short in furnishing protein, so vital in milk production. Happily, at least one of the legumes—alfalfa, clover, cowpeas, soybeans, vetch, etc.—can be grown on almost every American farm to correct the deficiency. The dairyman who grows great crops of corn or sorghum for grain and silage should also have broad fields of clover, alfalfa, or some other legume to help round out the ration.

It must be borne in mind that the value of any legume hay, even that from alfalfa or red clover, varies widely, depending chiefly on whether it is well cured and on the proportion of leaves to stems.

Poorly-cured legume hay with but few leaves may be little better than ordinary timothy hay for dairy cows and inferior to well-cured, early-cut timothy hay. The range in actual value is greatest in the case of such hay as sweet clover or soybean, which is often coarse and stemmy.

When one is fortunate enough to have for his cows an abundance of alfalfa hay, rich in protein, it is especially important to scrutinize the concentrate or "grain" mixture he is feeding to see if it does not supply more protein than is necessary or advisable.

865. Legume hay makes possible efficient home-grown rations.— Alfalfa hay is so rich in protein that when cows are fed all they will clean up, in addition to plenty of corn silage and such a grain mixture as equal parts of ground corn and oats, the ration will be adequately balanced in protein content for animals producing somewhat more than 1 lb. of butter fat daily. It is pointed out in the preceding chapter that such home-grown rations may be too low in phosphorus for efficient milk production, and therefore a phosphorus supplement, like bone meal or wheat bran, should be added.

Dairy cows yielding 1.25 lbs. of fat or more per head daily remained in nitrogen balance, losing no protein from their bodies, in metabolism experiments by Hart and Humphrey at the Wisconsin Station when fed a ration of alfalfa hay, corn silage, and grain.[50] On the other hand, they lost protein when clover hay, lower in protein than alfalfa, was substituted for the alfalfa hay.

In two Wisconsin experiments by the author and associates, dairy cows produced as much milk and butter fat on a home-grown ration consisting of an abundance of alfalfa hay and corn silage for roughage, with a grain mixture of only ground corn and oats, as when a mixture of half linseed meal and half cottonseed meal was substituted for part of the corn and oats.[51] The average production on this home-grown ration was 27.6 lbs. of 3.5 per cent milk daily. The nutritive ratios of the home-grown ration were 1:6.8 and 1:7.1 in the two experiments, showing that it supplied enough protein to meet the recommendations of modern standards for cows of such production. Like results have been secured in similar trials at other stations.[52]

For cows producing much over 1 lb. of fat daily, a limited amount of protein-rich concentrates should be fed, even when an abundance of alfalfa hay is fed with corn or sorghum silage. Obviously, if a liberal amount of good alfalfa hay is fed as the only roughage, with no protein-poor roughage like corn silage, the amount of protein furnished by the large amount of alfalfa hay will be much greater. The supply of protein will then be ample, even for high-producing cows, when farm grains are fed as the only concentrates. For example, a cow fed only alfalfa hay and ground corn in an Ohio trial produced 11,276 lbs. of milk and 351 lbs. of fat in a year.[53]

866. Wasting protein supplements with legume hay.—Often when dairymen who have been growing but little legume hay change their cropping practices and provide their cows with an abundance of good legume hay, they fail to reduce the amount of protein supplements in the concentrate mixtures they feed. For example, in the northeastern states many dairymen have continued to feed concentrate mixtures containing as high as 20 to 24 per cent total protein, after they have provided their cows with plenty of alfalfa hay. Since protein supplements, such as linseed meal and cottonseed meal, are usually higher in price than the cereal grains or other low-protein concentrates, this is then decidedly uneconomical. The cows would produce just as much milk and fat if only sufficient amounts of protein supplements were fed to balance the ration according to the recommendations of modern feeding standards.

Certain farm-survey data have been said to show that dairymen who feed an abundance of alfalfa hay secure larger milk production and greater net returns when they feed concentrate mixtures just as high in protein as they would use with low-protein hay.[54] From the standpoint of the fundamentals of animal nutrition this conclusion does not seem correct. The higher production secured by the farmers who fed high-protein concentrate mixtures when also supplying an abundance of alfalfa hay was doubtless a result of their being better dairymen, on the average, than the men who fed concentrate mixtures lower in protein. They took such pains with their cows that they fed high-priced, protein-rich mixtures, believing that they were thereby giving their cows the best feed possible. Naturally such men would be apt to have high-producing cows and would take excellent care of them.

The experiments just reviewed, as well as our general knowledge of the protein requirements of dairy cows, show that these good dairymen would have secured just as high production and would have obtained greater net returns if they had fully appreciated the richness of alfalfa hay in protein and had changed their feeding methods accordingly.

Even with good mixed hay for roughage, smaller amounts of protein supplements are needed than have been fed by many dairymen, especially in the eastern states. This is shown clearly by the experiments at the New York (Cornell) Station, which have been reviewed in the preceding chapter. With mixed clover-and-timothy hay containing 30 to 50 per cent clover and corn silage for roughage, good cows gave practically as much milk and fat on a concentrate mixture containing only 16 per cent total protein as on concentrate mixtures containing 20 to 24 per cent protein. (801) With pure clover hay instead of mixed hay, still less protein is needed in the concentrate mixture.

867. Legume hay makes possible saving of concentrates.—When cows are fed all the good legume hay they will consume, they will eat considerably more than they will of such roughage as ordinary-quality timothy hay or corn fodder. They will therefore get from the legume hay a larger proportion of the nutrients they need, and consequently will need less grain and other concentrates for a given amount of milk.

The saving of concentrates made possible by feeding plenty of legume hay has been proved in several experiments. For example, in a trial at the Ohio Station, cows full-fed on alfalfa hay and corn silage, with only 5.9 lbs. of ground corn in addition, yielded about as much as others fed 9.3 lbs. of concentrates (cottonseed meal, wheat bran, and corn meal) with corn stover and corn silage for roughage.[55]

Since the question as to how much grain or other concentrates should be fed to dairy cows under various conditions is one of the most important problems for a dairyman, it has been discussed in detail in the previous chapter. (**804-809**) It has there been shown that when cows are fed no concentrates at all, but only all the high-quality legume hay they will eat, either with or without corn or other silage, they will produce fair amounts of milk.

Such a system may be the most profitable in such areas as certain alfalfa districts of the West, where alfalfa hay supplies nutrients much more cheaply than do the grains or other concentrates. On the other hand, in the corn belt and eastward it generally pays best to supply cows of good productive capacity with sufficient concentrates, in addition to roughage of the best quality, so that their nutritive requirements will be fully met. Only then can the high levels of production be maintained that are most profitable under such conditions.

868. Legume hay as the only roughage.—Legume hay gives satisfactory results when fed as the only roughage during the usual winter feeding period. However, some experienced dairymen prefer to feed other roughage in addition, for cows seem to prefer such a combination as alfalfa hay and mixed clover-and-timothy hay or alfalfa hay and corn silage to alfalfa hay fed continuously as the only roughage.

869. Alfalfa hay.—Good alfalfa hay is unexcelled as a dry roughage for dairy cows, on account of its large yield, its palatability, its high content of protein, its richness in calcium, and its superiority in vitamins A and D. (**373**) Because of these excellencies, if good cows have an abundance of well-cured alfalfa hay as part of a balanced ration, they will produce a high yield of milk and will need less grain and other concentrates than when less palatable and efficient roughage is fed.

The experiments reviewed previously show that alfalfa hay is so rich in protein that a ration consisting only of this hay, fed with corn silage and such a mixture as ground corn and oats, supplies sufficient protein for cows producing 1 lb. of butter fat daily. (**865**) Cows of greater productive capacity should receive a small amount of protein supplements in addition.

If cows are fed grain and all the good-quality alfalfa hay they will eat, with no non-legume roughage like corn silage, they will eat much more alfalfa than when they have both alfalfa and a non-legume roughage. The ration will therefore provide an abundance of protein for all cows, except perhaps for those producing an unusually large amount of milk. The extravagance of feeding protein-rich concentrate mixtures with an abundance of alfalfa hay has been pointed out previously. (**866**)

It has been shown in the previous chapter that it is wise to add a phosphorus supplement to a ration of grain and alfalfa hay, with or without corn or sorghum silage, but without any protein supplement, unless the roughage has been grown on soil rich in phosphorus. (**812**)

Recent investigations have shown that when alfalfa hay is fed less than about 4 hours before milking time, the flavor of the milk may be impaired.[56] The effect is greater when a large amount of alfalfa hay is used, and is most marked when the hay is fed less than 2 hours before milking. The hay should therefore be fed after milking, instead of before. When cows are fed nothing but alfalfa hay, the butter may be undesirably hard.[57] This condition can be corrected by adding corn silage to the ration.

Early-cut alfalfa hay is usually more palatable to dairy cattle and is worth more than late-cut hay.[58] The relative values of various cuttings of alfalfa hay and of brown alfalfa hay have been discussed in Part II. (**372, 333**) In general, the leafier the hay is, the higher is its value. (**370**)

The value of alfalfa leaves is illustrated in a Michigan trial.[59] A mixture of alfalfa leaf meal, ground oats, and ground hulled oats, fed with alfalfa hay and silage, produced as much milk as the usual type of concentrate or "grain" mixture, consisting of corn, oats, wheat bran, linseed meal and cottonseed meal.

The value of good alfalfa hay for dairy cows is not usually increased appreciably by cutting or grinding it. This has been shown by the experiments reviewed in the previous chapter. (**820**)

870. Feeding alfalfa hay alone or as the only roughage.—In some sections of the West alfalfa hay is so much cheaper than other feeds that dairy cows are fed only alfalfa hay during the winter and sometimes even throughout the year, perhaps with green alfalfa soilage or alfalfa pasturage in addition during the summer. Such a ration is too bulky and low in digestible nutrients for high production and is also very high in protein. Reproductive troubles have been attributed to this ration, but investigations at western stations indicate that the excess of alfalfa hay and of protein is not usually responsible for such troubles, but that they are commonly due to contagious abortion.[60]

Whether or not it will be most economical to feed only alfalfa hay to good cows in such districts, will depend on the relative price of alfalfa and other feeds and also on the price received for the milk, as has been pointed out in the previous chapter. (**806**) Adding corn or sorghum silage to the ration may sometimes be more profitable than adding grain.

It is pointed out later that when cows are fed alfalfa hay as the only roughage throughout the entire year, without any pasture or other green feed, they may tire of the alfalfa and produce decidedly better results when fed some other roughage in addition, even grass hay of ordinary quality. (**882**)

871. Alfalfa meal; alfalfa-molasses meal.—The relative value of *alfalfa meal* and wheat bran for dairy cows has often been discussed. Since alfalfa meal contains about three times as much fiber as wheat bran and supplies only three-fourths as much total digestible nutrients, we would hardly expect it to equal bran in feeding value as a source of digestible nutrients. In nearly all the trials where these feeds have been compared for dairy cows, wheat bran has had a higher value per ton.[61] Probably if no legume hay was otherwise available, a moderate amount of high-quality alfalfa hay in the ration would be fully as valuable for high-producing cows as the same weight of wheat bran. This would be due not to its content of digestible nutrients, but to other virtues of good alfalfa hay—its richness in calcium and in vitamins A and D.

Alfalfa-molasses meal is sometimes fed to dairy cows, especially in the West, as a substitute for part of the concentrates or in place of hay. It is very palatable but is not worth much more than good-quality alfalfa hay. In an Arizona trial alfalfa-molasses meal was worth 37 per

CONTENTED COWS WITH MANGERS FULL OF ALFALFA HAY

Alfalfa hay is unexcelled as a roughage for dairy cows, because it is not only high in protein and rich in lime, but also because it is exceedingly palatable. The farmer who provides alfalfa for his herd can save much purchased concentrates.

RED CLOVER FOR HAY AND CORN FOR SILAGE MEAN PROFITS

The dairyman who has an abundance of clover or alfalfa hay and plenty of corn for silage has the foundation of an economical, efficient ration for his herd. (From Wisconsin Station.)

SOYBEAN HAY IS A GOOD SUBSTITUTE FOR ALFALFA OR CLOVER

Soybeans are especially useful as an emergency hay crop for dairy cows when alfalfa or clover winterkills. They are also grown regularly for hay by many dairymen.

SWEET CLOVER IS AN EXCELLENT TEMPORARY PASTURE CROP

Sweet clover has been used with success on thousands of farms as a temporary pasture for dairy cows. With a good stand on fertile soil it will carry more than a cow to the acre.

cent more than rather stemmy and weedy alfalfa hay, of which the cows refused 20 per cent.[62]

872. Clover hay.—Hay from the clovers, cut while yet in bloom, is one of the best roughages for dairy cows and other dairy cattle. By the use of clover hay—red, alsike, or crimson—the dairyman may reduce the amount of concentrates needed to supply a well-balanced ration in the same manner as in the case of alfalfa hay. Cutting or grinding clover hay of good quality for dairy cattle is usually not economical. (**820**)

When cows are fed concentrate mixtures containing no more protein than they actually require, pure clover hay is worth somewhat less per ton than alfalfa hay of the same quality, because clover hay is usually considerably lower in protein content than alfalfa hay. With clover hay a greater amount of protein supplements must therefore be used to balance the ration. This was shown clearly in the metabolism trials at the Wisconsin Station which have been previously reviewed. (**865**)

Since clover hay slightly surpasses alfalfa in amount of total digestible nutrients and net energy, we should expect that the milk production would be just as high on clover hay as on alfalfa, when an abundance of protein is furnished by the other feeds in the ration. On the other hand, the production should be less on clover than on alfalfa, if the ration is somewhat deficient in protein.

Red clover hay was compared with alfalfa hay for dairy cows in 4 trials at the Ohio Station, in which these hays were added to corn grain or corn grain and wheat bran, with corn silage or silage and corn stover for roughage.[63] The clover rations had nutritive ratios ranging from 1:8.5 to 1:8.8, in comparison with 1:6.8 to 1:7.3 for the alfalfa rations. The clover rations therefore provided somewhat less protein than is commonly recommended. The alfalfa-fed cows had better appetites, consumed somewhat more feed, maintained their live weights better, and yielded 9.3 per cent more milk and 7.5 per cent more fat. In a trial at the Pennsylvania Station[64] cows fed clover hay produced 6.5 per cent less milk than those receiving alfalfa hay.

873. Mixed legume-and-grass hay.—Early-cut mixed clover-and-timothy hay, mixed alfalfa-and-timothy hay, or other similar mixed hay is excellent for dairy cows, if it contains a considerable proportion of legumes and if it is well cured. (**364, 368, 382**) Since such hay is lower in protein than pure legume hay, a greater amount of protein supplements is needed to balance the ration when it is fed. Except for this fact, the value of such mixed hay may be nearly as high as that of pure alfalfa or clover hay.

874. Sweet clover hay.—The value of sweet clover hay for dairy cows will vary widely, depending on the quality. Hay cut during the fall of the year in which the crop is seeded may be fully equal to alfalfa. Also, in the drier districts, where the first cutting the second year does not grow too rank, it may nearly equal alfalfa hay.[65] On the other hand, in humid districts this cutting is usually coarse, stemmy, and inferior in quality. In using second-year sweet clover hay for feeding cattle, the danger from the sweet-clover disease must always be borne in mind. (**392**)

875. Soybean hay.—Soybean hay has recently become of much importance for feeding dairy cattle in many sections. Soybeans are especially useful as an emergency legume-hay crop when alfalfa or clover winter-kills, and they are also grown regularly for hay by many dairymen. While soybean hay compares favorably with alfalfa in composition, it is coarser and the stems are often somewhat woody. There is therefore usually considerably more waste in feeding it than in the case of alfalfa hay.

Numerous experiments have been conducted to determine the value of soybean hay for dairy cows, in comparison with that of alfalfa hay.[66] The results of the various experiments have differed somewhat, chiefly because of the considerable difference in the quality of the soybean hay. Considering all of the data, it may be concluded that 100 lbs. of the portion of good-quality soybean hay actually eaten by cows is worth about as much as the same weight of alfalfa hay. This would mean that if 16 per cent of the soybean hay is refused (an average figure in these trials), a ton of the usual grade of soybean hay would be worth about 84 per cent as much as a ton of good alfalfa hay. The value of soybean hay as commonly produced will usually range between 70 to 90 per cent of that of good-quality alfalfa hay.

The chief difference between the two kinds of hay in these experiments has usually been that the cows refused to eat about 10 to 20 per cent of the soybean hay, this portion consisting of the coarse stems. On the other hand, there was much less waste of the alfalfa hay. Where equal amounts of hay have been fed, this greater wastage of soybean hay has generally caused a lower milk production on the soybean-hay ration, or the cows have lost in weight while the alfalfa-fed cows maintained their weights satisfactorily. In some of the experiments the investigators have not fully considered the loss in live weight on soybean hay in drawing their conclusions.

By chopping soybean hay, cows can be induced to eat practically all of it, and such preparation increased its value 19 per cent in 3 trials at the Wisconsin Station.[67] However, it must be borne in mind that the stemmy portions refused are high in fiber and low in digestible nutrients. Probably it would generally be more economical to feed a larger amount of the hay and let the cows leave the stems.

Feeding good soybean hay in place of timothy or mixed hay of ordinary quality makes possible a great saving in the amount of protein-rich concentrates needed to balance a dairy ration, and also a saving in the total amount of grain or other concentrates required for high production. For example, in three trials at the Minnesota Station feeding soybean hay in place of timothy effected a saving of 46 per cent in the concentrates fed and reduced the expenditure for purchased protein supplements 93.6 per cent.[68]

When soybean hay containing a considerable proportion of soybean seed is fed, along with a concentrate mixture containing ground soybeans, the ration may be too laxative or the cows may tire of the excessive amount of soybeans.[69] This may be avoided by feeding some other roughage in place of part of the soybean hay.

Soybean hay cut when the seed had practically reached full development and the lower leaves were turning yellow was of higher value per ton for dairy cows in 3 trials at the Indiana Station[70] than hay cut at an earlier stage. In these trials the soybeans were seeded with a grain drill in rows 7 inches apart and were therefore much finer-stemmed than when grown in cultivated rows. Due to this and because the hay was well cured, only 4 to 7 per cent of the late-cut hay was refused by the cows. Similar results were secured in Illinois trials with dairy heifers.[71]

876. Cowpea hay.—In the South cowpeas furnish excellent hay for dairy cows, even richer in protein than is alfalfa hay. For dairy cows and heifers this hay may, when it is well cured, be considered equal to alfalfa.[72]

877. Hay from other legumes.—In addition to the legume hay crops that have been discussed in this chapter, several others, which are discussed in Chapter XIII, are of importance in various districts. These include lespedeza, field peas, pea vines from canning factories, the vetches, moth beans, mung beans, tepary beans, and kudzu.

The composition and value of artificially-dried, or dehydrated, hay or immature grass have been considered in Chapter XI. (**336-338**)

IV. DRY ROUGHAGES LOW IN PROTEIN

878. Hay from the grasses.—Hay from timothy and other grasses is generally much inferior to legume hay for dairy cattle. It is low in protein when cut at the usual stage of growth, is not high in calcium, is commonly even lower in phosphorus than legume hay, and is decidedly lower in vitamin A than well-cured legume hay. Such grass hay is also much less palatable to dairy cows than is good legume hay, and therefore the cows will not eat so much of it. As a result, in order to secure good production they must be fed a larger amount of grain and other concentrates than is needed with legume hay.

Timothy hay or hay from other grasses, cut not later than full bloom and preferably even earlier, is greatly superior for dairy cattle to grass hay cut at the usual stage of maturity. This is because it is much more palatable and is considerably higher in protein, especially when grown on well-fertilized land. As is pointed out later, such hay is a satisfactory substitute for legume hay in districts where it is difficult to grow sufficient legume hay for the dairy herd. (**880**)

When there is insufficient legume hay to feed liberally throughout the barn-feeding period to all the herd, it is best to give the cattle one feed of legume hay a day, rather than to use it all up during a part of the winter and then confine them to non-legume roughage for the rest of the time. Foresight is needed to store the various kinds of hay in the barn so this will be possible.

Feeding some legume hay during the dry period is important, for it is at this time that cows have the greatest ability to store calcium and phosphorus in their bodies, which minerals may have been depleted during their lactation periods. They are therefore benefited particularly by well-cured legume hay, rich not only in calcium, but also in vitamin D, which they must have in abundance to enable them to assimilate and use the calcium and phosphorus in their feed. (**159, 190**)

If grass hay is fed, with or without silage, as the chief roughage to dairy cows, it may be wise to add a calcium supplement to the ration. (813) The large proportion of protein supplements needed to balance such a ration will usually provide sufficient phosphorus. (812)

879. Timothy hay.—Timothy hay cut at the usual stage of maturity is a poor roughage for dairy cows, for it is low in protein, in calcium, and in vitamin A; it is not very palatable to cows; and it has a constipating effect quite opposite to the beneficial laxative action of legume hay. (449) On the other hand, early-cut timothy hay, especially from fields well fertilized with commercial nitrogenous fertilizer or manure, can successfully be substituted for legume hay in feeding dairy cows during the usual winter feeding periods. When timothy or other grass hay is used as the only roughage or when such hay is fed with corn silage or sorghum silage, it may be wise to add a calcium supplement to the ration. (813) The value of mixed legume-and-timothy hay for cows will depend largely on the proportion of clover or alfalfa present.

880. Early-cut timothy hay from nitrogen-fertilized fields.—Much of the hay fed to dairy cows in the northeastern states is from timothy or other grasses. To make this hay suitable for dairy cows, it is important that the field be fertilized with some nitrogenous fertilizer (either a commercial fertilizer or farm manure) and that it be cut not later than early to full bloom. Such hay will generally be considerably higher in protein than timothy hay of the usual sort, and it is soft and well-liked, instead of being harsh, stemmy, and unpalatable. (302, 303)

The value of such timothy hay is shown in two New York experiments and in a Wisconsin experiment.[73] In the trials at the New York (Cornell) Station one group of cows was fed each winter on a ration of early-cut, nitrogen-fertilized timothy hay (cut in early to full bloom), corn silage, and a suitable concentrate mixture. Another lot was fed a ration of good alfalfa hay, corn silage, and a concentrate mixture lower in protein (so as to provide the same amount of protein in each ration). Bone meal and ground limestone were added to each ration. This timothy-hay ration produced as much milk as the alfalfa-hay ration and maintained the live weights of the cows just as well. Also, the cows liked the timothy hay fully as well as the alfalfa and refused no larger proportion, the refuse of both kinds of hay being less than 2 per cent. Similar results were secured in the Wisconsin trial.

Timothy hay cut before bloom furnished 44 per cent more net energy in New Hampshire experiments with dairy cows than did that cut after the seed had formed.[74] While only about one-third the protein in the latter hay was digestible, about 60 per cent of that in the early-cut hay was digested. When supplied as the only feed, the late-cut hay barely furnished enough nutrients for maintenance, but the early-cut hay supplied sufficient for maintenance and the production of 8 to 10 lbs. of milk a day.

The results of these experiments show that early-cut timothy hay from well-fertilized fields is a satisfactory roughage for dairy cows during the usual barn-feeding period, when fed with corn silage and in a properly-balanced ration. It is obvious that where alfalfa or clover can be grown satisfactorily and economically, dairymen should grow these legumes for dairy cattle, instead of grass hay, on account of their higher yield, their higher protein content, and their effect in soil improvement.

881. Ordinary timothy hay for cows.—The milk production on timothy hay of the usual quality will be decidedly less than on good legume hay, even when the deficiency in protein is made good by an additional amount of protein supplements. In Virginia experiments[75] a ration of timothy hay (United States Grade No. 1) and a suitable protein-rich concentrate mixture, without any calcium supplement, produced only 84 to 88 per cent as much milk during periods of several months as did a ration of No. 1 alfalfa hay and a concentrate mixture correspondingly lower in protein.

If timothy hay is fed as the chief roughage, or if timothy is fed with other roughages low in protein, such as corn silage, without the addition of enough protein supplements to balance the ration, the yield of milk will be seriously reduced.[76] When timothy or other grass hay must be fed to dairy cows without legume hay, it will give better results if fed in combination with silage than when forming the only roughage.

882. Poor-quality timothy hay dangerous if fed over long periods.—The unsatisfactory nature of late-cut timothy hay for dairy cows, when fed continuously as the only or chief roughage, is well shown in experiments by the United States Department of Agriculture.[77] Cows broke down on the average in about a year and a half and died or became sterile, when fed for long periods, without any pasture, on timothy hay of low quality, either as the only roughage or with corn silage, along with suitable concentrate mixtures. The calves from cows thus fed were born dead, or else weak and usually blind, because of the lack of vitamin A in such hay. In contrast to these results, a cow kept on only grain and good timothy hay (United States Grade No. 1) for 4 years gave birth during this period to 3 normal calves.

The cows fed poor-quality timothy hay showed a great desire to steal alfalfa hay from their neighbors fed this kind of hay, and when they were fed alfalfa in addition, the disasters were prevented. It was surprising that although cows were successfully fed on good alfalfa hay as the only roughage for similar lengths of time, they showed an eagerness for hay of some other kind. The best results were secured when high-quality alfalfa and timothy hay were both fed, so the cows could eat as much as they wished of each.

It should be pointed out that the conditions of these experiments were unnatural and most severe, since the cows had no pasture or other fresh green feed at any time. Though poor-quality timothy hay is unsatisfactory for dairy cows, it will not produce such disastrous results when fed as the only or the chief roughage during the usual barn-feeding period.

883. Prairie or native hay.—The value for dairy cattle of prairie hay or hay from other native meadows will vary widely, and depends both on the stage of maturity at which it is cut and on how well it is cured. **(456)** Wyoming trials show that prairie hay of excellent quality may be more palatable to dairy cows than some alfalfa hay.[78]

In Oklahoma experiments mentioned previously, dairy cows have been successfully fed for long periods on good-quality prairie hay as the only roughage, with cottonseed meal as the only concentrate. **(583)**

On this restricted ration reproduction and milk production were both normal. On the other hand, very unsatisfactory results were secured in Arkansas trials when cows were fed prairie hay, without pasture, as the only roughage and with a concentrate mixture containing practically no vitamin A.[79] When the cows were continued on this ration, normal reproduction was prevented and the milk yield was poor, apparently due to a lack of vitamin A. The results were much better when alfalfa hay was fed in place of the prairie hay.

In recent Kansas tests the results were satisfactory when good-quality prairie hay was fed to dairy cows with sorghum silage and a concentrate mixture supplying plenty of protein and containing bone meal and ground limestone.[80] When prairie hay was thus supplemented, the production of the cows was as great as when alfalfa hay was fed.

884. Hay from other grasses.—The value of hay from the other grasses in general resembles that of timothy hay. For detailed information on the value and usefulness of other non-legume hay, including brome hay, Bermuda grass hay, Johnson grass hay, Sudan grass hay, and hay from the small grains, the reader is referred to Chapter XV.

885. Corn fodder.—Though inferior to corn silage, well-cured corn fodder, especially that from thickly-planted corn, is relished by cows and may be used as a substitute for hay from the grasses. (**430**) Instead of being fed as the only roughage, it should be used with some legume hay, and it should be cut or shredded to reduce waste. Corn fodder was practically equal to timothy hay in a Pennsylvania trial, and in an Iowa trial the milk production was only 3.5 per cent less when cut corn fodder was fed with alfalfa hay, than when corn silage and alfalfa hay were fed as roughages.[81] However, in the latter experiment the return over feed cost was 12 per cent greater on the silage ration. Similar results have been secured in other tests with cut or ground corn fodder or ground corn-and-soybean forage.[82] Ground corn fodder may be decidedly unpalatable to cows, and cutting or shredding is a preferable and a less expensive method of preparation.

Whole corn fodder was not a good substitute for corn silage in feeding dairy cows at the North Carolina Station.[83] It was not palatable and a large proportion was refused. In an Iowa trial dairy cows refused 23 per cent of whole corn fodder, but only 12 per cent of corn fodder cut into one-fourth inch lengths.[84] The saving in feed was sufficient to cover a cost of $2.00 per ton for cutting.

886. Corn stover.—Corn stover is too low in nutrients to form any large part of the roughage for high-producing cows, but a limited amount of bright, well-cured stover, fed after cutting or shredding, may sometimes be economical. (**432**) However, better use of this feed can generally be made by such animals as well-grown heifers, stocker steers, or idle horses, which do not need so much digestible nutrients. In trials by Henry at the Wisconsin Station 1 ton of mixed clover-and-timothy hay was equal to 3 tons of uncut corn stover.[85] Thirty-four per cent of the coarse, uncut stover was uneaten in these trials, which loss would have been reduced by shredding. As is pointed out later, corn-stover silage (made from field-cured stover) is more palatable than dry corn stover and is consumed with much less waste.

Ground corn stover was inferior to shredded stover in an Indiana trial, and it caused some of the cows to go off-feed and decrease markedly in milk production.[86]

887. Sorghum fodder and stover.—In the South and in the plains states fodder and stover from the sorghums are common feeds for dairy cattle, resembling corn fodder and stover in feeding value. (**441, 442**) They may be successfully used to replace part of the hay in a dairy ration, but are usually inferior to sorghum or corn silage for milk production.[87] Cutting or shredding sorghum fodder or stover is advisable to lessen the waste.

888. Straw.—Straw is too low in nutrients to have much usefulness under usual conditions in feeding good dairy cows in milk. (**468**) Where plenty of better roughage is available, it is best to fill good cows up with more nutritious feed than straw. If there is a shortage of hay or other good roughage on the farm but plenty of straw, the straw may be fed once a day in place of one of the feedings of hay.

To induce the cows to clean up more straw than they would otherwise eat, it may be sprinkled with diluted molasses. When straw is thus used, it is necessary to feed a somewhat larger allowance of concentrates than usual and to use an ample amount of protein supplements in the mixture. The most satisfactory results are secured with this method when the cows are given at least one feeding of legume hay a day. When good straw is used for bedding, some dairymen place the straw in the manger first and allow the cows to pick it over and eat what they will, before throwing it under them for bedding.

Well-cured legume straw, with the exception of coarse and woody soybean straw, is generally of higher value than straw from the cereals. (**418**)

889. Cottonseed hulls.—Cottonseed hulls are one of the common roughages for dairy cattle in the cotton belt. (**588**) They should not be fed as the only roughage over long periods, because they lack vitamin A and are very low in calcium and phosphorus. However, they are satisfactory when some well-cured hay (especially legume hay) or good silage is fed in addition, or when the cattle are on good pasture a considerable part of the time. Care should be taken to add a calcium supplement to the ration, when necessary, if cottonseed hulls are used as the chief roughage.

When fed with silage and with a good concentrate mixture supplying ample protein and containing a calcium supplement (oyster shell flour), cottonseed hulls were almost equal to good Bermuda grass hay in Louisiana tests with dairy cows and superior to late-cut Bermuda grass and carpet grass hay.[88] Two cows on good pasture ate as much as 18 lbs. of cottonseed hulls per head daily. This indicates that the lack of palatability sometimes observed when cottonseed hulls are fed as the only roughage, has probably been due to the nutritive deficiencies in the ration.

In other experiments cottonseed hulls have been worth somewhat less per ton than good corn stover, Bermuda grass hay, Johnson grass hay, Sudan grass hay or sorghum hay for dairy cows or heifers.[89] When bulky concentrates, such as oats and wheat bran, are not available or are high in price, cottonseed hulls may be useful to increase the bulkiness of a mixture of heavy concentrates.

V. Succulent Feeds

890. Value of succulent feeds.—Succulent feeds are of much importance in the efficient and economical feeding of dairy cattle. Due to their cooling, slightly-laxative action, succulent feeds aid greatly in keeping the digestive tracts of high-producing dairy cows in good condition. Furthermore, succulent feeds are usually highly palatable, and thus they whet the appetite so that larger amounts of roughage are consumed than when only hay and other dry forages are fed. As a result, the cows have more nutrients available for milk production, after the maintenance needs of their bodies have been met.

The mild laxative effect of silage is especially desirable when there is not an abundance of legume hay in the ration. This laxative effect often makes easier the problem of providing desirable concentrate or grain mixtures, for laxative concentrates such as wheat bran and linseed meal are often relatively high in price. If cows are watered only once a day, succulent feeds also help to supply plenty of water.

While succulent feeds are highly desirable for feeding dairy cows during the winter, they are not absolutely necessary for good production. If cows are fed a liberal amount of excellent legume hay, with some good-quality carbonaceous roughage for variety, such as early-cut grass hay or bright corn fodder, they may produce nearly as much milk as when they are fed good hay and either silage or roots. (**893-894**) However, unless the dry roughage is excellent, their production will be decidedly greater if they receive succulent feeds in addition.

Whether or not to supply silage or other succulent feeds is therefore primarily a question of farm economics and farm management. (**342**) In the corn belt the use of corn silage is generally advisable, on account of its high value and its economy. On the other hand, in certain of the western alfalfa districts nutrients can be provided so much more cheaply in alfalfa hay than in any form of succulent feed that it may not be profitable to use silage or other succulent feeds in winter.

In early years it was thought that the feeding of roots or silage produced watery milk, but the extensive experiments with these feeds have proved beyond a doubt that the milk of the cow cannot be watered by supplying succulent feeds.

891. Corn silage.—Throughout the chief dairy sections of the United States corn silage is the cheapest succulent feed available, as well as the most satisfactory. (**426**) So thoroughly has the high value of corn silage for dairy cows been demonstrated that in the leading dairy districts of the corn belt a dairyman usually apologizes if he does not have a silo on his farm. Not only does corn silage furnish a steady and uniform supply of high-quality succulent feed for winter, but large numbers of progressive dairymen have found that silage is much more economical than soiling crops to feed in summer when pastures become parched and scanty, provided only that a sufficient number of cows are fed to keep the silage from spoiling.

Largely because the silage made during the early years was frequently of poor quality and fed in a careless manner, a widespread belief existed that silage injured the flavor of the milk. Silage may cause a slight odor or taste in the milk if fed soon before milking, especially in a poorly-ventilated barn. (837) However, experience has abundantly demonstrated that when good silage is fed under proper conditions the quality of the milk is not injured at all. The silage should be fed after milking, the mangers should be cleaned out regularly, and silage should not be left scattered on the floor of the stable. The air of the stable should also be kept wholesome by proper ventilation.

Though animals fed continuously on silage consume considerable quantities of organic acids, these do not cause acidosis, or an injurious acid condition of the body tissues. (183, 340)

The type of corn to grow for silage, the thickness of planting, and the value of silage cut at various stages of maturity are important problems for dairymen. These are discussed in detail in Chapter XIV.

892. Corn silage vs. dry corn fodder.—A much greater feeding value for dairy cattle is secured from an acre of corn when it is ensiled than when it is cured as dry fodder. In 9 early trials at various stations in which corn silage was compared with corn fodder, on the average 7.4 lbs. more milk were produced from each 100 lbs. of dry matter in the rations containing silage than in those containing corn fodder.[90]

The actual difference in the feeding value of the dry matter in the two forms of corn forage was obviously much greater than 7.4 per cent in these trials, because the silage or fodder was fed in addition to hay and concentrates, and therefore formed only part of the ration. In a trial at the Iowa Station corn fodder fed with alfalfa hay and a good concentrate mixture produced only 6 per cent less milk than corn silage.[91] However, on account of the greater losses in curing corn fodder and the waste in feeding it, an acre of dry corn fodder was estimated to be worth but 45 per cent as much as an acre of corn silage.

Since corn silage is no more digestible than good-quality dry corn fodder, the superiority of 100 lbs. of dry matter in corn fodder compared with the same amount of dry matter in corn silage, must be largely due to the fact that while silage is eaten with little or no waste, a considerable part of the corn fodder is usually left uneaten. Another reason is that cows getting the succulent, palatable silage consume more feed than those fed the dry fodder, and hence they have a larger amount of nutrients available for milk production after the maintenance requirements of the body have been met.

893. Is silage an economical feed?—In spite of the wide use of corn silage in feeding dairy cows, experimental data are rather limited concerning the effect on milk production when corn silage is added to a ration of good hay and concentrates, and concerning the relative value per ton of silage and hay. There is no question but that the production of good cows is increased materially when silage is added to rather poor dry roughage, such as ordinary timothy hay or dry corn fodder. The better the quality of the dry roughage, the less will be the increase in production resulting from the addition of silage. A ration consisting of excellent legume hay and a good concentrate mixture may give about as great a production of milk as when corn silage is added to it, provided the cows have access to water in drinking cups.

In a study by the United States Department of Agriculture of records from cow-testing-association herds, it was found that the average production of cows fed silage, legume hay, and grain was 305 lbs. fat a year; of those fed only legume hay and grain, 299 lbs.; of those fed silage, mixed hay and grain, 279 lbs.; of those fed only mixed hay and grain, 248 lbs.; and of those fed only non-legume hay and grain, 229 lbs.[92] It will be noted that the addition of silage to a ration of legume hay and grain increased the average production much less than adding it to a ration of poorer hay and grain.

Where the effect of silage feeding has been studied in surveys made in various states on the cost of milk production, it has usually been found that silage-fed herds produced more milk and fat than those fed only dry roughage in winter. However, in some studies the net return has been no larger or even smaller where silage has been fed.

In deciding whether or not to provide silage for his dairy cows, a farmer should consider not only the relative cost per ton of producing hay and silage, but also the other factors that have been discussed in Chapter XII. (**342**)   The economy of silage will depend primarily on whether the farm is well adapted to growing large yields of a good silage crop, usually either corn or the sorghums. It will also depend on whether the soil and the climate are such that large acreages of alfalfa or other legumes can be grown with high yields and made into good hay at a decidedly lower cost than an equivalent amount of nutrients in silage.

894. Corn silage and hay vs. hay as roughage.—Several experiments have been conducted to determine the value of silage per ton in comparison with hay or other dry roughage, and the effect of adding silage to a ration of dry roughage and grain. When corn silage was added to a ration of mixed hay and concentrates in early trials at the Maine and Vermont Stations the production of milk was increased 7 to 8 per cent.[93] In a similar trial at the Montana Station the milk production was increased only 2.5 per cent when immature corn silage was substituted for part of the clover hay in a ration of hay and concentrates.[94]

A ration consisting of an abundance of good alfalfa hay and a proper amount of concentrates is ideal for dairy cows, except that it contains no succulent feed. It is therefore of much interest to determine whether the production will be increased when corn silage is added to such a ration, in place of part of the hay. Corn silage increased the production of milk 9.9 per cent and of fat 5.7 per cent under such conditions in 3 Indiana experiments, and in similar tests at the Utah Station there was an increase of 2 per cent in milk and 4 per cent in fat through silage feeding.[95] On the other hand, in Nebraska and New Mexico trials the production was just as large on a ration containing no silage.[96] In an experiment by the United States Department of Agriculture there was likewise no increase in yield when silage was added to a ration of alfalfa hay and concentrates, but this result was not surprising, because less concentrates were fed in the silage ration.[97]

When cows were watered only once a day in Connecticut trials, the addition of corn silage to a ration of hay and grain increased the milk production 5 per cent; but when cows fed only hay and grain had access to water continuously in drinking cups, they produced even more than those watered once a day and fed silage, grain, and hay.[98] This indicates that some of the advantage secured from silage feeding in the early experiments may have been due to the additional water furnished by the silage.

In these experiments in which silage has been added to a ration of hay and concentrates, it has usually required from 250 to 300 lbs. of well-eared corn silage to equal 100 lbs. of hay in actual feeding value. In these trials good corn silage has therefore been worth 33 to 40 per cent as much per ton as good hay. This is a somewhat lower value for silage in comparison with hay than has been found in the experiments with fattening cattle and lambs, where it has required only 2 tons of corn silage, or less, to replace a ton of good legume hay. The possible explanations of this difference are discussed in Chapter XIV. (**426**)

895. Amount of silage for dairy cows.—The daily allowance of silage commonly fed to dairy cows ranges from 20 to 40 lbs. per 1,000 lbs. live weight. When cows are fed twice a day all the good corn silage and legume hay they will eat, they consume about 3 lbs. of silage and 1 lb. of hay per 100 lbs. live weight, in addition to the usual amount of concentrates. Most dairymen who have plenty of silage let their cows have all they will clean up, except perhaps in the case of cows on official test. Limiting the amount of silage and hay for such animals induces them to eat more concentrates.

To determine the effect of feeding only about half the usual amount of corn silage, 3 trials were conducted at the Connecticut (Storrs) Station.[99] In each trial one lot of cows was fed a little more than 3 lbs. corn silage per 100 lbs. live weight, while another lot was fed half as much. Both lots received equal amounts of concentrates, and the cows in each lot were given all the hay they cared for, those fed the light silage allowance eating 3.6 lbs. more per head daily than the others. The milk yield and fat production were maintained as well on the light allowances of silage as on the heavy one.

In Ohio trials cows produced a little less milk, but almost as much fat, when fed 30 lbs. of mixed alfalfa and timothy hay and 15 lbs. of corn silage a day, with a somewhat reduced allowance of a concentrate mixture consisting chiefly of grain, as they did when fed normal amounts of silage, hay, and concentrates.[100] The feed costs were lower and the net returns over feed costs were higher on the heavy hay ration. These results are of much significance in sections where the cost of silage is relatively high, in comparison with the cost of hay.

896. Silage as the only roughage.—While silage is not usually fed to dairy cows as the only roughage, without any hay or other dry fodder, this method of feeding seems to produce satisfactory results, providing there is an ample supply of protein, calcium, phosphorus, and vitamins in the ration. In Ohio trials good results were secured when the only roughage cows received during the winter (except for straw they picked up from their bedding) was corn silage or mixed corn and legume silage.[101] Similar results were obtained with corn silage as the only roughage in an Iowa trial.[102]

Soybean silage and corn silage, fed together as the only roughages, produced nearly as much milk in Florida trials as did a ration in which corn silage and good alfalfa hay were the roughages.[103] Cows fed silage as the only roughage will eat as much as 6 lbs. of silage daily per 100 lbs. live weight.

It should be borne in mind that ordinarily the easiest way to provide ample amounts of vitamins A and D in the dairy ration is through feeding well-cured legume hay. Such hay is apt to be richer in vitamin A than good silage and probably also much richer in vitamin D.

897. Corn-stover silage.—It is a mistake to remove the ears from corn fodder which is to be made into silage for dairy cattle. (**429**) If this is done, it will be necessary to feed a correspondingly larger amount of grain to replace the corn ears removed. The labor of removing the ears will be worse than wasted, for experiments have proved that better results will be secured from normal well-eared silage than from stover-silage, fed with the ground corn from the ears that were removed.[104]

Silage made from dry corn stover, fed with alfalfa hay and a suitable concentrate mixture, produced 10.6 per cent less milk than when normal corn silage replaced the stover silage in a trial at the Wisconsin Station.[105] The stover silage contained 73 per cent water, which is about the average for normal corn silage. Taking into consideration the reduced milk yield and the greater amount of other feeds required per 100 lbs. of milk, the stover silage was worth only 61 per cent as much as the normal corn silage.

898. Sorghum silage; sorghum-stover silage.—Next in value to corn silage for dairy cows is that from the grain sorghums and the sweet sorghums. (**443**) Sorghum silage is worth somewhat less per ton than such corn silage as is normally produced in the corn belt. However, where the climatic conditions are more favorable to the sorghums than to corn, as in the southern plains states, sorghum silage may be nearly as valuable per ton as the corn silage grown there.[106] In such sections the yield of sorghum silage per acre is usually much greater than that of corn, which makes sorghum decidedly the more economical silage crop.

There is apparently not much difference in the value per ton of silage from the grain sorghums and from the sweet sorghums for dairy cows. Kafir silage was slightly better than sweet sorghum silage in Kansas trials, but sweet sorghum silage was equal to kafir silage in palatability and feeding value per ton at the Oklahoma Station.[107]

Sorghum silage has this high value for dairy cows in spite of the fact that a much larger proportion of the seed passes through the animal unmasticated and undigested than in the case of corn silage. It has been found that one-fourth or more of the seeds in sorghum silage are voided in the manure with little change.[108] This is a much larger loss than occurs in the case of corn silage.

Because of this loss, experiments were conducted at the Oklahoma Station to find the relative value for dairy cows of silage made from green sorghum stover (sorghum from which the heads had been removed) in comparison with that of normal sorghum silage.[109] It was found that darso stover silage was worth 87 per cent as much a ton as darso silage containing the heads. In these tests each 100 lbs. of darso heads were worth only as much as 40 lbs. of alfalfa hay. These tests indicate that under certain conditions it may be advisable to remove the heads from grain sorghum in making silage for dairy cows.

899. Silage from the legumes.—Where more reliable silage crops do not thrive or when rain prevents making satisfactory hay from the first cutting of alfalfa or clover, the legumes are sometimes used as silage for dairy cattle. The precautions to be taken in ensiling alfalfa, clover, soybeans, etc., are pointed out in Chapter XIII, and the value of such silage is there discussed. In the pea cannery districts, *pea-vine silage* is often available for dairy cattle. This is considerably richer than corn silage in protein, and is nearly equal to corn silage for dairy cows, when fed so as to take advantage of this higher protein content. (**403**)

Such combination crops as oats and peas, oats and vetch, and corn and soybeans make good silage for dairy cattle. *Oat-and-pea silage* is of slightly less value than is corn silage, but is often useful for feeding in summer to supplement pasture, permitting double use of a silo during the year. (**402**)

The combination of *oats and vetch* is one of the best silage crops for dairy cattle in the northern Pacific-Coast section, greatly excelling corn in yield in that district. (**404**)

Whether to grow *corn and soybeans* for silage in place of corn alone is discussed in Chapter XIII. (**309**) The combination crop will make silage higher in protein, but it will usually be lower in total digestible nutrients than silage from well-eared corn grown alone. Perhaps this is the reason why corn-and-soybean silage was not worth appreciably more per ton than corn silage in 2 trials at the Iowa Station and that there was no great difference between the two kinds of silage in Arkansas and Pennsylvania experiments.[110] The value for milk production of a soybean crop was practically the same in an Ohio experiment when it was ensiled and when it was made into hay.[111]

Corn and cowpeas make an excellent silage crop in the South, and in the sections better adapted to the sorghums (sweet or grain sorghums), a combination of *sorghum and soybeans* or of *sorghum and cowpeas* provides silage equal or slightly superior to sorghum grown alone.

Soybeans alone made satisfactory silage in Florida, where it was impossible on account of rainy weather in the autumn to cure soybeans into hay that would be eaten by dairy cows. Such silage was less palatable than corn silage and about 20 per cent was left uneaten, but 2.9 tons, as fed, were equal in value to 1 ton of No. 1 alfalfa hay.[112]

900. Other silages.—The value and use of several other kinds of silage suitable for dairy cattle have been discussed in Part II. These silages include sunflower silage, silage from the small grains, apple-pomace silage, wet-beet-pulp silage, and beet-top silage.

901. Roots for dairy cows.—Though roots are an excellent succulent feed for dairy cows, they are raised but little for this purpose in the United States, as has been shown in Chapter XVI. (**470-472**) Over most of the country corn or sorghum silage provides much cheaper succulence than do roots, and where the growing season is too short for these crops, sunflower silage or such silage as oats and peas is usually more economical. Roots should be run through a root chopper or sliced before feeding, to avoid danger of cattle choking on them.

Roots are a very useful feed for dairy cows where a dairyman does not keep sufficient stock so that he can feed silage fast enough to keep it from spoiling, or where a silo is not available. They are highly esteemed for cows on official test, because in such cases the object is maximum yield, rather than low cost of production. Even for this purpose, however, soaked beet pulp has largely taken the place of roots, on account of the greater convenience.

Roots have a "cooling" effect on the digestive organs, helping to prevent digestive trouble when the cows are heavily fed on concentrates. In addition, experiments have shown that adding roots even to a palatable ration containing good corn silage seems to increase slightly the yield of milk and fat.[113] This is doubtless because roots are especially well-liked by cows, and their feed consumption is therefore greater when roots are fed. A slight increase in yield produced by feeding roots may be important for the breeder seeking high records of production. However, this practice is rarely economical for dairymen in general, for in these trials the increase in production was not great enough to offset the cost of the roots, with milk at usual prices.

While the dry matter of roots is considerably more digestible and lower in fiber than that in corn silage, in actual feeding trials with dairy cows the dry matter of silage has been as valuable or nearly as valuable for dairy cows as that in roots.[114] Since roots are much lower than corn silage in dry matter, they are worth correspondingly less per ton when used as a substitute for corn silage. For example, it requires about 3.0 tons of mangels, 2.5 tons of rutabagas, or 1.7 tons of sugar beets to furnish as much dry matter as 1 ton of good corn silage, and these figures therefore represent approximately the amounts of these root crops it takes to equal a ton of corn silage in feeding value for milk production.

When roots are fed to dairy cows as the only succulent feed in place of corn silage, the production of milk and fat will be about as high and perhaps even slightly higher than on corn silage. However, in good corn-growing sections, the production on the silage ration will be much more economical.[115] Compared with root crops, silage of the kind that can be grown in Great Britain, where corn does not thrive, has given varying results. In some trials the production has been more economical on roots than with such silage as combinations including oats, peas, vetch, beans, and tares, and in other tests the silage ration has been cheaper.[116]

902. Wet beet pulp.—Wet beet pulp is liked by cows and produces milk of good quality when not fed in excess. (643) In Utah trials during 4 years Holstein cows were fed either wet beet pulp or corn silage and a limited amount of concentrates, with pasture in summer and alfalfa hay when pasture was not available.[117] The cows ate on the average 68.1 lbs. of beet pulp per head daily, in comparison with 32.1 lbs. of silage, and the production was fully as high on the beet-pulp ration. In these trials it required 2.1 lbs. of wet beet pulp, containing 11.5 per cent dry matter, to replace 1 lb. of corn silage, containing 26.0 per cent dry matter. Thus, a pound of dry matter in the beet pulp was worth slightly more than a pound of dry matter in corn silage.

When cows are fed large allowances of wet beet pulp, without feeds rich in calcium and phosphorus, weak calves may result, doubtless due to a lack of these minerals. Plenty of legume hay should therefore be fed with heavy allowances of beet pulp, and a phosphorus supplement should be provided, unless the concentrate mixture is sufficiently high in phosphorus. In the Utah experiments the cows fed wet beet pulp continuously became lame. Possibly this was due to a shortage of phosphorus in the ration.

Beet pulp which has passed through the fermentation process in a silo seems to be more palatable and satisfactory than fresh pulp. As there are occasional reports of beet pulp tainting the milk, it should be fed after milking and in a sanitary manner, the same as in the case of corn silage.

903. Soiling crops; other succulent feeds.—The use and value of soiling crops for dairy cows are discussed in detail in Chapter XII. Corn silage usually furnishes just as satisfactory and much cheaper feed to supplement short summer pasture than does a succession of soiling crops, such as red clover, peas and oats, sweet corn, and field corn. The same is true of other good silage crops, such as the sorghums. Where too few cows are kept to consume the silage fast enough to prevent its spoiling or where silage is not available for any other reason, the wise dairyman will provide a well-planned succession of soiling crops to keep up the milk flow when pastures are poor, or else will provide temporary grazing crops, such as Sudan grass, sweet clover, etc.

Several other succulent feeds that are treated in Part II are sometimes used for dairy cows in certain districts. Thus, cull potatoes can well be utilized for this purpose. Cull cabbage and the waste left after the heads are harvested are satisfactory for dairy cows, if care is taken to feed them only immediately after milking, in order to avoid tainting the milk. In certain sections of the Pacific-Coast district kale provides economical succulent feed during much of the winter.

904. Pastures.—Luxuriant pasture furnishes unexcelled feed for dairy cows. Not only is the supply of nutrients liberal, but also the feed is succulent and palatable, and good pasturage is rich in protein, mineral matter, and vitamins. Unfortunately, in most sections the season of ideal pasturage is short, and in midsummer permanent pastures are too often parched and brown. The importance of pasture fertilization to provide good forage throughout the grazing season, and also rotational grazing and general pasture management are discussed in Chapter XI.

To supplement permanent pasture, such pastures as sweet clover, Sudan grass, alfalfa, or red clover are exceedingly useful, for they provide forage when there is otherwise apt to be a serious deficiency. When pasture is poor, cattle have to spend practically all day searching for enough to satisfy their hunger. On the other hand, if there is plenty of good forage, they will soon be able to eat their fill and will then lie down, preferably in a shady spot, and chew their cud.

The carrying capacity of pastures varies widely, depending on the soil and climatic factors and especially on how wisely the pasture has been handled. If no soiling crops or summer silage are provided for periods of drought, 1.5 to 2.5 acres of fairly-good pasture should be provided per cow, but if such additional feed is furnished and the pasture is properly fertilized, the pasture allowance can be reduced to 1 acre per cow or even less. In the West, irrigated pasture which is well fertilized may carry more than 2 cows per acre throughout the season.[118]

Though dairy cows have been maintained for several years without much pasture, or even with none at all, this practice is usually uneconomical and, moreover, does not promote the health of the animals.

The value of the various pasture crops is discussed in detail in Chapters XIII and XV. Throughout the northern states, bluegrass and combinations of bluegrass with other grasses and with white clover are the most common permanent pastures. Bluegrass alone furnishes excellent grazing in spring, early summer, and autumn, but in midsummer the feed is scanty. Therefore for the best permanent pasture a mixture of grasses and clovers should be seeded.

Red clover provides excellent pasture in the regular crop rotation, though care must be taken to avoid bloat. With alfalfa there is more danger of bloat, except in a few favored districts, but it provides such excellent feed that many dairymen, nevertheless, make a practice of pasturing it.[119]

In rotated pastures, timothy in combination with the clovers and other grasses furnishes excellent pasturage. Timothy is even more palatable than bluegrass to cattle when in the actively-growing pasture stage, but the usual hay types of timothy will not endure continued close-grazing, year after year. Timothy endures much better under rotational grazing.

Sweet clover furnishes excellent temporary pasture for dairy cows and is especially useful to supplement permanent pasture.[120] In the second year of its growth up to midsummer it will usually produce more pasturage per acre than any other corn-belt crop, provided the soil is suited to its growth. Yearling dairy heifers failed to make good gains on sweet-clover pasture in Wisconsin tests, while it was satisfactory for cows.[121] This was apparently because the sweet clover was unpalatable to the younger animals, and they ate too little.

In the sections adapted to it Sudan grass is an excellent temporary-pasture crop, being especially useful to supplement short pasture after midsummer. Winter rye and wheat provide fall and early spring pasture even in the northern states, and farther south furnish feed during much of the winter. Cows should not be grazed on rye within 3 hours of milking, or the milk may be tainted.

QUESTIONS

1. Discuss the use of corn for feeding dairy cows and the value of various methods of preparation.
2. Compare hominy feed and ground corn as feeds for dairy cows.
3. Discuss the value and use of oats in dairy rations.
4. What is the value of ground barley for milk production in comparison with that of corn?
5. Discuss the value and use for dairy cows of any of the following that are important in your locality: (a) Wheat; (b) rye; (c) grain sorghums.
6. How is molasses used in feeding dairy cows, and what is its value under various conditions?
7. Discuss the use and value of dried beet pulp and dried molasses-beet pulp.
8. Why is wheat bran such a popular dairy feed?
9. Compare standard wheat middlings and wheat mixed feed with wheat bran as feeds for dairy cows.
10. What are the merits of linseed meal as a protein supplement for dairy cows?
11. Discuss the use of cottonseed meal for milk production.
12. Compare corn gluten feed and linseed meal as dairy feeds; corn gluten meal and cottonseed meal.

13. What is the value for dairy cows of soybeans in comparison with that of linseed meal or cottonseed meal? What is the effect of feeding too large a proportion of soybeans?

14. Discuss the value of soybean oil meal for dairy cows.

15. Compare brewers' dried grains with wheat bran and with corn gluten feed for dairy cows.

16. Discuss the value of distillers' corn dried grains for milk production; of distillers' dried rye grains.

17. Discuss fully the value of legume hay for dairy cows, showing how it makes possible home-grown rations and a saving of concentrates.

18. Why is alfalfa hay unexcelled as a dry roughage for dairy cows?

19. Under what conditions may it be economical to feed cows chiefly or exclusively on alfalfa hay?

20. Compare alfalfa meal and wheat bran as feeds for dairy cows.

21. Compare the values of red clover hay and of alfalfa hay for dairy cows; of mixed legume-and-grass hay and of alfalfa hay.

22. Discuss the values of any of the following that are important for dairy cows in your district: (a) Sweet clover hay; (b) soybean hay; (c) cowpea hay.

23. Compare the value for dairy cows of hay from the grasses with that of legume hay.

24. Contrast the value for dairy cows of ordinary timothy hay and of early-cut timothy hay from nitrogen-fertilized fields.

25. What are the effects when poor-quality grass hay is fed to cows as the only roughage for long periods?

26. What results have been secured in experiments where prairie hay has been fed to dairy cattle?

27. How can corn fodder be best used as a feed for dairy cows?

28. Discuss the use and value of the following for dairy cows: (a) Corn stover; (b) sorghum fodder and stover; (c) straw; (d) cottonseed hulls.

29. Why are succulent feeds desirable in feeding dairy cows?

30. Why is corn silage such a popular feed for dairy cattle?

31. Discuss the relative value of corn silage and of hay for dairy cows. Under what conditions is silage an economical feed and when is it uneconomical?

32. Discuss the use of limited allowances of silage; of using silage as the only roughage.

33. Is it economical to remove the ears from corn forage before ensiling it for dairy cows?

34. Compare sorghum silage and corn silage as feeds for dairy cows.

35. What other silage crops are used for dairy cattle in your locality?

36. Discuss the use of roots for dairy cows.

37. Are soiling crops fed to dairy cattle in your district? If so, what crops are chiefly used?

38. Discuss the importance of good pastures for dairy cattle. In your section, what kinds of pasture are used chiefly?

REFERENCES

1. Fraser and Hayden, Ill. Bul. 159.
2. Patterson, Md. Bul. 84.
3. McCandlish and Weaver, Iowa Bul. 195; Shaw and Norton, Mich. Bul. 242; Olson, S. D. Rpt. 1929; Darnell and Copeland, Tex. Rpt. 1932.
4. Wilbur, Ind. Bul. 372.
5. Hilton, Wilbur, and Heinton, Ind. Bul. 373; McCandlish, Iowa Res. Bul. 51; Otis, Kan. Bul. 126; Fain and Jarnagin, Va. Bul. 172.
6. Shaw and Norton, Mich. Bul. 242.
7. McCandlish and Weaver, Iowa Bul. 195.
8. Fitch, Cave, Riddell, and Merrill, Kan. Rpts. 1928-30, 1932-34; Cook, N. J. Rpt. 25.
9. Lindsey, Mass. Rpt. 1913, Part I.
10. Ind. Rpt. 1927; Shaw and Norton, Mich. Bul. 242; see also Darnell and Copeland, Tex. Rpt. 1932.
11. Morrison, Humphrey, and Hulce, Wis. Bul. 319; Cunningham, Ariz. Bul. 127; Burnett and Reed, Mich. Quar. Bul., 10, 1927, No. 1.
12. Woll and Voorhies, Cal. Bul. 305.

13. Headley, Nev. Bul. 119.
14. Bohstedt, Roche, Rupel, and Duffee, Wis. Buls. 420, 421.
15. Fitch and Cave, Kan. Rpt. 1930-32; Ky. Rpt. 1931; Bartlett, Me. Rpt. 1895; Dice,
    N. D. Bul. 256; Hayden and Monroe, Ohio Buls. 497, 516, 532; Jacobs, Okla.
    Panhandle Sta. Bul. 29; Copeland, Tex. Bul. 480.
16. Tretsven, Mont. Bul. 303; Hayward, Penn. Bul. 52.
17. Tretsven, Mont. Bul. 282; Hirst and Eckles, Minn. Sta., information to the author.
18. Fitch and Wolberg, Jour. Dairy Sci., 17, 1934, pp. 343-350.
19. Cave and Fitch, Kan. Cir. 119; Fitch, Cave, Riddell, and Merrill, Kan. Rpt. 1932-34.
20. Cunningham, Ariz. Bul. 127; Moore, Miss. Rpt. 1928, 1929.
21. Cave and Fitch, Kan. Cir. 110; Fitch and Cave, Kan. Rpt. 1930-32; Fitch, Cave,
    Riddell, and Merrill, Kan. Rpt. 1932-34.
22. Fitch, Kan. Bien. Rpt. 1928-30.
23. Bohstedt, Roche, et al., Wis. Bul. 430; see also: Lindsey, Holland, and Smith,
    Mass. Bul. 118; Britnall, Miss. Cir. 38; Arnett, Mont. Rpt. 1929; Williams,
    Jour. Dairy Sci., 8, 1925, pp. 94-104; Grisdale, Canada Expt. Farms, Rpt. 1913.
24. Woodward, et al., U. S. Dept. Agr. Bul. 1272.
25. Tretsven, Mont. Bul. 282.
26. Henke, Hawaii, Bul. 73.
27. Lindsey, Mass. Rpt. 1913; Part I; Rothwell, Canada Expt. Farms, Anim. Husb.
    Div., Interim Rpt. 1922.
28. White and Johnson, Conn. (Storrs) Bul. 198; Billings, N. J. Bul. 189; Foster,
    N. Mex. Bul. 122; Monroe, Hayden, and Perkins, Ohio. Bul. 470.
29. Woodward, Shepherd, and Graves, U. S. Dept. Agr., Misc. Pub. 130; Henderson
    and Teague, Jour. Dairy Sci., 16, 1933, pp. 363-368.
30. Billings, N. J. Rpt. 1904; Lindsey, Mass. Rpt. 1913.
31. Cunningham, Ariz. Bul. 127; Caine and Bateman, Utah Bul. 235.
32. Smith and Beals, Mass. Bul. 146.
33. Waters and Hess, Penn. Rpt. 1895; Hills, Vermont Rpt. 1907; Michels, N. C. Rpt.
    1910.
34. Huffman and Moore, Jour. Dairy Sci., 12, 1929, pp. 410-418; Copeland and Fraps,
    Tex. Bul. 473.
35. Eckles and Palmer, Mo. Res. Bul. 27; Keith, Kuhlman, Weaver, and Gallup, Okla.
    Rpts. 1930-32, 1932-34; Shields and Raitt, S. C. Rpt. 1917; Harrington and
    Adriance, Tex. Bul. 29.
36. Keith, Kuhlman, Weaver, and Gallup, Okla. Rpt. 1932-34.
37. Caldwell, Ind. Bul. 203.
38. Soule and Fain, Va. Bul. 156.
39. Moore, Miss. Bul. 70; see also Michels and Burgess, S. C. Bul. 117.
40. Caldwell, Ind. Bul. 203.
41. Hackleman, et al., Ill. Bul. 310; Fairchild and Wilbur, Ind. Bul. 289; McCandlish,
    Weaver, and Linde, Iowa Bul. 204; Fitch, Kan. Rpts. 1924-26; 1926-28; Schaefer,
    Minn. Bul. 239; Hayden and Perkins, Ohio Bimo. Bul. 121; Olson, S. D. Bul. 215.
42. Brooks, Mass. (Hatch) Rpt. 1894; Moore and Cowsert, Miss. Bul. 235; Cook,
    N. J. Rpt. 1913; Price, Tenn. Bul. 80.
43. Overman and Garrett, Jour. Agr. Res., 45, 1932, pp. 51-58; Ind. Rpt. 1932; Otis,
    Kan. Bul. 125; LaMaster and Elting, S. C. Rpt. 1929; Olson, S. D. Rpt. 1926.
44. Nevins, Ill. Rpt. 1924; Fairchild and Wilbur, Ind. Bul. 289; McCandlish, Jour.
    Dairy Sci., 5, 1922, pp. 27-38; Moore and Cowsert, Miss. Bul. 235; Hayden and
    Perkins, Ohio Bimo. Bul. 121; Perkins, Bachtell, and Weaver, Ohio Bul. 516;
    Holdaway, Ellett, and Harris, Va. Tech. Bul. 28, Gilchrist, Mark Lane Express,
    100, 1909, p. 667; Hansen, Deutsche Landw. Presse, 36, 1909.
45. Fairchild and Wilbur, Ind. Bul. 289.
46. Lindsey, Mass. Bul. 94; Hills, Vt. Rpt. 1903.
47. Lindsey, Mass. Bul. 94; Hills, Vt. Rpt. 1907; see also: Armsby and Risser, Penn.
    Bul. 73; Billings, N. J. Rpt. 1907.
48. Archibald, Mass. Bul. 321.
49. Cannon, Iowa Sta., information to the author; Petersen, Minn. Sta., information
    to the author.
50. Jour. Biol. Chem., 38, 1919, pp. 515-527; 44, 1920, pp. 189-201; Wis. Bul. 417.
51. Morrison, Hulce, and Humphrey, Amer. Soc. Anim. Prod., Proc. 1922, pp. 68-72;
    Wis. Buls. 339, 352; Hart and Humphrey, Wis. Bul. 417.
52. Hilton, Ind. Rpt. 1934 and information to the author; Iowa Rpt. 1924; Savage,
    Harrison and Work, N. Y. (Cornell) Sta., unpublished data; Monroe and Hay-
    den, Ohio Bimo. Bul. 158; Olson, S. D. Rpts. 1922, 1933.
53. Hayden and Perkins, Ohio Bul. 402.
54. Misner, N. Y. (Cornell) Bul. 438; N. Y. State Col. of Agr., Farm Economics, No.
    57, Feb., 1929.
55. Caldwell, Ohio Bul. 267; see also: Fraser and Hayden, Ill. Bul. 146; Fraser,
    Dairy Farming, 1930; Billings, N. J. Bul. 190.
56. Weaver, Kuhlman, Fouts, and Reder, Okla. Rpt. 1932-34.
57. Richardson, Amer. Dairy Sci. Assoc., Abstr. of Papers, 29th Annual Meeting, 1934.
58. Cunningham, Ariz. Rpts. 1932, 1933; Willard, Wyo. Rpt. 1932.
59. Huffman and Bowling, Mich. Quar. Bul. 14, 1931, No. 2.
60. Woll, Cal. Bul. 256; Mont. Rpt. 1931; Headley, Nev. Rpt. 1933, Bul. 119.
61. Lindsey, Mass. Rpt. 1909, Part II, pp. 158-166; Snyder, Nebr. Bul. 164; Mairs,
    Penn. Bul. 80; Hills, Vt. Rpt. 1906; Rothwell, Canada Expt. Farms, Anim. Husb.
    Div. Rpt. 1924.
62. Cunningham, Ariz. Bul. 127.
63. Hayden, Ohio Bul. 327.

64. Bechdel, Penn. Bul. 188.
65. Iowa Rpt. 1924; Kan. Bien. Rpt. 1926-28; Olson, S. D. Rpt. 1933.
66. Nevens, Ill. Cir. 369; Ill. Bul. 310; Caldwell, Ind. Bul. 203; Cannon and Johnston, Iowa Exten. Bul. 196; Fitch, Kan. Rpts. 1926-28, 1928-30, 1930-32; Moore and Cowsert, Miss. Bul. 235; Hayden, Ohio Bul. 470; Bechdel, Penn. Bul. 201; Olson, S. D. Bul. 215; Anthony and Henderson, West Va. Bul. 181; Henderson, West Va. Bul. 244; Morrison, Savage, and Hulce, Wis. Bul. 362; Morrison, Humphrey, and Rupel, Wis. Buls. 373, 388.
67. Morrison, Humphrey, and Rupel, Wis. Buls. 373, 388; Rupel, Roche, and Bohstedt, Wis. Res. Bul. 102.
68. Schaefer, Minn. Bul. 239; see also Bierman, Md. Bul. 277.
69. Nevens, Ill. Cir. 369.
70. Hilton, Wilbur, and Epple, Ind. Bul. 346.
71. Nevens, Ill. Rpts. 1931, 1932.
72. Duggar, Ala. Bul. 123; Dvorachek, Ark. Bul. 203; Wing, Ga. Bul. 49; Lane, N. J. Bul. 174.
73. Morrison and Salisbury, N. Y. (Cornell) Rpts. 1933, 1934; Musback, Wis. Station, information to the author.
74. Ritzman and Benedict, N. H. Bul. 270.
75. Holdaway, et al., Va. Tech. Bul. 45.
76. Fraser and Hayden, Ill. Bul. 146; McCandlish, Iowa Bul. 212.
77. Meigs and Converse, Jour. Dairy Sci., 15, 1932, pp. 171-183; 16, 1933, pp. 317-328; Converse, Wiseman, and Meigs, Amer. Soc. Anim. Prod., Proc. 1934.
78. Willard, Wyo. Rpts. 1931, 1932, 1933.
79. Jacobson, Ark. Bul. 318.
80. Fitch, Cave, Riddell, and Merrill, Kan. Rpt. 1932-34.
81. Hunt and Caldwell, Penn. Rpt. 1892; Iowa Rpt. 1929.
82. Dice and Jensen, N. D. Buls. 194, 217; LaMaster and Elting, S. C. Rpts. 1931, 1932, 1933, 1934.
83. Grinnells, N. C. Rpt. 1929.
84. Iowa Rpt. 1929.
85. Henry, Wis. Rpt. 1884.
86. Ind. Rpt. 1929.
87. Cunningham and Davis, Ariz. Rpt. 1920; Fitch and Cave, Kan. Rpts. 1928-30, 1930-32; Grinnells, N. C. Rpt. 1929.
88. Lush, Staples, Fletcher, and Stewart, La. Bul. 238.
89. Moore, Miss. Rpt. 1902; Michels, N. C. Bul. 199; Conner, S. C. Bul. 66; Soule, Tex. Bul. 47; Copeland, Tex. Bul. 451.
90. Henry and Woll, 6 trials, Wis. Rpts. 1888, 1889; Voorhees and Lane, 1 trial, N. J. Bul. 122, Armsby, 1 trial, Penn. Rpt. 1890; Cooke and Hills, 1 trial, Vt. Rpt. 1892; see also: Sanborn, Mo. Bul. 8.
91. McCandlish and Weaver, Iowa Bul. 212.
92. McDowell, U. S. Dept. Agr., information to the author.
93. Jordan, Me. Rpt. 1889; Hills, Vt. Rpt. 1901.
94. Clark, Mont. Bul. 94.
95. Fairchild and Wilbur, Ind. Bul. 297; Carroll, Utah Bul. 190.
96. Snyder, Nebr. Rpts. 1923, 1924, Foster and Weeks, N. Mex. Bul. 122.
97. Converse, Jour. Dairy Sci. 11, 1928, pp. 179-188.
98. White, Conn. (Storrs) Bul. 192; White and Johnson, Conn. (Storrs) Bul. 198.
99. White and Pratt, Conn. (Storrs) Bul. 169.
100. Monroe and Allen, Ohio Bul. 538.
101. Hayden, Monroe, Perkins, and Thatcher, Ohio Bul. 532; Monroe and Hayden, Ohio Bul. 548.
102. Cannon, Espe, and Goble, Amer. Dairy Sci. Assoc., Abstr. of Papers, 29th Annual Meeting, 1933.
103. Becker, et al., Fla. Bul. 255; see also: La. Rpt. 1931-33.
104. Hills, Vt. Rpt. 1892; Woll, Wis. Rpts. 1891, 1892.
105. Morrison, Humphrey, and Hulce, Wis. Bul. 323.
106. Cunningham and Reed, Ariz. Bul. 122; Woll and Voorhies, Cal. Bul. 282; Reed and Fitch, Kan. Cir. 28; Grinnells, N. C. Rpts. 1929, 1930; LaMaster and Morrow, S. C. Bul. 254.
107. Reed and Fitch, Kan. Cir. 28; Fitch, Kan. Bien. Rpts. 1926-28, 1928-30; Becker and Gallup, Okla. Bul. 177.
108. Cave and Fitch, Kan. Cir. 110; Fitch and Wolberg, Jour. Dairy Sci., 17, 1934, pp. 343-350; Moore, Miss. Rpt. 1927; Becker and Gallup, Okla. Bul. 164; LaMaster and Morrow, S. C. Bul. 254.
109. Kuhlman, McGilliard, and Weaver, Okla. Rpt. 1932-34.
110. Iowa Rpts. 1924, 1925; Dvorachek, et al., Ark. Bul. 196; Bechdel, Penn. Bul. 178.
111. Hayden and Perkins, Ohio Bimo. Bul. 122.
112. Becker, et al., Fla. Bul. 255.
113. Shaw and Norton, Mich. Bul. 240; Morrison and Humphrey, Wis. Sta. unpublished data; Rothwell, Canada Dept. Agr. Bul. 94.
114. Brooks, Mass. (Hatch) Rpt. 1893; Horwood and Putnam, Mich. Quar. Bul. 15, 1932, No. 1; Wing and Savage, N. Y. (Cornell) Bul. 268; Thorne et al., Ohio Bul. 50; Kuhlman, McGilliard, and Weaver, Okla. Rpt. 1930-32; Caldwell, Penn. Rpt. 1890; Hills, Vt. Rpt. 1895; Henderson and Morrow, West Va. Bul. 256; Hopkins, Rothwell, Elford, and Schutt, Canada Dept. of Agr. Bul. 94.
115. Kuhlman, Becker, McGilliard, and Weaver, Okla. Rpts. 1924-26, 1926-30; Rothwell, Canada Dept. Agr. Bul. 94; Ste. Marie, Canada Expt. Farms, 1930-32; Ste. Anne de la Pocatiere (Que.) Sta., Rpt. Supt. 1923.

116. Fishwick, Jour. Min. Agr., Great Britain, 31, 1924, pp. 50-8 ; McCandlish and McVicar, Scot. Jour. Agr., 9, 1926, pp. 194-201 ; Oldershaw, Jour. Roy. Agr. Soc., England, 86, 1925, pp. 112-128 ; Rae and Gardner, Jour. Min. Agr., Great Britain, 31, 1924, pp. 261-6 ; 32, 1925, pp. 635-9 ; Robertson and Pitcher, Jour. Min. Agr., Great Britain, 28, 1921, pp. 506-15 ; White and Roberts, Jour. Min. Agr., Great Britain, 29, 1922, pp. 34-7.
117. Bateman and Caine, Utah Bul. 239 ; see also : Wing and Anderson, N. Y. (Cornell) Bul. 183.
118. Hansen and Kopland, Mont. Rpts. 1929, 1931 ; Jones and Brandt, Ore. Bul. 264.
119. Dorrance and Rather, Mich. Quar. Bul. 15, 1932, Nos. 1 and 4 ; Olson and Robinson, S. D. Bul. 265.
120. Reed and Burnett, Mich. Quar. Bul. 4, 1922, No. 3 ; Kans. Rpt. 1926-28 ; Olson and Robinson, S. D. Bul. 265 ; West Va. Bul. 254 ; Holden, U. S. Dept. Agr., Dept. Cir. 289 ; Aune, U. S. Dept. Agr. Cir. 417.
121. Mortimer and Rupel, Wis. Bul. 410.

CHAPTER XXVI

FEEDING AND CARING FOR DAIRY COWS

I. Feeding for Milk Production

905. Essentials in feeding and care.—The net returns a dairyman receives from his dairy business depend equally on the productive capacity of his cows and on the feed and care he gives them. It has previously been shown that poor dairy cows are such inefficient producers of milk that, even if they are well fed and cared for, they can never return a reasonable profit. Just as essential as well-bred cows, capable of high yields, are efficient rations and intelligent care. Without these, good cows are forced to become poor and unprofitable producers.

The chief essentials in the proper feeding and care of dairy cows are:

1. The use throughout the year of economical, well-balanced rations, which provide the nutritive essentials that have been previously stated. (**794**)

2. Adjusting the amount of concentrates for each cow to her actual production.

3. Palatable rations, containing a reasonable variety of feeds.

4. Some succulent feed in the ration, except when succulent feeds are unduly expensive.

5. Rations that are slightly laxative, instead of constipating.

6. Dry periods of proper length.

7. Comfortable surroundings, both in winter and during the pasture season.

8. Plenty of good water, conveniently accessible. (**819**)

9. Regularity in feed and care.

10. Kindness on the part of the herdsman.

Neglect of these simple essentials will seriously reduce the net income from the dairy herd.

906. Guides in selecting well-balanced rations.—Any intelligent dairyman can compute an economical, well-balanced ration for his cows by following the methods explained in Chapters IX and X, and familiarizing himself with the nutrient requirements for milk production which are stated in Chapter XXIV. However, the computing of a balanced ration requires considerable time if one is not experienced in the process.

To simplify the selection of efficient rations for milk production, convenient feeding guides are given in Appendix Tables VII and IX. By the use of these guides the balancing of dairy rations is reduced to a recipe basis, and practically all computations are eliminated.

First, there are given in Appendix Table VII a considerable number of good concentrate mixtures which are adapted for feeding with the various kinds of roughages there stated. It has been explained previ-

559

ously that the percentage of protein required in the concentrate mixture depends primarily on the protein content of the roughage which is fed. These concentrate mixtures are therefore grouped according to their protein content, and simple directions are given for determining which group is suitable for feeding with any common combination of roughages.

One can readily find which of the several concentrate mixtures in the proper group is most economical at the local prices for various feeds. If one desires to use some particular feed that is not included in the suggested concentrate mixtures, these formulas will serve as useful guides in making up a special mixture. The manner in which various substitutions can be made in these formulas is explained in the paragraphs which immediately precede the formulas.

After selecting an economical concentrate mixture that will make a balanced ration with the roughage to be fed, it is next necessary to know how much of the concentrate mixture each cow in the herd should receive. Various "thumb rules" are often used for estimating this. A more convenient and also more accurate method is to use the "Grain Feeding Tables" given in Appendix Table IX.

The first of these tables is for use when the cows are not on pasture. It states the number of pounds of a good concentrate mixture, or so-called "grain mixture," that are required by cows producing various amounts of milk of different fat percentages, when various amounts of roughage are consumed. The second table similarly shows the amounts of concentrates needed by cows on excellent, good, and fair pasture. The feeding of cows on poor pasture is discussed later in this chapter.

Sufficient amounts of concentrates are advised in these tables to meet the recommendations of the feeding standards and to maintain good yields of milk under usual conditions. Since heifers need additional feed for the growth of their own bodies, it is wise to feed them a trifle more liberally than stated in the tables. Also, the allowance should be increased somewhat over the amounts shown in the tables in the case of excellent cows during the latter part of the lactation period, if they have run down in flesh during the height of milk production.

When concentrates are very expensive in comparison with roughages, then it may be most economical to feed less concentrates, as has been shown previously. (**805–806**) Though these feeding guides are exceedingly simple, it will be found that they are sufficiently exact from the scientific standpoint to be reliable in practical feeding.

It is well worth while for a dairyman to understand thoroughly the method of computing economical rations which are balanced in accordance with the feeding standards. He will then know how to make balanced rations under any special conditions that may arise. However, from the standpoint of his net returns, the most important point is to be sure to feed balanced rations, even though he has not taken time to figure them out himself. In any case of doubt as to the best ration to use, a farmer will find his agricultural college and experiment station or his county agent ready to advise him.

In computing rations for dairy cows, it is necessary to know their approximate weights. If one does not have suitable scales available for weighing the individual cows, their weights can be estimated from a

measurement of the heart girth. Appendix Table X shows the approximate weights of dairy cows having different heart girths.

907. Cows should be fed individually.—It is well known that the
amount of total digestible nutrients or of net energy needed by a particular cow depends on the amount of milk and fat that she is actually
producing. (**787, 794**) A high-producing cow cannot consume much
more roughage, per 100 lbs. live weight, than a low producer. The high
producer will therefore need a far greater weight of grain or other
concentrates than the low producer. Indeed, if a dairyman retains the
poor cow in his herd, instead of discarding her, it may not pay to feed
her any grain at all, but merely all the roughage she will eat.

In spite of the great difference in the real needs of the various
cows in a herd, many dairymen make the mistake of feeding all their
cows the same amount of grain mixture, regardless of their actual
yields. This practice seriously underfeeds the high producers and
therefore reduces the net returns from the herd. It just as seriously
overfeeds the poor cows. They are unable to convert the excess nutrients
into milk, but instead turn them into body fat or waste them entirely.
It is therefore very important to adjust the amount of grain mixture
fed each cow to her actual production of milk and fat.

908. "Thumb rules" not accurate guides.—Since it would be very
time consuming to compute rations according to the feeding standards
for each cow in a herd, convenient "thumb rules" have been widely
used for determining the amount of "grain mixture," or concentrates,
each cow should receive, in addition to all the good roughage she will
clean up. However, none of these thumb rules is so convenient or so
accurate as the grain feeding tables which are given in Appendix
Table IX.

Two "thumb rules" that have been widely used are as follows:

1. Feed 1 lb. of concentrates per day for each 2½ to 4 lbs. of milk, depending
on the richness of the milk and the quality of roughage fed, or

2. Feed 1 lb. of concentrates per day for each pound of butter fat the cow
produces a week.

These rules are simple and easy to use, but they have one exceedingly serious fault. Under most conditions they underfeed the high
producers and overfeed the poor cows. This is because these rules do
not take into consideration the important fact that when a cow is fed a
liberal amount of good roughage, she receives a greater amount of nutrients than she needs for mere body maintenance.

Thus, a Holstein cow fed all the good hay and silage she cares for
will get in this roughage sufficient nutrients for maintenance and for
the production of 10 to 20 lbs. of milk. Her concentrate allowance
should accordingly be based, not on the total amount of milk she yields,
but on the amount she is producing beyond the amount which she can
make from the roughage.

Various "thumb rules" have recently been devised which take these
facts into consideration, and which are therefore more accurate than the
older rules. The following convenient "thumb rules" are recommended
by Woodward, Shepherd, and Graves of the Bureau of Dairy Industry,
United States Department of Agriculture, for use when good roughage
is fed in the usual amounts.[1]

Holsteins: Feed 0.4 lb. of concentrates for each pound of milk above a yield of
16 lbs.
Ayrshires and Brown Swiss: Feed 0.45 lb. of concentrates for each pound of milk
above a yield of 14 lbs.
Guernseys: Feed 0.55 lb. of concentrates for each pound of milk above a yield of
12 lbs.
Jerseys: Feed 0.6 lb. of concentrates for each pound of milk above a yield of
10 lbs.

While these rules are more accurate than the older "thumb rules,"
they are less convenient than the grain feeding table in Appendix Table
IX. Also, they are based merely on the usual amounts of good roughage, and cannot be used when a very liberal amount of excellent roughage
is fed, or when, on the other hand, only a scanty allowance of roughage
is used. The grain feeding table in Appendix Table IX gives specific
recommendations to fit these varied conditions.

909. Palatable feeds.—It is important that both the roughages
and the concentrate mixture for dairy cows be palatable and eaten
readily. This is especially necessary in the case of high producers. If
the roughage is not palatable, the cows will eat much less of it than they
would of well-liked roughage, such as well-cured legume hay and silage.
To secure a good yield of milk it will therefore be necessary to feed
them an unusually large allowance of concentrates. (**867**)

Such roughages as corn stover, grass hay cut at the usual stage of
maturity, and even straw can be fed to dairy cows in limited amounts,
along with better roughage. (**878, 886, 888**) However, for the best
results they should not form the chief roughage for good cows. It is
preferable to feed two kinds of roughage to dairy cows, for when fed
even good alfalfa hay continually as the only roughage, they show a
keen desire for other roughage in addition and seem to thrive better
when receiving it. (**882**)

It is usually easy to provide a palatable concentrate mixture, or
"grain mixture," for dairy cows, for they like most all of the common
grains and by-product concentrates, if the feeds are of the ordinary
quality. Sometimes it is economical to include in the grain mixture
some feed like malt sprouts or rye feed, which is not itself palatable.
This may be done without making the whole mixture unpalatable, if
only a reasonable amount is mixed with well-liked feeds, such as ground
corn, ground oats, wheat bran, linseed meal, molasses, etc.

910. Variety.—There is considerable difference of opinion concerning the need of "variety," or of several different ingredients, in a
concentrate mixture for dairy cows. It has been shown previously that
when cows have a liberal allowance of alfalfa hay and corn silage or
of alfalfa hay as the only roughage, good production can be secured
when they receive in addition such a simple grain mixture as one-half
ground corn and one-half ground oats. (**865, 869**)

When cows of ordinary productive capacity have good roughage,
including a reasonable amount of legume hay, it is not necessary to go
to any unusual expense to provide a concentrate mixture containing
several ingredients. For example, in an Iowa experiment the milk
production of cows fed good roughage was practically the same when
they were fed a mixture of grain and cracked soybeans, as when the
mixture also included linseed meal and cottonseed meal.[2]

The palatability and nutritive merits of the individual feeds in a concentrate mixture are of greater importance than the number of ingredients. "Variety" in itself is no guarantee of palatability or of high nutritive value. A concentrate mixture containing a reasonable variety of well-liked ingredients is, however, apt to be more palatable than a simple combination, such as a mixture of grains, or of grains and a single protein supplement. Many dairy experts therefore advise that for high-producing cows, especially those on official test, the concentrate mixture contain 5 or 6 ingredients.

If a good ration is being fed which amply meets the nutrient requirements for milk production, there is no advantage in changing the ration from time to time, in order to supply additional variety. While humans would tire of such a monotonous fare, stock fortunately do not have such fickle appetites.

If cows which are accustomed to one good grain mixture are changed to another equally good, but having a decidedly different taste, they may at first not show a desire for the new mixture. However, in nearly all cases they will soon become used to it. When cows which have been fed on advanced registry test and have had their whims for special feeds indulged by expert herdsmen are returned to the regular herd, it often takes them some time to become accustomed to the less-luxurious manner of life.

911. Bulkiness of concentrate mixture.—Most dairymen believe that when high-producing cows are fed a liberal amount of concentrates, there will be less tendency for them to go off feed if some bulky feeds, such as wheat bran, ground oats, or dried beet pulp, are included in the mixture. Many experienced men prefer a concentrate mixture which does not weigh more than about 1 lb. to a quart.

This point is of less importance with cows of average production. In trials at the Michigan Station cows were successfully fed roughage and a separate mixture of linseed meal and ground corn, without the addition of any bulky material.[3] In these trials and also in Illinois trials[4] where ground corn or linseed meal was fed separate from the roughage to cattle which were slaughtered soon afterward, most of the concentrate was found well-mixed with the previous contents of the paunch and the honeycomb, and only a small part was in the form of separate lumps or boluses.

In general herd-feeding if it is cheapest to feed a heavy mixture which contains no bulky feeds, the mixture may readily be distributed over silage after the latter has been placed in the mangers. This will insure adequate mixing of the concentrates and silage in the digestive tract.

When bulky concentrates are expensive, considering the amounts of nutrients they actually furnish, it is wise to bear in mind the fact that they are not necessary for cows fed the usual amounts of concentrates. On the other hand, it is wise to use only a bulky concentrate mixture for cows that are fed very liberal amounts of concentrates, such as cows on advanced registry test.

912. Succulent feeds.—The importance of succulent feeds in the dairy ration has been emphasized in the preceding chapter. **(890)** Cows fed silage or other succulent feed in winter, along with good hay, will usually produce appreciably more milk than those fed only hay with the same allowance of concentrates. (892–894) The sole exceptions are when the cows have an abundance of hay of excellent quality and when they also have constant access to water in drinking bowls. The poorer the quality of hay or other dry roughage, the greater will be the benefit from supplying succulent feed in addition. Therefore, where silage or other succulent feeds can be supplied at reasonable expense, some succulence should usually be included in the winter ration.

913. Rations that are slightly laxative.—In order to secure the most efficient production, dairy cows should be fed rations that are slightly laxative. There is no difficulty from this source when plenty of well-cured legume hay or good silage is included in the ration. If all the roughage is of rather constipating nature, such as ordinary grass hay, corn stover, or straw, care should be taken to include in the grain mixture, a sufficient amount of laxative feeds, such as wheat bran, linseed meal, or molasses, to counteract the constipating effect of the roughage.

II. Care of the Milking Herd

914. Shelter and comfort.—During the barn-feeding months, dairy cows should be comfortably housed in dry, well-ventilated, and well-lighted quarters. When the cows are confined by stanchions or stalls in the usual type of dairy stable, the temperature should not be lower than 45° to 50° F. in winter.[5] This is no higher than can readily be secured without artificial heat, even during severe weather in the northern states, if the stable is well-built and thoroughly insulated and is provided with an efficient ventilating system. (133) Farther south less shelter is required in winter than in the northern states.

Dairy cows require somewhat warmer shelter than fattening steers, for they are spare instead of being protected by fat, and consequently they have more body surface to radiate heat than steers per 100 lbs. live weight. Also their hides are usually thinner and their coats more scanty than in the case of steers.

In studies conducted by the United States Department of Agriculture in co-operation with the Wisconsin Station it was found that cows were more comfortable in a stable temperature of 50° to 55° F. than when the temperature was 60° F. or over.[6] At the lower temperature the cows were more alert, their appetites were better, and their eyes were brighter and their hair more glossy than at the higher temperatures. Also, the lower temperature was preferred by the milkers, and the stable odors were less pronounced.

It has been shown previously that weather which is too hot for the comfort of the cows may cause a decided drop in milk yield and produce changes in the composition of milk. (834) Since the air in green pasture fields is cooler during very hot weather than in a bare, dry yard or corral, cows are more comfortable when on good pasture.

On dairy farms in the northern states the cows are generally housed during winter in closed stables where the individual animals are confined by stanchions or sometimes by stalls. For the comfort of the cows, swinging stanchions are much preferable to the old-fashioned rigid stanchions. Sufficient bedding should always be used for comfort and cleanliness. The various common bedding materials are discussed in Chapter XX. So that milk of good sanitary quality can be produced, the barn and the cows should be kept clean. Though grooming the cows may not increase the yield of milk appreciably, it is important from the sanitary standpoint. (836)

High-producing cows may yield slightly more milk when they have the freedom of individual box stalls, instead of being confined in stanchions. However, this increase, which will probably be less than 4 per cent, is not enough to pay for the extra labor and bedding required and the extra cost of housing, except in the case of cows fed on advanced registry test.[7]

The importance of an efficient ventilating system to provide fresh air, to maintain a proper temperature, to reduce the humidity, and to remove dampness and foul odors, has been emphasized in Chapter IV. (133) To aid in keeping the cows healthy, as well as for sanitary reasons, it is advisable to have at least 4 square feet of window glass for each animal. It is well to disinfect the stable thoroughly at least once each year, to aid in checking any possible spread of disease. The benefits from dehorning cows have been pointed out previously. (836)

915. Milking room and loose-stabling method.—On some dairy farms the cows have the freedom of a large stable or open shed, except at milking time when they go to a milking room. Here they are confined in stanchions, fed their grain, and milked. In this method the stable is usually cleaned only when considerable manure has accumulated. Much more bedding is therefore needed to keep the cows clean than when they are confined by stanchions in a stable of the ordinary type. On the other hand, somewhat less labor may be required with this method, if the milking room is conveniently arranged.

In experiments by the United States Department of Agriculture in Maryland and by the Pennsylvania Station in central Pennsylvania, there was no marked difference in production when cows were housed during winter in an open shed and when they were confined by stanchions in a closed stable.[8] Slightly more feed was required per 100 lbs. of milk in the open shed. Very satisfactory results were secured with the loose-pen method or the open-shed method of housing in other trials.[9]

Trials by the North Dakota Station show that even during the cold winter weather in that state, good production can be secured from cows housed in a partially-open shed, provided it is free from drafts and provided that the cows are liberally fed, well bedded, and kept dry.[10]

916. Flies and fly sprays.—Many farmers believe that the sharp decline in milk production which often occurs during midsummer is due to the annoyance of the cows by flies. Undoubtedly, however, this is most often due to a shortage of feed and to the heat. Many different fly sprays have been extensively used to repel flies, and the best of those on the market do, for varying periods of time, cause a considerable reduction in the number of flies on cows that are sprayed with them.

In numerous tests at various experiment stations, spraying cows with commercial or home-mixed fly sprays has usually produced little or no increase in milk production.[11] In some of the tests the use of oil fly sprays has even caused a decided reduction in milk yield, especially during hot weather. This is probably because the film of oil on the hair and skin raises the body temperature appreciably in hot weather, since it prevents the evaporation of water from the skin. (**121**) Some fly sprays may temporarily injure the parts of the skin exposed to the sunlight, if applied daily for considerable periods of time. Medicated stock salts, sold as a fly repellant, were found entirely ineffective in Kansas and Oklahoma tests.[12]

917. Exercise; trimming hoofs.—During the winter in the northern states, the cows should be turned out daily for exercise for about 1 to 2 hours, except in stormy or unusually severe weather, in a sunny yard that is sheltered from the prevailing winds. Such exercise will aid in keeping them thrifty, and it has been pointed out in Chapter XXIV that moderate exercise tends to increase slightly the yield and the percentage of fat. (**836**) The exposure to direct sunlight also helps to provide vitamin D. (**191**) Forcing cows to stay outside a good share of the day in cold weather is a waste of feed and may reduce the milk yield severely. In the South, winter pasture should be provided whenever possible.

The hoofs of dairy cattle should be trimmed when necessary to prevent them from becoming so long that the feet are injured. When the cattle are on pasture, the hoofs generally wear down sufficiently, but during the winter trimming is often necessary.

918. Frequency and order of feeding.—The most common practice in dairy herds is to feed the grain mixture before milking, and then after milking to feed the silage or other succulent feed which might taint the milk if fed before milking. (**837**) The hay is usually fed after the silage has been cleaned up. In the case of cows milked more than twice a day, part of the daily allowance of grain mixture is usually fed before each milking and the hay and silage only at morning and night.

Hay and other dry forages should not be fed until after milking, as they are apt to fill the air with dust. Also, alfalfa hay may produce a marked flavor in milk if fed less than 4 hours before milking. (**869**)

The particular order of supplying the various feeds is not important, but the same order should be followed from day to day and the cows should be fed and milked at regular times. In tests by the United States Department of Agriculture regularity in feeding and milking increased the yield of milk 3.9 per cent and of fat 5.2 per cent, in comparison with a lack of regularity.[13]

Some dairymen put the grain mixture on top of the silage in the manger, and this is a good plan if one is feeding a liberal allowance of a heavy concentrate mixture which contains no bulky feeds. Cows which are accustomed to getting their grain before milking may tend to be restless and "hold up" their milk if the grain is not fed until after milking, but it will not take them long to get accustomed to the change.

919. Milking.—While milking is often regarded as a simple task that anyone can do, there may be a great difference in the returns which two different milkers can get from the same cow. A cow should be milked quietly and rapidly with dry hands. (**234**) The milker should be especially careful to milk each cow dry and to get all the strippings, for the last-drawn milk may contain 10 times as much fat as that drawn first. (**824**) If a cow does not let down her milk when milking is started, massaging her udder will usually accomplish the result.

It is always desirable to have the same man milk each cow at every milking, but a change will not usually affect the yield of milk appreciably, if the new man is as good a milker as the former one.[14] Regularity in the time of milking is highly desirable, especially in the case of high-producing cows. However, cows of average production can apparently be milked with occasional irregularity, without any appreciable decline in yield, providing they are fed regularly.[15]

In milking cows thoroughly so as to get all the strippings, the best milkers generally manipulate the udder to some extent toward the end of milking. An upward pressure on each quarter for a few times when milking is nearly completed helps to bring the last milk into the teats, where it can be drawn.

Somewhat elaborate methods have been advocated for massaging and manipulating the udder before milking and especially after nearly all the milk has been drawn. The method known as the Allgau method has long been used extensively in certain districts of Germany, and a similar method was advocated by Hegelund of Denmark. In tests of the Hegelund method many years ago at the New York (Cornell) and Wisconsin Stations there was no material advantage in this method over milking by the ordinary method, provided the milker was careful to perform his task thoroughly and milk the cows dry.[16] Similar results were secured in recent Washington trials.[17]

It has been the general belief that incomplete milking tends to reduce the yield, to decrease the persistency in production, and to cause more trouble from mastitis and other udder troubles than when the cows are milked dry at each milking. While there were no such injurious effects from incomplete milking in recent tests by the United States Department of Agriculture,[18] it does not seem wise to recommend incomplete milking as a general practice unless further experiments prove that good results can always be secured by this method. On the basis of their experience, many veterinary experts believe that incomplete milking very definitely increases udder trouble in cows infected with mastitis.[19]

In trials by the Iowa Station the milk yield of cows milked by milking machines was increased 2.5 per cent by hand stripping.[20] For each hour of labor spent in stripping 1.16 lbs. of extra fat were secured.

920. Milking machines.—Because of the saving of labor through their use and also the difficulty of securing good hand milkers, milking machines are used in many dairy herds. Numerous and long-continued trials by the experiment stations show that satisfactory results, both in yield and in quality of milk, can be secured when good milking machines are handled by careful operators, who use well-adjusted teat cups and who properly cleanse and disinfect the machines. Efficient machine milking is equal to ordinary hand milking in maintaining the yield of milk, but probably somewhat inferior to the best hand milking.

While with most cows a machine does not draw quite all the milk and the cows are generally stripped by hand, nevertheless a considerable saving of labor results from using a machine. For example, in a Wisconsin study on 71 farms where milking machines were used in herds averaging 20 cows, 18 less hours of total man labor per cow a year were required, on the average, for milking, feeding, and care than on 91 farms without machines.[21] Owing to the first cost of a machine and the labor involved in the operation and cleaning, various authorities consider machine milking economical under usual conditions only where there are 15 to 30 cows or more in the herd.

Care must be taken not to spread udder diseases by the use of a milking machine. Cows affected with mastitis should always be milked last, or else be milked by hand.

921. Regularity and kindness.—For the best results with dairy cows, as with other farm animals, they should be treated with kindness at all times, and regularity in feeding and care should be observed. The highest-yielding cows are usually of nervous temperament, and especially with such animals, excitement often causes a sharp decrease in yield. Cows being driven should not be hurried, and attendants should never strike or otherwise abuse them.

Good dairymen now realize the fact brought to public attention by W. D. Hoard of Wisconsin that dairying is based on the maternity of the cow, and treat their animals accordingly. As Haecker wrote: "If you so handle the cows that they are fond of you, you have learned one of the most important lessons that lead to profitable dairying. . . . A cow's affection for the calf prompts the desire to give it milk; if you gain her affection she will desire to give you milk."[22]

III. Feed and Care Before and After Calving

922. Dry period important.—A dairy cow will produce considerably more milk annually if dried off 6 weeks before freshening, than if she is milked continuously.[23] A cow that is in thin flesh should be dry 8 weeks. Experienced dairymen always provide this rest period so that their cows will be in good body condition for the hard work of the next lactation.

During the peak of lactation high producers frequently secrete in their milk considerably more nutrients than they can assimilate from the feed they are able to eat. Therefore, if they have stored a reserve supply of fat and other nutrients in their bodies before freshening, they can maintain a materially higher level of production during the time they are "milking off" this store. It has also been shown in Chapter XXIV that during the dry period cows fed good rations can replenish the store of calcium and phosphorus in the skeleton that has been drawn upon during the flush of milk production. (**814**) For this reason alone, it is undoubtedly important that cows have a dry period of reasonable length.

Various methods are used in drying off persistent producers. Probably the best and most rapid method is to discontinue milking abruptly.[24] Then, if the udder fills so much with milk that there is danger of its becoming congested, the cow should be milked out clean, and only milked again as it may be necessary. This method dries off a cow much more rapidly than the older method of gradually decreasing the frequency of milking, first to once a day, then once in 2 days, etc.

If the cow is a most persistent producer and is giving a large yield when it becomes time to dry her off, her feed should be severely reduced, so as to check the milk flow. If possible, she should be put in a box stall where she can not steal feed from her neighbors. Then she should be fed only rather inferior hay and no grain at all. Also, she should be supplied with only about one and one-half pailfuls of water a day. This treatment, combined with the method of discontinuing milking, will commonly dry off the cow in a few days. Then she should again receive a normal ration.

923. Feeding during the dry period.—Proper feeding during the dry period is important to get the cow in shape for heavy production and also to prevent trouble at calving time. During the barn-feeding season no better ration can be provided than good legume hay and silage, if the latter is available, with enough concentrates to get the cow in proper condition before she freshens.

Plenty of well-cured legume hay is especially important at this time, because it is the richest source of vitamin D among common feeds and this vitamin is necessary for the assimilation of calcium and phosphorus. It is during the dry period that high-producing cows can most readily rebuild the store of these minerals that may have been lost during the flush of milk production. (**814**)

If dry cows are fed legume hay as the only roughage, a mixture of farm grains alone, such as one-half ground corn or barley (by weight) and one-half ground oats, will provide sufficient protein. If they are fed legume hay with corn silage, corn fodder or stover, or roots, the grain mixture need not contain more than 12 per cent protein. If they must be fed only low-protein roughage, the grain mixture should contain at least 16 per cent protein. Unless the grain mixture contains at least one-fifth of feeds high in phosphorus, such as wheat bran, linseed meal, or cottonseed meal, 1 lb. of bone meal or other safe phosphorus supplement should be added to each 100 lbs. of the concentrate mixture. (**166**)

A popular mixture for dry cows is 100 lbs. of ground corn, hominy feed, or ground barley; 100 lbs. of ground oats; 100 lbs. of wheat bran; and 50 to 100 lbs. of linseed meal. The concentrate mixtures in Appendix Table VII that contain the proper percentage of protein and that are laxative and bulky in nature are suitable for dry cows, as well as for cows in milk.

If a cow is in fairly good condition when she is dried off, an allowance of 2 to 4 lbs. of concentrates a day with good roughage should be sufficient. On the other hand, if she is thin, the amount should be increased to 5 or 6 lbs., or even more. Cows that are to be on advanced registry test are usually fed with great liberality when dry, so they will be fat at time of freshening. (**938**)

During the pasture season, no additional feed need be furnished dry cows if there is plenty of forage. However, if pastures become short, enough additional feed should be fed to get them in the desired condition. This feed may be silage, soiling crops, or hay, with grain if necessary.

The net returns from good cows are undoubtedly increased when they are so fed during the dry period that at calving they are in thrifty condition and carry a reasonable amount of flesh. This is well shown by results secured at the New York (Cornell) Station in which a group of good cows were purchased, shortly before calving, from dairymen for use in a feeding experiment.[25] Of the entire group, 18 were in rather thin condition when they calved, because they had not been well fed during the dry period. These cows were given good rations during the following lactation period and produced an average of 8,577 lbs. milk and 270 lbs. fat during the first 35 weeks of lactation.

The cows were well fed during the following dry period and after calving weighed 112 lbs. more, on the average, than the previous year. They were fed the same rations during lactation that they had received the year before, and produced an average of 9,282 lbs. milk and 293 lbs. fat in a 35-week period. There was thus an average increase of 705 lbs. milk and 23 lbs. fat because of proper feeding during the dry period. To make this increase, an average of less than 440 lbs. additional concentrates were fed during the dry period and during lactation. For each additional 100 lbs. of milk, only 62 lbs. of concentrates were fed, with no additional roughage. Except when milk is very cheap in comparison with the price of concentrates, this would make it decidedly profitable to feed sufficient concentrates during the dry period to get such cows into fairly good condition before calving.

Experiments conducted by the United States Department of Agriculture show that except when cows are to be on official test, or when the price of milk is high in comparison with the price of concentrates, it may not pay to feed them so liberally during the dry period that they become very fat.[26]

It is often recommended that for a week or so before calving a concentrate mixture should be fed which is very bulky and laxative. Such mixtures are advised as: (1) Equal parts by weight of ground oats and wheat bran; (2) equal parts by weight of ground oats, wheat bran, and linseed meal. There is, however, no need of feeding a special mixture at this time, if the ration previously fed has been sufficiently laxative to prevent constipation. The recommendation is also often made that the allowance of concentrates be reduced at this time to only 3 or 4 lbs. a day, if more has been fed. Unless the cow's udder shows a tendency to become congested, it is not, however, necessary to reduce the allowance in this manner.

A cow that is soon to calve should be turned out for exercise each day when the weather is suitable. She must not be chased by dogs or be crowded through narrow doors or gates. Care should also be taken that she is not injured by slipping on the stable floor or on ice.

924. Gestation period; frequency of calving.—The average gestation period of cows is placed by most writers at 280 to 285 days. However, in studies of the gestation periods for cows of the leading dairy breeds, the average period has generally been only 278 to 280 days.[27] Male calves are apt to be carried a trifle longer than females, and the gestation period is shorter, on the average, for twin calves than for single calves. Knott of the Washington Station found, on studying the records of 2,910 gestations of Holstein cows, that as the cows increased in age from 2 to 6 years, the average length of the gestation period increased 1.5 days.[28] After that, there was a tendency for the periods to shorten slightly. Calves sired by some bulls seemed to have a definitely shorter or longer gestation period than the average.

Unless dairymen wish to change the period of freshening in their

IMITATE SUMMER CONDITIONS THE YEAR ROUND

The most successful dairymen imitate summer conditions as closely as possible during the rest of the year.

FEEDING ALFALFA HAY TO COWS ON PASTURE

When the pasture is short, it is essential that other feed be provided to keep up the milk flow. This may be soilage, silage, or legume hay.

Luxuriant Pasture Is Unexcelled for Dairy Cows

Not only is the supply of nutrients liberal on good pasture, but also the feed is succulent and palatable. Furthermore, good pasturage is rich in protein, mineral matter and vitamines.

Feeding Green Corn to Keep Up the Milk Flow

If additional feed is not supplied when pastures become parched in mid-summer, the milk flow will surely decrease and it will not be possible to bring the cows back to their normal yield even should the pastures improve later.

herds, as from spring freshening to fall freshening, they usually plan to have their cows freshen at intervals of about 12 months. Especially in the case of high-producing cows, the annual production is apt to be reduced if the interval is much less than a year between calving dates. Apparently, lengthening the calving intervals at least a month or two beyond a year does not reduce the average production for consecutive calendar years.[29]

925. Calving time.—Unless the herd is at pasture, the cow should be placed in a suitable box stall at least 2 or 3 days before the expected time of calving. Even during the summer when the cows are on pasture, it is wise to separate the cow that is soon to calve from the herd and put her in a box stall or in a small pasture lot where she can be given any needed attention. Before the cow is put in the box stall, any old bedding should be removed and the stall thoroughly cleaned and disinfected. Plenty of dry bedding should then be provided for the comfort of the cow.

As calving time approaches, the udder of a good cow will become swollen with milk. It is not advisable, however, to remove part of the milk prior to calving. If the udder becomes unduly congested, it is well to rub it twice a day with a mixture of one-half cod-liver oil and one-half ethyl alcohol, or with some other suitable mixture. When the muscles on each side of the tail head of the cow relax, leaving a hollow on each side, the calf may be expected within 24 hours, or usually 2 to 3 days at the longest.

If the cow is constipated, she should be given a warm bran mash or else a dose of mineral oil or of Epsom salts. The bran mash is made by placing 3 or 4 quarts of wheat bran in a pail and pouring enough boiling water over it to moisten thoroughly. After it has stood for 10 to 15 minutes, sufficient cold water should be added to bring it to a comfortable temperature for the cow to eat.

It is sometimes advised that but little feed or water be given the cow for several hours before calving, but this is unnecessary. Also, it is often difficult to estimate exactly when the cow will calve. She may be allowed feed and water as usual up to calving time, but will not generally have much appetite soon before calving.

The cow should not be molested during the calving, unless assistance is required. To avoid injury to the cow, assistance should then be given only by a veterinarian or some other experienced person. During calving time and also following calving, the cow should be protected from drafts.

As soon as the calf arrives, it should be given any needed attention. Sometimes a slimy membrane covers its nose. This should be removed, so that the calf can breathe easily. If the cow does not dry the calf by licking it vigorously, it should be dried by rubbing with a cloth or dry straw. If the afterbirth is not expelled naturally within about 48 hours after the birth of the calf, the services of a qualified veterinarian should be secured, if possible. The cow should not be allowed to eat the afterbirth.

If the calf is weak and does not nurse within a half hour, it should be helped to get its first meal. As has been shown previously, it is very important that the calf receive the colostrum. (**210**) To guard against navel infection, the navel should be disinfected with tincture of iodine soon after birth.

It is advisable to separate the calf from the cow about 24 hours after birth. If left with the cow longer, a vigorous calf may get so much milk that scours will result. It is also usually less difficult to teach a calf to drink from a pail when it is separated from its dam not more than a day after birth, than when it remains with her for a longer time.

It is customary to save the seventh milking after the cow calves for human use, although sometimes the milk is not normal before the eighth or ninth milking. A simple test for normal milk, is to heat a small quantity to boiling. If the sample does not thicken because of a high content of albumin, the milk is usable.

926. Feed and care after calving.—To secure a large yearly production from a cow, it is highly important that she be properly fed and cared for during the first month after calving. It is especially necessary to increase the concentrate allowance gradually, or udder troubles and digestive disturbances are apt to result.

Immediately after calving, the cow is in a weakened condition and her digestive system is sluggish. She should therefore be kept warm and comfortable, and should be blanketed, if the stall is too cold. The amount of feed should be very limited for the first day, and the cow should be given lukewarm water to drink, unless there is a drinking bowl in the stall. During the first day after calving she may be given what hay and other roughage (including silage) that she cares for, but she should have only a small amount of concentrates. If calving has been normal and the cow is doing well, she may have for the first feed about 1 lb. of the same concentrate mixture that was fed during the dry period.

After the first day, the allowance of concentrates may be gradually increased. Three weeks or more should be taken to get high producers on a full feed of concentrates, while lower producers can be fed their usual allowance somewhat sooner. If the udder of a cow becomes swollen and congested, the amount of concentrates should be reduced. Applying cold water to the udder with a hose, followed by thorough milking, will relieve the congestion. This process should be repeated 4 to 6 times a day, if necessary.

927. Milk fever; acetonemia.—All experienced dairymen know that their best cows are apt to have milk fever during the first few days after calving. This is caused by a lack of calcium in the blood, produced by the heavy drain on the supply of this mineral as the cow begins to secrete a large amount of milk. It has been stated previously that the parathyroid glands normally regulate the amount of calcium in the blood in some manner. (**63**) Later in lactation the cow is able to draw on the store of calcium in her skeleton when she does not assimilate enough from her food. At the outset of lactation the parathyroid glands seem to be unable in some cases to meet the demand for calcium, and milk fever results.

Checking the milk secretion decreases the tendency towards milk fever. Therefore in the case of high-producing cows, except heifers, only enough milk should be milked out during the first 2 or 3 days to supply the calf. This increases the pressure in the udder and consequently lessens the milk secretion until the parathyroid glands increase their activity sufficiently to maintain a normal calcium content in the blood.

If milk fever develops, no time should be lost in securing a competent veterinarian to treat the cow. The older method of inflating the udder with air is effective, but there is danger of infecting the udder with mastitis by this method, even when care is used. For this reason the newer method is to be preferred, in which a solution of calcium gluconate or other calcium salt is injected into the jugular vein or the mammary veins.

In some instances cows are affected from 8 to 10 days after calving by a disease called acetonemia, or acetonuria. This disease sometimes resembles milk fever. However, it is caused by a deranged metabolism of fats in the body and the consequent excretion in the urine of partially-oxidized products of fat metabolism (called ketone bodies). In this condition there is a lack of glucose in the blood, and the disease is usually treated by the injection of a glucose solution into the veins. Cows affected by a chronic form of the disease may be benefited by the feeding of molasses.

IV. FEEDING COWS ON PASTURE

928. Feeding the herd on pasture.—No factor is of greater importance in reducing the cost of milk production than the providing of excellent pasture for the herd over just as long a period as possible. The economy and importance of good pasture for dairy cows is well shown in studies by the United States Department of Agriculture in seven of the leading dairy districts of this country.[30] **(305)** In these districts pasturage furnished nearly one-third of the total nutrients consumed by the cows during the year. Yet the cost of the pasturage was only one-seventh of the annual feed cost.

When well-fertilized and properly-managed pastures are provided, a high yield of milk can be maintained throughout the summer with a minimum amount of grain or other harvested feed. On the other hand, when little effort is made to improve the pastures, a large amount of additional feed must be supplied in order to keep up a good milk flow and to prevent the cows from running down in flesh.

The proper feeding of milk cows on pasture is much simpler than during the winter, and doubtless this is the reason that so many farmers, busy with their crops, fail to give their herd the necessary attention in summer. Often the cows are merely turned to pasture after milking at night and in the morning, with no further thought as to the supply of feed actually available for them. It is then no wonder that when the pasturage becomes scanty in midsummer, the cows run down in flesh and fall off severely in yield of milk. Even if fed liberally when barn feeding starts in the fall, commonly they cannot then be brought back to their usual production.

Many also make the mistake of turning the herd to pasture before the grass is well started. This not only injures the pasture but also is apt to decrease the yield of milk, for the cows cannot get much nourishment from the scanty forage. **(307)** It is important, however, that grazing start as soon as the grass is ready. Otherwise, the cattle may be unable to keep the forage grazed down during the period of most rapid growth, and it will then become too mature and will be unpalatable.

When cows in milk are first turned on pasture in the spring, the feeding of some concentrates and hay should be continued until they become used to pasture and until the grass becomes abundant. If this is not done, good cows will run down in condition, for the young grass stimulates them to produce more milk than on their winter ration, but yet it is often low in dry matter and nutrients. The cows are therefore unable to eat enough of it to meet their needs.

929. Feeding concentrates on pasture.—It is often difficult for a dairyman to decide how much concentrates to feed cows on good pasture, or whether or not to feed them any concentrates at all. The answer to this problem depends on the amount and quality of the forage the pasture furnishes and on the actual production of the cows.

Good pasture alone will provide sufficient nutrients for body maintenance and the production of 10 to 20 lbs. of milk or more, depending on its richness. If the pasture is excellent, it will provide sufficient nutrients for still more milk. Cows of high productive capacity that are fed no concentrates on pasture may continue to yield more milk than these amounts, but they must draw on their bodies for the additional nutrients they need. Consequently, they will lose weight and run down greatly in condition.

The "Grain feeding table for cows on pasture" in Appendix Table IX provides a convenient guide for the feeding of concentrates, or "grain," to cows on various grades of pasture. Separate recommendations are made for cows on excellent, good, fair and poor pasture, and for specific yields of milk containing various percentages of fat. These recommendations are based upon the results of the various studies that have been made of the feed requirements of cows on pasture.[31]

It is the opinion of the author that good cows should be fed about as much concentrates as shown in this table, except when milk is unusually low in price in comparison with the price of grain and other concentrates. It may then be most economical to feed no grain to cows on good pasture unless they are producing more than 1 lb. of butter fat a day, and to feed higher producers only one-half to two-thirds as much concentrates as stated in the table.

Even when the feeding of concentrates to cows on good pasture does not result in enough higher production during the summer to show an immediate profit, it may nevertheless be wise. This is because it will prevent good cows from running down in condition on pasture and will result in higher yields during the following fall and winter.

When cows are grazed on luxuriant, intensively-fertilized pastures, it may be wise to provide them with a little hay or other dry roughage, and to reduce the allowance of concentrates. In Massachusetts trials cows on such pasture which were fed 2.7 lbs. hay and only 3.1 lbs. concentrates (1 lb. to each 8.2 lbs. of milk) produced nearly as much milk as others fed 5.7 lbs. concentrates (1 lb. to each 5.7 lbs. of milk).[32] The feed cost was considerably lower on the combination of hay and concentrates. When hay was high in price, oat mill feed was a good substitute for feeding cows on pasture.

It has been emphasized previously that young pasture grass contains even more protein, on the dry basis, than does alfalfa hay. (**297**) There is therefore no need of using a concentrate mixture rich in protein for cows on good pasture. Merely a mixture of farm grains or a concentrate mixture containing 12 per cent protein will provide an ample amount of protein for cows on excellent pasture, except in the case of unusually heavy producers.

In experiments during 3 summers at the Ohio Station cows on pasture which were fed a concentrate mixture containing only 11 to 12 per cent protein produced nearly as much milk as others fed a mixture containing much more protein.[33] In no case was the yield on the high-protein mixture enough greater to pay for the additional cost. In Michigan tests with cows on good pasture a concentrate mixture containing 9.3 per cent digestible protein (about 12 per cent total protein) produced just as much milk as one containing 16.7 per cent digestible protein.[34]

Unless the grass is kept growing actively by liberal fertilization and proper pasture management, it will be considerably lower in protein content, on the dry basis, during midsummer. It will then be necessary to increase the protein content of the concentrate mixture. Unless the pasture is decidedly poor, however, it will not be necessary to have more than 16 to 18 per cent protein in the mixture.

Various concentrate mixtures adapted for feeding on excellent, good, fair, and poor pasture are given in Appendix Table VII.

930. Supplementing scanty pasture.—If pastures become parched in midsummer, it is much more economical to rely largely on summer silage or soiling crops to supplement them than to try to keep up the production by feeding only concentrates. It has been shown previously that when the number of cows is large enough to use up the silage fast enough to keep it from spoiling, silage is usually a much more economical feed than soiling crops. (**341, 355–356, 903**)

If soiling crops are used, it should be borne in mind that as a rule they are more watery than good corn silage, and hence it is necessary to feed a considerably greater weight. Hay can also be fed to supplement short pasture, when silage or soiling crops are not available.

QUESTIONS

1. State 10 essentials in the proper feeding and care of dairy cows.
2. Why is it important that the amount of concentrates for each cow be adjusted to her actual yield of milk and fat?
3. Why are the grain feeding tables in Appendix Table IX more accurate guides than the thumb rules for feeding grain to dairy cows?
4. Discuss the importance of the following for dairy cows: (a) Palatability of feeds; (b) variety in the ration; (c) bulkiness of the concentrate mixture; (d) rations that are slightly laxative.
5. Discuss the requirements of dairy cows for shelter and comfort.
6. What are the advantages and disadvantages of the loose-stabling method of housing dairy cows?
7. Discuss the use of fly sprays on dairy cows.
8. Why is exercise important for dairy cows?
9. Discuss the frequency and order of feeding dairy cows.
10. Discuss the milking of dairy cows, considering (a) regularity of milking, (b)

milking cows thoroughly, (c) massaging the udder, (d) the use of milking machines.

11. Why is it important that cows have a dry period?

12. How would you dry off a persistent producer?

13. Discuss the feeding of cows during the dry period.

14. What is the approximate gestation period for dairy cows?

15. Discuss the feed and care of a cow at calving time; after calving.

16. What is the cause of milk fever? What two methods of treatment are used?

17. Discuss the feeding of concentrates to cows on pasture.

18. About what is the minimum percentage of protein there should be in a concentrate mixture for cows on excellent, actively-growing pasture?

19. Discuss the use of various feeds to supplement scanty pasture.

REFERENCES

1. Woodward, Shepherd, and Graves, U. S. Dept. Agr., Misc. Pub. 130; Fraser, Dairy Farming, pp. 140-146; Headley, Nev. Bul. 116.
2. Cannon and Espe, Iowa Rpt. 1931; see also: Jacobson, Ark. Bul. 312; Mich. Rpts. 1933, 1934; N. C. Rpt. 1927.
3. Moore, Huffman, and Plumb, Jour. Agr. Res. 44, 1932, pp. 789-796; Mich. Rpt. 1928-30.
4. Nevens, Jour. Agr. Res. 36, 1928, pp. 785-788.
5. Kelly, U. S. Dept. Agr. Farmers' Bul. 1393; Kelly, Agr. Engin., 14, 1933, pp. 271-273.
6. Kelly, Agr. Engin., 14, 1933, pp. 47-49.
7. Woodward and Dawson, U. S. Dept. Agr., Farmers' Bul. 1470.
8. Woodward et al., U. S. Dept. Agr. Bul. 736, Farmers' Bul. 1470; Davis, Penn. Rpt. 1914.
9. Foord, Mass. Bul. 293; Buckley, Md. Bul. 177; Jefferson, Mich. Quar. Bul. 16, 1933, No. 3; Johnson, Tretsven, Ezekiel, and Wells, Mont. Bul. 264.
10. Dice, N. D. Bul. 256; Jour. Dairy Sci., 18, 1935, pp. 447-448.
11. Eaton, Ala. Rpt. 1931; Freeborn, Regan, and Folger, Jour. Econ. Entom. 18, 1925, pp. 779-790; 21, 1928, pp. 494-501; Cal. Rpts. 1928, 1932; Beach and Clark, Conn. (Storrs) Bul. 32; Cannon and Richardson, Iowa Rpt. 1932; Wilson, Pearson and Cannon, Jour. Dairy Sci., 16, 1933, pp. 427-433; Kan. Rpts. 1926-28, 1928-30; Eckles, Mo. Bul. 68; Grinnells, N. C. Rpts. 1930, 1931; Bartlett, N. J. Rpts. 1930, 1931; Bartlett, N. J. Agr., 15, 1933, pp. 2-3; Ohio Bul. 402; Kuhlman, McGilliard and Weaver, Okla. Rpt. 1930-32.
12. McCampbell, Amer. Soc. Anim. Prod., Proc. 1929; Baer, Okla. Rpt. 1924-26.
13. Woodward, U. S. Dept. Agr. Cir. 180.
14. Carlyle, Wis. Rpt. 1899; Linfield, Utah Bul. 68; Woodward, U. S. Dept. Agr. Cir. 180.
15. Woodward, U. S. Dept. Agr. Cir. 180.
16. Wing and Foord, N. Y. (Cornell) Bul. 213; Woll, Wis. Rpt. 1902.
17. Ellington and Knott, Wash. Bul. 229.
18. Woodward, Amer. Dairy Sci. Assoc., Abstract of Papers at Annual Meeting, 1932; U. S. Dept. Agr., Yearbook, 1935.
19. Udall, Veterinary Medicine, p. 235.
20. Wilson and Cannon, Jour. Dairy Sci., 17, 1934, pp. 331-338.
21. McNall and Mitchell, Wis. Bul. 421.
22. Minn. Bul. 130.
23. Dow, Me. Bul. 361; Carroll, Utah Bul. 127; Sanders, Jour. Agr. Sci., England, 20, 1930, pp. 145-185; Dix-Arnold and Becker, Amer. Dairy Sci. Assoc., Abstract of Papers at Annual Meeting, 1934.
24. Wayne, Eckles, and Petersen, Jour. Dairy Sci., 16, 1933, pp. 69-78.
25. Harrison, N. Y. (Cornell) Station, unpublished data.
26. Woodward, Shepherd, and Graves, U. S. Dept. Agr., Misc. Pub. 179.
27. Wing, N. Y. (Cornell) Bul. 162; Knott, Jour. Dairy Sci., 15, 1932, pp. 87-98; Id. Bul. 179; Knoop and Hayden, Ohio Bimo. Bul. 166; McCandlish, Jour. Dairy Sci., 5, 1922, p. 301; see also: Fitch, McGilliard, and Drumm, Jour. Dairy Sci., 7, 1924, pp. 222-233.
28. Knott, Jour. Dairy Sci., 15, 1932, pp. 87-98
29. Headley, Nev. Bul. 119; Gaines and Palfrey, Jour. Dairy Sci., 14, 1931, pp. 294-306; Matson, Jour. Agr. Sci., England, 19, 1929, pp. 553-562; Sanders, Jour. Agr. Sci., England, 17, 1927, pp. 21-32.
30. Semple, Vinall, Enlow, and Woodward, U. S. Dept. Agr., Misc. Pub. 194; see also: Moore, Miss. Rpts. 1927, 1930; Kuhlman, McGilliard, and Weaver, Okla. Rpt. 1930-32; La Master, Elting and Mitchell, S. C. Rpts. 1931, 1933; Bateman and Caine, Utah Bul. 239.
31. Ind. Rpts. 1925, 1928, 1930; Lush, La. Bul. 241; Moore, Miss. Rpts. 1925, 1926; Roberts, N. Y. (Cornell) Buls. 36, 49; Ohio Spec. Cir. 43; Kuhlman, McGilliard, and Weaver, Okla. Rpt. 1930-32; Jones and Brandt, Ore. Bul. 264; Ore. Rpt. 1922; LaMaster, Elting and Weaver, S. C. Rpts. 1931, 1932; Bateman and Caine, Utah Bul. 239; Knott, Hodgson, and Ellington, Wash. Bul. 295; Dawson, U. S. Dept. Agr. Leaflet 7; Moseley, Stuart, and Graves, U. S. Dept. Agr., Tech. Bul. 116.
32. Foley, Jour. Dairy Sci., 16, 1933, pp. 407-411.
33. Perkins, Ohio Bul. 548.
34. Horwood and Putnam, Mich. Quar. Bul. 16, 1933, No. 1; Mich. Rpt. 1930-32.

CHAPTER XXVII

COST OF MILK PRODUCTION—FEEDING TEST COWS

I. THE COST OF MILK PRODUCTION

931. Factors in the cost of milk production.—Many investigations have been conducted by the state experiment stations and the United States Department of Agriculture to find the cost of milk production under different conditions. These investigations have not only furnished much accurate information on this subject, but have also pointed out ways in which the individual farmer can reduce his own cost of production, so that in many cases he can secure a satisfactory profit where otherwise there might be a loss.

In determining the cost of milk production it is most convenient to group the various items of expense into certain classifications. The following is a common classification of the different factors which enter into the cost of producing milk.

1. The combined cost of feed and bedding is by far the largest single item in the cost of producing milk, generally making up from one-half to two-thirds the total gross cost. This expense will of course vary widely, depending on the price of the various feeds, the productive capacity of the herd, and the economy of the rations used.

2. The cost of man labor is next in importance. This includes the labor of milking, feeding and caring for the cows, cleaning the stables, handling and hauling milk, and all miscellaneous work connected with the herd. The labor cost will make up at least one-fifth the total gross cost.

3. The building charge includes interest, taxes, and depreciation on the proportion of the barn actually occupied by the cows and by the feed storage for the dairy herd. Repairs should also be included under this item or under "miscellaneous."

4. The equipment charge covers interest, insurance, depreciation, and any taxes on milk utensils or machinery, tools, etc.

5. The cow charge, which covers depreciation, interest, taxes, and mortality risk on the cows themselves, is a larger item than often believed. First of all, the average useful life of dairy cows in the herd after they first freshen has been found to be only 4 to 5 years. While many cows have a much longer period of usefulness, on the average the cows will be replaced within this period, because of low milk yield, failure to breed, or injury or contraction of disease.

The annual depreciation is computed by finding the probable difference between the cost or value of the cow when she first freshens or is purchased and the price she will bring for beef when she is discarded. For example, if a cow is worth $125 when she first freshens, then has a useful life of 5 years, and finally brings $60 when sold for beef, the annual depreciation will be one-fifth of $65, or $13.00. The taxes paid on the cows, interest on their average valuation, and the mortality risk must also be included in the charges. With dairy cows the annual mortality risk is usually about 1.5 per cent, when the health of the herd is properly safeguarded.

6. The cost of keeping the sire must be pro-rated among the cows, or the cost of bull service must be included in herds where a bull is not owned.

7. Under "miscellaneous" are included such items as cash paid for hauling milk, cost of consumable supplies, veterinary services, cow-testing association fees and other miscellaneous items. Some of these expenses are sometimes carried under the "cow charge."

In computing the labor cost, commonly all the man labor, both of hired laborers and of the owner and manager, is figured at the current rate for ordinary farm labor. Then an item is sometimes added to cover managerial ability and business risks, a common estimate for this being 10 per cent of the other total costs.

932. Credits in determining cost of production.—From the total gross cost of maintaining dairy cows, which will include the various items just enumerated, must be deducted the value of the manure secured and the value of the calves at a few days of age. Commonly, the value of the manure produced on pasture is not deducted directly, but the pasture charge is based upon the fact that the fields will be improved by the manure voided on them.

The value of the calves will of course vary widely, depending on the breeding of the cows and the sire. In studies of the cost of milk production where some herds include purebred cows, these are commonly valued at the price of high grades of similar productive capacity, and the calves credited at usual veal or grade prices. This is done so as to differentiate between the financial returns from the two enterprises —the breeding of purebred stock and the producing of milk.

933. Annual cost of keeping cows.—From the large amount of data which has been secured in recent years on the cost of milk production, the summaries of investigations carried on in 6 states are presented on page 579.[1] Since costs are constantly changing, these figures must be regarded as examples, rather than averages for any particlar district. From the amounts of feed consumed and labor required annually, one can readily compute the cost of these major items under his own conditions. The other costs do not vary as widely from year to year, and furthermore, they make up only one-fourth or less of the total gross cost.

These data represent the cost of milk production for dairymen who were undoubtedly more efficient than the average. This is shown clearly by the fact that the yields of milk in most of these studies were decidedly higher than the general average for the particular state. The average cost of milk production for all dairymen would therefore be somewhat higher than is shown in these figures.

It will be noted that the cows in the New York and Virginia herds were fed most liberally on concentrates, the average amount fed annually per cow being 2,683 lbs. and 2,959 lbs., respectively. This liberal feeding of concentrates is characteristic of the most intensive dairy districts of the eastern states, for there it generally produces the best net returns.

LARGE AVERAGE PRODUCTION IS NECESSARY TO REDUCE COSTS

Of all the factors affecting the cost of milk production, a large average yearly production per cow is the most important. This herd of Jerseys has been bred and selected for high production.

WELL-PLANNED CROP ROTATIONS PROVIDE LOW-COST RATIONS

A corn-belt farm with a good system of crop rotation, including corn for grain and silage and a liberal acreage of legumes for hay. Legume hay field in the foreground with corn for grain in the background.

Excellent Pasture Cuts Cost of Milk Production

To produce milk cheaply in summer, it is necessary to provide excellent pasture during just as long a period as is possible. There should be abundant feed, so the cows can eat their fill, without hunting for grass all day.

Enough Cows Should Be Kept to Make an Economical Unit

If dairy cows are to provide the main source of income on the farm, a sufficient number must be kept to make an economical unit. The exact number should depend on the local conditions.

The cows in the Michigan herds received slightly less grain but produced an average of 7,457 lbs. milk a year.

The Oklahoma herds represent a much less intensive system of milk production, such as is common in the newer dairy districts of the western states. The average production was relatively low, being only 185 lbs. of butter fat a year, but the feed cost was low because the cows were on pasture for an average of 299 days. The cows in the Oregon herds received an average of only 1,293 lbs. concentrates, but they were fed liberally on hay (chiefly alfalfa) and on silage and other succulent feeds. Because of this, the average production of milk was nearly as high as in the Virginia herds, where over twice as much concentrates were fed.

Yearly cost of keeping dairy cows

	New York 1934	Michigan 1933	New Hampshire 1929–30	Virginia 1931–32	Oklahoma 1931	Oregon 1932
No. of cows.........	458	881	5,566	2,958	680	8,352
Av. yield per cow						
Milk, lbs.........	7,994	7,457	5,217	6,099	.....	6,088
Fat, lbs...........	.....	333	.....	.....	185	270
Feed and bedding						
Concentrates, lbs...	2,683	2,031	1,596	2,959	1,261	1,293
Hay, lbs..........	3,800	3,317	} 4,449 {	3,230	2,397	4,984
Other dry roughage, lbs.	1	216		370		
Succulent feeds, lbs.	8,000	4,660	3,409	7,740		4,818
Pasture, days......	1	153	1	187	299	148
Bedding, lbs........	1	1	1	1	1	1
Labor						
Man, hrs..........	144	153	140	199	88	130
Costs						
Feed and bedding..	$ 94.99	$ 49.49	$ 81.07	$ 93.48	$ 26.58	$ 55.91
Man labor.........	38.55	22.92	39.04	48.49	14.00	28.66
Building charge....	6.09	7.68	5.90	6.78	1.27	5.99
Equipment charge..	6.91[2]	2.11	2.78	4.70	4.23	2.32
Cow charge........	8.71	9.12	11.06	17.18	4.97	8.98
Bull charge........	3.25	3.23	1.90	3.94	3	2.40
Miscellaneous	12.38	9.83	19.00	30.68	1.86	4.51
Total gross cost......	$170.88	$104.38	$160.75	$205.25	$ 52.91	$108.77
Credits						
Manure	$ 8.32	$ 11.14	$ 15.50	$ 6.86	4	$ 4.71
Calves	4.40	3.75	4.80	3.05	3	2.29
Miscellaneous	.08	.....	.01	.38	.....	4.08
Total credits........	$ 12.80	$ 14.89	$ 20.31	$ 10.29	.....	$ 11.08
Net cost.............	$158.08	$ 89.49	$140.44	$194.96	$ 52.91	$ 97.69
Av. yearly cost						
Per 100 lbs. milk...	$1.98	$1.20	$2.69	$ 3.20	.....	$ 1.60
Per lb. fat........	....	.27	....	....	.29	1.36

[1] Amount not stated, but cost included in total cost of feed and bedding.
[2] Including horse labor.
[3] Bull charge offset by value of calf.
[4] No credit allowed for manure.

934. Formulas for cost of milk production.—Since it is no easy task to convert such data as are presented in the preceding table from one set of prices to the prices current at another time, various simple formulas have been worked out for estimating the cost of milk production. In these formulas all the costs are reduced to terms of feed and labor. Therefore, by taking the current prices for feeds and for labor, a more or less approximate estimate of the cost of producing milk can readily be made at any time.

In using these items as a basis for calculating the cost of producing milk, it is assumed that as the prices of feeds and labor rise or fall the other items of expense and the credit items will fluctuate more or less in the same proportion. Though the costs of all the factors probably never change in exact unison, they usually keep closely enough together for purposes of comparison.

One of the formulas which has been used most widely is that of Warren of the New York (Cornell) Station. According to this formula, the cost of producing 100 lbs. of milk under New York conditions is found by first totalling the cost of 33.8 lbs. concentrates, 43.3 lbs. hay, 10.8 lbs. of other dry roughage (corn stover, corn fodder, straw, etc.), 100.5 lbs. silage, and 3.02 hours of man labor. This total represents 80 per cent of the entire cost. Therefore it must be increased by one-fourth to determine the approximate total cost of 100 lbs. of milk, according to the formula. The Warren formula has been simplified by Misner, as shown in the following table. This presents some of the formulas that have been proposed to meet conditions in various districts.[2]

Comparison of formulas for cost of milk production

Factors in formula	Warren (N. Y.)	Misner (N. Y.)	Pearson (Ill.)	Food Adminis- tration	Indiana	Michigan
Concentrates, lbs.	33.80	30.0	44.00	33.50	28.9	23.50
Hay, lbs.	43.30	60.0	50.00	45.30	38.1	34.90
Other dry roughage, lbs.	10.80	.....	39.00	11.50	9.9	15.20
Silage, lbs.	100.50	100.00	188.00	102.60	104.8	110.40
Labor, hours	3.02	2.5	2.42	2.88	2.4	2.11
Corrective factor, per cent	25	25	0	23.7	.....	45.8

To illustrate the method of estimating the cost of milk production according to a formula, let us estimate the cost, using the Misner formula. We will assume that the cost of a good concentrate mixture is $26 a ton; of hay, $12 a ton; of silage $4 a ton; and of farm labor, 25 cents an hour, including board. At these prices the total cost of 30 lbs. concentrates, 60 lbs. hay, 100 lbs. silage, and 2.5 hours man labor will be $1.575. Increasing this total by 25 per cent to cover the other costs, will give us $1.97 as the estimated total cost of producing 100 lbs. of milk.

935. Seasonal cost of production.—Every experienced dairyman knows that it costs much more to produce milk in winter than in summer when the cows are on pasture. This is because pasture is a cheap feed, and also because much less labor is required in producing each 100 lbs. of milk when the herd is on pasture than under winter feeding conditions. In studies by Pearson in Illinois it was found that the other expenses of producing milk were more or less constant through the year.[3] When all expenses were included, the net cost of producing 100 lbs. of milk in June was about 60 per cent of the average cost for the year, and in December about 120 per cent of the yearly cost.

Since it costs less to produce milk in the summer, the natural tendency will be for dairymen to concentrate production in the more profit-

able months. Therefore in order to secure a steady supply of milk for
city consumption, the price paid farmers must be enough higher in winter than in summer to offset the difference in cost of production.

936. Reducing the cost of milk production.—The studies of the
cost of milk production have shown that the following are the most important factors in reducing the cost of milk production:

1. Large average yearly production. Of all the factors affecting
the cost of milk, a large average yearly production per cow is the most
important. The effect of this in reducing the cost of feed per 100 lbs.
of milk has been emphasized previously. (**785**) To secure a large average production the dairyman must first of all have good cows and cull
his herd each year to get rid of the unprofitable animals. (**789-790**)
Next, he must feed and care for these good cows so that they are given
an opportunity to yield a profitable amount of milk.

2. Balanced rations. Cows of high productive capacity cannot produce a good yield unless they are fed adequate rations, properly-balanced
in protein and supplying ample minerals and vitamins. (**794**) It has
been clearly shown in the studies of the cost of milk production on
dairy farms that an insufficiency of protein seriously reduces the yield
of milk and consequently the net returns.

Thus, in studies on 95 Wisconsin dairy farms it was found that in
herds where decidedly unbalanced rations were fed which had a nutritive ratio of 1:11.5, the average milk yield was only 74 per cent as large
as where balanced rations were fed having a nutritive ratio of about
1:7.0.[4] Similarly, on rations having a nutritive ratio of 1:9.0, the
yield was only 86 per cent of that secured with the ample supply of
protein.

3. A liberal but not wasteful amount of feed. Large production is
impossible without a liberal supply of feed, as has been emphasized
previously. (**804-807**) When concentrates are very expensive in comparison with roughage, it is most economical to feed less concentrates
than are needed to meet the recommendations of the feeding standards.
However, it is then especially important that the roughage be of excellent
quality and that it be fed with great liberality.

Wasteful feeding of concentrates must be avoided at all times. The
amount fed to the individual cows in the herd should be strictly adjusted
to their milk yields.

4. Low-cost rations throughout the year. The annual feed cost
must be kept as low as possible and yet high production must be maintained. To achieve this result, good yields of crops of the best feeding
value must be produced. The cost of efficient rations during the barn-
feeding season can generally be kept at a minimum by providing an
abundance of legume hay or of mixed hay high in legumes, along with
good silage where silage is an economical feed. (**864-867, 891-894**)
With such roughage it is not necessary to feed as great an amount of
concentrates to secure high production, as when the roughage is poorer
in quality.

For economical summer feeding it is necessary to provide excellent
pasture. This must be so fertilized and managed that it will provide a
liberal supply of nutritious forage over just as long a period as is
possible. (**305-312**) The pasture must be so supplemented with con-

centrates and other feed that a high yield of milk can be maintained throughout the season. (928–930) It is especially important that plenty of supplementary feed be provided whenever the pasturage becomes scanty. Otherwise the yield of milk will be seriously reduced.

5. *Maintaining health and avoiding heavy depreciation.* Unless great care is taken to prevent disease and maintain the health of the herd, disease will destroy all possible profits. In keeping the cost of milk production low, it is especially important to eradicate Bang's disease (infectious abortion), if it exists in the herd, and to handle the herd so that mastitis is reduced to a minimum.

The necessary replacements for the milking herd can usually be provided most economically by raising properly the heifer calves from the best cows in the herd, sired by a bred-for-production purebred bull. In dairy districts where the cost of feed is not unduly high, many farmers reduce the cost of depreciation to a minimum by selling cows when they are in their prime and will bring a good price, instead of waiting until they must be discarded as culls. They replace these animals with good heifers which they have raised. Careless dairymen may sometimes raise just as many calves for replacement, but because of disease and poor management, never have any cows to sell except culls.

6. *A herd of sufficient size.* If dairy cows are to provide the main source of income on a farm, a sufficient number must be kept to make an economical unit. If there are only a few cows in the herd, the gross income will necessarily be small, labor will be employed less efficiently, and if a bull is kept, the bull cost per cow will be greatly increased.

7. *Efficiency in the use of labor.* Many dairymen do not fully realize the importance of efficiency in the use of labor to reduce the cost of milk production. There is a great range in the number of hours of labor spent in feeding and caring for the cows on individual farms, even where the milk is of the same quality from the sanitary standpoint. For example, in New Hampshire studies the number of hours of man labor per cow a year ranged from less than 100 hours to 241 hours.[5]

To reduce the time spent in doing chores the barn must be arranged conveniently and labor-saving equipment must be provided, such as automatic drinking bowls for the cows. Also, considerable time can often be saved by efficient planning of the daily routine.

The studies of the cost of milk production have shown that those dairymen generally secure the better net returns who have a reasonable degree of efficiency in all these factors that have just been discussed. They secure larger net profits than the men who excel in one or two factors, but rank low in the others.

II. Feeding and Caring for Cows on Test

937. Official testing of dairy cows.—In the improvement of the breeds of dairy cattle in this country the systems of advanced registry testing have been of great importance. (792) It is but natural that the methods of official testing have undergone changes as additional knowledge has been gained concerning the fundamentals of breeding for milk production. For example, the 7-day and 30-day official tests, which once were most popular among Holstein breeders, have been entirely superseded by tests covering a 305-day period or the entire year. The brief tests were discarded because they were less reliable than the long-time tests as an index to the real productive capacity of various cows. (**829**)

All dairymen recognize that successful reproduction within a normal period is fully as important as a record of high milk yield. To an ever increasing extent experienced breeders now favor, instead of the 365-day test, the 305-day test with the additional requirement that the cow calve within a definite period.

While a test covering one lactation period is an excellent index to the maximum productive capacity of a cow, a still better measure of her worth is a record over several consecutive years. Likewise, the best index to the value of the blood lines represented in a herd is provided by the records of all the cows in the herd, year after year. This is far more reliable than official tests on a few selected cows which are pushed to the utmost when they are being run on test. For these reasons, the herd-test plan is becoming increasingly popular with breeders.

The feeding and management of cows on official test is fully as much of an art as of a science. Starting with a cow of high productive capacity, which is always necessary, the completion of a notable record depends largely upon the intelligent feeding and painstaking care of an expert herdsman. The rations and methods employed by leading breeders differ widely in many details. In fact, nearly every champion cow has received a somewhat different ration from other record-breaking cows. This indicates that there are no secret formulas or methods of management which are outstanding in their superiority over all others.

The following brief summary on the feeding and care of test cows is presented with the hope that it may be helpful to those who have not had experience in this field. This summary is based to a considerable extent on recommendations made by Harrison of the New York (Cornell) Station.[6]

938. Fitting cows for official test.—The highest production of which a cow is capable can be secured only when she is carefully fitted, or fattened, before she freshens. It has been shown previously that when a cow calves in high condition her production of milk and fat is considerably increased during the early part of the lactation period, because she is able to draw on the store of fat in her body. (**829, 923**) In the case of cows of the lower-testing breeds, not only is the yield of milk and fat thus increased, but also the percentage of fat is generally raised to a marked extent during the first few weeks of lactation.

A cow that is to be run on official test should be completely dry about 60 days before she is due to freshen. A longer dry period is not necessary for proper fitting, though some breeders prefer a dry period of 10 to 12 weeks. If the cow is not in fair flesh during the latter part of the lactation period, she should be fed a little more liberally than if she were not to be tested during the next lactation. Then she can be gotten into the desired condition in a 60-day dry period.

The same concentrate mixture, or so-called "fitting ration," may be used in fitting cows for official test that is used for the rest of the herd during the dry period. (**923**) The amount to be fed will depend entirely on the condition of the individual cow. It should not be necessary to feed more than about 12 lbs. of the concentrate mixture daily. Extremely heavy feeding during the dry period is not economical, and may result in the cow having a poor appetite at the start of the test period. Some breeders feed as much as 20 lbs. of concentrates daily during the fitting period, but when this is done one must be very careful not to get the cow off feed.

It is a good plan to feed during the dry period the same roughages that will be used when the cow is on test. A liberal amount of well-cured legume hay or of mixed hay rich in legumes should be fed, so that the cow may receive a plentiful supply of vitamins A and D. Corn or sorghum silage is also excellent at this time.

939. Feed and care before and after calving.—When the cow is to be kept in a box stall during the test period, she should be put in it a few weeks in advance of calving, so she will become used to her surroundings. The cow should be in the proper condition for freshening about 2 weeks before calving, because it may be necessary to reduce the concentrate allowance considerably to prevent extreme congestion of the udder.

Some congestion is normal with cows of high productive capacity that are well fitted. However, the udder must not be allowed to become caked and hard. If this occurs, the cow must be fed scantily for a time after she freshens. This will result in her using up her body reserve of fat very rapidly. Rubbing the udder twice daily with a mixture of one-half cod-liver oil and one-half ethyl alcohol will do much to prevent undue congestion and to keep the udder soft.

Many breeders discontinue feeding the regular fitting concentrate mixture 10 days to 2 weeks before calving and give instead a "cooling ration." However, no change in the mixture is necessary if the cow is not constipated. It is essential that her bowels be in a laxative condition before calving. A warm bran mash is an excellent mild laxative; if necessary, the cow should be given a dose of mineral oil or Epsom salts.

Those who prefer to use a special "cooling ration" before calving feed such a mixture as 2 parts wheat bran, 2 parts ground oats, and 1 part linseed meal. For a day or so before calving, some breeders even feed no concentrates except a bran mash, or a warm mash made of equal parts of bran and whole oats.

The care of a test cow at calving time is little different from that for any other cow. (**925**) The danger from milk fever is greater, however, and preventive measures should be taken at the first signs of its appearance. The calf should be removed after it has had one feeding. In the Cornell University herd all cows in the dairy herd receive a subcutaneous injection of pituitrin after calving. This hastens the complete contraction of the uterus and greatly reduces the danger of metritis, or inflammation of the uterus. If metritis occurs, it can take off in a few days all the bloom and condition that has been put on the cow during the entire dry period.

940. Getting the test cow on feed.—The cow must be gotten on feed as quickly as possible, but extreme care must be used not to force her too fast. For several days after calving the cow should be fed the same concentrate mixture used during the dry period (the so-called "fitting ration"). Only a very small amount of the mixture should be fed during the first 24 hours after calving. At each feeding 1 lb. of the mixture may be sprinkled over an allowance of soaked beet pulp.

The amount to be fed after this must be determined by the condition of the udder and by the cow's appetite. If the cow has been properly fed and cared for during the latter part of the dry period and if her udder is in good, pliable condition, 6 to 8 lbs. a day of the fitting ration may be fed during the second to the fifth day. On the other hand, if the udder is badly congested, but little of the fitting ration can be fed until the congestion is over. Though this extremely scanty feeding of concentrates is necessary under these conditions, it is undesirable from the standpoint of a high record. During this time the cow will not get nearly enough feed to cover her nutrient requirements, and therefore must draw heavily on the fat she has stored during the dry period.

After the fifth day, if the cow has a good appetite and her udder is in satisfactory condition, the concentrate allowance should be gradually increased by adding a small amount of the concentrate mixture which is to be fed throughout the lactation period (the so-called "test ration"). The increase must be made very gradually, a good plan being to increase the amount at the rate of 0.1 lb. per feed until full feed is reached. When the cow is on full feed, the fitting ration is then gradually replaced by the test ration.

At the first sign of a dull appetite, no further increase should be made until the cow seems ready to handle more feed. Concentrates should never be left before a cow hoping she will eat the remainder. If she needs the feed, she will eat it at once. In case the cow does not show an eager appetite, most experienced feeders of test cows advise reducing the concentrates for one or two feeds to allow her to become hungry.

Only a good herdsman can decide when a cow is actually on full feed. The object should be always to feed no more concentrates than are needed for maximum production. Forced feeding is a foolish practice. By crowding them on rich feeds beyond the safety point in an attempt to secure a little higher production, many valuable animals have unfortunately been sacrificed. In such cases they have failed to breed afterwards, their udders have been spoiled, or their digestive systems have been injured.

The upper limit of the concentrate allowance should be about 25 lbs. per head daily, not including soaked beet pulp which is often fed in addition, as is mentioned later. It is best not to feed first-calf heifers more than 15 lbs. per head daily of the concentrate mixture.

941. Necessity of liberal feeding.—When maximum yields are desired from cows on test, they must be fed even greater amounts of nutrients than are recommended in the feeding standards. This is well shown in tests by Woodward of the United States Department of Agriculture.[7] In these experiments the records of cows on official test were compared with the records of the same animals made under the usual system of feeding and care for cows not on test.

When on official test the cows were full fed on concentrates, with a large quantity of alfalfa hay, a small amount of silage, and soaked beet pulp in addition. They consumed somewhat more nutrients than were required according to feeding standards for the amount of milk and fat they yielded. While on test the cows were milked 3 times a day, they were kept in box stalls, and they were bred to freshen about 15 months from the previous date of calving.

Because of the liberality of feeding and the other conditions favorable for a maximum yield, the cows yielded approximately 50 per cent more milk than during other lactation periods when they were fed according to usual good dairy practice. When not on test, the cows received fully as great an amount of nutrients as advised in the feeding standards for the amount of milk they yielded. They were kept in stanchions, were milked twice a day, and were bred to freshen about 12 months from the date of previous calving.

In addition to showing the necessity of liberal feeding and the best of care when maximum records are desired, these experiments emphasize the difference between records of production under such test conditions and records under ordinary herd conditions. As Woodward concludes, "A 400-pound record under herd conditions is equal to 600 lbs. under test conditions."

942. Rations for test cows.—The "test rations," or concentrate mixtures, used by various breeders for test cows differ widely, but nearly all have certain general characteristics. They are usually made up of a considerable variety of palatable feeds; they include a goodly proportion of such bulky feeds as wheat bran, ground oats, distillers' corn dried grains, and dried beet pulp, and in addition a sufficient amount of protein-rich feeds, such as linseed meal, soybean oil meal, cottonseed meal, coconut oil meal, distillers' corn dried grains, and gluten meal or gluten feed.

When the cows are fed a liberal amount of legume hay or of mixed hay high in legumes, it is advisable to use a concentrate mixture that contains about 16 to 18 per cent protein. If a mixture is used which is considerably higher than this in protein, a large excess of protein will be furnished, which will throw an increased load on the kidneys. When little or no legume hay is fed, the concentrate mixture should have 19 to 20 per cent protein.

In order to provide plenty of fat for maximum production, the concentrate mixture should contain at least 5 per cent of fat. (801) Since certain feeds may have a slight effect in increasing the fat content of milk, it is a good plan to include one or more of these feeds in the test mixture. Such feeds are coconut oil meal, soybeans, and palm-kernel oil meal. (832)

A concentrate mixture that has given excellent results when used with legume hay in the Cornell University herd is: 400 lbs. ground corn or hominy feed, 370 lbs. ground oats, 400 lbs. wheat bran, 300 lbs. distillers' corn dried grains, 300 lbs. coconut oil meal (old process), 200 lbs. linseed meal, 10 lbs. salt, and 20 lbs. steamed bone meal. This mixture contains about 18.5 per cent protein.

A concentrate mixture containing about 20 per cent protein, which is recommended by Bender of the New Jersey Station is as follows: 600 lbs. ground corn or hominy feed, 400 lbs. ground oats, 300 lbs. wheat bran, 250 lbs. linseed meal, 150 lbs. corn gluten meal, 150 lbs. cottonseed meal, and 150 lbs. brewers' dried grains.[8] To each ton of the mixture are added 20 lbs. ground limestone, 20 lbs. steamed bone meal, and 20 lbs. salt.

A concentrate mixture containing about 19 per cent protein, which is recommended by Nevens of the Illinois Station, is: 560 lbs. ground corn, 200 lbs. ground oats, 200 lbs. wheat bran, 200 lbs. dried beet pulp, 400 lbs. linseed meal, 200 lbs. corn gluten feed, 200 lbs. cottonseed meal, 20 lbs. steamed bone meal, and 20 lbs. salt.[9]

The considerable difference in these formulas well shows that no one concentrate mixture is preferable to all others. In these mixtures ground barley or other grain may be substituted for part or all of the corn.

A test cow should be supplied with as much well-cured hay as she will eat, for this is the best insurance that she will receive a plentiful supply of vitamins A and D. Legume hay or mixed hay high in legumes is much preferable to grass hay. If the latter is used, it should be early-cut and of good green color. First-cutting alfalfa hay is satisfactory, if it is well cured, and may even be preferable to second-cutting or third-cutting hay, which is sometimes too laxative. Second-cutting mixed hay, high in clover or alfalfa, is excellent.

Opinions differ concerning the feeding of silage to test cows. When silage is fed, the allowance should be limited to 20 or 25 lbs. per head daily. If test cows are provided all the silage they will eat, they will consume so much of this bulky feed that they will not be able to eat as much concentrates as needed for maximum production.

Many experienced feeders of test cows prefer to use soaked beet pulp as a succulent feed instead of silage. The allowance is usually about 5 or 6 lbs. of dried beet pulp per head daily for cows of the smaller breeds and up to 9 or 10 lbs. for Holsteins. The dried beet pulp is soaked from one feeding time to the next in twice its weight of water or of water to which a little cane molasses has been added. A good way to feed the beet pulp is to put the weighed allowance in a water-tight bushel measure and then pour on enough water to cover it. The beet pulp is allowed to soak until the next feeding time, when the allowance of concentrates is mixed with the soaked pulp.

Some years ago the feeding of sliced mangels or sugar beets to test cows was a common practice in the United States. There is no doubt that roots are an excellent feed for test cows, but it has been found that just as good results can be secured when dried beet pulp is fed. As roots are not an economical feed for stock in most sections of this country, they are now used much less frequently for feeding cows on test. (**470–472**)

In summer, test cows should, if possible, be turned out on good pasture each day, but they should not be kept on pasture for so long a period that they will fail to eat the desired amount of concentrates. When they are started on pasture at the beginning of the season, they should not be left on the pasture more than an hour the first day, for too large an amount of the green feed will be unduly laxative. The feeding of hay should be continued throughout the pasture season, to avoid an over-laxative condition.

Test cows are generally fed concentrates as many times a day as they are milked. When soaked beet pulp is fed, it is a good plan to mix it with the concentrate allowance, so as to moisten the latter. This seems to make the concentrates a trifle more palatable.

If the cows are in box stalls, the hay may be kept before them at all times in racks. Before each new supply of hay is put in the rack, any waste should be removed.

943. General problems.—It is advisable to have cows freshen in the fall when they are to be placed on test, for their production will usually then be appreciably greater than if they freshen at another period of the year. (**835**) A cow that calves in the fall produces most of her milk during the cooler part of the year when her appetite is best and when she does not suffer from heat or flies. Also, the percentage of fat in milk is slightly higher during cool weather than in summer. (**834**)

Where maximum records are desired, Holstein cows on test are usually milked 4 times a day and cows of the other breeds at least 3 times a day. (**826**) Box stalls should be provided for test cows when maximum records are desired, for this slightly increases the yield that can be obtained. (**914**)

During the winter, test cows should be turned out for exercise about an hour a day when the weather is good. Exercise aids in keeping the cows healthy and in developing a keen appetite. Also it keeps their legs in condition and prevents their hoofs from growing too long. In extremely cold weather the time they are outdoors should be reduced to one-half hour, and they should not be turned out during storms.

At all times cows should have comfortable quarters and regular care and attention, always by the same herdsman, if possible. The stable should be kept free from flies during the summer. It must always be borne in mind that only when a test cow is comfortable, contented, and in the best of health will she respond with continued production of the maximum yield of which she is capable.

There is much difference of opinion as to whether or not the useful life of a dairy cow is shortened by feeding her all the concentrates she will consume, in an effort to secure maximum production while she is on official test. Without much question, many cows have been injured and their future usefulness even destroyed by injudicious crowding when on test. On the other hand, by following such methods as have previously been described, experienced herdsmen are usually able to feed cows so as to secure very high records of production without apparent injury.

In this connection studies by Eckles of the records in the dairy herd at the Minnesota Station over a 29-year period are of interest.[10] In this herd there was no marked increase in breeding troubles in the case of cows having high records of production. Of 37 cows with records of over 600 lbs. of butter fat, only 2 became non-breeders.

QUESTIONS

1. Discuss the various items of cost in producing milk, stating the 7 classifications into which the expenses are commonly grouped.
2. Estimate the approximate cost of producing milk in your locality according to a formula, and using local prices for feeds and for man labor.
3. Discuss the effect of season of year on cost of milk production.
4. State 7 important factors in reducing the cost of milk production.

5. What is the advantage of a 305-day official record of production over a 365-day record?

6. Why is the herd-test of testing cows becoming more popular?

7. Discuss the fitting of cows for official test.

8. In what respects do the feeding and care of a test cow before and after calving differ from the feed and care of other cows at this time?

9. State a good method of getting a test cow on feed.

10. Describe the feeding of cows on test, considering (a) concentrate mixture; (b) dry roughage; (c) succulent feed; (d) pasture.

11. Discuss the following points in running cows on official test: (a) Best time of year for freshening; (b) number of times cows are milked a day; (c) exercise; (d) importance of comfort and regular care.

REFERENCES

1. Williamson, Hertel, Hughes, Efferson, and Hedlund, N. Y. (Cornell) Sta., mimeo. rpt.; Wright, Mich. Quar. Bul. 17, 1934, No. 1; Eastman, N. H. Bul. 260; Stephens, Okla. Bul. 208; Selby, Burrier, and Brandt, Ore. Bul. 318.
2. King, The Price of Milk, p. 121; Misner, N. Y. (Cornell) Sta., Farm Economics, No. 42, Feb. 1927; Pearson, Ill. Bul. 216.
3. Pearson, Ill. Buls. 216, 224.
4. Ezekiel, McNall, and Morrison, Wis. Res. Bul. 79; see also: Pond and Ezekiel, Minn. Bul. 270; Misner, N. Y. (Cornell) Memoir 64.
5. Woodworth, Harris, and Rauchenstein, N. H. Bul. 275.
6. Harrison, N. Y. (Cornell) Station, mimeo. rpt.; see also: Savage and Maynard, Better Dairy Farming, pp. 49-60; Larson, Putney, and Henderson, Dairy Cattle Feeding and Management, pp. 113-124; Eckles, Dairy Cattle and Milk Production, pp. 490-495.
7. Woodward, Jour. Dairy Sci., 10, 1927, pp. 283-291; see also: Converse, Jour. Dairy Sci., 9, 1926, pp. 388-406.
8. Bender, N. J. Cir. 302.
9. Nevens, Ill. Cir. 372.
10. Eckles, Minn. Bul. 258.

CHAPTER XXVIII

RAISING DAIRY CATTLE

I. Nutrients Required for Growth of Dairy Cattle

944. Importance of raising good heifers.—It has already been emphasized that the most important single factor in determining the financial outcome from a dairy herd is the productive capacity of the individual cows. (785) The most certain method of developing a high-yielding herd is by replacing the poor producers with well-bred, home-raised heifers of greater productive capacity. Such heifers should be from the best cows in the herd; they should be sired by a purebred bull which has been selected for ability to transmit high production; and they must be so raised that they will have a large capacity for converting feed into milk.

The dairyman who follows the opposite plan of purchasing his replacements will often be badly disappointed, even if he is careful to buy only heifers or cows whose appearance is promising. The farmer from whom he buys will naturally desire to retain for his own herd the heifers out of his very best cows. In addition to the difficulty of buying animals that will prove profitable, there is also much more danger of introducing disease when the replacements for the milking herd are continually purchased.

945. Nutrient requirements.—Before discussing the various rations suitable for raising dairy cattle, we should have clearly in mind the nutrient requirements for growth, which have been considered in Chapter VII. (201-216) In raising dairy cattle especial attention must be given to providing: (1) Plenty of protein; (2) protein of satisfactory quality; (3) enough total digestible nutrients to permit normal growth; (4) sufficient minerals, especially calcium, phosphorus, and common salt; and (5) liberal amounts of vitamins. These requirements are discussed in detail on the following pages.

In the revised Morrison feeding standards, given in Appendix Table III, recommendations are made concerning the amounts of dry matter, digestible protein, and total digestible nutrients that should be supplied young dairy cattle at various stages of growth. These recommendations are based on the results of the experiments that have been conducted, especially by American experiment stations, to determine the nutrients needed for the normal growth and development of young dairy cattle.

946. Amount of protein required.—In common with other young animals, calves require a relatively large proportion of protein in their rations to provide the material needed for the rapid growth of the protein tissues of the body. The proportion of protein needed becomes less as the animal becomes older, because less of the gain in weight then consists of protein.

590

Investigations at several experiment stations have shown that young dairy cattle after the age of 6 months require considerably less protein for normal growth than was recommended in the Wolff-Lehmann and the Armsby feeding standards.[1] But little definite information is available concerning the minimum amounts of protein required by calves under 6 months of age.

The results of the various studies on the protein requirements for growing dairy cattle have been taken fully into consideration in the recommendations made in the revised Morrison feeding standards, presented in Appendix Table III. It will be noted that while the narrow nutritive ratio of 1:3.9 to 1:4.5 is recommended for calves 100 lbs. in weight, the nutritive ratio advised becomes wider as the animals grow older, reaching 1:8.0 to 1:8.4 for cattle weighing 1,000 lbs.

947. Quality of protein.—Milk provides the best possible kind of protein for calves, and, furthermore, protein that makes good the deficiencies in the proteins of the cereal grains. Therefore, when calves are fed a normal amount of whole milk or skimmilk until 4 to 6 months of age, no special attention need be given to the quality of the protein furnished by the rest of the ration. As is pointed out later, an excellent ration for calves after 3 to 4 weeks of age is skimmilk plus plenty of cereal grain and good legume hay.

In raising calves on calf meals or "calf starters," which are substitutes for whole milk or fluid skimmilk, the quality of protein is of great importance until they are 3 to 4 months of age. After this, if they are fed sufficient legume hay, satisfactory quality of protein is provided by a combination of such hay with the cereal grains and the common protein-rich feeds of plant origin, such as wheat bran, wheat middlings, linseed meal, cottonseed meal, soybeans, etc. Up to this age, a considerable part of the protein in the concentrate mixture should come from an animal by-product, such as dried skimmilk or buttermilk, dried blood, or fish meal, and at least some of it should preferably come from a milk by-product.

When calves are raised on whey, which is relatively low in protein, care must be taken to provide plenty of protein in the concentrate mixture, but it is not necessary that any of this protein be of animal origin. This is because the small amount of protein in whey is particularly well suited to make good the deficiencies in the proteins of the grains and the common protein supplements of plant origin. Suitable concentrate mixtures for use in the various methods of raising calves are given later in this chapter.

948. Total digestible nutrients required.—Since the digestive tract of a young calf has not yet developed so that it can digest hay or other roughage it must be fed chiefly on milk and on concentrates high in digestible nutrients and low in fiber. As the calf grows older, it can utilize more and more roughage, until after 10 months of age the ration may even consist entirely of roughage, if it is of excellent quality.

The amounts of total digestible nutrients advised in the revised Morrison feeding standards for young dairy cattle at various stages of growth are based on investigations conducted at several experiment stations, especially at the Minnesota and Missouri Stations.[2] It will be noted that the amount of total digestible nutrients required per head daily increases gradually from 1.5 to 2.2 lbs. at 100 lbs. live weight up to 11.4 to 12.6 lbs. at 1,000 lbs. live weight.

949. Mineral requirements.—If growing dairy cattle are fed rations that are otherwise adequate and satisfactory, there will commonly be no deficiency of mineral nutrients, except of common salt, which should always be supplied. As soon as calves begin to eat grain, salt should be provided where they can have access to it and take what they wish. Under certain conditions there may also be a lack of calcium or of phosphorus. The importance of these minerals is discussed in detail on the following pages.

Iodine is furnished in ample amounts by the ordinary rations fed growing dairy cattle in most districts.[3] If any calves at birth show evidence of goiter, or "big neck," this should be prevented in the future by the use of iodine, as previously explained. (**172**) The use of iodized stock salt is a good means of preventing this trouble in iodine-deficient areas, and of supplying iodine to calves showing a tendency to have goiters.

The addition to the ration of Manamar (a commercial preparation composed of dried kelp, fish meal, and calcium carbonate, which is rich in iodine and certain other minerals) has not produced any significant benefit in New Jersey and Ohio tests.[4]

Milk is very low in *iron* and *copper*. However, when calves are raised according to any of the ordinary methods and given concentrates and hay to eat as soon as they desire these feeds, iron and copper will be adequately supplied.[5] (**173**)

Magnesium is provided amply by all normal rations for calves. Contrary to earlier opinions, feeding a ration high in magnesium to calves in Michigan and Minnesota experiments did not interfere with the building of calcium into the skeleton, nor did it prevent the cure of rickets when plenty of calcium, phosphorus, and vitamin D were provided.[6]

950. Calcium and phosphorus.—The necessity of ample supplies of calcium, phosphorus, and vitamin D for the formation of bones by growing animals has been explained in Chapter VI. (**159-163**) If there is a deficiency of one or more of these essentials, rickets or other serious nutritional trouble will result.

Milk is rich in both calcium and phosphorus, and therefore there will be no lack of these minerals during the period when calves are fed normal amounts of whole milk or skimmilk. Since legume hay is always high in calcium, calves will get plenty of it if they are fed the usual amounts of legume hay, or even of mixed hay containing a considerable proportion of legumes. Also, there will generally be no lack of calcium when young dairy cattle are on pasture, even on pasture consisting only of grasses, unless the soil is unusually low in this mineral. If there seems to be any danger of a lack of calcium, it may be readily furnished in the manner stated in Chapter VI. (**165, 181**)

There will be no deficiency of phosphorus, after calves are weaned from milk, if they are fed 2 to 3 lbs. per head daily of a concentrate mixture containing 10 to 20 per cent of such protein supplements as wheat bran, wheat middlings, linseed meal, or cottonseed meal, which are rich not only in protein, but also in phosphorus. When growing cattle are fed only cereal grains and legume or other hay, with or without corn or sorghum silage, there may be a serious lack of phosphorus if the soil on which the roughage is grown is deficient in this mineral.[7] In all such cases bone meal or some other safe phosphorus supplement should be provided, as previously advised. (166-171, 181) Whether or not there will be any benefit from adding a phosphorus supplement to a ration for growing dairy cattle will depend entirely on the actual phosphorus content of that particular ration.[8]

Experiments at the Michigan and Massachusetts Stations show that the rations for dairy heifers should contain at least 10 grams (0.35 ounce) of phosphorus per head daily up to the time of first calving.[9] During milk production the supply must be much larger than this. (812) This amount of phosphorus is the minimum that should be supplied when heifers are fed plenty of sun-cured hay and when they are turned outside daily where they are exposed to sunlight, thus receiving plenty of vitamin D. (191-192) Under less favorable conditions it is wise to furnish more phosphorus than this minimum amount.

In Michigan experiments good growth and normal bone development were obtained when dairy heifers were fed a ration supplying only 6 to 12 grams of calcium per head daily from birth to about 2 years of age.[10] However, it was concluded from Massachusetts investigations that heifers should receive about 20 grams of calcium per head daily for the first year and somewhat more during the second year.[11] Since bone contains a much greater amount of calcium than of phosphorus, it would seem wise, as a policy of safety, to supply somewhat more calcium than of phosphorus in the ration.

So long as sufficient calcium and phosphorus are provided, the proportion between the amounts of these minerals (the calcium-phosphorus ratio) can differ considerably, without producing any detrimental results. (162)

951. Vitamin requirements.—Vitamins A and D are of great importance in raising dairy cattle, for they often suffer from deficiencies of these vitamins. As is shown later, there is no lack of the other vitamins in the rations ordinarily fed to young cattle.

Calves will receive sufficient vitamin A during the whole-milk period if they are fed milk from cows on normal rations, containing a reasonable amount of well-cured hay or other roughage high in vitamin A value (carotene content). (187-189) Later, when the calves are eating roughage, there will be no lack of vitamin A if they are fed good legume hay or even mixed hay containing one-third or more of legumes. Even when calves are changed from whole milk to skim-milk or milk substitutes at the usual ages for making such changes, vitamin A will not be deficient if they are encouraged to eat well-cured legume hay or mixed hay high in legumes as soon as they normally will take it.

It is essential that growing dairy cattle get plenty of this vitamin, for a lack of it will produce disaster, even in animals 1 to 2 years old.[12] It has been shown previously that when cows have been fed poor-quality timothy hay, deficient in vitamin A, as the only roughage for long periods, the milk has contained but little vitamin A. As a result it was impossible to raise calves on the milk, without some other source of vitamin A, when they were changed from whole milk to skimmilk at the usual time. (**189**)

An ample supply of vitamin D is necessary in raising calves, for a lack of it will cause serious trouble from rickets.[13] The symptoms of this nutritional disease have previously been described. (**163, 190**) Sometimes calves that have been making excellent growth develop mild cases of rickets, showing especially the characteristic sag in the back, just behind the shoulders. Such animals are growing rapidly in skeleton and therefore need especially liberal amounts of vitamin D.

Good-quality hay which has been cured in the sun, especially legume hay or mixed hay high in legumes, is the best safeguard against a lack of vitamin D in raising dairy cattle. Since whole milk is not rich in this vitamin, even a liberal amount of it may not furnish enough to protect calves against rickets. Fortunately, calves will begin to eat hay at 2 to 3 weeks of age and if then supplied with good hay, they will soon eat sufficient to furnish the needed amount of the vitamin.

Michigan experiments indicate that even 2 lbs. per head daily of sun-cured alfalfa or grass hay will furnish sufficient vitamin D for young calves, but that later more should be provided.

Direct sunlight which has not passed through ordinary window glass has an anti-rachitic effect, due to the ultra-violet light in it. Exposure to direct sunlight in spring, summer, and fall will prevent rickets in calves, if they are receiving sufficient calcium and phosphorus. Winter sunlight in the northern states does not have enough anti-rachitic power to prevent the trouble, unless calves are getting some vitamin D in their ration. If calves are supplied with sufficient good-quality, sun-cured hay, they will seldom suffer from rickets, even during the winter, when they may not be turned out of doors at all. Indeed, calves and heifers have made entirely normal growth in experiments where they were never exposed to sunlight, but were fed plenty of good legume hay.[14]

When calves are fed the usual type of satisfactory ration, including plenty of good hay, there is no need to add a vitamin A or D supplement, such as cod-liver oil, or a vitamin concentrate.[15] Such an addition is not even necessary when a calf meal is fed in place of milk, if care is taken to get the calves to eat high-quality legume hay as early as possible.[16] In case there has been any trouble from rickets, it is wise to add 0.25 per cent of a cod-liver oil concentrate or 0.5 per cent of cod-liver oil to the calf meal as an insurance against further trouble.

There is usually no lack of *vitamins B and G* in raising dairy calves and heifers. Most rations contain considerable of these vitamins. Furthermore, at least in certain instances these vitamins can apparently be synthesized in the paunch of ruminants. (**196**) Calves have been raised successfully on rations so deficient in the vitamin B complex that rats would die on the same rations in a few weeks.[17]

The addition of *yeast* to normal rations of whole milk or skimmilk, grain, and hay has not produced any beneficial effect in feeding dairy calves.[18]

Vitamin C is of no importance in the raising of dairy cattle. Calves have grown normally for a year on a ration so deficient in this vitamin that it would produce scurvy in guinea pigs within a month.[19] (**199**)

HEIFER CALVES FROM SUCH COWS BUILD UP THE HERD

A dairyman who raises no heifer calves, but replenishes his herd by buying cows, can only with great difficulty keep up a high average of production.

THRIFTY, PROMISING HEIFERS RAISED ON SKIM MILK

With proper feeding and care, skim milk calves develop into just as good cows as those fed whole milk until weaning time. When calves have plenty of skim milk, they need little or no purchased protein-rich concentrates.

HEIFERS NEED CONCENTRATES TO MAKE GOOD GROWTH

Many heifers are permanently stunted and never develop their maximum productive capacity on account of insufficient feed or an unbalanced ration.

SAFETY BULL PEN WITH BREEDING CHUTE AND BREEDING RACK

This bull pen is equipped with a breeding chute and a breeding rack at the right, next to the shed, so that it is not necessary to handle the bull at time of service. The bull can exercise at will in the strongly-fenced pen. Note the steel oil drum in the pen near the corner. The bull plays with this and bunts it about, thus getting more exercise. (From Goodman, New York State College of Agriculture, Cornell University.)

There is no lack of *vitamin E* in normal rations for dairy calves and heifers, so far as is known. (**200**)

952. Importance of water.—Calves over 8 weeks of age should have plenty of fresh water at least twice a day, even when they are fed normal amounts of milk. Up to 8 weeks of age, they will drink but little water if they have a liberal amount of milk, and there is then probably little advantage from supplying water in addition during this period. After this, they will drink rapidly-increasing amounts of water, and should be furnished it.

In Idaho trials calves fed 12 to 16 lbs. of skimmilk a day to 6 months of age drank the following amounts of water per day: At 4 weeks of age, 0.07 lb.; 6 weeks, 0.5 lb.; 8 weeks, 2.2 lbs.; 10 weeks, 4.3 lbs.; 12 weeks, 6.6 lbs.; 16 weeks, 12.9 lbs.; 20 weeks, 18.0 lbs.; and 26 weeks, 33.4 lbs.[20] It is especially important to provide plenty of water when calves are raised on a minimum of milk or on dry calf meals.

The importance of supplying water even when calves receive a fairly liberal amount of milk is shown by Wisconsin trials in which calves were fed not to exceed 14 lbs. skimmilk per head daily to 6 months of age.[21] Calves supplied with water twice daily gained an average of 1.80 lbs., while others given no water gained only 1.36 lbs. Up to 6 months of age the calves supplied with water drank an average of 2,535 lbs. water. Calves fed no skimmilk, but only 400 lbs. of whole milk, with a concentrate mixture fed dry and clover hay, drank an average of 4,897 lbs. water up to 6 months of age.

II. RAISING DAIRY CALVES

953. The new-born calf.—The care of the cow at calving time and the care of the new-born calf have been considered in a previous chapter. (**925**) A new-born calf is very sensitive to the treatment it receives and has but little resistance to certain diseases. Great care is therefore necessary to prevent infections, as has been emphasized in the previous discussion. The calf should always be protected from drafts and from cold and dampness, and the navel should be disinfected with tincture of iodine soon after birth.

When a calf does not begin breathing promptly after birth, any mucus or membrane should be removed from its nostrils, and attempts should be made to start respiration by slapping the chest vigorously or by alternately compressing and relaxing it. If the cow's udder is soiled, it should be washed with soap and water and dried with a clean cloth before the calf nurses. The calf should nurse within an hour after birth, and if it is weak and fails to nurse, it should be helped patiently to get its first meal.

It is very important that the calf get one and preferably more feeds of the first milk, or colostrum. As has been shown in a previous chapter, this protects the new-born young against certain diseases, especially of the digestive system. (**210**) Missouri experiments show that if for any reason a calf cannot receive colostrum milk, an egg-white emulsion may be used as a substitute.[22] This is prepared by mixing the whites of 6 eggs with fresh cow's milk for the first feeding. For the following feedings, one less egg is used each time.

954. Starting the calf on whole milk.—No matter what method of feeding is followed later, a calf should receive whole milk in normal amounts for at least 2 weeks, and preferably for 3 or 4 weeks or more if it is especially valuable or if it is not strong. For very young calves there is no satisfactory substitute for milk. This is because of the special virtues of milk as a food for young animals, which have been previously discussed. (207) When calf meals are substituted for milk at too early an age, the calf is unable to digest its food thoroughly, and digestive disturbances and scours usually follow.[23] The digestive organs develop rapidly, however, and at 2 to 3 months of age the paunch has developed so that the calf can get a considerable part of its nutrients from ordinary concentrates and hay.[24]

Except when calves are raised on nurse cows, a method which is discussed later, a calf is usually not allowed to remain with its dam more than 2 to 4 days. During this time the milk is not fit for human use on account of the colostrum characteristics. For the reasons stated previously, it is probably the best plan to separate the calf from the cow about 24 hours after birth. (925)

Genuine hunger is a great aid in teaching a calf to drink, and therefore the first lesson had better be postponed until 12 to 18 hours after it is separated from its dam. One should be patient with the calf and remember that its instinct is to seek its food at a level above its nose and not down in a pail, and also that it frequently bunts the udder of its dam while nursing, thus massaging it. The calf cannot be blamed if it follows these instincts for a time.

After putting a quart of fresh, warm milk in a clean pail, one is ready for the first lesson. A common method is to back the calf into a corner and stand astride it to hold it fast. Then hold the pail in one hand, dip the fingers of the other in the milk, and while the calf is sucking the fingers, bring its nose down into the milk. Then gradually withdraw the fingers, holding them at the end of the nose for a little while. Above all, use patience in repeating the process as needed.

The calf pails in which milk is fed must be kept scrupulously clean and should be sterilized, if possible. A good rule is to cleanse them as thoroughly as the milk pails. Sometimes calf-feeding devices are used, in which the calf sucks the milk through an attached nipple. Especial care is necessary in keeping such equipment sanitary.

The young calf should be fed sparingly, for there is much more danger of overfeeding the first few days than of underfeeding. For the first day or two 5 or 6 lbs. of milk daily is a safe allowance for an average calf, with 8 lbs. as a maximum for a large, lusty one. This allowance should be divided between 2 or 3 feedings and the amount of each should be measured or weighed and not estimated. The milk should be fed as fresh as possible and at a temperature of 90° to 100° F., determined by a thermometer, instead of guessing at it. Feeding 3 times a day is slightly better for the calf during the first week or so and is advisable if the cows are milked thrice daily. If they are milked only twice a day, most dairymen consider that there is not enough benefit from feeding the calves at noon to warrant the trouble of warming the milk.

If possible, it is a good plan to feed the calf milk from its dam for the first few days, unless the milk is very high in fat. In this case it may be wise to use milk from a low-testing cow for a week or two, or else to add warm skimmilk or water to lower the fat percentage. In recent Iowa tests there was, however, no apparent difference in the rate of digestion of milk containing 3 per cent fat and of that having 6 per cent fat.[25]

The allowance of milk should be gradually increased as the calf grows older, if it is thriving. Overfeeding, the cause of much trouble in calf rearing, should be avoided at all times. A safe plan is to keep the calf a little hungry. A good rule to follow is to feed whole milk at the rate of 1 lb. daily per 10 lbs. live weight. Weak or sickly calves should be fed even less, and the allowance should not usually exceed 12 lbs., even for a large and vigorous calf. In case of indigestion or scours, the allowance should immediately be cut in half until the calf recovers.

Especially with Guernsey or Jersey milk, some advise adding one-half pint of limewater to each feeding of milk until the calf is 3 or 4 weeks old. This helps prevent the formation of hard curd that cannot be readily digested.

Hand-reared calves should be confined in stanchions for a time after the milk is drunk, until they consume their concentrate allowance and overcome the desire to suck each other's ears or udders. When this precaution is neglected, the shape of the udder may be injured or a heifer may later persist in sucking herself or other cows.

955. Precautions in rearing calves.—In addition to suitable feed intelligently supplied, attention to the following points is necessary for success in rearing calves: The stable should be well ventilated and lighted, and reasonably warm in winter. Cold drafts must be avoided. The stalls must be kept clean and should be well bedded. In all cases the calves should be fed at regular intervals and any increase or change in the feed should be made gradually. Water and salt should always be supplied. In summer shade should be provided for calves on pasture. The feeder should watch for any signs of scours and at once take suitable measures to overcome the trouble. If necessary, the calves should be treated for lice or ringworm.

956. Various methods of raising calves.—When it is desired to raise dairy calves so they will make maximum growth, regardless of expense, there is no better method than to continue the feeding of a considerable amount of whole milk for 6 months or longer. On account of the expense involved, however, relatively few dairy calves are raised by this method, except when they are reared by the "nurse-cow method." After calves have a good start on whole milk, they may be raised successfully by several different methods. When skimmilk is available, the calves are usually changed to this by-product at 2 to 4 weeks of age. Whey and buttermilk are also satisfactory substitutes for whole milk, if properly fed. Dried skimmilk, dried buttermilk, or semi-solid buttermilk may be diluted with water to the same concentration as skimmilk or buttermilk and fed in this form as a milk substitute. Another method is to raise the calves on a minimum amount of whole milk, weaning them at 7 to 9 weeks of age, or even earlier, and then feeding them only a dry calf meal, or "calf starter," and hay.

Still another method is to wean them at an early age and then feed them a calf meal in gruel form as a milk substitute. These various methods of raising calves are all discussed in later paragraps of this chapter.

957. Feeding grain and other concentrates.—When the calf is 1 to 2 weeks old, it should be taught to eat concentrates. Though certain mixtures are especially popular for feeding young calves, almost any mixture of the farm grains is satisfactory, or even a single grain, or else a simple mixture, such as a combination of grain and wheat bran or linseed meal or with both these feeds. As long as the calf gets plenty of whole milk, skimmilk, or buttermilk, it will receive sufficient protein in the milk, and it is not necessary to feed a large proportion of a protein supplement. Adding a small amount of such a feed as wheat bran or linseed meal to grain will usually make the mixture more palatable to calves, and therefore may be advisable, merely from this standpoint.

Such mixtures as the following are excellent in teaching calves to eat concentrates:

(1) Corn, 30 lbs.; oats, 30 lbs.; wheat bran, 10 lbs.; linseed meal, 10 lbs.

(2) Corn, 40 lbs.; oats, 30 lbs.; wheat bran, 20 lbs.; linseed meal, 10 lbs.

(3) Equal weights of corn or barley and of oats or wheat bran.

(4) Corn, 30 lbs.; wheat bran, 10 lbs.

(5) Corn, 30 lbs.; linseed meal, 5 lbs.

(6) Corn, 40 lbs.; wheat bran, 10 lbs.; linseed meal, 10 lbs.

Whole or ground oats are also often used as the only concentrate. In these mixtures other grains may be substituted for the corn and oats. These mixtures all provide sufficient protein for calves raised on plenty of milk (whole milk, skimmilk, or buttermilk). If the amount of milk is limited and especially if calves are weaned at an early age and raised on concentrates and hay alone, the mixture must contain much more protein. Also, a larger proportion of protein supplements is required when calves are raised on whey. Suitable mixtures to use under these various methods of feeding are stated later in the discussions of these methods.

The calf is taught to eat concentrates by putting a handful or less in the bottom of the pail after it has finished drinking its milk. Some add the concentrates to the milk, but this is inadvisable, as the meal is then often chewed less thoroughly. The calf that is backward may be taught to eat the mixture by rubbing some on its muzzle when it is through drinking milk, or by putting a little in its mouth. After the calf has learned to eat concentrates, the mixture should be fed dry in a suitable feed box or in the manger. Until the calf is 2 to 3 months old, it can be allowed to eat as much of the mixture as it desires, a supply being kept before it in a feed box. Care should be taken to clean the box out regularly.

Calves fed a liberal allowance of skimmilk may be permitted to eat up to 4 lbs. of the concentrate mixture a day, and those raised on a calf meal, up to 5 lbs. a day. If the calves begin to exceed these limits, the proper amount should be hand-fed twice daily, instead of letting them have as much as they will eat. Otherwise, they will fail to consume sufficient roughage, and also the cost will be unduly high.

958. Concentrates for calves.—The *grains* most commonly used for calf feeding are corn, oats, and barley, but the other grains can all be used satisfactorily. It was shown in a Wisconsin trial that white corn is as satisfactory for feeding to calves as yellow corn, if they are fed well-cured, green-colored hay, which is rich in vitamin A.[26]

Calves chew corn or oats thoroughly up to an age of 6 to 8 months and, after they have learned to eat concentrates, show a preference for the whole grain. Therefore, the whole grain gives as good or better results than when ground.[27] When such a mixture as corn and linseed meal is fed, the corn is often ground to prevent the linseed meal from separating out. After calves are 6 to 8 months old, they chew grain less thoroughly, and corn and oats should then be ground. Such hard grains as barley, wheat, and the grain sorghums should always be ground. Coarse grinding is preferable to fine grinding for calves.

Dried beet pulp may be used as a substitute for part of the grain for calves 2 to 3 months old or more. (**644**)

Cane molasses, or *blackstrap molasses,* which is often a cheap feed in the South, is apt to produce scours, if young calves are allowed all the molasses they will eat. However, in Louisiana trials it was found that if calves were fed 1 to 2 ounces of molasses, along with concentrates, at the start and the amount of molasses was then increased only about 2 ounces per head daily each week, there was no trouble from scouring.[28] At the end of 21 weeks the calves were safely fed 2 lbs. of molasses a head daily with an equal weight of concentrates. (**641**)

Wheat bran and *linseed meal* are the most popular protein-rich feeds of plant origin for use in calf feeding, due to their palatability and general nutritive effect. (**539, 591**)

Flour wheat middlings and *standard wheat middlings* are excellent ingredients for calf meals, especially for young calves. *Red dog flour* is often used in mixtures for calves raised on a minimum of milk, on account of its high digestibility. (**543-545**)

Cottonseed meal may be used satisfactorily in a concentrate mixture for calves, if the mixture does not contain more than about 20 per cent of cottonseed meal and if the calves are supplied with good roughage, high in vitamin A. For example, in South Carolina experiments good results were secured with a calf meal consisting of 20 lbs. cottonseed meal, 39 lbs. ground yellow corn, 40 lbs. ground oats, and 1 lb. salt.[29] At least after calves are 3 to 4 months old, they may be fed larger proportions of cottonseed meal with safety. (**583**)

Soybean oil meal is an excellent protein supplement for calves, because of the good quality of the protein and the high digestibility of the feed. (**595**)

Dried skimmilk provides the best possible quality of protein in calf meals for use in raising calves on a minimum amount of milk, but it is often an expensive source of protein. (**622**) Therefore care should be taken not to feed a larger proportion than necessary, and fish meal or soluble blood flour can be used as partial substitutes. As discussed later, calves are often raised on reconstituted skimmilk, made by dissolving dried skimmilk in water. (**966**)

Dried buttermilk is a satisfactory substitute for dried skimmilk, but is apt to be laxative in effect. Therefore in changing calves from whole milk to reconstituted buttermilk, more care is necessary than in the case of skimmilk. (**622**)

Blood meal, or *dried blood,* is often used as an ingredient in calf meals. (**632**) Soluble blood flour, produced at a lower temperature than ordinary blood meal, has been considered preferable, since the protein in the latter is not very well digested by calves.[30] However, in an Ohio test ordinary blood meal was as satisfactory as spray-dried soluble blood flour for use in the New Jersey calf meal mentioned later.[31] (**970**)

Blood meal is usually not palatable to calves at first, and if it is used as the chief protein supplement in a calf meal, special care may be required to get them started on it.

Fish meal is not equal to dried skimmilk as the chief source of protein for young calves but can be used satisfactorily as a partial substitute for it.[32] For example, 5 to 10 per cent of fish meal and 10 per cent of dried skimmilk can be used in place of 20 per cent of dried skimmilk. Fish meal dried at a low temperature supplies vitamin D and therefore should aid in preventing rickets. (**635**)

Meat scraps, or dry-rendered tankage, can also be used as a protein supplement in calf meals. It is best used as a partial substitute for dried skimmilk or dried buttermilk. (**627**)

959. Importance of hay for calves.—Since green-colored, sun-cured hay is the richest source of vitamin D among common feeds and is also high in vitamin A, it is very important that calves have access to good hay as soon as they will eat it. At about 2 weeks of age a handful of such hay should therefore be placed each day where the calf can get it. Little will be eaten at first, but even this may be very important in supplying needed vitamins and thus preventing rickets and other troubles. As the calf grows and its paunch develops, more hay will be eaten, until at 6 months of age it should be eating 3 to 5 lbs. a day. The best way to feed hay is in a slatted rack. All uneaten hay should be removed daily and fed to other stock, for calves do not like hay which has been picked over.

From the standpoint of the amount of protein, calcium, and vitamins A and D supplied, leafy, fine-stemmed legume hay is the best for calves. Sometimes young calves will eat so much of such hay that its laxative nature will cause them to scour. This can be avoided by limiting the amount or by starting them on mixed legume-and-grass hay. There is much unwarranted prejudice against pure legume hay for calves, especially on the part of those who have had little experience in using it. In experiments over 6 years by the author and associates at the Wisconsin Station, calves were allowed access to red clover hay from the start with uniform success, and in later trials were fed alfalfa hay with similar success.[33] Probably many cases of scours have been attributed to the laxative properties of legume hay when some other factor has been responsible.

In general, the leafier the hay is, the higher will be its value for calves. Therefore second-cutting clover or alfalfa hay is preferred to the first cutting. Good-quality soybean hay and cowpea hay are also very satisfactory for calves.[34] Hay from the grasses or cereal hay is inferior to legume hay, for it is much lower in protein, calcium, and vitamins. If it is necessary to use such hay for calves, it should be early-cut and well-cured.

The importance of legume hay in raising dairy cattle is well shown in Arkansas experiments in which dairy heifers were raised on either alfalfa hay or prairie hay as the only roughages, with a concentrate mixture lacking in vitamin A.[35] While satisfactory growth was produced on the prairie-hay ration, when the heifers freshened they were unable to produce a normal amount of milk, and one became sick, even though the ration contained plenty of protein, calcium, and phosphorus. Changing the heifers to alfalfa hay or green grass had a beneficial effect. In contrast to the results on prairie hay, the ration containing alfalfa hay as the only roughage was satisfactory for growth and also for reproduction and lactation.

It is never safe to attempt to raise calves without plenty of good hay or other good roughage. As has been shown earlier, most attempts to raise calves on milk alone or on milk and grain without roughage have ended in failure, and limited success is possible only when special mineral and vitamin supplements are skillfully added to such a ration. (**137, 208**)

Occasionally a calf will show an abnormal appetite and will eat the bedding or will gorge on an undue amount of hay, which may result in a serious digestive disturbance. Fortunately, this rarely happens with healthy calves. Some breeders keep muzzles at hand and if a calf shows such a tendency, they muzzle it for the first month, except at the time it is fed milk and concentrates. The use of muzzles on all calves for the first month has been advocated as a protection against such trouble, but on account of the nutritive benefits that young calves secure from good hay, this practice seems unwise, except perhaps where there have been severe losses from calf diseases.

960. Succulent feeds.—A small amount of good corn or sorghum silage, free from mold and not too acid, may be fed to calves after they are 6 to 8 weeks old,[36] but many prefer not to feed silage until the calves are 4 or 5 months old. The use of silage is not at all necessary in raising good calves, and feeding silage too early may cause more trouble from scours.

Adding silage to a ration including plenty of good hay may increase the rate of gain slightly and is often economical in the corn belt. However, corn or sorghum silage should not be used as a substitute for good hay, since it is not rich in protein or calcium, and since it also does not generally supply as much vitamin A or vitamin D as does well-cured hay. Calves will eat about 2 lbs. of silage per head daily from the second to the third month and gradually increase their consumption until they are taking about 10 lbs. at 6 months of age. Should the calves not be gaining rapidly enough, it may be necessary to reduce the allowance of silage and increase the amount of concentrates and hay.

Roots are a satisfactory succulent feed for calves, but are usually much more expensive than silage.

961. Pasture.—Pasture is excellent for calves old enough to make good use of it. However, if they are pastured at too early an age, there is more trouble from scours, and they may suffer from heat and flies.

Many prefer not to turn calves on pasture until they are 5 to 6 months old but keep them in the stable where they are more sure to receive the proper feed and attention. However, thrifty calves do well on pasture after they are 2 to 4 months old, or even earlier, providing they are accustomed to the green feed gradually, are fed plenty of other feed, and are supplied with shade and shelter, salt, and fresh water.[37] The scrawny, pot-bellied calves one often sees on pasture are usually not a result of the pasturage, but of the lack of milk and grain and of proper daily attention. As has been pointed out previously in this chapter, direct sunlight is an effective aid in preventing or curing rickets, and for this reason during warm weather it is well to let calves over 2 months of age have access to clean outside pens, if they are not on pasture.

962. Raising calves on skimmilk.—Whenever skimmilk is available, the calves should be changed from whole milk to this by-product as soon as they have a good start. Numerous experiments have shown that under proper management skimmilk calves will make excellent growth and gains.[38] For example, Holstein calves, changed to skimmilk at 3 or 4 weeks of age and continued on a moderate allowance to 6 months of age, will gain 1.50 to 1.75 lbs. a day, which is considered above the normal rate.

Calves raised on skimmilk may not make quite as rapid gains the first few months as when they are continued on a liberal allowance of whole milk. However, they will be just as large by the time they are 18 months to 2 years old and they will develop into just as productive cows.

Skimmilk should be fed, if possible, fresh and warm from the farm separator. If the milk is not warm, it should be heated to 90° to 100° F. before feeding. In very cold weather the skimmilk may not be warm enough as it comes from the separator and the temperature should be tested with a thermometer. Contrary to common opinion, Montana and South Dakota trials show that it is not injurious to calves to feed them the foam which normally collects on separated milk, providing the proper total amount of milk is fed.[39] Calves getting considerable foam may be a little bloated immediately after feeding, but the condition soon disappears.

After the calf is 2 to 4 months old, it can usually be accustomed to cool milk, if the temperature is reasonably uniform. Also, sour milk can then be fed, if it is not stale or contaminated with undesirable bacteria, and if it is uniformly fed sour, and not sweet at one feeding and sour at another.

In raising calves on skimmilk, the change from whole milk to skimmilk may begin when the calf is 2 to 4 weeks old, the exact age depending on the vigor of the calf. The change should be made at the rate of about 1 lb. a day over a period of 7 to 10 days. In the case of very valuable calves, some whole milk is often fed for 2 months or longer.

After the calf has been changed entirely to skimmilk, the allowance may be increased very gradually, if the calf is doing well. Not over 14 to 16 lbs. of skimmilk daily are needed to ensure good development, but if an excess is available after any pigs or poultry have been provided for, large vigorous calves may be fed somewhat more. The allowance should not exceed 18 lbs. daily until the calf is 6 weeks old, but after this vigorous calves may be allowed to drink as much as they wish in addition to their grain and hay.[40]

If only a small amount of skimmilk is available, very good gains can be secured on only 10 lbs. of skimmilk per calf daily, along with plenty of concentrates and good hay. In 2 trials at the Wisconsin Station calves thus fed gained an average of 1.52 lbs. a head daily, in comparison with 1.72 lbs. for others fed 14 lbs. of skimmilk a day.[41]

If the supply is sufficient, skimmilk feeding should be continued for at least 6 months, but when the supply is scanty, thrifty calves can be weaned at 2 to 3 months and then be fed on a calf meal, as is described later. In the case of a very valuable calf, it may be wise to continue skimmilk feeding until the calf is 7 or 8 months old.

The importance of pasteurizing skimmilk, buttermilk, or whey before they are returned from the factory to the farm has been emphasized previously. (**621**) If the herd is not free from tuberculosis, even farm-separated skimmilk should be heated to 170° F. to destroy any tuberculosis bacteria that might infect the calves.

963. Concentrates for skimmilk-fed calves.—Skimmilk differs in composition from whole milk only in having had most of the fat removed. Consequently, the proportion of protein to other nutrients is much higher in skimmilk than in whole milk, which is itself a protein-rich food. Accordingly, in choosing supplements to feed with an ample amount of skimmilk, the need is not for additional protein, but for an abundance of energy-giving, easily-digested carbohydrates or fat to replace the fat removed from the whole milk.

The concentrates for calves fed a liberal amount of skimmilk should consist chiefly or even entirely of farm-grown grains. Experiments have shown clearly that calves thus fed make just as rapid and much more economical gains than when their concentrate mixture contains a large proportion of protein-rich feeds, such as linseed meal or wheat bran.[42] Any of the concentrate mixtures are satisfactory that have been suggested earlier in this chapter for feeding with an ample supply of whole milk.

Grain gives very satisfactory results when used as the only concentrate for calves getting plenty of skimmilk. If such palatable protein-rich feeds as wheat bran and linseed meal are added to grain, the mixture is usually liked a little better by young calves and therefore they will eat more of it and make slightly more rapid gains.

For example, in each of three Wisconsin trials, one lot of Holstein and Guernsey calves was fed ground corn as the only concentrate, with not to exceed 14 lbs. of skimmilk per head daily and what clover hay they would eat.[43] In comparison another lot was fed the same, except that a concentrate mixture was used consisting of 40 lbs. ground corn, 30 lbs. ground oats, 20 lbs. wheat bran, and 10 lbs. linseed meal. The corn-fed calves were vigorous and growthy and gained, on the average, 1.69 lbs. per head daily to 6 months of age, which is an excellent rate of gain and considerably above the usual normal. Those fed the mixture ate slightly more concentrates, on account of the palatability of the mixture, and gained 1.80 lbs. a day, or only 0.11 lb. more than those fed corn as the sole concentrate. At 6 months of age the calves fed the mixture had gained 20 lbs. more, but their feed cost per head was $0.78 higher.

Oats, whole or ground, and ground barley also give good results as the only grain for skimmilk-fed calves. A mixture of grains may be more palatable than a single grain, and ground wheat or grain sorghums are satisfactory in such mixtures.[44] Rye is less palatable and should not form too large a part of a concentrate mixture for calves.

While various fats and oils may be used to supplement skimmilk, the cereal grains, rich in carbohydrates, are cheaper and more satisfactory than oils for calf feeding.[45] Unless oil is fed as an emulsion with the milk, it is apt to produce indigestion and scours, for young animals in general have but limited ability to digest fat.

964. Raising calves on buttermilk.—Where available, fresh buttermilk is a good substitute for skimmilk and should be used in the same manner and with the same precautions, being heated to 90° to 100° F. before feeding.[42] It is well not to begin changing calves to buttermilk until they are 4 weeks old, as buttermilk sometimes has a more laxative effect than skimmilk. The watery slop sometimes obtained from creameries, often from filthy tanks, is unfit for calves, as it is almost sure to cause scours.

965. Raising calves on whey.—Whey can be successfully used for calf feeding, if it is fed with a suitable concentrate mixture and if it is of good sanitary quality, and not from a filthy whey tank. It must be borne in mind that most of the protein has been removed in cheesemaking and that each 100 lbs. of whey supply only 0.8 lb. protein. Fortunately, this protein, though small in amount, is of the highest quality. Since whey is not a protein-rich feed like whole milk or skimmilk, a concentrate mixture rich in protein must be fed with it.

To prevent disease, whey should always be pasteurized or sterilized before being returned from the cheese factory to the farm. Whey that is allowed to ferment and putrefy in dirty whey tanks cannot be successfully used in calf feeding, but whey soured under sanitary conditions is satisfactory, if sour whey is fed every day. Changing from sweet whey one day to sour whey the next may cause scours. In making the change from whole milk to whey somewhat more care is necessary than in changing to skimmilk.

Two Wisconsin trials show the good results that can be secured from whey under proper conditions.[46] Calves were changed gradually from whole milk to skimmed whey at 3 weeks of age during a period of 10 days. In addition, they were fed clover hay and a protein-rich mixture, consisting of 30 lbs. ground corn, 30 lbs. standard wheat middlings, and 40 lbs. linseed meal. The allowance of whey was gradually increased to 14 lbs. per head daily at 6 weeks of age. These calves gained an average of 1.48 lbs. per head daily and were vigorous and thrifty. Calves fed a liberal allowance of skimmilk at the same time gained 1.72 lbs. Satisfactory results have also been secured with whey in other trials when properly fed.[47]

966. Dried skimmilk or buttermilk; semi-solid buttermilk.—In districts where whole milk is marketed and no dairy by-products are available on the farm, calves are often raised on reconstituted, or remade, skimmilk or buttermilk. This is made by mixing dried skimmilk or dried buttermilk with warm water at the rate of 1 lb. to 9 lbs. of water. First mix the dried product to a smooth paste with an equal weight of cold water and then add 8 parts more of warm water. This solution will have practically the same composition as fluid skimmilk or buttermilk.

When the reconstituted milk is fed in the same manner and in the same amounts as skimmilk or buttermilk, nearly as good results can be secured with it.[48] The only difficulty is that dried products are often expensive. Changes can be made freely from skimmilk to reconstituted skimmilk or from buttermilk to reconstituted buttermilk, if the supply of the fluid by-products is variable from day to day.

Semi-solid, or condensed, buttermilk may be used in the same manner as powdered buttermilk in making reconstituted buttermilk, but it requires about 3 lbs. of semi-solid buttermilk to 7 lbs. of water to make a solution of the same composition as fluid buttermilk.[49] If a more dilute solution is fed, as is often done, the feeding of a given amount of the solution will obviously not produce as good gains as the same weight of skimmilk or buttermilk. The acidity in semi-solid buttermilk sometimes causes calves to scour severely, and it is then necessary to neutralize it with lime water before feeding.[50]

On account of the usual high cost of dried skimmilk, dried buttermilk, or semi-solid buttermilk, the feeding of reconstituted skimmilk or buttermilk is often not continued as long as when fluid skimmilk or buttermilk is available. Instead, the calves are weaned at 2 to 3 months of age and then fed only a concentrate mixture and hay, the same as when they are raised on a minimum amount of whole milk or of skimmilk.

As is pointed out later, dried skimmilk and dried buttermilk are excellent protein supplements to include in a calf meal for young calves, to be fed either dry or in gruel form.

967. Raising calves on nurse cows.—Where dairy by-products are not available on the farm, some use the "nurse-cow method" of raising calves with much success.[51] In this method 2 to 4 calves of about the same age and vigor are kept in a box stall with a cow, competing for her milk. The calves should be taught to eat a dry calf meal and hay as soon as possible and may be weaned, if necessary, at 2 to 3 months of age. During her lactation one cow may thus raise several calves to the weaning age. Often a hard milker or low tester can well be used for this purpose. This system takes a minimum of labor and reduces the trouble from scours, if the number of calves is properly adjusted to the milk yield of the cow.

968. Raising calves on a minimum amount of whole milk and dry calf meals.—When no skimmilk, buttermilk, or whey is available, a method often followed in raising calves is to give them a good start on normal amounts of whole milk and teach them to eat a dry calf meal and good hay as soon as possible. Then, if they are thrifty, the amount of milk is gradually reduced and they are weaned entirely from fluid milk at 7 to 9 weeks of age, after this being fed only the dry calf meal, or "calf starter," with plenty of good hay and with water to drink. Such a method saves considerable labor in comparison with the feeding of reconstituted milk or of calf meal in gruel form, for there is no mixing and warming of a fluid food and washing and sterilizing of calf pails, after the calves are weaned.

This method of raising calves has been studied at several stations, with the following general results and conclusions:[52] The results are somewhat more variable with this method than when calves are raised on plenty of skimmilk or reconstituted milk. To secure the best results from this method, the calves must be well started on the dry calf meal and hay before they are weaned from milk. Excellent-quality legume hay or mixed hay high in legumes must be fed, and if a calf is delicate or sickly, whole milk feeding must be continued until it is strong and vigorous.

Calves are sometimes weaned from whole milk before 6 weeks of age, but they then often gain poorly for a month or more and become scrawny and pot-bellied. Later they may make good gains and reach normal weight and height at 12 to 24 months of age. Holstein and Brown Swiss calves can usually be successfully weaned under this method at 7 weeks of age, but in the case of the smaller breeds—Guernseys, Jerseys, and Ayrshires—it is best to continue whole milk feeding to 9 weeks of age or more. The total amount of milk per calf will be about the same, as calves of the smaller breeds do not require as much per head daily.

Some such schedule as the following should be followed under this plan: Feed whole milk as stated previously during the first 3 weeks, with a maximum of 10 lbs. a day for calves of the larger breeds and of about 8 lbs. for those of the smaller breeds. (**954**) Start feeding the dry calf meal and hay just as soon as the calf will eat them and reduce the milk allowance gradually, if the calf is thrifty. For example, feed calves of the larger breeds 9 lbs. of milk a day during the fourth week, 7 lbs. during the fifth week, 6 lbs. during the sixth week, and then gradually wean the calf during the next 7 to 10 days. In the case of Guernsey, Jersey, or Ayrshire calves, reduce the milk allowance more gradually and do not wean the calf until 9 weeks of age, unless it is doing unusually well.

Until the calf is 3 months old, let it have all the dry calf meal it will eat, up to a maximum of 4 or 5 lbs. a day, along with plenty of good legume hay, preferably alfalfa or clover. If a calf meal is being fed which contains expensive animal by-products, supply a more simple mixture in addition, when the calf is 3 months old. Any of the mixtures suggested for use with skimmilk-fed calves will be satisfactory that contain linseed meal, wheat bran, or other protein supplements. When the calf is 4 months old the more-expensive calf meal can be discontinued, and the cheaper mixture fed, along with the hay.

969. Calf meals to use in minimum-milk method.—When calf meals are fed which do not include dried skimmilk or other animal by-products, calves can usually be raised successfully on not to exceed 400 lbs. of whole milk, including colostrum. If part of the protein in the calf meal is furnished by dried skimmilk, dried buttermilk, blood flour, or fish meal, the amount of whole milk can be reduced to 350 lbs., and commonly the gains and growth will be slightly better.[53] However, the use of the animal by-products often increases the cost of the calf meal considerably.

A calf meal for use without fluid milk should contain 20 per cent protein and thus must include a rather large proportion of protein-rich supplements. It should not contain more than 5 per cent of fiber, and should be high in total digestible nutrients. For this reason, if considerable oats are to be included in a calf meal, rolled oats, not including the hulls, are often used, or most of the hulls are sifted out of the ground oats. However, mixtures containing 25 per cent or more of whole ground oats, including hulls, have been successfully used.

Experiments during 6 years at the Wisconsin station show the results that can be secured with proper care from a simple mixture that includes no animal by-product.[54] An equal number of Holstein and Guernsey heifer calves were fed each year a total of not to exceed 400 lbs. whole milk, including colostrum, with clover hay and a mixture of equal weights of ground yellow corn, ground oats, wheat bran, and linseed meal. They were weaned at 7 to 9 weeks of age, with an occasional exception, and but little trouble was experienced from scours.

On the average these calves gained 1.30 lbs. per head daily to 6 months of age, which would be considered a normal average for the combination of Holsteins and Guernseys. Up to this age they consumed an average of 369 lbs. whole milk (not including colostrum), 654 lbs. concentrates, and 353 lbs. hay, and drank 4,897 lbs. water. Similar calves fed not over 14 lbs. of skimmilk per head daily to 6 months of age gained 1.77 lbs. a day. Though the calves raised on the limited amount of whole milk did not make maximum gains up to 6 months, they would later make up all or most of this difference, if they were well fed up to calving time.

Some other simple mixtures, not including animal by-products, which have been used with success under this method are:

1. Ground yellow corn, 39 lbs.; ground oats, 40 lbs.; cottonseed meal, 20 lbs.; salt, 1 lb.[55]

2. Ground barley, 200 lbs.; ground oats, 150 lbs.; wheat bran, 150 lbs.; linseed meal, 50 lbs.; bone meal, 4 lbs.; and salt, 3 lbs.[56]

Various modifications can be made in the mixtures to suit local conditions. In some of the trials in which such calf meals have been used with a small amount of whole milk, the gains have not been very satisfactory up to 6 months of age. Even in such cases, however, the heifers would probably reach normal size later, if well fed up to calving time.

Unless it is essential to reduce the expense of raising the calves to a minimum, it is best to include some protein-rich feed of animal origin in the calf meal, as this will usually increase the gains somewhat. Experiments at the New York (Cornell) station indicate the results that can be secured on a calf meal containing a liberal amount of dried skimmilk.[57] A total of 15 Holstein calves were raised on not to exceed 350 lbs. whole milk, early-cut mixed clover-and-timothy hay, and a ''calf starter'' consisting of 25 lbs. ground yellow corn, 30 lbs. rolled oats (without hulls), 15 lbs. wheat bran, 8 lbs. linseed meal, and 22 lbs. dried skimmilk.

At 16 weeks of age the calves were changed to a mixture of 30 lbs. each of ground yellow corn, ground oats, and wheat bran, and 10 lbs. linseed meal. These calves gained 1.50 lbs. per head daily to 6 months of age and consumed, on the average, 340 lbs. of whole milk, 262 lbs. of calf starter, 277 lbs. of the other mixture, and 681 lbs. of hay.

Some other calf meals for dry feeding recommended by various authorities are:

(1) 32.25 lbs. ground yellow corn, 28 lbs. rolled oats (not including hulls), 10 lbs. wheat bran, 5 lbs. linseed meal, 3 lbs. white fish meal, 20 lbs. dried skimmilk, 0.5 lb. salt, 0.5 lb. ground limestone, 0.5 lb. steamed bone meal, and 0.25 lb. cod-liver oil concentrate.[58]

(2) 50 lbs. ground corn, 15 lbs. rolled oats, 15 lbs. linseed meal, 10 lbs. dried skimmilk, 10 lbs. blood flour, 1 lb. salt.[59]

(3) 20 lbs. ground barley, 20 lbs. ground oats, 15 to 10 lbs. wheat bran, 7 lbs. linseed meal, 25 lbs. dried skimmilk, 10 to 5 lbs. blood meal, 2 lbs. bone meal, and 1 lb. salt.[60]

(4) 34 lbs. ground yellow corn, 35 lbs. ground oats, 20 lbs. cottonseed meal, 10 lbs. dried skimmilk, 1 lb. salt.[61]

In these calf meals other grains can be substituted for the corn; fish meal for the blood flour or blood meal; and probably soybean oil meal or ground soybeans for the linseed meal. A calf meal containing much blood meal, or blood flour, may not be palatable to calves, and it may be necessary to force them to eat it at first by great hunger, as in the "New Jersey method."

970. The "New-Jersey dry-fed calf mixture."—A cheap method of raising calves in which a total of only about 150 lbs. whole milk is fed has been developed by the New Jersey Station.[62] The calf is started on whole milk, limited to 3 quarts a day, and when it is a week old the following "calf mixture" is put into the feed box and some is rubbed on its muzzle after each feeding of milk: 25.0 lbs. yellow corn meal, 37.5 lbs. ground oats, 12.5 lbs. wheat bran, 12.5 lbs. linseed meal, 12.5 lbs. soluble blood flour, 1 lb. steamed bone meal, 1 lb. pulverized limestone, and 1 lb. salt. If more than 3 quarts of milk are fed daily, the calf may not take readily to the calf meal. Good alfalfa, clover, or mixed hay is also supplied when the calf is a week old.

When the calf is 3 weeks old, the milk allowance is gradually reduced by diluting it with water, so that after 30 days of age the calf is fed only the dry calf meal, hay, and fresh water. At this time it should be eating about 1 lb. of the meal a day. Enough of the calf meal and hay should be fed each morning for the entire day, and the calf should have access to fresh water at all times. The calf should be allowed all the calf meal it will eat, up to a maximum of 6 lbs. a day. After 6 months of age the calf meal is discontinued, and the usual type of mixture for heifers fed in its place.

Holstein calves thus fed usually reached normal weight and height by 6 months of age, though their gains were below normal for a time after they were weaned from milk. Calves raised by this method have developed into excellent cows. In experiments at other stations in which this system or a similar system has been compared with raising calves on more expensive calf meals containing dried skimmilk in place of the blood flour, the calves fed the skimmilk calf meals have generally been somewhat thriftier up to 3 or 4 months of age, but later there has been less difference, or no difference at all.[63]

971. Calf pellets.—There has recently been considerable interest in the use of "calf pellets" in place of dry calf meals. The pellets are made in machines which compress the dry concentrate mixture into pellet form by great pressure. In using calf pellets the same general method is followed as in raising calves on a dry calf meal.

It is claimed that calves like the pellets better than a dry meal, and therefore learn to eat them sooner and make better gains than on dry meals. The relative value of calf pellets and dry meals has not yet been studied sufficiently by the experiment stations to warrant definite conclusions as to whether or not the pelleting of a calf meal increases its worth enough to justify the expense.[64]

972. Raising calves on a limited amount of skimmilk.—If a limited amount of skimmilk is available, but not enough to continue its use until the calves are 5 or 6 months old, they may be started on whole milk and changed to skimmilk at the usual time. They are then weaned from skimmilk at 7 to 9 weeks of age, just as in raising calves by the limited-whole-milk method.[65] The plan of feeding already described under that method should be followed and the same sort of calf meal used as is there suggested. Reconstituted skimmilk, made from dried skimmilk, may be fed in place of fluid skimmilk during the skimmilk period, to reduce the amount of whole milk needed. Calves may be raised by this method on only 200 lbs. whole milk or less and 400 to 600 lbs. skimmilk.

973. Raising calves on gruels.—Until the development of successful methods of raising calves on dry calf meals in recent years, a more common method was to feed the calf meal in gruel form. In gruel feeding the calf meal is mixed with warm water at the rate of 1 lb. of the meal to 5 or more lbs. of water. When the calf is about 4 weeks old, the amount of whole milk is reduced very gradually and the gruel added to it, until after 20 days or more the milk is discontinued. Good hay is supplied and also such a concentrate mixture as 30 lbs. each of ground corn, ground oats, and wheat bran and 10 lbs. of linseed meal. The ingredients in such a calf meal should be finely ground so they will not settle out of the gruel rapidly. There is no advantage in cooking the gruel before feeding it.[66]

A calf meal developed at the New York (Cornell) Station and used to a considerable extent in the northeastern states has the following formula: Yellow corn meal, 250 lbs.; oat flour, 150 lbs.; malted barley, 100 lbs.; red dog flour, 220 lbs.; linseed meal, 150 lbs.; soluble blood flour, 100 lbs.; precipitated bone meal, 10 lbs.; precipitated calcium carbonate, 10 lbs.; salt, 10 lbs.[67] In this formula ground barley can be substituted for the malted barley; flour wheat middlings, for the red dog flour; and ground oats with the hulls sifted out, for the oat flour. Many other formulas have been developed and used with more or less success.[68] If desired, the calf meals recommended previously for feeding dry can be fed in gruel form, if ground to a sufficient degree of fineness.

974. Commercial calf feeds.—There are on the market several brands of calf meals and calf pellets, which are somewhat similar to the mixtures that have been recommended in the previous paragraphs, but which often are more complex in nature. These should be fed in accordance with the recommendations of the manufacturers. (**665**)

975. Self-feeding calves.—Because the self-feeder is used so successfully in swine feeding, experiments have naturally been conducted to find whether calves can be raised satisfactorily by self-feeding them concentrates in addition to supplying milk and roughage.[69] These trials have shown that if calves or heifers are allowed access, free choice, to grains, such as corn and oats, and also to linseed meal, wheat bran, and other protein supplements, they will usually eat much more of the protein supplements than is needed to balance their ration. This will make the cost unduly high.

Also, even if the calves are self-fed a mixture containing the proper proportion of protein supplements, after 2 to 4 months they will often eat much more concentrates than they need and less hay than they should take. This is expensive, but even more important, the amount of hay may be so small that the calves may become unthrifty, due to a lack of the vitamins and minerals good hay provides. They may suffer from rickets and even have fits and convulsions.

By using a mixture of the proper proportions of chopped or ground legume hay and concentrates in a self-feeder this difficulty can be avoided, but the proportion of hay must be carefully adjusted, so that the calves will eat plenty of hay and yet make the desired gain.[70]

III. Dairy Heifers

976. Proper development of heifers important.—Raising dairy heifers after they are 6 months old is an easy task, and perhaps for this very reason many are stunted for lack of suitable feed. Such animals never develop into as profitable cows as would otherwise have been the case. Also, if a dairyman is raising surplus cattle for sale, he will find that buyers do not want undersized heifers or cows, but that they are looking for well-grown animals which give indications of large and profitable production. The proper development of the heifers is therefore an exceedingly important part of the dairy business.

977. Nutrient requirements.—The nutrient requirements for growing dairy cattle have been discussed in detail earlier in this chapter. In considering the feeding of heifers after 6 months of age the following points with reference to their nutrient requirements should be borne in mind.

In order to provide the necessary nutrients and also to reduce the cost of raising heifers, it is very important that they be fed all the good roughage they will eat during the winter and that they have plenty of good pasture during the grazing season. Far too often, heifers are fed only fair or poor roughage in winter and are turned on pasture and allowed to shift for themselves in summer, with but little attention, even when the feed becomes scanty. Such neglect is perhaps due to the fact that the heifers are not bringing in any immediate cash income, and a lack of sufficient appreciation that the future income will depend on how the heifers are developed.

If possible, at least half of the winter roughage, on the dry basis, should be well-cured legume hay, for it supplies needed protein, calcium, and vitamins A and D. If legume hay is not available, grass hay of the best quality should be fed, that is early-cut and well-cured.

Normal growth cannot be made unless heifers receive a sufficient supply of total digestible nutrients in their rations. Since hay and other roughages are bulky and relatively low in digestible nutrients, young heifers fed roughage alone, without grain or other concentrates, cannot consume enough of the bulky feed to provide sufficient digestible nutrients for normal growth. After they are a year old, their digestive tracts are sufficiently developed so they can be wintered satisfactorily on roughage with little or no concentrates, if the roughage is of satisfactory quality.

Raising heifers on an abundance of good hay and other roughage, with just enough concentrates to keep them growing properly, is nearly always much more economical than feeding them a large allowance of concentrates with less roughage.[71] Heifers fed liberally on concentrates will make rapid growth and be sleek and fat, but there is apt to be more difficulty in getting them in calf than in the case of heifers in moderate flesh. Also, such overfed animals will certainly not develop into better cows than those raised more economically, and perhaps they will not be as good producers.

There is probably more apt to be a deficiency of phosphorus than of calcium in raising heifers. They will get sufficient calcium if they are fed a liberal amount of legume hay, mixed hay, or even early-cut, well-cured grass hay, unless the soil on which the latter is grown is very deficient in calcium. (950)

Heifers will get ample phosphorus if their roughage is grown on soil well supplied with phosphorus or if they are fed a concentrate mixture which includes a reasonable proportion of phosphorus-rich feeds, such as wheat bran, linseed meal, or cottonseed meal. When fed roughage grown on phosphorus-deficient soil, with or without cereal grain, but with no phosphorus-rich concentrates, there may be a serious lack of phosphorus in the ration. Whenever there is danger of a lack of phosphorus or of calcium, a suitable mineral mixture should be provided where the heifers can have access to it, or 1 or 2 per cent of such supplements as steamed bone meal or ground limestone should be included in the concentrate mixture. (181)

If heifers are fed early-cut, well-cured hay in winter, especially legume hay, and are on good pasture in summer they will receive an abundance of vitamins.

978. Raising heifers on roughage alone.—Numerous experiments have been conducted to find the minimum amount of grain or other concentrates required by dairy heifers and to determine whether they can be wintered satisfactorily on roughage alone.[72] These experiments show in general that if heifers are fed only roughage, even of excellent quality, before they are 10 to 12 months of age, they will not make normal growth. They will make somewhat better gains on legume hay plus corn or sorghum silage than on legume hay alone, but even on this combination the gains will usually not be normal.

They will make up their growth to some extent later, if well-fed, and may even reach normal size, if fed liberally after they freshen. However, unless grain is unusually high in price in comparison with roughage, it is advisable to feed heifers under a year of age sufficient concentrates, in addition to an abundance of good roughage, so that they will make normal growth.

If heifers have made proper growth the first year, they may then be fed roughage alone up to 3 or 4 months before calving, if the roughage is of first-class quality. During this period before calving it is advisable to feed them enough concentrates to get them into good condition for calving and for their first lactation period.

979. Feeding heifers from 6 to 12 months of age.—The feeding of milk or special calf meals is usually discontinued by the time heifers are 6 months of age. They should have an abundance of other feeds at this time, so that their growth will not be checked. Even if the heifers are later to be raised on roughage alone, the feeding of concentrates should be continued in the winter until they are at least 10 to 12 months old. The amount of concentrates required will depend on the quality of roughage fed. With good roughage 2 to 3 lbs. of concentrates per head daily should be enough, while with that of only fair quality 4 to 5 lbs. may be needed to keep the heifers gaining properly. Heifers 6 to 12 months of age should be fed 8 to 15 lbs. of hay a day, or 5 to 10 lbs. of hay and 8 to 15 lbs. of silage.

Whether it will be necessary to feed grain or other concentrates to heifers of this age on pasture will depend on the amount and the quality of the pasture. If there is plenty of good feed, they may make satisfactory growth on pasture alone, but it is often necessary to feed a small amount of concentrates to keep them growing well. Whenever the pasture becomes scanty, it is especially important to provide plenty of other feed, including concentrates and also hay, silage, or green soiling crops. In the spring when young heifers are first turned to pasture, it is best to continue feeding some hay until they get used to the lush, laxative green feed.

If the heifers are fed plenty of alfalfa, clover, or other legume hay as the only roughage, or if they are on excellent pasture which is kept well grazed, no protein supplements need be included in the concentrate mixture. Merely ground grain alone, even corn, is satisfactory. The mixture may then be any desired combination of the common cereals. If only about half the dry matter in the roughage is legumes, the concentrate mixture should contain 12 to 14 per cent total protein. For example, such a combination of roughage would be 3 lbs. of corn or sorghum silage to each pound of alfalfa or clover hay. If little or no legume hay is fed, then the concentrate mixture should contain 18 to 20 per cent protein.

Appendix Table VII gives a considerable number of concentrate mixtures containing various percentages of protein which are excellent for dairy heifers and also for dairy cows. These mixtures will show the sort of combinations that are commonly used for feeding heifers.

980. Feeding heifers over one year of age.—After heifers are a year old, their capacity to use roughage is well developed, and they need but little concentrates, if plenty of high-quality roughage is provided. When on good pasture, no concentrates are required, but care should be taken to supply additional feed if the pasturage becomes scanty at any time.

Heifers of this age may be wintered satisfactorily, up to 3 or 4 months before calving, without concentrates, if fed either an abundance of good legume hay and corn or other silage, or else all the well-cured legume hay they will eat. They will not carry as much flesh as some breeders desire, but if well fed before calving and during their first lactation period, will reach normal size and weight. With roughage of less excellent quality, it is necessary to feed a small amount of concentrates to keep them growing properly. If the roughage is fair in quality, not over 2 to 4 lbs. of concentrates should be needed up to 3 or 4 months before calving. At this time they should be fed more liberally in order to meet the need for nutrients in the development of the fetus and also so they will be in good condition for high production during their first lactation. With plenty of good roughage 4 to 5 lbs. of concentrates are sufficient for this purpose.

The same concentrate mixtures may be used for heifers of this age as have been advised for those up to a year old. If desired, the proportion of protein supplement in the mixture may be reduced slightly, as heifers need somewhat less protein as they become older.

981. Concentrates for heifers.—All the grains may be used satisfactorily, when ground or crushed, for feeding heifers, and their relative values for this purpose will be about the same as for dairy cows. The reader is therefore referred to Chaper XXV for further information.

Though corn is somewhat lower in protein than barley, oats, wheat, or the grain sorghums, it may be used satisfactorily as the only concentrate, if fed with plenty of good legume hay, especially alfalfa hay.[73] Hominy feed is equal to ground corn, and dried beet pulp may be used as a partial substitute for one-third the grain, when economical in price. Molasses, either cane or beet, may be useful in getting heifers to clean up unpalatable roughage, like straw, but such poor roughage should not form a large part of the ration except when necessary.

Wheat bran and linseed meal are the most popular protein supplements for use in feeding heifers, but other supplements may be used with entire success. Soybeans and soybean oil meal are about equal to linseed meal,[74] and cottonseed meal is a good supplement to use when there is plenty of well-cured legume or mixed hay in the ration. As has been shown previously, heifers over 3 to 4 months of age may even be fed cottonseed meal as the only concentrate without injury, if roughage is fed which supplies plenty of vitamins and if there is ample calcium in the ration. (**583**) The other protein supplements successfully used in feeding dairy cows may likewise be used for heifers.

982. Roughages for heifers.—Early-cut, well-cured legume hay is the best roughage for heifers, and if possible such hay should be fed as part of the ration. Clover hay is a close second to alfalfa hay, if of equal quality.[75] Soybean hay and cowpea hay are also excellent, and the part actually eaten is probably equal to the same weight of alfalfa or clover.[76]

Timothy hay, prairie hay, or hay from other grasses is inferior to legume hay for heifers,[77] and is unsatisfactory as the only roughage if cut late or poorly cured. Early-cut hay is much better, but even such grass hay should be fed, if possible, along with some legume hay or with silage.

Straw or chaff from the legumes, such as pea straw, may be fed as part of the roughage to heifers. Cut or shredded corn or sorghum fodder or stover, and even straw from the grains can be used satisfactorily, if fed along with better roughage. For example, in a Wisconsin trial heifers fed 7 lbs. oat straw and 26 lbs. corn silage a head daily, with 3 lbs. of a concentrate mixture consisting of 2 parts cottonseed meal, 3 parts gluten feed, and 1 part wheat bran, made practically as large gains as others fed alfalfa hay, corn silage, and 2.5 lbs. of a concentrate mixture consisting chiefly of corn.[78] The heifers actually ate but 4.5 lbs. straw a day, being allowed to pick it over and eat the finer parts. The rest was used for bedding.

To get heifers to eat unpalatable roughage, diluted molasses may be poured over it. Thus fed on cut corn stover in a Wisconsin trial, molasses was worth as much as or even more per pound than ground corn.[79]

Oat feed may be used as a substitute for half the hay, on a pound for pound basis, in a ration for heifers.[80] Cottonseed hulls may also be used satisfactorily, if fed with some legume or other hay, silage, or pasture to furnish the vitamins the hulls lack.[81]

Silage, especially from corn or the sorghums, is excellent for heifers when fed as part of the roughage, along with legume or mixed hay. However, silage is not at all necessary if an abundance of good hay is fed. For heifers, just as with dairy cows, it requires about 3 tons of corn silage to equal 1 ton of legume or mixed hay in feeding value.[82] Heifers may be wintered satisfactorily on corn or sorghum silage as the only roughage, if a concentrate mixture is fed which furnishes plenty of protein,[83] but often they show a great desire for some dry forage. It is therefore wise to feed some hay or even dry fodder or stover from corn or the sorghums along with the silage.

It must be borne in mind that silage, fodder, or stover from corn or the sorghums, and also grain straw, oat feed, cottonseed hulls, and the usual kinds of grass hay are all low in protein. Therefore when most of the roughage is of this character, care must be taken to balance the ration by feeding a sufficient amount of protein supplements. If necessary, a calcium or a phosphorus supplement should also be supplied.

983. Age for first calving.—Well-grown heifers may be bred to freshen at 24 months of age or soon thereafter, and they should be fed liberally during their first lactation period, so their growth will not be stopped.[84] Heifers calving at about 24 months of age will not produce quite as much milk in their first lactation as when calving is delayed a few months. However, considering the additional cost of carrying a non-producing heifer a longer time, it is generally more profitable to have them calve at this age.

From studies of Advanced Registry and Register of Merit records of production, Turner of the Missouri Station concluded that the yield of milk in the first lactation would be within 5 per cent of the maximum possible for that lactation, when Guernseys, Jerseys, and Holsteins calved at 26 months and Ayrshires at 28 months of age.[85] If the first breeding is delayed beyond 16 to 18 months, it is often considerably more difficult to get a heifer in calf.[86]

984. Normal growth of dairy cattle.—In order to determine whether young dairy cattle are making the proper rate of growth for the particular breed, it is helpful to have a normal standard with which they can be compared. At several experiment stations the weight and also the height at the withers have therefore been recorded each month during growth for young heifers and bulls of the chief dairy breeds.

The following table summarizes the available data of this kind for young cattle up to 2 years of age. Records are included from the Missouri, Iowa, Kansas, Nebraska, South Carolina, and West Virginia Stations, and from the United States Department of Agriculture.[87] For each breed the averages represent data for a larger number of animals at early ages than later ages. The weights up to 1 year of age are averages of 387 animals or more for the Holstein heifers, 281 head or more for the Ayrshire heifers, 251 head or more for the Jersey heifers, and 87 head or more for the Guernsey heifers. The average heights shown in the table are for smaller numbers of animals, and the number of bulls included in the studies was much less than of heifers.

Normal growth in weight and height of dairy cattle

Age	Ayrshire heifers		Guernsey heifers		Holstein heifers		Jersey heifers	
	Weight	Height	Weight	Height	Weight	Height	Weight	Height
Months	Lbs.	Inches	Lbs.	Inches	Lbs.	Inches	Lbs.	Inches
Birth ..	73	27.4	65	26.6	91	28.9	54	25.8
1	88	28.2	79	28.4	113	30.5	68	26.9
2	115	29.6	105	30.0	150	32.2	92	28.8
4	194	33.4	177	33.7	250	36.2	164	32.7
6	287	36.7	267	37.2	365	39.8	250	36.2
8	384	39.5	350	39.9	474	42.4	331	39.1
10	467	41.4	427	41.7	568	44.6	402	41.0
12	535	43.0	490	43.3	653	46.2	462	42.3
14	598	44.3	556	44.6	725	47.6	518	43.5
16	652	45.4	605	45.3	795	48.8	568	44.5
18	709	46.1	663	46.4	861	49.7	615	45.3
20	766	47.0	712	47.0	928	50.6	658	46.0
22	815	47.6	763	47.7	999	51.3	702	46.6
24	860	48.0	818	48.0	1075	51.9	750	47.0

Age	Ayrshire bulls		Guernsey bulls		Holstein bulls		Jersey bulls	
	Weight	Height	Weight	Height	Weight	Height	Weight	Height
Months	Lbs.	Inches	Lbs.	Inches	Lbs.	Inches	Lbs.	Inches
Birth ...	80	27.9	71	27.7	96	29.4	60	26.2
1	99	28.9	87	29.3	120	30.9	78	27.9
2	131	30.4	113	30.6	157	32.8	104	29.7
4	216	34.0	190	34.2	265	36.4	184	33.6
6	320	37.4	291	37.8	401	40.6	282	37.2
8	432	40.2	401	40.3	529	43.4	371	39.5
10	532	42.2	494	42.5	649	45.6	452	41.4
12	599	43.3	609	44.5	773	47.8	531	43.0
14	670	44.7			906	49.3	613	45.0
16	724	45.6			1063	51.0	679	46.1
18	751	46.4			1216	52.8	745	47.5
20	819	47.0			1320	53.7	856	48.6
22	895	47.6			1376	55.3	904	49.3
24	990	48.1			1452	56.0	969	50.3

At one year of age the Ayrshire heifers averaged 535 lbs. in weight; the Guernseys, 490 lbs.; the Holsteins, 653 lbs.; and the Jerseys, 462 lbs. The gains during the first year averaged 1.54 lbs. per head daily for the Holsteins; 1.27 lbs. for the Ayrshires; 1.16 lbs. for the Guernseys; and 1.12 lbs. for the Jerseys. The gains during the second year were somewhat less rapid, averaging 1.16 lbs. per head daily for the Holstein heifers; 0.90 lb. for the Guernseys; 0.89 lb. for the Ayrshires; and 0.79 lb. for the Jerseys.

The bulls made distinctly more rapid gains than the heifers of the same breed, and except in the case of the Ayrshires, the bulls were also decidedly taller at a given age.

985. Cost of raising heifers.—The cost of raising dairy heifers up to the time of first calving differs rather widely in various sections, the cost depending chiefly on the prices of feeds and the method of feeding that is employed. Feed and bedding make up more than one-half of the total cost. To this expense must be added the initial value of the calf and the expenses for labor, shelter, interest, taxes, and miscellaneous items. From the gross cost should be deducted a credit for the manure produced.

During the past few years the net cost of raising heifers to the age of first calving has generally ranged from $60 to $100 or more per head in the cost studies that have been conducted by various stations. Except in sections where feed is cheap, the cost of raising heifers is often greater than the selling price of grade dairy heifers of but ordinary quality.

Care should therefore be taken to raise only heifers that are out of high-producing cows and that are sired by a good purebred bull. Such heifers are the best source of replacements for the milking herd, and if more of such heifers are raised than are needed for this purpose, they are the kind that will bring good prices. Heifer calves that are out of poor cows or those that are otherwise undesirable should not be raised, for they will not be worth the expense involved.

In order to keep the cost of raising heifers as low as possible, great care is necessary to prevent scours and other calf diseases. Otherwise, the death losses will be heavy, or some of the calves will not develop into thrifty heifers of good size.

The following table shows the amounts of feed that are required to raise dairy heifers either to 2 years of age or to the time of first calving, as found in various studies.[88]

Amounts of feed required to raise dairy heifers

	Ohio Jerseys	Ohio Holsteins	Louisiana Holsteins	Oregon Various breeds
Whole milk, lbs.	465	499	844	552
Skimmilk, lbs.	3,015	2,960	2,724	1,209
Concentrates, lbs.	1,382	1,526	785	230
Hay and other dry roughage, lbs.	2,041	2,448	2,570	3,260
Silage and other succulent feeds, lbs.	2,884	2,833	2,386	1,180
Pasture, days	281	281	*	358

*Number of days of pasture not stated.

In these studies most of the calves were raised on skimmilk, with a limited amount of whole milk during the first few weeks. The amounts of concentrates were low in the Louisiana and Oregon studies, chiefly because pasture could be provided over a longer season than is possible in the central and northeastern states.

IV. The Bull

986. Selection of the bull.—Since improvement in the productive capacity and profitableness of the dairy herd depends fully as much on the sire as on the cows, the selection of a bull is one of the most important problems every dairyman must meet. No improvement can be expected if nondescript scrub or grade bulls are used. Therefore every dairyman who raises heifers for his replacements should breed his cows to a purebred sire, selected primarily on the basis of actual records of production of his immediate ancestors and their offspring. Due attention must also be given to the conformation and type of the bull and his ancestors. If a poor bull is used, it will take years of constructive breeding to undo the damage.

As the average production of the cows in a herd increases, it becomes more and more difficult to select a bull whose daughters will be better than their dams, or that will even maintain a high level of production in the herd. In such herds it is especially desirable to use a "proved sire," whose ability to transmit high production has been definitely proved by the actual records of his daughters in comparison with the records of their dams. In the past most dairymen have preferred to use young bulls, because they are less apt to be vicious, they are often surer breeders, and they are increasing in weight and in salvage value for beef. In countless instances the real value of a bull is realized only a considerable time after he has been sold for slaughter, when his daughters come into milk.

Dairymen with good-sized herds of high-producing purebred cows will find it highly advantageous to secure a sire proved for high production, if possible. Unfortunately, but few such sires are available and these are often high in price. The best substitute for a proved sire is a young bull which is selected with the greatest care after making a detailed study of the production records of his ancestors and their direct offspring. Through belonging to a "bull association," a dairyman can often greatly reduce the expense of using an excellent sire in his herd.

After a bull has been carefully selected, it is then just as important to feed and care for him so that he will remain a sure breeder.

987. The young bull.—The same principles apply to the rearing of the young bull as to the heifer, and the same methods of feeding can be used, except that it is wise not to limit the amount of milk so much as to check his growth. A young bull should always be fed so as to make good growth and reach normal size. One which has been stunted by insufficient feed may sire just as large calves, but a purchaser does not desire such an animal. He never knows whether the small size is due to heredity or to scanty feed.

After 5 to 6 months of age, when a bull calf should be separated from the heifers, he should be fed a somewhat larger amount of concentrates than a heifer. This is because a young bull makes more rapid gains than a heifer and consequently needs more nutrients. If well grown, a bull should be sufficiently mature for very light service at 10 to 12 months of age, but not more than 1 or 2 services in any one week should be permitted until he is 2 years old.

The bull should be halter broken as a calf, and at about 1 year of age should have a stout ring inserted in his nose. When he is about 2 years old this should be replaced by a larger one and the ring should never be allowed to wear thin. He should be so handled from calfhood that he will recognize man as his master and he should never be given an opportunity to learn his great strength. Stall and fences should always be so strongly built that there is no possibility of his learning how to break loose.

988. Feed and care of the bull in service.—The bull in service should be fed good legume hay or mixed legume-and-grass hay with sufficient concentrates to keep him in thrifty condition, but not fat. A limited amount of corn or sorghum silage may also be fed, but the allowance should be limited to 10 or 15 lbs. a day. Feeding a large allowance of silage or even too much hay may make the bull paunchy, so that he will be clumsy and slow at service. Green soiling crops are excellent for the bull, when available. When hay is fed as the only roughage, 15 to 20 lbs. will be required, depending on the size of the bull. When silage is fed, each 3 lbs. of silage will replace 1 lb. of hay.

If good roughage is fed, from 4 to 6 lbs. of concentrates should be sufficient to keep the bull in the desired condition, depending on his size and the amount of service.[89] A bull does not need nearly so much protein in his ration as a high-producing cow in milk, and should therefore be fed the same sort of concentrate mixture as has been advised for dry cows or growing heifers. The percentage of protein needed in the mixture will depend on the kind of roughage that is used.

Except perhaps in unusually cold climates, the best quarters for a bull are a well-built open shed with an adjoining roomy paddock where he may exercise. This should be constructed as a "safety bull pen," with breeding chute and breeding rack so arranged that the necessity of handling the bull at time of service is eliminated. In such quarters a mature bull, even a vicious one, can be handled in safety.

Though this open-air treatment is admirable for the health of the animal, it results in a heavier and rougher coat of hair, and hence breeders offering animals for sale usually prefer to keep the bulls in comfortable box stalls, turning them out only on fair days. Rather than confine the bull in isolation, it is well to have his stall so located and built that he can see the other members of the herd. The hoofs of the bull spending most of his time in the stall need regular trimming.

From the standpoint of safety it is always desirable to dehorn the bull. Often breeders dislike to do this, because in the opinion of some it detracts from the appearance of the animal. In reaching a decision on this point one should bear in mind that many men have been killed by bulls with horns, who might have otherwise escaped.

A bull should always be handled with a strong, safe staff attached to the ring in his nose. Even with a quiet, peaceable bull, safety lies only in handling him without displaying fear and yet as if he were watching for an opportunity to gore his attendant. Nearly all the accidents occur with "quiet" bulls that have been too much trusted.

To keep a bull healthy and a sure breeder it is essential that he have plenty of exercise. It was found in Washington trials that exercising bulls not only decreased the time required for service but also increased the motility and length of life of the sperm.[90] Some breeders who have two or more dehorned bulls turn them into one paddock, where they get plenty of exercise mauling each other about. Others exercise the bull on a tread power, where he may run the separator, pump water, do other useful work, or run the power for exercise only. Still others fix a long sweep on a post and tie the bull to it, so he will walk around in a circle.

Another device is a light cable stretched between two high posts, the bull being attached to it by a sliding chain so that he is able to walk back and forth the length of the cable. A tractable bull may also be harnessed and hitched to cart or wagon for such odd jobs as hauling manure or feed. Electric bull exercisers, which are motor-driven devices that lead bulls in a circular path, are convenient for breeders having several bulls. Whatever the plan adopted, it is essential that the bull receive ample and regular exercise, else he is almost certain to develop an ugly disposition and he may become impotent.

After a bull is 2 years old, he may be bred to 50 or 60 cows a year, and even more if the services are well distributed throughout the year. The bull should not be permitted to run with the herd at pasture, and only one service should be allowed when a cow is bred.

A good sire should be retained in the herd until it is necessary to make a change to prevent too close breeding. If he has proved to be a desirable sire and if he is still potent, he should be sold to some other breeder. No commoner mistake is made than discarding a likely bull at 3 to 4 years of age, before his heifers have come into milk to demonstrate how valuable a sire he may be.

QUESTIONS

1. State 5 essentials in satisfactory rations for raising dairy cattle.
2. Discuss the protein requirements of dairy calves, considering both amount and quality of protein.
3. State the importance of each of the following minerals for young dairy cattle: (a) Salt; (b) calcium; (c) phosphorus; (d) iodine; (e) iron and copper.
4. Discuss the vitamin requirements of dairy calves, stating which vitamins may be deficient and the best ways of providing each of these vitamins.
5. Discuss the importance of water for dairy calves.
6. State the important points in caring for a calf after birth.
7. Tell how a dairy calf is started on whole-milk feeding.
8. What sort of concentrate mixtures should be used for calves fed whole milk?
9. Name 5 concentrates that are commonly fed to dairy calves in your section of the country, and tell how they are used.
10. Discuss the importance of good-quality hay for calves.
11. Discuss the use of silage for calves; of pasture.
12. Describe the method of raising calves on skimmilk, stating the sort of concentrate mixtures that are most economical for feeding with skimmilk.
13. How may calves be raised satisfactorily on whey?
14. Discuss the use of dried skimmilk and dried buttermilk in calf feeding.
15. Describe the "nurse-cow method" of raising calves.
16. Describe the raising of calves on a minimum amount of whole milk and dry calf meals.
17. What sort of a concentrate mixture should be used in this method?
18. What are the distinguishing features of the "New Jersey" method of raising calves?
19. State the most important points concerning the following: (a) Raising calves on a limited amount of skimmilk; (b) raising calves on gruels; (c) self-feeding calves.
20. Discuss the nutrient requirements of dairy heifers.
21. Discuss the raising of heifers on roughage alone.
22. Describe: (a) The feeding of heifers from 6 to 12 months of age; (b) the feeding of heifers over one year of age.
23. What concentrates and what roughages are used most commonly for heifers in your district? What improvements can you suggest in the usual methods of feeding heifers?
24. Discuss the age for first calving of heifers.

25. About how much should a Holstein heifer weigh at 1 year of age; a Jersey heifer?
26. Discuss the cost of raising heifers.
27. How would you select a bull to head a herd of high-producing grade cows?
28. State the most important points in the feed and care of a young bull.
29. Discuss the feed and care of the bull in service.

REFERENCES

1. Coöperative experiments by several experiment stations, summarized by Armsby and by Forbes, Armsby et al., Bul. of National Res. Council, No. 12; Forbes et al., Bul. of National Res. Council, No. 42. See also: Swett, Eckles, and Ragsdale, Mo. Res. Bul. 66; Nevens, Davis, et al., Nebr. Buls. 181, 184.
2. Eckles and Gullickson, Jour. Agr. Res., 42, 1931, pp. 603-616; Ragsdale, Mo. Bul. 336; see also: Fitch and Lush, Jour. Dairy Sci., 14, 1931, pp. 116-124; Henderson and Anthony, West Va. Bul. 232.
3. Krauss and Monroe, Ohio Bul. 497; Forbes et al., Jour. Agr. Res., 45, 1932, pp. 113-128.
4. N. J. Rpt. 1930; Monroe and Krauss, Ohio Bul. 516.
5. Hart and Elvehjem, Wis. Bul. 410.
6. Huffman, Robinson, Winter, and Larson, Jour. Nutr., 2, 1930, pp. 471-483; Eckles, Gullickson, and Palmer, Minn. Tech. Bul. 91.
7. Eckles, Gullickson, and Palmer, Minn. Tech. Bul. 91; Huffman et al., Jour. Dairy Sci., 16, 1933, pp. 203-223; Lamb et al., Jour. Dairy Sci., 17, 1934, pp. 233-241.
8. Salmon and Eaton, Jour. Dairy Sci., 8, 1925, pp. 312-317.
9. Huffman et al., Mich. Tech. Bul. 134; Archibald and Bennett, Jour. Agr. Res., 51, 1935, pp. 83-96; see also: Henderson and Weakley, West Va. Bul. 231.
10. Huffman, Am. Soc. Anim. Prod., Proc. 1934.
11. Lindsey, Archibald, and Nelson, Jour. Agr. Res., 42, 1931, pp. 883-896; Mass. Bul. 271.
12. Jones, Eckles, and Palmer, Jour. Dairy Sci., 9, 1926, pp. 119-139; Bechdel, Honeywell, and Dutcher, Penn. Bul. 230; Kuhlman, Gallup, and Weaver, Jour. Dairy Sci., 18, 1935, pp. 433-434.
13. Bechdel, Landsburg and Hill, Penn. Bul. 291; Rupel, Bohstedt, and Hart, Wis. Res. Bul. 115; Huffman, Mich. Quar. Bul. 14, 1931; No. 1 and Mich. Rpt. 1930-32.
14. Gullickson and Eckles, Jour. Dairy Sci., 10, 1927, pp. 87-94; S. D. Rpts. 1931, 1932; Morrison and Rupel, Wis. Bul. 396.
15. Insko and Rupel, Wis. Bul. 405; Isaachsen, Jour. Agr. Sci., England, 22, 1932, pp. 460-484.
16. N. J. Rpt. 1930.
17. Bechdel, Eckles, and Palmer, Jour. Dairy Sci., 9, 1926, pp. 409-438.
18. Eckles et al., Jour. Dairy Sci., 7, 1924, pp. 421-439.
19. Thurston, Eckles, and Palmer, Jour. Dairy Sci., 9, 1926, pp. 37-49; 12, 1929, pp. 394-404.
20. Atkeson, Warren, and Anderson, Jour. Dairy Sci., 17, 1934, pp. 249-256.
21. Morrison, Hulce, and Humphrey, Wis. Bul. 352; Rupel, Wis. Bul. 404.
22. Ragsdale, Brody, and Nelson, Mo. Buls. 210, 228.
23. Norris, N. Y. (Cornell) Memoir 90.
24. Iowa Rpt. 1930.
25. Espe and Cannon, Jour. Dairy Sci., 18, 1935, pp. 141-147.
26. Morrison, Hulce, and Humphrey, Wis. Bul. 339.
27. Hilton, Wilbur, and Heinton, Ind. Bul. 373; McCandlish, Iowa Res. Bul. 51; Kildee, Iowa Cir. 16; Otis, Kan. Bul. 126; S. C. Rpt. 1924; Fain and Jarnagin, Va. Bul. 172; Ireland Dept. Agr. and Tech. Instr. Jour., 20, 1920, pp. 201-204.
28. Calloway, La. Bul. 180.
29. Elting and La Master, S. C. Bul. 293; see also: Kuhlman, Weaver, and Gallup, Okla. Rpt. 1932-34.
30. Carr, Spitzer, Caldwell, and Anderson, Jour. Biol. Chem., 28, 1917, pp. 501-509.
31. Krauss and Monroe, Ohio Bul. 548.
32. La Master and Elting, S. C. Rpt. 1930.
33. Morrison, Hulce, and Humphrey, Wis. Bul. 362; Morrison and Rupel, Wis. Bul. 396; Rupel, Wis. Bul. 404.
34. Ragsdale and Turner, Mo. Bul. 197.
35. Dvorachek, Ark. Buls. 246, 257; Jacobsen, Ark. Bul. 280.
36. White and Kuelling, Conn. (Storrs) Bul. 102; Iowa Rpt. 1923.
37. Cunningham, Ariz. Rpt. 1932.
38. Spitzer and Carr, Ind. Bul. 246; Krauss and Crawford, Ohio Bimo. Bul. 137; Ellington and Knott, Wash. Bul. 178; Morrison and Rupel, Wis. Bul. 388; Rupel, Wis. Bul. 404; Canada Expt. Farms, Kentville, N. S., Station, Rpt. of Supt. 1922.
39. Tretsven and Keyes, Mont. Bul. 304; Olson, S. D. Bul. 304.
40. Woodward, Jour. Dairy Sci., 6, 1923, pp. 243-4.
41. Morrison and Rupel, Wis. Bul. 362.
42. Otis, Kan. Bul. 126.
43. Rupel, Wis. Bul. 404; see also: Woll and Voorhies, Cal. Bul. 271.
44. Kan. Rpts. 1924-26, 1928-30.
45. Lindsey, Mass. Rpts. 1893, 1894.
46. Morrison, Hulce, and Humphrey, Wis. Buls. 339, 362; Rupel, Wis. Bul. 404.
47. Otis, Kan. Bul. 126; Paterson, West of Scotland Agr. College, Rpt. 15.
48. Id. Buls. 160, 179; Ingham, Meade and Berry, Md. Bul. 319; Berry, Md. Bul. 330; Eckles and Gullickson, Minn. Bul 215; Lindsey and Archibald, Mass. Bul. 253; Krauss and Crawford, Ohio Bimo. Bul. 137; Ellington and Knott, Wash. Bul. 178; Morrison and Rupel, Wis. Bul. 388; Rupel, Wis. Bul. 404; Bohstedt and Rupel, Am. Soc. Anim. Prod., Proc. 1930, pp. 167-169.

49. Id. Bul. 164; Eckles and Gullickson, Minn. Bul. 215; Ellington and Knott, Wash. Buls. 178, 208; Rupel, Wis. Bul. 404.
50. Riddell, Kan. Rpt. 1932-34.
51. Weaver, Shay, and Ely, Iowa Cir. 91; Berry, Md. Bul. 330; Kuhlman, McGilliard, and Weaver, Okla. Rpts. 1930-32, 1932-34.
52. Atkeson and Warren, Id. Buls. 192, 197; Hulce and Nevens, Ill. Cir. 202; Riddell, Kan. Rpt. 1932-34; Snell, La. Rpt. 1929-31; Ingham, Meade, and Berry, Md. Bul. 319; Berry, Md. Buls. 330, 354; Lindsey and Archibald, Mass. Buls. 271, 280, 293; Mich. Bien. Rpt. 1928-30; Eckles and Gullickson, Minn. Bul. 215; Ragsdale and Turner, Mo. Buls. 179, 189, 210; Ragsdale and Turner, Jour. Agr. Res., 26, 1923, pp. 437-446; Mead, Regan, and Bartlett, Jour. Dairy Sci., 7, 1924, pp. 440-459; Savage and Crawford, N. Y. (Cornell) Bul. 622; Krauss, Monroe, and Hayden, Ohio Buls. 497, 516, 532, 548; Krauss and Crawford, Ohio Bimo. Buls. 137, 141; Jones, Brandt, and Wilson, Ore. Bul. 290; Bechdel and Williams, Penn. Buls. 213, 243, 266; Elting and LaMaster, S. C. Bul. 293; Knott, Hodgson, and Ellington, Wash. Bul. 273; Morrison and Rupel, Wis. Bul. 388; Rupel and Bohstedt, Wis. Bul. 410.
53. Berry, Md. Bul. 354; Morrison and Rupel, Wis. Bul. 388; see also: Elting and LaMaster, S. C. Bul. 293.
54. Morrison and Rupel, Wis. Bul. 388; Rupel, Wis. Bul. 404.
55. Elting and LaMaster, S. C. Bul. 293.
56. Mead, Cal. Bul. 478.
57. Savage and Crawford, N. Y. (Cornell) Bul. 622.
58. Savage and Crawford, N. Y. (Cornell) Bul. 622.
59. Shepherd and Miller, U. S. Dept. Agr., Farmers' Bul. 1723.
60. Knott, Hodgson, and Ellington, Wash. Bul. 273.
61. Elting and LaMaster, S. C. Bul. 293.
62. Bender and Perry, N. J. Exten. Bul. 73; N. J. Rpts. 1930, 1931; Bender and Bartlett, Jour. Dairy Sci., 12 1929, pp. 37-48; N. J. Cir. 263.
63. Berry, Md. Bul. 354; Savage and Crawford, N. Y. (Cornell) Bul. 622; Krauss, Monroe, and Hayden, Ohio Buls. 497, 516, 548; Williams and Bechdel, Penn. Bul. 266.
64. Atkeson and Warren, Id. Bul. 205; Savage and Newman, N. Y. (Cornell) Sta., unpublished data.
65. Mead, Cal. Bul. 478; Fraser and Brand, Ill. Bul. 164; Gullickson, Minn. Spec. Bul. 91; Swett, Mo. Cir. 91; Crawford and Krauss, Ohio Bimo. Bul. 141.
66. Archibald, Jour. Dairy Sci., 11, 1928, pp. 119-135.
67. Maynard, Norris, and Krauss, N. Y. (Cornell) Bul. 439.
68. Davis and Cunningham, Ariz. Bul. 111; Hunziker and Caldwell, Ind. Bul. 193; Spitzer and Carr, Ind. Bul. 246; Lindsey and Archibald, Mass. Buls. 223, 230, 253; Ellington and Knott, Wash. Bul. 178; Morrison and Rupel, Wis. Bul. 396.
69. Hulce, Ill. Sta., information to the author; McCandlish, Iowa Res. Bul. 51; Jour. Dairy Sci. 6, 1923, pp. 572-587; 7, 1924, pp. 160-162; Tretsven, Mont. Bul. 282; S. C. Rpt. 1924; Olson, S. D. Bul. 236; Henderson and Anthony, West Va. Bul. 232.
70. Nevens, Jour. Dairy Sci., 2, 1919, pp. 435-443.
71. Eckles, Mo. Res. Bul. 31; Mo. Buls. 135; 158; Eckles and Swett, Mo. Bul. 163.
72. Woll, Jour. Dairy Sci., 1, 1917, pp. 447-461; Id. Buls. 131, 149, 164, 179; Ind. Rpt. 1925; Reed, Fitch, and Cave, Kan. Bul. 233; Eckles, Mo. Bul. 158; Eckles and Swett, Mo. Bul. 163; Nevens and Davis, Nebr. Bul. 181; Headley, Nev. Rpt. 1933; Bender and Bartlett, N. J. Cir. 263; Ore. Rpt. 1920-22; LaMaster, S. C. Rpt. 1926; Willard, Jour. Dairy Sci., 15, 1932, pp. 435-444; Shepherd and Miller, U. S. Dept. Agr., Farmers' Bul. 1723.
73. Nevens, Davis, et al., Nebr. Bul. 181; Hayden, Ohio Bimo. Bul. 120.
74. Hilton, Wilbur, and Hauge, Ind. Bul. 354; Snell, La. Rpt. 1929-31.
75. Ohio Buls. 362, 373.
76. Ark. Bul. 215; Hayden, Ohio Bimo. Bul. 120.
77. Dvorachek, Ark. Bul. 257 and Ark. Rpt. 1931-32; Ore. Rpt. 1924-26.
78. Morrison, Oosterhuis, and Bohstedt, Wis. Bul. 275; see also Ore. Rpt. 1918-20.
79. Morrison and Hulce, Wis. Sta., unpublished data.
80. Berry, Md. Bul. 332; Beam, Penn. Bul. 266.
81. Copeland, Tex. Bul. 451.
82. Harrison and Kahn, N. Y. (Cornell) Rpt. 1931.
83. Hunt, Va. Buls. 219, 225; Kan. Rpt. 1926-28.
84. White, Jour. Dairy Sci., 1, 1917, p. 139; Plum and Lush, Jour. Dairy Sci., 17, 1934, pp. 625-638; Reed, Fitch, and Cave, Kan. Bul. 233; Ky. Rpt. 1924; Towles, Md. Bul. 217; Eckles, Mo. Bul. 135; Beam, Penn. Rpt. 1916; Shepherd and Miller, U. S. Dept. Agr., Farmers' Bul. 1723.
85. Turner, Mo. Res. Bul. 164.
86. White, Rettger, et al., Conn. (Storrs) Bul. 135.
87. Ragsdale, Mo. Bul. 336; Eckles, Mo. Res. Bul. 36; Espe, Cannon, and Hansen, Iowa Res. Bul. 154; Fitch, Kan. Sta., mimeo. rpt.; Davis, Nebr. Sta., information to the author; Elting and LaMaster, S. C. Bul. 293; Henderson, West Va. Sta., information to the author; Moseley, Stuart, and Graves, U. S. Dept. Agr., Tech. Bul. 116. (The last-mentioned publication includes Montana and South Dakota data.)
88. Hayden, Ohio Bul. 289; Staples and Lush, La. Cir. 9; Selby and Kuhlman, Ore. Bul. 324; see also: Hulce and Nevens, Ill. Cir. 202; Dow, Me. Bul. 361; Watkins, Md. Bul. 356; Ragsdale, Mo. Bul. 338; Eke, West Va. Bul. 224; McNall and Mitchell, Wis. Bul. 405.
89. Schaefer and Eckles, Jour. Dairy Sci., 13, 1930, pp. 165-173.
90. Woodward, Wash. Bul. 158; Ellington, Wash. Buls. 175, 196.

CHAPTER XXIX

GENERAL PROBLEMS IN BEEF PRODUCTION

I. Nutrient Requirements of Beef Cattle

989. Knowledge of nutrient requirements increasingly important.—The systems of beef production in this and many other countries have undergone profound changes during the past score of years, and these trends are still continuing. Chief among these is the fattening of cattle for market at much younger ages than formerly. This change has made it even more necessary than before that the beef producer have a thorough knowledge of the nutrient requirements of his cattle, in order to secure from them the best possible returns.

Until rather recently beef cattle were commonly raised to the age of 2 or 3 years, and then were fattened for market. They made most of their growth on cheap pasture and were carried through the winters on what roughage was available, usually without any concentrates whatsoever. If the pasture was reasonably good, it took care of the requirements of the cattle for protein, minerals, and vitamins, under this system of moderate rate of growth and development.

These well-grown cattle, 2 years old or more, were taken from the western ranges or other pasture districts to sections of the country where grain was cheaper, and there fed for market until they reached the desired degree of fatness. Since their protein tissues and their skeletons were already largely grown, the requirements for protein and minerals were materially less than with younger animals. Also, since the feeding period was not commonly so long as is needed for the fattening of calves and yearlings, there was less tendency for a deficiency of vitamins to produce injury, unless the lack was too serious.

The desire of consumers for smaller cuts of beef that are tender but have a minimum of waste fat, has brought about the fattening of cattle for market at a much earlier age. As is shown in Chapter XXXI, the cattle raised for beef on farms in the corn belt and eastward are, to an ever-increasing extent, fattened as they grow. Such cattle are ready for slaughter as "heavy fat calves" at weaning time or soon afterwards, or are fattened for marketing at 12 to 18 months of age as "baby beeves," or "fat yearlings."

A similar change has taken place in the case of cattle produced on the ranges. Instead of being grown under range conditions to 2 years of age or more, a large proportion of the calves are now sold as feeders in the fall of their first year. Most of the rest are sold as yearlings, after being carried through one winter and the following summer on the range. To reach the desired degree of fatness these range calves must be fed liberal fattening rations for approximately 200 days or more, nearly doubling their initial weights during this time.

Calves that are raised for baby beef on farms or range calves that are fattened for market are growing rapidly in protein tissues and skeleton, as well as laying on fat. Therefore to secure the cheapest gains it is much more necessary than in the case of older cattle that their rations fully meet their nutritive requirements.

990. Nutrient requirements of various classes of cattle.—Before proceeding to a detailed discussion of the requirements of beef cattle for the various nutrients, it will be helpful to consider the differences in the general requirements for the different classes of cattle.

The nutrient requirements of beef breeding cows are far different from those of dairy cows, for their milk yields are much lower. Also, they are usually dry during the winter feeding period and produce their milk while on pasture. Normally, beef cows need no supplementary feed during the pasture period.

It is shown in Chapter XXXI that they may be wintered cheaply on roughage alone, if it is of fairly good quality and if sufficient legume hay is fed to meet their limited need for protein. (**1104-1108**) If no legume hay is fed, they can be wintered adequately on non-legume roughage, such as corn or sorghum silage or fodder, with only 1 lb. per head daily of cottonseed meal, linseed meal, or some other high-protein supplement. It is wise to add 0.1 lb. per head daily of a calcium supplement to such non-legume rations to provide an ample supply of this mineral.

When calves or yearlings are being carried through the winter to be fattened later, they may likewise be maintained entirely or chiefly on roughage, if it is of good quality. As is shown in Chapter XXXI, even calves will make satisfactory growth and will improve in condition on a full feed of corn or sorghum silage with 3 or 4 lbs. of alfalfa or other legume hay as a protein supplement. (**1118**) With no legume hay in the ration, 1 lb. per head daily of protein supplement is needed to balance the ration, and a calcium supplement is also advisable.

The requirements of cattle that are being fattened rapidly are in strong contrast to those of beef breeding cows or of cattle that are merely being carried through the winter. To enable them to make rapid gains, they must receive rations rich in total digestible nutrients and net energy. The data summarized later in this chapter show that, except when grain is unusually high in price in comparison with roughage, it is generally advisable to give a liberal allowance to cattle being fattened in dry lot. (**1004-1006**) Unless this is done, they will make less rapid gains and will not reach as good a finish.

Especially with calves and yearlings, good gains cannot be expected unless the ration provides ample protein, minerals, and vitamins. These needs are considered in detail in the paragraphs which follow.

The nutrient requirements of beef cattle of the various ages and classes are shown in the Morrison feeding standards. These recommendations are based chiefly upon extensive studies by the author and associates, of the many experiments that have been conducted during recent years by the American experiment stations. It is believed that rations computed according to these standards will amply meet the requirements of beef cattle, provided due attention is given to vitamins, minerals, and quality of protein, and to the general suitability of the feeds for the particular class of stock to be fed.

991. Protein requirements.—Recent investigations have proved definitely that beef cattle do not need nearly as much protein as was recommended in the Wolff-Lehmann and other older feeding standards. This fact is of great financial importance in beef production, for protein supplements ordinarily cost much more per ton than grain. Therefore, if farm animals are fed larger amounts of supplements than they actually need, the profits will be materially reduced.

Whether or not it will be advisable to add a protein supplement to a ration for fattening cattle which consists of farm-grown grain and roughage, will depend on the kind of roughage and also to some extent on the kind of grain. This is shown in the following paragraphs that review the results of the feeding experiments which have been conducted to study this problem. The protein requirements for wintering young stock and beef breeding cows are discussed in Chapter XXXI.

When beef cattle are fed even a rather limited amount of legume hay, the ration will usually provide proteins of adequate kind or quality. (**153**) On the other hand, if little or no legume roughage is fed, then due attention should be given to the kind of protein supplied by various protein supplements.

For example, corn gluten meal or corn gluten feed should not be used as the only supplement to balance a ration of grain and non-legume roughage. These corn by-products should instead be combined with linseed meal, soybeans, soybean oil meal, etc., which will make good the deficiencies in the proteins of the cereal grains. The experiments reported in the following chapter show that, even with a small amount of legume hay in the ration, the value of gluten meal as a protein supplement for fattening cattle has been greatly increased by combining it with linseed meal or with both linseed meal and cottonseed meal. (**1067**)

992. Amounts of protein required by fattening cattle.—It is highly important in fattening cattle for market to know definitely whether any supplement is required, and, if any is needed, just how much should be added to the ration. These questions have therefore been given much study by the author, and the recommendations given in the Morrison feeding standards are based upon a careful analysis of the experiments which bear upon this problem. Due to limitations of space, only certain typical experiments on this subject can be reviewed in the following paragraphs.

As shown in Appendix Table III, it is the belief of the author that rations for fattening calves should have nutritive ratios not wider than 1:6.5 to 1:7.3; for yearlings, not wider than 1:7.0 to 1:8.0; and for 2-year-olds, not wider than 1:7.5 to 1:8.5. When rations contain less protein than provided by these nutritive ratios, the gains will usually be considerably less rapid and more feed will be required per 100 lbs. gain. Also, the cattle will generally sell for a lower price, on account of inferior finish.

The net returns will therefore generally be increased when sufficient protein supplement is fed so that the ration is no wider than the limits here indicated. If care is taken to feed only enough protein supplement to balance the ration according to these recommendations, each 100 lbs. of such a supplement as linseed meal, cottonseed meal, or soybean oil meal will be equal in value to 250 to 300 lbs. of grain or grain equivalent. This value considers not only the saving in amount of feed required per 100 lbs. gain, but also the higher selling price, due to better finish.

993. Adding a supplement to grain and alfalfa hay.—Legume hay of good quality is so rich in protein that when fattening cattle are fed a liberal amount, along with corn or other grain, the ration contains sufficient protein to produce good gains. Whether or not it will pay to add any protein supplement will depend on the amount of hay actually eaten, the protein content of the hay, and the age of the cattle.

Good alfalfa hay is sufficiently high in protein to balance fully the ration for 2-year-old fattening cattle full-fed on corn grain and the hay. This is shown by Nebraska experiments in which 2-year-old steers ate an average of 16.6 lbs. corn and 10.9 lbs. alfalfa hay per head daily, gaining 2.41 lbs. a day, and requiring 695 lbs. corn and 460 lbs. hay per 100 lbs. gain.[1] The nutritive ratio of this ration was 1:7.1, which is even narrower than necessary for 2-year-old steers. The addition of linseed meal or cottonseed meal to this ration did not increase the rate of gain or decrease the amounts of feed required per 100 lbs. gain. Neither did it increase the selling price of the steers.

Fattening calves require a larger proportion of protein than do older cattle, and it would therefore be expected that for them there would be more advantage in adding a supplement to a ration of corn and alfalfa hay. In three South Dakota experiments in which fattening calves were fed liberally on alfalfa hay, with corn as the grain, they received an average of 6.5 lbs. hay and 13.5 lbs. corn per head daily and gained 2.42 lbs. a day.[2] Adding about 1 lb. per head daily of linseed meal to the ration increased the daily gain only 0.04 lb., and each 100 lbs. of linseed meal saved only 64 lbs. corn plus 51 lbs. hay. It was therefore not profitable to add the supplement.

Fattening calves that consumed somewhat less alfalfa hay in 3 other similar experiments, received 4.6 lbs. hay per head daily and gained an average of 2.27 lbs.[3] Adding linseed meal or cottonseed meal to the ration increased the gain to 2.45 lbs. and produced a somewhat better finish. The cattle fed the supplement sold for 30 cents more per hundredweight, on the average, and returned $2.82 more per head over cost of feed than those fed no supplement.

From these trials it may be concluded that it does not usually pay to add a supplement to corn and a liberal feed of good alfalfa hay for 2-year-olds and also for yearlings. The addition of a supplement to this ration will also not generally be profitable in the case of calves, if they consume a liberal amount of good-quality alfalfa hay. These statements apply also to soybean hay and cowpea hay, which contain even more protein, on the average, than does alfalfa hay.

If the amount of alfalfa hay is nearly as large as this, it will require only a small amount of protein supplement to balance the ration. For example, a ration of 11 lbs. corn grain and 5 lbs. average alfalfa hay has a nutritive ratio of 1:7.7, which is slightly too wide for fattening calves. Adding to this ration only 0.5 lb. of cottonseed meal of 41 per cent protein grade will provide plenty of protein to meet the recommendations of the Morrison feeding standards, for the nutritive ratio will then be 1:6.9.

When the grain fed with alfalfa hay is barley, wheat, or oats, there is obviously less advantage in adding a supplement than with corn, owing to the higher protein content of these grains.[4]

994. Adding a supplement to grain and clover hay.—Since clover hay of average quality contains less protein than alfalfa hay, a ration of corn and clover hay does not provide quite enough protein for maximum gains, even of 2-year-old cattle. This is shown by 5 experiments in which 2-year-old steers fed 18.7 lbs. shelled corn and 9.9 lbs. clover hay gained 2.08 lbs. per head daily and required 910 lbs. corn and 485 lbs. hay per 100 lbs. gain.[5] Adding 2.75 lbs. of linseed or cottonseed meal to this ration increased the daily gain to 2.38 lbs., and each 100 lbs. of supplement saved 130 lbs. corn, plus 70 lbs. hay.

The saving in feed per 100 lbs. of supplement was hardly large enough to make the use of the supplement profitable, chiefly because much more supplement was fed than is now known to be necessary for cattle of this age. The nutritive ratio of the ration of corn and clover hay alone was 1:9.0, which provides nearly enough protein for 2-year-olds. Adding merely 0.5 lb. per head daily of cottonseed meal (41 per cent protein grade) would provide sufficient protein, for the nutritive ratio would then be 1:8.4. This is within the limits advised in the Morrison feeding standards.

When no more supplement is fed than is actually needed, it will probably be profitable under usual conditions to add a protein supplement to corn and clover hay for fattening 2-year-old cattle. There will be still more advantage in the case of yearlings, and with calves the proper amount of supplement should always be added. The amount of supplement needed with mixed clover-and-grass hay will depend on the proportion of clover actually present in the hay.

995. Supplement needed with non-legume roughage.—When legume hay forms only part of the roughage for fattening cattle, the amount of protein in the ration is correspondingly lessened and the need of a supplement increased. The amount of supplement required for any combination of roughages and grain can readily be found by computing a ration which is balanced according to the feeding standards.

When fattening cattle are fed all the corn or sorghum silage they will eat in addition to corn or other grain, the silage is so palatable that they will generally eat but 2 to 5 lbs. of hay a day, even when it is legume hay of good quality. This small amount of legume hay is insufficient to balance the ration, and therefore the gains will be increased considerably if a supplement is added.

The effect of adding a protein supplement to a ration of a liberal amount of corn silage, with corn grain and clover hay, is shown in the following table, which summarizes the results of 14 comparisons in which 2-year-old steers averaging 935 lbs. in weight were fed for an average of 161 days.[6]

The steers in Lot II, fed 2.6 lbs. of protein supplement (cottonseed meal or linseed meal) in addition to shelled corn, corn silage, and clover hay, gained 0.4 lb. more per head daily than those in Lot I, which had no supplement. They also ate slightly less feed per 100 lbs. gain, but their feed cost per 100 lbs. gain was $0.65 higher, because the cost of the supplements was much more per ton than that of corn. However, the selling price for the steers fed the supplement was enough higher to more than offset the greater cost of the gains, and their net return per head over cost of feed was slightly greater.

Adding a supplement to corn, corn silage, and clover hay

	Daily gain Lbs.	Concen- trates Lbs.	Hay Lbs.	Silage Lbs.	Feed cost per 100 lbs. gain Dollars	Selling price Dollars	Net return per head Dollars
Average ration			Feed per 100 lbs. gain				
Lot I, no supplement							
Shelled corn, 12.7 lbs.							
Corn silage, 28.6 lbs.							
Clover hay, 3.6 lbs.......	2.1	619	177	1,390	13.19	9.03	9.62
Lot II, fed a supplement							
Supplement, 2.6 lbs.							
Shelled corn, 12.4 lbs.							
Corn silage, 28.3 lbs.							
Clover hay, 3.5 lbs.......	2.5	612	144	1,186	13.84	9.36	9.91

Considerably more supplement was fed in these trials than is actually needed, according to our present information. If only 1.25 lbs. of supplement had been used, instead of 2.6 lbs., the nutritive ratio would have been 1:8.4, which is narrow enough for 2-year-old fattening cattle. The rate of gain and the selling price would then probably have been about as high as with the larger amount of supplement, and the net return would have been materially greater.

On account of the high protein content of alfalfa hay, a ration of corn grain, corn silage, and alfalfa hay is more nearly balanced than when clover is fed. Therefore less supplement is needed. In 6 experiments 2-year-old steers fed this ration (4.0 lbs. of alfalfa hay being fed daily) gained 2.22 lbs. per head daily, in comparison with a gain of 2.47 lbs. when 2.34 lbs. of cottonseed meal or linseed meal were added.[7] However, there was not sufficient saving in the amount of feed required per 100 lbs. gain or enough increase in the selling price to make the use of the supplement profitable for cattle of this age.

The nutritive ratio of the ration of corn grain, corn silage, and alfalfa hay was 1:9.0, which is nearly narrow enough for fattening 2-year-old cattle. It would have required only 0.5 to 0.75 lb. of cottonseed meal to provide as much protein as now advised in the Morrison feeding standards. If only this amount had been fed, the use of the supplement would probably have been profitable.

996. Supplement more necessary for calves.—Because fattening calves need more protein than do older cattle, there is more benefit from feeding them a protein supplement in addition to corn grain, corn or sorghum silage, and legume hay. In 8 experiments the addition of 1.5 lbs. per head daily of linseed meal or cake to a ration of corn grain, corn silage, and alfalfa hay increased the daily gain from 2.01 lbs. to 2.29 lbs. and raised the selling price 42 cents per 100 lbs.[8] (In 6 of the trials the calves were fed a mixture of corn and oats while they were being started on feed.) The average net return per head over feed costs was $2.60 more for the supplement-fed calves, being greater than for those fed no supplement in all except one of the tests. In these experiments each 100 lbs. of linseed meal were worth as much as 230 lbs. of corn grain, considering all factors.

Similar results were secured in three Kansas trials in which calves were fed corn grain and sorghum silage, with only 2 to 3 lbs. of alfalfa hay.[9] The addition of 0.9 lb. cottonseed meal to the ration increased the net returns in each test, and each 100 lbs. of cottonseed meal were worth as much as 287 lbs. of corn grain.

997. Mineral requirements.—Beef cattle should always be supplied regularly with salt, as shown in the following paragraphs. Whether there will be any need of furnishing additional mineral supplements to provide either calcium or phosphorus will depend entirely on the amounts in the ration, as is shown in later paragraphs.

Wherever there is trouble from goiter, or "big neck," in calves at birth, iodized salt should be supplied the breeding cows during the latter part of the pregnancy period. (**172**) In a few districts, the soil is so deficient in iron or in both iron and copper that poor results follow unless cattle on pasture are provided a mineral mixture containing these minerals. (**173**)

There is no need of adding to the usual rations for beef cattle any other minerals, such as sulfur, potassium, sand, or dirt.[10] (**182**) Also, the addition of kelp to well-balanced rations is not usually profitable. (**671**)

998. Salt.—Salt should be supplied regularly to all beef cattle. (**158**) The best plan is to provide it where they can have access to it and can take what they wish, instead of salting them only once or twice a week.

For feeding where the salt is not exposed to the weather, loose salt, rock salt, and block salt are all satisfactory, but flake salt is not desirable for feeding in the open, on account of the great loss through weathering. Cattle prefer the softer kinds of block salt to that which is very hard. In Iowa tests with fattening cattle fed under shelter, there were no differences in rate or economy of gain when salt was fed in flake form or in blocks.[11] Cattle usually eat somewhat more salt when fed flake salt than when supplied with block salt.

In Iowa experiments in which a record was kept of the amount of block salt consumed by cattle fattened in dry lot with shelter, it was found that the average for 2-year-olds was 0.022 lb. per head daily in 14 tests and the average for calves 0.021 lb. per head daily in 10 tests.[12] The salt consumption was thus about two-thirds pound per month. Where salt is fed in the open, about twice this amount must be fed, to allow for wastage.

Cattle on pasture consume much more salt than those fed in dry lot on harvested feeds, and they eat more in spring and early summer when the forage is abundant and succulent than later in the season. In a Kansas test yearling and 2-year-old steers on pasture consumed about 2.8 lbs. of block salt per head in July, 1.8 lbs. in August, and 1.2 lbs. in September and in October.[13] Nearly equal amounts were lost by weathering of the salt blocks. In another Kansas test, when a salt mixture was fed which was advertised as repelling flies from cattle, no such effect was noted.[14]

Under range conditions a total of about 20 lbs. of salt is provided for each cow during the year.[15] The salt allowance should be from 2.0 to 2.5 lbs. per head a month when the feed is succulent or when the cattle are subsisting largely on browse. Later in the season 1.0 to 1.5 lbs. per month are usually sufficient.

999. Calcium.—When beef cattle are fed a sufficient amount of legume hay or other legume roughage (as silage containing considerable legumes), there will be no lack of calcium in the ration. Consequently, there is no advantage in adding a calcium supplement like ground limestone to such rations.[16] **(161)**

Experiments conducted several years ago, which are summarized in the next chapter, showed that fattening cattle did not make as rapid gains or reach as good a finish when fed only non-legume roughage of good quality, as when they received some legume hay. **(1071)** This was true even when care was taken to furnish plenty of protein in the non-legume ration, by the use of sufficient amounts of protein supplements.

Extensive experiments by McCampbell and associates at the Kansas Station and also later studies by others have shown conclusively that the poor results on non-legume roughage of good quality are due to a lack of calcium.[17] For example, in the Kansas tests fattening cattle made decidedly smaller and less economical gains on rations of grain, protein supplement, and either sorghum silage or sorghum silage and prairie hay for roughage, than they did when fed a limited amount of alfalfa hay.

However, when 0.1 lb. ground limestone or similar calcium supplement was added to the non-legume ration, the results were as good, or nearly as good, as when alfalfa hay was fed. This does not mean that prairie hay or other grass hay would then be equal to legume hay in value per ton, for a greater amount of protein supplement is needed to balance the ration when no legume hay is fed. **(993-996)**

When only non-legume roughage is used, there is more apt to be a lack of calcium for fattening cattle than for cattle that are being carried through the winter for later fattening. This is because even non-legume hay, fodder, or silage contains considerably more calcium than the grains. Therefore fattening cattle that are liberally fed on grain, and consequently eat only limited amounts of roughage, receive much less calcium than stock cattle being wintered on roughage with little or no grain.

However, especially in the case of calves, it is wise to add 0.1 lb. per head daily of ground limestone or other calcium supplement to a wintering ration that contains no legume roughage, unless the roughage has been raised on soil rich in calcium. In Nebraska trials there was a marked benefit for wintering calves from adding ground limestone to a ration of corn silage or sorghum silage plus 1 lb. per head daily of cottonseed meal.[18] Similarly, in a Wyoming test it was profitable to add ground limestone to a ration for wintering beef cattle which was composed of native grass hay, sunflower silage, and 1 lb. cottonseed cake per head daily.[19]

If good-quality non-legume roughage, such as grass hay or corn or sorghum fodder or silage, is grown on calcium-rich soil, there may be no lack of this mineral in the ration when these feeds are the only roughages for beef cattle. There will then be no benefit from adding a calcium supplement.[20] However, since ground limestone and other calcium supplements are cheap, it is advisable to add to such rations the small amount needed as an insurance against any deficiency, unless there is definite knowledge that the calcium supply is ample.

When fattening calves eat only 2 lbs. or less of legume hay per head daily, along with a full feed of grain and corn or sorghum silage, it may be wise to add 0.05 to 0.10 lb. calcium supplement per head daily to the ration.[21] Such a small amount of legume hay may not provide quite enough calcium for them, since their calcium requirements are considerably higher than for older cattle.

1000. Phosphorus.—The recent investigations that are summarized in Chapter VI have shown that throughout many districts in this and other countries the soil is so deficient in phosphorus that the forage produced on it provides insufficient of this mineral for cattle or other stock. (**163**) As a result, the animals become unthrifty and fail to make normal gains. They may even die as a result of the phosphorus deficiency, or because of disease contracted through chewing decomposed and putrid bones in an effort to get the needed phosphorus. Under such conditions there is a striking benefit from providing bone meal or other safe phosphorus supplements. (**166**)

It is of interest to note that a serious lack of phosphorus in pasture forage may even impair the quality of beef from cattle fattened on such pastures. In a Kansas test beef from cattle fattened on phosphorus-deficient pasture had a higher shrinkage loss in storage and did not stand ripening for so long a period as beef from normal animals.[22]

Recommendations are made in Chapter VI concerning suitable methods of furnishing phosphorus. (**181**) But little information is yet available to show the minimum amounts of phosphorus or calcium required by beef cattle of various ages. The requirements for young beef cattle are probably about the same as for young dairy cattle. (**950**) In New Mexico experiments yearling steers were able to store phosphorus in their bodies when their ration contained 14.8 grams (about one-half ounce) per head daily.[23]

When fattening cattle are fed rations which include 1.0 lb. or more per head daily of cottonseed meal, linseed meal, soybean oil meal, soybeans, or other protein supplements rich in phosphorus, they will have an ample supply of this mineral. There is therefore no need of adding a phosphorus supplement to such rations. In some experiments there has been no improvement whatsoever from adding to good rations of this kind either bone meal or a mineral mixture containing bone meal or other phosphorus supplements.[24] In other tests the improvement has been but slight.[25]

When no protein supplement that is rich in phosphorus is included in a ration for fattening cattle, there may be a marked advantage in adding bone meal or some other phosphorus supplement. This is especially the case when a considerable part of the ration consists of wet beet pulp, beet molasses, or other feeds very low in phosphorus. In Utah experiments, summarized in the next chapter, the gains of fattening cattle were doubled when 0.1 lb. per head daily of bone meal was added to a ration of wet beet pulp, beet molasses, and alfalfa hay. (**1054**)

In contrast to these results, there was no advantage in an Idaho experiment with fattening cattle from adding bone meal to rations consisting of only alfalfa hay or of a liberal amount of alfalfa hay, fed with barley and dried beet pulp.[26] The difference between the Utah and Idaho results was probably due to the larger amount of alfalfa hay eaten in the Idaho test, and to the fact that barley contains much more phosphorus than does beet pulp or beet molasses. Also, if feeder cattle come from a range where the forage is rich in phosphorus and in calcium, they may make good gains during the usual fattening period on a ration rather low in these minerals.

Whenever there is any probability that there is insufficient phosphorus in a ration for fattening cattle, a phosphorus supplement should be added as insurance. If there is a decided lack of phosphorus, 0.1 lb. per head daily of bone meal or the equivalent amount of another safe phosphorus supplement should be used. When the feeds probably supply nearly enough phosphorus, half this amount of phosphorus supplement is ample.

1001. Vitamin requirements.—The only vitamin that is of importance in feeding beef cattle under any usual conditions is vitamin A. Even when they receive no feeds rich in vitamin D, they are generally protected against any lack because they are commonly outdoors most of the daytime throughout the year, in all usual methods of commercial beef production. (**191**) So far as is known, there is no lack of the other vitamins in feeding beef cattle. (**195-200**)

Beef cattle will receive plenty of vitamin A when they are on green pasture and also when they are fed a reasonable amount of well-cured hay or corn or sorghum fodder. Good silage will also provide sufficient of this vitamin under most conditions. On the other hand, if they receive only such roughage as cottonseed hulls, straw, or hay of very poor quality, they will sooner or later be seriously affected by the deficiency of this vitamin. (**186**)

For a limited time fattening cattle that have previously been properly fed may make normal gains on a ration low in vitamin A. For instance, cattle will usually not show evidences of a lack of vitamins for 2 to 3 months when fattened on a ration consisting only of cottonseed hulls, fed with cottonseed meal or other usual concentrates. However, if they do not have a good store of vitamin A in their bodies, they will be affected sooner. In a Georgia trial, steers began to show the effects of such an inadequate ration before the end of the second month of fattening.[27]

Care should be taken not to feed beef cattle for any long period on a ration that does not include at least 3 to 5 lbs. per head daily of good-quality roughage, which will supply the necessary amounts of vitamin A. While beef breeding cows are often wintered in the wheat-growing districts of the West on nothing but straw plus 1 lb. per head daily of protein supplement, such a ration cannot be advised except under emergency conditions. (**1107**) There should be added a limited amount of well-cured hay or other roughage high in vitamin A, and also a calcium supplement.

California investigations have shown that when range cattle are forced to subsist for long periods on mature and weathered grass or similar forage, they may suffer from a serious deficiency of vitamin A.[28] This is due to the fact that the carotene has been nearly all destroyed in such forage. Furnishing a limited amount of well-cured alfalfa hay or other hay rich in vitamin A will prevent the injury that may otherwise result.

If the roughage fed to beef cattle contains sufficient vitamin A, there will be no difference in the value of yellow corn and white corn. On the other hand, yellow corn is superior to white corn when fed with vitamin-deficient roughages.[29]

1002. Need of roughage for fattening cattle.—Good roughage is the chief source of vitamin A and of calcium in most rations for cattle. It is therefore not surprising that fattening cattle have not made good gains when such roughage has been omitted from the ration.

In two Nebraska tests yearlings fed nothing but ground ear corn and cottonseed cake for only 65 days made decidedly less rapid gains than others fed alfalfa hay as roughage.[30] In an Illinois trial cattle fed for 112 days, only a mixture of ground oats, wheat, and corn, with cottonseed meal as a protein supplement, gained but 1.63 lbs., in comparison with 2.45 lbs. for others fed alfalfa hay in addition.[31]

1003. Water.—It is important that beef cattle have an abundant supply of good water at all times. During winter in the northern states, water in tanks or troughs should be kept from freezing by using suitable heaters, but there is no need otherwise of warming the water.[32] Separate water troughs should be provided for pigs running with the steers. While it is best to have water before beef cattle at all times, they readily adapt themselves to taking a fill once daily.

The water provision should be not less than 10 gallons per head daily for 2-year-old steers or breeding cows. In Ohio tests beef calves, averaging about 800 lbs. in weight, drank 6.5 to 7.1 gallons of water per head daily during the latter part of the fattening period.[33] In summer the average daily consumption of various groups was 6.8 to 8.0 gallons per head.

1004. Amount of concentrates for fattening cattle.—One of the most important problems in cattle feeding is deciding how much grain or other concentrates to feed during the fattening period. Upon a wise decision of this problem depends in no small measure the financial outcome of the feeding operations.

In early years when corn and other grains were usually very cheap in price, fattening cattle were ordinarily fed all the grain they could be induced to eat, after they had been gotten on feed. Commonly 2-year-old steers were fed an average of over 20 lbs. of corn per head daily, in addition to hay and other dry roughage. Later, when corn silage came into wide use for fattening cattle, it was found that when steers are fed all they will eat of silage from well-eared corn, they will not consume so much corn grain in addition to the roughage.

Usually 2-year-old steers full-fed shelled corn in addition to corn silage, hay, and enough protein supplement to balance the ration will not average throughout the fattening period over 15 to 16 lbs. of corn per head daily, not including that in the silage. Full-fed yearlings will average about 3 lbs. less corn per day than 2-year-olds, and calves about 5 to 6 lbs. less.

Many experiments have been conducted to determine the most profitable amounts of grain for the dry-lot fattening of cattle of the various ages under different conditions. In these tests the feeding of a very limited amount of grain, either throughout the entire feeding period or only during the first part, has been compared with the full-feeding of grain. Other trials have been conducted to find what results could be secured when fattening cattle were fed only all the well-eared corn silage they would clean up, with legume hay and just enough protein supplement to balance the ration.

These extensive investigations have shown that it is most profitable to feed grain liberally throughout the entire fattening period, unless the price of grain is unusually high in comparison with the prices of hay or other roughage, or unless the local market pays no premium for well-fattened cattle. It is shown in the next chapter that in certain sections of the West where alfalfa hay is very cheap and but little premium is paid for thoroughly-finished cattle, the best returns are secured when 2-year-olds or yearlings are fed little or no grain. (1075) Also, the price of grain occasionally rises so high in comparison with that of roughage, as during the World War, that it pays to limit the amount of grain, even in the corn belt. The feeding of concentrates to cattle that are being fattened on pasture is discussed in Chapter XXXII. (1128)

While 2-year-olds and yearlings will reach a fairly satisfactory degree of fatness on a very limited allowance of grain or other concentrates, liberal grain feeding is required to make calves really fat. If fed only good roughage, even including an abundance of well-eared silage, they will make fair gains in weight, but will merely grow and will not put on much fat. Experiments have shown that unless grain is extremely high in price in comparison with roughages, it is practically always most profitable to give calves a liberal allowance of grain throughout the entire fattening period.[34]

1005. Feeding no grain except that in silage.—It was found in several experiments that when first placed on feed 2-year-old steers would make excellent gains for some time on only corn silage or sorghum silage, hay, and 2 to 3 lbs. of linseed meal or cottonseed meal.[35] Trials were then conducted to find whether 2-year-olds could be made fat enough for the large markets when fed such rations throughout the entire fattening period. The following table presents the results of 16 tests in each of which one lot of 2-year-old steers, averaging 979 lbs. in weight, was fed for an average of 125 days only well-eared corn silage, legume or mixed hay, and a limited amount of protein supplement, while another lot received a full feed of corn grain in addition.[36]

The steers fed no corn grain except that in the well-eared corn silage made the surprisingly good average gain of 2.1 lbs. per head daily. Before the introduction of the silo and the use of modern, well-balanced rations this would have been considered a good rate of gain on a liberal feed of grain. However, the steers full-fed corn made considerably more rapid gains, averaging one-half pound more a day. As a result, they were much better finished at the end of the fattening periods than the steers fed no corn grain except that in the silage.

Some of these tests were carried on during the World War when corn was as high as $1.50 per bushel, while others were conducted when corn was cheap in price. The feed costs per 100 lbs. gain accordingly varied widely in the individual trials. On the average, the feed cost per 100 lbs. gain was $1.93 higher for the steers full-fed on corn than for the no-corn ration.

Feeding no grain except that in corn silage

Average ration	Lot I No corn except in silage	Lot II Full-fed corn grain
Corn grain, lbs.	...	14.1
Supplement, lbs.	2.9	2.8
Hay, lbs.	3.8	2.9
Corn silage, lbs.	49.2	27.6
Average daily gain, lbs.	2.1	2.6
Feed per 100 lbs. gain		
Corn grain, lbs.	...	542
Supplement, lbs.	142	110
Hay, lbs.	199	117
Corn silage, lbs.	2,427	1,091
Feed cost per 100 lbs. gain	$14.25	$16.18
Selling price per 100 lbs	$10.47	$11.17
Net return per head	$—0.03	$2.55

Other factors are fully as important as the cost of the gains in deciding the financial outcome. Much more pork is produced by pigs following full-fed steers than when no shelled corn is fed the cattle. Furthermore, full-fed steers reach a better finish and hence bring a higher price on the market. There was not, however, as much difference in the actual selling price in these trials as many experienced cattlemen would predict. In fact, the "no corn" steers brought only 70 cents less per hundredweight than the others.

Because of the higher selling price and the greater pork credit, the full-fed steers made a much better average financial showing than those fed no corn except that in the silage. While the full-fed cattle returned an average of $2.55 per head over cost of feed, the no-corn cattle did not quite pay for their feed. However, in some of the experiments conducted when corn was extremely high in price, the cost of gains was so much lower for the no-corn cattle that they returned the greater profit.

In other similar experiments with yearling or 2-year-old cattle the results have generally been similar to those here summarized.[37] It is not possible to fatten calves satisfactorily without feeding considerable grain in addition to that in corn or sorghum silage.

1006. Feeding limited amounts of corn.—When it seems problematical whether it will be more profitable to feed 2-year-olds or yearlings no corn except that in the silage, or on the other hand to feed a liberal allowance of corn, a middle course may be taken and a limited amount of corn grain may be supplied the cattle. This method has been tested in a number of trials in which various amounts of corn grain have been fed.

The following table summarizes the results of 11 trials in each of which one lot of 970-lb. 2-year-old steers has been full-fed on shelled corn in addition to corn silage, legume or mixed hay, and a small allowance of cottonseed meal or linseed meal. In each trial another lot has been fed about half as much corn grain throughout the feeding period which averaged 131 days in length.[38]

CHAMPIONSHIP YEARLING FAT STEERS AT THE INTERNATIONAL

Yearlings usually make less expensive gains than older steers, but require a somewhat longer feeding period to reach the same finish. The proportion of steers marketed as yearlings has increased considerably in recent years.

A FINE BUNCH OF BABY BEEVES

Blocky calves of good type and conformation must be selected for baby beef production, as others will not usually reach the desired maturity and finish at this early age. (From U. S. Department of Agriculture.)

HAND-FEEDING STEERS EAR CORN ON PASTURE

Commonly the concentrates are fed to cattle on pasture in broad troughs or "feed bunks." Hand-feeding cattle is a more common practice than self-feeding.

SELF-FEEDING EAR CORN TO STEERS ON PASTURE

Self-feeders are sometimes used for fattening cattle after they are on full feed.

Full feed of corn versus half allowance for fattening steers

Average ration	Daily gain	Feed for 100 lbs. gain			
		Corn	Supplement	Hay	Silage
	Lbs.	Lbs.	Lbs.	Lbs.	Lbs.
Lot I, full feed of corn					
Shelled corn, 13.8 lbs.					
Supplement, 2.6 lbs.					
Corn silage, 28.5 lbs.					
Hay, 2.4 lbs.........................	2.66	521	98	95	1,103
Lots II, half feed of corn					
Shelled corn, 6.9 lbs.					
Supplement, 2.5 lbs.					
Corn silage, 41.0 lbs.					
Hay, 2.7 lbs.........................	2.31	306	114	128	1,825

In these trials the steers fed only a half allowance of shelled corn made the very satisfactory gain of 2.31 lbs. a head daily at a feed cost of 67 cents less per 100 lbs. gain than those full-fed on shelled corn, and they sold for only 44 cents less per hundredweight. The difference in selling price and the difference in the amount of pork produced by the pigs following the steers more than offset the cheaper gains, and the full-fed steers returned $3.35 more profit per head on the average.

When it seems desirable to limit the amount of corn grain for yearlings or 2-year-olds, it is best during the first part of the period to feed them only silage and hay, with enough linseed meal or cottonseed meal to balance the ration. They will make excellent gains on such a ration for some time, and then about 40 to 60 days before they are to be sold, they should be started on corn grain and finished on a full feed.

Trials at the Indiana and Missouri Stations show that this method takes less corn than where a half allowance of corn is fed throughout the entire feeding period.[39] Yet it produces fully as large gains and as good a finish. Consequently the profit is greater than where a limited amount of corn is fed over the entire period.

II. GENERAL FACTORS INFLUENCING BEEF PRODUCTION

1007. The necessary margin.—Under usual conditions the cost per 100 lbs. of the gains made by feeder cattle that are being fattened for market is greater than the selling price of the finished animals per hundredweight. Therefore, in order to make a profit or even to prevent loss on the fattening process, a higher price per 100 lbs. must be secured for the fat cattle when marketed than their original cost per 100 lbs. as feeders. This is also generally the case in the fattening of feeder lambs or older sheep for the market.

The difference between the cost per hundredweight of the feeder animals and the selling price per hundredweight of the same animals when fattened is called the *margin*. The term *necessary margin* means the margin that is required for any particular lot of animals to avoid loss.

To determine the margin that will be necessary in feeding a particular class of cattle, the other expenses must be taken into consideration, in addition to the cost of feed for each 100 lbs. of gain. Where full value can be secured from the manure, this and the credit for the pork produced are commonly assumed to cover the cost of labor, housing, taxes, interest, incidental expenses, and the mortality risk.

However, one must include in his financial estimates the expenses incident to the purchase of the feeder cattle and of bringing them to the feed lot, and also the expenses of marketing them after they are fattened. These marketing expenses include the cost of transportation, the loss through the shrinkage in live weight during shipment, and the expenses at the central stockyards, such as yardage fees, commission, and cost of feed supplied at the stockyards.

1008. Factors affecting necessary margin.—The following factors have an influence on the margin that is necessary for any particular lot of cattle:

1. Other conditions being equal, the more the animal weighs when placed on feed, the less is the necessary margin. This is because the increased selling price is obtained on a greater number of pounds of initial weight. This factor may be offset, however, if the heavier cattle are older and therefore make more expensive gains.

2. The higher the initial cost is of the feeder cattle per hundredweight, the smaller is the necessary margin. This is because the initial cost of the animals per 100 lbs. will then more nearly equal the cost of the gain per 100 lbs.

3. The greater the cost of the gains, the higher will be the necessary margin. Thus, a large margin is necessary when feeds are high in price. Also, a much greater margin is needed when animals are carried to a high degree of fatness.

4. The larger the total amount of gain made per head by the cattle, the greater will be the margin needed to prevent loss. This is because the margin on the initial weight of the animal must cover a greater number of pounds of expensive gains.

5. Obviously, a greater margin is needed when the expenses are heavy for getting the steers to the feed lot and then to the market, after fattening.

Since these factors all have an influence at the same time on the necessary margin, computations are necessary to find approximately how great a margin will be needed to prevent loss under any particular set of conditions. One can estimate the necessary margin by computations based on the cost of feeders at any given time; the prices of the available feeds; the average amounts of feed required for 100 lbs. of gain (as shown in this and the following chapter); and the other expenses that must be considered.

The effects of the various factors upon the necessary margin are shown by the following examples:

Let us suppose that 700-lb. yearling steers cost $8.00 per hundredweight when put in the feed lot. They are to be fed 180 days, and it is expected that they will gain 2.0 lbs. per head daily at a feed cost of $11.00 per 100 lbs. gain. Assuming that the pork produced by pigs following the steers and the value of the manure will offset the labor and miscellaneous expenses, what will be the necessary selling price and the necessary margin, after deducting the marketing expenses?

The steers will make a total gain per head of 360 lbs., and the total feed cost of this gain will be $39.60 at $11.00 for each 100 lbs. gain. Adding this to the total initial cost of the cattle per head, which was $56.00, we will have $95.60 as the total cost per head of the fat cattle. Dividing this total by the final weight of the cattle, which is 1,060 lbs. (700 lbs. plus 360 lbs.), we find that the cattle must bring $9.02 per hundredweight in the feed lot to break even.

To determine the necessary margin, we subtract the initial cost per hundredweight from this necessary selling price. This gives us $1.02 as the necessary margin under these particular conditions.

In general, it may be stated that the necessary margin is usually smaller for fattening calves than for older cattle. This is because they make much cheaper gains and also because their initial cost per 100 lbs. is commonly higher than for yearlings or 2-year-olds.

1009. Yield of dressed carcass.—According to the United States Census the average live weight of cattle slaughtered at wholesale slaughtering and meat packing plants was 946.5 lbs. for the period 1922-1929. The average weight of dressed carcass was 504.0 lbs., making the average dressing percentage 53.2 per cent. Because of the increasing demand for smaller cuts of beef, the average weights are now probably less.

Good to choice fat steers will range from 56 to 59 per cent in dressing percentage, and show steers, which are of extra good type and in high condition, will usually dress 59 to 63 per cent.[40] Fat cows dress about 56 per cent, and canners from 35 to 43 per cent.

The veal calves slaughtered at wholesale slaughtering plants averaged 173.2 lbs. in live weight and yielded 103.2 lbs. dressed carcass for the period 1923-1929. The average dressing percentage was 59.6 per cent, being higher than for cattle because the hide is left on the veal carcass to protect the flesh.

1010. Value of beef blood for beef production.—All those with considerable experience in the cattle business know that "blood tells" in beef production, just as it does in other types of stock farming. Good returns cannot be expected when calves are raised for beef out of scrub or inferior cows, sired by a scrub bull or one lacking in the desired beef characteristics. This has been shown conclusively by careful tests at the experiment stations and by the results secured on a host of farms where scrub cattle have been replaced by well-bred beef animals.

The greater earning capacity of purebred or high-grade beef cattle over scrubs was well shown in an inquiry conducted by the United States Department of Agriculture among 2,000 farmers in 36 states who had improved their herds in a national "Better Sires—Better Stock" campaign.[41] These men estimated that purebred beef cattle had an average earning power 37 per cent greater than that of common or scrub stock, based on utility alone and not considering the greater pride and pleasure in caring for well-bred cattle. Those who had replaced scrub bulls with purebred sires reported an average increase of 48.0 per cent in returns traceable to the use of the purebred sires. These figures show clearly that no stockman who persists in keeping scrubs can expect a profit.

In comparison with scrubs, well-bred beef cattle have the following advantages: (1) They make more rapid gains and are therefore heavier at a given age; (2) the gains are usually cheaper; (3) the animals mature earlier; (4) they furnish a higher percentage of dressed carcass; (5) they produce a greater proportion of the more valuable cuts of meat; (6) their carcasses have less internal fat; and (7) their beef is superior in quality.

1011. Rapidity and cost of gains.—When they are raised and finished for market under the same conditions, beef-bred cattle will make appreciably more rapid gains than most scrubs. Also, they will usually require a little less feed for 100 lbs. gain. This has been the case in experiments conducted by the Georgia, North Carolina, Oklahoma, and South Carolina Stations in which scrub calves have been compared with better-bred calves.[42]

In 6 Oklahoma tests, for example, calves from scrub dams gained only 1.67 lbs. per day on the average during the fattening period, and their feed cost of 100 lbs. gain was $8.58. Calves from purebred sires and scrub dams gained 1.88 lbs., with a feed cost per 100 lbs. gain of $8.32. Well-bred beef calves from a purebred sire and high-grade beef cows gained 1.97 lbs. and required only $7.72 worth of feed per 100 lbs. gain.

On the other hand, in Arkansas experiments calves from a scrub sire and scrub dams gained fully as rapidly to market age as purebred beef calves or calves from the scrub sire and grade beef cows.[43] In considering these results, it must be borne in mind that the scrub cattle in all these tests were vigorous, thrifty animals and were fed and cared for as well as the well-bred beef cattle. Commonly, it is found that on farms where scrub animals are raised, the methods of feeding and management are no more improved than are the stock.

In all of the tests the chief difference in the results between the well-bred beef calves and the scrubs has been in the value of the animals on the market. Thus, in the Oklahoma trials the scrub steers sold for $1.71 less per 100 lbs. than the steers from purebred bulls and high-grade cows, and for 92 cents less per 100 lbs. than the steers from purebred bulls and scrub cows. Likewise, in the Arkansas tests the purebred steers sold for $1.26 more per 100 lbs. than the scrubs. Second-cross calves from purebred bulls and the scrub cows sold at nearly as high a price as the purebreds, while first-cross steers were intermediate in value.

Occasionally the claim is still made that well-bred beef cattle eat less than scrubs. The very opposite is true. They are heartier eaters, for they have greater ability to digest feed and convert it economically into meat. It is for this very reason that they make more rapid and more economical gains than scrubs.

It is shown later in this chapter that dairy-bred steers of the larger dairy breeds may make as large and as cheap gains as beef-bred steers. However, their carcasses are of considerably lower value for beef.

1012. Early maturity of well-bred beef cattle.—It is well known that well-bred beef steers "mature," or reach the degree of fatness demanded by the market, earlier than scrubs or dairy-bred steers. Indeed, only calves of good beef type are suited for fattening at an early age as baby beeves. Though dairy steers may grow rapidly, they do not become well fleshed at a sufficiently early age.

1013. Superior carcasses of well-bred beef cattle.—Well-fattened steers of good beef type have a somewhat higher dressing percentage than scrub or dairy steers that have been fattened equally. Also, the beef steers have a higher percentage of loins and ribs, which are the most valuable cuts, and a smaller proportion of the cheap cuts. The actual differences in dressing percentage and in percentage of different cuts is not large, however.

There is a more marked difference between beef-bred steers and either scrubs or dairy steers in the distribution of fat in the body. In the carcass of a well-bred beef steer more of the fat is distributed throughout the muscular tissues, and less is deposited about the internal organs, where its only value is for tallow. Fat distributed throughout the lean meat makes it tender, juicy, and toothsome. On the other hand, when it is deposited in separate masses anywhere about the body, it has but low value.

One of the most important differences between beef cattle and scrub or dairy-bred cattle is in the quality of beef produced. The thick-fleshed cuts from well-fattened beef cattle command a much higher price on discriminating markets than the thin-fleshed cuts from scrubs or dairy animals. Due to these differences in quality of the carcass, fat cattle of good beef type sell for a considerably higher price on the market and therefore bring a much larger return to the man who has raised them.

1014. Fattening cattle of the various market grades.—The preceding paragraphs show clearly that for the beef producer who raises the animals he fattens or for the man who raises cattle for sale as feeders, well-bred animals of the beef breeds are the most profitable. The matter is more complicated for one who fattens feeder cattle that he purchases on the market. He must consider not only the cost of the gains he can expect from cattle of the various grades, but also the differences in their initial cost per hundredweight and the probable differences in their selling prices when fattened.

Fortunately, the results from feeding cattle of the various market grades have been carefully compared in several experiments. The results of these studies are of much importance to those who make a business of the fattening of purchased feeders for the market. The table on page 640 summarizes the data secured in 15 trials in each of which a group of good or choice western feeder steers has been fed a good ration in direct comparison with a group of medium feeder steers and also with a group of common steers, all being fed the same ration.[44] A total of 423 steers were fed in these tests for feeding periods averaging 173 days.

The good to choice groups of cattle in these experiments were high-grade beef animals of good type and conformation. The medium steers were of less desirable type and were usually somewhat thinner, but were of the beef breeds. Many of the common feeders were of dairy breeds or showed admixture of dairy blood. Although the common steers were thrifty, they were thinner and averaged lighter in weight than the better grades.

There was but little difference in the rate of gain by the steers of the different grades in these trials. Because the medium and common feeders were thinner at the start than the better steers, their average gains were a trifle more rapid. For the same reason, the feed cost per 100 lbs. gain was slightly the lowest for the common grade and was a trifle less for the medium grade than for the choice to good grades of cattle.

These trials therefore show that common feeder cattle will gain as rapidly, provided they are equally thrifty, as the cattle of the higher grades. Also, there will be a tendency for them to require slightly less feed per 100 lbs. gain, because they usually carry somewhat less flesh when purchased.

Comparison of various grades of feeder cattle

	Good to choice feeders	Medium feeders	Common feeders
Initial weight, lbs...................................	624	607	550
Daily gain, lbs......................................	2.31	2.37	2.35
Feed cost per 100 lbs. gain..........................	$8.37	$8.23	$8.03
Initial cost per 100 lbs.............................	$7.54	$6.30	$5.20
Selling price per 100 lbs............................	$8.30	$7.82	$7.14
Actual margin per 100 lbs...........................	$0.76	$1.52	$1.94
Net return per head over feed cost..................	$2.75	$6.32	$5.17
Dressing percentage, per cent.......................	60.6*	58.7*	56.9*

*Average of 5 experiments.

The table shows that the average initial weight of the common feeders was considerably less than that of the better grades. Since they were fully as old or even older, this means that they had made considerably less rapid gains than the better animals up to the time they were sold as feeders.

The average initial cost of the good to choice feeders in these tests was $2.34 more per 100 lbs. than for the common feeders, and $1.24 more than for the medium feeders. While the better cattle also sold for higher prices when fat, there was much less difference in the selling price than there was in the initial cost. The good to choice steers sold for only $1.16 more per hundredweight than the common grade, and the medium steers for only 68 cents more than the common cattle.

The average actual margin per 100 lbs. between initial cost and selling price was only 76 cents for the best grade, while it was $1.52 for the medium feeders and $1.94 for the common feeders. As a result of their cheaper gains and the greater margin, the net return per head over cost of feed was decidedly greater for the medium and for the common feeders than it was for the cattle of the better grade. The average dressing percentage, in 5 experiments where this was determined, was only 56.9 per cent for the common feeders, while it was 58.7 per cent for the medium group and 60.6 per cent for the best cattle.

Computations from the data in the table will show that if the good to choice feeders had been bought for $6.97 per hundredweight, instead of $7.54, the net return from them would have been the same as from the medium feeders, which were purchased at the average price of $6.30. Thus, the good to choice feeders were actually worth only 67 cents more per 100 lbs. than the medium feeders, while they cost $1.24 more.

To make the same net return per head from the common feeders as from the medium grade, it would have been necessary to buy them for $4.99 per 100 lbs. instead of at the actual cost of $5.20. There was, therefore, a difference of $1.31 per 100 lbs. in the real value of the common and the medium feeders, while the difference in the actual cost was only $1.10.

1015. Choosing between the grades of feeder steers.—One should not conclude from the foregoing summary that the best profits are always made from buying the lower grades of feeder cattle. The financial outcome from the various grades will depend primarily on the margin that can be secured between their purchase price as feeders and their selling price as fat cattle.

The spread in price between the prices for good to choice fat cattle and for those of the lower grades is usually the greatest in summer and fall. This is because there are fewer such cattle then coming on the market. The spread is apt to be smallest in late winter and spring, when a large number of well-fattened cattle are coming to market from the feedlots.

In purchasing feeders one should not base his decision on the spread in price between the various grades at that time, but upon the difference there will probably be, based on average prices, when he has them fattened and ready for market. If one has access to a special market that pays an unusually large premium for thoroughly fat cattle of high quality, obviously he can not hope to secure the premium unless he fattens animals of the best grades.

In purchasing feeders of the lower grades it is especially important that they be carefully selected and that only thrifty animals are bought. Otherwise the results may be disappointing. Some experienced feeders specialize in fattening cattle that do not even come up to the common grade. Such animals are in disfavor on the market, for most good stockmen do not want them on their premises. Therefore, they can often be bought for a price that offers good possibilities of profit. Many such animals are unthrifty, and therefore the death losses during the fattening process are higher than for good cattle. Also, more skill is necessary in feeding these cheap cattle. The fattening of such cattle should therefore be undertaken only by an expert who knows cattle and market conditions.

1016. Dairy steers vs. beef steers vs. cross breds.—The question is often asked as to the value for beef of steers from the dairy breeds, especially Holsteins, in comparison with steers of the beef breeds. Three Wisconsin experiments supply information on this question and also on the value of cross-bred steers from Holstein cows bred to a beef bull.[45]

In these trials Holstein calves fed for an average of 217 days gained 2.37 lbs. per head daily, in comparison with 2.19 lbs. for Aberdeen-Angus calves and 2.05 lbs. for cross-bred Holstein-Angus calves. The feed cost per 100 lbs. gain was also slightly the lowest for the dairy steers. These differences were probably due to the fact that they did not carry quite so much flesh when the fattening period began.

The average selling price was $13.00 for the Angus steers, in comparison with $12.16 for the cross-breds and $10.08 for the Holsteins. Though the dairy steers made excellent gains, they were not well covered with flesh over the back and ribs, the forequarters were rough, and they lacked thickness of flesh over the shoulders. These faults were much more noticeable in the live animals than in the carcasses, for the well-fattened Holstein steers made a desirable grade of medium beef. In fact, there was no outstanding difference in the quality of the cooked beef from the three lots.

The cross-bred steers in these tests made very desirable baby beeves, both on foot and when slaughtered, though they were not quite so smoothly covered with fat as the Angus steers. The cross-breds and the Angus steers both had an average dressing percentage of 62 per cent, while that of the Holsteins was only 59 per cent.

These and also other experiments show that young steers of the larger dairy breeds make acceptable beef when well fattened.[46] However, such steers usually sell at a considerably lower price on the market and therefore are worth much less as feeders than are beef steers.

1017. Relation between conformation and gains.—It is well known that there are great differences in the rate of gain and in the economy of gain made by individual cattle of the same breed. Relatively few experiments have yet been conducted to determine just what points of conformation are of importance as indications that an animal will make rapid and cheap gains. In the studies thus far reported there has been much difference in the results secured.[47]

In considering this question it must be borne in mind that steers of dairy type which lack the desired beef conformation may make just as rapid and economical gains as beef steers. However, their carcasses will be less valuable. Experienced judges of cattle are generally much more successful in picking out young cattle that will rank high when fattened than they are in predicting just which animals will make the largest gains or will require the least feed per pound of gain. They prefer animals that are low-set, deep, broad, and compact, with roomy digestive tracts and evidences of strong constitutions. Cattle feeders also know that temperament is of great importance in determining gains in the feed lot. The calm, quiet animal which eats its fill and then lies down is almost sure to outgain the nervous, restless beast.

Studies at the Minnesota Station indicate that there may be possibilities for great improvement in the efficiency of beef production by selection of breeding animals on the basis of a record of performance of their offspring in the feed lot.[48]

1018. Influence of age on economy of gains.—It is well known that young animals require less feed per pound of gain in live weight than do older ones of the same kind, and that their gains are therefore much cheaper. The reasons for this marked difference, which is of much practical importance in beef production, have been fully explained in Chapter VII. (204-206)

Studies conducted by Haecker at the Minnesota Station over a period of several years well show the effect of age upon the amount of feed and of digestible nutrients required per 100 lbs. gain in weight.[49] In these experiments a careful record was kept of all feed eaten by grade beef steer calves from birth to two years of age or over. So that all the feed consumed could be accurately determined, the calves were raised by hand, instead of nursing their dams.

During the various periods the steers were allowed all the roughage (corn silage and prairie hay) they would eat, but the amount of concentrates was somewhat smaller than is commonly fed to cattle that are being fattened for market. When the steers reached a weight of 1,200 lbs. they were sufficiently well fleshed for the market, but some were continued on trial until they reached 1,500 lbs. and were very fat. The following table presents certain of the most important data for the steers that were not on pasture during the experiments.

Feed required for 100 lbs. gain by steers of various ages

| Period | Av. daily gain | Feed for 100 lbs. gain | | | | Total dig. nutrients per 100 lbs. gain | Feed cost of 100 lbs. gain |
		Skim and whole milk	Concentrates	Hay	Silage		
	Lbs.	Lbs.	Lbs.	Lbs.	Lbs.	Lbs.	Cents
100– 200 lbs............	0.93	1,252	91	103	6	225	7.50
200– 300 lbs............	1.33	575	196	232	126	319	4.90
300– 400 lbs............	1.44	160	251	291	326	376	5.00
400– 500 lbs............	1.51	...	291	322	481	429	5.50
500– 600 lbs............	1.85	...	283	314	438	426	5.30
600– 700 lbs............	1.71	...	362	440	327	529	6.50
700– 800 lbs............	1.79	...	425	480	135	553	7.50
800– 900 lbs............	1.53	...	558	550	364	708	9.50
900–1,000 lbs............	1.62	...	550	455	715	731	9.30
1,000–1,100 lbs............	1.53	...	623	449	876	808	10.00
1,100–1,200 lbs............	1.48	...	714	455	899	885	11.20
1,200–1,300 lbs............	....	...	821	774	1,050	...	14.40
1,300–1,400 lbs............	....	...	870	785	1,200	...	15.20
1,400–1,500 lbs............	....	...	911	563	1,746	...	15.40
From calf to 600 lbs...	1.39	433	232	264	279	...	6.30
From calf to 1,200 lbs...	1.52	194	407	385	423	...	7.80
From calf to 1,500 lbs...	....	153	506	454	618	...	9.30

The daily gains of the steers increased until they reached 600 lbs. in weight, after which they decreased slightly. The amount of feed required for 100 lbs. gain rose steadily as the steers grew and fattened. While only 225 lbs. total digestible nutrients were required for 100 lbs. gain between the weights of 100 to 200 lbs., over 800 lbs. total digestible nutrients were required for 100 lbs. of gain after the steers reached the weight of 1,000 lbs.

The feed cost of 100 lbs. gain was higher for the first period than for those immediately following, due to the whole milk that was fed. The cost then rose gradually from $4.90 per 100 lbs. gain between 200 and 300 lbs. live weight up to $15.40 between the weights of 1,400 and 1,500 lbs. The feed cost of the gains was especially high after the steers had reached 1,200 lbs., at which time they were sufficiently well fleshed for the market, but not fat enough for "prime" beef.

Some steers were turned to pasture the second summer and then returned to the barn and fattened the next winter. These animals made much more rapid and economical gains than those that had not been on pasture. This was because they carried less flesh, and also possibly owing to a greater supply of vitamins or unknown nutritive essentials which they secured from the green forage, that put them in the best condition to make profitable gains.

In these investigations it was found that the older steers actually stored as much energy in their bodies for each 100 lbs. of total digestible nutrients in the feed they ate, as did the younger steers. However, as the body gains made by the young steers were high in water and low in fat, while those of the older steers consisted chiefly of energy-rich fat, much more feed was required by the older steers per 100 lbs. of gain in weight, as has already been pointed out.

In a previous comparison of the economy with which the various farm animals convert their feed into human food, it has been shown that beef cattle rank along with sheep in the economy with which they produce edible meat, but are greatly excelled by swine. (231) In these Minnesota investigations it was found that well-finished 1,200-lb. steers yielded in their carcasses 10.95 lbs. of edible meat and fatty tissues, containing 6.02 lbs. dry matter, for each 100 lbs. total digestible nutrients they had consumed during their growth and fattening.

During the entire lives of these steers they converted about 10 per cent of the gross energy in the feed they ate into the energy stored in their body tissues.[50] Thus the "over-all" efficiency of the steers was 10 per cent.

1019. Calves vs. yearlings vs. older cattle.—On account of the great practical importance of the matter, many experiments have been conducted to compare the costs of gains and the net returns from fattening cattle of various ages. The table on page 645 presents an average of the results secured in 17 experiments in which calves, yearlings, and 2-year-olds were directly compared.[51] In these trials special efforts were made to secure feeder cattle of equal quality for the different ages. Cattle of good beef type and conformation were used in practically all the tests.

The cattle were fed grain (corn in all except one experiment) and legume or mixed hay. In addition they received a small allowance of cottonseed meal or linseed meal in certain of the tests and had silage in addition to hay for roughage in 6 of the trials. Similar results have been secured in several other experiments in which not all the age-groups of cattle were used, or in which somewhat different rations have been fed.[52]

An average feeding period of 197 days was needed to fatten the calves sufficiently to meet market demands, while the feeding period was only 174 days for the yearlings and 162 days for the 2-year-olds. Often it will take 225 days or more to fatten calves properly, if they are thin when put on feed.

When young cattle are fed liberally from calf-hood, the daily gains will reach their maximum during the first year, and then the rate of gain will gradually decline. However, in the case of feeder cattle which are in thin condition when fattening begins, yearlings and 2-year-olds will make slightly more rapid gains than calves.

In these experiments the average daily gains were 2.40 lbs. for the 2-year-olds, 2.26 lbs. for the yearlings, and 2.19 lbs. for the calves. These are somewhat larger gains than are secured, on the average, in commercial cattle feeding. In these experiments cattle of good quality were fed excellent rations under careful supervision. Therefore the data in the table show the results that can be secured by experienced stockmen and under favorable conditions.

Comparison of calves, yearlings, and 2-year-olds

	Calves	Yearlings	2-year-olds
Av. initial wt., lbs..............................	414	638	840
Length of feeding period, days.................	197	174	162
Av. daily gain, lbs.............................	2.19	2.26	2.40
Av. total gain, lbs.............................	431	393	389
Av. ration:			
Grain, lbs.	10.1	13.1	15.8
Supplement, lbs.	1.1	1.1	1.1
Hay, lbs.	4.2	5.4	5.8
Silage, lbs.	4.1	5.8	7.5
Total feed consumed per head:			
Grain, lbs.	1,990	2,279	2,552
Supplement, lbs.	217	188	170
Hay, lbs.	827	935	941
Silage, lbs.	808	1,014	1,221
Feed per 100 lbs. gain by steers:			
Grain, lbs.	462	586	667
Supplement, lbs.	47	45	41
Hay, lbs.	198	241	246
Silage, lbs.	186	258	308
Feed cost per 100 lbs. gain..................	$ 9.14*	$10.98*	$12.07*
Initial cost per 100 lbs......................	$ 8.78*	$ 8.21*	$ 8.24*
Selling price per 100 lbs.....................	$10.32*	$10.08*	$10.14*
Net return per steer.........................	$ 9.39	$ 4.08	$ 3.25
Dressing percentage, per cent...............	58.9†	59.8†	60.7†

*Average of 16 experiments.
†Average of 11 experiments.

There was not a great difference in the total gains, though a total of about 40 lbs. more gain was necessary to finish the calves properly than for the yearlings or 2-year-olds. Often the total amount of gain needed to finish calves properly will be somewhat more than was made by the high-quality calves in these experiments.

The amounts of feed eaten per head daily by the calves were considerably less than for the older cattle. However, since the calves were fed for a longer period, there was much less difference in the total amount of feed consumed by the cattle of the different ages.

The economy of the younger cattle is shown by the amounts of feed required per 100 lbs. gain and by the feed cost per 100 lbs. gain. While the feed cost of each 100 lbs. of gain made by the calves was only $9.14, it was $10.98 for the yearlings and $12.07 for the 2-year-olds.

Calves usually cost more per 100 lbs. as feeders than do yearlings or 2-year-olds, and this is shown in these experiments. While the average initial cost of the yearlings and 2-year-olds was approximately the same, the cost of the calves was 57 cents per 100 lbs. higher than for the yearlings.

This greater cost of the calves was more than offset by their cheaper gains and by the further fact that they sold for an average of 24 cents more per hundredweight than the yearlings and for 18 cents more per hundredweight than the 2-year-olds. As a result, the average net return over the cost of feed, after allowing credit for the pork produced by the pigs following the cattle, was $9.39 per head for the calves, in comparison with $4.08 for the yearlings and $3.25 for the 2-year-olds. The table shows that the dressing percentage was distinctly higher for the older cattle, averaging 58.9 per cent for the calves, 59.8 per cent for the yearlings, and 60.7 per cent for the 2-year-olds.

Three-year-old cattle will usually require even more feed per 100 lbs. gain than 2-year-olds. Old cows generally do not make as rapid gains as yearlings or 2-year-olds, and their gains cost considerably more.[53]

1020. Which age of feeders should be purchased?—One should not conclude from the preceding summary that it is always more profitable to feed calves than older cattle. Whether or not this will be the case depends on the conditions at any particular time. In deciding which age of feeders to purchase, the following factors should be considered:

If the cost of yearling or 2-year-old feeders per 100 lbs. is enough below that of calves to offset fully the cheapness of the gains by calves, then the profit may be greater from feeding the older cattle. Somewhat more care is necessary in feeding calves than in the case of yearlings or 2-year-olds.

Calves are not well suited to utilize roughage of poor quality. Therefore, if one wishes to use considerable low-grade hay, corn stover, or straw, he will prefer older cattle. Also, calves must have a liberal amount of grain to fatten properly, while 2-year-olds will reach a fair market finish on nothing but good corn silage, a little hay, and enough protein supplement to balance the ration.

Some people decidedly prefer the beef from well-finished older cattle of good quality to that from baby beeves, as it has more flavor. Therefore, there still is, without question, a definite demand for such carcasses. At certain times the supply is not sufficient to meet this demand, and then the price for fat yearlings or 2-year-olds of choice quality may be higher than that for baby beeves.

Calves have another advantage that is sometimes of importance, in addition to their cheaper gains and higher average selling price per hundredweight when well fattened. They will continue to make good gains for some time after the end of the ordinary feeding period, and if not continued on feed too long their carcasses will not be wastefully fat. Therefore if the prices for fat cattle happen to drop at the time when it has been planned to market them, and one believes the prices will be better a few weeks later, calves can successfully be continued on feed for a reasonable length of time.

On the other hand, when 2-year-olds are already well fattened, further gains are very expensive. Also, the cattle will soon become so fat and heavy that they will not bring a satisfactory price, even if there is improvement in the general level of cattle prices.

1021. Excessive fattening does not pay.—Experienced cattle feeders know that it never pays to carry fattening cattle to an unnecessarily high "finish." After an animal is already well fattened, any further gains are much more expensive.

This is because the gains in weight then consist chiefly of fat and contain but little water. Also, after an animal has become fat, its appetite is less hearty, and consequently it eats less feed in proportion to its weight than does one in moderate condition. As a result, it has a smaller proportion of its food available for making body tissue, after the maintenance requirements have been met.

Not only are the gains exceedingly expensive when cattle are carried to extreme fatness, but also the carcasses from such animals do not meet the desires of most consumers. The lean meat will, it is true, be of the highest quality, but too large a proportion of the various cuts will consist of masses of fat which are not usually eaten. It has been pointed out in Chapter VII that the primary object of fattening stock for slaughter is the improvement of the quality of the lean meat through the depositing of fat between the bundles of muscular fibers. This gives the meat from well-fleshed animals the characteristic "marbled" appearance. The accumulation of the separate masses of fat in the carcass is only a necessary accompaniment in the process. (**218**)

Any excess fat beyond that which is required to make the meat attractive, juicy, and well-flavored is waste, because the consumer will generally not eat it, though it has been a heavy expense to the producer. In former years, when cattle were usually fattened after they were well grown, it was necessary to carry them to a high finish to make the meat tender and juicy. Now, however, with our changed methods of beef production in which cattle are fattened while yet young and growing, such extreme finishing is no longer needed to produce beef of good quality.

The demand for highly-fattened steers is limited, even on the large central markets, for most consumers cannot afford this wasteful class of beef. Often such steers will bring some premium over those which are well fattened, but not "ripe." However, unless one is so fortunate as to have a special market outlet for highly-fattened cattle, the difference in price is commonly so small that it fails to offset the high cost of carrying the steers to this degree of finish.

The wise beef producer will therefore keep posted with reference to the market prices of the various grades of cattle and will sell his steers just as soon as they are sufficiently well fleshed to return the most profit. While it would be a source of pride to him to sell a load of steers that would "top the market," he knows that often this reduces rather than increases the net return.

An experienced stockman can easily tell the degree of fatness of an animal. On thin cattle the flesh on the back and over the ribs and shoulders is relatively hard and unyielding, while after proper fattening the flesh feels mellow, yet firm and springy. Other indications that a steer is well fattened are a well-filled flank, and a full "twist" and "cod." If a steer is carried to an extreme degree of fatness, as is sometimes done in fitting for shows, the flesh will be soft and blubbery, due to the large accumulation of fat.

1022. Wastefulness of excessive fattening.—The wastefulness of carrying cattle to an extreme degree of fatness is well shown by a Missouri experiment in which one steer was slaughtered before fattening, at a weight of 756 lbs., and the entire carcass analyzed.[54] Another was slaughtered after being fed a fattening ration for 153 days, when it weighed 1,266 lbs. and would have graded as a choice steer but lacked

40 to 50 days of feeding of being in prime condition. A third was fed until it reached the weight of 1,805 lbs., when it was extremely fat.

Compared with the animal slaughtered before fattening, it was found that the 1,266-lb. steer had stored in its body 152.6 lbs. lean meat and 151.7 lbs. fatty tissue. From this stage the gains are chiefly fatty tissue. Compared with this 1,266-lb. steer, the 1,805-lb., very fat steer had stored 255.5 lbs. more fatty tissue and only 89.5 lbs. more lean meat. Furthermore, for each pound of gain in weight the 1,266-lb. steer had required only 4.51 lbs. digestible organic nutrients in its feed, while the very fat steer had consumed 8.16 lbs.

1023. Heifers vs. steers.—On the large markets in the United States fat beef heifers commonly sell for a definitely lower price than steers of similar quality and condition. However, recent investigations have shown conclusively that when young heifers are properly fattened, but are not over-fat, they yield carcasses that are equal to those from steers.[55] In these experiments there have been no appreciable differences due to sex in the dressing percentage, in the retail value of the carcasses, in the color of the meat, or in its tenderness and palatability when cooked.

Heifers become fat sooner than steers and therefore do not require so long a feeding period. If fed for the length of time needed to finish steers properly, they become wastefully fat and do not meet the market demands. They should therefore be marketed just as soon as they become sufficiently fat, which will be fully 30 to 40 days earlier than in the case of steers of the same age. If properly-finished heifers are sold at weights not over 700 to 750 lbs., they will generally bring a better price than if fattened to a weight of 900 lbs. or more.

The lower selling price of fat heifers in this country is probably due for the most part to the fact that many of them are pregnant when marketed. This lowers the dressing percentage and may affect the value of the carcass. This situation is due to the unwise practice sometimes followed of breeding heifers during the fattening period, so they will be more quiet and make a trifle larger gains. Unless a buyer on the market can be certain that none of a particular lot of heifers is pregnant, he must discount the price he offers, in order to be safe. It is of interest to note that in England there is no discrimination in price against well-finished heifers.

Many experiments have been conducted to compare the results from fattening heifers and steers of the same age and quality. Most of these tests were carried on before it was fully realized that heifers should not be fed for as long a period as is required to fatten steers. In the great majority of the trials the feeding periods have therefore been the same length for the two sexes.

In 6 experiments in which heifer calves have been fattened for an average of 165 days in comparison with steer calves fed for an average of 233 days, the daily gains have been the same for both sexes, 2.24 lbs. per head daily.[56] The average feed cost of 100 lbs. gain was 19 cents less for the heifers than for the steers.

On the other hand, in 19 experiments in which heifer calves and steer calves have been fattened for periods of the same length, the heifers have gained only 1.99 lbs. per head daily on the average, in comparison with 2.14 lbs. for the steers.[57] In these trials the feed cost per 100 lbs. gain averaged 63 cents more for the heifers, because they were fatter at the close of the experiments. This is shown by the fact that in the tests in which the dressing percentages were determined, the average was 59.9 per cent for the heifers and only 58.0 per cent for the steers.

Including the results of all the 25 experiments, the initial cost was 86 cents less per 100 lbs. for the heifers than for the steers, but the selling price was also 69 cents less per 100 lbs. The more expensive gain and the lower selling price more than offset the lower initial cost in these trials, and as a result the net return per head over cost of feed was $4.92 less for the heifers than for the steers. In these experiments it would have been necessary to buy the heifer calves at $2.15 less per 100 lbs. than the steers to make an equal net return per head. This is probably a somewhat more unfavorable result for the heifers than there will be if care is taken not to carry them to an undue degree of fatness before they are marketed.

In 4 experiments in which yearling heifers were compared with yearling steers, fed for the same length of time, the gains were slightly more rapid, the cost of gains less and the selling price 81 cents more per 100 lbs. for the steers.[58] However, these factors were more than offset by the fact that the initial cost of the heifers was $1.66 less per 100 lbs. than for the steers. The net return per head was therefore greater from the heifers.

Spayed heifers may make slightly better gains than open heifers after they have recovered from the effects of the operation, but the difference is not sufficient to make up the gain lost until they recover, and to cover the expense and risk.[59]

If possible, heifers should be fed apart from steers, to lessen the disturbance at the heat periods. However, in a Minnesota test about as good results were secured from a mixed lot of heifers and steers as from the two sexes fed separately.[60]

1024. Preparation of feeds.—The general principles which determine whether any particular method of feed preparation for stock will prove profitable have been fully discussed in Chapter IV. (97-104) Information is presented in the following chapter on whether or not it pays to grind each of the grains for beef cattle.

In general, the small grains should all be ground for beef cattle. In the case of corn, there is usually not enough saving through grinding to warrant the expense, if pigs follow the cattle to utilize any unmasticated grain.

Statements are sometimes made that rolling small grain is preferable to grinding it. However, a mixture of ground wheat and oats proved better for fattening cattle in an Illinois test than rolled wheat and oats.[61] The bulkiness of the rolled grain decreased the amount eaten and therefore lessened the gains.

1025. Chopping or grinding dry roughage.—There has been considerable discussion as to whether it pays to chop or grind hay or other dry roughage for beef cattle. Under certain conditions, as is shown later, chopping hay, fodder, or stover will increase its value sufficiently to warrant such preparation.

Grinding of hay or other dry roughage into a meal is much more expensive than chopping it. In experiments to study the effect of grinding roughage for beef cattle, such preparation has generally made no more saving than chopping it or has not been profitable, except in the case of sorghum fodder, which is mentioned later.[62]

Grinding corn stover and alfalfa hay for fattening calves produced no better results than chopping it in an Ohio trial.[63] Likewise, in a test at the University of Alberta, Canada, grinding oat sheaves, prairie hay, and legume hay for fattening cattle was not profitable, while chopping the roughage was justified.[64] Grinding hay for fattening cattle in Arizona, North Dakota, and South Dakota experiments did not pay.[65]

It is pointed out in the next chapter that grinding fodder from the sorghums in a machine that grinds or cracks the seed increases its value considerably more than merely chopping the fodder. However, the ground fodder has a much lower feeding value per acre than sorghum silage. In a Colorado test it was not profitable to grind sweet sorghum fodder having fine to medium-sized stalks for calves being carried through the winter.[66]

Whether it will pay to chop or cut hay or other dry roughage for beef cattle will depend on the quality and on the price of the roughage, and also on the manner in which it is fed. If the forage is consumed with but little waste when fed uncut, chopping it will generally not be advisable. On the other hand, where the wastage is considerable, chopping the roughage may make sufficient saving in feed to justify the expense.

In the West, where alfalfa hay is usually cheap, it is commonly fed to fattening cattle in very liberal amounts and the wastage is hence greater than when only as much is supplied as will be cleaned up reasonably well. Chopped alfalfa hay was compared with uncut hay in 25 Idaho and Oregon comparisons in which fattening cattle were fed alfalfa hay and usually a limited amount of grain or silage in addition.[67] On the average the cattle fed chopped hay gained 0.17 lb. more per head daily. From the standpoint of the amount of feed required per 100 lbs. gain, chopping the hay increased its value about 25 per cent.

Chopping soybean hay for fattening cattle in a Louisiana test increased its value 25 per cent.[68] In three Wisconsin tests chopped alfalfa hay was compared with uncut hay for beef cows nursing calves during the winter.[69] The cows and calves were fed corn silage and grain and other concentrates in addition to the hay. Chopping the hay for the cows made possible a saving of about 10 per cent of the concentrates fed. With the concentrate mixture at $30 per ton, this saving amounted to $1.82 for each ton of hay fed. In an Ohio trial and in Wyoming experiments chopping hay for beef cattle was not profitable.[70]

When cattle are fattened chiefly on alfalfa hay, as in some sections of the West, more care is necessary in starting them on chopped hay than on long hay. As the chopped hay is much less bulky, the cattle may at first over-eat if they are fed an unlimited amount.

It is pointed out in the next chapter that when cattle are fattened on alfalfa hay alone it is not wise to chop low-quality hay in order to force them to eat the poorer parts that they would otherwise discard.

1026. Mixing chopped or ground hay with grain.—It is shown in Chaper XXXIV that for fattening lambs heavily fed on grain it is sometimes advisable to mix chopped or ground hay with the grain, in order to lessen digestive troubles. In the case of fattening cattle, however, experiments have shown that there is no advantage from the use of such combinations, in place of feeding the grain and hay separately.[71]

1027. Self feeding.—When it is desired to feed fattening cattle all the grain they will eat, self-feeders are often used. As the hopper which holds the grain can be of considerable capacity, it requires less labor to keep it filled than to feed the grain by hand twice a day. Also, self-fed cattle generally gain a trifle more rapidly than when hand-fed, even by experienced men. With an inexperienced person doing the hand-feeding, the difference is more marked.

There is also probably less tendency for self-fed cattle to "go off feed" than with those that are hand-fed. This is because each animal soon learns he can eat what he wishes at any time, and therefore there is not the tendency for greedy steers to gorge, as they sometimes do at feeding time when fed by hand.

These advantages are offset to some extent by the fact that more grain and less roughage are consumed per 100 lbs. gain by self-fed animals, and generally their gains are more expensive than those of cattle hand-fed by good stockmen. The greater expense of the gains is offset, as a rule, by a higher selling price of the self-fed cattle, due to better finish. Ear corn is not well suited to self-feeding, as it tends to clog the feeder. Therefore corn must be shelled or ground for self-feeding.

Cattle unaccustomed to grain feeding can not be self-fed grain separately until they have been brought to full feed, and then the change must be made with care, or some animals will overeat and "founder." Sometimes chopped or ground hay is mixed with the grain in starting the cattle on the self-feeder, but this is not a common practice. The grain in the self-feeder should be protected from rain and snow, and care is necessary to avoid clogging, as an abundance of feed must be available at all times.

Self-feeding of grain has been compared with hand-feeding in 13 experiments in each of which one lot of cattle has been self-fed grain after they were safely on feed, while another lot was given the same grain by hand twice a day.[72] The roughages (hay or hay and silage) were hand-fed in the usual manner. In most of the trials the grain was shelled corn, but in three tests a mixture of equal parts shelled corn and whole oats was fed at first, the oats being decreased later and entirely omitted during the last part of the fattening period.

In these trials the self-fed cattle gained 0.13 lb. more per head daily than the hand-fed animals, but their feed cost per 100 lbs. gain was 26 cents greater. This was more than offset by a slightly higher selling price, and on the average the net return per head over cost of feed was 48 cents per head more for the self-fed cattle, not considering the saving in labor. In these tests self-feeding was just as well suited to the fattening of calves as of older cattle.

1028. Shelter.—An important advantage of beef production is that expensive buildings are not required. Several experiments have shown that, even in climates like that of the northern United States, cattle make fully as rapid and economical gains when fattened during winter in an open shed with an adjacent exercise lot, as when more warmly housed in a barn.[73]

With such animals ample heat is unavoidably produced in the body through the mastication, digestion, and assimilation of their food to keep them warm under all ordinary conditions, without diminishing at all the amount of nutrients available for fattening. A reasonable degree of cold is a benefit rather than a detriment to liberally-fed fattening cattle, for in warm weather they have an excess of heat which they must get rid of. (**119-125**)

In cold climates where there is considerable rain or snow during winter, it is advisable, however, to provide a shed for shelter. Otherwise, the loss of heat in the evaporation of water from a wet skin, coupled with the loss by radiation, may be so great that food nutrients must be oxidized merely to keep the animal warm.

Unless the winters are unusually severe, there is probably no great advantage in providing warmer winter shelter than an open shed for beef breeding cows or for young stock, except young calves. For cattle being fed little more than a maintenance ration, warmer shelter will save a small amount of feed in cold climates, but it is doubtful if the saving will be sufficient to justify much additional expense.[74]

The feeding of fattening cattle in open yards, with no shelter other than windbreaks, is common in western sections with little rainfall, even in regions where the winters are severe. Furnishing shelter in an open shed or barn, did not appreciably increase the gains of fattening cattle, even of calves, in tests conducted in eastern Oregon and Washington and in Manitoba.[75] Neither was there sufficient saving of feed to justify the expense of such shelter.

In humid sections with mild winters it may likewise not pay to provide shelter for beef cattle. In Mississippi trials shelter was not necessary for wintering beef cows, yearlings, or weanling calves, providing that they were in good condition in the fall and if they were properly fed.[76] The small saving of feed through providing shelter was not enough to warrant the expense. Likewise, in Alabama steers fattened in the open during winter made practically as rapid gains as those allowed access to an open shed.[77] Shelter reduced the feed cost of 100 lbs. gain by only 6 cents.

When cattle are fattened in a dry lot during the summer it may be advisable to confine them to a barn or open shed, merely so that their coats do not become harsh and sunburned. Otherwise, the buyers at the central market may think that they have been fattened on grass and not be inclined to offer the premium for them that cattle well fattened in the dry lot generally command.[78]

1029. Confinement and exercise.—Beef breeding cattle and young stock being wintered should be allowed plenty of exercise in outside paddocks during the winter. Not only does the exercise itself aid in keeping them thrifty, but also the exposure to sunlight will prevent any deficiency of vitamin D. (**191**)

On the other hand, too much exercise for fattening cattle will make the gains less rapid and more expensive. This is shown in three Kentucky experiments in which fattening steers confined in winter to a barn with a covered barnyard were compared with others which had the run of a similar barn and were allowed to range at will on a 20-acre bluegrass pasture.[79] The steers confined to the barn gained an average of 0.16 lb. more per head daily and also sold at a slightly higher price. Including credit for the pork produced by the hogs following the steers, the confined steers returned $6.86 more profit per head.

The ordinary method of feeding fattening cattle in which they are fed as a group, having access to a common feed bunk and hay rack, is decidedly preferable to confining them in stanchions. Not only is there a saving of labor and equipment, but also the group-fed cattle will eat more feed, due to competition at the feed bunk, and will make more rapid gains.

For example, in an Ohio test steers fed in a group gained 0.4 lb. more per head daily than others fed the same ration, but confined to stanchions.[80] Similar results were secured in Canadian experiments.[81]

1030. The paved feed lot.—Where the soil and the climate are such that a feed lot will otherwise become a sea of mud and mire in winter, paving the lot will pay. It will make the cattle more comfortable and will increase their gains, and also the pigs following the steers will be able to utilize the grain in the droppings more completely. In addition there will be much less waste of manure.

In an Iowa test steers with a paved lot and adjacent open shed gained slightly more and sold for a trifle higher price than where the feed lot was unpaved.[82] Due chiefly to the greater amount of pork produced by the pigs following the steers in the paved lot, the net returns per head were $4.49 greater for this group of cattle. The profit was also greater in a similar Illinois trial from the steers in the paved lot.[83]

It is not necessary to have a large outside lot for fattening cattle. For cattle 2 years old or older, 60 square feet of space per head in an outside lot and 30 square feet in an adjoining open shed are ample.[84]

1031. Dehorning.—Horned cattle are at a distinct disadvantage in the feedlot. They require more room than dehorned or polled cattle, they make less rapid gains, and they commonly sell at a lower price on the large markets, due to the damage caused to hides and carcasses. Therefore it pays well to dehorn feeder cattle before they are fattened for market.[85]

1032. Variations in weight.—Cattle show surprising variations in weight from day to day, and from week to week. Even when weighed at the same time on consecutive days and under apparently similar conditions, the weight of a steer or a cow on any particular day may vary 20 to 40 lbs., and sometimes even more, from the weight on the previous day.

These variations show how difficult it is to know the true weight of an animal at any given time. Experiment stations now generally weigh all experimental animals for 3 successive days at the beginning and end of feeding trials, taking the average as the true weight of the animal on the second day. These variations in weight are due chiefly to irregularity in voiding of feces and urine and to differences in amount of water drunk or amount of feed consumed shortly before the animals are weighed.

QUESTIONS

1. Why is it more necessary than formerly that beef cattle being fattened for market be fed well-balanced rations?
2. Compare the nutrient requirements of beef cows with those of dairy cows.

3. Under what conditions may the kind of protein in the concentrates be of importance in feeding beef cattle?

4. About how much will 100 lbs. of protein supplement, such as linseed meal or cottonseed meal, be worth for fattening cattle, in comparison with grain, when added to a ration that has insufficient protein?

5. Discuss the addition of a protein supplement to grain and alfalfa hay for fattening cattle.

6. Does it pay to add a supplement to a ration of corn and clover hay in fattening: (a) 2-year-olds; (b) calves?

7. Discuss the use of protein supplements with non-legume roughage for fattening cattle.

8. Discuss the requirements of beef cattle for: (a) Salt; (b) calcium; (c) phosphorus; (d) vitamin A; (e) water.

9. Under what conditions and for what ages of cattle is it economical to limit the amount of concentrates fed fattening cattle?

10. Define *margin* and *necessary margin*. State the effect of each of 5 factors on the necessary margin.

11. Discuss the value of beef blood for beef production, considering: (a) Rapidity and cost of gains; (b) early maturity; and (c) value of carcass.

12. How would you decide which grade of feeder steers to purchase?

13. What results have been secured in trials in which beef-bred steers have been compared with dairy-bred steers?

14. Discuss the influence of age upon the economy of gains by beef cattle.

15. Upon what factors would you base your decision concerning the age of feeder cattle to buy?

16. Why is it important both for beef producer and for consumer not to carry fattening cattle to an excessive degree of fatness?

17. Discuss the results secured from the fattening of heifers.

18. Discuss the chopping of hay and other dry roughage for beef cattle; the grinding of roughage.

19. When would you recommend the self-feeding of grain to fattening cattle?

20. Discuss the needs of beef cattle for shelter under various climatic conditions.

21. Contrast the requirements of breeding cattle and of fattening cattle for exercise.

REFERENCES

1. Gramlich, Nebr. Bul. 174 and mimeo. rpts.
2. Wilson and Wright, S. D. Bul. 293.
3. Peters, Minn. Bul. 300; Gramlich and Thalman, Nebr. Bul. 252 and mimeo. rpt.; see also: Thalman, Nebr. Sta., mimeo. rpt.
4. Hickman, Rinehart, and Johnson, Id. Bul. 209; Potter, Withycombe, and Edwards, Ore. Bul. 276.
5. Skinner and Cochel, Ind. Buls. 129, 136; Mumford, Ill. Bul. 103; Culbertson and Evvard, Iowa Sta., Amer. Soc. Anim. Prod., Proc. 1923; Peters and Carnes, Minn. Bul. 200.
6. Skinner and Cochel, Ind. Bul. 129; Skinner and Starr, Ind. Bul. 220; Skinner and King, Ind. Buls. 240, 249, 255, 265, 281, 291, 314; Allison, Mo. Bul. 112; see also Culbertson, Evvard, et al., Iowa Sta., Amer. Soc. Anim. Prod., Proc. 1923; Bohstedt, Ohio Bimo. Buls. 105-106.
7. Allison, Mo. Bul. 150; Gramlich, Nebr. Sta., mimeo. rpts.
8. Brown and Branaman, Mich. Quar. Buls., 7, 1924, No. 1; 8, 1925, No. 1; 9, 1926, No. 1; Branaman and Brown, Mich. Quar. Buls., 10, 1927, No. 1; 11, 1928, No. 1; 12, 1929, No. 1; Peters, Minn. Bul. 300; Bohstedt, Ohio Bimo. Bul. 117.
9. McCampbell et al., Kan. Circs. 105, 117, 128.
10. Evvard, Culbertson, et al., Iowa Rpt. 1931, Iowa Leaflet 16, and mimeo. rpts.
11. Evvard, Culbertson, et al., Iowa Sta., mimeo. rpts.
12. Evvard, Breeder's Gazette, 76, 1919, p. 307; Evvard, Culbertson, et al., Iowa Sta., mimeo. rpts.; see also: Becker, Neal, and Shealy, Fla. Bul. 231.
13. Hensel, Breeder's Gazette, 80, 1921, p. 181; Kan. Rpt. 1920-22.
14. McCampbell, et al., Fort Hays Branch, Kan. Sta., Cattlemen's Round-up, 1927.
15. Chapline and Talbot, U. S. Dept. Agr. Cir. 379.
16. Morton, Osland, and Tom, Colo. Press Bul. 82; King, Ind. Rpts. 1933, 1934.
17. McCampbell, Amer. Soc. Anim. Prod., Proc. 1932; Weber and Connell, Kan. Sta., mimeo. rpt.; Blizzard, Okla. Rpt. 1930-32 and mimeo. rpts.; J. M. Jones, Hall, Black, Mackey, Dickson, and J. H. Jones, Tex. Rpts. 1932, 1933, and mimeo. rpts.
18. Thalman, Gramlich, and Lewis, Nebr. Sta., mimeo. rpt.
19. Wyo. Rpt. 1933.

20. Guilbert, Cal. Bul. 481.
21. Rusk and Snapp, Ill. Sta., mimeo. rpt.; see also, Evvard, Culbertson, Hammond, and Wallace, Iowa Sta. mimeo. rpt.
22. King and Hall, Kan. Rpt. 1930-32.
23. Watkins, New Mex. Bul. 212.
24. Rusk and Snapp, Ill. Rpt. 1928; Skinner and King, Ind. Buls. 281, 291, 314; McCampbell et al., Fort Hays Branch, Kan. Sta., Annual Cattlemen's Round-up, 1933; Bohstedt, Ohio Buls. 373, 382; Wyo. Rpt. 1933.
25. Evvard, Culbertson, Wallace, and Hammond, Iowa Leaflet 16 and mimeo. rpts.
26. Hickman, Id. Sta., information to the author.
27. Edwards and Massey, Ga. Bul. 184.
28. Hart and Guilbert, Cal. Bul. 560.
29. Edwards and Massey, Ga. Bul. 184.
30. Gramlich and Thalman, Nebr. Sta., mimeo. rpt.
31. Rusk and Snapp, Ill. Rpt. 1932.
32. Hickman, Rinehart, and Johnson, Id. Bul. 209; Potter and Withycombe, Ore. Bul. 183.
33. Gerlaugh, Ohio Bimo. Buls. 159, 166.
34. Evvard, Culbertson, et al., Iowa sta., mimeo. rpt.; Culbertson and Hammond, Iowa Sta., mimeo. rpt.; McCampbell, Winchester, and Marston, Kan. Cirs. 86, 92, 97; Branaman and Brown, Mich. Quar. Bul., 13, 1930, No. 2; 14, 1931, No. 3: 15, 1932, No. 2; Vaughan, Minn. Bul. 237; Thalman and Gramlich, Nebr. Sta., mimeo. rpt.; Bohstedt, Ohio Bimo. Buls. 117, 123.
35. Skinner and King, Ind. Buls. 153, 163, 167; Trowbridge, Mo. Bul. 179; Trowbridge and Fox, Mo. Buls. 218, 228; Cochel, Penn. Bul. 118; Tomhave and Severson, Penn. Bul. 145.
36. Skinner, King, et al., Ind. Buls. 206, 220, 240, 249, 255, 265, and mimeo. rpt.; Evvard and Dunn, Iowa Sta., mimeo. rpt.; Evvard, Culbertson, Wallace and Hammond, Iowa Bul. 253; Peters and Carnes, Minn. Bul. 200; Trowbridge, Mo. Bul. 179; Trowbridge and Fox, Mo. Bul. 218; Gramlich, Nebr. Sta., mimeo. rpt.; Bohstedt, Ohio Sta., mimeo. rpt.; Fuller and Morrison, Wis. Bul. 319, and mimeo. rpt.
37. McCampbell and Winchester, Kan. Cir. 77; Trowbridge and Fox, Mo. Buls. 189, 197; Tomhave and Bentley, Penn. Buls. 181, 183.
38. Skinner, King, et al., Ind. Buls. 206, 220, 240, 249, 255, 265; Dunn, Evvard, and Pew, Iowa Bul. 182; Trowbridge and Fox, Mo. Bul. 218; Bohstedt, Ohio Bimo. Buls. 83-84, 93-94; see also: Anderson, McCampbell, and Alexander, Kan. Cir. 151; Christensen, N. D. Sta., mimeo. rpt.; Vinke and Pearson, Mont. Bul. 251; Sackville and Bowstead, Univ. of Alberta, Canada, Col. of Agr., Bul. 13, Sackville and Sinclair, Univ. of Alberta, mimeo. rpt.
39. Skinner, King, et al., Ind. Buls. 206, 220, 240, 249, 255, 265; Trowbridge and Fox, Mo. Bul. 218.
40. Wentworth, Progressive Beef Cattle Raising, Armour and Co.
41. Burch, U. S. Dept. Agr., Bur. Anim. Indus., press announcement.
42. Edwards and Massey, Ga. Bul. 184; Hostetler, Foster, and Case, N. C. Rpts. 1929, 1931, 1932; National Live Stock and Meat Board, Rpt. 1934-35; Hawkins, Blizzard, and Croft, Okla. Rpt. 1932-34; Starkey, S. C. Rpt. 1928.
43. Dvorachek and Semple, Ark. Bul. 247; Semple and Dvorachek, U. S. Dept. Agr. Tech. Bul. 203.
44. Evvard, Culbertson, et al., Iowa Sta., mimeo. rpt.; Peters, Minn. Bul. 300; Gerlaugh and Gay, Ohio Bimo. Buls. 152, 158, 166, 173; Bentley, Ziegler, and McKenzie, Penn. Buls. 279, 293, 308, and mimeo. rpt.; Knox, Tex. Sta., Amer. Soc. Anim. Prod., Proc. 1931; see also: Mumford, Ill. Bul. 90; Rusk and Snapp, Ill. Rpt. 1932; McCampbell and Winchester, Kan. Cir. 92; Gramlich, Nebr. Rpt. 1922 and mimeo. rpt.; Livesay, West Va. Bul. 225; Black, Warner, and Wilson, U. S. Dept. Agr. Tech. Bul. 217; Dowell, Bowstead, and Black, Univ. of Alberta, Canada, mimeo. rpts.
45. Fuller, Wis. Buls. 396, 405, 410; Am. Soc. Anim. Prod., Proc. 1930.
46. Williams, Ariz. Bul. 91; Bohstedt, Ohio Bimo. Bul. 83-84; Hayden, Ohio Bimo. Bul. 89-90.
47. Peters and Johnson, Minn. Sta., mimeo. rpt.; Smith, Nebr. Bul. 132; Bliss and Lee, Nebr. Bul. 151; Severson and Gerlaugh, Penn. Rpt. 1917; Lush, Tex. Buls. 385, 471; Lush, Jour. Agr. Res., 42, 1931, pp. 853-881; Hultz, Wyo. Bul. 153; Hultz and Wheeler, Wyo. Bul. 155.
48. Winters and McMahon, Minn. Tech. Bul. 94; see also: Sheets, Amer. Soc. Anim. Prod., Proc. 1933, Wentworth, Amer. Soc. Anim. Prod., Proc. 1933.
49. Haecker, Minn., Buls. 155, 193.
50. Armsby and Moulton, The Animal as a Converter of Matter and Energy, pp. 217-218.
51. Culbertson, Evvard, Hammond, and Bassett, Iowa Bul. 271 and mimeo. rpts.; Peters, Minn. Bul. 300; Gramlich, Nebr. Bul. 229; Gramlich and Thalman, Nebr. Bul. 252; Bohstedt, Ohio Bimo. Buls. 83-84, 93-94, 105-106; Hackedorn and McCall, Wash. Bul. 202.
52. Stanley and Scott, Ariz. Bul. 108; Howell, Cal. Bul. 421; Hickman, Rinehart, and Johnson, Id. Bul. 209; Rusk and Snapp, Ill. Rpt. 1932; McCampbell, Bell, and Winchester, Kan. Cir. 77; Trowbridge and Fox, Mo. Buls. 197, 210, 228, 272; Arnett, Mont. Rpt. 1923; Quesenberry, Baker, Krantz, and Hutton, Mont. Rpt. 1927; Hungerford and Foster, New Mex. Bul. 128; Snell, New Mex. Bul. 140; J. M. Jones, Lush, and J. H. Jones, Tex. Bul. 309; Livesay, West Va. Bul. 251; Sackville and Bowstead, Univ. of Alberta, Canada, Col. of Agr. Bul. 12.
53. Stanley and Scott, Ariz. Bul. 108; Rusk and Snapp, Ill. Rpt. 1932; Trowbridge and Moffett, Mo. Bul. 300; Gramlich and Thalman, Nebr. Sta., mimeo. rpt.
54. Trowbridge, Moulton, and Haigh, Mo. Res. Bul. 30.

55. Bull, Olson, and Longwell, Ill. Bul. 355; Helser, Culbertson, Thomas, Nelson, et al., Iowa Rpts. 1932, 1933; Brown, Mich. Rpt. 1930-32; Foster and Miller, Mo. Res. Bul. 186; Trowbridge, Moffett, and Hazen, Mo. Bul. 310; Sackville and Sinclair, Univ. of Alberta, Canada, Col. of Agr. Bul. 25.

56. Culbertson and Hammond, Iowa Sta., mimeo. rpts.; Rusk and Snapp, Ill. Rpt. 1928.

57. Stanley and Scott, Ariz. Bul. 116; Maynard, Colo. Press Bul. 65; Maynard and Osland, Colo. Press Bul. 70; McCampbell and Horlacher, Kan. Cir. 105; Culbertson, Evvard, et al., Iowa Sta., mimeo. rpt.; Vaughan, Minn. Bul. 237; Trowbridge and Moffett, Mo. Bul. 314; Bohstedt, Ohio Bimo. Bul. 129; Bohstedt, Bell, and Gerlaugh, Ohio Spec. Cir. 10; Sackville and Sinclair, Univ. of Alberta, Canada, Col. Agr. Bul. 25 and mimeo. rpt.; see also: Stanley, Ariz. Bul. 137; Howell, Cal. Bul. 421; Rusk and Snapp, Ill. Rpt. 1927; Brown and Branaman, Mich. Rpt. 1930-32 and mimeo. rpt.; Kiser and Peters, Minn. Bul. 261; Ruffner, N. C. Rpt. 1927; Potter, Withycombe, and Edwards, Ore. Bul. 276.

58. Stanley and Scott, Ariz. Bul. 108; Gramlich and Thalman, Nebr. Bul. 252 and mimeo. rpt.

59. Wilson and Curtis, Iowa Buls. 24, 33; Gramlich and Thalman, Nebr. Bul. 252.

60. Vaughan, Minn. Bul. 237.

61. Rusk and Snapp, Ill. Rpt. 1931.

62. Hickman, Rinehart, and Johnson, Id. Bul. 209; Potter, Withycombe, and Edwards, Ore. Bul. 276.

63. Bohstedt, Bell, and Gerlaugh, Ohio Sp. Cir. 10.

64. Shaw and MacEwan, Sci. Agr., Canada, 12, 1932, pp. 255-261.

65. Stanley and Scott, Ariz. Rpt. 1932; Thompson and Sander, N. D. Exten. Cir. 119; Wilson and Wright, S. D. Bul. 252.

66. Morton, Colo. Rpt. 1934.

67. Hickman, Rinehart, and Johnson, Id. Bul. 209; Potter, Withycombe, and Edwards, Ore. Bul. 276 and information to the author; see also: Thalman, Nebr. Sta., mimeo. rpt.

68. Snell, La. Sta., mimeo. rpt.

69. Fuller, Roche, and Bohstedt, Wis. Res. Bul. 102.

70. Gerlaugh, Ohio Bimo. Bul. 135; Quayle, Wyo. Rpt. 1929.

71. Bohstedt, Bell, and Gerlaugh, Ohio Spec. Cir. 10; Vaughan, Minn. Bul. 237; Peters, Minn. Bul. 274; Wilson and Wright, S. D. Bul. 252.

72. Pew, Evvard, and Dunn, Iowa Bul. 271; Anderson and Marston, Kan. Cir. 130; Brown and Branaman, Mich. Quar. Bul., 7, 1924, No. 1; 8, 1925, No. 1; 9, 1926, No. 1; Fuller, Bohstedt, and Roche, Wis. Buls. 410, 420; Sackville and Sinclair, Univ. of Alberta, Canada, Col. of Agr. Bul. 23; see also: Mumford, Ill. Bul. 142; Trowbridge, Moffett, and Hazen, Mo. Buls. 310, 328.

73. Trials at Alabama, Iowa, Kansas, Minnesota, Missouri, Ohio, Pennsylvania, Texas, and Utah Stations. Partially reviewed by Armsby, U. S. Dept. Agr., Bur. Anim. Indus., Bul. 108. See also Penn. Rpt. 1906 and Penn. Buls. 88, 102; Ala. Bul. 163; Mo. Bul. 76; Ingle, Trans. Highl. and Agr. Soc. Scotland, 1909.

74. Waters, Mo. Bul. 76.

75. Hickman, Rinehart, and Johnson, Id. Bul. 209; Potter and Withycombe, Ore. Bul. 183; Ottawa, Canada, Expt. Farms Rpts. 1910, 1911, 1912.

76. Templeton, Miss. Bul. 268.

77. Gray and Ward, U. S. Dept. Agr., Bur. Anim. Indus., Bul. 159.

78. Gerlaugh, Ohio Bimo. Bul. 144.

79. Good, Ky. Bul. 242.

80. Bohstedt, Ohio Bimo. Bul. 123.

81. Day, Ontario Agr. College, Canada, Rpt. 1907; Grisdale, Ottawa, Canada, Expt. Farms, Rpt. 1904.

82. Pew, Evvard, and Dunn, Iowa. Bul. 182.

83. Mumford, Beef Production, p. 155.

84. Snapp, Beef Production, 2nd edition, p. 456.

85. Williams, Stanley, and Smith, Ariz. Bul. 110; Baird, Canada Expt. Farms, Nappan, Nova Scotia, Rpt. Supt. 1923; Canada Expt. Farms, Charlottetown, Prince Edward Island, Station, Rpt. 1923.

CHAPTER XXX

FEEDS FOR BEEF CATTLE

I. Grains and Other Concentrates Low in Protein

Much information concerning the value of the various feeding stuffs for beef production has been furnished by the many feeding experiments, conducted chiefly by the American experiment stations. This chapter, which discusses the most important feeds for beef cattle, is based largely upon an extensive study of the results of these investigations.

For further information on the composition and general characteristics of these feeds, the reader is referred to the respective chapters of Part II. Detailed information is also presented in Part II concerning the feeds of lesser importance that are not considered in this chapter.

Most of the experiments to determine the relative value of feeds for beef cattle have been conducted with fattening animals. Therefore the discussions in this chapter are concerned chiefly with the use of feeds for this purpose. Further information on feeds and rations for breeding cattle and for raising beef cattle is given in the next chapter.

1033. The cereal grains.—In most grain-growing sections, the cereal grains are the chief concentrates fed to beef cattle, these grains being combined, if necessary, with protein supplements to balance the ration. All of the grains can be used satisfactorily for beef production; the choice between them will depend on the price and availability. In all sections where corn is a leading grain crop, it is commonly fed as the only grain or at least as the chief grain to fattening cattle. In the sorghum belt the grain sorghums take the place of corn, and in the northwestern states the small grains—barley, oats, wheat, and rye—are widely used.

To secure good returns from beef cattle it is imperative that one not only appreciate the merits of the cereal grains, but also that he understand thoroughly their limitations. For a full discussion on this subject the reader is referred to Chapter XVII. (**508**) It must be remembered that all of the cereals are low in protein, corn and some of the grain sorghums containing somewhat less than barley, oats, wheat, or rye. Also, the cereals are very low in calcium and are lacking in vitamin D. All except yellow corn are deficient in vitamin A.

1034. Correcting the deficiences of the cereals.—Experiments conducted many years ago showed clearly that, even for fattening cattle, which do not need large amounts of protein, poor results are secured when the cereal grains are fed with only protein-poor roughages, like timothy or prairie hay or forage from corn or the sorghums. Such rations are not only deficient in protein, but also they are apt to contain insufficient calcium and they may be rather low in phosphorus. An abundance of legume hay of good quality will largely or entirely make

657

good this deficiency of protein and will supply an abundance of calcium for beef cattle.

The value of legume hay for supplementing the grains is well shown by the results of 8 experiments in each of which one lot of steers, 2 years old or older, was fed a ration consisting of only corn and protein-poor roughage (timothy hay, prairie hay, corn stover, or kafir stover), while another lot was fed corn and good legume hay.[1] The steers fed the well-balanced ration of corn and legume hay gained 2.3 lbs. daily, on the average, and required only 689 lbs. corn and 575 lbs. hay for each 100 lbs. gain. On the other hand, those fed the unbalanced ration gained only 1.7 lbs. a day and consumed 930 lbs. corn and 832 lbs. hay per 100 lbs. gain, thus requiring 36 per cent more corn and 44 per cent more hay for each 100 lbs. of gain.

Similar results were secured in experiments where a protein supplement, such as linseed meal, cottonseed meal, or gluten feed, was added to a ration of only corn and protein-poor roughage.[2] It was found that cattle fed unbalanced rations not only made slow and expensive gains, but also they were apt to go off feed and to suffer from digestive disturbances. Even when fed for a long period, they did not reach as good a finish as those receiving balanced rations, and therefore they sold for a considerably lower price.

It should be borne in mind that these great differences occurred with cattle that were 2 years old or older. With calves or yearlings the results from feeding unbalanced rations would have been even worse. For example, in an Illinois trial fattening calves gained only 1.5 lbs. per head daily on an unbalanced ration of shelled corn, corn silage, and oat straw (with a small amount of bone meal added to supply calcium and phosphorus.)[3] Similar calves gained 2.4 lbs. a day on a well-balanced ration, and gave a net return over cost of feed more than double that of those on the poor ration.

Since barley, oats, wheat, rye, and kafir usually contain appreciably more protein than does corn, it is not necessary to use so large an amount of protein supplement to balance rations of these grains, fed with non-legume roughage, as in the case of corn. However, the use of the proper amount of supplement is very important. The amount of supplement needed with the various grains for fattening cattle of the various ages can readily be found by computing balanced rations according to the Morrison feeding standards, as has been explained in the previous chapter. (991-992) When no legume hay is included in the ration, care should be taken to add a calcium supplement, except perhaps when the roughage has been grown on soils that are well supplied with this mineral. (999)

1035. Adding a supplement to grain and legume hay.—If fattening cattle are fed all the good-quality legume hay they will eat in addition to a full feed of corn or other grain, they will consume sufficient of the protein-rich hay to provide enough protein for satisfactory gains. Whether or not it will pay to add a protein supplement to such a ration has been discussed in detail in the preceding chapter. (993-994) If legume hay is used as only part of the roughage for grain-fed cattle and it is fed in combination with such protein-poor feeds as silage or fodder from corn or sorghum, then it will commonly pay well to add sufficient protein supplement to balance the ration according to the recommendations of the Morrison feeding standards. (Appendix Table III.)

1036. Indian corn.—Of all the concentrates, Indian corn is by far the most important feed for fattening cattle in the United States. (**512**) It excels not only because of its richness in starch and oil, but also because no other grain is so palatable to cattle. Corn is therefore generally taken as the standard with which the values of other grains for fattening cattle are compared.

Corn is also entirely satisfactory for breeding cattle, if it is wisely fed. The prejudice that is often encountered against the use of much corn for such stock is due chiefly to poor results secured when corn has been carelessly fed, without attention being given to its composition. Breeding stock should not be fed so much corn that they will become too fat. Also, care must be taken to provide plenty of protein and minerals, and, if available, some legume hay should be included in the ration. If other feeds in the ration furnish sufficient vitamin A, there will be no difference in the value of white corn and yellow corn. On the other hand, if this is not the case, then yellow corn will be superior, because it supplies this vitamin.[4]

Whether to feed fattening cattle all the corn or other grain they will eat or to limit the amount of grain, is a problem of the utmost importance. This has been fully discussed in the preceding chapter. (**1004-1006**)

1037. Preparation of corn for beef cattle.—If pigs follow beef cattle to consume the corn grains that escape mastication and digestion, corn is most commonly fed as ear corn or shelled corn. Numerous experiments have shown definitely that in such cases there is not sufficient saving through grinding the grain to warrant the expense. On the other hand, it pays to grind shelled corn or ear corn for cattle that are not followed by pigs. Coarse or medium-fine grinding is preferable to fine grinding, for such grain is more palatable and also less apt to cause heavily-fed fattening cattle to go off feed. (**99**) Ear corn should be ground finely enough so that the cattle will eat the fragments of cobs. Up to 6 or 8 months of age, calves chew corn and oats so thoroughly that it does not pay to grind these grains for them.

Cattle that are being fitted for show or sale are generally fed ground corn, instead of shelled corn or ear corn, because the gains are usually somewhat more rapid on ground corn. For the same reason, the expense of grinding is warranted when one wishes to force cattle to make maximum gains, so as to be ready for market before an expected decline in the price of fat cattle.

The use of shock corn for beef cattle is discussed later in this chapter. (**1085**)

1038. Ear corn.—Where corn is raised on the farm for cattle feeding, it is most commonly fed as broken ear corn. Experiments have shown that this is generally the most profitable manner in which to feed farm-raised corn during the fall, winter, and spring to fattening cattle that are followed by pigs.[5]

Ear corn is usually broken into pieces before being fed, so that the grain can be more readily eaten. The ears are broken over the edge of the manger, or are sliced by means of a corn knife or a special machine.

While breaking the ears into two or three pieces is sufficient for older cattle, the best results are secured with calves when the pieces are not over an inch to an inch and one-half long.[6]

Because of the bulk furnished by the cobs, broken ear corn is especially good in starting cattle on feed. Ear corn is best suited to feeding in winter and early spring, before the ears dry out and become hard. For summer feeding, shelled corn and ground corn are more popular. Unless a special machine is used to slice the ear corn, it takes more time to break the ears by hand before feeding than to shell the corn in large quantities by machinery.

1039. Snapped corn.—Snapped corn, which is ear corn, with some husks adhering, that has been snapped from the corn stalks, is often fed to beef cattle during the fall and early winter. It gives good results in the fattening of older cattle, especially during the first part of the feeding period.[7] Due to the bulky nature of the husks, it is less well suited to calves.[8] Even for yearlings and 2-year-olds it had best be replaced by broken ear corn or shelled corn during the latter part of the fattening period.

1040. Shelled corn; ground corn.—Next to ear corn, shelled corn is the most common form in which corn grain is fed to beef cattle. In nearly all of the experiments in which shelled corn and ground corn have been compared for fattening cattle that were followed by pigs, shelled corn has proved more economical.[9]

As shelled corn is the form in which corn is sold on the large markets, it is ordinarily the manner in which the grain is fed by those who purchase corn for fattening cattle.

1041. Corn-and-cob meal; ground snapped corn.—Unless there is a lack of roughage on the farm, it does not usually pay to grind ear corn into *corn-and-cob meal* for fattening yearlings or older cattle, if pigs follow them.[10] The results of experiments in which corn-and-cob meal has been used for fattening calves have differed somewhat.

It was concluded from Minnesota tests with fattening calves that the full-feeding of corn-and-cob meal was preferable to the full-feeding of shelled corn, because the ground cobs slightly limited the amount of grain the calves ate.[11] As a result, they showed less tendency to bloat or to go off feed, and they returned a greater profit than those full-fed on shelled corn. With pigs following the calves, still better results were secured when the calves were fed somewhat less shelled corn than they would clean up.

In Ohio tests in which corn-and-cob meal was compared with shelled corn, any benefit from using corn-and-cob meal was hardly sufficient to cover the additional cost of grinding.[12]

Ground snapped corn is too bulky for feeding throughout the fattening period, especially in the case of calves. Some beef producers use ground snapped corn during the first of the feeding period, then change to ground ear corn, and perhaps finish the cattle on ground corn. From Nebraska experiments it seems doubtful whether this method is preferable to feeding shelled corn or broken ear corn throughout the fattening period.[13]

1042. Soft corn; ear-corn silage.—Soft corn that has not fully matured before frost is well utilized by fattening cattle. The various ways of using such corn have been discussed in Chapter XVII. (516) In Illinois experiments with fattening cattle the highest value has been secured from soft corn when fed in the form of ear-corn silage.[14] Other good methods were to feed the crop as shock corn or to husk the corn from the standing stalks as needed for the cattle.

A given weight of dry matter in soft corn is about equal to the same amount of dry matter in mature corn. The gains will usually be somewhat less rapid on the soft corn, because the cattle will consume less actual dry matter. For example, it will take 30 to 60 days longer to fatten calves thoroughly on ear-corn silage than on shelled corn.

1043. "Cattling down" corn.—Particularly in the corn belt fattening cattle are sometimes turned into standing corn to harvest the crop. Cattle that are 2 years old or older are much better for this purpose than younger animals. The cattle should always be brought to a full feed of grain before they are turned into the field, or they may overeat and suffer from indigestion. In using this method it is important to feed sufficient protein supplement to balance the ration, and to have about twice as many pigs following the cattle as would be needed in dry-lot feeding.

1044. Barley.—In the sections of the western and northern states where corn does not thrive, barley is of great importance in beef production, for it closely approaches corn in feeding value. (551) Barley is not only an excellent grain for fattening cattle, but it is also well suited to breeding cattle.

Though barley usually gives entirely satisfactory results when fed as the only grain to fattening cattle, sometimes they tire of it during a long fattening period. Also, there is sometimes a tendency for cattle to bloat when fed barley as the only grain. In either of these conditions it is helpful to mix corn or ground oats with the barley. Except in such instances, there is no advantage in mixing oats with barley for fattening cattle, after they are on full feed, unless the cost of oats per ton is considerably less than that of barley.

Barley should be ground or rolled for cattle, but should not be ground into a very fine meal. (99) In Minnesota and South Dakota trials cattle fattended on whole barley made fairly satisfactory gains, but the amount of grain required per 100 lbs. gain was much higher than with ground barley.[15] These trials show that grinding barley will increase its value 20 to 40 per cent for fattening cattle.

Many experiments have been conducted to determine the value of ground barley in comparison with that of corn for fattening cattle. In 24 experiments in which ground barley has been fed as the only or the chief grain in direct comparison with corn, the average gains of the barley-fed cattle have equalled those of the corn-fed cattle.[16] This average of these many experiments shows that the opinion, often expressed, that cattle will gain faster on corn than on ground barley is incorrect.

Ground barley also fully equalled corn in these experiments so far as the amount of feed required per 100 lbs. gain by the cattle was concerned. However, the selling price of the barley-fed cattle was generally a little lower than for those fed corn, in the experiments in which the selling prices were reported. Also, where pigs followed the fattening cattle, considerably more pork was produced in the corn lots than in the barley lots.

The best measure of the relative value of these grains, when pigs follow the fattening cattle, is furnished by the results of 14 of these experiments in which ground barley was directly compared with shelled corn, pigs following the cattle on each ration. In these trials the barley-fed cattle gained 2.27 lbs., on the average, and those fed corn 2.25 lbs. On the barley ration a trifle less feed was required per 100 lbs. gain by the cattle, but much more pork was produced by the pigs following the corn-fed cattle, and the corn-fed steers sold for 13 cents more per hundredweight than those fed barley. Due to the smaller pork credit and the slightly lower selling price on the barley ration, ground barley was actually worth only 88 per cent as much as shelled corn in these trials.

The cost of grinding barley must be deducted from this value of ground barley, to find the relative value of whole barley (to be ground before feeding) in comparison with that of corn. If the cattle are not sold on a discriminating market and if no pigs follow the cattle in the feed lot, then the value of ground barley per ton will be as high as that of shelled corn, or probably even as high as that of ground corn.

There was no appreciable difference in the value of Trebi barley and of ordinary barley in North Dakota tests.[17] Hull-less barley is similar to wheat in composition, and when ground is about equal to ground wheat for fattening cattle.[18] Scabbed barley gives satisfactory results when fed to beef cattle. (503)

1045. Oats.—Due to the hulls, oats are less concentrated than corn or barley and are lower in total digestible nutrients. (528) Hence they are generally worth correspondingly less per ton for fattening cattle, if they form any large part of the concentrates. On account of the bulky nature of oats, if fattening cattle are fed oats as the only or the chief grain, their consumption of nutrients will be less than on corn, and their gains will therefore frequently be somewhat slower.

Oats are often included in the grain mixture when cattle are being started on feed, being omitted when they are safely on feed or at least during the latter part of the fattening period. Oats are popular as part of the concentrates for breeding cattle, for they have somewhat more protein and minerals than corn, and their bulk is no disadvantage for such cattle.

Experiments have shown that, except for calves, it pays to grind oats for beef cattle, even when they are followed by pigs. It was found in 3 Indiana experiments, in which 2-year-old steers were fattened on a mixture of 1 part oats by weight and 2 parts shelled corn, that grinding the oats to a medium or a coarse degree of fineness slightly increased the gains and resulted in greater net returns.[19] On the other hand, finely-ground oats were not as valuable as whole oats.

For calves, there was no benefit in grinding oats in a Kansas trial when they were fed as the only grain during the first half of the fattening period.[20] Likewise, in a Minnesota test with fattening calves it did not pay to grind a mixture of shelled corn and oats.[21]

The relative value of ground oats and shelled corn for fattening cattle, when each is fed as the only grain, is shown by 3 Michigan experiments with calves and 3 Indiana trials with 2-year-old steers.[22] In each series of tests either ground oats or shelled corn was fed with legume hay, corn silage, and either linseed meal or cottonseed meal. Pigs followed the cattle in all cases.

In these comparisons there was practically no difference in the rate of gain on the two rations. However, the oat-fed cattle were not quite so well finished and consequently sold for a slightly lower price than those fed corn. Also, the credit for pork produced was much less for the oat-fed cattle. Considering all the factors, ground oats were actually worth only 89 per cent as much as shelled corn in the experiments with calves and 79 per cent as much in the trials with 2-year-old cattle.

In some experiments ground oats have had a higher value than this when they have been used to replace not more than one-third of the corn. For example, in 4 Indiana trials 2-year-old steers were fed, throughout the fattening period, a mixture of one-third ground oats and two-thirds corn, by weight, in comparison with others fed shelled corn.[23] Substituting oats for part of the corn slightly increased the rate of gain and improved the finish of the cattle. When thus fed, ground oats were worth even more per ton than shelled corn.

On the other hand in Iowa experiments with calves and with 2-year-old steers and in a Minnesota trial with calves it was uneconomical to substitute ground oats for part of the corn throughout the fattening period.[24] In these trials oats were worth less per ton than corn.

In experiments in which ground oats have been directly compared with ground barley as the only feed for fattening cattle, the gains on oats have been nearly as rapid, on the average, but ground oats have been worth only about 86 per cent as much as ground barley.[25]

1046. Wheat.—When wheat is unusually low in price, it is often fed to beef cattle in the western states. (**537**) Even when fed as the only grain, it usually gives very satisfactory results, if it is coarsely ground, or cracked, or else rolled. Finely-ground wheat is less palatable, apparently because it tends to form a sticky mass in the mouth, and cattle are apt to tire of it. Sometimes it is difficult to keep cattle on feed when wheat is fed as the only grain, and occasionally there is a tendency for them to bloat.

In 13 recent experiments where ground wheat was directly compared with ground or shelled corn, the cattle fattened on wheat gained 2.14 lbs. per head daily, in comparison with 2.20 lbs. for those fed corn, and they usually required somewhat less feed per 100 lbs. gain.[26] In these trials ground wheat would have produced gains at an equal cost, even if priced 12 per cent higher per ton than corn. In some of the tests the wheat-fed cattle were not quite so well finished as those fed corn, and consequently they sold for a slightly lower price. This would correspondingly reduce the relative value of wheat in comparison with corn.

These trials show a surprisingly high value for wheat in comparison with corn, especially when we consider that in the experiments with fattening lambs, summarized in Chapter XXXIII, wheat has been worth considerably less than corn and has been about equal to barley. The high value of wheat for fattening cattle is corroborated by the results of 6 experiments in which ground wheat has been compared with ground barley as the only grain.[27] The wheat-fed cattle made fully as rapid gains as those fed barley and required less feed for 100 lbs. gain. Considering the amounts of grain and roughage needed per 100 lbs. gain, ground wheat was worth about 18 per cent more than ground barley.

In comparing the values of corn and wheat for beef cattle it should be borne in mind that there is no need of grinding corn if pigs follow the cattle, while wheat is not utilized well unless ground. The cost of grinding must obviously be deducted to find the value of whole wheat per ton, before being ground, in comparison with shelled corn. Sometimes this will be partly offset by the fact that wheat is richer than corn in protein. Therefore no supplement may be required with wheat, while it may be needed with corn.

Considering all the data available, it may be concluded that whole wheat (which is to be ground before feeding) is worth about as much per ton as a good grade of shelled corn for beef cattle. Frosted or shrunken wheat may be fully equal in feeding value to wheat of good milling grade.

By feeding ground wheat mixed with shelled or ground corn, or with ground barley or oats, any difficulty in keeping fattening cattle on feed can be avoided. Several experiments have shown that on such mixtures as one-half wheat by weight and one-half of these other grains the gains are generally fully equal to those on corn.[28] Also, the cattle have good appetites throughout the fattening period, are not apt to bloat, and do not tend to go off feed. Therefore when other grain is available, it is well to mix it with wheat, especially toward the end of the feeding period.

1047. Rye.—When not appreciably contaminated with ergot, rye is a satisfactory feed for beef cattle. (561) Like wheat, it should be ground coarsely, cracked, or rolled. Since rye is often not so palatable as other grains, it is best to mix it with corn, oats, or barley. Doubtless some of the poor results secured with rye have been due to the presence of ergot in the grain.

Steers fed only ground rye and alfalfa hay in 4 experiments gained 2.31 lbs. per head daily on the average and required 451 lbs. rye and 334 lbs. hay per 100 lbs. gain.[29] Others fed shelled corn and alfalfa hay gained 2.44 lbs. a day and required 520 lbs. corn and 241 lbs. hay per 100 lbs. gain. On the basis of the amount of feed for 100 lbs. gain, ground rye was fully equal to corn in these trials.

1048. Grain sorghums.—In the sorghum belt the grain sorghums largely take the place of corn for feeding beef cattle. (565) Ground grain sorghum is well liked by fattening cattle, produces nearly as rapid gains as does corn, and is not far below corn in feeding value.

The grain sorghums should commonly be fed to cattle either in the form of the ground heads or as the ground threshed grain, because the seeds are so small that they are poorly utilized unless ground. In 3 Texas experiments with fattening calves that were followed by pigs, grinding threshed milo increased its value 41 per cent, on the average, and grinding milo heads increased the value 62 per cent.[30] Though these large savings were made through grinding, the calves fed the whole threshed milo or the whole milo heads made satisfactory gains.

Few experiments have been conducted to determine the relative value of the various grain sorghums, or their value in comparison with corn. However, judging from the available data, the grain sorghums probably do not differ much in feeding value.

Ground kafir has been directly compared with corn in 9 experiments with fattening steers.[31] The cattle fed kafir gained 2.18 lbs. per head daily on the average, in comparison with 2.24 lbs. for those fed corn. The kafir-fed steers required for each 100 lbs. gain 572 lbs. kafir, 51 lbs. supplement, 410 lbs. hay or other dry roughage, and 238 lbs. silage.

Those fed corn required 534 lbs. corn, 51 lbs. supplement, 404 lbs. hay, and 217 lbs. silage. Considering the slightly greater amounts of feed required per 100 lbs. gain, ground kafir was worth about 92 per cent as much as corn in these trials.

Ground milo was about equal to ground kafir for fattening calves in an Oklahoma test,[32] and *cracked hegari* was equal to rolled barley in 2 Arizona trials.[33] Steers fed *ground darso* in 2 Oklahoma trials gained 0.33 lb. less per head daily than those fed ground corn and required considerably more feed per 100 lbs. gain.[34]

Ground feterita heads were about equal to ground snapped corn, including husks, in a Texas experiment, while ground hegari heads were worth somewhat less, on the average, than ground snapped corn in 2 other trials.[35]

1049. Sweet sorghum seed.—When ground, the seed from the sweet sorghums, or sorghos, is satisfactory for beef cattle, though it is somewhat less valuable than the grain sorghums. (566) In a Kansas trial beef calves fed ground sweet sorghum seed made nearly as rapid gains as others fed shelled corn, but they required considerably more feed per 100 lbs. gain.[36] Considering this, the sorghum seed was worth only about 60 per cent as much as shelled corn.

1050. Hominy feed.—Though hominy feed is not extensively used for beef cattle, it is entirely satisfactory for them. (519) It may be used as a substitute for corn, and in Kansas and Nebraska experiments with fattening cattle was about equal to shelled corn or ground corn in value per ton.[37]

1051. Cane molasses.—Cane or blackstrap molasses is widely used for feeding beef cattle in the sugar-cane districts of the South, as it is often considerably lower in price per ton than corn or other grains. (641) It should be used to replace not more than about one-half the concentrates ordinarily fed and is commonly diluted and poured over silage or over hay or other dry roughage. If the roughage is not of very good quality, this will frequently induce the cattle to consume more of it than they would otherwise.

Molasses can be self-fed to fattening cattle by placing a barrel of it in a tight feed-bunk and opening the bung, so the molasses will fill the feed-bunk to the level of the bung. It will then gradually flow out as it is eaten by the cattle.

The value of cane molasses when added to southern rations is shown by the results of 12 tests in each of which one lot of cattle was fattened on cottonseed meal as the only concentrate, with silage or Johnson grass hay for roughage, or else a combination of silage and hay.[38] In each trial molasses was added to the ration of a second lot of cattle. The molasses-fed cattle, which were given 3.5 lbs. molasses per head daily, gained an average of 1.99 lbs., in comparison with 1.81 lbs. for the cattle receiving no molasses.

In these experiments 100 lbs. of molasses replaced an average of 20 lbs. cottonseed meal plus 88 lbs. hay and 79 lbs. silage, in addition to the increase in the rate of gain. From these data, the value of molasses with feeds at local prices can readily be estimated. The molasses was diluted and poured over the cottonseed meal or silage in these trials, and not over hay. Perhaps molasses would have had an even higher value if it had been used to induce the steers to eat more hay or coarse dry forage.

1052. Adding molasses to an excellent ration.—Cattle feeders in other sections of the country have been much interested in knowing definitely whether it would pay to add a small amount of molasses to an already excellent ration for fattening cattle, such as grain, legume hay, corn silage, and protein supplement. The statement is often heard that the addition of molasses will appreciably increase the gains and the selling price of the cattle, and that molasses, thus fed, will be worth more per ton than corn.

This question has been studied in 19 experiments, in each of which one lot of steers has been fed a well-balanced ration, usually consisting of corn and legume hay, with or without silage, and in nearly all cases with a protein supplement.[39] Another lot has received a small amount of cane molasses in addition, the average being 2.0 lbs. per head daily.

Including molasses in the ration made only a trifling increase in the rate of gain (an increase of only 0.04 lb. per head daily). The molasses-fed cattle sold for a slightly lower price than the others, and they required more concentrates for 100 lbs. gain. Considering all factors, molasses was actually worth only 53 per cent as much per ton as grain in these experiments.

To find whether there was an advantage in adding a small amount of molasses to a good ration during only the latter part of the fattening period 2 Iowa tests were conducted with beef calves.[40] In neither of the trials did the addition of molasses to the ration increase the gains or the selling price, and the molasses was worth considerably less per ton than corn.

The effect of using a larger amount of cane molasses to replace part of the grain in a good ration for fattening cattle has been tested in 7 similar experiments.[41] The molasses-fed cattle, which received an average of 5.1 lbs. molasses in place of part of their corn, gained 0.08 lb. less per head daily on the average than those fed no molasses, and they sold at only 5 cents more per hundredweight. To make the same profit per head on the molasses-fed cattle as on the others, it would have been necessary to buy the molasses at only 56 per cent of the price of corn per ton, on the average.

These numerous experiments show definitely that there is no advantage in adding molasses to a palatable ration for fattening cattle, unless the cost of molasses is very much less per ton than that of grain. Similar results have been secured in experiments where molasses has been thoroughly mixed with the other concentrates or with the concentrates and chopped hay.[42]

In considering the results of these trials in which molasses has had a relatively low value for fattening cattle when added to an already excellent ration, it must be borne in mind that the no-molasses rations were made up of feeds of high quality and that the feeding was done by experienced stockmen. Under less favorable conditions it seems probable that the value of cane molasses in comparison with grain would at least be proportional to the amount of digestible nutrients supplied. This is about 70 per cent of the amount furnished by corn grain.

1053. Beet molasses.—In the beet-sugar districts of the West beet molasses is extensively used for fattening cattle. (**642**) It is usually poured over hay or other roughage, either undiluted or thinned with

SILAGE IS FAST REVOLUTIONIZING BEEF MAKING

Wherever corn or the sorghums thrive, silage from these crops has proved of great value in cheapening the cost of beef production.

Pasture Gains Are Cheap Gains

Bluegrass is the most common pasture for beef cattle in the North, but clover makes excellent pasture, if care is taken to avoid bloat.

Meal Time in a Corn-belt Feed Lot

The steers are being fattened on an efficient well-balanced ration, including corn grain, corn silage, and a protein-rich supplement. Where cattle are fed ear corn, shelled corn, or well-eared corn silage, pigs should follow them to utilize the waste grain.

water. Because of the laxative effect of beet molasses, not more than 4 to 8 lbs. should be fed per head daily to cattle.

When fed in limited amounts, beet molasses is worth about as much per ton as cane molasses for beef cattle.[43] In 3 Colorado experiments in which 2.3 to 5.0 lbs. of beet molasses were fed per head daily to fattening cattle, 100 lbs. of molasses saved 79 lbs. of barley plus 33 lbs. of hay.[44]

1054. Sugar beet pulp.—In the vicinity of the western beet-sugar factories many thousands of cattle are fattened annually on wet sugar-beet pulp. (643) This is usually fed with alfalfa hay, which makes good the lack of protein and calcium in the pulp. Generally, a limited amount of grain or of beet molasses is also fed in addition. If the cattle are not supplied with a liberal amount of alfalfa hay, sufficient cottonseed cake or meal or some other protein supplement should be added to balance the ration.

Because beet pulp and beet molasses are very low in phosphorus, care should be taken to supply this mineral when these beet by-products form a large part of the ration. The importance of this has been recently shown in 3 experiments by Maynard and Greaves of the Utah Station.[45] Steers fed wet beet pulp, beet molasses, and all the alfalfa hay they would eat gained only 1.07 lbs. per head daily on the average. Adding 0.1 lb. daily of bone meal to this ration doubled the gains and reduced the feed cost per 100 lbs. gain by 44 per cent. The addition of either cottonseed cake or wheat mixed feed (which are rich both in protein and phosphorus) produced no more rapid gains than the bone meal, and the gains were more expensive.

The value of wet beet pulp is well shown by 4 Colorado trials in each of which one lot of calves was fattened on a ration of ground barley, alfalfa hay, and 1.0 lb. of cottonseed cake per head daily.[46] Another lot was fed beet pulp in addition, eating an average of 27 lbs. The beet-pulp ration produced slightly more rapid gains in each trial and on the average 1 ton of beet pulp replaced 148 lbs. of barley and 344 lbs. of hay. In addition, the pulp-fed calves sold for an average of 10 cents more per hundredweight, due to better finish.

The relative value of siloed beet pulp and corn silage is shown by the results of 7 experiments in which cattle have been fattened on concentrates, alfalfa hay, and either beet pulp or corn silage.[47] The pulp-fed cattle gained 0.28 lb. more per head daily and each ton of wet pulp replaced 1,040 lbs. of silage plus 34 lbs. grain and other concentrates. From the values shown for wet beet pulp in these tests there must be deducted any losses in hauling pulp from the sugar factory and also any spoilage.

Sometimes cattle are fattened on only wet beet pulp and alfalfa hay, but the gains are much slower than when a limited amount of concentrates is fed, and also the cattle do not reach as good a finish.[48] Cattle should be accustomed to the pulp gradually, but later they may be allowed to eat all they will clean up, if there is a plentiful supply.

1055. Dried beet pulp; dried molasses-beet pulp.—When cheaper per ton than grain, dried beet pulp and dried molasses-beet pulp are economical substitutes for not over one-half of the grain in a ration for fattening cattle. (644) When thus used, these beet by-products are about equal to ground barley in value per ton and produce good gains.[49] Less satisfactory results are secured when they are fed as a substitute for all of the grain in a ration for fattening cattle.[50]

1056. Molasses feeds; alfalfa-molasses meal.—Many different brands of commercial mixed feeds containing various proportions of cane or beet molasses are manufactured for beef cattle. (647) The better grades of these feeds are well liked by fattening cattle and are often used as part of the concentrate mixture in fitting cattle for show or sale. Most molasses feeds are not high in protein, and therefore should be used chiefly as substitutes for grain, rather than to replace protein supplements.

In several trials at corn-belt stations rations including various brands of commercial molasses feeds have been compared with such standard rations as the combination of corn grain, corn silage, legume hay, and a small amount of linseed meal or cottonseed meal.[51] In nearly all of these tests the gain was lower instead of higher on the molasses feed, and the profit was less than on the standard rations. These trials show that in the commercial fattening of cattle in the corn belt, corn grain must commonly be used as largely as possible in order to secure the greatest net returns.

Alfalfa-molasses meal, composed of a mixture of alfalfa meal and molasses, is sometimes fed in the western states as a substitute for alfalfa hay or grain. Its value per ton is not greatly different from that of alfalfa hay.[52] Since alfalfa-molasses meal is not rich in protein, it should not be used as a substitute for cottonseed meal or linseed meal.

II. Protein Supplements

1057. Cottonseed meal or cake.—In the United States cottonseed meal or cake is used more extensively for beef cattle than any of the other protein supplements. (**581-584**) This is due to the good results secured with this high-protein supplement and also to the fact that in this country a much larger supply is available than of linseed meal or soybean oil meal.

The popularity of these cottonseed by-products is also due to the fact that they are well liked by cattle, and that they are so rich in protein that only relatively small amounts are needed to balance rations low in this nutrient. In addition, cottonseed meal and cake are unusually high in phosphorus. They therefore serve as phosphorus supplements, as well as protein supplements.

In the southern states cottonseed meal is often cheaper per ton than corn or other grain, and under these conditions is then frequently fed to fattening cattle as the only concentrate. On the other hand, in the North cottonseed meal generally costs considerably more per ton than grain. It is accordingly used distinctly as a protein supplement, only sufficient being fed to balance the ration in protein content.

To avoid wastage, cottonseed cake is generally used instead of cottonseed meal for beef cattle under ranch conditions and for fattening cattle in western feed lots where little or no shelter is provided. In feeding cottonseed cake as a winter supplement for range cattle, a common practice is to distribute it on the ground, the larger sizes of cake being preferred. It makes little difference whether cake or meal is used when it is fed under shelter and in feed bunks. In these chapters the term "cottonseed meal" is frequently used for both the meal and the cake.

1058. Value of cottonseed meal as a supplement.—The experiments summarized in the preceding chapter show that when cottonseed meal is added to a ration deficient in protein, each 100 lbs. will usually equal in value 250 to 300 lbs. of corn or other grain, provided that no more cottonseed meal is fed than is needed to balance the ration. (**992-996**) Not only will less feed be required for each 100 lbs. gain on the properly balanced ration, but also the cattle will reach a better finish and consequently sell for a higher price.

In several experiments cottonseed cake has been compared with alfalfa hay as a supplement for calves that were being wintered on non-legume roughages. In these tests each 100 lbs. of cottonseed cake, fed at the rate of 1 lb. per calf daily, have equalled 300 to 400 lbs. of alfalfa hay in actual feeding value. (1118) Where cottonseed cake or meal has been compared with grain as a supplement to non-legume roughage for wintering cattle in similar experiments, it has required about 2 lbs. of grain to take the place of 1 lb. of cottonseed meal.

While cottonseed meal or cake is satisfactory as the only protein supplement for fattening cattle, it is shown later in this chapter that even better results are secured if it is fed in combination with linseed meal. As is there shown, in most of the experiments where cottonseed meal has been fed as the only supplement to fattening cattle in direct comparison with linseed meal, the value of linseed meal per ton has been considerably higher. (1062) On the other hand, a mixture of one-half cottonseed meal and one-half linseed meal has produced as good results as when linseed meal has been fed as the sole supplement.

Under certain conditions, however, cottonseed meal or cake is definitely superior to linseed meal as the supplement for fattening cattle. This is because it tends to counteract the laxative effect of such feeds as wet beet pulp, beet molasses, or early-cut alfalfa hay. For example, in Colorado tests cottonseed cake produced better results than linseed meal with cattle fed liberal amounts of wet beet pulp and also beet molasses.[53] Similar results were secured in an Idaho trial in which fattening calves were fed alfalfa hay as the only roughage with ground barley and oats.[54]

In rations that tend to be too constipating, linseed meal will be preferable to cottonseed meal, as it helps to correct this condition.

1059. Correcting deficiencies in cottonseed meal and hulls.—Because cottonseed meal is often cheaper than grain in the cotton belt, it is frequently fed to fattening cattle as the only concentrate, along with such roughages as cottonseed hulls, corn or sorghum silage, or hay. Some years ago the most common ration for fattening cattle in the South was cottonseed meal and cottonseed hulls, without any hay or silage. When cottonseed meal was low in price, 10 lbs. or more per head daily were frequently fed to cattle a year old or more.

On this restricted ration cattle usually make satisfactory gains for about 2 to 3 months. Later they generally become unthrifty and show marked symptoms of "cottonseed meal injury." The recent investigations summarized in Chapter XVIII have shown definitely that the injurious effects of such a ration for cattle are due to the lack of vitamins, especially vitamin A, and of calcium. This trouble is therefore caused by deficiencies in the ration and not by a toxic effect of cottonseed meal for cattle. (583)

When care is taken to provide an ample supply of vitamins and of calcium, cattle can ordinarily be fed large amounts of cottonseed meal with good results, and without any injury whatsoever. The best sources of vitamins, especially vitamin A, are well-cured hay, particularly legume hay, and green pasture or forage crops. Good silage also aids in supplying vitamin A, but probably varies too much in this vitamin to be as reliable a vitamin supplement as green-colored hay. Unless a reasonable amount of legume hay is fed, a calcium supplement should also be added to the ration.

For breeding cattle or for fattening cattle that are to be fed for several months, it is of the utmost importance that vitamin-rich roughage be fed with a ration of cottonseed meal and cottonseed hulls, or disaster may result. Even in the case of cattle that are to be fattening for only 100 days or less, better results will usually be secured if a limited amount of good hay or silage is supplied.

1060. Feeding large amounts of cottonseed meal.—The relative prices of cottonseed meal and of grain will determine whether it will be more economical to use cottonseed meal as a substitute for grain in feeding fattening cattle, or to feed only enough meal to balance the ration. Several experiments have shown conclusively that the gains of cattle are not increased by feeding more cottonseed meal than is necessary to balance the ration. Also, when cottonseed meal is thus used as a grain substitute it is definitely worth less per ton than grain.

For example, in each of 8 experiments one lot of cattle was fed corn with just enough cottonseed meal to balance the ration, along with good hay or silage, or both hay and silage. This amount of cottonseed meal was 1.3 lbs. per head daily, on the average.[55] In each trial other cattle were fed similarly, except that they received 4.4 lbs. of cottonseed meal per head daily, which was much more than was needed to supply sufficient protein. The amount of grain they received was reduced so that they had the same total amount of concentrates as the first lot.

There was no appreciable difference in the gains made on the two rations, the cattle fed the smaller amounts of cottonseed meal gaining 0.03 lb. more per head daily, on the average. The cattle receiving the larger amounts of cottonseed meal as a grain substitute required somewhat more feed per 100 lbs. gain, and did not sell at any higher price than those on the other ration. In these trials each 100 lbs. of cottonseed meal fed as a corn substitute, beyond the amount needed to balance the ration, was only worth about as much as 87 lbs. of corn.

Similar results were secured in 6 Arizona experiments in which cottonseed meal was used as a substitute for ground barley.[56] In these trials 100 lbs. of cottonseed meal were equal in value to about 95 lbs. of barley. These experiments show that it does not pay to use cottonseed meal as a grain substitute for fattening cattle, unless the price of the meal is decidedly below that of grain.

In some experiments in which different amounts of cottonseed meal have been fed, the gain has been much more rapid on the larger allowances. However, in these trials the total amount of concentrates (grain plus cottonseed meal) has been greater. The increase in the rate of gain has thus been due to the larger amount of total concentrates, and not to any superiority of cottonseed meal over grain, when fed merely as a grain substitute.

1061. Whole-pressed cottonseed; cottonseed feed.—Whole-pressed *cottonseed,* often called "cold-pressed cottonseed cake," is well liked by cattle and may be used in the same manner as cottonseed meal. Since it contains the hulls, the value is correspondingly lower per ton than that of cottonseed meal. In 3 experiments where whole-pressed cottonseed has been compared with high-grade cottonseed meal, it has required 138 lbs. of the whole-pressed cottonseed to replace 100 lbs. of cottonseed meal for fattening cattle.[57]

Cottonseed feed, a mixture of cottonseed meal and hulls, was compared with cottonseed meal in a Pennsylvania trial as a protein supplement for fattening cattle.[58] Due to the lower protein content of the cottonseed feed, considerably more was needed to balance the ration than of cottonseed meal. With cottonseed feed costing 19 per cent less per ton than cottonseed meal, the latter was much more economical. Rarely is it economical for northern farmers to buy cottonseed feed instead of cottonseed meal.

1062. Linseed meal or cake.—Throughout the northern states linseed meal or cake is used extensively as a protein supplement for beef cattle. (591) In referring to these feeds, the term "linseed meal" will commonly be used for both the meal and the cake form. Linseed meal is of particularly high value for fattening cattle, as it produces rapid gains and also tends to give excellent finish. Cattle fed linseed meal usually have a trifle sleeker coats than those fed other common protein supplements. On account of this more attractive appearance, they tend to sell for a slightly higher price on the large markets, though the actual value of their carcasses may be no greater.

This ability of linseed meal to produce excellent finish and sleek coats is the reason why this supplement is commonly included in concentrate mixtures for cattle that are being fitted for show or for sale. Linseed meal is also excellent as part of the concentrates for young stock or breeding cattle, on account of its conditioning effect, its mild laxative property, and its richness in phosphorus.

Linseed meal or cake is appreciably lower in protein content than is cottonseed meal of the higher grades. Since cottonseed meal is a very satisfactory protein supplement for fattening cattle, we would naturally expect that the actual feeding value of cottonseed meal per ton would be fully as high or even higher than that of linseed meal. Many experiments have been conducted in which these two important protein supplements have been directly compared, when each has been fed as the only supplement.

A careful analysis of the data from 36 such experiments shows that the results have been somewhat surprising.[59] On the average, the cattle fed linseed meal as the only supplement gained 2.30 lbs. per head daily while those fed cottonseed meal averaged 2.21 lbs. This difference is only slight and not especially significant, for the cottonseed-meal-fed cattle gained fully as rapidly as those fed linseed meal in 10 of the trials.

There was also a slight advantage in favor of the linseed-meal-fed cattle in the amount of feed required per 100 lbs. gain. Considering only this factor, cottonseed meal would have been worth about 90 per cent as much as linseed meal in these trials.

However, in nearly all of the experiments the cattle that had been fed linseed meal sold for a slightly higher price, either because of better finish or a sleeker appearance. On the average, there was a difference of 18 cents per hundredweight in selling price in favor of the linseed-meal-fed cattle. Though this difference may seem small, it is of importance, because it applies to the entire weight of the cattle when they are marketed.

Primarily because of this difference in average selling price, the average net return per head over cost of feed was distinctly higher for the cattle fed linseed meal, even though the cost of the linseed meal was $1.86 per ton higher than that of the cottonseed meal.

To ascertain the relative actual values of these supplements in the 36 experiments, there has been computed for each experiment the price at which it would have been necessary to purchase the cottonseed meal, in order to make the same net return per head as with the cattle fed the linseed meal. These computations show that it would have been necessary to buy cottonseed meal at only 60 per cent of the price of linseed meal to make equal profit, on the average, in these many experiments.

These experiments do not mean at all that cottonseed meal is not efficient when fed as the only supplement to fattening cattle. They show that good results are secured with cottonseed meal, but that the gains are usually a little more rapid and the selling price appreciably higher with linseed meal. When the cattle are sold on a discriminating market, where small differences in the appearance or the finish of the animals affect the selling price, the latter fact should be considered.

As stated earlier in this chapter, cottonseed meal is superior to linseed meal as a supplement when the ration would otherwise have too laxative an effect. For example, cottonseed meal gives better results than linseed meal where steers are fed liberal amounts of wet beet pulp and beet molasses.

1063. Combining cottonseed meal and linseed meal.—Some years ago, after the author and associates had compared cottonseed meal and linseed meal in experiments with fattening steers, it occurred to him that a mixture of one-half linseed meal and one-half cottonseed meal might be fully equal to linseed meal alone. Accordingly 3 experiments were carried on at the Wisconsin Station to study this matter, and the same comparison was made in 6 later trials at the Iowa and Kansas Stations.[60]

In these 9 experiments the gains were fully as rapid, on the average, on the combination of cottonseed meal and linseed meal as on linseed meal fed as the only supplement. Though the selling price averaged 13 cents higher on the latter ration, slightly less feed was required per 100 lbs. gain on the mixed supplement. Considering all factors, the average value per ton of the cottonseed-linseed meal mixture was 97 per cent that of linseed meal.

These trials show that although under most conditions linseed meal is considerably superior to cottonseed meal as the only supplement for fattening cattle, a mixture of these two supplements is practically equal to linseed meal in value per ton. It is pointed out later that similar excellent results were secured when gluten meal was combined with linseed meal, although gluten meal was inferior to linseed meal when fed as the only supplement.

1064. Soybeans.—Where soybeans thrive, the beef producer can provide in the seed of this legume an excellent protein supplement for his cattle. (594) Even in the South, soybeans far excel cowpeas for this purpose.[61] Soybeans may be used satisfactorily to balance rations for fattening cattle and are also excellent for breeding cattle and young stock.

Probably because of the high oil content, fattening cattle sometimes tire of soybeans when fed as the only supplement for more than about 100 days. This is especially apt to be the case when more than 1.5 to 2.0 lbs. are fed per head daily. Large allowances are also apt to be too laxative and to cause scouring. Only a sufficient amount of soybeans should therefore be used to balance the ration in protein content, and if there is a tendency for the cattle to go off-feed, it is best to reduce the amount of soybeans and mix them with cottonseed meal, linseed meal, or some other protein supplement.

There is no need of grinding soybeans for beef cattle which are followed by pigs. In fact, in Illinois tests whole soybeans gave better results than ground soybeans.[62] Cooking soybeans does not apparently increase their value for beef cattle, as it does for swine, for roasted soybeans were not superior to uncooked soybeans in Indiana trials.[63] Other Indiana experiments show that there is no benefit from adding a mineral mixture supplying calcium and phosphorus, when soybeans are used as the supplement for fattening cattle, provided the cattle are fed a reasonable amount of legume hay.[64]

Soybeans have been directly compared with cottonseed meal in several experiments, when used as the protein supplement for fattening cattle fed corn, with hay or silage or with both these roughages. The results of 13 such comparisons are summarized in the following table:[65]

Soybeans vs. cottonseed meal as the protein supplement

	Soybean ration	Cottonseed meal ration
Average initial weight, lbs.	646.1	643.6
Average daily gain, lbs.	2.21	2.22
Average ration		
Corn, lbs.	10.4	10.6
Supplement, lbs.	1.9	1.9
Clover or alfalfa hay, lbs.	2.8	3.0
Corn silage, lbs.	17.0	17.9
Feed for 100 lbs. gain		
Corn, lbs.	466	477
Supplement, lbs.	84	85
Clover or alfalfa hay, lbs.	127	134
Corn silage, lbs.	752	798
Selling price per cwt., dollars	10.07	10.13
Return per head over feed cost, dollars	16.81	14.96

The table shows that the rates of gain on the two rations were almost identical. The soybean-fed cattle required a little less feed per 100 lbs. gain, but their average selling price was 6 cents lower. The net return over cost of feed, including credit for the pork produced by the pigs following the steers, was $1.85 higher for the soybean-fed cattle, chiefly because the average price of soybeans per ton was considerably lower than that of cottonseed meal. Considering all factors, soybeans were about equal in feeding value per ton to cottonseed meal in these experiments, except that there was sometimes a tendency for the steers to go off feed on the soybean ration.

Soybeans have been compared with linseed meal in 7 similar experiments with fattening cattle.[66] In these trials the soybean-fed steers gained 0.14 lb. less per head daily, on the average, and sold for 22 cents less per 100 lbs., than those fed linseed meal. Therefore, although no more feed was required per 100 lbs. gain on the soybean ration, the actual value of the soybeans per ton was considerably less than that of linseed meal.

1065. Soybean oil meal.—With the great increase in the production of soybean oil meal in this country during the past few years, this protein-rich feed has become of increasing importance as a supplement for beef cattle. (595) Because soybean oil meal is not high· in fat, like soybeans, fattening cattle do not usually show the tendency to tire of the feed during a long fattening period, as is sometimes the case with soybeans. Also, there is much less tendency to an undue laxative effect with soybean oil meal. While soybean oil meal that has been thoroughly cooked in the manufacturing process is more palatable and decidedly superior to raw-tasting oil meal for swine and poultry, Illinois tests indicate that this is not the case with cattle.[67]

In 3 experiments with fattening calves in which soybean oil meal has been directly compared with soybeans as a protein supplement, the average daily gain on the soybean oil meal has been 0.27 lb. greater.[68] Also, the selling price of the calves fed soybean oil meal has been higher in each trial, the average difference being 42 cents per hundredweight. As a result, the soybean oil meal was worth considerably more per ton than soybeans in these tests. On the other hand, in 4 experiments with 2-year-old cattle, the gains have been practically as rapid and the selling price of the cattle fully as high on soybeans as with soybean oil meal as the supplement.[69] For these older cattle soybeans were worth as much per ton as soybean oil meal.

Soybean oil meal has been compared with cottonseed meal as a supplement for fattening cattle in 7 Illinois and Indiana tests.[70] The cattle fed cottonseed meal gained a trifle more rapidly (the average difference being only 0.17 lb.) and also sold for 8 cents more per hundredweight in 5 of the experiments in which the selling price was reported. On the other hand, the cattle fed soybean oil meal required 19 lbs. less concentrates, 9 lbs. less hay, and 23 lbs. less silage per 100 lbs. gain. On the whole, the soybean oil meal was just about equal to cottonseed meal in value per ton.

Soybean oil meal has also been equal to cottonseed meal in 3 South Carolina comparisons in which these two feeds have been compared as the only concentrate for fattening cattle, when fed with corn silage or cottonseed hulls.[71] In an Illinois test soybean oil meal was slightly superior to cottonseed meal when fed as a protein supplement for steers fed corn on bluegrass pasture.[72]

Soybean oil meal does not seem to produce quite so good a finish on fattening cattle as does linseed meal. For example, in 3 Iowa comparisons cattle fed soybean oil meal gained nearly as rapidly as others fed linseed meal, but their average selling price was 22 cents less per 100 lbs.[73] Due to this, the actual value of the soybean oil meal per ton was considerably less than that of linseed meal, even though slightly less feed was required per 100 lbs. gain when soybean oil meal was used as the supplement.

1066. Wheat bran.—For beef cattle the use of wheat bran is limited chiefly to the breeding herd and young calves. (542) It is excellent as part of the concentrate mixture for such stock, for it is palatable, bulky, fairly rich in protein, and especially high in phosphorus.

Bran is also sometimes mixed with the grain when fattening cattle are being started on feed. After the cattle are on full feed, the bran is generally replaced by more concentrated protein supplements, such as linseed meal, cottonseed meal, or soybean oil meal. This is because a much larger amount of bran than of these high-protein feeds must be fed to balance a ration. Since bran is bulky and relatively low in total digestible nutrients, the considerable amount needed in the ration will lessen the gains and result in a poorer finish.

In Pennsylvania experiments conducted some years ago, a ration of wheat bran, corn, mixed hay and corn stover, which was frequently fed by farmers at that time, was decidedly inferior to a ration of cottonseed meal, corn, mixed hay, and corn silage.[74] This was due not only to the superiority of cottonseed meal as the supplement in a fattening ration, but also because silage is a much better feed than corn stover.

Similarly, in 4 Nebraska trials wheat bran produced somewhat smaller and more expensive gains than linseed meal or cottonseed meal, when used as a supplement to corn and prairie hay.[75]

1067. Corn gluten meal.—Corn gluten meal is used much more commonly for dairy cattle than for beef animals. (524) For fattening cattle it gives fairly satisfactory results when fed as the only supplement, if the ration contains a reasonable amount of legume hay. Gluten meal should not be used as the only supplement when little or no legume hay is fed, as the quality of the protein in the ration may then be inferior. (148)

Even when some legume hay is fed, the best results are secured from gluten meal when it is combined with linseed meal or certain other supplements. This is shown by the results of 3 Kansas experiments in which fattening calves were fed various supplements and mixtures of supplements, in addition to shelled corn, corn silage, and alfalfa hay.[76] Although the gains on gluten meal were fairly satisfactory, the calves sold for 47 cents less per 100 lbs. than others fed linseed meal. Therefore the value per ton of the gluten meal was much lower than that of linseed meal, when each was fed as the only supplement. The results from gluten meal and cottonseed meal were about equal, except that gluten meal was less palatable.

A mixture of one-half gluten meal and one-half linseed meal, or a mixture of one-third of each of these supplements and one-third cottonseed meal, produced fully as rapid gains as linseed meal. Also the selling prices of the calves fed these combinations were practically as high as in the case of those fed linseed meal as the only supplement. On the other hand, a mixture of gluten meal and cottonseed meal was not much better than either gluten meal or cottonseed meal fed as the only supplement.

Though no experiments have apparently been conducted to test such mixtures, it would seem that a combination of gluten meal and either soybeans or soybean oil meal should produce excellent results, for soybean seed should well supplement the deficiencies of the proteins of gluten meal.

1068. Corn gluten feed.—Though most commonly fed to dairy cows, corn gluten feed is a fairly satisfactory protein supplement for fattening cattle, when the ration includes some legume hay. There is, however, but little information concerning its exact value in comparison with the protein supplements more generally used for beef cattle.

When used as the only supplement for fattening cattle in a trial at the Iowa Station and one at the Minnesota Station, gluten feed was worth much less per ton than linseed meal.[77] Judging from the Kansas experiments with gluten meal reviewed in the preceding paragraphs, a combination of gluten feed and linseed meal or a mixture of gluten feed, cottonseed meal, and linseed meal should be much better than gluten feed as the only supplement.

1069. Meat scraps; tankage.—Recent experiments have shown that meat scraps (dry-rendered tankage) and digester tankage are satisfactory protein supplements for beef cattle.[78] Because of the high protein content of the best grades of meat scraps and tankage, less of these feeds is needed to balance a ration than in the case of such supplements as linseed meal, cottonseed meal, or soybean meal. The relative value of meat scraps or tankage in comparison with these supplements of plant origin will depend on the amounts of digestible protein and of total digestible nutrients contained in the feeds, and may be estimated by the method explained in Chapter X. (**281-283**) For beef cattle fed the usual kinds of rations, 1.0 lb. of digestible protein in tankage or meat scraps probably has about the same value as 1.0 lb. of digestible protein in good supplements of plant origin. The condition is thus different than in the case of swine and poultry, where 1.0 lb. of digestible protein in these meat by-products has a decidedly higher value than protein from plant sources. (**143, 155**)

Sometimes cattle may not like meat scraps or tankage at first, but after a few days they will generally eat the small amount that is needed to balance a ration. It is best to accustom cattle to these feeds gradually by mixing a small proportion at the start with better-liked feeds, such as linseed meal, cottonseed meal, or ground grain.

As is shown in the following paragraphs, especially good results have been secured where fattening cattle have been fed mixed protein supplements that contained meat scraps or digester tankage.

1070. Combinations of protein supplements.—It has been found in recent experiments with fattening cattle that certain combinations of protein supplements produce better results than most single supplements. While cottonseed meal and corn gluten meal have generally been of much lower value than linseed meal when one of these feeds has been used as the only supplement, combinations of these feeds with linseed meal have proved fully equal to linseed meal. (**1063, 1067**) It has been shown previously that any one of the following combinations is equal to linseed meal as the protein supplement for fattening cattle. This is probably also true for other classes of beef cattle. (1) One-half cottonseed meal and one-half linseed meal; (2) one-half corn gluten meal and one-half linseed meal; (3) one-third each of cottonseed meal, corn gluten meal, and linseed meal.

Excellent results were also secured in experiments at the Ohio Station with a mixture of one-third each of ground soybeans, cottonseed meal, and linseed meal, and in experiments at the Iowa Station with a combination of one-fourth each of ground soybeans, cottonseed meal, corn gluten meal, and linseed meal.[79] Undoubtedly soybean oil meal can be substituted for ground soybeans in these mixtures with equally good results.

The all-purpose protein supplement developed by the Ohio Station has been mentioned previously. (**629**) This combination has proved excellent for fattening cattle, being slightly superior to the mixture of one-half cottonseed meal and one-half linseed meal. It has likewise been very satisfactory as a protein supplement for dairy cattle, sheep, swine, and poultry. This supplement is a combination of 30 lbs. meat scraps, 30 lbs. soybean oil meal, 20 lbs. cottonseed meal, 15 lbs. linseed meal, and 5 lbs. minerals (equal parts by weight of steamed bone meal, ground limestone, and salt). Modifications can be made in this formula to adapt it to local feed prices.

A combination of one-third each of meat scraps, cottonseed meal, and linseed meal was also slightly superior to the mixture of one-half cottonseed meal and one-half linseed meal in Ohio tests with fattening cattle.[80] In Iowa trials excellent results were likewise secured with a combination of 50 lbs. cottonseed meal, 10 lbs. linseed meal, 10 lbs. corn gluten meal, 5 lbs. white fish meal, 10 lbs. soybean oil meal, 5 lbs. peanut oil meal, 5 lbs. coconut oil meal, and 5 lbs. cane molasses.[81]

It is evident from the foregoing that there are several supplemental mixtures of proven high value which will produce fully as good results as will linseed meal when it is used as the only supplement. Some of these supplemental mixtures are apparently a trifle superior to any single supplement for fattening cattle.

III. Legume Hay and Other Dry Roughages

1071. Value of legume hay.—The great importance of well-cured legume hay in making good the deficiencies of the cereal grains has already been emphasized in this chapter. (**1034**) On account of the richness in protein, calcium, and vitamins A and D, legume hay of good quality is the most valuable of all roughages for beef cattle. It is especially useful in keeping breeding stock in thrifty, vigorous condition.

Even in the case of fattening cattle, much better results are usually secured when the ration includes at least some legume hay than when the only roughage is grass hay or other non-legume dry forage. This is true even when sufficient protein supplement is fed to make good the lack of protein in the latter ration. The results with legume hay can generally be equalled only when excellent silage, such as that from corn or sorghum, is fed as the chief roughage, and there is supplied in addition not only a sufficient amount of a good protein supplement, but also about 0.1 lb. per head daily of ground limestone or some other calcium supplement.

The usual results that are secured when such dry forages as timothy hay, prairie hay, or corn fodder are fed as the only roughage to fattening cattle are well shown by the data from 4 experiments.[82] In each trial one lot of 2-year-old steers was fed a ration of legume hay and corn grain, and another lot a ration of non-legume hay or fodder, corn grain, and sufficient cottonseed meal or linseed meal to balance the ration.

The steers fed the non-legume roughage gained 2.0 lbs. per head daily and required 719 lbs. corn, 197 lbs. supplement, and 387 lbs. hay or fodder per 100 lbs. gain. Many would consider these results satisfactory. However, the steers fed the legume hay gained 0.3 lb. more per head daily, reached a decidedly better finish, and made much cheaper gains. It should be noted especially that a considerable amount of expensive protein supplement was needed to balance the non-legume ration while none was fed to the steers receiving legume hay. Because of this and also the higher selling price of the legume-fed steers, the non-legume roughage had an exceedingly low value in comparison with the clover and alfalfa hay.

From recent investigations that are summarized elsewhere, it seems evident that these non-legume rations would have been materially improved by the addition of a calcium supplement. (999) However, even then the value of the legume hay would undoubtedly have still been much higher than that of the non-legume roughage, merely because no expensive protein supplement was needed with the former to make good a lack of protein.

Whether it will pay to chop or grind legume hay or other dry roughage for beef cattle has already been discussed in the previous chapter. (1025)

1072. Feeding non-legume roughage with legume hay.—Even on farms where considerable legume hay is raised, much non-legume dry roughage, such as corn and sorghum stover, straw, and hay from the grasses, is normally produced in addition. In economical beef production these roughages should be wisely and fully utilized. While they do not equal legume hay in nutrients or palatability, excellent results are secured when cattle are fed such roughage along with a limited amount of good legume hay.[83]

Sometimes the addition of non-legume roughage to legume hay may be a distinct advantage. For example, alfalfa or soybean hay may occasionally be unduly laxative when fed as the only roughage. Also, cattle fattened on only alfalfa hay and ground wheat or barley sometimes show a tendency to bloat. Supplying some non-legume roughage will tend to correct these conditions.

1073. Legume hay with cottonseed meal.—Since legume hay is rich in protein, it should not be fed as the chief roughage with cottonseed meal, which is itself so rich in this nutrient. In Texas trials very poor results were secured when peanut or alfalfa hay was fed to steers with 5 lbs. of cottonseed meal per head daily.[84] When shelled corn was substituted for a part of the cottonseed meal or when prairie hay was fed in place of the legume hay, the gains became normal.

Where cottonseed meal is the chief concentrate, legume hay should be fed in limited amount, along with such carbohydrate-rich roughages as forage from corn or the sorghums, or cottonseed hulls.

1074. Alfalfa hay.—Alfalfa hay may well be taken as the standard with which other roughages for beef cattle are compared, for it has no superior. (373) Not only is it an excellent roughage for fattening cattle, but also its value for the breeding herd is perhaps even more outstanding. When even a reasonable part of the roughage consists of well-cured alfalfa hay, one can rest assured that there will be no deficiency in the quality of protein in the ration, or in calcium or vitamins.

It has been shown in the previous chapter that when fattening cattle are fed a liberal amount of alfalfa hay as the only roughage with corn or other grain, it generally does not pay to add a protein-rich concentrate, such as cottonseed or linseed meal. (993) This is because alfalfa hay is sufficiently rich in protein to balance the ration in protein content.

However, when the cattle are fed silage in addition to alfalfa hay, this succulent feed is so palatable that they will not eat enough alfalfa to balance the ration completely. To secure the best results it is then necessary to add a small amount of a protein supplement. If this is not done, the gains are slower and the cattle usually sell at a materially lower price, on account of poorer finish. This will generally result in decidedly lower net returns.

For information on the relative value of alfalfa hay cut at different stages of maturity and of hay from the first, second, or third cutting, the reader is referred to Chapter XIII. (370, 372)

1075. Fattening cattle on alfalfa hay and other roughage.—In some sections of the West, when cattle are not marketed directly from the range, they are fattened on alfalfa hay alone or on alfalfa and other roughages. Sometimes they are fed such roughage alone during most of the feeding period, and then a limited amount of grain or other concentrates is added for the last month or so to produce better finish.

Whether it will be more profitable to fatten cattle on alfalfa hay or other roughage alone, instead of adding grain and fattening them more thoroughly, will depend entirely on local conditions. In spite of the fact that cattle cannot be made really fat on roughage alone, this method is often most profitable when alfalfa hay is very cheap in comparison with grain, and when the local market does not pay much of a premium for well-fattened cattle.

In 16 tests cattle fattened on alfalfa hay alone for periods averaging 110 days were fed 32 lbs. of hay per head daily (including the wastage) and gained only 1.20 lbs. daily.[85] For each 100 lbs. of gain there were required 2,985 lbs. of hay.

When cattle are fattened on alfalfa hay alone, poor-quality hay should not be chopped or ground in the attempt to reduce the wastage. This will force the cattle to eat the stems or weeds that they could otherwise discard, and is therefore apt to reduce the gains and be a disadvantage, instead of a benefit.[86] The refuse hay can often be used advantageously for breeding cows or idle horses that are being wintered. Idaho and Oregon tests show that chopping good-quality alfalfa hay increases its value about 18 per cent for cattle that are being fattened on hay alone.[87]

Adding grain or other concentrates to a ration of alfalfa hay increases the rate of gain and results in better finish, but it often makes the gain much more expensive, owing to the low price of hay and the high price of grain in these sections. In 8 of the experiments in which cattle were fattened on alfalfa hay alone, another lot was fed a limited amount of grain in addition. Feeding the grain increased the gains of the steers 0.45 lb. per head daily and each 100 lbs. of grain saved 308 lbs. of hay, without considering the much better finish of the grain-fed cattle.

Adding corn silage or other good silage to alfalfa hay increases the rate of gain fully as much as using a limited amount of grain, and often the gains are decidedly cheaper than with grain. In 9 trials cattle fed silage and alfalfa hay gained 1.64 lbs. per head daily, while others fed nothing but alfalfa hay gained only 1.12 lbs.[88] Each 100 lbs. of silage actually saved an average of 115 lbs. of alfalfa hay in these tests, and in addition the silage-fed cattle were much better finished.

1076. Red clover hay.—Red clover hay of good quality is an excellent roughage for beef cattle, being worth about as much per ton for fattening cattle as alfalfa hay of equal quality. (382) The effective manner in which clover hay makes good the deficiencies of the grains is shown in 2 experiments at the Indiana and Missouri Stations.[89] In each trial one lot of 2-year-old steers was fed clover hay and shelled corn, while another lot was fed timothy hay and shelled corn, without any protein supplement.

The steers fed clover hay and corn ate 9.8 lbs. clover hay and 21.5 lbs. shelled corn per head daily, gained 2.4 lbs. daily, and required 919 lbs. corn and 416 lbs. hay for each 100 lbs. gain. Those fed the unbalanced ration of timothy hay and corn gained only 1.8 lbs. a day and required 18 per cent more corn per 100 lbs. gain. The steers fed clover hay had much better appetites throughout the experiments, were much easier to keep on feed, and were decidedly better finished at the end of the experiments. With younger cattle the differences between these rations would have been even greater.

Since red clover hay contains somewhat less protein than alfalfa hay, a slightly larger amount of protein supplement may be needed to balance the ration with clover than with alfalfa. It might naturally be supposed that this would give alfalfa hay a higher value per ton. However, in 4 Wisconsin experiments it was found that clover hay was equal to alfalfa hay for fattening cattle, even when just enough protein supplement was fed with each kind of hay to balance the ration properly.[90]

In each of these tests one group of steers was fed clover hay, corn silage, corn grain, and sufficient cottonseed meal to provide enough protein. Another group was fed the same weights of alfalfa hay and corn silage and the same total amount of concentrates (corn plus cottonseed meal). However, this group was fed less cottonseed meal and a correspondingly larger amount of corn, so that each ration would provide the same amounts of protein.

In 5 earlier experiments in which equal amounts of protein supplements were fed in clover-hay and alfalfa-hay rations, clover hay was likewise equal to alfalfa hay for fattening cattle.[91] It must therefore be concluded that these two different kinds of excellent legume hay have about the same value per ton for beef cattle.

1077. Soybean hay.—Soybean hay differs rather widely in value, depending on how well it has been cured, on the leafiness, and on the coarseness of the stems. (398) For this reason there has been a considerable range in the results of the experiments in which soybean hay has been directly compared with alfalfa hay or clover hay for beef cattle.

The portion of soybean hay that is actually consumed is probably equal in value per pound to alfalfa or clover hay, but often cattle will leave 10 per cent or more of the soybean hay. Sometimes soybean hay which contains a considerable proportion of beans is unduly laxative for fattening cattle, if they are fed too large amounts. Therefore the allowance had best be restricted to what they will clean up reasonably well. In a Kentucky trial soybean hay cut when the seeds were three-fourths matured was slightly more palatable to steers than hay cut when just past the bloom stage.[92]

Good-quality soybean hay has been compared with red clover hay for fattening cattle in 4 experiments in which the hay was fed with corn silage, shelled corn, and a protein supplement.[93] The gains were as rapid on the soybean hay, and on the average it was fully equal to clover hay in value per ton. In trials in which soybean hay has been fed as the only roughage, it has been nearly equal to alfalfa in some cases but much inferior in others, the results probably depending on the relative quality of the two kinds of hay used in the various experiments.[94]

1078. Cowpea hay.—In the southern states cowpea hay is a valuable roughage for beef cattle. (401) Good-quality cowpea hay has been about equal to alfalfa hay or clover hay for fattening steers in Georgia and Missouri tests.[95]

The value of cowpea hay as a source of protein to balance rations is well shown by 3 New Mexico experiments.[96] Steers fattened on a ration of cowpea hay, ground milo grain, and sweet sorghum silage gained as rapidly as others fed cottonseed meal in place of the cowpea hay and sold for just as high an average price. On the average the home-grown cowpea hay was worth 59 per cent as much per ton as cottonseed meal in balancing the ration.

1079. Sweet clover hay.—Sweet clover hay cut in the fall of the same year that it is sown is eaten by cattle with little or no waste, and it is about equal to alfalfa or red clover hay.[97] **(391)** Second-year sweet clover hay is apt to be coarse and stemmy, and therefore is usually lower in feeding value, as shown by Minnesota trials.[98]

To reduce the wastage of stemmy sweet clover hay it may be advisable to run it through a silage cutter or hay chopper. When rather-coarse sweet clover hay was chopped, it was worth much more than uncut prairie hay for fattening calves in a Minnesota test, and was nearly equal to alfalfa hay in a South Dakota trial.[99]

To avoid trouble from the "sweet clover disease" in feeding sweet clover hay to cattle, the precautions mentioned in Chapter XIII should always be taken. **(392)**

1080. Other legume hay.—Several other kinds of legume hay that are discussed in Chapter XIII are also excellent for beef cattle. These include lespedeza, alsike clover, field pea, peas-and-oats, and peanut hay.

1081. Making efficient use of non-legume roughage.—When no legume hay is fed to beef cattle, it is exceedingly important to see that any deficiencies in the ration are corrected, so that efficient results can be secured. The deficiencies that must be guarded against are a lack of protein, insufficient calcium, and deficiencies of vitamins A and D.

The lack of protein in rations which do not include legume forage can readily be corrected by furnishing sufficient of some good protein supplement to meet the recommendations of the feeding standards. An adequate amount of phosphorus will ordinarily be provided by the protein supplement. On the other hand, there will often be a lack of calcium in such rations for fattening cattle. Therefore when little or no legume forage is fed, it is wise to add to the ration about 0.1 lb. per head daily of ground limestone, ground oyster shell, or other calcium supplement.

As has been shown in the previous chapter, there may be no need of this addition if the non-legume hay, fodder, or silage has been grown on soil rich in calcium. **(999)** However, since calcium supplements are cheap, it is wise to supply one when fattening cattle are fed no legume roughage, unless one is certain there is no deficiency of this mineral.

There will ordinarily be no lack of vitamins when the only roughage fed beef cattle is well-cured hay from the grasses, good silage, or properly-cured dry fodder or stover from corn or the sorghums. On the other hand, it is not wise to use vitamin-poor roughage like poor hay, straw, or cottonseed hulls as the only roughage for long periods, or the cattle may suffer from a deficiency of vitamins, especially of vitamin A. **(186)**

1082. Hay from the grasses.—While hay of the usual quality from the grasses is much less valuable than legume hay for beef cattle, such hay will produce satisfactory results if it is properly supplemented. Grass hay can be used best when fed with a limited amount of legume hay or else with silage. Also, it more nearly equals legume hay in value for wintering beef cows than for fattening cattle. Proper fertilization and early cutting of grass hay undoubtedly increase its value for beef cattle in the same manner that has been shown in experiments with dairy cows. (302-303, 880-881)

That fattening cattle will make satisfactory gains when fed good-quality grass hay as the only roughage, if it is properly supplemented, is shown by 3 Oklahoma experiments.[100] In each of these tests one lot of calves was fed shelled corn and alfalfa hay plus an average of 1.0 lb. cottonseed meal per head daily. Another lot was fed prairie hay in place of the alfalfa hay, and the amount of cottonseed meal was increased to 2.3 lbs. to provide the same amount of protein in each ration. A small amount of ground limestone was fed to both lots, but was undoubtedly not needed by the alfalfa-fed calves.

On both rations the average daily gain was 1.9 lbs., but the calves fed prairie hay required 27 lbs. more total concentrates (corn plus cottonseed meal) per 100 lbs. gain. Still more important was the fact that they needed for each 100 lbs. gain more than twice as much cottonseed meal as the calves fed alfalfa, and the cost of cottonseed meal per ton was considerably higher than that of corn. Due to these facts, to produce gains at an equal cost, prairie hay was actually worth only 39 per cent as much per ton as alfalfa hay in these trials, even though it was well supplemented with cottonseed meal and ground limestone.

When grass hay is fed to fattening cattle in combination with good silage and with proper protein and calcium supplements, the gains may be just as economical as with legume hay. This is shown by 3 Kansas experiments in which calves were fed either prairie or alfalfa hay with sorghum silage, shelled corn, and cottonseed meal.[101] To furnish sufficient calcium 0.1 lb. of ground limestone or other calcium supplement per head daily was added to the prairie hay ration.

When prairie hay and sorghum silage were fed as the roughages, without a calcium supplement, the gains were distinctly less than on alfalfa hay and sorghum silage. The selling price was also lower and the profit $6.90 less per head than on the alfalfa ration. On the other hand, when a calcium supplement was added to the prairie-hay ration, the gains were fully as rapid as with alfalfa hay, the selling price nearly as high, and the profit even greater, with prairie hay at $10 a ton and alfalfa at $15 per ton.

1083. Timothy hay; mixed hay; other grass hay.—*Timothy hay* of the ordinary quality has usually been much inferior to alfalfa or other legume hay in the experiments that have been conducted to study this question. (449) For example, in 2 Missouri trials with calves that were being wintered, it required considerably more concentrates to produce a certain amount of gain with timothy hay as the roughage than with alfalfa hay.[102] Also, a protein supplement was needed with the timothy hay, but not with alfalfa. In these experiments a mineral mixture supplying calcium and phosphorus was fed to both lots of calves.

In an Iowa experiment 2-year-old steers fed timothy hay, shelled corn, and cottonseed meal gained 0.5 lb. less per head daily than others fed clover hay, and the net return per head over cost of feed was $9.26 less on the timothy ration.[103] *Mixed clover-and-timothy hay,* containing one-third to one-half clover was midway between timothy and clover in value.

That timothy hay grown on well-fertilized fields and cut early may be much better than ordinary timothy hay is indicated by Minnesota tests.[104] When fed hay alone, steers gained 1.2 lbs. a day on timothy hay from well-fertilized peat soil, but only 0.8 lb. on ordinary timothy. When fed with shelled corn and linseed meal, the timothy hay from the well-fertilized land produced as good gains as did alfalfa hay.

Western native hay was decidedly inferior to alfalfa hay as the only feed for wintering beef calves in a Wyoming trial, but it was equal to alfalfa in a similar experiment with yearling steers.[105] **(456)**

Sudan grass hay was as good as alfalfa hay as the sole feed for wintering beef cows or 2-year-old heifers in Kansas tests.[106] However, it was inferior to alfalfa for wintering calves, which had greater requirements for protein and calcium.

1084. Cereal hay; sheaf oats.—In certain sections of the western states hay from the cereals is important for beef cattle. *Oat hay* was even superior to alfalfa hay as the only feed for wintering beef cows in 5 Montana trials.[107] Rye and wheat hay were also satisfactory.

For wintering beef calves *wheat hay* was decidedly inferior to alfalfa hay in a Washington test, but a combination of one-half wheat hay and one-half alfalfa was as efficient as alfalfa alone.[108]

Wild oat hay, fed with barley and cottonseed meal to yearling steers in a California test, produced nearly as good results as alfalfa hay.[109]

Sheaf oats, a common feed in western Canada, were worth about one-fifth more per ton than prairie hay for fattening steers in a trial at the University of Alberta.[110]

1085. Shock corn; corn fodder.—Both shock corn and corn fodder are often used for beef cattle. **(420)** Shock corn is frequently fed to fattening cattle, especially during the first part of the fattening period. The cattle soon become used to eating the unhusked ear corn and will also eat most of the leaves and even some of the stalks. In feeding shock corn there is more wastage of grain than in feeding ear corn or shelled corn, even when pigs follow the cattle. It is also rather difficult to adjust the amount of grain as the fattening progresses. Therefore the gains are apt to be slower from shock corn, especially during the latter part of the feeding period.

Corn fodder and shock corn are excellent feeds for wintering beef cattle, when a limited amount of legume hay is supplied to balance the ration or when a small amount of protein supplement is fed. A considerably greater feeding value per acre is secured when the crop is ensiled, but the dry fodder is a very useful feed for those who do not have silos.

There is considerable wastage of the stalks when corn fodder is fed whole. This may be reduced by chopping the fodder or by grinding it. Whether or not such preparation will pay will depend on the price of feeds and the cost of chopping or grinding under the local conditions.

In 2 Michigan tests whole shock corn, ground shock corn, and corn silage were compared for fattening yearling steers, which were also fed cottonseed meal as a supplement and a limited amount of alfalfa hay.[111] The amount of beef and pork produced per acre of corn fed was 50 per cent greater for corn silage than for the shock corn and 12 per cent more than for the ground shock corn. The difference was even more striking in the net return per acre over the cost of growing, harvesting, and preparing the corn. The net return per acre from corn silage averaged $23.07, for shock corn $13.48, and for ground shock corn only $6.68.

Corn silage was likewise much more profitable than ground shock corn in an Ohio trial.[112] It also excelled ground corn fodder in New Mexico experiments with fattening cattle, even though molasses was mixed with the ground fodder to increase its palatability.[113] In 3 Colorado trials chopped corn fodder was slightly less economical for fattening cattle than corn silage when the cost per ton of the cut fodder was 2.5 times that of the silage.[114] Chopped corn fodder produced nearly as good gains as corn silage in North Dakota trials, when fed with alfalfa hay, grain, and protein supplement.[115] In these tests 100 lbs. of chopped fodder were about equal in feeding value to 184 lbs. of corn silage.

When uncut shock corn or corn fodder has been compared with corn silage, there has usually been a large difference in feeding value per acre. For example, in an Illinois trial the corn silage from an acre was worth 30 per cent more than the shock corn from the same area for feeding growing beef calves.[116] In a Missouri test with fattening steers an acre of corn silage was worth 50 per cent more than an equal area of shock corn.[117] Fodder corn was similarly much less efficient for fattening cattle than corn silage in Iowa experiments.[118]

In an Indiana experiment excellent results were secured when steers were fattened on a ration of shock corn combined with corn silage and cottonseed meal.[119] However, shock corn fed in a similar manner in Ohio tests was inferior to shelled corn.[120]

Ground corn fodder, fed with 1 lb. of cottonseed meal or 4 lbs. of alfalfa hay, was very satisfactory for wintering beef calves in 3 Nebraska experiments.[121] In these tests ground corn fodder produced about 85 per cent as much gain per acre, while in similar Kansas and Missouri trials it made only 60 per cent as much gain per acre as did corn silage.[122]

1086. Corn stover.—Corn stover (shock corn or corn fodder minus the ears) can often be fed advantageously as part of the ration for wintering beef cows or even for wintering young cattle. (**432**) However, it is too low in nutrients to be of much value in feeding fattening cattle.

For example, in an Ohio trial corn stover was compared with corn silage for fattening yearling steers, when fed with mixed hay, shelled corn, and linseed meal.[123] With corn stover at $7 a ton and corn silage at $4, the steers fed silage returned $6.14 each over the cost of feed, while the net return for those fed stover was only 81 cents.

As is pointed out later in this chapter, greater feeding value can be secured from corn stover when it is ensiled than when the dry stover is fed. (**1096**)

1087. Sorghum fodder or hay.—Cured forage from both the sweet sorghums, or sorghos, and from the grain sorghums can be used for beef cattle in the same manner as corn fodder and stover. (**441**) Sorghum hay, or "cane hay," made from thickly-planted sweet sorghum, is about equal to good prairie or timothy hay, for there is but little waste in feeding it.

Sorghum forage gives especially good results when fed with a limited amount of legume hay. However, chopped or ground sorghum fodder of good quality has been satisfactory as the only roughage for fattening cattle when fed with a sufficient amount of cottonseed meal or other protein supplement to balance the ration.[124] When no legume hay is fed, about 0.1 lb. per head daily of ground limestone or other calcium supplement should also be supplied, unless the fodder has been grown on soil rich in calcium.

While sorghum fodder is a very satisfactory feed for beef cattle, much more economical results are secured when the crop is ensiled. For example, in Kansas experiments with cattle being carried through the winter, kafir silage produced more than twice as much gain per acre as kafir fodder.[125] In a similar Nebraska test sorghum silage produced two-thirds more gain an acre than did chopped sorghum fodder.[126]

Sweet sorghum fodder, fed with ground milo grain and cottonseed meal, produced as rapid gain in 3 New Mexico trials as did sorghum silage.[127] However, per pound of dry matter the sorghum silage had a considerably higher value than the sorghum fodder. Similar results were secured in 3 Texas experiments, except that there was a greater difference in feeding value in favor of the sorghum silage.[128]

In the Kansas experiments mentioned previously, chopping kafir fodder in a silage cutter did not increase its value for cattle being carried through the winter. On the other hand, chopping rather poor-quality grain sorghum fodder in a Texas trial increased the value for fattening cattle more than enough to justify the expense.[129]

Chopping sorghum fodder does not crack the grain and thus does not lessen the loss of nutrients through seed escaping mastication and digestion. Therefore the effect of grinding kafir fodder was also studied in the Kansas experiments. Even when the fodder was ground in a mill that cracked most of the grain, the value of the fodder per acre was still much below that of kafir silage. However, grinding the fodder in this manner did increase its value 46 per cent in one test, in comparison with feeding it uncut.

The choice between the various kinds of sorghums for forage will depend chiefly on their relative yields under the local conditions. In Texas tests with fattening cattle there was not much difference in the feeding value per ton of ground sweet sorghum fodder and of ground fodder from kafir, milo, feterita and hegari.[130]

1088. Sorghum stover.—Sorghum stover (not including the heads) is a useful feed for carrying through the winter animals that are not being fattened. Its value per ton will be somewhat less than that of the fodder including the heads, and will depend on the leafiness and on how it has been cured. Kansas tests show that by making silage from sorghum stover the feeding value can be increased very greatly.[131]

Ground hegari stover, undoubtedly of good quality, was satisfactory as the only roughage for fattening steers in Texas trials.[132] However, unless sorghum stover is well-cured, palatable, and leafy, it is better for animals that are being wintered than for those that are being fattened.

1089. Straw.—*Straw from the small grains* can be used satisfactorily as the chief feed or even as the only roughage for wintering beef breeding cows, if it is properly supplemented. (**1107**) On the other hand, straw is too low in nutrients to form any considerable part of the ration for fattening cattle. (**468**)

If, because of drought or for any other reason, there is a shortage of better roughage, straw can replace part of the hay or silage usually fed fattening cattle. In such cases the lack of protein, calcium, phosphorus, and vitamin A in straw must be remembered.

Reasonably good gains can even be produced on cattle a year old or more with straw as the only roughage, if a liberal amount of grain is fed and protein and calcium supplements are provided. For example, in a Nebraska trial 660-lb. steers were fed a ration consisting of 4.3 lbs. straw, 14.1 lbs. shelled corn, 1.6 lbs. cottonseed cake, and 0.07 lb. mineral mixture. These steers gained 2.04 lbs. per head daily, in comparison with a gain of 2.23 lbs. for others which were fed 2.9 lbs. of alfalfa hay in addition.[133]

Providing the ration is properly supplemented with protein and also with calcium if needed, cattle that are fed a liberal amount of silage or wet beet pulp may make just as rapid gains with straw for the dry roughage as when fed legume hay.[134] The actual value of the straw per ton will, of course, be much lower than that of the hay, due to the larger amount of protein supplement needed with the straw.

Straw from the legumes is somewhat more valuable than cereal straw with the exception of soybean straw, which is as low in protein and digestible nutrients as straw from the small grains. (**418**) Straw from alfalfa, clover, peas, or field beans can form a considerable part of the roughage for wintering beef cattle. In an Illinois test 1,110-lb. steers even made good gains when soybean straw was fed as the only roughage, along with a liberal amount of shelled corn and enough soybean oil meal to balance the ration.[135]

1090. Cottonseed hulls.—Cottonseed hulls have long been used extensively for feeding beef cattle in the cotton belt of the South. (**588**) Formerly, cattle were commonly fattened on nothing but cottonseed meal and cottonseed hulls, but recent investigations have shown that this ration can be greatly improved.

The cottonseed meal makes good the lack of protein in the hulls, but there is a lack of calcium and vitamins in both these feeds. While cattle make satisfactory gains for a time when fed only cottonseed meal and hulls, if fed this restricted ration too long they will suffer from nutritive deficiencies. (**582**)

Even during the usual fattening period, the results are considerably improved if well-cured hay or good silage is added to the ration to furnish vitamins, and also a calcium supplement, unless legume hay is fed. When hay or silage is not available, even the calcium supplement alone is beneficial, though the cattle will be affected by the vitamin deficiency if the ration is continued too long. Cottonseed hulls are well-liked by cattle, and 2-year-old steers will eat 20 to 30 lbs. a day when the hulls are the only roughage.

Cottonseed hulls were compared with sorghum silage in 6 Mississippi trials in which the cattle were fed cottonseed meal and also a limited amount of Johnson grass hay.[136] The steers fed hulls made nearly as rapid gains as those fed silage, and 100 lbs. of hulls replaced about 270 lbs. of sorghum silage. When hulls were fed in combination with both silage and hay, the value was even higher.

When fed with cottonseed meal and ground limestone to fattening cattle in 3 Oklahoma experiments, cottonseed hulls proved fully equal to prairie hay in rate of gain produced and in value per ton.[137] Fed in this manner, the hulls produced as rapid gains as did alfalfa hay. In 3 North Carolina trials cottonseed hulls were of slightly more value than corn stover when fed with shelled corn and cottonseed meal.[138] In a Texas trial cottonseed hulls were slightly superior to chopped sorghum fodder, when fed with alfalfa hay.[139]

Cattle fed cottonseed meal with cottonseed hulls as the only roughage, and without any calcium supplement, have gained 0.2 lb. less per head daily, on the average, in 12 experiments than others fed corn silage in place of the hulls.[140] In these trials each 100 lbs. of hulls replaced only about 145 lbs. of corn silage. This is a much lower value than has been secured in the recent experiments previously mentioned in which the hulls have been fed in more complete rations.

IV. SILAGE; ROOTS; PASTURE

1091. Importance of silage in beef production.—Wherever corn or the sorghums thrive, silage from these crops has proved of great value in cheapening the cost of beef production. (**340**) In cooler sections silage from such crops as sunflowers or peas and small grain is frequently an economical substitute.

Breeding cows and stock cattle may be maintained in winter in good condition on silage with a small amount of legume hay or else with 1.0 lb. or less of such a protein supplement as cottonseed meal or linseed meal. For wintering calves and yearlings silage cannot be excelled, when thus fed. On well-balanced rations in which silage is the chief roughage, fattening cattle will make rapid gains and reach a high finish on a moderate allowance of expensive concentrates. At first it was thought that silage-fed cattle shrank more in shipment than those finished on dry roughage. Trials have now abundantly demonstrated, however, that even when silage-fed cattle shrink a trifle more during shipment, they take on such a good "fill" at the market that the net shrinkage is no more than for cattle fed only dry roughage.

Trials at various stations have shown that it is commonly more economical to give fattening cattle twice a day all the silage they will clean up without undue waste, rather than to limit the amount of silage fed.[141] Two-year-old steers full-fed on corn, legume hay, and silage will eat 30 to 40 lbs. of silage a day during the first month of fattening and gradually less as feeding progresses, until during the last month they will eat only 10 to 20 lbs. a day. Calves and yearlings will, of course, eat considerably less silage per head daily. Kentucky experiments show that if the supply of silage is used up before fattening cattle are ready for the market, they can be changed gradually to good hay as the only roughage without difficulty.[142]

The question as to how much corn or other grain it is profitable to feed to steers given an unlimited allowance of silage is fully discussed in the preceding chapter. (1004-1006)

1092. Feeding a supplement with a full feed of silage.—It has been shown in the previous chapter that when fattening cattle are fed alfalfa or clover hay as the only roughage, they will eat sufficient of the protein-rich legume hay to balance their ration satisfactorily. Hence, the addition of a protein supplement, such as linseed meal or cottonseed meal, does not make much increase in the gains. (993-994)

However, when cattle are fed all the corn silage or sorghum silage they will eat in addition to corn and legume hay, they like the silage so well that they will then generally eat only 2 to 4 lbs. per head daily of the hay. Sometimes they will not even eat an average of 2 lbs. of the legume hay throughout the fattening period, unless the silage allowance is slightly restricted.

These small amounts of legume hay are not enough to balance the ration entirely. Therefore the gains will be more rapid and the cattle will reach a better finish if a protein supplement is added. (995) Unless protein supplements are unusually expensive, compared with grain, it will generally pay to add sufficient supplement to balance the ration according to the recommendations of the Morrison feeding standards. If more supplement is used than is actually needed, the cost may be increased to such an extent that the advantage secured through the better selling price will be largely offset.

1093. Corn or sorghum silage as the only roughage.—Whether as good results can be secured from fattening cattle fed corn or sorghum silage as the only roughage as when they are fed some legume or mixed hay in addition, is often a problem of importance to cattle feeders. Such silage is not only low in protein, but it is also apt to be rather low in calcium, unless grown on soil rich in this mineral. (999)

The fact that corn silage and sorghum silage often do not supply enough calcium for maximum gains by fattening cattle has been shown recently by McCampbell and associates in experiments at the Kansas Station.[143] In previous experiments with fattening calves, they had compared sorghum silage as the only roughage with a combination of sorghum silage and 2.0 lbs. of alfalfa hay per head daily, corn grain being fed in each ration with sufficient cottonseed meal to furnish ample protein.

In 3 such experiments the calves fed sorghum silage as the only roughage gained 2.02 lbs., which is a good rate of gain for calves. However, those fed alfalfa hay in addition did still better, gaining an average of 2.27 lbs. a day. On account of superior finish they sold for 58 cents more per 100 lbs., and the net return over cost of feed was $7.55 more per head. In 10 experiments at other stations it had likewise been found that usually the gains were slightly more rapid when legume hay was added to a ration of corn silage, corn grain, and cottonseed meal or linseed meal.[144]

Since these silage rations contained sufficient protein, the Kansas investigators now conducted trials to find whether a lack of calcium might be responsible for the difference in results. It was found that when 0.1 lb. per head daily of ground limestone or other calcium supplement was added to the silage ration, the gains were fully as rapid and the selling price just as high as when the calves received alfalfa hay in addition to silage for roughage. With prevailing prices in that section, the net return per calf was even larger on silage as the only roughage, fed with the calcium supplement, than with the alfalfa hay.

These and other experiments indicate that corn or sorghum silage, fed with a calcium supplement to fattening cattle, will produce just as satisfactory results as when legume hay is also supplied. The calcium supplement is probably not needed if the corn or sorghum has been grown on soil rich in calcium, but such supplements are cheap, and therefore it is wise to supply one unless there is unquestionably no lack in the ration. In using corn or sorghum silage as the only roughage for breeding cattle over long periods, it would seem wise always to add a calcium supplement as an insurance against any possible lack of this necessary mineral.

Undoubtedly, very satisfactory results can be obtained when fattening cattle are fed corn or sorghum silage as the only roughage with a calcium supplement. However, the author believes it wise to furnish a small amount of hay or other dry roughage whenever it is conveniently available. Cattle fed silage as the only roughage often seem to show a desire for some dry forage. Also, well-cured hay is the best source of vitamin A among common harvested feeds, and is a much more reliable source of this vitamin than is silage.

1094. Corn silage.—Silage from well-matured corn, carrying an abundance of ears and consequently a high proportion of corn grain, is the best of all silages for beef cattle. **(426)** Such silage aids materially in reducing the amount of concentrates which need be supplied in addition.

To show the good results from feeding corn silage, there are summarized in the following table the results of 33 trials in which a full feed of corn silage was added twice a day to the already excellent ration of shelled corn, cottonseed or linseed meal, and good clover or alfalfa hay.[145] In these trials a total of 574 steers (chiefly 2-year-olds) were fed for an average of 145 days.

Value of corn silage when added to an already excellent ration

Average ration	Daily gain Lbs.	Corn Lbs.	Supple-ment Lbs.	Hay Lbs.	Silage Lbs.	Feed cost of 100 lbs. gain Dollars	Selling price per cwt. Dollars
Lot I, no silage							
Legume hay, 9.9 lbs.							
Shelled corn, 17.3 lbs.							
Supplement, 2.3 lbs.....	2.48	698	96	405	...	12.39	9.31
Lot II, fed silage							
Corn silage, 23.6 lbs.							
Legume hay, 3.1 lbs.							
Shelled corn, 14.3 lbs.							
Supplement, 2.6 lbs.....	2.49	580	102	129	954	11.82	9.28

The steers in Lot II, which ate 23.6 lbs. silage per head daily, consumed 6.8 lbs. less hay and 4.0 lbs. less corn than those in Lot I. To partly offset the low protein content of the silage, a somewhat larger amount of supplement was fed in the silage ration. It will be noted that the silage did not produce appreciably larger gains or better finish than did good legume hay fed as the only roughage.

The chief advantage from feeding silage was the cheapness of the gains. Silage feeding reduced the feed cost of 100 lbs. gain from $12.39 to $11.82, thus saving 57 cents on each 100 lbs. gain made by the cattle. This might make the difference between a profit and a loss on the feeding operations.

In these trials each ton of corn silage saved an average of 247 lbs. corn plus 580 lbs. legume hay, but minus 14 lbs. protein supplement. With corn at $20.00, supplement at $40.00, and legume hay at $10.00 a ton, this would give silage a value of $5.09 per ton. Thus, with feeds at these representative prices, corn silage was worth fully one-half as much per ton as good clover or alfalfa hay. These trials show that except where alfalfa or other hay crops thrive better than corn or sorghum for silage, the use of silage will generally increase the profits from the feeding of cattle for the market.

For silage in the northern states a variety of corn should be grown which will nearly mature in the average season, rather than attempting to grow a rank-growing, late-maturing kind. Immature, watery silage is of much lower feeding value per ton than that from corn cut when the kernels have hardened and glazed, but while most of the leaves are still green.[146] The value of the dry matter in immature silage will also probably be somewhat lower than that in well-eared corn silage, due to the great difference in the amount of grain contained. (428)

Corn for silage to be used in fattening cattle should not be planted so thickly as to prevent the development of good ears. This is because the grain is needed to furnish the liberal supply of digestible nutrients required for rapid fattening. If the silage is to be used only for wintering beef breeding cows, somewhat thicker planting may be advisable.

1095. Adding corn silage to alfalfa hay and grain.—In the western alfalfa districts it is important to know whether it will be economical to add corn silage to the common ration of alfalfa hay and grain for fattening cattle. This question has been studied in 16 tests at western experiment stations with the results shown in the following table.[147] In these trials cattle averaging 863 lbs. in weight were fed for an average of 127 days, with no pigs following the cattle. The grain was ground barley in 11 of the trials and corn in the others.

Adding corn silage to a ration of alfalfa hay and grain

	Daily gain Lbs.	Grain Lbs.	Feed per 100 lbs. gain Hay Lbs.	Silage Lbs.
Lot I, no silage				
Alfalfa hay, 20.2 lbs.				
Grain, 10.0 lbs.	1.90	515	1,117	....
Lot II, fed silage				
Corn silage, 20.4 lbs.				
Alfalfa hay, 14.1 lbs.				
Grain, 8.4 lbs.	1.99	426	733	1,019

Adding corn silage to the excellent ration of grain and alfalfa hay slightly increased the rate of gain in these experiments. Though the difference in gain was but small, the tendency would be for the silage-fed steers to sell at a trifle higher price on a discriminating market. In these trials each ton of corn silage saved 754 lbs. of alfalfa hay plus 175 lbs. of grain, without considering the slightly more rapid gains on silage. With grain at even twice as much per ton as hay, this would make 1 ton of silage fully equivalent in value to 1,004 lbs. of hay. Similar results have been secured in California and Colorado experiments in which corn silage has been added to alfalfa hay and ground barley, either with or without a protein supplement.[148]

These tests show that where a ton of corn silage can be provided at not more than one-half the cost of alfalfa hay per ton, the use of silage in addition to alfalfa hay for fattening cattle is economical. Where the cost of silage is more than this, in comparison with that of hay, it may be more profitable to feed hay as the only roughage. (342)

It has been shown previously in this chapter that when corn silage is added to a ration of nothing but alfalfa hay for fattening cattle the gains are greatly increased. Each 100 lbs. of silage actually replaces about 115 lbs. of hay, without giving credit for the better finish produced by the silage feeding. (1075)

1096. Corn stover silage.—Silage made from corn forage from which the ears have been removed is often an economical feed for wintering beef breeding cows, as is shown in the next chapter. (1106) This is because such stock do not require rations very rich in digestible nutrients. Accordingly, for these animals corn stover silage can be used as a cheap substitute for normal corn silage.

On the other hand, corn stover silage cannot replace well-eared corn silage for fattening cattle, as they must have a liberal supply of digestible nutrients and net energy. If the ears are removed from corn forage before it is ensiled, it will be necessary to feed with such silage a correspondingly larger amount of grain or other concentrates. Otherwise, the cattle will not make rapid gains or reach the desired degree of fatness.

Even in wintering beef calves that are to be fattened later, normal silage is usually more economical than grain-less silage. In an Illinois trial calves fed corn stover silage, with a little hay and 1 lb. of cottonseed meal per head daily, gained only 0.65 lb. daily in comparison with 1.16 lbs. for others receiving normal corn silage.[149] To secure good gains on stover silage, it was necessary to supply as much grain as the other calves received in the normal silage.

In wintering yearlings or 2-year-olds, better use can be made of stover silage, unless considerable gain is desired during the winter. For feeding all classes of beef cattle, corn stover silage is more valuable than an equivalent amount of whole or cut dry corn stover, for it is more palatable and is consumed with less waste.

Several experiments have shown conclusively that it is a mistaken attempt at economy to remove the corn ears from corn forage that is to be ensiled for fattening cattle. For example, in 3 Tennessee trials stover silage, made from corn forage from which the ears had been snapped as soon as the grain was mature, was compared with normal silage.[150] Both lots of cattle were given the same amounts of concentrates each year (not including the corn in the silage), along with a little hay or dry stover. The gain on normal corn silage was 1.84 lbs. per head daily and on stover silage only 1.40 lbs. The average feeding value of an acre of normal silage was $74.63 and of the stover silage from an acre only $16.81.

Some farmers think that a considerable part of the value of the corn grain is lost when the whole crop is ensiled. They believe that if they husk the corn and later feed it with silage made from the stover, the crop will have a higher value. This was tested in 3 Michigan trials in each of which one lot of steers (Lot I) was fed normal, well-eared silage with a limited amount of shelled corn, a protein supplement and clover hay.[151] Lot II was fed similarly, except that the cattle received silage made from dry stover, and their allowance of shelled corn was increased by the amount of corn grain in the silage that was fed Lot I.

The steers fed stover silage gained only 1.90 lbs. per head daily, while those receiving the normal silage gained 2.35 lbs., though they had no more total corn grain. Since these steers were much better fattened, they sold for a higher price in each test than the cattle fed stover silage. In each trial a third lot of steers was fed corn stover silage with only 0.7 lb. more shelled corn per head daily than the steers in Lot I received. These steers gained only 1.70 lbs. a day and did not reach a good finish. Corn stover silage has also been decidedly inferior to normal corn silage for fattening cattle in Kansas, Mississippi, and Virginia experiments.[152]

1097. Silage from the sorghums.—Sorghum silage is of great importance for beef production in those sections where the climatic conditions are such that the sorghums yield much more forage per acre than does corn. It has previously been shown that the feeding value per acre is far greater when a sorghum crop is ensiled than when it is fed as dry forage. (**1087**)

The choice between the various types of sorghums for silage depends chiefly on the yield per acre. Sweet sorghum silage is generally worth somewhat less per ton for beef cattle than silage from kafir or the other grain sorghums, as it contains much less grain. However, in many districts the yield of the sweet sorghums is enough greater to more than make up this difference. (**439-440**)

When sorghum silage is added to a ration for fattening cattle in which the only roughage is hay, the rate of gain may not be increased, if the hay is of excellent quality. However, there usually will be a sufficient saving of other feed to make the addition of silage profitable, just as in the case of corn silage. In Kansas and Oklahoma experiments in which kafir, darso, or sweet sorghum silage has been added to good rations for fattening cattle, the value of the silage per ton has been about 35 per cent as much as that of alfalfa, or about half as much as that of prairie hay.[153]

Sweet sorghum silage approaches corn silage in value per ton for beef calves that are being wintered on moderate rations. In seven tests in which calves have been fed either sorghum silage or corn silage with 1 lb. per head daily of cottonseed meal or linseed meal, the gain has been nearly as great on the sorghum silage.[154] Each 100 lbs. of sorghum silage have been equal in average feeding value to 87 lbs. of corn silage in these trials.

For fattening cattle the value of sweet sorghum silage has been considerably lower in comparison with that of well-eared corn. This is probably because fattening cattle do not utilize the grain in sorghum silage so completely as that in corn silage. Even if pigs follow them, considerable of the seed is lost. In spite of this wastage, a much greater feeding value is secured per acre from a sorghum crop when it is ensiled, than when the fodder is cured and then ground or chopped before it is fed. (**1087**)

In 12 experiments where one lot of cattle was fed good-quality sorghum silage and another lot corn silage, the average daily gain was 1.87 lbs. on sorghum silage and 2.07 lbs. on corn silage.[155] On account of poorer finish the cattle fed sorghum silage generally sold for a slightly lower price. Due to this and because somewhat more feed was required per 100 lbs. gain on sorghum silage, the actual feeding value of sorghum silage was only 58 per cent as great per ton as that of corn silage.

These results show that sweet sorghum should not be grown in place of corn silage for fattening cattle, unless the average yield is enough larger to make up the difference in value per ton. In the sorghum belt this will generally be the case, and also it will often be true in certain districts of the South, where sorghum far outyields corn for forage. On the other hand, in the corn belt and eastward corn surpasses the sorghums as a silage crop.

Sorghum stover silage, made from sorghum forage after the heads have been removed, corresponds in feeding value to corn stover silage and may be similarly used in wintering beef breeding cows. For fattening cattle and even for wintering calves or yearlings, silage from the entire crop, including the heads, is preferable.[156]

1098. Silage from soybeans or cowpeas with corn or sorghums.—Soybeans are frequently grown with corn or the sorghums and the combination crop ensiled. In the South cowpeas are used for the same purpose. The relative value of such combination crops in comparison with corn or sorghum grown alone is discussed in Chapter XIII. (399) To secure a larger proportion of soybeans in the silage, the corn and the soybeans are sometimes grown separately and then mixed as the forage is ensiled, usually at the rate of 1 ton of soybean forage to each 2 or 3 tons of corn forage.

Such *corn and soybean silage* (made from 1 ton of soybean forage to 2 tons of corn forage) was compared with well-eared corn silage in 4 Indiana trials with fattening steers.[157] The protein-rich corn and soybean silage did not have an appreciably higher value, ton for ton, than the corn silage, even when fed with shelled corn and clover hay, which ration, as we have seen, does not contain quite enough protein for maximum gains. That the corn and soybean silage was not worth more per ton than the corn silage was probably due to the fact that it was lower in net energy, because the soybean forage did not contain as much grain as the corn forage. This would offset the higher protein content of the mixed silage.

In 7 Louisiana tests corn and soybean silage (containing about one-third soybeans) was worth about 8 per cent more than corn silage per ton for fattening cattle.[158] Also sorghum and soybean silage was slightly more valuable than sorghum silage. In these trials the silages were fed with 4 to 5 lbs. of cottonseed meal, so no advantage was gained from the higher protein content of the mixed silage. In a similar Mississippi trial corn and soybean silage was worth more per ton than corn silage, but this was primarily because the mixed silage happened to contain much less water.[159]

In general, it would seem desirable to use these combination silage crops for beef cattle only when fully as large a yield per acre can be secured as from corn or sorghum grown alone. To get full advantage from the higher protein content of such combination silage, it is important that only sufficient supplement be fed to balance the ration instead of using as much as is necessary with corn or sorghum silage.

1099. Silage from other crops.—Several crops which are discussed in Part II, furnish satisfactory silage for beef production. In fact, some economical silage crop can be grown in nearly every section of the United States. Other silage crops used for beef cattle are Russian sunflowers, peas-and-oats, oats, Japanese cane, millet, etc.

1100. Roots.—Wherever corn or the sorghums thrive, silage from these crops provides cheaper succulence than do roots. In northern districts where root crops flourish but where corn will not mature sufficiently for silage, roots are a valuable feed for beef cattle.

In Canadian trials corn silage was worth considerably more per ton than roots for fattening cattle, due to the fact that it contains much more dry matter.[160]   When only a few pounds per head daily of roots are fed to cattle as an appetizer, they may be worth as much, pound for pound, as corn silage.[161]   As has been shown in Chapter XVI, cull potatoes may be an economical feed for beef cattle in potato-growing districts.   (480)   Cull sweet potatoes can be similarly used.

In Great Britain and the countries of Northern Europe where corn does not thrive, roots are extensively fed to beef cattle. A general practice is to allow fattening stock to eat all the chopped or sliced roots they will clean up. Because of the high water content of roots, the amounts eaten are surprisingly large. Often cattle 2 years old or over will eat well over 100 lbs. of roots per head daily.

In addition to the roots and a limited amount of concentrates, fattening cattle are fed hay or straw, this often being chopped and mixed with roots. By this means the animals may be induced to eat a considerable amount of straw or rather unpalatable hay. Only a limited amount of concentrates is commonly fed, consisting largely of the various oil meals and other by-product feeds. Much less grain is used than in our country. This system produces good gains and carcasses of excellent quality.[162]

One lot of cattle in each of 3 recent Scotch experiments was fed 80 lbs. of roots per head daily, another lot 40 lbs. and a third lot no roots.[162a]   All groups received hay, straw, and a concentrate mixture. The gains were equal on the heavy and the medium allowances of roots, but were less rapid when no roots were fed. Under Scotch conditions, feeding the large allowance of roots was the most economical.

1101. Pastures.—Good pasture is the foundation of economical beef production, for it commonly furnishes much cheaper feed than harvested crops. Unless the beef herd is maintained on adequate pasture during as large a part of the year as possible, the costs will generally be increased and the profits reduced.

Under western ranch conditions the breeding herds in some districts get practically all their feed the year around from the range forage, being given supplemental feed only if the grass or browse is buried deep under snow. In other sections the cattle must be wintered largely on harvested feeds.

In the humid regions of the United States beef cattle are most frequently grazed on permanent pastures during the growing season. These may be either native pastures or improved pastures of tame grasses and legumes. When there is but little land on the farm that is not tillable, the pasture fields are frequently in the regular crop rotation. In such cases the most common practice is to use mixed timothy and clover, or perhaps timothy and alfalfa, for pasture after hay has been cut from the field for one or more seasons. Such mixed pasture is excellent for all classes of beef cattle, having proved superior to bluegrass, alfalfa, or sweet clover in Illinois tests.[163]

Alfalfa may also be used successfully for the breeding herd or for fattening cattle, if care is taken to avoid bloat.[164]   **(375-376)** Red clover is likewise a valuable pasture crop for beef cattle. Sweet clover is one of the best rotation pasture crops for beef cattle in some districts, especially where grass pastures become parched in midsummer.[165]   However, sweet clover has sometimes been disappointing for fattening cattle, as it may be too laxative early in the season, and it is often woody and unpalatable late in the summer.

In the southern states lespedeza is of much importance, as it greatly improves permanent pastures. Throughout the South soybeans, cowpeas, or velvet beans are often grown with corn, and cattle turned into the field to graze after the corn ears have been picked. By such means much of the feed needed to carry cattle through the winter can be provided.

Frequently cattle on pasture fail to make the proper growth or gain in condition because the soil is seriously deficient in fertility or the pasture has not been well managed. In such cases a striking improvement will result from proper fertilization and management, as has been shown in Chapter XI. (305-310) In many areas the soil is so low in phosphorus that cattle on pasture suffer from a deficiency of this mineral. When it is not practicable to apply a phosphorus fertilizer to the pasture, care should be taken to provide the cattle with a phosphorus supplement. (163)

The fattening of cattle on pasture is discussed in detail in Chapter XXXI.

QUESTIONS

1. How should the deficiencies of the cereal grains be corrected in feeding beef cattle?
2. Discuss the value of corn for breeding cattle; for fattening cattle.
3. How is corn usually fed to beef cattle? Discuss the use of: (a) Ear corn; (b) snapped corn; (c) shelled corn; (d) ground corn; (e) corn-and-cob meal; (f) ground snapped corn; (g) soft corn.
4. What is the value of ground barley for fattening cattle in comparison with that of corn? How should barley be fed to beef cattle?
5. Discuss the use and value of oats for beef cattle.
6. Compare the value of wheat and corn for fattening cattle. In what form should wheat be fed to beef cattle?
7. How would you use rye for beef cattle?
8. Discuss the use and value of the grain sorghums for beef cattle.
9. Summarize the results of experiments which show the value of cane molasses for beef cattle.
10. What is the relative value of beet molasses and cane molasses for beef cattle?
11. Discuss the use for beef cattle of: (a) Wet beet pulp; (b) dried beet pulp; (c) molasses feeds.
12. Discuss the value and use of cottonseed meal for beef cattle. How should the deficiencies be corrected in such a ration as cottonseed meal and cottonseed hulls?
13. What is the relative value of cottonseed meal in comparison with that of corn or barley when larger amounts of cottonseed meal are fed than are necessary to balance the ration?
14. What have experiments shown concerning the value of linseed meal for beef cattle? What is the advantage of combining cottonseed meal with linseed meal?
15. Discuss the use and value for beef cattle of: (a) Soybeans; (b) soybean oil meal; (c) wheat bran; (d) corn gluten meal; (e) corn gluten feed; (f) tankage or meat scraps.
16. Summarize the advantages of legume hay for beef cattle.
17. Compare the value of alfalfa and of red clover hay for beef cattle.
18. What is the value of: (a) Soybean hay; (b) cowpea hay; (c) sweet clover hay?
19. How can most efficient use be made of non-legume roughage?
20. Discuss the value and use for beef cattle of the following: (a) Timothy hay; (b) native hay; (c) Sudan grass hay; (d) corn fodder and shock corn; (e) corn stover; (f) sorghum fodder or hay; (g) sorghum stover; (h) straw.
21. What is the value of cottonseed hulls for beef production in comparison with other common feeds?

22. Discuss: (a) The importance of silage in beef production; (b) the use of corn or sorghum silage as the only roughage.
23. Summarize the results of the feeding trials in which corn silage has been added to an already excellent ration.
24. How should corn stover silage be used in beef production?
25. Discuss the value of silage from the sorghums.
26. What other silage crops are of importance for beef cattle in your section?
27. Why are roots used extensively for beef cattle in northern Europe?
28. What pastures are of most importance for beef cattle in your section?

REFERENCES

1. Mumford, Ill. Bul. 83; Skinner and Cochel, Ind. Buls. 115, 129; Haney, Kan. Bul. 132; Smith, Nebr. Buls. 90, 93; Burtis, Okla. Rpts. 1900, 1901.
2. Mumford, Ill. Bul. 83; Skinner and Cochel, Ind. Bul. 115; Smith, Nebr. Buls. 90, 93.
3. Rusk and Snapp, Ill. Rpt. 1928.
4. Edwards and Massey, Ga. Bul. 184.
5. Mumford, Ill. Bul. 103; Good and Horlacher, Ky. Cir. 26; Peters, Minn. Bul. 300; Allison, Mo. Bul. 149; Trowbridge and Moffett, Mo. Bul. 310.
6. Snapp, Beef Cattle, 2nd edition, p. 369.
7. Gramlich, Nebr. Bul. 174.
8. Thalman and Gramlich, Nebr. Rpt. 1934 and mimeo. rpts.
9. Cochel, Kansas Station, information to the author; Allison, Mo. Bul. 149; Trowbridge, Moffett, and Hazen, Mo. Bul. 328; Thalman and Gramlich, Nebr. Rpt. 1935; Gerlaugh, Ohio Bul. 446; see also: Thalman and Cathcart, Nebr. Sta., mimeo. rpt.
10. Mumford, Ill. Bul. 103; Allison, Mo. Bul. 149; Thalman and Gramlich, Nebr. Rpt. 1935 and mimeo. rpts.; Gerlaugh and Rogers, Ohio Bimo. Bul. 173.
11. Vaughan, Minn. Bul. 237; Peters, Minn. Bul. 300.
12. Gerlaugh, Ohio Bimo. Bul. 135; Gerlaugh and Rogers, Ohio Bimo. Bul. 173.
13. Thalman and Gramlich, Nebr. Rpts. 1934, 1935 and mimeo. rpts.
14. Rusk and Snapp, Ill. Bul. 313, Ill. Rpt. 1933; Bull, Olson, and Longwell, Ill. Bul. 355; see also: Kennedy and Rutherford, Iowa Bul. 75; Wilson and Bushey, S. D. Bul. 219.
15. Kiser and Peters, Minn. Bul. 261; Peters, Minn. Bul. 274; Wilson and Wright, S. D. Bul. 262.
16. Hickman, Rinehart, and Johnson, Id. Bul. 209; Rusk and Snapp, Ill. Sta., mimeo. rpt.; Haney, Kan. Bul. 128; Branaman and Brown, Mich. Quar. Bul., 10, 1927, No. 1; 11, 1928, No. 1; 12, 1929, No. 1; 13, 1930, No. 2; 14, 1932, No. 3; 15, 1932, No. 2; Peters and Carnes, Minn. Bul. 200; Peters, Minn. Buls. 274, 300; Foster and Simpson, New Mex. Bul. 101; Blizzard, Okla. Bul. 147; Potter, Withycombe, and Edwards, Ore. Bul. 276; Wilson, S. D. Bul. 160; Fuller, Morrison, and Fargo, Wis. Bul. 323; see also: Morton, Colo. Rpt. 1927; Hostetler and Foster, N. C. Rpt. 1932.
17. Christensen, N. D. Bul. 264.
18. Vinke and Pearson, Mont. Bul. 251.
19. Skinner and King, Ind. Bul. 371.
20. Weber and Connell, Kan. Rpt. 1932-34.
21. Peters, Minn. Bul. 300.
22. Branaman and Brown, Mich. Quar. Buls. 13, 1930, No. 1; 14, 1932, No. 3; 15, 1932, No. 2; Skinner and King, Ind. Bul. 371; see also: Weber and Connell, Kan. Sta., mimeo. rpt.; Wilson, S. D. Bul. 160.
23. Skinner and King, Ind. Buls. 330, 371.
24. Evvard, Culbertson, et al., Iowa Rpt. 1924; Culbertson and Hammond, Iowa Sta., mimeo. rpt.; Peters, Minn. Bul. 300; see also: Rogers and Gerlaugh, Ohio Bimo. Bul. 134.
25. Kiser and Peters, Minn. Bul. 261; Linfield, Mont. Bul. 58; Fuller, Wis. Sta., mimeo. rpt.
26. Weber and Connell, Kan. Bul. 261; Good and Harris, Ky. Bul. 332; Trowbridge and Moffett, Mo. Bul. 325; Baker, Nebr. Buls. 263, 295; Blizzard, Okla. Rpt. 1930-32; Blizzard, Cattleman, 11, 1925, pp. 49-51; Potter, Withycombe, and Edwards, Ore. Bul. 276; see also: Haney, Kan. Bul. 128; Linfield, Mont. Bul. 58; Burnett and Smith, Nebr. Bul. 75; Hostetler and Foster, N. C. Rpt. 1932.
27. Morton and Osland, Colo. Press Bul. 78; Peters, Minn. Bul. 300; Vinke and Pearson, Mont. Bul. 251.
28. Morton and Osland, Colo. Press Bul. 78; Rusk and Snapp, Ill. Rpt. 1931; Skinner and King, Ind. Bul. 396; Weber and Connell, Kan. Bul. 261; Peters, Minn. Bul. 300; Thalman and Gramlich, Nebr. Sta., mimeo. rpt.; Baker, Nebr. Bul. 295; Christensen, N. D. Bul. 256.
29. Baker, Nebr. Bul. 295; Wilson and Wright, S. D. Bul. 271; see also: Peters, Minn. Bul. 330; Kiser, Christgau, and Peters, Minn. Sta., mimeo. rpt.; Vinke, Morgan, and Sandberg, Mont. Sta., mimeo. rpt.
30. J. M. Jones, Keating, Black, and J. H. Jones, Tex. Sta., mimeo. rpts.
31. Haney, Kan. Bul. 132; Cochel, Kan. Sta., mimeo. rpts.; Foster and Simpson, New Mex. Bul. 101; Burtis, Okla. Rpts., 1899, 1900, 1901; Blizzard, Okla. Rpt. 1922-24 and mimeo. rpt.; Burns, Tex. Bul. 110.

32. Blizzard, Okla. Rpt. 1922-24.
33. Stanley, Ariz. Bul. 137.
34. Blizzard, Okla. Bul. 147; Blizzard and Hawkins, Okla. Rpt. 1932-34.
35. Jones et al., Tex. Rpts. 1921, 1932, and mimeo. rpts.
36. McCampbell, Winchester, and Marston, Kan. Cir. 97.
37. Cochel, Kan. Sta., mimeo. rpt.; Gramlich, Nebr. Sta., mimeo. rpt.
38. Grimes, Ala. Bul. 231; Templeton and Goodell, Miss. Bul. 242; Quesenberry, U. S. Dept. Agr. Cir. 65.
39. Edwards and Massey, Ga. Bul. 184; Skinner and King, Ind. Buls. 183, 191; Evvard, Culbertson, et al., Iowa Sta., mimeo. rpts.; Snell and Bray, La. Rpt. 1931-33 and mimeo. rpts.; Peters, Minn. Bul. 300; Trowbridge, Mo. Bul. 223; Gramlich and Thalman, Nebr. Sta., mimeo. rpt.; Gerlaugh, Ohio Bimo. Buls. 154, 159, 166, 173; Ohio Bul. 463; see also: Guilbert, Cal. Bul. 481; Jacob, Tenn. Rpts. 1931, 1932, 1933; Hunt, Va. Rpt. 1920-27.
40. Culbertson, Evvard, Hammond, and Bassett, Iowa Leaflet 27.
41. Edwards and Massey, Ga. Bul. 184; Evvard and Culbertson, Iowa Sta., mimeo. rpts.; Gerlaugh, Ohio Bul. 463; Tomhave and Bentley, Penn. Bul. 183; Burns, Tex. Bul. 110.
42. Peters, Minn. Bul. 300; Bohstedt, Fuller, et al., Wis. Bul. 428.
43. Evvard and Culbertson, Iowa Sta., mimeo. rpts.; Gerlaugh, Ohio, Bul. 463.
44. Maynard, Breeder's Gazette, 79, 1921, p. 213.
45. Maynard and Greaves, Utah Buls. 235, 250, and mimeo. rpts.
46. Maynard and Osland, Colo. Press Buls. 65, 70; Morton, Maynard, and Osland, Colo. Press Bul. 74; Morton and Osland, Colo. Press Bul. 77.
47. Morton, Osland, et al., Colo. Press Buls. 74, 77; Colo. Information Bul., Jan. 1918, and information to the author; Carroll, Utah Bul. 192.
48. Carlyle and Griffith, Colo. Bul. 102; Quayle, Wyo. Rpt. 1929.
49. Kiser, Christgau, and Peters, Minn. Sta., mimeo. rpt.; Morton and Maynard, Colo. Sta., mimeo. rpt.
50. Shaw and Norton, Mich. Bul. 247.
51. Evvard, Culbertson, et al., Iowa Sta., mimeo. rpts.; Skinner and King, Ind. Buls. 183, 191; Trowbridge, Mo. Sta., Am. Soc. Anim. Prod., Proc. 1931, and mimeo. rpt.; Gramlich and Thalman, Nebr. Sta., mimeo. rpts.
52. Hickman, Rinehart, and Johnson, Id. Cir. 18; Gramlich, Nebr. Rpts. 1921, 1922, 1927, and mimeo. rpts.
53. Morton, Colo. Rpt. 1927; Morton and Osland, Colo. Press Bul. 78.
54. Hickman, Rinehart, and Johnson, Id. Bul. 209.
55. Edwards and Massey, Ga. Bul. 184; McCampbell, Anderson, and Marston, Kan. Cir. 128; Blizzard and Hawkins, Okla. Rpt. 1932-34; see also: Barnett and Goodell, Miss. Bul. 214; J. M. Jones, Lush, and J. H. Jones, Tex. Bul. 309; Ward, Curtis, and Peden, U. S. Dept. Agr. Bul. 628; Ward, Jerdan, and Lloyd, U. S. Dept. Agr. Buls. 631, 761.
56. Stanley, Ariz. Bul. 137; Scott and Stanley, Ariz. Sta., mimeo. rpts.
57. Kennedy and Robbins, Iowa Sta., Breeder's Gaz., 58, 1910, p. 303; Burns, Tex. Bul. 198; Ward, Jerdan, and Lloyd, U. S. Dept. Agr. Bul. 761.
58. Tomhave and Bentley, Penn. Bul. 183.
59. Morton and Osland, Colo. Press Bul. 78; Hickman, Rinehart, and Johnson, Id. Bul. 209; Evvard, Corn Belt Meat Prod. Assoc., 1913; Evvard, Culbertson, et al., Iowa Sta., mimeo. rpts.; Culbertson and Hammond, Iowa Sta., mimeo. rpts.; McCampbell and Marston, Kan. Cir. 117; Anderson and Marston, Kan. Cir. 130 and mimeo. rpts.; Anderson, McCampbell, and Alexander, Kan. Cir. 152 and mimeo. rpts.; Weber and Connell, Kan. Rpt. 1932-34; Allison, Mo. Bul. 150; Smith, Nebr. Bul. 100; Gramlich and Thalman, Nebr. Sta., mimeo. rpts.; Gerlaugh, Ohio Bimo. Bul. 140; Gerlaugh and Hackett, Ohio Bimo. Bul. 146; Tomhave and Bentley, Penn. Bul. 183; Wilson, S. D. Bul. 148; Morrison, Fuller, and Roche, Wis. Bul. 388 and mimeo. rpts.
60. Morrison, Fuller, and Roche, Wis. Buls. 388, 396; Fuller and Roche, Wis. Bul. 405; Culbertson, Evvard et al., Iowa Sta. mimeo. rpt.; Culbertson and Hammond, Iowa Sta., mimeo. rpt.; Weber and Connell, Kan. Rpt. 1932-34.
61. Willson, Tenn. Bul. 114.
62. Rusk and Snapp, Ill. Rpts. 1927, 1928.
63. King, Ind. Sta., mimeo. rpts.
64. Skinner and King, Ind. Buls. 281, 291, 314.
65. Rusk, Ill. Cir. 369; Skinner and King, Ind. Buls. 281, 291, 314, 330; King, Ind. Sta., mimeo. rpt.; Gerlaugh, Ohio Bimo. Bul. 140; Gerlaugh and Hackett, Ohio Bimo. Bul. 146; see also: Hickman, Rinehart, and Johnson, Id. Bul. 209.
66. Rusk, Ill. Cir. 369; Evvard, Culbertson, Hammond, and Wallace, Iowa Sta., mimeo. rpt.; Culbertson and Hammond, Iowa Sta., mimeo. rpt.; Gerlaugh, Ohio Bimo. Bul. 140; Gerlaugh and Hackett, Ohio Bimo. Bul. 146.
67. Rusk and Snapp, Ill., Rpts. 1933, 1934.
68. Rusk, Ill. Cir. 369; Culbertson and Hammond, Iowa Sta., mimeo. rpt.
69. Skinner and King, Ind. Buls. 281, 291, 314; Evvard, Culbertson, et al., Iowa Sta., mimeo. rpt.
70. Rusk and Snapp, Ill. Cir. 369 and mimeo. rpt.; Skinner and King, Ind. Buls. 281, 291, 314.
71. Starkey, S. C. Rpts. 1926, 1927, and information to the author.
72. Rusk and Snapp, Ill. Rpt. 1932.
73. Evvard, Culbertson, et al., Iowa Sta., mimeo. rpt.; Culbertson and Hammond, Iowa Sta., mimeo. rpt.
74. Tomhave, Severson, and Gerlaugh, Penn. Buls. 133, 145.
75. Smith, Nebr. Buls. 100, 132.

76. Weber and Connell, Kan. Rpt. 1932-34; see also: Culbertson et al., Iowa Rpt. 1931 and mimeo. rpts.
77. Evvard, Dunn, and Savin, Iowa Sta., mimeo. rpt.; Kiser and Peters, Minn. Bul. 261; see also: Mumford, Mo. Bul. 90.
78. Rusk, Ill. Sta., National Live Stock Producer, Jan. 1935; Skinner and King, Ind. Sta., mimeo. rpt.; Culbertson and Hammond, Iowa Sta., mimeo. rpt.; Weber and Connell, Kan. Sta., mimeo. rpt.; Johnson, Minn. Sta., information to the author; Thalman, Nebr. Sta., mimeo. rpt.; Hackedorn and McCall, Wash. Bul. 302.
79. Gerlaugh and Hackett, Ohio Bimo. Bul. 146; Culbertson and Hammond, Iowa Rpt. 1931 and mimeo. rpt.
80. Gerlaugh, Ohio Bimo. Bul. 159.
81. Culbertson and Hammond, Iowa Rpt. 1931 and mimeo. rpt.
82. Mumford, Ill. Bul. 83; Skinner and Cochel, Ind. Bul. 115; Smith, Nebr. Bul. 90; Bliss and Lee, Nebr. Bul. 151; see also: Smith, Nebr. Buls. 100, 116, 132.
83. Waters, Mo. Bul. 76; Snyder, Nebr. Bul. 105.
84. Craig and Marshall, Tex. Bul. 76.
85. Williams, Ariz. Bul. 91; Hickman, Rinehart, and Johnson, Id. Bul. 209; Vinke and Pearson, Mont. Bul. 251; Foster and Simpson, New Mex. Bul. 101; Potter and Withycombe, Ore. Bul. 193; Carroll, Utah Sta., information to the author; Hackedorn, Sotola, and Bean, Wash. Bul. 208.
86. Hickman, Rinehart, and Johnson, Id. Bul. 209.
87. Hickman, Rinehart, and Johnson, Id. Bul. 209; Potter and Withycombe, Ore. Bul. 193.
88. Williams, Ariz. Bul. 91; Hickman, Rinehart, and Johnson, Id. Bul. 209; Potter and Withycombe, Ore. Bul. 193; Hackedorn, Sotola, and Bean, Wash. Bul. 208.
89. Skinner and King, Ind. Bul. 129; Waters, Mo. Bul. 76.
90. Fuller and Morrison, Wis. Buls. 362, 373, 388.
91. Skinner and King, Ind. Buls. 178, 183, 191, 206, 245; Evvard, Culbertson, Wallace, and Hammond, Iowa Bul. 253.
92. Good and Harris, Amer. Soc. Anim. Prod., Proc. 1934.
93. Skinner and King, Ind. Buls. 314, 330, 396; Bohstedt, Ohio Bimo. Bul. 105-106.
94. Dvorachek, Ark. Bul. 203; Rusk and Snapp, Ill. Rpt. 1933; Rusk, National Livestock Producer, Jan. 1935; Good, Ky. Rpt. 1933; Trowbridge, Mo. Sta., mimeo. rpt.; see also Means, Miss. Rpt. 1932.
95. Edwards and Massey, Ga. Bul. 184; Waters, Mo. Bul. 76.
96. Lantow, Black, and Burnham, New Mex. Bul. 156; Black, Lantow, and Burnham, U. S. Dept. Agr. Tech. Bul. 30; see also: Foster and Smith, New Mex. Bul. 108; Lantow and Clemmer, New Mex. Bul. 131.
97. Cochel, Kan. Sta., mimeo. rpt.
98. Kiser and Peters, Minn. Bul. 261.
99. Peters and Mayo, Minn. Sta., mimeo. rpt.; Wilson, S. D. Bul. 160.
100. Blizzard, Okla. Rpt. 1930-32; Blizzard and Hawkins, Okla., Rpt. 1932-34.
101. McCampbell, Am. Soc. Anim. Prod., Proc. 1932; Anderson et al., Kan. Cirs. 130, 143, 151.
102. Trowbridge and Moffett, Mo. Buls. 285, 300.
103. Evvard, Culbertson, Wallace, and Hammond, Iowa Bul. 253.
104. Peters, Minn. Bul. 274.
105. Hays, Wyo. Rpt. 1922; Wyo. Bul. 128.
106. McCampbell et al., Fort Hays Branch, Kan. Sta., Cattlemen's Round-up, 1933, 1934, 1935.
107. Vinke and Dickson, Mont. Bul. 275; Dickson and Bergstedt, Mont. Sta., mimeo. rpt.
108. Hackedorn and McCall, Wash. Bul. 302.
109. Guilbert, Cal. Bul. 481.
110. Dowell and Bowstead, University of Alberta, Canada, mimeo. rpt.
111. Branaman and Hudson, Mich. Quar. Bul., 16, 1933, No. 1; 17, 1934, No. 1; see also Mich. Quar. Bul., 18, 1935, No. 1.
112. Gerlaugh and Rogers, Ohio Bimo. Bul. 157.
113. Lantow, New Mex. Bul. 211.
114. Morton, Colo. Rpt. 1927.
115. Christensen, N. D. Sta., mimeo. rpt.
116. Mumford, Ill. Bul. 73.
117. Allison, Mo. Bul. 112.
118. Evvard, Culbertson, et al., Iowa Bul. 253 and mimeo. rpts.
119. Skinner and King, Ind. Bul. 396.
120. Bohstedt and Rogers, Ohio Bimo. Bul. 129.
121. Thalman, Gramlich, and Lewis, Nebr. Sta., mimeo. rpts.; see also: Trowbridge and Moffett, Mo. Bul. 328.
122. McCampbell et al., Fort Hays Branch, Kan. Sta. Annual Cattlemen's Round-up, 1931; Trowbridge and Moffett, Mo. Sta., mimeo. rpt.
123. Bohstedt, Ohio Bimo. Buls. 83-84; see also: Gerlaugh and Rogers, Ohio Bimo. Bul. 139.
124. Scott and Stanley, Ariz. Sta., mimeo. rpts.; Jones, Keating, Black, and Smith, Tex. Rpt. 1931.
125. McCampbell et al., Fort Hays Branch, Kan. Sta., Annual Cattlemen's Round-up, 1934.
126. Thalman, Gramlich, and Lewis, Nebr. Sta., mimeo. rpt.
127. Lantow, Black, and Burnham, New Mex. Bul. 156; U. S. Dept. Agr. Tech. Bul. 30.
128. Jones, Black and Keating, Tex. Bul. 363; see also Ariz. Rpt. 1922; Williams and Smith, Ariz. Bul. 107.
129. J. M. Jones, Dickson, Black, and J. H. Jones, Tex. Rpt. 1932.

130. J. M. Jones, Dickson, J. H. Jones, Texas Rpt. 1933; see also: Willham, Okla.,
     Panhandle Sta., Bul. 54; McCampbell and Aichen, Fort Hays Branch, Kan. Sta.,
     Annual Cattlemen's Round-up, 1932.
131. McCampbell, Fort Hays Branch, Kan. Sta., Annual Cattlemen's Round-up, 1920,
     1922, 1928.
132. J. M. Jones, Hall, and J. H. Jones, Tex. Rpt. 1933.
133. Thalman, Nebr. Sta., mimeo. rpt.
134. Rusk, Ill. Sta., mimeo. rpt.; Skinner and King, Ind. Buls. 163, 167, 396; Morton,
     Osland, and Tom, Colo. Press Bul. 82.
135. Rusk, Ill. Cir. 369.
136. Buchanan, Miss. Bul. 278; Means, Miss. Bul. 301.
137. Blizzard, Okla. Rpt. 1932 and mimeo. rpt.
138. Hostetler et al., N. C. Rpts. 1929, 1930, 1931.
139. Jones, Keating, Black, and Smith, Tex. Rpt. 1931 and mimeo. rpt.
140. Lloyd, Miss. Sta., information to the author; Curtis, N. C. Buls. 199, 218, 222;
     Smith, S. C. Bul. 169; Starkey, S. C. Rpts. 1926, 1927, and information to the
     author; Willson, Tenn. Bul. 104; Ward and Gray, U. S. Dept. Agr. Bul. 762.
141. Stanley and Scott, Ariz. Sta., mimeo. rpt.; Hickman, Rinehart and Johnson, Id.
     Bul. 209; Peters and Carnes, Minn. Bul. 200; Hackedorn, Sotola, and Bean,
     Wash. Bul. 186.
142. Good and Horlacker, Ky. Bul. 264.
143. McCampbell, Amer. Soc. Anim. Prod., Proc. 1932.
144. Ariz. Rpt. 1922; Rusk, Ill. Sta., Breeder's Gaz., 61, 1912, p. 1041; Skinner, Cochel,
     and King, Ind. Buls. 136, 153, 163, 167; Evvard, Iowa Sta., Breeder's Gaz., 61,
     1912, p. 1040; Allison, Mo. Bul. 112; Tomhave and Hickman, Penn. Bul. 133.
145. Skinner, Cochel, and King, Ind. Buls. 129, 136, 153, 167, 178, 191, 206; Evvard
     and Pew, Iowa Bul. 182 and Breeder's Gaz., 61, 1912, p. 1040; Evvard, Culbert-
     son, et al., Iowa Sta., mimeo. rpts. and Amer. Soc. Anim. Prod., Proc. 1923;
     Peters and Carnes, Minn. Bul. 200; Allison, Mo. Bul. 112; Gramlich, Nebr. Sta.,
     mimeo. rpts.; Blizzard, Okla. Bul. 147.
146. Wilson and Thompson, S. D. Bul. 182; Wilson and Kuhlman, S. D. Bul. 189.
147. Hickman, Rinehart, and Johnson, Id. Bul. 209; Gramlich, Nebr. Sta., mimeo. rpts.;
     Hackedorn, Sotola, and Bean, Wash. Bul. 186.
148. Maynard, and Osland, Colo. Press Buls. 74, 77; Osland, Colo. Bul. 380; Guilbert,
     Cal. Bul. 418.
149. Rusk and Snapp, Ill. Rpts. 1929, 1931.
150. Jacob and Duncan, Tenn. Bul. 144.
151. Brown, Mich. Rpt. 1927.
152. McCampbell and Winchester, Kan. Cir. 92; Gayle, Miss. Bul. 182; Hunt, Va.
     Rpt. 1920-27.
153. McCampbell and Winchester, Kan. Cir. 77; McCampbell, Anderson, and Marston,
     Kan. Cir. 128; Blizzard, Okla. Rpt. 1930-32 and mimeo. rpts.; see also: Stanley,
     Ariz. Bul. 137.
154. Cochel, Kan. Sta., Amer. Soc. Anim. Prod., Proc. 1915-16; McCampbell et al.,
     Fort Hays Branch, Kan. Sta., Annual Cattlemen's Round-up, 1931; Thalman,
     Gramlich, and Lewis, Nebr. Sta., mimeo. rpts.
155. Good, Horlacher, and Grimes, Ky. Bul. 233; Goodell, Miss. Bul. 222; Buchanan,
     Miss. Bul. 278; Blizzard, Okla. Bul. 139; Quesenberry, U. S. Dept. Agr. Bul. 1318.
156. McCampbell, et al., Fort Hays Branch, Kan. Sta., Annual Cattlemen's Round-up,
     1928.
157. Skinner and Starr, Ind. Bul. 220; Skinner and Vestal, Ind. Bul. 240; Skinner and
     King, Ind. Buls. 249, 255.
158. Quesenberry, U. S. Dept. Agr. Bul. 1318; U. S. Dept. Agr. Cir. 65.
159. Goodell, Miss. Bul. 222.
160. Day, Ont. Agr. Col., Canada, Rpts. 1901, 1902; Blair, Rpt. Dominion Expt. Farms,
     Canada, 1917, p. 72.
161. Wilson, S. D. Bul. 137.
162. See the summary by Ingle, Highl. and Agr. Soc. Scot., Trans. 1909.
162ª. Paterson, Highl. and Agr. Soc. Scot., Trans. 1930, pp. 37-50.
163. Rusk and Snapp, Ill. Rpts. 1931, 1933.
164. Morton, Colo. Rpt. 1931; Rusk and Snapp, Ill. Rpt. 1931 and mimeo. rpt.; Snyder,
     Nebr. Bul. 239; Baker, Nebr. Bul. 281.
165. Selvig, Crookston Substa., Minn., Rpts. 1924, 1925; Thalman, Gramlich, Lyness,
     and Kiesselbach, Nebr. Sta., mimeo. rpt.; Shepperd, N. D. Bul. 211; Snapp and
     Knox, Ill. Bul. 328.

CHAPTER XXXI

FEED AND CARE OF BEEF CATTLE—METHODS AND COSTS OF BEEF PRODUCTION—VEAL PRODUCTION

I. The Beef Breeding Herd

1102. Establishing a beef herd.—In establishing a beef breeding herd, one should start with as good foundation cows as possible, in order to secure offspring that will make economical gains, mature early, and yield carcasses with a large percentage of the high-priced cuts of meat. (**1010-1014**) Ordinarily, well-bred grade cows of one of the beef breeds should be selected. Where this cannot be done, a start may be made with selected commoner cows, but the progress will then be less rapid.

The cows should be of the recognized beef type and conformation; i.e., low-set, deep-bodied, broad, and compact, with vigorous constitutions. A purebred bull of good quality should always be used, for only then is it possible to build up a herd which will return the most profit.

There are three general systems of handling beef breeding herds. These are: (1) The usual beef method; (2) "baby beef" production; and (3) the "dual-purpose" system. In the first two systems the calves run with their dams until weaned, none of the cows being milked. Cows producing calves intended for baby beef are, however, commonly fed a little more liberally, as is pointed out later. (**1133**) In the dual-purpose system beef production is combined more or less with dairying. (**1110**)

1103. Feeding beef breeding cows.—Where cows are kept only to raise calves for beef, the cost of their maintenance for an entire year must be charged against the calf at weaning time. To reduce the cost of beef production it is therefore essential that the breeding herd be maintained as cheaply as possible, yet kept in vigorous breeding condition. Only a breeder of purebred stock who wishes to keep his herd in somewhat of "show condition" as an advertisement can afford to feed much grain to his beef cows.

Cows kept solely for beef production are commonly grazed on pasture during the growing season, the suckling calves running with their dams and no additional feed being given to cows or calves. Usually the pastures thus utilized will be the land least suited to tillage. In the fall the cows can get their living chiefly from feed that might be otherwise wasted, such as stubble or stalk fields and the aftermath of meadows. With a little foresight, the amount of such cheap feed may be increased by seeding rape or clover in the small grain, and rape in the corn fields. Shade should always be supplied the herd at pasture.

The winter feed and care may range from the most intensive system, where the herd is fed in barn or shed with the freedom of exercise paddocks, to the practice yet followed in some of the grazing districts of the West, where the only feed is that furnished by the winter range on which the grass has been allowed to grow up and mature. However, bitter experience has taught the western stockman that he must provide against winter's rigors by having available a supply of feed to supplement the range when necessary.

1104. Nutrient requirements of beef cows.—The nutrient requirements of breeding animals have been discussed in detail in Chapter VII. (217) In order to produce thrifty, vigorous offspring, the dams must receive rations containing sufficient protein, minerals, and vitamins. Fortunately, much smaller quantities of these nutritive essentials are needed for wintering beef breeding cows than for feeding dairy cows in milk. This is because beef cows usually calve in the spring and are dry during the winter. Therefore they need nutrients merely for the maintenance of their own bodies and for the growth of the fetus. As we have seen in Chapter VII, the amounts of nutrients required for the development of a calf to birth are not so large as often believed. (217)

It is for this reason that beef cows can be wintered satisfactorily on roughage alone, when some legume hay is available. If only non-legume roughage is fed, there should be added to the ration 1 lb. per head daily of linseed or cottonseed cake or meal or one of the other high-protein supplements. Beef cows should be supplied with sufficient feed during the winter to keep them in thrifty condition. Otherwise, they may be unable to produce strong calves and nourish them with a good flow of milk. If they go into the winter in poor flesh, due to a shortage of feed on pasture, a little grain may be needed to get them in suitable condition before calving.

Too-liberal feeding of grain is not only extravagant but also may prove actually injurious. Experienced beef producers know that the best calf crop is apt to be secured from cows kept in vigorous condition on a properly-balanced ration, rather than from cows which are fat.

If the cows receive at least 5 to 6 lbs. per head daily of properly-cured alfalfa, clover, or other legume hay, there will be no shortage of protein, calcium, or vitamins. Also, there will be no deficiency of phosphorus in such rations unless the roughage has been raised on soil very low in this mineral. When non-legume roughage is fed with 1 lb. per head daily of protein supplement, the ration will contain ample phosphorus, but there may be a lack of calcium, unless the roughage was grown on soil well supplied with calcium. Therefore when no legume hay is fed, it is wise to feed 0.1 lb. or slightly more of ground limestone or other calcium supplement per head daily.

Beef cows that have been on good pasture during the summer go into the winter with a considerable reserve of vitamin A, and their vitamin needs are not large. Therefore, unless the winter is too long, they can be wintered successfully on straw as the only roughage, which is very low in vitamins. However, as an insurance against a lack of vitamin A, it is wise to feed along with straw at least a limited amount of well-cured hay, good fodder from corn or sorghum, or good silage. This is especially important if the cows go into winter in poor condition and depleted of vitamins, because of drought-stricken pastures. Beef breeding cattle that are outside in the sunlight most of the day are amply protected against any lack of vitamin D.

Plenty of salt and a proper supply of water should always be furnished the cattle. If trouble is experienced from goiter, or "big neck," in new-born calves this may be prevented by supplying the cows with iodized salt during at least the latter one-half of the pregnancy period. (**172**)

If one is in doubt as to whether the ration he intends to feed his breeding cows is balanced, he should calculate the dry matter, digestible protein, and total digestible nutrients in it and see how the amounts correspond with the Morrison feeding standards, which are based on the investigations at American experiment stations. (Appendix Table III.) If the ration does not contain as much digestible protein as is there advised (0.6 to 0.7 lb. daily for a 1,000-lb. cow), enough of some protein supplement should be added to balance the ration.

In the case of mature cows the amount of total digestible nutrients may fall slightly below the minimum in the standard, if the cows go into winter in good flesh. On such a ration, however, the animals will probably lose in weight slightly during the winter. Cows which are not yet mature should be fed a little more liberally than full-grown ones, as they need additional nutrients to provide for growth. Cows nursing calves in winter require more feed than those which are dry.

1105. Wintering cows chiefly on corn or sorghum forage.—Where corn or the sorghums thrive, these premier forage crops should generally furnish much of the roughage for the breeding herd. The crop may be fed, grain and all, as silage or dry fodder, or the grain may be removed and the stover fed either as dry stover or stover silage.

Experiments have shown that corn or sorghum silage is much more economical than the dry fodder, for it is consumed with less waste and will maintain the cows in better condition.[1] Beef cows may be wintered very satisfactorily on 50 to 60 lbs. of corn or sorghum silage per head daily and 1 lb. of cottonseed meal, linseed meal, or similar protein supplement.[2] This will keep them in good condition. Even an allowance of 40 lbs. per head daily of corn silage with 1 lb. of supplement maintained cows in fair condition in an Illinois test.[3] Though the cows did not carry as much flesh as many breeders would desire, their health was not injured, and they produced vigorous calves.

Often it is most economical to use silage in combination with hay, straw, or other dry roughage. An excellent combination is 5 lbs. or more of legume hay and 25 to 30 lbs. or more of corn or sorghum silage.[4] If grass hay, straw, or corn or sorghum stover is used as the dry roughage with corn or sorghum silage, 1 lb. of protein supplement per head daily should be added to balance the ration.[5]

While cows that are in good condition in the fall can be wintered on only corn or sorghum silage or the silage and dry non-legume roughage, they will maintain their weights much better if a supplement is fed. Therefore they will be able to yield more milk for their calves in the spring.

A combination of 20 to 25 lbs. corn silage, 7.5 lbs. soybean or mixed clover-and-grass hay, and 2 to 3 lbs. of wheat straw proved very satisfactory and economical in four West Virginia trials.[6] Good results were also secured on a ration of 24 lbs. silage, 7 lbs. wheat straw and 1.5 lbs. cottonseed meal. When corn or sorghum silage is fed as the only roughage or else with non-legume forage, a calcium supplement should be supplied, unless the soil is high in lime. (**999**)

WELL-BRED CATTLE AND A PROSPEROUS FARM

What single-crop, grain-growing farm can furnish a scene of such beauty as this? Sleek, contented cattle; fertile fields; and well-kept fences.

ABERDEEN-ANGUS COWS AND CALVES ON A CORN-BELT PASTURE

To reduce the cost of beef production it is essential that the breeding herd be maintained as cheaply as possible, yet kept in vigorous breeding condition.

SHADE AND FRESH WATER ARE IMPORTANT ON PASTURE

For all cattle on pasture it is important that shade, fresh water, and salt be provided. Fattening steers nearly ready for market may get rough coats, however, if they spend much time standing in deep water in midsummer to escape the flies.

1106. Stover silage a cheap feed.—To reduce the cost of wintering the cows, stover silage, made from corn stover or grain sorghum stover, may be used instead of normal silage containing the grain. Much more feeding value is secured from an acre of stover when fed in the form of silage than when fed as dry stover. While stover silage is not well suited for feeding to fattening cattle, it is satisfactory as the chief feed for wintering breeding cows, due to the fact that they need much less total digestible nutrients. (**1096**)

In Illinois tests it was found that beef cows could be wintered on about 60 lbs. of corn stover silage and 1 lb. of protein supplement per head daily, preferably with a few pounds of straw in addition.[7] Though cows thus fed were rather spare in condition, they produced thrifty calves, and the cost of feed was only one-third as much as when corn silage was used which contained all the ears. In these trials corn stover silage was worth about two-thirds as much per ton as normal corn silage, while in an Ohio test it was not worth one-half as much per ton.[8]

1107. Wintering cows chiefly on straw.—In the wheat-growing districts of the West beef cows are frequently wintered on straw as the only roughage. Montana and Oregon trials show that cows in medium to good condition in the fall can be wintered satisfactorily on 12 to 20 lbs. of straw daily plus 1 lb. of cottonseed cake or meal or other protein supplement, or on straw and 4 to 5 lbs. of alfalfa or other legume hay.[9]

If the cows are in good condition in the fall and the winter is mild and not too long, they can even be carried through the winter on straw alone. However, they will then lose 50 to 200 lbs. per head and may not be thrifty enough in the spring to provide sufficient milk for their calves. Such an inadequate ration should therefore be used only in emergencies. Straw is also often fed with grass hay or with corn or sorghum fodder, stover, or silage. Such combinations are likewise very low in protein, and 1 lb. of protein supplement per head daily should be added. Also, a calcium supplement should be supplied when straw is fed as the only roughage or with non-legume forage.

1108. Wintering on hay and other feeds.—In the alfalfa districts of the West alfalfa hay is widely used as the chief roughage for wintering beef cows. They can be kept in excellent condition on 18 to 25 lbs. of alfalfa hay a day, but often the cost can be reduced by combining the alfalfa with some cheaper roughage, such as prairie hay, corn or sorghum fodder or stover, or straw.[10] One ton of hay, or the equivalent in hay and other roughage, is a common estimate of the amount needed to winter a breeding cow under range conditions, if the feeding season is not too long.

In five Montana trials oat hay proved to be even better than alfalfa hay as the only feed for wintering beef cows.[11] Sweet clover hay, native bluejoint hay, and corn fodder were also satisfactory as the only feeds.

1109. Supplementing winter range.—In range sections where the grass or other forage is not usually covered by snow in winter, the beef herd is wintered as largely as possible on the range. Supplementary feed should be provided for use if feed becomes scanty, in order to keep the cattle from running down seriously in condition.

In New Mexico tests cottonseed cake, fed at the rate of 0.5 to 1.0 lb. per head daily was an excellent supplement.[12] It could be fed with little waste and produced decidedly better results than an equal weight of corn. Often a supply of hay or silage (usually in a trench or pit silo) is kept on hand to meet shortages of feed on the range during the winter.

1110. Feeding dual-purpose cows.—Where dual-purpose cows are kept and milked so as to secure dairy products as well as a crop of calves, the cows should be fed the same as dairy cows and the calves raised much like dairy calves, except that the calves should be forced to rapid growth through more liberal feeding. Since many dual-purpose cows do not have marked dairy temperament, it is especially important that they be fed strictly according to their actual production, instead of being given concentrates for which they will not pay at the milk pail.

Sometimes the "double nursing" method is followed, in which about half the cows in the herd nurse two calves each and the others, from which the calves have been taken, are milked. For this plan it is essential that all the cows nursing calves be good milkers, as otherwise the calves will not make the gains desired.

1111. The beef bull.—Under farm conditions the bull should be kept separate from the herd of cows except at the breeding season. This plan is also often followed in range herds, so that the calves will come within a certain time and so that the bulls will have an opportunity to get in good condition before the next breeding season.

A vigorous bull 3 years old or over should serve 40 to 50 cows when hand-mated, and 25 to 30 when he runs with the cows on pasture during the breeding season. On the western ranges the average number of cows per bull is about 25, except in rough and mountainous country, where a bull to every 15 to 20 cows is a common proportion. A yearling bull should be hand-mated to no more than 10 to 12 cows during the breeding season and a 2-year-old to no more than 25 to 30 cows. It is not wise to allow young bulls to run with the cows on pasture during the breeding season.

The same general principles apply to the feed and care of the beef bull as for the dairy bull. (**987-988**) The bull should be kept in good, thrifty condition but not fat. Previous to the breeding season he should be well fed, and concentrates should be added at other times, as needed, to keep him in condition. It is best to feed only a limited amount of silage to a bull prior to the breeding season or during it, as he may become too paunchy for active service. If a bull is a "hard keeper" and requires an abnormal amount of feed to keep him in proper flesh, he should be discarded, for he cannot be expected to sire cattle which will make economical gains.

The importance of using a good purebred sire has been emphasized in Chapter XXIX. (**1010-1013**)

II. Raising Beef Cattle

1112. The beef calf.—Most beef producers prefer to have the calves born in the spring, as the cows may then be wintered more cheaply, with less shelter and less care.[13] When the cows are suitably fed during the winter and have proper shelter, it is generally best to have them calve early, from February to April. They can then receive more careful attention, and the winter rations will produce plenty of milk for the young calves.

When the cows are turned to pasture in the spring, the calves will be old enough to use to advantage the increased milk flow. Also, early calves can utilize the summer pasturage better than those born late in the spring or in the early summer. Early calves are not only much larger in the fall, but also, if sold as feeders, will bring a better price per 100 lbs. on account of being in better flesh.

When the calves are born on pasture, the cows usually have no difficulty in calving and need little attention. Even when they calve under winter conditions, beef cows are not apt to require assistance at calving time, as is sometimes the case with dairy cows. This is because their calves are rather small at birth, generally weighing only 60 to 75 lbs.

All bull calves that are not to be retained for breeding should be castrated, preferably before fly time and when from 1 to 2 months of age. Calves to be fed for the market should be dehorned, unless it is the intention to sell them as fat calves at weaning time. A good plan, where practicable, is to prevent the growth of the horns by using the caustic pencil before the calves are 3 weeks old.

Spring calves are commonly weaned in the fall by separating them from their dams. To avoid a loss of weight at this time, it is best to teach farm-raised calves to eat grain and hay before they are weaned, and then feed them well when they are taken from their mothers.

1113. Gains of suckling calves.—Suckling calves should gain 1.25 to 1.75 lbs., or over, per head daily if their dams give a good flow of milk. In a Pennsylvania test 3 calves fed whole milk containing 4.6 per cent of fat for 161 days, gained 1.77 lbs. each daily, requiring 8.8 lbs. of whole milk, 1 lb. of hay and 1 lb. of grain for each pound of growth.[14]

Martiny found that from 3.5 to 6 lbs. of whole milk were sufficient to produce a pound of gain, live weight, with calves between the first and fifth weeks, while older ones required from 16 to 20 lbs.[15] In Utah experiments calves required less dry matter than pigs for 1 lb. of gain up to 14 weeks of age, and after that more, possibly because of the greater amount of roughage then fed in the ration.[16] In Connecticut studies calves required 1.03 lbs., lambs 1.08 lbs., and pigs 1.36 lbs. of dry matter in whole milk for each pound of gain made.[17]

1114. Creep-feeding suckling calves.—Beef calves are not generally fed grain while they are nursing their mothers and are on good pasture, except in the case of purebred calves on which maximum growth is desired or sometimes with calves to be fattened for market at as early an age as possible. Several recent experiments have shown that creep-feeding is generally profitable for well-bred beef calves that are to be sold for beef at weaning time or shortly thereafter. It is doubtful if it is advisable, except when pasture is scanty, for calves that are to be full-fed on grain for 5 months or more after weaning.

Creep-fed calves are heavier in the fall at weaning time. They will also then sell at a higher price as feeders, unless grain is cheap and farmers prefer calves that do not carry much flesh to those which are fatter, because they can put on fat cheaper than they can buy it in well-fleshed calves. The cows also keep in better flesh when their calves are creep-fed, and thus need not be fed so much during the winter.

The creep should be built at a spot in the pasture where the calves tend to gather, as at the watering place. It is an enclosure with openings about 16 inches wide and 4 feet high, so that the calves can enter and the cows can be kept out. At first the cows should be allowed to enter the enclosure with the calves and eat grain, in order that the calves will learn to take it. Even then, it is sometimes difficult to get certain calves to eat grain, if their mothers are good milkers and there is an abundance of pasturage. The grain can be conveniently fed in the creep by means of a covered self-feeder which will hold a supply for several days.

Creep-feeding is particularly advantageous for calves that are to be sold as fat calves at an early age. Early-spring calves creep-fed during the summer on good pasture and then full-fed after weaning can often be made fat enough for market by October or November, then weighing 600 lbs. or more. The experiments show that even when the calves are to be sold as feeders in the fall, they usually bring enough more, because of additional weight and better flesh, to show a profit on the grain that is fed.

1115. Tests of creep-feeding.—In 14 tests of creep-feeding, the calves that were creep-fed while nursing their dams gained an average of 1.79 lbs. per head daily, which was 0.42 lb. more than others that did not receive the additional feed.[18] In these trials, which averaged 152 days in length, the difference in total gain per calf was 64 lbs. The total amount of grain and other concentrates eaten per calf during this time was 495 lbs., including that consumed by the cows while the calves were learning to eat. For each 100 lbs. of additional gain, the creep-fed calves therefore were to be charged with 758 lbs. of concentrates. In 9 tests in which the selling prices were reported, the creep-fed calves were worth $1.23 more per hundredweight at weaning time. The greater gains and the increased selling price paid well for the concentrates fed in most of these tests.

In Missouri tests the creep-feeding of calves that were running with their dams on pasture proved preferable to keeping the calves in a separate enclosure where they were fed grain, and turned with the cows to nurse only twice a day.[19]

Because milk is rich in protein and also because good pasture is likewise fairly high in protein, there is no need of a high protein content in the concentrates fed to calves while suckling their dams on pasture. Good results will be secured even with corn as the only grain. Mixtures of corn and other grain and a small proportion of protein supplement are often preferred, as such mixtures may be slightly more palatable. There is no advantage in grinding corn or oats for suckling calves.

In Missouri tests during 3 summers calves creep-fed a mixture of 8 parts by weight of shelled corn and 1 of cottonseed meal gained slightly more than those fed only shelled corn or a mixture of 2 parts corn and 1 part oats.[20] They also sold for 50 cents more per hundredweight. However, the feed cost per 100 lbs. gain was somewhat less for the calves fed only shelled corn.

1116. Wintering calves.—Until recently, nearly all the young beef cattle intended for market were carried through one or more winters before they were fattened for market. Now an ever-increasing number are put into feed lots in the fall and fattened for marketing when not much over a year of age. When this plan, which is discussed later, is followed, the calves must be fed liberally during the winter on good roughage with grain in addition and also a protein supplement, if the latter is needed to balance the ration. (**1134**)

Calves that are being wintered for later fattening must be fed primarily on roughage, in order to keep the cost as low as possible. While the ration must be cheap, it is essential that the calves be kept growing thriftily. Sufficient protein, minerals, and vitamins must be provided to meet the requirements of animals of this young age, or they will fail to make the desired growth.

Many experiments have been conducted to determine the best methods of wintering calves under various conditions.[21] These experiments show that if the calves are to be fattened the following spring and summer in dry lot, or if they are to be fed grain on pasture, it is usually best to feed sufficient grain or other concentrates during the winter to keep them improving somewhat in condition, or degree of fatness.

Calves will make considerable growth when gaining only 0.50 to 0.75 lb. per head daily, but they will then carry less flesh in the spring than when they came off pasture in the fall. Usually a gain of about 1.0 lb. per head daily is required to keep them from losing in condition, and the rate of gain must be even greater if any fattening is desired during the winter.

When calves are to be pastured during the following summer without grain in addition, the gain during the winter should not be too great, or the summer gains on pasture will be greatly reduced. If the summer grazing will probably be good, it is generally best to feed calves so they will gain 0.75 to 1.00 lb. per head daily. This will keep them thrifty, produce good growth, and prevent them from losing much in condition. The gains will be sufficient to pay for the feed consumed during the winter, and hence the cost of the calves per 100 lbs. in the spring should be no greater than in the previous fall when they came off pasture.

If the calves will be on rather poor range in summer, it may be best to limit the winter feed so that they will gain only about 0.50 lb. per head daily. It is almost always advisable to secure at least this much growth during the winter, instead of feeding the calves so scantily that they grow in skeleton, but merely maintain their weights. If they do not gain during the winter, all the feed and labor is spent just for carrying them over to spring. The cost of the calves per 100 lbs. live weight in the spring will then be considerably greater than if they had been fed so as to make reasonable gains.

Many men who fatten western feeder cattle during the spring and summer, buy calves in the fall and carry them through the winter, instead of making their purchases in the spring. They find that they can generally get calves of good quality more readily in the fall, when the supply on the market is greatest. By carrying the calves through the winter, they dispose of much farm-grown roughage. Also, if the calves are fed economical rations, the cost per 100 lbs. will usually be less in the spring than the price at that time for animals of similar quality on the feeder markets.

1117. Nutrient requirements and example rations.—The amounts of dry matter, digestible protein, and total digestible nutrients needed by calves of various weights to make daily gains of approximately 0.75 to 1.00 lb. per head daily are stated in the Morrison feeding standards. (Appendix Table III.) Also, several example rations suited to conditions in various parts of the country are given in Appendix Table VII.

The amounts of feed there suggested are only approximate, but should be helpful as a general guide. Where the winters are unusually cold, somewhat more feed will be required. Also, if the hay or other roughage is of rather inferior quality, it will be necessary to supply enough grain or other concentrates to keep the calves in the desired condition.

1118. Rations for wintering calves.—In the West where alfalfa hay is cheap, it is a standard ration for wintering calves or older cattle. If calves are fed all the good alfalfa hay they will clean up reasonably well, they will eat 12 to 20 lbs. of hay a day, depending on their size, and will gain approximately 1.0 lb. per head daily, or perhaps even more. When thus fed, they may waste about 2.0 to 2.5 lbs. of hay a day, but this refuse hay can often be fed to older stock being carried through the winter. To winter calves under western conditions without making any gains in weight, it will usually take about 2.0 lbs. of hay daily per 100 lbs. live weight.

Clover hay or mixed clover-and-grass hay is about equal to alfalfa hay in value for calves. Unless hay from the grasses is cut earlier than usual, it is too low in protein to give the best results when used as the only feed for wintering calves. Good results are secured when good-quality timothy hay, prairie hay, native hay, or other grass hay is fed with 0.5 to 1.0 lb. of cottonseed meal or other protein supplement per head daily.

To reduce the cost, it is often advisable to feed, along with alfalfa hay or other legume hay, some cheap roughage, such as corn or sorghum fodder or stover, or even straw. Calves fed 4 to 6 lbs. of alfalfa hay per day, with what straw they will eat, do not make much gain in weight, but can be carried through the winter in thrifty condition. By adding to such a ration 2 or 3 lbs. of grain per head daily, satisfactory gains can be secured.

In many sections of the country silage from corn or the sorghums provides the cheapest roughage for calves. An excellent ration is 3 to 4 lbs. alfalfa hay and sufficient silage to produce the desired gain in weight. On this amount of legume hay and 25 lbs. of good silage, calves should gain a pound a day or more. Unless this much legume hay is fed with corn or sorghum silage, a protein supplement should be added. Contrary to some earlier opinions, cattle fed silage during the winter will make just as good gains on grass the following summer as others that have made similar winter gains on dry feed.

Very satisfactory gains have been made when calves have been wintered on a sufficient amount of silage with 0.5 to 1.0 lb. per head daily of a protein supplement. When thus used to balance the ration, each 100 lbs. of cottonseed meal or cake has been worth as much as 300 to 400 lbs. of alfalfa hay. Kansas and Nebraska trials show that when protein supplements are high in price compared with farm grain, 2.0 lbs.

of ground barley, oats, wheat, or grain sorghum can be used in place of 0.75 to 1.00 lb. of protein supplement, such as cottonseed cake or meal.[22] Corn is rather too low in protein to be thus used, but an allowance of 1.0 lb. corn and 0.5 lb. cottonseed cake, fed with silage or other suitable non-legume roughage, gives good results.

Corn-stover silage or silage made from grain-sorghum stover should not be used as the only roughage for calves, if more nutritious roughage is available. If such silage or dry corn or sorghum stover is the chief roughage, it will be necessary to feed some grain to keep the calves in good condition.

Sometimes straw is used as the only roughage for wintering calves, but this is not advisable under usual conditions, for straw is very low in vitamin A. When straw is thus fed, the calves should receive 1.0 lb. of protein supplement, such as cottonseed meal or linseed meal, per head daily, and 0.1 lb. of ground limestone or other calcium supplement should also be supplied. At least 4 or 5 lbs. of well-cured hay had best be fed with straw, instead of using straw as the only roughage, or else it should be fed in combination with a limited amount of corn silage or other silage.

On the ranges of the Southwest the calves often get most of their winter feed from a winter range. New Mexico tests show that it is advisable to supplement such feed with 0.5 to 1.0 lb. of cottonseed cake, the amount depending on whether the calves are to be sold in the spring or carried on the range until the following fall.[23]

1119. Wintering yearlings and older stocker cattle.—Yearlings and older stocker cattle that are being carried through the winter for later fattening can make even greater use of cheap roughages than can calves. Hence, unless grain is very low in price, they should generally be wintered on roughage alone, when they are to be grazed on pasture without grain the following summer. Of course, a small amount of a protein supplement should be added when it is needed to balance the ration. If the cattle are to be finished for a summer or early fall market by feeding them grain or other concentrates in addition to pasture, then some grain is commonly fed during the winter, especially towards spring.

Extensive experiments have been conducted at various stations and by the United States Department of Agriculture to compare various rations for wintering yearlings and older stocker cattle.[24] The recommendations given in the Morrison feeding standards for such cattle are based upon the results of these investigations. (Appendix Table III.) Likewise, the example rations given in Appendix Table VII have been computed from the results of these studies.

While stock cattle must be wintered cheaply, they should be fed so as to make some gain in weight. The most desirable amount of gain will depend on how they are to be handled the following summer.

Yearlings and older cattle will make good gains when wintered on a full feed of legume hay or of mixed legume-and-grass hay. Even grass hay of good quality, which has been cut reasonably early and is therefore fair in protein content, is satisfactory as the only feed for such stock cattle. If the hay is late-cut or of poor quality, it is best to add about 1 lb. per head daily of cottonseed meal or other protein supplement. To reduce the expense somewhat, the allowance of alfalfa hay or other good hay is often kept somewhat below the amount the cattle would clean up.

Except in certain alfalfa districts of the West, feeding hay alone often makes the ration unduly expensive. To reduce the cost, such cheap dry roughage as straw or else corn or sorghum stover can be satisfactorily fed with 3 or 4 lbs. or more per head daily of legume hay. When most of the roughage is of low grade, it will be necessary to add 2 to 3 lbs. per head daily of grain or other concentrates, if it is desired that the cattle make fair gains during the winter.

Corn or sorghum silage or silage from other suitable crops is excellent as part of the roughage, or even as the only roughage for wintering stock cattle. Since corn or sorghum silage is low in protein, at least 3 to 4 lbs. of legume hay per head daily should be fed with it, or else 1 lb. of protein supplement. The trials reviewed in the preceding chapter show that a crop of corn or sorghum has a much greater feeding value for wintering cattle when it is ensiled than when it is fed as dry fodder. (1085, 1087)

Stalk and stubble fields can often furnish much of the feed for stock cattle during the fall and early winter. In certain sections of the Southeast, stock cattle are often wintered chiefly on rough land on which no cattle have been grazed in summer.

In those Western range sections where there is not much snow in winter, winter range is commonly used as much as possible for stock cattle. Provision should always be made for supplemental feed when the supply of feed on the range is insufficient. For this purpose hay may be stacked against time of need or silage can be stored in a trench silo. Cottonseed cake, fed at the rate of 1.0 lb. per head daily, is also an excellent supplement to scanty winter range.

1120. Raising beef heifers and bulls.—In raising beef heifers and bulls for the breeding herd, the rations should be somewhat more liberal during the first and second winters than in the case of stocker cattle which are later to be fattened for market. It is very important that they be fed so that they will develop into vigorous animals of the proper size for their breed.

Care should therefore be taken that the ration supplies not only enough total digestible nutrients, but also sufficient protein, minerals, and vitamins. In particular, it is wise to include in the ration some well-cured hay (legume, if possible) to furnish plenty of vitamin A. If no legume hay is fed, a calcium supplement should be supplied, and if there is any probability of a lack of phosphorus, bone meal or some other safe phosphorus supplement had better be fed.

In purebred herds young cattle are commonly fed with more liberality than in commercial beef herds. The rations which have been suggested for wintering dairy heifers and young dairy bulls are well suited for use with such cattle, except that more concentrates (chiefly farm grain) will be needed in the case of animals which are being fitted for sale or show.

In commercial beef herds the heifers must be raised as economically as possible, and therefore they must be wintered almost entirely on roughage. With good legume hay and corn or sorghum silage for roughage, little or no grain is necessary. If lower grade roughages are used, enough concentrates should be aded to keep the cattle in thrifty, growing condition at all times.

Unless at least 3 to 5 lbs. of good legume hay are fed per head daily, sufficient protein supplement should be added to balance the ration. Even with no legume roughage whatsoever, 1 lb. of cottonseed meal, linseed meal, soybean oil meal, or soybeans will supply enough protein, either for calves or yearlings. Any additional amount of concentrates that is needed may consist of corn, barley, oats or other grain. When half the roughage is legume hay, the remainder may consist of straw, corn or sorghum stover, or other rather low-grade roughage.

1121. Age to breed.—Under farm conditions beef heifers are commonly bred to calve when 24 to 36 months old.[25] When heifers calve as 2-year-olds, they must have made excellent growth prior to calving and must have plenty of feed during the next year, or they are apt to be permanently stunted in size.[26]

Under ranch conditions it is essential that sufficient size be maintained in the herd of breeding cows, and yet the cost of feeding a heifer up to the time of her first calf must be kept as low as possible. Experiments have therefore been conducted, especially by the Oregon and Kansas Stations, to study the effect of breeding various groups of heifers to calve as 2-year-olds and as 3-year-olds, respectively.[27] Some of the heifers have been fed liberally during the winter and others have received only sufficient feed for fair growth.

In the Oregon trials, which covered a period of 6 years, it was most profitable to breed the heifers to calve at 2 years of age, even when they were not fed liberally during the winter up to calving time. Calving at 2 years of age somewhat reduced the percentage of calves dropped by the same cows when 3 and 4 years old.

However, at the age of 6.5 years the cows that had produced their first calves as 2-year-olds had produced an average of 0.7 more calf for the entire period than those which first calved as 3-year-olds. For this reason, the net return from them was decidedly higher. At 4 years of age the cows which had first calved as 2-year-olds averaged about 100 lbs. less in weight than those that had their first calves a year later.

In the Kansas trials heifers raised on roughage alone were compared with others which received a limited amount of concentrates in addition. When calving at 2 years of age was combined with a winter ration of roughage alone, not only did the heifers fail to reach as large size as the others, but the average weight of their calves at weaning time for 3 consecutive years was only 348 lbs. Compared with this, the average weaning weight of the calves from heifers raised similarly, but calving as 3-year-olds, was 405 lbs.

The indications were also that a considerable percentage of the heifers which were raised on roughage alone and calved as 2-year-olds became non-breeders later. Feeding the heifers a liberal allowance of grain in winter largely prevented the ill-effects of early breeding, but this method was expensive under range conditions. It was concluded that the development of heifers without grain and breeding them to drop their first calves at 3 years of age, was the most practical method under range and semi-range conditions.

In economic studies of range beef production it has been found that when the heifers calve as 2-year-olds under ordinary systems of winter feed and care, they are apt not to have calves the following year, because they become run down in condition.[28] This may seriously reduce the percentage calf crop in the herd. Therefore the best returns are secured when breeding is delayed, unless the heifers are fed adequately.

1122. Normal growth of beef cattle.—Very few data have been published showing the weights of beef cattle of the various breeds at different ages. The following table gives the weights of females and of steers of the 3 important beef breeds in the purebred herds of the California College of Agriculture, as recorded by Guilbert and McDonald.[29] While these figures are averages for only a relatively few animals and in one herd, they will be of interest in showing the rates of growth of beef cattle.

Weights of purebred beef cattle at various ages

Females	1 Mo. Lbs.	6 Mos. Lbs.	12 Mos. Lbs.	18 Mos. Lbs.	24 Mos. Lbs.	30 Mos. Lbs.	Mature Lbs.
Aberdeen-Angus	127	414	669	861	1,018	....	1,292
Hereford	129	401	676	855	1,031	1,097	1,453
Shorthorn	124	440	703	869	1,033	1,166	1,468
Steers							
Aberdeen-Angus	122	433	...	...	....	....	....
Hereford	132	476	850	...	....	....	....
Shorthorn	131	474	819	...	....	....	....

It will be noted that at 1 month of age there was no significant difference in the weights of the heifers and the steers, but at 6 months and 12 months the steers were heavier.

III. Methods and Costs of Beef Production

1123. Fattening cattle on pasture.—Whether it will be more profitable to fatten cattle on pasture during the summer or to finish them in dry lot on harvested feeds will depend on several factors. In farming districts where much land is unsuited for tillage, the fattening of cattle on grass is common, for a maximum utilization is thus made of pasturage. On the other hand, on farms where there is but little untillable land, dry-lot fattening is more common, for more feed can be produced on an acre of tilled crops than on an acre of pasture.

In late summer and fall large numbers of cattle fat enough for slaughter come to the central markets from the western ranges and other grazing areas. This large supply of grass-fat cattle generally depresses the price for ordinary grades of fat cattle. This competition may be avoided by getting cattle that are fed grain on pasture fat enough to market before the rush of grass-fat cattle arrives.

Another plan is to fatten steers of high quality sufficiently by feeding a liberal amount of grain on pasture, so that they will sell as choice or prime fat steers. The prices for such cattle are usually good in late summer and early fall, due to a scanty supply. It is generally unwise to finish steers of medium to common grade or heifers for marketing at this time. Steers to be fattened on pasture should carry some flesh when grazing begins in the spring, or they will not be fat enough for market by the end of the pasture season.

1124. Advantages and disadvantages of pasture fattening.—Fattening cattle on pasture has certain definite advantages over dry-lot feeding: (1) Pasture gains are cheaper. This is because less grain is required per 100 lbs. gain; because pasture is a cheaper roughage than hay or silage; and because little or no protein supplement is needed. (2) Less labor is required, for the cattle need be fed only once a day, and no roughage is given. Therefore the farmer has more time for his crops. (3) Pigs following pasture-fed cattle make larger gains and the death loss is lower than in dry-lot feeding. (4) The manure is well distributed on the field, and fertility is saved. (5) No shelter is required, except that shade in the pasture is highly desirable.

These advantages are more or less offset by the following:[30] (1) A farmer has less time to care for fattening cattle in summer than in winter. (2) Feeder cattle are scarce and high in price in the spring. (3) In extremely hot weather cattle may not make good gains, on account of the heat or flies. (4) Gains may also be checked by drought. (5) When a permanent pasture is grazed, the manure does not benefit the fields in the regular crop rotation. (6) On pasture fields in the rotation, it is often difficult to provide shade and water.

1125. Quality of beef from grass-fattened cattle.—In the past many butchers and meat experts have believed that beef from grass-fattened cattle was dark in color, unattractive, difficult to sell, and inferior in quality when cooked. This opinion has tended to lower the price of such cattle on the markets. Recent investigations have shown, however, that if cattle are equally well fattened on pasture and in dry lot, there will be little or no difference in the color of the lean meat.[31]

When the pasture is growing luxuriantly and is high in carotene, there may be a tendency for the fat to be a trifle yellower than in the case of cattle fattened in dry lot. This yellowish tinge is undoubtedly due to a higher carotene content in the fat, and thus increases the vitamin value of the beef, instead of injuring it in the slightest. (**187**) Beef from cattle that are thoroughly fattened on pasture alone is of excellent quality, being well-flavored and tender. However, young cattle cannot generally be made fat enough for discriminating markets on pasture alone, without grain.

1126. Gains on pasture; amount eaten; area per head.—The gains of cattle fed no grain on pasture will vary widely, depending on the supply of forage throughout the season and on the nutritive value of the pasturage. On good pasture where there is an abundance of feed, yearlings should average 1.25 to 1.50 lbs. a day for the season and 2-year-olds 1.50 to 2.00 lbs.[32] In the Gulf States the rate of gain is usually not over 1.0 lb. per head daily. The gains are generally most rapid during the period of flush growth of pasturage in May and June and become small if the forage becomes scanty during the season.

In experiments at the Illinois Station the amount of forage eaten by steers on various pastures was estimated by an ingenious method.[33] Digestion trials were conducted with each steer to find the percentage of dry matter digested from the various pasture forages. Then the steers were pastured on each plot, a special sack being attached to a suitable harness, so that the feces voided each day could be accurately collected. The total dry matter in the forage eaten daily was estimated from the amount of dry matter in the feces.

In these tests the steers ate as much as 35 lbs. of dry matter daily per 1,000 lbs. live weight, which made over 100 lbs. of green forage daily in some instances. On 5-weeks-old bluegrass and on red clover they consumed more than twice as much forage as they needed for maintenance. Therefore they had more than half their feed available for gain in weight. On alfalfa the feed consumption was considerably less.

The area of pasture required per head for cattle fed no grain on pasture will range all the way from 2 acres or less per 1,000 lbs. live weight on fertile pasture in the humid districts, up to 7 to 10 acres or more on good grazing lands of the western ranges. When concentrates are fed to cattle on pasture, the area of pasture needed per head is considerably reduced.

1127. Pasture vs. dry-lot fattening.—The summer fattening on pasture of feeder cattle that have not previously been fed much grain has been compared with fattening in dry lot in 8 trials.[34] In each of these one lot of steers has been fed corn or corn plus supplement while another lot has been full-fed the same concentrates in dry lot.

In these trials the average rate of gain in dry lot was 2.19 lbs. per head daily and only 0.04 lb. more on pasture. The feed cost per 100 lbs. gain averaged 94 cents less for the pasture-fed steers. This was partly offset by their selling price being 15 cents lower, but their average net return per head over feed cost was $2.02 more than for the steers fattened in dry lot.

Cattle that are fairly fleshy in the spring, because they have been wintered on considerable grain in addition to good roughage, may make larger and cheaper gains if continued on full feed in the dry lot instead of being turned to pasture.[35] The fatter they are in the spring, the greater will be the advantage from finishing them in dry lot.

1128. Feeding concentrates on pasture.—When cattle are finished on pasture, no concentrates at all may be fed, a small allowance may be given during the entire pasture period, concentrates may be fed during only the last few weeks, or an unlimited allowance of grain may be given throughout the entire period. In most of the recent experiments where cattle have been fed concentrates on pasture in comparison with others fattened on grass alone it has usually paid to feed some concentrates.[36] The amount to be fed will depend on the quality of the pasture and on how rapidly it is desired to fatten the cattle.

The gains on pasture alone will commonly be cheaper than when grain is fed in addition, but the cheapness of the gains may be more than offset if the cattle do not reach a good finish, and hence sell as feeders or low-grade slaughter cattle. Cattle that are 2 years old or more become much fatter on pasture alone than those that are younger, for the latter tend to grow as well as fatten. To fatten yearlings sufficiently for the large markets, it is usually necessary to feed grain in addition to pasture, or to finish them in dry lot for a short feeding period before they are marketed.

In certain districts the pasture is so nutritious that cattle 2 years old or older can be well finished on grass alone. For example, many cattle are brought from the Texas and other southwestern ranges for fattening without grain on the bluestem pastures of the Flint Hills district of Kansas.[37] From there, they are shipped on to the large central markets.

Also, many cattle are finished for market without grain on excellent bluegrass pastures, especially in certain areas from Virginia to Tennessee and Kentucky. Some years ago the grass fattening of steers 3 years old or more was common in this district. Now, with the market demand for lighter carcasses of beef, the practice of fattening younger cattle and feeding some grain on pasture is increasing.

In the northern states the concentrate most commonly fed on pasture is corn, with perhaps a small amount of a protein supplement in addition. In the South, however, cottonseed cake or meal is often the cheapest concentrate available, and therefore an allowance of 3 to 4 lbs. per head daily is frequently fed as the only concentrate to cattle on pasture.

1129. Feeding a protein supplement with corn on grass pasture.— Due to the richness of immature grass in protein, corn and actively-growing grass make a well-balanced ration for fattening cattle, even for calves soon after weaning. The rate of gain can generally be increased slightly by feeding 1 lb. of protein supplement to each 10 or 12 lbs. of corn.[38] Whether this will increase the profit, will depend primarily on the relative prices of corn and of the protein supplement.

The benefit from the addition of a supplement will be much greater in midsummer and later, when the supply of grass is often scanty and when the protein content is lower than in spring and early summer. If the cattle are on legume pasture, or if the grass pasture contains a considerable proportion of white clover, lespedeza, or other legumes, there is no need of a protein supplement.

There is more advantage in feeding a protein supplement to cattle of high grade that will sell near the top of the market when well finished, than to low-grade animals that will not bring the best price, no matter how they are fed.

1130. Hints on fattening cattle on pasture.—Care should always be taken in changing cattle from dry lot to pasture, especially when they are in good flesh, else they may not continue to gain or may even shrink severely. As young pasture grass is laxative, if silage has been fed during the winter, the allowance should be reduced or entirely withdrawn as soon as the cattle are turned to pasture. Dry roughage which is palatable should be fed during the change, for otherwise the cattle may refuse the dry feed, preferring the grass.

When cattle are turned to pasture early in the season and there is no dry grass standing over from the preceding fall, it is wise to leave them on pasture for only a short time the first day and increase the period gradually, or severe scouring may result. If grain has been fed during the winter, it should be continued until the cattle are accustomed to grass. Supplying cattle on pasture with salt, shade, and plenty of good water should never be overlooked.

Cattle that have been fed a fairly liberal allowance of grain or other concentrates during the winter and that are fully half fat at the beginning of the pasture season, had best be finished in the dry lot.

If they are turned to pasture, they will usually make very poor and expensive gains during the first month or so.[39]

It has been mentioned in the previous chapter that cattle are sometimes turned into standing corn in the fall to harvest the crop, pigs following the cattle to get the corn not eaten by the cattle. (**1043**)

1131. Various methods of beef production.—Several efficient methods of beef production are followed in various parts of the United States. Each of these methods has advantages that make it desirable under certain local conditions.

At one extreme is the production of heavy, fat calves, or "super" or "ultra" baby beeves, which are marketed when only 7 to 9 months of age. Next comes the production of baby beeves and fat yearlings, then the fattening of yearling feeder cattle, and last the fattening of cattle 2 years old or more when placed on feed.

1132. Production of heavy, fat calves.—The production of heavy, fat calves is a recent development, brought about by the market demand for light-weight carcasses that will furnish small cuts of tender beef. These calves are often called "super" or "ultra" baby beeves, but these terms are somewhat misleading, as they imply that the carcasses of such animals are superior to baby beef. On the contrary, the beef from these calves, marketed when only 7 to 9 months old and weighing but 500 to 700 lbs., lacks the color and flavor of beef from older animals. It is lighter in color, being slightly like veal. Nevertheless, it is tender and is well liked by many consumers.

In this method, calves of good quality are fed liberally by means of a creep while they are running with their dams on pasture in the summer. Calves born in January or February may be fat enough to market directly off the cows in the fall. If the calves are born in early spring or if the season is not favorable for the best gains during the summer, it may be necessary to full-feed them in dry lot for a couple of months before they are marketed.

This method requires animals of superior beef breeding, suitable winter quarters, good pasture, and careful feed and care of the calves. It makes but relatively small use of roughage or pasturage, in comparison with the marketing of cattle when approaching 2 years old or older.

1133. Baby beef production.—Next in age at which the cattle are marketed, comes baby beef production. Under this system well-bred beef calves are so fed that they can be marketed as choice to prime fat cattle when 12 to 18 months of age and weighing 700 to 1,000 lbs. Such cattle are also classified as fat yearlings.

The carcasses from these cattle provide popular-sized cuts of beef that is tender and satisfactory in flavor, although not as high in flavor as that from older cattle.[40] If the calves are well fattened, the carcasses will have a good exterior covering of fat and the meat will show a sufficient degree of marbling. Since the lean meat is more tender than that from older animals, less marbling is needed to make the meat satisfactory in quality.

Baby beef production requires, first of all, calves of good quality that can be made into high-grade fat cattle at an early age. Common, scrub, or dairy-bred calves will not reach the desired maturity and degree of fatness at this age.

Since the natural tendency of calves is to grow, rather than fatten, calves intended for baby beef must be fed liberally on grain and other concentrates. Therefore this method is not adapted to farms where beef is produced primarily to dispose of roughage. It is best suited to corn-belt farms, where pasture is relatively expensive, and corn is cheaper in price than in other sections of the country.

Baby beef production is especially adapted to the beef producer with a good beef herd who raises his own calves. He can be sure of having thrifty calves of the proper beef type for this intensive system. If one buys feeder calves for baby beef production, he must be sure to secure animals of the proper quality.

In producing baby beef, the breeding cows are fed and cared for much the same as in the more common type of beef production, but they are often fed a little more liberally, so as to ensure a good milk flow. The cows must be maintained economically, however, or profits will be eaten up. The calves are usually dropped from the latter part of March to May.

In producing baby beef in the corn belt, the object is to fatten the calves as they grow and to retain their "calf fat." If the calves suffer from lack of feed at any time, it is much more difficult to get them well finished at the desired weight. During summer the calves run with their dams on pasture, and in addition are often fed grain or a concentrate mixture by means of a creep, at least during the latter part of the summer if pastures are short. They will then be used to grain, and will suffer no setback at weaning time.

1134. Fattening calves for baby beef.—Steer calves must usually be fattened for 200 days or longer to reach the desired finish for baby beef. (**1019**) Heifers can generally be made sufficiently fat in 160 to 170 days, and bring the best price when marketed at a weight of about 750 lbs. or less. (**1023**)

Calves that are in good condition in the fall at weaning time and are full-fed on a proper ration should be ready for market from May to August, after most of the older fat cattle from the feed lots of the corn belt and other districts have been marketed. Even though pasture is available in the spring, it is best to continue fattening the calves in dry lot, instead of turning them to pasture. (**1127**)

When western range calves are bought on the market to be fattened for baby beef, they will not usually carry as much fat as home-raised calves. However, if they are thrifty, well-bred, and of good quality, they can be fattened satisfactorily for baby beef by feeding them good rations, though they will not be ready for market at as early an age as calves fed liberally at all times.

Unless grain is unusually high in price in comparison with other feeds, calves being fattened for baby beef should be brought to a full feed of grain as soon as possible and should be fed liberally throughout the fattening period. (**1004**) When grain is extremely expensive compared with roughage, it may be most profitable to feed the calves chiefly on good roughage during the first half of the feeding period, and then finish them on a liberal allowance of grain.[41]

Calves need a larger proportion of protein in their rations than do older fattening cattle, and therefore care must be taken that the ration is properly balanced. A protein supplement should be fed, unless the calves receive a liberal amount of good alfalfa hay, or other legume hay equal in protein content, as the only roughage.

The amount of supplement required to balance any particular ration can readily be found by computing a balanced ration according to the Morrison feeding standards. (Appendix Table III.) Example rations which are suitable for fattening calves in various parts of the country are given in Appendix Table VII.

The amounts of feed consumed by calves fattened for baby beef and the gains made are shown in Chapter XXIX. (1019) It is there shown that calves require considerably less feed per 100 lbs. gain and therefore make cheaper gains than do older cattle.

1135. Finishing cattle as fat yearlings.—On farms where an important object in beef production is the utilization of roughages, the finishing of cattle somewhat later as fat yearlings offers marked advantages over the method of baby beef production. In this system the cattle are handled according to various methods, the choice depending on local conditions. Investigations by the Kansas, Missouri and Nebraska Stations show that the following methods give excellent results.[42]

Where the desire is to use the maximum amount of roughage in winter and of pasturage in summer, the calves are wintered so they will gain 1.0 lb. per head daily or slightly more. As shown previously, this will require only good roughage, such as corn or sorghum silage, with 3 to 5 lbs. of legume hay or else 1 lb. per head daily of protein supplement to balance the ration. (1118)

During the pasture season they are grazed, without grain feeding, on good pasture. In midsummer or in fall, they are put in the dry lot and full-fed on grain and good roughage for 100 days or longer, until they are fat enough to meet the market demands. Under this method the cattle are marketed in early winter, before the rush comes on the market of fat older cattle from the feed lots.

In another method steer calves of high quality are wintered similarly on roughage and then full-fed grain on pasture until fat. They should be ready for market from August to November, at the time when there is an over supply of half-fat, grass-fed cattle from the range and other grazing districts, but a shortage of well-finished fat cattle of quality.

If it seems best to have the cattle ready for market somewhat earlier, the calves should receive a limited amount of grain during the winter (3 to 5 lbs. per head daily) in addition to good roughage and also a protein supplement, if the latter is needed. They can then be finished by full-feeding grain on pasture for 75 to 150 days, the length of time depending on their condition in the spring and on the degree of fatness in demand on the market. Such cattle will come within a strict definition for baby beeves.

When the cattle are of such quality that they will grade choice to prime when finished sufficiently well, it may be best to feed them in dry lot for 4 to 6 weeks, before marketing. This will not only improve their actual condition slightly but will also better their appearance still more, for it will help to overcome the sunburned appearance of the coats of pasture-fed cattle. Since the buyers often still have a prejudice against cattle fattened on pasture, this change in appearance will usually increase the selling price.

Instead of turning the cattle on pasture in the spring, it may be advisable to full-feed them in dry lot during spring and summer, until they are ready for market. This will increase the feed cost per 100 lbs. gain, but it may improve the selling price more than enough to offset the cheaper gains. Except perhaps when the pasturage is unusually nutritious and abundant, it is not advisable to graze the cattle without grain in summer, if they have been wintered on a fair allowance of grain and good roughage. They will then usually be too fleshy in the spring to do well on grass alone.

1136. Finishing cattle as 2-year-olds or older.—Where pasturage and roughage are cheap and abundant, cattle are not usually finished for market until 2 years old or older. When cattle are to be fattened as yearlings during their second winter, they are generally fed during the first winter on roughage alone, or roughage plus 1 lb. per head daily of protein supplement or 2 to 3 lbs. of grain. (**1118**) They are then pastured without grain feeding during the summer and put into the feed lot for fattening at the close of the pasture season.

Such yearlings can be fattened sufficiently for market in 150 to 180 days, if they come off the pasture in good condition. Weighing 600 to 750 lbs. when placed on feed, they are generally fat at weights of 1,000 to 1,100 lbs. when about two years old, and meet the market demand for well-finished light-weight fat cattle.

In another method cattle are carried through their second winter chiefly on roughage, and either fattened on grass the second summer, with or without grain feeding, or else fattened in dry lot. Kentucky experiments have shown that it is better to feed grain on grass than to use the same amount of grain in carrying the cattle through the previous winter, and then pasture them during the summer without grain feeding.[43]

Still other cattle are put into the feed lot as 2-year-old feeders in the fall and fattened for sale the following spring when approaching 3 years of age. The results that can be expected from fattening yearlings or 2-year-olds, in comparison with calves, are shown in the discussion on this subject in Chapter XXIX. (**1019**) In a few sections cattle are still carried through 3 winters before they are fattened. However, such cattle are too heavy when fat to meet present-day demands, and therefore they have practically disappeared from the large central markets.

1137. Beef cattle production on western ranges.—About three-fourths of the beef breeding cattle in the United States are in the western states and in the great plains district from North Dakota to Texas. Here they are mostly kept under range conditions.

The methods used in range beef-cattle production differ considerably in various districts.[44] In some range sections, as in parts of Texas, the grazing land is privately owned and generally fenced. On the other hand, in the mountainous districts of the West much of the grazing is in the National Forests and on the public lands.

In the early days of the western ranges little effort was made to provide harvested feed to carry cattle through the winter. Therefore the losses of stock by starvation were sometimes appalling in winters with heavy snowfall. Now most western ranchmen have some land on which hay or other crops are raised for winter feed. In the mountain districts the cattle are commonly wintered on range land at lower elevations adjacent to the ranch headquarters. The feeding of harvested feeds is delayed as long as possible in the autumn or winter, so the cattle will get as much of their living as they can from the winter range.

Spring calving is general in range herds, the date depending on the system of management and the climate. Occasionally sheds are provided for shelter and the cows are bred for early spring calving, so the calves will be heavier in the fall.

In the typical range areas of the West the cattle graze in spring on the lower foothills, and then as the season advances they go to the more elevated and more rugged areas. By the end of June they are usually on this summer range, where the forage remains green and palatable until late in the season. Then in the fall they are brought back to the spring range.

The cattle are looked after by experienced riders or herders who see that they are kept on good grazing areas, and away from areas infested with poisonous plants. These men also provide salt at proper salting grounds and prevent the cattle from straying. The various ranchmen grazing cattle in a given district usually coöperate in the spring and fall round-ups.

In the spring round-up the cattle belonging to each ranch are identified by means of the brand and are counted. The calves are branded and castrated, and also the breeding cattle are sometimes separated from the steers and yearling heifers. In the fall round-up, which takes place in September or October, the cattle to be sold are sorted out, and any calves are branded that have been dropped since the spring round-up.

Generally the percentage calf crop is considerably smaller in range herds than under farm conditions. In the northern range districts the number of calves weaned per 100 cows bred usually does not average more than 65, and in the semi-desert range areas of the Southwest the number is even less. The calf crop is often seriously lessened by a lack of suitable feed for the cows in winter, by an inadequate supply of bulls or poor condition of the bulls, and by permitting heifers that have not been well fed to be bred to calve when only 2 years old.

1138. Fattening range cows.—The purchase and fattening for the market of range cows which have been discarded on account of age or for other reasons, is a hazardous undertaking. Experiments have shown that the gains made by such cows are generally very expensive.[45] Also, many prove to be so far advanced in pregnancy that they must be kept over and fattened for market after they have raised calves. In addition, there is danger of introducing infectious abortion or other diseases unless such cows are carefully isolated from other breeding cattle.

1139. Cost of keeping beef cows and of beef calves up to weaning.—The following table shows the approximate amounts of feed and labor required in keeping a beef cow a year on corn-belt farms, and the costs with feeds and labor at the prices indicated, as determined in cost studies by the United States Department of Agriculture.[46] These data represent averages for 11,261 beef cows handled according to the usual methods, 4,572 beef cows kept for baby-beef production, and 1,541 cows that were partially milked, the calves taking the rest of the milk.

Cost of keeping beef cows and raising beef calves on corn-belt farms

	Beef cows	Beef cows for baby beef	Cows partially milked
Feed per year			
Pasture, days	194	197	200
Hay, lbs.	1,900	1,940	1,940
Silage, lbs.	700	740	600
Straw, lbs.	660	500	580
Corn, bu.	1.2	2.5	4.8
Corn stalks, acres	1.4	2.0	1.8
Labor per year			
Man hours	15.3	16.7	47.2
Horse hours	10.4	9.6	9.8
Feed cost per year*	$23.78	$24.78	$25.61
Labor cost per year*	$ 4.10	$ 4.30	$10.42
Other expenses per year	$ 6.97	$ 7.27	$ 7.38
Total gross cost per cow	$34.85	$36.35	$43.41
Credit for manure	$ 4.00	$ 4.00	$ .4.50
Credit for milk*	....	....	$17.67
Net cost per cow	$30.85	$32.35	$21.24
Calves raised per 100 cows	85	86	87
Cow cost per calf	$36.37	$37.63	$24.28
Bull cost per calf	$ 2.36	$ 2.45	$ 3.47
Cost per calf at weaning	$38.73	$40.07	$27.75

*Prices as follows: Pasture, $1.50 per cow a month; hay, $10.00 per ton; silage $4.00 per ton, straw or fodder $2.00 per ton; corn stalks, $1.00 per acre; corn, $0.50 per bushel; protein supplement, $35.00 per ton; man labor, $ .20 per hour; horse labor, $ .10 per hour; manure credited at $1.00 per load.

It will be noted that these cows were maintained almost entirely on pasture and roughage, the beef cows receiving only 1.2 bushels of corn a year and the cows that were partially milked only 4.8 bushels. (Any protein supplement fed is reduced to the corn equivalent.) The labor required per year was only 15.3 hours of man labor and 10.4 hours of horse labor for the cows kept for ordinary beef production.

The total yearly gross costs per cow at the prices indicated for feeds and labor were $34.85 for the cows kept for ordinary beef production, $36.35 for the cows kept for raising baby beeves, and $43.41 for the cows partially milked. Deducting a credit for the manure at $1.00 per load and also for the milk secured from the partially-milked cows, the net costs were $30.85, $32.35, and $21.24, respectively.

A calving percentage of 80 per cent is excellent in farm herds, and the percentage is much lower on the western ranges. By calving percentage is meant the number of calves raised to weaning age per 100 cows. In these herds the calving percentage was 85 or over for all groups.

The "cow cost per calf" is found by dividing the "net cost per cow" by the percentage of calves raised. To this must be added the "bull cost per calf" to secure the cost per calf at weaning time. Under the conditions in this survey, this cost per calf was $38.73 for the beef calves, $40.07 for the calves being raised for baby beef, and $27.75 for the calves from the cows partially milked.

By good management the cost of producing calves for baby beef can be brought even below the costs in this study. Cost records were kept for 3 years on an Iowa farm where a herd of 75 to 90 Hereford cows was used for the production of calves to be fattened for baby beef.[47] The cows were fed no grain and were wintered as largely as possible on meadow aftermath and stalk fields, with what hay and silage was necessary.

In summer the cows and calves were grazed on bluegrass pasture without additional feed, except that 20 lbs. of silage per head daily were fed one summer when the pasture had been parched by drought. No grain was fed the calves until July or August, when they were started on a mixture of equal parts shelled corn and whole oats. After they were accustomed to grain, they were fed according to appetite, and consumed about 3.25 lbs. a head daily up to weaning time.

On this farm the calf crop ranged from 84 to 90 per cent and the average weight of the calves at weaning time was 413 lbs. The average cost per calf at weaning age under pre-war conditions was $30.40, including the grain eaten by the calves and all the costs of keeping the cows. It was found that each year the cost of raising the calves was less than calves of similar quality could have been bought for on the market, the saving averaging $5.08 a head during the 3 years.

The costs of producing beef calves will vary widely in different sections of the country. However, these data are helpful in showing the approximate feed and labor requirements under conditions similar to the corn belt, and the costs with feed and labor at the prices indicated.

1140. Reducing the cost of producing beef calves.—Even under the same general conditions there is often a great difference in the cost of keeping beef cows on individual farms. In a study of methods of wintering beef cows on corn-belt farms by the United States Department of Agriculture, it was found that on some farms the cost was twice as high as on others.[48] This was due largely to a failure to use cheap roughages in wintering the cows. Many farmers were overfeeding their cows and hence wasting feed, without securing any better calves. One of the greatest wastes was found to be the feeding of unhusked corn fodder, in place of husking out the corn for other stock and feeding the cows the stover, after cutting or shredding it.

Another important factor in reducing the cost of producing calves is to build up, by selection, a herd of cows which are all regular breeders and satisfactory mothers, producing good yields of milk.

The possibilities in keeping beef cows at low cost on corn-belt farms are well shown in a recent Illinois test.[49] The cows were maintained principally on pasture for 9 months of the year, being on meadow aftermath and corn stalk fields half of this time. During the 3 months of dry-lot feeding the cows were fed clover hay and oat straw, with but 2.5 bushels of grain. With prices at 1933 levels, the feed cost for the year was only $16.80 per head, while the value of the calves was $22.41 per cow.

1141. Cost of producing yearling stockers or baby beeves.—In the studies conducted on corn-belt farms by the United States Department of Agriculture the costs were also determined for carrying beef calves from weaning time through the winter and of fattening calves for baby beef. The following table presents the averages for 7,236 beef calves, 4,009 baby beeves, and 1,015 calves from cows partially milked. The calves fattened as baby beeves averaged 14 to 15 months of age and 825 lbs. in weight when marketed.

Cost of producing yearling stockers or baby beeves on corn-belt farms

	Beef calves carried through winter	Beef calves fattened for baby beef	Calves from cows partially milked
Feed per head			
Hay, lbs.	1,218	1,150	1,080
Silage, lbs.	266	658	218
Straw, lbs.	110	40	114
Fodder, lbs.	159	...	204
Corn, bu.	8.6	41.0	6.1
Protein supplement, lbs.	7	141	12
Corn stalks, acres	0.1	0.03	0.1
Pasture, days	9.0	48.0	10.0
Labor per head			
Man labor, hours	8.6	12.2	12.5
Horse labor, hours	6.8	9.1	4.7
Feed cost per head*	$11.86	$32.51	$10.01
Labor cost per head*	$ 2.40	$ 3.35	$ 2.97
Other expenses per head	$ 2.52	$ 5.13	$ 2.11
Total gross expense	$16.78	$40.99	$15.09
Credit for manure*	$ 1.50	$ 1.50	$ 1.00
Credit for pork	....	$ 2.85	....
Net expense per head	$15.28	$36.64	$14.09
Cost at weaning time	$38.73	$40.07	$27.75
Total production cost	$54.01	$76.71	$41.84

*Prices the same as in preceding table.

With prices for feeds and labor the same as in the preceding table, the net expense of wintering the beef calves was $15.28 per head, after allowing credit for the manure, and $14.09 for the calves from the partially-milked cows. The net expense for fattening the baby beeves was $36.64 per head, after allowing credit for the manure and also for the pork produced by pigs following the calves.

This brought the total production cost of the stocker yearlings to $54.01 a head for those from the cows that were not milked and to $41.84 for the yearlings from the cows that were partially milked. The total production cost per head for the 825-pound fat baby beeves was $76.71 per head.

1142. Cost of fattening cattle.—The cost of fattening cattle will vary widely in different sections of the country and at various times. The chief items of cost are the initial cost of the feeder cattle and the cost of the feed. Other expenses which must be charged against the feeding operations are man and horse labor, building and equipment charges, interest, mortality risk, any veterinary services, insurance, taxes, marketing costs, and incidental expenses.

The cost of the feed will generally form 80 per cent or more of the operating expenses, not including the initial cost of the cattle or the expenses of marketing them. Thus, in studies by the United States Department of Agriculture on corn-belt farms from 1918 to 1923, the cost of feed formed 84 per cent of the operating expenses; interest, 6 per cent; labor (man and horse), 5.5 per cent; and taxes, building and equipment cost, mortality risk, and miscellaneous expenses, 4.5 per cent.[50]

In similar studies on Illinois farms from 1913 to 1923, feed formed 85.5 per cent of the operating expenses; interest, 4.0 per cent; man labor, 4.1 per cent; horse labor, 1.8 per cent; mortality risk, 0.7 per cent; and miscellaneous expenses, 3.9 per cent.[51]

It is commonly assumed that when cattle are full-fed on corn, the by-products of the fattening operations (the manure secured and the pork produced by the pigs following the steers) will usually pay for all costs other than the initial costs of the cattle and the cost of the feed. Except when pork is unusually cheap, these credits will certainly cover all these costs, except the expense of marketing the steers. Sometimes the manure and pork credits will even cover the marketing expenses as well.

For example, in studies on Illinois farms from 1913-1922, the average credit per steer for manure was $5.87 with manure at 75 cents per ton, and the average credit for pork $6.30 per steer.[51] The total credit of $12.17 per steer more than offset the expenses other than feed, totalling $10.53. These expenses included $2.17 per steer for man labor, $0.94 for horse labor, $2.12 for interest, $0.43 for buildings and equipment, $0.35 for mortality loss, $1.65 for taxes and miscellaneous expenses, and $2.87 for marketing expenses. In other Illinois cost studies from 1919 to 1923 the manure and pork credits per steer amounted to $12.69 per steer and just about covered all expenses except the initial cost of the cattle, the cost of feed, and the marketing expenses.[52]

It must be borne in mind that when cattle are fattened in winter on a general farm, most of the man and horse labor comes at a time of the year when it might not otherwise be utilized. Therefore much of it does not represent any real additional expense.

The probable cost of fattening cattle on various rations may be estimated approximately from the data in the previous chapters, showing the feed required for 100 lbs. gain under various conditions. It should be borne in mind that most of the trials reviewed were carried on with cattle of good quality, given first-class feed under expert supervision. Under farm conditions, slightly more feed will often be required for 100 lbs. gain than was needed in these trials.

In an extensive survey of the fattening of beef cattle on corn in Indiana, Illinois, Iowa, Nebraska, and Missouri (including data on 34,934 cattle), the United States Department of Agriculture found that on the average the cattle weighed 786 lbs. when placed on feed, were fed for 174 days, and made daily gains of 1.63 lbs. and an average total gain of 284 lbs. during the feeding period.[53] For each 100 lbs. gain there were required 680 lbs. grain (chiefly corn), 62 lbs. commercial concentrates (chiefly linseed and cottonseed meal), 391 lbs. hay and other dry roughage, 863 lbs. silage, and 20 days of pasturage.

It was found in these studies that in making each 100 lbs. gain there were required 4.5 hours man labor and 3.0 hours horse labor in the feeding operations.[54] When the equipment is arranged conveniently, the labor can be reduced even below these amounts.

IV. Counsel in the Feed Lot

1143. Cattle fattening requires business judgment.—Even more than in other types of livestock farming, the commercial fattening of cattle requires sound business judgment, or the venture is apt to result in loss. This is because the fattening of purchased feeder cattle is a much more speculative enterprise than most ventures in animal husbandry. To secure good profits it is therefore especially necessary that the several factors which make for success be kept clearly in mind.

Before purchasing feeder cattle one should estimate the quantity of feeds on hand and determine how many and what class of cattle he had best buy to consume the feed. From a study of market reports he can estimate how much his feeders will cost, including the cost of getting them to his feed lot. Then he can figure out approximately how much the gains will cost him, by using the data in the preceding chapters, in which are shown the actual results on typical rations. He can then estimate the necessary selling price he must secure to break even, taking into consideration the marketing costs. If the outlook for a profit does not seem reasonably good, it is usually best not to buy just at that time.

The kind of feeder cattle should always be chosen which seem to offer the best opportunity for profit. The summaries presented in Chapter XXIX show the results that can be expected from various grades of feeders and from calves, yearlings, and 2-year-olds. It is an old adage among stockmen that "cattle bought right are more than half sold." A man may be a skillful feeder and lose money year after year because of poor judgment in buying. The beginner should hire an experienced cattleman to purchase animals that will best suit his needs, or deal with a reliable commission firm that is acquainted with his conditions. If choice feeders are commanding a high premium in the market over commoner animals, and it does not seem probable that the premium will be correspondingly large for the cattle of better quality when they are fattened, the commoner grade had better be purchased. (**1014-1015**)

By following the various market reports for preceding years, one can tell approximately when his cattle can be marketed to greatest advantage. They should then be fed so as to be finished at that time. It has been emphasized in Chapter XXIX that the cattle should be fattened only enough to return the greatest profit under the particular market conditions. (**1021**) It is much more important to have a good net return than it is to "top the market."

When the cattle are ready for market, it is usually not advisable to hold them for better prices, unless they continue to make gains at a reasonable cost. The extra feed consumed by finished cattle will soon more than offset any ordinary increase in price that may be obtained. When the cattle are almost finished, the owner should watch the market reports and find out from his commission firm what they consider the best date for shipment.

1144. Rations for fattening cattle.—The numerous trials reviewed in the preceding chapters show forcefully that much greater profits are secured when fattening cattle are fed properly-balanced rations.

Whenever there is any question as to whether a ration is balanced, it will take but a short time to compute the approximate amounts of dry matter, digestible protein, and total digestible nutrients it contains and see how closely the ration meets the recommendations of modern feeding standards (Appendix Table III). The time it takes to work out suitable and economical balanced rations is commonly the most profitably spent of all the year. Example rations suited to various conditions are given in Appendix Table VII.

To determine which of the several available feeds are actually the most economical, one should refer to the summaries in Chapter XXX which give definite information concerning the relative value for beef cattle of the most important feeds. The usefulness and value of the other feeds of lesser general importance are discussed in the chapters of Part II.

1145. Equipment for feeding cattle.—Some cattle feeders do not realize that proper equipment is an important factor in securing profits from the fattening of cattle. The character of shelter required for fattening cattle under various climatic conditions has been discussed in Chapter XXIX. (**1028**) Where the soil and climate are such that the feed lots often become a sea of mud in winter or early spring, paving them with concrete is an economy. Not only do the steers make larger and more economical gains, but also much loss of manure is prevented. (**1030**)

Cattle of the same age, or at least those of equal size and strength, should be fed in the same lot. From 2.5 to 3 feet of feed racks or bunks should be provided per steer, so there will not be undue crowding at meal time. Some feeders use combination feed racks for grain and roughage, while others prefer a separate rack for hay and a bunk or flat manger for silage and grain. Feed racks and bunks should always be cleaned after each feeding. Salt and fresh water should always be provided beef cattle. (**998, 1003**)

1146. Getting cattle on feed.—Cattle that are not accustomed to grain or other concentrates must be started on feed gradually, or serious digestive trouble may result. When feeder cattle are first brought to the feed lot, it is best to restrict the amount of hay or other roughage slightly for a day or so, until they have recovered from the effects of their trip.

They should then be started on grain. A safe plan is to feed not more than 1 lb. of grain per head at the first feed, or 2 lbs. for the day. The allowance may be gradually increased at the rate of 1 lb. per head daily or less, care being taken not to increase the amount unless the cattle are eager for each feed and clean up the grain properly. When they are approaching a full feed, the increases should be much more gradual, probably not over 1 lb. per head every third day.

When cottonseed meal or linseed meal is to be fed to balance the ration, it is best to feed no more than one-quarter to one-half pound per head daily at first and then gradually increase the amount at the rate of one-quarter pound per head daily until the full amount needed to balance the ration is supplied.

1147. Frequency and order of feeding.—Most cattlemen feed concentrates and roughage twice a day to fattening cattle not on pasture.

Often cattle being fitted for shows are fed grain more frequently, so as to induce them to consume a larger amount.

The feeding should always be at the same time each day. The cattle should not be disturbed until after daylight, and they should have time to clean up the evening feed before dark. Usually the concentrates are fed first and then the silage is put in the feed bunk, if this excellent feed is being used. Hay or other dry roughage is fed in suitable racks, also twice daily as a rule. However, if two kinds of roughage are fed, sometimes one is fed in the morning and the other at the evening feed. In this case, the less-palatable roughage should be fed in the morning. So that each animal can get its share of protein supplement, such as linseed meal or cottonseed meal, it should be mixed with the grain or else distributed over the silage.

Commonly, when cattle are given grain or other concentrates on pasture, they are fed but once a day. This is largely as a matter of convenience, for they may be grazing on a pasture at some distance from the farmstead.

Though it is the usual practice to feed fattening cattle twice a day, in 2 Wisconsin tests steers fed both grain and roughage only once a day (at 8:00 A.M.) made as rapid gains as those fed twice a day and returned practically as much profit.[55]

1148. The eye of the master fattens his cattle.—There is so much truth in the old adage, "The eye of the master fattens his cattle," that every stockman should bear its significance in mind. In all phases of animal husbandry the discernment of a good stockman is essential for success, and in no phase is it of more importance than in the fattening of cattle for market.

Being versed in the science of stock feeding is not enough. For the greatest profits not only must one feed his stock economical and well-balanced rations, but also he must have the watchful eye and good judgment of a true stockman. The best results are secured only when the cattle are fed at regular hours, and when the attendant is quiet and kind at all times, so that the animals trust rather than fear him.

Experience counts for much in stock feeding. Many an experienced stockman can carry steers through the fattening period without getting them once "off feed," but yet cannot well describe to others just why he is so successful. In general, when steers are to be full-fed on grain, they should be supplied all they will readily consume at each feeding, after they have been gradually brought onto feed. Any feed left in the feed bunk or manger should be cleaned out before the next feeding, for it will not usually be eaten by the cattle afterwards, but will spoil and contaminate the fresh feed put in later.

Scouring, the bane of the stock feeder, should be carefully avoided, since in a single day it may cut off a week's gain. This trouble is generally brought on by overfeeding, by unwholesome food, or by a faulty ration. Overfeeding comes from a desire of the attendant to push his cattle to better gains, or from carelessness and irregularity in measuring out the feed supply.

The droppings of the steers are an excellent index of the progress of fattening. While they should never be hard, they should still be thick enough to "pile up" and have that unctuous appearance which indicates a thrifty condition. There is an odor from the droppings of thrifty, well-fed steers known and quickly recognized by every good feeder. Thin droppings and those with a sour smell indicate something is wrong in the feed yard.

1149. Pigs following steers.—Whenever cattle are fed ear corn, shelled corn, or corn silage, pigs should be kept with them to utilize the unmasticated and undigested corn in the droppings. The margin in cattle feeding is frequently so narrow that the gains made by the pigs return the only profit. It is therefore essential that pigs be provided to follow the cattle, except when they are fattened on a ration from which the pigs would not secure much waste feed, such as a ration of hay and ground grain, without corn silage, or a ration of cottonseed meal and cottonseed hulls.

The number of pigs per steer varies with the kind of feed and the age of the cattle being fed. Enough should be provided to utilize the waste feed fully. The younger the steers, the better they masticate their feed and the smaller are the gains made by the pigs following.

For cattle full-fed on the common corn-belt ration of shelled corn, corn silage, legume hay, and a small amount of protein supplement, 1 pig will be needed for approximately 1 to 2 steers in the case of 2-year-olds, 1 pig to 2 steers with yearlings, and 1 pig to 3 steers with calves. When ear corn or snapped corn is fed, the wastage of corn by the steers is considerably greater, and twice as many pigs may be required as with shelled corn. In the case of ground corn or corn-and-cob meal, only one-half to one-third as many pigs are needed as with shelled corn.

The best pigs for following cattle weigh from 50 to 150 lbs., and when they become fat they should be replaced. Any extra grain given the pigs to ensure their making satisfactory gains should be fed in nearby separate pens before the cattle are fed, so that the pigs will not crowd around the feed troughs or under the wagon and team while the cattle are being fed. It pays to feed pigs following steers 0.2 to 0.3 lb. per head daily of tankage, or an equivalent amount of other protein-rich feeds, to balance the ration.[56]

In experiments at the Iowa Station the approximate amount of feed recovered by pigs from the droppings of steers full-fed on shelled corn was estimated by feeding similar pigs separately.[57] On studying the data secured from 53 separate lots of experimental cattle, it was found that the average pig, following 1.9 steers, picked up the equivalent of 312 lbs. of corn during the average feeding period of 120 days. On the average, 4.7 per cent of the cost of the feed given to the steers was saved by the pigs.

1150. Shrinkage; preparation for market.—Unless cattle are shipped under proper conditions, the shrinkage between their weights at home and the selling weights on the market may be so large that it will eat up no small part of the profits. The shrinkage between the loading weights and the sale weights at the stockyards of either range cattle or fat cattle in transit 36 hours or less is usually about 3 to 5 per cent; when in transit 70 hours or over the shrinkage is 5 to 6 per cent of their live weight.[58] In addition there will be a slight shrinkage in weight from the feed lot to the loading station.

Silage-fed cattle show a larger gross shrinkage but usually fill so well at market that the net shrinkage is even lower than with cattle fed no silage. Pulp-fed cattle shrink more than any other class.

Well-fattened cattle shrink a smaller percentage of their live weight than those that are not so fat. For example, the percentage shrink of feeder cattle is higher than for the same animals shipped the same distance after fattening.

Calves that are well-fattened have no higher percentage shrinkage than older fat animals. In 10 comparisons steer calves shrank 3.2 per cent on the average; yearling steers, 3.5 per cent; and 2-year-olds, 3.6 per cent.[59]

The shrinkage can be reduced to a minimum by the proper handling of cattle before shipment and by care in loading. The cattle should be handled quietly and should never be driven faster than a slow walk. If they are hurried, they will begin to scour and will shrink unduly. The car should be cleaned, if necessary, and should always be well bedded, so the cattle will have a firm footing. If different kinds of livestock are put in the same car, they should be separated securely.

Formerly, it was generally advised that feeds of a laxative nature, such as silage or excellent-quality alfalfa hay, should be greatly reduced in amount 48 hours before shipment, and that only half as much grain as usual should be fed during the last day. Many still prefer to feed chiefly grass hay and oats during the last day or so.

In spite of these beliefs, probably there is little or no real advantage in decided changes in the ration before shipment. If cattle have been receiving a full feed of silage, legume hay, and grain, they will lose weight when changed to grass hay and a reduced grain allowance. This may result in a smaller shrinkage per head between the weights at the loading point and at the market. However, this may merely be the result of a shrinkage that took place prior to shipment, due to the great change in the ration.

If very laxative feeds have been used during fattening, such as pea-green alfalfa hay, it is wise to reduce the amount the day before shipment. Also, the amount of the various feeds supplied at the last feeding should be reduced, since cattle travel better when not too full.

It is a mistake to withold salt from the cattle for a few days, and then salt them liberally just before shipment, so that they will take on a large fill of water at the stockyards. If this is done, the cattle will generally scour in transit, shrink heavily, and arrive in poor shape. Buyers both of fat cattle and of feeder cattle can easily recognize animals which have taken on an abnormal fill, and they will discriminate against them by offering a lower price per hundredweight.

When cattle reach the market just before being sold, the fill is small, but when they arrive about daylight of the sale day, or the afternoon of the day before, they generally take a good fill.

V. Veal Production

1151. Veal production.—Only dairy calves are commonly fattened for veal. For producing the highest grade of veal whole milk is the only feed generally used, for otherwise the desired light-colored flesh and white fat may not be produced. Furthermore, growth must be pushed as rapidly as possible by liberal milk feeding and the calves must be marketed before the carcass takes on the appearance of beef. Calves being fattened for veal should be confined in stalls that are not too roomy, so they will not exercise too much.

1152. Milk consumption and gains of veal calves.—In Pennsylvania tests some years ago calves fed whole milk alone for an average of 53 days after birth gained 1.85 lbs. per head daily, required 9.4 lbs. of milk for each pound of gain in weight, and sold for 9.7 cents per pound, live weight.[60] Calves fed on milk substitutes gained only 0.93 lb. per head daily and brought but 5.6 cents a pound, live weight. Feeding only a small amount of milk substitutes in place of milk injured the color of the carcass.

Holstein calves fed whole milk for an average of 52 days in a recent Wisconsin trial gained 2.05 lbs. a day on the average, averaged 203 lbs. in live weight, required 10.6 lbs. of milk per pound gain, and sold for an average of $11.54 per 100 lbs. on the Milwaukee market.[61] In comparison with marketing the calves at 10 days of age, without fattening, each 100 lbs. of whole milk fed brought a return of $1.61, without making a deduction for the labor in feeding the calves. Calves weighing less than about 145 lbs. or more than about 215 lbs. brought a somewhat lower price per hundredweight than those within these live weights.

Records kept on 122 calves fed for veal on Ohio farms from 1926 to 1928 showed that the calves, which were fed for an average of 50 days, consumed a total per head of 130 gallons of whole milk and 10 gallons of skimmilk.[62] One farmer fed a small amount of meal in addition to milk. Most of the calves nursed cows, only 20 per cent being bucket-fed. Charging whole milk at 10 cents per gallon when the calf nursed and at 12 cents per gallon when hand-fed, the average feed cost per calf was $13.79. The calves averaged 185 lbs. in weight when marketed and brought $25.65, leaving a net return above feed cost of $11.86.

Where the market does not pay a premium for veal calves raised exclusively on milk, they can be fed a limited amount of milk supplemented with grain, or the whole milk can be gradually replaced with grain, as in raising calves for the dairy herd. With the latter method, considerable skill is necessary to feed the calves so they will gain rapidly and fatten, without going off feed.

QUESTIONS

1. Describe the usual methods of feeding beef breeding cows throughout the year when they are kept solely for beef production.
2. State a satisfactory ration for wintering beef cows in the corn belt.
3. Compare the usefulness of stover silage for wintering beef cows and for fattening cattle.
4. State a satisfactory ration for wintering beef cows chiefly on straw.
5. About how much hay does it require to carry a beef cow through the winter?
6. How does the feeding of dual-purpose cows differ from that of cows kept solely for raising calves for beef?
7. What are the most important points in the feed and care of the beef bull?
8. What are the advantages of having beef calves born in the spring?
9. Under what conditions is it profitable to creep-feed suckling calves?
10. Discuss the feeding of beef calves being carried over the winter, stating the amount of gain that should be made under various conditions.
11. What sort of rations should be used for wintering yearlings and older stocker cattle?
12. Discuss the raising of beef heifers, including the age at which they should drop their first calves.
13. State 5 advantages and 6 disadvantages of the fattening of cattle on pasture.
14. Discuss: (a) The quality of beef from pasture-fattened cattle; (b) the gains made by cattle on pasture; (c) the results secured in tests of pasture vs. dry-lot fattening.
15. Is it usually profitable to feed concentrates to cattle being fattened on pasture?
16. Discuss the feeding of a protein supplement with corn to cattle being fattened on grass pasture.

17. Describe the following methods of beef production: (a) Production of heavy, fat calves; (b) production of baby beef; (c) production of fat yearlings; (d) fattening cattle 2 years old or older; (e) fattening old range cows.
18. Describe a method of feeding and management common on the western ranges.
19. Discuss briefly the cost of keeping beef cows and producing beef calves up to weaning.
20. How may the cost of producing beef calves be decreased?
21. Discuss the cost of producing yearling stockers and of producing baby beeves.
22. Summarize the information on the costs and the credits in fattening cattle.
23. Why is good business judgment especially necessary in the fattening of purchased feeder cattle?
24. What equipment is necessary for fattening cattle?
25. Describe the method of getting fattening cattle on feed.
26. Discuss the frequency and order of feeding for fattening cattle.
27. Summarize the chief facts concerning the use of pigs to follow fattening cattle.
28. About how much do cattle shrink that are 36 hours or less in transit to market? How can shrinkage be reduced to a minimum?
29. Discuss the production of veal.

REFERENCES

1. Mumford, Ill. Bul. 111; McCampbell, Fort Hays Branch, Kan. Sta., Annual Cattlemen's Round-up, 1920; Sheets and Tuckwiller, West Va. Bul. 190, U. S. Dept. Agr. Bul. 1024.
2. Tomhave and Severson, Penn. Buls. 138, 150, 170.
3. Rusk, Ill. Sta., information to the author.
4. McCampbell, Fort Hays Branch, Kans. Sta., Annual Cattlemen's Round-up, 1922, 1924; Gerlaugh, Ohio Spec. Cir. 10.
5. McCampbell et al., Fort Hays Branch, Kan. Sta., Annual Cattlemen's Round-up, 1921; Templeton, Miss. Rpt. 1928; Gerlaugh, Ohio Spec. Cir. 10; Kyzer and Clyburn, S. C. Rpt. 1931.
6. Sheets and Tuckwiller, West Va. Bul. 190, U. S. Dept. Agr. Bul. 1024.
7. Rusk, Hoard's Dairyman, 57, 1919, pp. 1106-1107; Rusk, Ill. Rpts. 1926, 1927; Hamilton and Rusk, Ill. Bul. 291.
8. Bohstedt, Ohio Sta., information to the author.
9. Arnett, Baker, and Vinke, Mont. Bul. 187; Arnett and McChord, Mont. Bul. 211; Vinke and Dickson, Mont. Bul. 275; Ore. Rpt. 1928-1930.
10. Vinke and Dickson, Mont. Bul. 275; Hulme, Utah Bul. 237.
11. Vinke and Dickson, Mont. Bul. 275.
12. Lantow and Snell, New Mex. Bul. 144; Lantow, New Mex. Bul. 202.
13. Jacob, Tenn. Rpts. 1931, 1932.
14. Hunt, Penn. Rpt. 1891.
15. Martiny, Die Milch, 2, 1871, pp. 9-15.
16. Linfield, Utah Bul. 57.
17. Beach, Conn. (Storrs) Rpt. 1904.
18. Osland and Morton, Colo. Press Bul. 87; Bray, La. Bul. 249; J. M. Jones and J. H. Jones, Tex. Bul. 470; Black and Trowbridge, U. S. Dept. Agr. Tech. Bul. 208; Black, McComas and Wilson, U. S. Dept. Agr., mimeo. rpt. and West Va. Bul. 263; Powell, Amer. Soc. Anim. Prod., Proc. 1934; see also: Means, Miss. Rpt. 1932; Hawkins, Okla., Rpt. 1932-34.
19. Black and Trowbridge, U. S. Dept. Agr. Tech. Bul. 208; Trowbridge et al., Mo. Buls. 244, 256, 272, 285.
20. Black and Trowbridge, U. S. Dept. Agr. Tech. Bul. 397.
21. Morton, Colo. Rpt. 1934; Rusk and Snapp, Ill. Rpt. 1930; Cochel, Kan. Sta., Amer. Soc. Anim. Prod., Proc. 1915-16; McCampbell, Kan. Sta., Amer. Soc. Anim. Prod., Proc. 1922; Anderson, McCampbell, and Alexander, Kan. Cirs. 151, 152; McCampbell, Weber, and Connell, Kan. Sta., mimeo. rpts.; McCampbell et al., Fort Hays Branch, Kan. Sta., Annual Cattlemen's Round-up, 1932, 1933; Trowbridge and Moffett, Mo. Buls. 285, 300; Templeton, Miss. Bul. 268; Arnett, McChord, and Tretsven, Mont. Bul. 176; Arnett, Baker, and Vinke, Mont. Bul. 188; Snyder, Nebr. Buls. 105, 117; Gramlich, Thalman, et al., Nebr. Rpts. 1927, 1929, 1932, 1934, and mimeo. rpts.; Blizzard, Okla. Sta., mimeo. rpt.; Potter and Withycombe, Ore. Bul. 182; Maynard and Hulme, Utah Bul. 250; Hultz, Wyo. Bul. 134, Wyo. Rpts. 1928, 1929; Sheets and Tuckwiller, U. S. Dept. Agr. Buls. 1042, 1431, West Va. Bul. 186; Black, U. S. Dept. Agr. Cir. 408.
22. McCampbell et al., Fort Hays Branch, Kan. Sta., Annual Cattlemen's Round-up, 1932; Nebr. Rpts. 1932, 1934.
23. Lantow, New. Mex. Buls. 161, 185.
24. Grimes, Ala. Bul. 231; Grimes, Sewell, and Cottier, Ala. Cir. 71; Shealy, Fla. Rpts. 1929, 1930; McCampbell and Winchester, Kan. Cir. 92; McCampbell, Winchester, and Marston, Kan. Cir. 97; McCampbell, et al., Fort Hays Branch, Kan. Sta., Annual Cattlemen's Round-up, 1922, 1923, 1925, 1926, 1927, 1928, 1929, 1930, 1931, 1932, 1934; Good, Ky. Bul. 267, Ky. Cir. 75; Good and Harris, Ky.

Rpts. 1927, 1928, 1929; Waters, Mo. Bul. 75; Curtis, Farley, and Peden, N. C. Bul. 243 and U. S. Dept. Agr. Bul. 954; S. C. Rpt. 1923; Willson, Tenn. Bul. 125; Hunt, Va. Bul. 215; Nobles, Va. Rpt. 1919-1927; Sheets and Tuckwiller, West Va. Bul. 186 and U. S. Dept. Agr. Bul. 870; Sheets, Livesay, Tuckwiller, and Semple, West Va. Bul. 191 and U. S. Dept. Agr. Bul. 1251; Wilson, Tuckwiller, and Sheets, West Va. Bul. 218; Livesay, West Va. Cir. 40; Hays, Wyo. Cir. 17; Sheets, U. S. Dept. Agr. Cir. 166; Black and Mathews, U. S. Dept. Agr., Tech. Bul. 192.

25. Wilson, West Va. Bul. 198.
26. Tomhave and Severson, Penn. Buls. 138, 150.
27. McCampbell, Amer. Soc. Anim. Prod., Proc. 1920; Withycombe, Potter, and Edwards, Ore. Mont. Rpt. 1931; see also Mont. Rpt. 1931.
28. Brennen, Fleming, Smith, and Bruce, Nev. Bul. 124; Lantow, New Mex. Cir. 74; Johnson, N. D. Bul. 237 and S. D. Bul. 255.
29. Guilbert and McDonald, Amer. Soc. Anim. Prod., Proc. 1934.
30. Snapp, Beef Cattle, 2nd ed., pp. 342-357.
31. McCampbell, Mackintosh, et al., Amer. Soc. Anim. Prod., Proc. 1927 and Kan. Rpts. 1926-28, 1928-30, 1930-32, 1932-34; Bull. Ill. Sta., The National Provisioner, 92, 1935, No. 1: Longwell, West. Va. Bul. 244.
32. Shealy, Fla. Rpt. 1930; McCampbell, Winchester, and Marston, Kan. Cir. 97; Templeton, Miss. Bul. 268; Waters, Mo. Cir. 24; Shepperd, N. D. Bul. 217; Potter and Withycombe, Ore. Bul. 193; Sarvis, U. S. Dept. Agr. Bul. 1301; Snapp, Beef Cattle, 2nd ed., p. 355.
33. Garrigus, Am. Soc. Anim. Prod., Proc. 1934.
34. Snapp and Knox, Ill. Bul. 328; McCampbell, Anderson, and Marston, Kan. Cir. 117; Trowbridge, Mo. Sta., mimeo. rpt.; Gramlich, Nebr. Rpt. 1925 and mimeo. rpt.; Thalman and Gramlich, Nebr. Sta., mimeo. rpt.; Gerlaugh, Ohio Bimo. Buls. 138, 144; see also: Mumford and Hall, Ill. Cirs. 79, 88; Skinner and King, Ind. Buls. 265, 281, 291; Culbertson and Hammond, Iowa Sta., mimeo. rpt.; Waters, Mo. Bul. 76; Baker, Nebr. Bul. 281.
35. McCampbell, Weber, and Connell, Kan. Sta., mimeo. rpts.; Thalman and Gramlich, Nebr. Sta., mimeo. rpt.
36. Grimes, Ala. Bul. 231; Grimes, Sewell, and Cottier, Ala. Cir. 71; McCampbell, Anderson, and Alexander, Kan. Sta., mimeo. rpt.; Bray, La. Sta., Amer. Soc. Anim. Prod., Proc. 1934 and mimeo. rpt.; Barnett and Goodell, Miss. Cir. 50; Jacob, Tenn. Rpts. 1931, 1933; J. H. Jones, Hall, and J. M. Jones, Tex. Sta., mimeo. rpt.; Hunt, Va. Rpts. 1918, 1927-31; Wilson and Livesay, West Va. Buls. 244, 254, 263; Ward, Gray, and Lloyd, U. S. Dept. Agr. Bul. 777; Black, Warner, and Wilson, U. S. Dept. Agr., Tech. Bul. 217; Holden, U. S. Dept. Agr. Cir. 5; Paterson, Highl. and Agr. Soc. Scotland, Trans. 1927.
37. Wilcox, Grimes, Evans, and Henney, U. S. Dept. Agr. Bul. 1454.
38. Mumford, Mo. Bul. 90; Trowbridge and Moffett, Mo. Sta., Amer. Soc. Anim. Prod., Proc. 1931; Gerlaugh, Ohio Bimo. Bul. 173.
39. Skinner and Cochel, Ind. Bul. 142; Culbertson and Hammond, Iowa Sta., mimeo. rpt.; Bohstedt, Ohio Bimo. Buls. 123, 129.
40. Mitchell, Hamilton, Bull, and Olson, Ill. Rpts. 1931, 1932.
41. McCampbell and Winchester, Kan. Cirs. 86, 92.
42. McCampbell, Anderson, and Alexander, Kan. Rpt. 1928-30 and mimeo. rpts.; McCampbell, Weber, and Connell, Kan. Rpts. 1930-32, 1932-34; Moffett and Trowbridge, Mo. Sta., Amer. Soc. Anim. Prod., Proc. 1929; Thalman and Gramlich, Nebr. Rpt. 1934 and mimeo. rpts.
43. Good and Harris, Ky. Bul. 332.
44. For detailed discussions of range beef cattle production, see: Sampson, Livestock Husbandry on Range and Pasture; Hultz, Range Beef Production; Hart and Guilbert, Cal. Bul. 458; Burdick, Reinholt, and Klemmedson, Colo. Bul. 342; Saunderson and Richards, Mont. Bul. 244; Hedges, Nebr. Bul. 215; Brennen et al., Nev. Bul. 133; Walker and Lantow, New Mex. Bul. 159; Shepperd and Johnson, N. D. Sta., Amer. Soc. Anim. Prod., Proc. 1928; Potter, Ore. Bul. 220; Johnson, S. D. Bul. 255; Peterson et al., Utah Bul. 203; Vass and Pearson, Wyo. Bul. 197; Wilcox and Parr, U. S. Dept. Agr., Farmers' Bul. 1395; Wilson et al., U. S. Dept. Agr. Bul. 1454, U. S. Dept. Agr. Tech. Bul. 45.
45. Williams, Ariz. Rpt. 1920; Rusk and Snapp, Ill. Rpt. 1932; Trowbridge and Moffett, Mo. Bul. 300; Gramlich and Thalman, Nebr. Sta., mimeo. rpt.
46. Sheets, Baker, Gibbons, Stine, and Wilcox, U. S. Dept. Agr., Yearbook, 1921; see also: Tomhave and Severson, Penn. Buls. 138, 150; Cotton, U. S. Dept. Agr. Bul. 615; Sheets and Tuckwiller, U. S. Dept. Agr. Bul. 1024; Black, U. S. Dept. Agr., Farmers' Bul. 1218.
47. Pew and Evvard, Iowa Bul. 181.
48. Cotton, U. S. Dept. Agr. Bul. 615.
49. Rusk and Snapp, Ill. Rpt. 1933.
50. Wilcox, Jennings, Collier, Black, and McComas, U. S. Dept. Agr., Tech. Bul. 23.
51. Case and Myers, Ill. Bul. 261.
52. Snapp, Beef Cattle, 2nd ed., p. 431.
53. Black, U. S. Dept. Agr., Farmers' Bul. 1218.
54. Wilcox, Jour. Farm Economics, 3, 1921, pp. 62-72.
55. Fuller, Bohstedt, and Roche, Wis. Buls. 410, 420.
56. Rusk and Snapp, Ill. Sta., mimeo. rpt.
57. Evvard and Henness, Amer. Soc. Anim. Prod., Proc. 1924.
58. Ward, U. S. Dept. Agr. Bul. 25.
59. Culbertson, Evvard, and Hammond, Iowa Bul. 271; Gramlich, Nebr. Bul. 229; Gramlich and Thalman, Nebr. Bul. 252; Bohstedt, Ohio Bimo. Bul. 93-94.
60. Bechdel, Penn. Rpt. 1917.
61. Bohstedt, Humphrey, and Roche, Wis. Bul. 420.
62. Dowler, Ohio Bul. 495.

A PROFIT-MAKING FARM FLOCK AT PASTURE

On many farms where most of the income is derived from other sources, a flock of sheep would bring additional profits, since they consume much food which would otherwise be wasted.

THE SHEEP HAS WON THE TITLE OF "THE GOLDEN HOOF"

Thru increasing the fertility of the pastures it grazes, this animal has won the title of "The Golden Hoof." As sheep graze, their droppings are distributed more uniformly than with other stock.

SHEEP KEEP LANES AND FENCE CORNERS CLEAN

Most weeds are eaten readily by sheep. They therefore help the farmer keep his lanes and fence corners clean.

LAMBS BRING QUICK RETURNS

If lambs are properly fed concentrates in addition to their dams' milk, they will be ready for market before weaning, bringing a high price and quick returns.

CHAPTER XXXII

GENERAL PROBLEMS IN SHEEP PRODUCTION

I. Factors Affecting Sheep Husbandry

1153. Sheep production in the United States.—The importance of the sheep industry in the United States is shown by the fact that from 1920 to 1935 the number of sheep on farms on January first of each year averaged 44,900,000. The number on January 1, 1935, was estimated at 49,766,000. These totals do not include the large proportion of the lambs which are born after January 1 and are marketed within the same year.

About two-thirds the total number of sheep are in the western range states and Texas, where most of them are kept under range conditions in bands of from 1,000 to 3,000 head. Differing widely from this type of sheep production, sheep raising in the rest of the country is usually combined with other types of farming and commonly there are only 25 to 100 breeding ewes in each flock. Farm flocks are most numerous in the North Central States and also in a section of the South including Kentucky, Tennessee, West Virginia, and Virginia. In this latter district and also in California many farmers specialize in the production of early lambs for marketing as fat lambs in the spring. (**1270**)

1154. The farm flock.—Usually sheep raising is not the main source of income on farms where there are farm flocks, but, due to its particular advantages, it is combined with other farm enterprises. Sheep do not require expensive buildings or equipment, the foundation animals are relatively cheap, and under good management the flock can be increased rapidly. Sheep require but little labor during the busy summer season, and the cares of lambing time can be over before the rush of spring work begins. The wool and the market lambs provide two sources of income each year, and returns come quickly, for lambs may be marketed 9 months after the ewes are bred. While surpassed by pigs in economy of meat production, lambs require slightly less feed per pound of gain in weight than do fattening calves.

Sheep are especially adapted to grazing on rough and hilly land, and therefore in the eastern states farm flocks are most common where much of the land is unsuited for tillage. Sheep are without equals as weed consumers and destroyers, for they will eat nearly all of the common weeds and they grind their feed so finely that they destroy most weed seeds. A moderate-sized farm flock can often secure no small part of its feed from material that would otherwise be wasted. They will clean up the lanes, stubble fields, and fence rows, thus helping to keep weeds in check. Although such waste feed should be fully utilized, in order to cut down the cost of maintaining the flock, one should not rely too largely on it. Good returns cannot be expected unless care is taken to provide a plentiful supply of the proper kinds of feed throughout the year.

For success with sheep, it is even more essential than with other classes of stock that they be given careful attention, especially at certain seasons, as during breeding, lambing, and weaning. However, the principles of feeding and management are relatively simple and easily understood. In some districts the dog nuisance is a serious obstacle in raising sheep, but fortunately several states have enacted effective dog laws which protect the sheepman. Also, the flock may be safeguarded by means of fences, corrals, and trained dogs.

Usually there should be at least 40 ewes in a farm flock in order to reduce the expense per head for shelter, equipment, and labor, and the cost of keeping a good ram. When there are proper facilities, often the flock can advantageously be much larger than this, but if a farm is too heavily stocked with sheep, the troubles from stomach worms and other parasites are greatly increased. For this reason, but few farm flocks contain more than 200 ewes. The beginner in sheep raising had best begin with a small flock, increasing the number as he gains experience.

1155. Types of sheep.—The original fine-wool or Merino sheep were developed primarily for the production of wool and had bodies which, like those of dairy cows, were inclined to be angular in form. At the other extreme are the mutton sheep, comprising the middle- and long-wooled breeds, which were developed in Great Britain primarily for the production of meat, with wool secondary. In shape of body these breeds resemble the beef breeds of cattle, being blocky and compact. The Delaine-Merinos and the Rambouillets were developed from the original Spanish Merinos with the object of securing a fine-wool sheep that would furnish more mutton. These are of dual-purpose type, between the two extremes in form of body.

1156. Breeds of sheep.—It is outside the field of this volume to discuss the characteristics or merits of the different breeds of sheep. Experiments have been conducted at several experiment stations to compare various breeds or to test the relative value of rams of different breeds for crossing on native or scrub ewes.[1] These studies show, as is well known, that lambs of the Merino type are slower in maturing than those of the mutton breeds and therefore usually make smaller daily gains and require somewhat more feed for each pound of gain. This slowness in maturing may, however, sometimes be of advantage when it is desired to fatten lambs for the late winter market.

Among the mutton breeds, there may be quite as much difference in gaining capacity and economy of gain between various strains of one breed as there is between the different breeds. In deciding upon the breed to raise, one should therefore select the breed that seems best adapted to his own local conditions and to the requirements of his particular market.

1157. Building up the farm flock.—Often the most economical way for a farmer to establish a flock of sheep is to buy young, thrifty western range ewes of good conformation. These are commonly less infested with internal parasites than native eastern ewes. By the continued use of good purebred rams of the same mutton breed, a flock of excellent mutton type and conformation may soon be built up that can scarcely be distinguished from purebreds. The lambs of even the first cross will show pronounced improvement in mutton characteristics.

If native ewes are purchased locally to start the flock, it is important that they be vigorous, thrifty, free from disease, and of as uniform breeding as possible. In certain sections, especially in the eastern states, native Delaine-Merino ewes can be purchased more cheaply than ewes of mutton type. Providing they are thrifty, they make desirable foundation stock for building up a farm flock by the use of purebred mutton rams.[2]

If one already has a flock of ewes, but they are of rather poor quality, he can make rapid improvement and thereby greatly increase the income from his sheep by using only a good purebred ram. For example, in experiments at the Kentucky Station[3] lambs from purebred rams and native "mountain" ewes averaged 72 lbs. in weight at 4 months of age, while lambs from a scrub ram and similar ewes weighed only 56 lbs. Similar striking examples of the rapid improvement made through the use of a good purebred ram have been reported by the Mississippi, Nevada, Oklahoma, North Carolina, and South Carolina Stations.[4] In the North Carolina trials 2-year-old ewes from a purebred Shropshire ram and native ewes averaged 121 lbs. in weight and sheared 6.8 lbs. of good wool, while their dams averaged but 75 lbs. in weight and sheared only 2.9 lbs. of poor-quality wool.

1158. Cross breeding for the western ranges.—In early years the sheep on the western ranges were of Merino blood, for wool was the product sought. When the demand for lamb and mutton increased, rams of the mutton breeds were used on the range ewes to improve the mutton qualities of the offspring. It was found, however, that the introduction of mutton blood cannot go beyond a certain degree in the range flocks of breeding ewes. Otherwise, they will lose both their hardiness and their Merino herding instinct and will scatter on the range so that many are lost or fall prey to wild animals. A rather troublesome system of cross-breeding must accordingly be followed in range flocks, in order to produce lambs of good mutton conformation and yet retain sufficient Merino blood in the breeding ewes.

To avoid this, the Corriedale breed was developed in New Zealand by crossing Lincoln and to a lesser extent Leicester rams on Merino ewes, mating the crossbreds together, and selecting the offspring with the desired qualities. The value of this breed for American range conditions is being tested by the United States Department of Agriculture and various ranchmen, and there are being developed along similar lines American breeds: the Columbia, the Panama, and the Romeldale.

1159. Lambs preferred to older sheep.—The tender, juicy, well-flavored meat from lambs is in much greater demand than mutton from older sheep, even though they are well fattened. Hence, fat lambs sell for a much higher price per hundredweight on the market than fat yearlings or older animals. For this reason and also because lambs make much cheaper gains than older sheep, ordinarily lambs which are not to be retained for the breeding flock are never carried over to the second year.

Experiments in which lambs have been fattened in comparison with yearlings or older sheep show that lambs will make as large daily gains, or nearly as large gains as older animals, in spite of the fact that they consume considerably less feed.[5] Therefore their gains are much cheaper. For example, in a Kansas trial the feed cost of 100 lbs. gain was 56 per cent more for yearlings than for lambs, and in a Texas test 35 per cent greater.[6]

For these reasons most stockmen who fatten western feeder sheep for the market prefer lambs. Though they cost more per hundredweight as feeders than do older animals, they sell for so much more when fat that there is usually a greater margin between cost and selling price per hundredweight and hence a greater profit in fattening them. Some men make a practice of fattening old ewes, which can often be obtained at low prices. Such animals require expert care and good feed. In the West they are often fed largely on beet pulp, as this is especially suited to those with "broken mouths," or poor and missing teeth.

II. Nutrient Requirements of Sheep

1160. Nutrient requirements of sheep and lambs; feeding standards.—Sheep are very fond of good roughage and have a high ability to utilize it. For these reasons their rations should consist largely of suitable roughage—plenty of pasturage during the growing season and well-cured hay and other forage in winter. Sufficient well-cured legume hay during the barn-feeding period will not only provide most of the necessary protein but also is an insurance that the sheep will receive an abundance of calcium and of vitamins, especially vitamins A and D.

Good roughage alone will usually provide ample nutrients for breeding ewes in winter up to about a month before lambing. Then additional nutrients are needed on account of the rapid growth of the unborn lamb at that time, and a small amount of grain or other concentrates should be fed. The nutrient requirements of ewes which are nursing lambs are much like those of dairy cows in milk, and they need considerably more protein and a more liberal supply of total digestible nutrients than before lambing.

In order to fatten lambs rapidly so that they will reach the desired degree of fatness before they become too large, it is necessary to feed them a liberal amount of grain or other concentrates in addition to plenty of good roughage. Fattening lambs make more rapid gains in proportion to their live weight than do beef cattle, and therefore they require somewhat more total digestible nutrients daily per 1,000 lbs. live weight.

For detailed information on the nutrient requirements of the various classes of sheep, the reader is referred to Appendix Table III, which presents the Morrison feeding standards for breeding ewes up to one month before lambing, for ewes during the last month of pregnancy, for ewes nursing lambs, for maintaining mature sheep, and for fattening lambs.

1161. Amount of protein.—Since wool fibers are composed of protein, sheep need somewhat more protein than would be the case if they were not producing this protein product. The amounts of protein recommended in the Morrison standards are based on a study of the various experiments that furnish information on the protein requirements of the various classes of sheep. Unfortunately, but few investigations have been conducted to determine definitely the minimum amount of protein required by breeding ewes, growing lambs, or fattening lambs. It is believed that the amounts advised are ample when feeds of average quality are used.

When protein-rich feeds are unusually high in price, it may be most economical to supply somewhat less protein than recommended, though such rations may not give maximum production. Fattening rations for light-weight feeder lambs, weighing 45 to 55 lbs., should provide a somewhat larger proportion of protein than for larger lambs which have completed more of their growth.

It will be noted that in the Morrison standards nutritive ratios of 1:6.5 to 1:8.0 are advised for fattening lambs on full feed, depending on their weights. Mitchell has recommended amounts of digestible protein very much lower than advised in these standards.[7] However, in an experiment by the author and Willman at the New York (Cornell) Station, lambs fed such a low amount of protein, in a ration otherwise presumably adequate, failed to make good gains, went off feed repeatedly, and could not be brought back to a full ration.[8]

1162. Quality of protein.—If sheep are fed a reasonable amount of good legume hay, there will be no deficiency in the *quality* or *kind* of protein. This is because alfalfa hay, clover hay, and presumably other legume hay furnish protein of excellent quality for sheep, as has been shown in Chapter VI. (**153-154**) In feeding sheep, such hay fully makes good any deficiencies in the quality of protein in the cereal grains and their by-products.

If there is little or no legume hay in the ration, it is not wise to use a feed like corn gluten feed, corn gluten meal, or distillers' corn dried grains as the only protein supplement. Instead, such a feed should be combined with a supplement that provides protein of better quality, like linseed meal, cottonseed meal, soybean oil meal, etc. (**148**) For sheep feeding, the protein supplements of animal origin commonly produce no better results than such supplements as linseed meal, cottonseed meal, soybean oil meal, or soybeans.

Wool is very rich in cystine, the chief sulfur-containing amino acid, but there is apparently no lack of cystine in ordinary rations for sheep that are otherwise satisfactory. For example, although certain experiments indicate that both alfalfa hay and soybeans may be low in cystine, nevertheless these feeds furnish protein of satisfactory quality for wool production. (**150, 154**) Oklahoma experiments also indicate that any ordinary balanced ration will supply ample cystine for normal growth of wool.[9]

If sheep are fed a ration unusually low in cystine, there may possibly be a benefit from using a protein supplement high in this amino acid. Thus, in an Australian test with Merino sheep, whose wool production is high, blood meal (a feed rich in cystine) gave excellent results as a supplement to pasture grass that was exceedingly low in cystine.[10]

1163. Determining whether a supplement is needed.—Since protein supplements are generally much more expensive than the farm grains, it is important to know whether or not a supplement is needed in any particular ration. Specific information is given on this subject in the following paragraphs and also in later discussions.

When there is any doubt concerning the need of a protein supplement for a given ration, the best guide is to find whether the ration provides sufficient protein to meet the recommendations of the feeding standards. It will usually pay to balance the ration according to the standards, unless protein supplements are unusually expensive in comparison with the grains.

The relative values of the various protein supplements are discussed in the following chapter.

1164. Adding a supplement to legume hay and grain.—Numerous experiments have been conducted to determine whether it pays to add a protein supplement to various rations for fattening feeder lambs, especially to combinations of legume hay and grain. These trials have shown that when a liberal amount of alfalfa or clover hay is fed with corn or other grain, there is usually sufficient protein to produce very satisfactory gains, without the addition of any protein supplement. If fattening lambs are full fed both legume hay and grain, they will continue to eat considerable hay, even during the latter part of the fattening period. The ration is therefore more completely balanced than in the case of fattening calves, which often eat but little hay toward the end of the fattening period if full fed on grain.

Adding a small amount of a protein supplement (0.10 to 0.15 lb. per head daily) to a ration of legume hay and grain for fattening lambs will commonly make a slight increase in the rate of gain. However, the increase will not average more than 0.05 lb. per head daily. The addition of the supplement usually stimulates the appetites of the lambs slightly, so that they eat more total concentrates (grain plus supplement) than those fed only grain and hay. This may be the cause of the slight increase in rate of grain.

Nearly as much feed will be required for 100 lbs. gain as on the unsupplemented ration. Therefore, it is doubtful whether it will ordinarily pay to add a supplement to such a ration, unless one desires to force the lambs to make maximum gains, so as to be ready for market at a particular time. Otherwise, it is usually the best plan to omit the supplement and to lengthen the fattening period the few days that will be needed for the lambs to reach the desired finish.

During the last few weeks of the fattening period, when lambs full-fed on corn tend to eat less hay than previously, there may be more advantage in adding a small amount of supplement to the ration. Also, it may pay to add a supplement when lambs are self-fed on corn and legume hay, fed separately, since they usually eat more corn and less hay than lambs that are hand-fed.[11] (**1265**)

In 30 experiments with fattening lambs, the effect of adding a small amount of linseed meal to a ration of alfalfa hay and shelled corn, both full-fed, has been studied.[12] Lambs fed an average of 0.19 lb. linseed meal per head daily gained only 0.05 lb. more than others receiving only hay and corn, and each 100 lbs. of linseed meal saved only 101 lbs. corn and 81 lbs. hay. In 19 similar experiments, adding cottonseed meal or cake to a ration of alfalfa hay and corn likewise increased the daily gain only 0.05 lb. on the average, and each 100 lbs. of cottonseed meal or cake saved only 87 lbs. corn and 114 lbs. hay.[13]

Not considering the very small increase in rate of gain produced by adding a supplement to the ration of corn and alfalfa hay, each 100 lbs. of linseed meal or cottonseed meal or cake has not been worth more than the equivalent of about 150 lbs. of corn in these trials. Usually the price of these supplements is higher than this in comparison with the farm price of corn in the corn belt. Therefore adding the supplement will usually increase the cost of the gains materially, and will generally not be profitable.

Lambs were fed linseed meal as a supplement to corn and alfalfa hay in Pennsylvania trials, but they were not allowed to eat any more total concentrates or any more hay than others fed only corn and hay.[14] In these trials the addition of linseed meal did not increase the rate of gain, as it usually does when lambs are allowed all the corn they will eat.

Probably because barley is richer in protein than corn, adding a supplement to a ration of barley and alfalfa hay for fattening lambs does not cause even as much increase in the rate of gain as adding the supplement to corn and alfalfa hay. Adding linseed meal or cottonseed meal or cake to barley and alfalfa hay has increased the average gain of fattening lambs only 0.03 lb. in 25 experiments. In these trials each 100 lbs. of supplement has saved only 92 lbs. barley and 116 lbs. hay.[15] Similar results have been secured, as a rule, in experiments in which a protein supplement has been added to a ration of alfalfa hay and other grains, such as oats or the grain sorghums.[16]

Red clover hay contains somewhat less protein than alfalfa hay. Nevertheless, adding linseed or cottonseed meal to a ration of only clover hay and shelled corn for fattening lambs increased the daily gain only 0.01 lb., on the average, in nine trials and did not decrease the amount of concentrates or hay required per 100 lbs. gain.[17]

If the roughage for fattening lambs is mixed legume-and-grass hay or a combination of a limited amount of legume hay with non-legume roughage, then a protein supplement is usually needed to balance the ration.

1165. Adding a supplement when silage is fed.—When fattening lambs are fed all the corn or sorghum silage they will eat, along with a full feed of legume hay and corn or other grain, they will naturally eat somewhat less of the protein-rich hay than when hay is the only roughage. However, they will generally eat 0.75 to 1.00 lb. of hay per head daily, if it is of good quality. This will provide enough protein to make good gains, but it will usually pay to add 0.15 to 0.20 lb. of a protein supplement to the ration. Such an addition will aid in keeping the lambs on feed, will increase the gains slightly, and will produce a better finish. Consequently, it will increase the selling price. When protein supplements are unusually high in price compared with grain, it may be most profitable to omit the supplement.

In 12 experiments with fattening lambs, the addition of 0.16 lb. per head daily of linseed or cottonseed meal to a ration of alfalfa hay, corn silage, and corn grain increased the daily gain 0.05 lb. on the average, raised the average selling price by 23 cents per hundredweight, and increased the average net return per lamb by 37 cents.[18] Not taking into consideration the more rapid gains or the increased selling price, each 100 lbs. of supplement saved 132 lbs. corn, plus 114 lbs. hay and 100 lbs. silage.

In six similar trials the addition of 0.16 lb. cottonseed meal per head daily to a ration of clover hay, corn silage, and shelled corn increased the daily gain 0.03 lb., on the average, and increased the selling price 7 cents per hundredweight.[19] Each 100 lbs. of cottonseed meal saved a total of 121 lbs. corn, plus 63 lbs. clover hay and 50 lbs. corn silage. Similar results have been secured in trials where a supplement has been added to a ration of other grains fed with corn silage and legume hay.[20]

Whether or not it will pay to add a protein supplement to a ration of alfalfa hay, wet or dried beet pulp, and grain, will depend primarily on the amount of hay the lambs eat and on its quality.[21]

1166. Salt.—Sheep show an especial fondness for salt and under any ordinary conditions should be furnished with it regularly. When sheep are accustomed to salt, it is the best plan to let them have access to it in suitable boxes or other containers, so they can take what they wish.

Sheep consume considerably more salt per 100 lbs. live weight than dairy cattle or beef cattle. Pregnant ewes allowed access to salt during seven winters in Iowa trials ate slightly less than one-half ounce daily, on the average.[22] Better results were secured from ewes receiving one-fourth to one-half ounce salt daily than when larger amounts were mixed in the ration or when no salt was furnished. For fattening lambs an allowance of 0.20 to 0.25 ounce per head daily is sufficient. This is about the amount they will usually consume when allowed free access to salt.[23]

On the western ranges allowances of salt equivalent to one-quarter to one-half ounce per ewe daily (not counting the lambs) are considered reasonable.[24] Often the sheep are salted at intervals of 3 to 7 days, instead of daily. In the alkali districts, sometimes range sheep are not salted, but merely allowed to eat alkali. This is safe if the alkali contains 85 per cent salt.[25]

1167. Calcium and phosphorus.—Whether or not there will be any advantage in adding a calcium or a phosphorus supplement to rations for breeding sheep or growing and fattening lambs will depend entirely on the amounts of these minerals supplied by the feeds they receive. (**161**) For information on the use of calcium and phosphorus supplements, the reader is referred to Chapter VI. (**165-171**) As is shown later in this discussion, there is more apt to be a lack of calcium in rations for sheep than of phosphorus.

Since breeding sheep and even fattening lambs consume large amounts of roughage, they will receive sufficient phosphorus when fed plenty of good-quality roughage, unless the roughage has been grown on soil seriously deficient in this mineral.[26] Also, the phosphorus supply will be ample if there is included in the ration a protein supplement, such as wheat bran, cottonseed meal, or linseed meal, which is rich in phosphorus.[27] If there is a deficiency of phosphorus in the ration, or if it seems wise to supply a phosphorus supplement as an insurance against a possible lack, one of the simple mineral mixtures recommended in Chapter VI may be provided. (**181**)

When at least one-third of the roughage (on the dry basis) for sheep and lambs is legume hay or other legume forage, they will receive an abundant supply of calcium. Experiments have shown that under such conditions there is no benefit from adding ground limestone or some other calcium supplement to the ration. In experiments with pregnant ewes at the Iowa and Ohio Stations the addition of a mineral mixture supplying calcium and phosphorus to good winter rations containing plenty of legume hay, did not prove beneficial to the ewes or their lambs.[28] Also, in trials with fattening lambs there has been no benefit from adding a calcium supplement to rations including any reasonable proportion of legume hay.[29]

When no legume hay is fed sheep or lambs, there may be a decided lack of calcium in the ration, especially where the forage is grown on soils very low in calcium. Adding ground limestone or some other calcium supplement will then be a decided benefit. In metabolism studies at the Texas Station sheep 1 to 3 years old which were fed maintenance rations stored calcium and phosphorus when fed legume hay, but lost these minerals from their bodies when they were fed non-legume forage.[30]

Experiments at the Kansas, Nebraska and Texas Stations show that a lack of calcium may be one cause of the poor results often secured when lambs are fattened on rations including no legume hay.[31] Fattening lambs fed silage or ground or chopped fodder from the grain or sweet sorghums, with corn or sorghum grain and cottonseed meal, made decidedly poorer and more expensive gains than others fed alfalfa hay for roughage. However, when 0.25 to 0.40 ounce per head daily of ground limestone or pulverized oyster shell was added to the ration, much better results were secured. Similar results were secured in Minnesota experiments in which fattening lambs were fed rations in which prairie hay was the only roughage.[32]

Likewise, in Ohio trials satisfactory results were secured with breeding ewes fed only timothy hay and corn silage for roughage, when the hay was cut in early bloom and when there were added to the ration 0.8 ounce of ground limestone per head daily and a sufficient amount of protein supplement.[33]

In certain other trials there has been an advantage from adding a calcium supplement to a ration containing no legume hay, while in others no advantage has resulted.[34] This difference in results is probably due to the fact that non-legume roughage varies widely in amount of calcium, depending on the calcium content of the soil.

If non-legume roughage is grown on soil fairly well supplied with calcium, it will take relatively little legume hay to provide enough of this mineral for fattening lambs. For example, in a trial at the Indiana Station there was no benefit in adding a calcium supplement when fattening lambs were fed corn silage, corn grain and cottonseed meal, with a full feed of clover hay only every fifth day.[35]

Considering all the data available, it seems wise, whenever the roughage for sheep or lambs is only non-legume roughage grown on soils low in calcium, to add to the ration one-quarter ounce or more per head daily of ground limestone or other calcium supplement, or else to provide free access to a mineral mixture supplying calcium. (181) The latter is probably the better plan, unless one is sure that there is a lack of calcium in the ration. If a suitable mineral mixture is supplied, the sheep will then take enough to meet their needs and will not consume an excess.

When there is already a liberal supply of calcium and phosphorus in the ration, forcing sheep to consume a calcium or phosphorus supplement may even be detrimental. For example, in the case of breeding ewes too liberal a supply of these minerals may even perhaps cause more cases of difficult lambing, because of an increase in the size of the skeleton of the lambs.

1168. Iodine; other minerals.—In districts where there is trouble from goiter in new-born lambs, the ewes should receive iodized salt during at least the latter half of pregnancy. (172) Only one-twentieth grain per head daily of potassium iodide is sufficient to prevent goiter, and too large doses may be injurious.[36] It is doubtful whether it is advantageous to supply fattening lambs with iodized salt in place of ordinary salt, except perhaps in areas where there is a decided deficiency of iodine. In recent California tests, however, fattening lambs supplied with iodized salt made more rapid and economical gains than others fed ordinary salt.[37]

There is no need of adding to the usual rations of sheep other mineral supplements, such as sulfur, iron, copper, potash salts, etc.[38]

1169. Vitamin requirements.—Vitamin A is probably the only vitamin that may be deficient in any usual method of feeding and caring for sheep. The fact that sheep are generally outdoors and exposed to sunlight much of the time, even in winter, protects them against any deficiency of vitamin D. (191) Also, hay and other good dry roughage supplies this vitamin. So far as is known, there is no need of adding to ordinary sheep rations any special supplements to furnish vitamins B, G, C, and E. (196-200)

A large proportion of the feed eaten by sheep is roughage, even in the case of fattening lambs. If a considerable part of the roughage is early-cut, well-cured hay or other roughage high in vitamin A value (carotene content), there will therefore be no lack of this vitamin. (188) On the other hand, there will be a decided lack of vitamin A if sheep are fed only cereal straw, poor-quality hay, or cottonseed hulls as the only roughage.

Sheep seem to have a higher requirement for vitamin A than do beef cattle. At least, it is more essential that they be provided with roughage of good quality, and such roughage is usually much higher than poor-quality roughage in the vitamin. While beef breeding cows can be wintered successfully on straw plus a small amount of a protein supplement, such a ration is not satisfactory for breeding ewes.

1170. Water.—Plenty of fresh water should always be furnished sheep, under all ordinary circumstances. Ewes on dry feed in the winter may drink as much as 1 gallon per head daily before lambing and 1.5 gallons or more when nursing lambs. Lambs that are being fattened on dry feed will drink 1.2 to 2 quarts or more of water a day.[39] When sheep are fed succulent feeds, such as silage or roots, they drink correspondingly less water. More water will be required in warm weather than when cooler, and fattening lambs will drink more as their grain allowance increases.

Because of the danger of infestation with internal parasites, drinking from stagnant pools must be avoided. In districts with very heavy dews, sheep on pasture may get along without other water, and likewise when they are fed large quantities of roots in winter. It is not necessary to warm water for sheep in winter, but ice should be kept out of the troughs. They should not be forced to eat snow to satisfy their thirst, or digestive trouble may result.

III. Miscellaneous Problems in Sheep Husbandry

1171. Grinding or crushing grain.—Of all farm animals sheep are best able to do their own grinding, and with few exceptions they should be fed whole grain. Better results are usually secured from whole corn, oats, ordinary barley, wheat, or grain sorghums, than from the ground or crushed grain. Such grains should be ground only for old sheep with poor teeth, for young lambs up to 5 or 6 weeks of age, or perhaps when fattening lambs are being self-fed such a mixture as grain and chopped hay.

It is wise to grind such hard seeds as hull-less barley or millet, and also screenings containing a considerable proportion of small weed seeds. If grain is prepared for sheep, it should be ground coarsely or crushed, instead of being ground to a fine meal, for this is not so palatable to them. Similarly, pea-size linseed cake or cottonseed cake is somewhat preferable to linseed meal or cottonseed meal for sheep feeding.

1172. Chopping or grinding hay, fodder, or stover.—Whether or not it will pay to chop (cut) or grind hay for sheep will depend on the quality of the hay, on the manner in which it is fed, and on the price of the hay and the cost of such preparation. When legume hay of good quality is fed in suitable racks or bunks and the allowance is limited to the amount the sheep will clean up reasonably well, it is questionable whether there will usually be enough waste to warrant the expense of chopping or grinding it. Often the refused part can be fed to idle horses or cattle being roughed through the winter. With poor-quality hay there is more advantage in chopping or grinding. Chopping good-quality first-cutting alfalfa hay for breeding ewes fed the hay in a suitable rack did not increase the value appreciably in trials at the New York (Cornell) Station.[40] Also, in a Minnesota trial chopping sweet clover hay for fattening lambs was of no advantage.[41]

When fattening lambs are fed hay (even good alfalfa hay) with great liberality, as is a common practice in the western states, there is an appreciable saving through chopping or grinding it. Chopped alfalfa hay has been compared with uncut hay in 23 experiments with fattening lambs (9 trials at the Oregon Station and 14 trials at other stations).[42] The lambs fed the chopped hay did not gain appreciably more rapidly, on the average, than those fed the long hay, but there was a considerable saving in hay. They were fed 747 lbs. hay and 328 lbs. grain per 100 lbs. gain, in comparison with 875 lbs. hay and 333 lbs. grain for the lambs fed long hay. In these trials 100 lbs. of chopped hay were equal in value to 117.1 lbs. uncut hay plus 0.6 lb. grain. Considering the slight saving in grain, it may be concluded that chopping the hay increased its value 18 to 19 per cent.

Ground alfalfa hay has been compared with uncut hay as the only roughage for fattening lambs in 9 Oregon experiments and 4 experiments at other western stations.[43] The lambs fed ground hay gained 0.32 lb. per head daily, on the average, in comparison with 0.29 lb. for those fed uncut hay. A considerable saving of hay and a slight saving of grain were made, and 100 lbs. of ground hay were equal in feeding value to 138 lbs. uncut hay plus 5 lbs. of grain. Similar results were secured in an Arizona trial in which the roughage for fattening lambs was alfalfa hay, ground or unground, and sorghum silage.[44]

In these western trials as much as 16 to 28 per cent of the hay was not eaten by the lambs. Probably when hay of good quality is fed in racks that will reduce the wastage, the saving through grinding will not average as much as in these trials. The grinding of alfalfa hay for fattening lambs did not increase the average gains in 2 Oklahoma trials, even though the hay was not of very good quality.[45] In these trials the saving of feed through grinding the hay was so slight that it was of doubtful economy.

If hay is ground for sheep, it should not be ground too finely, as such a product is very dusty.

When self-feeders are used for feeding grain to fattening lambs, often a mixture of cut or ground hay and ground grain is self-fed, instead of grain and hay separately, in order to lessen digestive disorders and reduce the death losses. (**1265**) Feeding a mixture of cut or ground hay and grain may also be advisable when lambs are fattened rapidly by hand-feeding them as much grain as possible. Except when lambs are being thus forced, the use of such mixtures is not advantageous.[46]

In 3 Nebraska trials the death loss was considerably less and the gains were more rapid and economical with lambs hand-fed a mixture of alfalfa meal, shelled or ground corn, and linseed meal than in the case of others fed long alfalfa hay and a very liberal amount of the concentrates separately.[47] Merely considering the amounts of feed required per 100 lbs. gain, each 100 lbs. of alfalfa meal was equal in feeding value to 144 lbs. of long alfalfa hay plus 7 lbs. of concentrates.

Whether it will pay to chop or shred dry corn fodder or stover or sorghum forage for sheep will depend on the proportion they would waste if the roughage were fed uncut, and also on the cost of such preparation. In a Texas test chopping sorghum hay for fattening lambs slightly increased the gains and saved one-third the hay, while in Colorado and Oklahoma trials it did not pay to chop sorghum hay or fodder or Sudan hay for lambs.[48]

1173. Shelter.—Sheep are so well protected from cold by their fleeces that they do not need warm shelter. Even in the northern states one thickness of matched boards will make a barn or shed sufficiently warm, except for winter lambs. In the drier sections of the West often no winter shelter is provided other than a windbreak to protect the sheep from cold winds and driving storms. If they are kept dry, sheep will stand a great degree of cold with no harm. On the other hand, too-warm quarters are injurious, for sheep sweat badly in winter when kept in a barn sufficiently warm for dairy cows, and they are then apt to catch cold.

Ample ventilation is of great importance, but drafts should be avoided. With sheep it is more important than with other livestock that they be kept dry as to coat and to feet. Neglect of either of these essentials is apt to result disastrously. Stone basements are usually unsatisfactory for sheep on account of dampness, and if used, good ventilation is especially necessary. Damp walls are a sure indication of lack of ventilation. Even in the South sheep should be protected from winter rains.

Sunlight, good drainage, and conveniences for feeding are the other requisites of a good sheep barn. From 12 to 18 square feet of ground space, not including feed racks, should be provided for each ewe. The doorways should be wide, lest the animals suffer injury when all attempt to rush through at once, in true sheep fashion.

In late spring and early summer the flock should be sheltered from cold rains, if possible, for exposure is dangerous, especially to young lambs. In summer, if there is no natural shade in the pastures, a movable shelter should be provided for shade, or the flock should have access to a darkened but well-ventilated shed. A fringed curtain of cloth or sacking through which the sheep may pass, will keep back flies from this retreat.

Fattening lambs or sheep have an excess of heat on account of their liberal rations and therefore need less shelter than breeding ewes. A well-bedded shed, opening to the east or south into a well-drained yard, is ideal for winter shelter, except in the extreme northern states. In experiments during 5 years at the Indiana Station lambs thus sheltered made as rapid and as cheap gains and returned more profit than others housed in a well-ventilated barn.[49] In 3 trials at the Wisconsin Station, where the winters are more severe, lambs housed in a well-ventilated barn and turned out for exercise daily gained 0.395 lb. a head daily in comparison with 0.386 lb. for others housed in an open shed, partly boarded up to provide additional protection.[50] The average cost of feed per 100 lbs. gain was only 4.6 per cent higher for the latter lambs.

In the lamb-feeding districts of the plains states and westward, no shelter is usually provided for fattening lambs, except perhaps a windbreak. Any slight saving in feed through providing sheds is not sufficient to justify the expense. In Nebraska and Idaho tests, providing an open shelter did not increase the gains or decrease the feed required per 100 lbs. gain.[51] In 3 trials in eastern Oregon lambs having access to an open shed made slightly larger gains than others fed in a yard with no shelter, and required 3 per cent less feed for 100 lbs. gain.[52] Where there is considerable rainfall or snowfall in winter, a shed may make more saving in feed. For example, in a Missouri trial yearling wethers fed in a yard without shelter required 19 per cent more feed than others which had access to a barn.[53]

1174. Feed troughs and racks.—Grain and roughage should be fed separately to sheep, except when a mixture of grain and chopped or ground hay is used for fattening lambs. (**1171**) Grain troughs should have a wide, flat bottom, forcing the sheep to consume the grain slowly. Hay racks should be so built that chaff and seeds will not fall upon the necks of the sheep and injure the quality of the wool. Combination grain and hay racks are convenient and satisfactory, if properly constructed. About 15 to 18 inches of linear feed trough and rack space should be provided for each ewe and 12 to 15 inches for each fattening lamb. The use of self-feeders for fattening lambs is discussed in Chapter XXXII. (1265)

1175. Exercise.—Abundant exercise is essential for breeding ewes in winter, to insure strong, healthy lambs. The ewes should have access to a dry, sunny yard, well protected from wind and storm. To force them to exercise on all fair days, roughage may be scattered in small bunches over a nearby field. If the snow is deep, paths should be broken out with snow plow or stone boat. On stormy days the sheep should remain indoors, for wet fleeces dry but slowly in winter.

For fattening lambs or sheep it is preferable to limit the exercise. Fattening lambs when closely confined may make slightly more economical gains than those allowed a reasonable amount of exercise in a small outside lot, but they may possibly be more apt to suffer from overeating disease, or digestive troubles.

1176. Yield of dressed carcasses; shrinkage in shipment.—Slaughter tests conducted in connection with the feeding experiments at various experiment stations show that the lambs have usually yielded 47 to 51 per cent of dressed carcass, based on the market weights. The prime grades of unshorn fat lambs will dress slightly higher than this, and very fat sheep or lambs may dress 60 per cent or even more. Such fat carcasses are very wasteful, however, and do not meet the demands of the market.

The shrinkage of fat lambs on shipment to market will vary widely, depending chiefly on the distance and the time in transit. Tests at various experiment stations show that the shrinkage on shipment for less than 150 miles will usually range from 4 to 7 per cent, and for greater distances may be as high as 8 to 10 per cent or even higher.

There is generally no need to make any decided change in the ration fed fattening lambs before shipment. It may be advisable to reduce the amount of grain somewhat the day before shipment, but the lambs may be allowed the usual amount of roughage. Oats are an excellent feed for sheep in transit, as they are bulky and not laxative. When sheep are marketed off pasture, especially rape pasture, shrinkage from scouring may be avoided by giving them hay or other dry feed for a day or two before shipment.

1177. Wool production.—The composition and structure of wool have been discussed in Chapter VIII. (250-251) It has also been there shown that adverse conditions, such as sickness, undue exposure, or a decided lack of feed, will not only decrease the yield of wool but will also injure its quality.

By proper culling of the flock of breeding ewes and using the weight and quality of the individual fleeces as one basis of selection, a marked improvement can be made in the yield of wool from the flock.[54] The first year's fleece of a ewe is usually a less reliable index of the fleece weight during succeeding years than the fleece of the second or third year.

The tendency in the case of certain breeds to place undue emphasis on wool covering over the face, ears, and legs is undesirable.[55] The greater the number of characteristics on which a breeder attempts to base his selection of breeding stock, the greater are his difficulties in making uniform improvements. It is therefore wise to base the selection on characteristics which are of basic economic importance.

To prevent injury to the wool, feeding racks should be so constructed that seeds and chaff will not lodge on the neck and shoulders of the sheep. The feed lot or barn must be kept well bedded, so that the wool will not become soiled.

1178. Shearing sheep.—Formerly, it was the common practice in many districts to wash sheep before shearing, by driving them repeatedly through a stream or by holding them in the water and squeezing the dirt out by hand. This removes most of the suint and dirt but does not remove much of the wool fat. Such washing is of no benefit to the manufacturer, for the wool must in any event be scoured to remove the wool fat before it can be used, and the washing does not improve the quality of the wool or reduce the cost of scouring. The price a manufacturer pays for any lot of wool is based entirely on the estimated yield and quality of the scoured wool. The shrinkage of wool in scouring ordinarily ranges from 30 to 80 per cent, being highest for fine-wooled sheep.

In the corn belt and eastward sheep are usually shorn between the middle of April and the middle of May, when the weather has become settled and there have been a few days too warm for the comfort of unshorn sheep. The yolk has then risen into the wool in sufficient quantity to make it "full of life" and to make shearing easy. If shearing is delayed too long, the wool becomes dead and lifeless, the sheep suffer from the heat and are troubled more with maggots about the breech, due to the wool becoming foul. Sheep should not be shorn when the fleeces are wet or even damp. The fleeces should always be tied with paper twine or a strand made from the wool. Binder twine or sisal twine should never be used, as the fibers adhere to the wool and cannot be dyed uniformly with the wool.

Though it is not of practical importance, it is of interest to note that where the climate is mild in summer, sheep may remain healthy when not shorn for a long time. In Washington tests a wether was first shorn when over 5 years old, the fleece weighing 76 lbs.[56] The wether had as good a frame as its mate, shorn regularly, but was 20 lbs. lighter in body weight. In hot climates sheep are often shorn twice a year, producing somewhat more wool under this system.[57]

Lambs and sheep that are to be fattened for market are often shorn either before being placed on feed or during the early part of the fattening period, for the purpose of stimulating their appetites and making them more comfortable. This practice is followed especially when the animals are on feed late in the spring and the weather becomes warm. Unless the weather is so warm that they would be uncomfortable if unshorn, lambs or other sheep that are shorn will not usually make materially larger or more economical gains than when unshorn.[58] They should never be shorn during cold weather, unless good shelter is available.

Before shearing fattening lambs or sheep, one should find the probable difference in price between fat shorn and unshorn sheep, and also know about how much wool he will secure by shearing and the price it will bring. Often shorn sheep sell for so much less than those which are unshorn, that shearing is unprofitable, even though it may cause the animals to make a trifle more economical gains. On the other hand, a person who is posted on market conditions cannot infrequently make

a good profit by shearing the sheep before they are sold. If shorn, more
sheep can be shipped in a car.

QUESTIONS

1. State some of the important advantages of sheep production under farm conditions.
2. Give an example of the improvement that can be made by the use of a purebred ram on common ewes.
3. Why must some Merino blood be retained in the flocks on the Western ranges?
4. Why are lambs that are not to be retained for the breeding flock practically never carried over to the second year?
5. Compare the nutrient requirements of pregnant ewes and of ewes nursing lambs.
6. Discuss the nutrient requirements of fattening lambs, considering proportion of protein and amount of total digestible nutrients.
7. Of what importance is quality of protein in sheep feeding?
8. Discuss the addition of a protein supplement to a ration of grain and alfalfa hay for fattening lambs.
9. Should a protein supplement be added to a ration of corn silage, legume hay, and corn or other grain for fattening lambs?
10. Discuss the salt requirements of sheep.
11. Under what conditions should a calcium supplement be added to sheep rations?
12. When is a phosphorus supplement needed for sheep?
13. Discuss the use of other mineral supplements for sheep.
14. Of what importance are vitamins in sheep production?
15. Discuss the water requirements of sheep.
16. Under what conditions should grain be ground for sheep?
17. Discuss the chopping and grinding of hay for sheep.
18. Discuss the requirements of sheep for shelter.
19. Compare the requirements of breeding ewes and of fattening lambs for exercise.
20. What is the usual dressing percentage of fat lambs? What precautions should be taken in preparing fat lambs for shipment?
21. On what basis would you cull a flock of breeding ewes?
22. Discuss the shearing of sheep and of fattening lambs.

REFERENCES

1. Miller, Cal. Rpts. 1931, 1932; Harper, Ind. Bul. 343; Hammond, Ohio Bul. 367; Bell, Ohio Spec. Cir. 16; Joseph, Mont. Bul. 250; Tomhave and McDonald, Penn. Bul. 163; Keith and Henning, Penn. Bul. 288; Ikeler, Utah Bul. 220; Wilson and Livesay, West Va. Bul. 244.
2. Harper, Ind. Cir. 183; Tomhave and Severson, Penn. Bul. 163; Henning, Penn. Bul. 188.
3. Horlacher and Good, Ky. Bul. 243.
4. Miss. Sta., mimeo. rpt.; Fleming, Nev. Rpts. 1924, 1925, 1928; Hostetler, Foster, and Nance, N. C. Rpts. 1930, 1931, 1933; Darlow, Okla. Bul. 151; Starkey, S. C. Rpt. 1926.
5. Shaw, Montana Buls. 35, 47, and 59.
6. Paterson and Winchester, Kan. Cir. 96; Jones and Dickson, Tex. Bul. 379.
7. Mitchell and Kammlade, Ill. Rpt. 1932.
8. Morrison and Willman, N. Y. (Cornell) mimeo. rpt.
9. Darlow, Heller, and Felton, Okla. Bul. 220.
10. Marston, Australian Council Sci. and Indus., Res. Bul. 61; see also: Marston, Jour. Agr. Sci., England, 25, 1935, pp. 103-112.
11. Brown, Mich. Quar. Bul. 16, 1933, No. 1 and mimeo. rpt.
12. 20 experiments at Nebr. Station and 8 experiments at other stations. Gramlich, Nebr. Bul. 173 and mimeo. rpts.; Savin, Nebr. Bul. 197; Fox, Nebr. Buls. 204, 211; Weber, Nebr. Sta. mimeo rpts.; Brown, Mich. Sta. mimeo. rpt.; Jordan and Peters, Minn. Bul. 306 and mimeo. rpt.; Carmichael and Hammond, Ohio Bul. 245.
13. Kammlade, Ill. Rpt. 1930; Jordan and Peters, Minn. Bul. 306; Gramlich and Alexander, Nebr. Sta., mimeo. rpts.; Holden, Nebr. Buls. 194, 216; Darlow, Okla. Bul. 213 and mimeo. rpt.; Quayle, Wyo. Bul. 191.
14. Keith and Henning, Penn. Bul. 307.
15. Miller, Cal. Sta. mimeo. rpt.; Maynard, Morton, and Osland, Colo. Bul. 379, Colo. Press Bul. 76; Morton and Fairbanks, Colo. Press Bul. 79; Rinehart, Hickman, and Johnson, Id. Bul. 194 and mimeo. rpts.; Jordan and Peters, Minn. Bul. 306; Vinke and Bergstedt Mont. Sta., mimeo. rpt.; Holden, Nebr. Bul. 216; Maynard, Esplin, and Boswell, Utah Bul. 238; Quayle, Wyo. Bul. 191.

16. Wilson, Wright, and Fenn, S. D. Bul. 278 and mimeo. rpt.; Mackey and Jones, Tex. Bul. 465.
17. Coffey, Ill. Sta., information to the author; Skinner and King, Ind. Buls. 162, 168; Smith and Mumford, Mich. Bul. 113; Carmichael and Hammond, Ohio Buls. 187, 245.
18. Dunn and Evvard, Iowa Bul. 185; Paterson and Winchester, Kan. Cirs. 79, 88; Brown, Mich. Spec. Bul. 233; Brown, Mich. Quar. Bul., 14, 1931, No. 1; Savin, Nebr. Bul. 197; Fox, Nebr. Bul. 211; Holden, Nebr. Sta. mimeo. rpt.; Hackedorn, Bean, and Sotola, Wash. Bul. 185.
19. Skinner and King, Ind. Buls. 162, 168, 179, 184; Bell, Ohio Sta., misc. rpt.
20. Brown, Mich. Spec. Bul. 233; Johnson, Rinehart, and Hickman, Id. Bul. 176.
21. Miller, Cal. Sta., mimeo. rpts.; Maynard, Morton, and Osland, Colo. Bul. 379; Richards and Vinke, Mont. Exten. Cir. 26; Quayle, Wyo. Bul. 191.
22. Evvard et al., Iowa Res. Bul. 94.
23. J. M. Jones, Bayles, and J. H. Jones, Tex. Sta., mimeo. rpt.
24. Jardine and Anderson, U. S. Dept. Agr. Bul. 790; Sotola, Smith, and Ellington, Wash. Pop. Bul. 127.
25. Potter and Nelson, Western Live Stock Management, p. 146.
26. Miller, Cal. Sta., mimeo. rpt.; Hickman, Id. Bul. 205 and mimeo. rpts; Dickson and Hansen, Mont. Sta., mimeo. rpt.; Maynard, Utah Sta., mimeo. rpt.
27. Morton, Leinbach, and Tom, Colo. Press Bul. 83; Harper, Ind. Sta., mimeo. rpt.
28. Culbertson, Iowa Rpt. 1931; Bell, Ohio Bul. 417 and Ohio Bimo. Bul. 143: see also: Winter, Ohio Bul. 382; Winter, Amer. Jour. Physiol., 73, 1925, pp. 379-86.
29. Miller, Cal. Sta., mimeo rpt.; Morton, Leinbach, and Tom, Colo. Press Bul. 83; Jordan and Peters, Minn. Sta., mimeo. rpt.
30. Fraps, Tex. Bul. 232.
31. Reed, Kans. Sta., mimeo. rpt.; Cox and Connell, Kans. Rpt. 1932-34 and mimeo. rpts.; Alexander, Nebr. Sta., mimeo. rpt.; Jones, Stangel and Dickson, Tex. Rpts., 1929, 1930, 1931, 1932, 1933.
32. Jordan and Peters, Minn. Sta., mimeo. rpt.
33. Bell, Ohio Sta., information to the author.
34. Miller, Cal. Rpt. 1928; Morton and Osland, Colo. Rpt. 1920; Morton, Leinbach, and Tom, Colo. Press Bul. 83; Bell, Ohio Sta., mimeo. rpt.; Bowstead, University of Alberta, Canada, mimeo. rpt.
35. Harper, Ind. Sta., mimeo. rpt.
36. Culbertson and Thomas, Iowa Rpt. 1931; Evvard, Lamb, and Gaessler, Jour. Amer. Vet. Med. Assoc., 67, 1925, N. S. 20, p. 1.
37. Miller, Cal. Sta., mimeo. rpts. and information to the author.
38. Evvard and Culbertson, Iowa Rpts. 1921, 1922, 1923, and information to the author.
39. Evvard et al., Iowa Bul. 234; F. B. Mumford, Mich. Buls. 113, 128; H. W. Mumford, Mich. Bul. 136; Plumb, Amer. Soc. Anim. Prod., Proc. 1925-26; Ore. Rpt. 1926-28; Pontius, Carr, and Doyle, Amer. Soc. Anim. Prod., Proc. 1931.
40. Willman and Morrison, N. Y. (Cornell) Sta., mimeo. rpt.
41. Jordan and Peters, Minn. Sta., mimeo. rpt.
42. Miller, Cal. Rpt. 1923; Carlyle and Morton, Colo. Bul. 151; Morton, Colo. Bul. 187; Hickman, Rinehart, and Johnson, Id. Buls. 135, 194 and Id. Cir. 19; Potter, Ore. Sta., information to the author; Darlow, Okla. Sta., mimeo. rpt.; Hackedorn, Sotola, and Singleton, Wash. Bul. 258.
43. Potter, Ore. Sta., information to the author; Morton, Colo. Bul. 187; Johnson, Rinehart, and Hickman, Id. Bul. 177, Cir. 19; Hackedorn, Sotola, and Singleton, Wash. Bul. 258; see also: Quayle, Wyo. Bul. 191.
44. Scott, Ariz. Sta., mimeo. rpt.
45. Darlow, Okla. Rpt. 1932-34.
46. Wilson and Wright, S. D. Bul. 252 and mimeo. rpt.
47. Weber and Fox, Nebr. Bul. 259.
48. Mackey and Jones, Tex. Sta., mimeo. rpt.; Colo. Rpt. 1934; Darlow, Okla. Bul. 213.
49. Skinner and King, Ind. Buls. 168, 179, 184, 192, and 202.
50. Morrison and Kleinheinz, Wis. Bul. 323; unpublished data.
51. Gramlich, Nebr. Bul. 173; Johnson, Rinehart, and Hickman, Id. Buls. 176, 205, and mimeo. rpts.
52. Withycombe and Potter, Ore. Bul. 175.
53. Mumford, Trowbridge, and Hackedorn, Mo. Bul. 115.
54. Lush, Amer. Soc. Anim. Prod., Proc. 1922; Lindgren, Ore. Agr. Col., mimeo. rpt.; Hill, Wyo. Bul. 127.
55. Ritzman, N. H. Bul. 238.
56. Hackedorn and Sotola, Wash. Bul. 260.
57. Jones, Tex. Rpt. 1929.
58. Stanley and Scott, Ariz. Rpt. 1932; Coffey, Ill. Bul. 167; Skinner, King, and Starr, Indiana Buls. 168, 202, 221; Rinehart, Hickman, and Johnson, Id. Bul. 194; Mumford, Mich. Bul. 128; Gramlich, Nebr. Buls. 167, 170; Fox, Nebr. Bul. 204; Henning et al., Penn. Buls. 293, 308; Craig, Wis. Rpt. 1904.

CHAPTER XXXIII

FEEDS FOR SHEEP

I. Grains and Other Concentrates Low in Protein

Most of the feeding trials with sheep at the various experiment stations have been conducted with fattening lambs, rather than with breeding ewes or with lambs during the suckling period. The following paragraphs, which discuss the value of various feeds for sheep, must therefore be based largely on the results of the experiments with fattening lambs. Further information on efficient rations for breeding ewes, young lambs, and also fattening lambs is given in the next chapter.

In the discussions of the experiments with fattening lambs, where the weight of the lambs and the duration of the fattening period are not stated, it may be assumed that western lambs weighing 55 to 65 lbs. were generally used, and that the feeding period covered from 12 to 15 weeks.

1179. Indian corn.—Corn is the grain used most commonly for fattening lambs in the United States as far west as Colorado, beyond which barley and wheat are more commonly fed. (**512**) It is also widely used as part of the concentrates for breeding ewes and young lambs.

Since legume hay is rich in protein of good quality and also in calcium, as well as being high in vitamins A and D, it admirably supplements corn and the other grains. (**358**) On account of its excellence, the ration of corn grain and alfalfa or clover hay is a standard for fattening lambs and sheep over a large part of our country. In this chapter other rations are compared, so far as possible, with this successful combination. It has been shown in the previous chapter that it is not necessary to add any protein supplement, such as linseed or cottonseed meal, to a ration of grain and legume hay for fattening lambs. (**1164**) Although the gains will be a trifle more rapid when a small amount of such a supplement is fed, the addition of the supplement will generally be uneconomical.

To show the possibilities of the ration of corn grain and legume hay for fattening lambs, there are averaged in the table on page 751 the results from 12 experiment stations with 44 lots, including a total of 1,171 lambs, fed experimentally for periods averaging 80 days on a liberal allowance of shelled corn (1.1 lbs. a head daily or more, on the average) with alfalfa or clover hay for roughage. The results are also presented for 43 experiments in which a total of 2,300 lambs were fed for an average of 97 days on a limited allowance of shelled corn (average of less than 1.1 lbs. a head daily) and all the alfalfa or clover hay they would eat.

The lambs fed the liberal allowance of corn ate 1.3 lbs. corn and 1.4 lbs. alfalfa hay and gained 0.34 lb. per head daily. For each 100 lbs. gain in weight they consumed 387 lbs. corn and 418 lbs. hay. The

Corn and legume hay for fattening lambs

Average ration	Initial weight Lbs.	Daily gain Lbs.	Feed for 100 lbs. gain Corn Lbs.	Hay Lbs.
Corn allowance liberal				
Shelled corn, 1.3 lbs.				
Alfalfa or clover hay, 1.4 lbs..............	63	0.34	387	418
Corn allowance limited				
Shelled corn, 0.9 lb.				
Alfalfa or clover hay, 2.3 lbs...............	62	0.31	305	727

lambs fed the limited allowance of corn, with all the legume hay they would eat, gained only a little less rapidly (0.31 lb. per head daily), because of the good quality of the hay fed in the experiments. For each 100 lbs. of gain these lambs required 305 lbs. corn and 727 lbs. hay.

From the averages given in this table, one may readily calculate the cost and possible profits of fattening lambs on such a ration under reasonably favorable conditions. It should be borne in mind that in these experiments thrifty lambs were fed by experts. In the commercial fattening of lambs the average rate of gain will usually be somewhat less and the amount of feed required per 100 lbs. of gain will often be somewhat higher.

The richness of yellow corn in vitamin A probably does not make it superior under usual conditions to white corn for sheep feeding, for sheep generally receive hay and other roughage that is richer in vitamin A. (511)

1180. Corn requires supplement.—Numerous experiments have proved that fattening lambs will not make rapid or economical gains when they are fed only corn and non-legume roughage, without a protein supplement. For example, in 7 tests lambs fed corn with timothy or prairie hay, without any supplement, gained an average of only 0.19 lb. per head daily, in comparison with 0.32 lb. for others fed corn and clover or alfalfa hay.[1] The lambs on the unbalanced ration required 46 per cent more corn and 15 per cent more hay for each 100 lbs. gain than those fed the balanced ration of corn and legume hay.

In 4 other trials the addition of 0.2 lb. linseed meal or cottonseed meal to a ration of corn and timothy hay increased the gain from 0.23 lb. per head daily to 0.30 lb. and also made a large saving in the amount of feed required per 100 lbs. gain.[2] On the average, each 100 lbs. of protein supplement saved 186 lbs. corn and 173 lbs. hay, without considering the advantage of the more rapid gains. In these trials still better results would probably have been secured if a calcium supplement had also been added to the ration of corn and timothy hay.

1181. Corn as the only grain.—When fed in a properly-balanced ration, corn can be used successfully as the only grain for breeding ewes in winter, providing the allowance is limited so the ewes do not become too fat. However, shepherds quite generally prefer for this purpose more bulky mixtures, such as are mentioned in the next chapter. (1240)

In the corn belt, corn is extensively fed as the only grain to fattening lambs, after they are safely on feed. For fattening lambs which are hand-fed it gives excellent results when thus used, if it is properly balanced by feeds supplying plenty of good-quality protein and of calcium. When lambs are self-fed corn, some bulky feed like chopped hay or oats should be mixed with it to lessen digestive troubles, which may cause serious death losses. (1265)

Even in the hand-feeding of fattening lambs it may also be safer to mix such feeds with the corn, if they are being forced as rapidly as possible on all the grain they can be induced to eat. In these cases such a combination as 2 to 3 parts corn and 1 part oats, by weight, is excellent. Where lambs are not forced so rapidly, there is no advantage in mixing such a feed as oats with the corn. (1185)

1182. Feeding corn in various forms.—Corn grain is usually fed to sheep and lambs in the form of shelled corn or as ear corn. Experiments have shown clearly that there is usually no advantage in grinding shelled corn or in grinding ear corn for sheep, with the following exceptions:[3] (1) For sheep with poor teeth, (2) for young lambs up to 5 or 6 weeks of age, and (3) when fattening lambs are being self-fed such a mixture as corn grain and chopped hay, or even when they are being hand-fed all of such a mixture that they can be induced to eat. (1172) Usually hand-fed lambs will make slightly more rapid and economical gains on shelled corn than on ground corn. Likewise, ear corn or broken ear corn has given as good or even better results than corn-and-cob meal. Corn ground coarsely is preferable to fine meal for sheep or lambs.

For fattening lambs ear corn or broken ear corn has produced just as rapid gains on the average, in 9 trials as shelled corn, when each was fed as the only grain.[4] Also, the cost of feed per 100 lbs. gain was slightly less for the lambs fed ear corn.

Sometimes fattening lambs are fed shock corn, ears and all, usually being given a small amount of shelled corn or other grain at first, until they learn to husk the corn ears. In an Illinois trial lambs thus fed shock corn and clover hay gained 0.25 lb. per head daily, in comparison with 0.29 lb. for others fed shelled corn and clover hay, and required 62 lbs. more corn grain and 43 lbs. less hay per 100 lbs. gain than the lambs fed shelled corn.[5] Very satisfactory results were secured in a Michigan trial in which lambs were fattened on a ration of shock corn, linseed meal, and alfalfa hay, or on these feeds plus corn silage.[6] In another Michigan test ground shock corn was unsatisfactory for fattening lambs, probably because they were forced to eat too much of the corn stalks.[7]

Both ear corn and shock corn are better suited for feeding on a thick sod than in a dry lot or barn, for they may be scattered on the sod so that each lamb will have an equal chance to feed, and little will be wasted. In the lot or barn, lambs are apt to drop the ears where they become soiled, or to bunch them up in the trough so that each lamb does not get its share.

Fattening lambs in the corn field, which is a common practice in some localities, is discussed in the next chapter. (1268)

1183. Hominy feed.—This corn by-product, which closely resembles corn grain in composition, is about equal to shelled corn for sheep feeding. (519) In 6 trials with fattening lambs hominy feed has been directly compared with shelled corn when fed with legume hay (with corn silage and linseed or cottonseed meal in addition in certain of the tests).[8] The rate of gain was practically the same on the two feeds, the lambs fed hominy feed gaining 0.01 lb. less on the average. Also, the amounts of feed required per 100 lbs. gain were nearly identical on hominy feed and on shelled corn.

1184. Barley.—North of the corn belt and especially in the western range district, barley is used extensively for sheep feeding. (551) It is a very satisfactory grain for growing or fattening lambs and for breeding ewes. Numerous experiments have been conducted by the experiment stations to compare the value of barley and corn when fed as the only grains to fattening lambs. The following table summarizes the results of 29 trials, averaging 94 days in length, in which good-quality barley was compared with shelled corn when fed with alfalfa hay to lambs averaging 62 lbs. in weight at the start:[9]

Barley vs. corn for fattening lambs

Average ration	Daily gain Lbs.	Feed for 100 lbs. gain Grain Lbs.	Hay Lbs.
Lot I, total of 1,309 lambs			
Whole barley, 1.0 lb. Alfalfa hay, 2.4 lbs.............	0.30	343	804
Lot II, total of 1,310 lambs			
Shelled corn, 1.0 lb. Alfalfa, 2.4 lbs...............	0.31	318	762

In these numerous trials the lambs fed whole barley made nearly as rapid gains as those fed shelled corn, but they required 25 lbs. more grain and 42 lbs. more hay for 100 lbs. gain. Not considering the slight difference in rate of gain, 100 lbs. of barley were equal in feeding value to 92.7 lbs. corn minus 12.2 lbs. alfalfa hay. From these figures, one can readily compute the relative percentage value of barley compared with corn at local prices. For example, with shelled corn valued at twice as much per ton as alfalfa hay, barley would be worth 87 per cent as much per ton as corn.

In 10 other trials[10] whole barley has been compared with shelled corn for fattening lambs when fed with alfalfa or clover hay and corn or sorghum silage, with or without a protein supplement, and in 13 trials[11] these two grains have been compared when fed with alfalfa hay and a small amount of linseed meal or cottonseed cake. The results of these trials agree identically with those presented in the preceding table, barley being worth 87 per cent as much per ton as corn, on the average, not considering the fact that the barley-fed lambs gained .02 lb. less per head daily than the corn-fed lambs.

These 52 experiments therefore show that under average conditions good-quality barley is worth about 87 per cent as much per ton as shelled corn of equal quality. Usually it will take lambs fed barley 3 to 6 days longer to reach a certain degree of fatness than it will corn-fed lambs.

Although barley contains somewhat more protein than corn, it is relatively low in it, and therefore the ration should be balanced by feeding legume hay or by adding a protein supplement. It is not generally profitable to add a supplement to a ration of barley and legume hay for fattening lambs, for the ration already has enough protein to produce rapid gains. (1164)

Barley produces about as satisfactory results when fed as the only grain as when it is fed in combination with corn to fattening lambs.[12]

Light-weight barley and that with a large proportion of hulls is worth considerably less than plump, heavy barley. Barley damaged by scab gave satisfactory results with fattening lambs in an Illinois trial and was not unpalatable.[13] (**503**)

Numerous experiments have shown that for fattening lambs or for breeding ewes it does not usually pay to grind or roll barley, with the possible exception of the hard bald or hull-less barley.[14] Fattening lambs fed ground or rolled barley have usually gained less rapidly and required slightly more feed per 100 lbs. gain than those fed the whole grain.

1185. Oats.—This grain is well liked by sheep and is extensively used for the breeding flock, for young lambs, and for starting fattening lambs on feed. (**528**) On account of its bulky nature, it is one of the safest feeds to use for this last purpose. (**1260**) Commonly, when oats are thus used, the proportion is reduced gradually as the feeding progresses. After the lambs are on full feed, the oats are usually omitted or only a small proportion is fed, along with heavier grains, such as corn or barley. However, good-quality, heavy-weight oats may be successfully fed as the only grain throughout the fattening period. When this is done, the lambs should be given all the oats they will eat, after they are safely on full feed, for it must be borne in mind that oats are much less concentrated than corn or barley.

In 6 trials at the Indiana Station lambs were fed on the average 1.7 lbs. oats per head daily, along with 0.16 lb. cottonseed meal, 0.8 lb. clover hay, and 0.9 lb. corn silage.[15] Other lambs fed shelled corn in place of oats, ate only 1.1 lbs. corn, with 0.15 lb. cottonseed meal, 1.2 lbs. clover hay, and 1.2 lbs. silage. The oat-fed lambs gained 0.30 lb. a day, in comparison with 0.28 lb. for those fed corn, and they reached just as good a finish as the corn-fed lambs. In these trials, considering the saving in consumption of hay and silage by the oat-fed lambs and also their greater gains, each 100 lbs. of oats were equal in feeding value to the same weight of corn. It was found that lambs can be put on a full feed of oats in less than half the time it takes to get them on a full feed of corn.

In experiments where lambs have been fed approximately equal amounts of oats or of corn, the lambs fed oats have gained less rapidly than those receiving corn, and oats have been worth decidedly less per ton than corn. In 12 tests of this kind lambs fed oats as the only grain gained 0.33 lb. per head daily, in comparison with 0.37 lb. for those fed corn, and the oat-fed lambs required somewhat more feed per 100 lbs. gain.[16] Not considering the less rapid gains on oats, each 100 lbs. of this grain equalled in feeding value only 85.4 lbs. corn minus 0.3 lb. protein supplement and 10.5 lbs. hay or hay equivalent in hay and silage. With corn at $20, protein supplement at $40, and hay at $10 per ton, oats were worth about 80 per cent as much as corn in these trials. In certain Montana trials oats have been about equal to shelled corn and superior to barley for lambs fed wet beet pulp and alfalfa hay, but in other Montana tests oats have been worth about 90 per cent as much as barley.[17]

When fattening lambs are self-fed or when they are hand-fed all the grain they will eat, oats are an excellent grain to use as part of the mixture, on account of their bulk. (**1265**) However, under other conditions it is not generally profitable to include oats in the grain allowance, after the lambs are on full feed, unless oats are cheaper per ton than corn or barley.[18]

It is unnecessary to grind oats for sheep. On the average, fattening lambs have made more rapid and economical gains on whole oats than on ground oats.[19] Sheaf oats may be fed to breeding ewes in the winter, thus saving the expenses of threshing.

1186. Wheat.—Wheat is an excellent grain for sheep feeding, but it is not commonly used for this purpose unless unusually low in price or of too poor quality for milling. (537) Wheat that is frosted or otherwise unsuited for milling is usually almost as valuable as high-grade wheat for sheep. Durum wheat and common wheat have about the same feeding value.

Though wheat is an excellent feed for fattening lambs, for some unexplained reason its value for lambs in comparison with that of corn is somewhat less than for fattening cattle or for pigs. While wheat is fully equal to corn for fattening cattle and is definitely superior to barley, wheat is worth only about 83 per cent as much as corn for fattening lambs and is about equal to barley.

Whole wheat has been directly compared with shelled corn in 18 trials with fattening lambs fed alfalfa or clover hay.[20] The lambs fed wheat gained an average of 0.28 lb. per head daily, while those fed corn gained 0.31 lb. Also, the wheat-fed lambs required 394 lbs. wheat and 699 lbs. hay per 100 lbs. gain, in comparison with only 357 lbs. corn and 640 lbs. hay for those fed corn. Considering only the feed required per 100 lbs. gain and not the difference in rate of gain, 100 lbs. of wheat were equal to 90.6 lbs. shelled corn minus 15.0 lbs. hay. With corn at twice the price of hay per ton, this would make wheat worth 83 per cent as much per ton as corn.

Wheat and barley, fed with alfalfa hay as roughage, have been compared in 11 trials.[21] The lambs fed wheat made practically as rapid gains as those fed barley, on the average, and required about the same amounts of grain and hay per 100 lbs. gain.

Because wheat is not high in protein, it gives the best results when fed with legume hay. While it gives satisfactory results when fed as the only grain to fattening lambs, even better results seem to be secured when wheat is fed in combination with shelled corn, whole barley, or grain sorghum.[22] Lambs like such mixtures a little better than wheat alone, and there is sometimes less trouble with them going "off feed."

Experiments have shown that it does not usually pay to grind or crush wheat for sheep.[23] Indeed, the ground or crushed grain is less palatable to them and in the case of fattening lambs will usually produce less rapid and less economical gains than whole wheat.

1187. Sorghum grain.—In the southern plains states the various grain sorghums are of much importance for sheep feeding. (565) Extensive experiments have shown that the threshed grains of all the grain sorghums are about equal to shelled corn in feeding value for sheep. Milo, kafir, and feterita grain were compared with shelled corn for fattening lambs in 5 experiments at the Texas Station.[24] There was no appreciable difference between any of these and corn in the rate of gain or in the feed required per 100 lbs. of gain. Similar results have been secured in other experiments in which kafir, darso, and Atlas sorghum grain have been compared with corn for fattening lambs.[25]

Several tests have shown that it does not pay to grind the sorghums for sheep.[26] Neither is it necessary to thresh or grind the grain sorghum heads for sheep. The heads of unthreshed grain sorghum have proved equal to the threshed grain in feeding value, considering the actual amount of grain contained, and have produced practically as rapid gains on fattening lambs.[27] In wet weather there may, however, be considerable waste in feeding the unthreshed heads.

The seed of the sweet sorghums is apparently of slightly lower value for sheep than that of the grain sorghums, being worth 82 to 88 per cent as much as shelled corn for fattening lambs in tests at the Texas Station and 80 per cent as much as wheat in a Kansas trial.[28]

1188. Rye.—Rye is apparently liked better by sheep than by most other stock. (561) When fed as the only grain to fattening lambs it was fully equal to barley or wheat in a Minnesota trial and to wheat in Nebraska experiments.[29] In these trials rye, fed as the only grain, produced about as good results as a mixture of half rye and half barley, corn, or oats. There is no advantage in grinding rye for sheep.

1189. Beet molasses; cane molasses.—In the western beet-sugar districts beet molasses is often used for sheep feeding, especially for fattening lambs, and in other districts cane molasses is sometimes fed to sheep. (**641, 642**) Beet molasses and cane molasses probably have about the same value for sheep, when containing equal percentages of sugar. In Colorado and Iowa tests with fattening lambs beet molasses was worth somewhat more than cane molasses, but the cane molasses used was lower in sugar and higher in water than the beet molasses.[30]

Molasses has the highest value for fattening lambs when not more than one-third to one-half pound per head daily is fed. It then serves as an appetizer and usually increases the rate of gain slightly. It does not produce satisfactory gains when used as an entire substitute for grain. In 15 trials lambs fed an average of 0.38 lb. beet molasses a day in addition to grain and alfalfa hay, with or without linseed meal and corn silage, gained 0.34 lb. per head daily, in comparison with 0.32 lb. for others which received a full feed of grain, but no molasses.[31] Each 100 lbs. of molasses saved 58 lbs. of grain, 1 lb. linseed meal, 45 lbs. hay, and 5 lbs. silage. With feeds at usual prices, 100 lbs. of beet molasses were equal in value to about 84 lbs. of grain, not considering the slight advantage in rate of gain for the molasses-fed lambs.

To compare a concentrate mixture containing cane molasses for fattening lambs with one containing no molasses, tests were made at the Wisconsin Station with hand-fed and self-fed lambs.[32] Lambs fed a mixture containing ground corn, ground oats, wheat bran, linseed meal, iodized salt, and 10 per cent of molasses, with alfalfa hay and corn silage for roughage, gained only 0.02 lb. more per head daily than those fed a similar mixture, except that it contained no molasses. On the basis of the amounts of feed required per 100 lbs. of gain, the molasses was worth considerably less than corn, on the average.

Where a small amount of molasses is fed as an appetizer or to get lambs to clean up rather inferior hay or other dry roughage, it may have a higher value than grain per pound. In an Indiana trial when 0.15 lb. cane molasses was added to the excellent ration of shelled corn, cottonseed meal, clover hay and corn silage, there was no significant increase in the rate of gain and the molasses was equal to corn in feeding value.[33] Molasses is usually poured in the grain troughs as a "broad ribbon" or is mixed thoroughly with cut hay or straw. In feeding molasses to fattening lambs, care must be taken that their wool does not become smeared with molasses.

1190. Dried beet pulp; dried molasses-beet pulp.—These by-products of beet sugar manufacture are often economical substitutes for grain in the western states.[34] (664) In 10 experiments lambs fed a mixture of dried molasses-beet pulp and shelled corn made as rapid gains, on the average, as others fed corn for the only concentrate.[35] In these trials the dried pulp was worth about 95 per cent as much per ton as shelled corn. A mixture of one-half dried molasses-beet pulp and one-half ground barley was superior to ground barley for fattening lambs in Montana and Utah tests.[36]

Dried molasses-beet pulp, fed as the only concentrate with alfalfa hay, was fully equal to ground barley in California trials.[37] In 18 Nebraska and Wyoming trials dried molasses-beet pulp was worth about 80 per cent as much, on the average, as corn per ton.[38]

1191. Other concentrates low in protein.—In addition to the grains and other low-protein concentrates that have been discussed in this chapter, several others are sometimes used for sheep feeding. These include emmer, hog-millet seed, rice by-products, dried apple pomace, and raisin by-products. For detailed information on these feeds see the various chapters of Part II.

II. Protein Supplements

1192. Linseed meal or cake; cottonseed meal or cake.—These popular feeds are the most commonly used in sheep and lamb feeding of all the high-protein supplements. (582-584, 591) They are excellent for fattening lambs and are about equal in value for this purpose. Linseed meal or cake is also a first-class supplement for the breeding flock, and cottonseed meal or cake is satisfactory for breeding ewes, if not fed in excess. Linseed cake and cottonseed cake of pea or sheep size are relished somewhat better by sheep than the finely-ground meals, but the latter are satisfactory, except for outdoor feeding where wind may waste them.

Because of the richness of these supplements in protein, but relatively small amounts are needed to balance a ration for sheep. For example, in feeding fattening lambs only 0.10 to 0.15 lb. per head daily of linseed meal or cottonseed meal is sufficient to balance a ration of corn grain, alfalfa or clover hay, and corn or sorghum silage. (1165) Since high-grade cottonseed meal is richer than linseed meal in protein, slightly less of it is needed to balance a ration.

Linseed meal or cake and cottonseed meal or cake have been compared in a considerable number of feeding trials with fattening lambs, but in practically all of these tests equal weights of the two supplements have been fed. This has resulted in the lambs which were fed cottonseed meal receiving a little more of the supplement than was actually needed, which was a slight handicap to this feed.

In 2 trials at the Wisconsin Station these supplements were compared, when fed with shelled corn, a limited amount of legume hay, and all the corn silage the lambs would eat.[39] The basal ration was therefore relatively low in protein. Less cottonseed meal was fed than of linseed meal, to make the protein content of the two rations the same. There was practically no difference in the gains on the two rations, in the feed required for 100 lbs. gain, or in the finish of the lambs. Due to the fact that a little less cottonseed meal was needed to balance the ration, this supplement had a slightly higher value than linseed meal.

In 11 trials with fattening lambs, a small amount of linseed meal or cake or the same amount of cottonseed meal or cake has been added to a ration of corn and alfalfa hay, which, as we have seen in the previous chapter, is already nearly balanced in amount of protein.[40] The lambs fed linseed meal or cake gained 0.38 lb. per day in comparison with 0.37 lb. for those fed cottonseed meal or cake—not a very significant difference. They also required a little less feed for 100 lbs. gain, but there was no appreciable difference in the selling price of the lambs. Considering the differences in the feed required per 100 lbs. gain, cottonseed meal was worth about 98 per cent as much as linseed meal.

In 6 similar comparisons these feeds were compared as supplements to a ration of shelled corn, clover hay, and corn silage for fattening lambs,[41] and in 6 comparisons as supplements to the same ration, except that oat straw was fed in place of nearly all the clover hay.[42] When fed with clover hay, cottonseed meal was equal to linseed meal in rate of gain, in economy of gain, and in the finish of the lambs. However, when there was practically no clover hay in the ration, there was a slight advantage in favor of linseed meal in rate of gain and in feed required per 100 lbs. gain, though the lambs fed cottonseed meal sold at as high a price as those fed linseed meal. In these latter trials cottonseed meal was worth about 88 per cent as much per ton as linseed meal.

From these experiments and other trials in which different rations were fed,[43] we may conclude that for fattening lambs cottonseed meal or cake is fully equal to linseed meal or cake when considerable legume hay is fed and when care is taken not to feed more of the supplement than is actually needed to balance the particular ration used.

In the southern and southwestern states cottonseed meal, when low in price, is sometimes fed as the only concentrate to fattening lambs. If more cottonseed meal is fed than is needed to balance the ration, the additional amount is usually worth no more, pound for pound, than corn or other grains and may be worth even less. On such a ration there is danger of "cottonseed meal injury," unless the lambs get plenty of good legume hay or other roughage which will prevent this trouble. (582) For example, lambs have been successfully fed 0.7 to 1.0 lb. cottonseed meal per head daily with alfalfa hay for 90 to 100 days, but when cottonseed meal has been fed with cottonseed hulls as the only roughage for the entire fattening period, some lambs have died.[44]

1193. Wheat bran; wheat mixed feed.—*Wheat bran* is excellent as part of the concentrates for breeding ewes, as it is laxative and fairly rich in protein. (542) It is also often used as part of the concentrate mixture for young lambs and is frequently mixed with corn and other heavy concentrates in starting fattening lambs on feed, in order to prevent digestive disturbances. It should form no large part of the concentrate allowance for fattening lambs after they are on full feed, for it is too bulky and induces growth, rather than fattening.

In a trial at the Idaho Station, lambs fed 1 part wheat bran and 3 parts barley, with mixed hay for roughage, gained 0.27 lb. per head daily, while others fed linseed cake in place of bran gained 0.32 lb. daily.[45] In a North Dakota trial lambs fed a mixture of 20 lbs. bran and 80 lbs. barley with alfalfa hay gained 12 per cent less than those fed a mixture of 10 lbs. linseed meal and 90 lbs. barley, but nearly as rapidly as other lambs which were fed a mixture of 5 lbs. linseed meal and 95 lbs. barley.[46]

Wheat mixed feed (bran and middlings) was an excellent supplement to barley and alfalfa hay, fed with or without wet beet pulp, in a Colorado trial with fattening lambs.[47] When 0.6 lb. per head daily was fed in place of 0.2 lb. linseed meal or cottonseed meal, the wheat mixed feed was worth about 60 per cent as much as these high-protein supplements.

1194. Soybeans; soybean oil meal.—Both soybeans and soybean oil meal are excellent protein-rich supplements for sheep feeding. Experiments have shown that they are usually equal to linseed meal or cottonseed meal in value per ton.[48] There seems to be little choice between soybeans and soybean oil meal for feeding sheep, for the results with these two supplements have been practically the same, on the average, in 5 trials with fattening lambs.[49] It does not generally pay to grind soybeans for sheep.[50]

When soybeans were fed as a supplement to corn grain, clover hay and corn silage for fattening lambs in 3 Indiana trials, there was no advantage in adding a mineral mixture to furnish additional calcium and phosphorus.[51] With no legume hay in the ration, the use of a calcium supplement would be advisable. (**1167**)

1195. Corn gluten meal; corn gluten feed.—These corn by-products are satisfactory to use as the only protein supplement when there is considerable legume hay in the ration to make good the deficiencies in the quality of protein in corn grain. On the other hand, if little or no legume hay is fed, it is wise to combine either of these feeds with supplements that furnish protein of more complete nature, such as linseed meal or cottonseed meal. (148)

No experiments have apparently been reported in which *corn gluten meal* has been compared with either cottonseed meal or linseed meal as a supplement for sheep or lamb rations that are low in protein. Gluten meal has been compared with these supplements in 5 tests, but the supplements have been added to a ration of alfalfa hay and corn grain.[52] As we have seen in the previous chapter, alfalfa hay and corn grain, without any supplement whatsoever, supply nearly enough protein to enable fattening lambs to make maximum gains, and these feeds also provide protein of excellent quality. (1164) When thus fed, gluten meal has been equal or slightly superior to cottonseed meal or linseed meal, but this does not show that it would be equally efficient in balancing a ration low in protein.

Corn gluten feed, used as the only protein supplement for fattening lambs, has been less satisfactory than cottonseed meal or linseed meal in Kansas and Wisconsin trials.[53] The lambs fed gluten feed were not so well finished as those fed linseed meal. Judging from these tests, gluten feed had best be combined with such a supplement as linseed meal or cottonseed meal.

Occasionally, gluten feed is lower in price than corn grain. It may then be used as a partial or even a complete substitute for corn in fattening lambs or feeding other sheep. In 2 Iowa trials when gluten feed was thus fed as a substitute for all or most of the corn for fattening lambs it was worth, on the average, only 86 per cent as much as corn per ton.[54] However, in a Nebraska trial when it was substituted for half the corn fed fattening lambs, it increased the gains and was worth more per ton than corn.[55]

1196. Meat scraps; tankage; fish meal.—Recent experiments have shown that meat scraps, tankage, and fish meal may generally be used satisfactorily as protein supplements in sheep feeding. Though sheep may not like these animal by-products at first, after a few days they will usually eat the small amount needed to balance the ration. It is a good plan to mix these supplements with better-liked feeds until the sheep get used to the taste. Since these feeds, when of high grade, are considerably richer than cottonseed meal or linseed meal in protein, correspondingly less should be fed to balance a ration.

The results of experiments in which either *meat scraps* or *digester tankage* have been used as the only protein supplement for fattening lambs have differed somewhat.[56] In some of the trials these feeds have produced fully as good results or even slightly better results than cottonseed meal or linseed meal, but in other tests the gains have been better on the latter supplements. Excellent results have been secured at the Ohio Station in the use for sheep feeding of the all-purpose protein supplement which has been mentioned previously. (629) This contains 30 per cent of meat scraps.

Fish meal was an excellent supplement for fattening lambs in California trials.[57] Even when added to a ration of alfalfa hay and either barley or dried molasses-beet pulp (a combination already containing a good supply of protein), fish meal tended to increase the rate of gain more than did cottonseed meal. In these tests the average value of fish meal was considerably greater than that of cottonseed meal. The feeding of fish meal did not produce a taint in the meat.

1197. Other protein supplements.—In addition to the protein supplements that have been considered in this chapter, several others may be used satisfactorily when available at economical prices. These include field peas, cull beans, peanut oil meal, peanut oil feed, cottonseed, flaxseed, cowpeas, distillers' dried grains, brewers' dried grains, coconut oil meal, sesame oil meal, and other oil meals not common in the United States. The composition and uses of each of these feeds are discussed in Part II.

1198. Combinations of protein supplements.—Very few experiments have been conducted with sheep to compare the efficiency of combinations of protein supplements with standard single supplements, like linseed meal or cottonseed meal. In experiments at the Minnesota and Nebraska Stations the following mixtures were compared with linseed meal, cottonseed meal, or gluten meal alone, when fed as supplements to corn grain and alfalfa hay for fattening lambs:[58] (1) Equal parts of linseed meal and cottonseed meal, (2) equal parts of gluten meal and either linseed meal or cottonseed meal, and (3) a triple combination of equal parts of the 3 supplements.

In 4 trials the combinations of two supplements did not prove superior, on the average, to either linseed meal or gluten meal, fed as the only supplement. The triple combination was slightly superior, on the average, to the other mixtures or to linseed meal or cottonseed meal, fed as the only supplement. Gluten meal nearly equalled this triple combination in these tests.

It should be borne in mind that the check ration used in these tests (corn grain and alfalfa hay), is already well balanced both in quantity and in quality of protein. Possibly certain mixtures of protein supplements would show a marked superiority over single supplements when used to balanced a ration low in protein or one in which the protein was of inferior quality. However, in an Ohio trial with fattening lambs the "all-purpose" protein supplemental mixture (a combination of soybean oil meal, cottonseed meal, linseed meal, and dry-rendered tankage) was not superior to cottonseed meal as a supplement to a ration of shelled corn, corn silage, and either timothy or clover hay.[59]

III. Legume Hay

1199. Legume hay.—Well-cured legume hay is far superior to any other dry roughage for sheep feeding, because of its richness in protein of good quality, the high content of calcium, the ample supply of vitamins, and its palatability. It is much more important to supply some legume hay to sheep than to beef cattle or even to dairy cattle. It is also more important for sheep than for cattle that the hay be fine-stemmed and leafy.

Legume hay is unexcelled for the breeding flock and is of even greater importance in feeding pregnant and nursing ewes than in the case of fattening lambs. Merely an abundance of good legume hay, with a small amount of grain for a few weeks before lambing, makes a very satisfactory ration for wintering breeding ewes. (**1236**) Early-cut, leafy legume hay is nearly indispensable in raising early spring lambs that need good roughage for some weeks before they can be turned to pasture.

It has been emphasized earlier in this chapter that a ration of legume hay and corn or other grain is nearly ideal for fattening lambs, and that this ration is therefore taken as a standard with which other combinations of feed are compared. Though the addition of a small amount of such a supplement as cottonseed meal or linseed meal will commonly increase the gains a trifle, the use of the supplement does not generally increase the profits. (**1164**) Even when legume hay is fed in combination with non-legume roughage, such as corn or sorghum silage, the amount of protein supplement needed to balance the ration is much less than when no legume hay is furnished.

The great superiority for sheep of legume hay over grass hay of the usual quality is well shown by the results of 7 trials in which clover or alfalfa hay has been directly compared with timothy or prairie hay.[60] In each test one lot of lambs was fattened on the legume hay and corn, without any protein supplement, while another lot was fed the grass hay and corn, with 0.2 lb. of linseed meal or cottonseed meal.

Though the lambs fed grass hay had plenty of protein, they gained only 0.25 lb. a day, in comparison with 0.31 lb. for those fed legume hay. The lambs receiving grass hay required considerably more feed per 100 lbs. gain, including 92 lbs. of expensive protein supplement. Because of this, the grass hay was actually worth only the absurdly low figure of 58 cents a ton in these trials in comparison with $10 a ton for alfalfa.

Recent experiments have shown that the results on a grass hay ration are generally improved when a calcium supplement is added as well as a protein supplement. (**1210**) Even if this had been done in these trials, the grass hay would still have been worth much less than the legume hay.

1200. Alfalfa hay.—Alfalfa hay is unexcelled for sheep feeding and may be taken as the standard with which other forages are compared. (**373**) It has to a high degree all the virtues that have been pointed out in the preceding paragraphs. In general, the greener in color and the finer and more leafy the alfalfa hay is, the more valuable it will be for sheep. The relative value of the various cuttings of hay and the value of brown alfalfa hay in comparison with green alfalfa hay are discussed in Chapter XIII. The chopping and grinding of alfalfa hay for sheep have been considered in the preceding chapter. (1172)

Lambs cannot be fattened sufficiently for the large markets on alfalfa hay alone, even that of the best quality. Experiments by the Idaho, Nebraska, and Nevada Stations show that lambs fed all the good alfalfa hay they will eat will usually gain only 0.17 lb. or less per head daily, and they will not reach a satisfactory market finish.[61]

When it is desired to fatten lambs for marketing late in the winter or in the spring, it may be desirable to feed them hay alone during the first part of the fattening period and later to add grain. (1258)

1201. Alfalfa-molasses feed.—This feed, made by mixing cane or beet molasses with alfalfa meal, is often fed to sheep in certain sections of the West, especially to fattening lambs. When lambs are being given a very heavy allowance of grain to force them to fatten rapidly, alfalfa-molasses meal is sometimes fed in place of hay and the grain is mixed with it to help prevent digestive troubles.

When thus fed in two Nebraska experiments, alfalfa-molasses meal produced about the same gains and had approximately the same value per ton as alfalfa meal (without molasses).[62] In these trials and in an Idaho test alfalfa-molasses meal was worth, on the average, about 50 per cent more a ton than uncut alfalfa hay.[63] In the Nebraska trials there was no significant difference in the value of alfalfa-molasses meal made from beet molasses and from cane molasses, and in feeds containing 20, 30, or 40 per cent beet molasses.

In other trials with fattening lambs, when 0.5 lb. per head daily of alfalfa-molasses feed was added to a ration of shelled corn and alfalfa hay, with or without linseed meal, the gains were increased and the alfalfa-molasses feed was worth about 84 per cent as much as shelled corn.[64] Alfalfa-molasses feed is not high in protein, and therefore it should not be fed as a substitute for such protein supplements as linseed meal or cottonseed meal.[65]

1202. Clover hay.—Clover hay, one of the best roughages for sheep, should be cut early. *Red clover hay* has been about equal to alfalfa hay of the same quality for fattening lambs in several experiments in which plenty of protein has been furnished in the rations.[66] (382) Since alfalfa hay is richer than clover hay in protein, possibly it would have a somewhat higher value than clover in such a ration as corn grain, corn silage, and hay, with no protein supplement.

Alsike clover hay proved even slightly superior to alfalfa in a Montana trial.[67] (386) *Mammoth clover hay* is usually coarser and more stemmy than red clover. (385)

1203. Sweet clover hay.—Good-quality sweet clover hay is a satisfactory roughage for sheep, but the value per ton in comparison with alfalfa or red clover hay will vary quite widely, depending on the quality of the hay. (391) When sweet clover hay of the usual kind is fed, a considerably larger proportion of the hay will be refused, on account of its stemmy nature, than in the case of alfalfa.

Excellent sweet clover hay, well-cured and leafy, was equal to alfalfa for fattening lambs in Minnesota and Washington trials.[68] In 7 other experiments the value of sweet clover hay per ton for fattening lambs has ranged from less than 50 up to 95 per cent of the value of alfalfa hay, depending on the quality of the hay.[69]

Lambs Fattening in a Field of Corn and Soybeans

Many farmers fatten lambs in the fall on rape, stubble fields, or standing corn. Growing soybeans with the corn for "lambing down" is a good practice.

Straw Is Unsatisfactory as the Only Roughage

Poor results are secured when lambs are fed straw as the only roughage, but a limited amount of straw may well be used along with legume hay.

Fresh Pasture Is Important for Ewes with Lambs

To avoid infesting the lambs with stomach worms, it is important that fresh, uncontaminated pasture be provided. Winter rye and other winter grains provide good early pasture.

Fine Lambs on Excellent Clover Pasture

The clovers furnish valuable pasture for sheep, but great care is necessary to prevent bloat.

Sheep are rarely affected by the "sweet clover disease," caused by eating spoiled sweet clover hay. (**392**)

1204. Soybean hay.—Hay from soybeans is an excellent substitute for alfalfa or clover hay, but due to the coarse stems, sheep will usually leave uneaten a much larger percentage of soybean hay. (**398**) In 3 trials at the Illinois Station soybean hay, fed with corn, produced as rapid gains on fattening lambs as did alfalfa hay, but more hay and corn were required per 100 lbs. gain.[70] In these trials 100 lbs. of soybean hay, as fed, were equal in value to 89 lbs. of alfalfa hay. In 5 trials at the Indiana and Iowa Stations the average gain of fattening lambs fed soybean hay was practically as rapid as that of those fed clover hay, but somewhat more feed was required per 100 lbs. gain.[71] On the average, 100 lbs. of soybean hay were equal to 79 lbs. of clover hay in feeding value.

Soybean hay has also proved to be a very satisfactory roughage for breeding ewes and ewe lambs, ranking close to alfalfa hay in value.[72] It is well suited for feeding young lambs only when unusually fine and leafy.

1205. Cowpea hay.—Well-cured cowpea hay is finer-stemmed and more leafy than soybean hay, and is practically equal to alfalfa hay per ton for sheep feeding. (**401**) In 5 experiments with fattening lambs the gains on cowpea hay and on alfalfa hay were nearly equal, and the cowpea hay was worth 96 per cent as much per ton as alfalfa hay.[73]

1206. Field pea hay; pea-and-oat hay.—Both of these hays are satisfactory for sheep feeding, but they rank somewhat below alfalfa or clover in feeding value. (**402**) In a trial with fattening lambs at the South Dakota Station field pea hay was inferior to alfalfa or sweet clover hay, and in experiments by the Wyoming Station lambs fed pea-and-oat hay and barley gained 0.21 lb. per head daily, in comparison with 0.28 lb. for others fed alfalfa hay and barley.[74] On the average, the pea-and-oat hay was worth about 77 per cent as much as the alfalfa hay.

1207. Other legume forage.—When available, other kinds of legume hay can be used for sheep feeding in the same manner as alfalfa or clover hay. For information on the composition and value of lespedeza hay, vetch-and-oat hay, vetch-and-barley hay, and other kinds of legume hay the reader is referred to Chapter XIII. As is also shown in that chapter, legume straw, or chaff, may be used as a substitute for part of the hay in feeding sheep. (**418**)

IV. Other Dry Roughage

1208. Hay from the grasses.—Hay from timothy or other grasses, cut at the usual stage of maturity, is much inferior to legume hay for feeding all classes of sheep, as has been pointed out previously. (**1199**) Since such hay is low in protein, some supplement, like linseed meal or cottonseed meal, should always be added to the ration. Also, it is wise to add a calcium supplement, such as ground limestone, especially when the grass hay has been grown on soil low in calcium. (**1167**) Even when the hay is thus supplemented, the results from hay cut at the usual stage of maturity will usually be decidedly less satisfactory than when legume hay is fed.

Early-cut grass hay is much better than late-cut hay for sheep. This

has been shown clearly by Ohio trials with pregnant and nursing ewes.[75]
When timothy hay cut in early bloom was fed with corn silage and with
0.8 ounce of ground limestone per head daily and plenty of protein supplement to pregnant ewes, satisfactory results were secured. The results
on this ration were only slightly inferior to those with alfalfa hay and
corn silage for roughage. On the other hand, when late-cut timothy
replaced the early-cut hay as the only roughage, the ewes lost weight,
became thin and weak, produced lambs lacking in vigor, milked poorly,
and showed a decided tendency to shed the fleece because of weakened
wool fibers. Their living lambs gained 31 per cent less during the trial
than those from ewes fed legume hay.

Much better results are secured in sheep feeding when grass hay is
combined with some legume hay than when no legume hay at all is fed.
Thus, early-cut mixed clover-and-timothy hay containing a considerable
proportion of clover is a satisfactory roughage for sheep. In an Ohio
trial with fattening lambs timothy hay was decidedly inferior to alfalfa
hay as the only roughage, but a combination of equal amounts of the two
kinds of hay was only slightly inferior to the alfalfa hay.[76]

1209. Timothy hay; mixed clover-and-timothy hay.—*Timothy hay*
is unsatisfactory for sheep, unless cut early, as it is both unpalatable
and constipating. (449) The heads in the hay work into the wool, irritating the skin, lowering the quality of the wool, and making shearing
difficult. Timothy hay cut in early bloom is much better than late-cut
hay for sheep, but even such timothy hay gives best results when fed as
only part of the roughage, preferably with some legume hay. In case it
is necessary to feed early-cut timothy hay as the only roughage, or with
corn silage, then ground limestone or some other calcium supplement
should be supplied and plenty of protein supplement should be included
in the ration.

Mixed clover-and-timothy hay is much better than timothy hay, if
cut early and if a considerable proportion of clover is present.

1210. Other grass hay.—*Prairie hay* is worth considerably less than legume hay
as the only roughage for sheep feeding, even when a protein supplement is fed and
also a calcium supplement. (456) In two Minnesota trials fattening lambs fed
prairie hay and shelled corn, with 0.2 lb. linseed meal and one-quarter ounce ground
limestone per head daily, gained 0.39 lb. per head daily, in comparison with 0.41
lb. for others fed alfalfa hay and shelled corn.[77] The finish of the lambs fed
prairie hay was satisfactory, and they sold for the same price as those fed alfalfa
hay. However, largely because of the protein supplement needed with the prairie
hay ration, the prairie hay was actually worth only 59 per cent as much a ton as
the alfalfa hay. In these Minnesota trials and in other tests fattening lambs failed
to make good gains on a ration of prairie hay, corn, and linseed meal, without a
calcium supplement.[78]

In trials at the Alberta, Canada, College of Agriculture, it was found that while
pregnant ewes could be wintered satisfactorily on alfalfa hay alone, they lost 21
lbs. on the average, when wintered on prairie hay alone.[79] Prairie hay was more
satisfactory when fed with 0.25 to 0.50 lb. grain a day.

Marsh hay is too coarse and woody for sheep.

Millet hay was worth less than corn stover or oat straw for fattening lambs in
a Michigan trial, and in two Colorado trials was worth somewhat less than sorghum
fodder, on the average.[80]

The composition and feeding values of oat hay, Sudan grass hay, and other
kinds of grass hay are discussed in Chapter XV.

1211. Shock corn; corn fodder; corn stover.—As has been pointed out earlier in this chapter, well-eared *shock corn*, grown primarily for grain, may be fed to fattening lambs as a substitute for shelled corn or other grain. **(1182)** Usually each bushel of corn grain fed in this form is worth somewhat less than the same weight of shelled corn.

In Colorado trials well-eared shock corn or dry corn fodder, chopped in a roughage mill so finely that all the kernels were cracked, was fed to fattening lambs in comparison with corn silage, along with grain, cottonseed meal, and alfalfa hay.[81] The lambs fed the chopped fodder made fully as rapid gains as those fed silage, and 1.0 ton of dry fodder was equal in feeding value to 2.6 tons of corn silage. In New Mexico trials good gains were also secured on ground corn fodder and 1.0 ton of the ground fodder was equal in value to 2.5 tons of silage.[82] However, silage produced more gain per acre and also cheaper gains. Well-cured leafy *corn fodder*, grown thickly for roughage or that which has been stunted by drought and has failed to ear out, is a better roughage for sheep than most timothy hay or prairie hay.[83]

Even good-quality *corn stover*, without the ears, may be a useful feed in limited amount for wintering breeding sheep. By far the best results are secured when these forages form only part of the roughage, and some legume hay is fed in addition.

Corn stover is too low in nutrients to be well adapted for fattening lambs, even when a limited amount is fed along with legume hay and other good roughage. Adding corn stover to a ration of shelled corn, linseed meal, alfalfa hay, and corn silage reduced the average daily gain from 0.37 to 0.34 lb. in a Michigan trial and the corn stover was worth only one-fourth as much a ton as corn silage.[84] Substituting corn stover for corn silage in an Indiana trial, when fed with ear corn, cottonseed meal, and clover hay, caused an even greater reduction in the rate of gain and resulted in a financial loss instead of a good net return over feed costs.[85]

1212. Sorghum fodder; sorghum stover.—*Sweet-sorghum fodder*, often called "cane" hay, varies widely in value, depending on its fineness and leafiness. Very satisfactory results were secured with fattening lambs fed corn, cottonseed meal, and sorghum fodder in Colorado tests, but in an Oklahoma trial sorghum hay, fed with the same feeds, was of low value, even when chopped.[86]

In Kansas and Texas experiments when pulverized limestone was added to a ration of ground or chopped fodder from the grain or sweet sorghums, plus corn or sorghum grain and cottonseed meal, fattening lambs usually made nearly as rapid gains as when fed alfalfa hay in place of the sorghum fodder.[87] On the other hand, unsatisfactory results were secured without the calcium supplement. **(1167)**

Chopped *sorghum stover* was a better roughage for fattening lambs than cottonseed hulls or corn stover in New Mexico trials.[88]

1213. Straw from the cereals.—Straw should not be fed as the only roughage to sheep, as it is too low in nutrients, especially protein, calcium, and vitamins, and moreover, it is constipating. When hay is scarce or high in price, a limited amount of straw, especially oat straw, can be used along with legume hay or legume hay and silage for breeding sheep or fattening lambs. Oat, barley, or wheat straw has proved unsatisfactory as the only dry roughage for fattening lambs, even when they are fed silage, grain, and a protein supplement.[89] Feeding a mixture of half chopped barley straw and half chopped alfalfa hay with barley grain to fattening lambs was much less profitable in a California test than a ration of alfalfa hay and barley, without the straw.[90]

When sheep are to be fed such unpalatable roughage as straw, along with good legume hay, it is best to feed the straw in the morning and the better-liked hay for the evening meal.

1214. Cottonseed hulls.—In the southern states cottonseed hulls are sometimes used as the only or the chief roughage for fattening lambs, perhaps with cottonseed meal as the only concentrate. Experiments show that this combination produces much less rapid gains than grain and legume hay, and if the feeding of only cottonseed meal and hulls is too long continued, "cottonseed meal injury" may result due chiefly to the lack of vitamin A and of calcium.[91]

Lambs showing slight injury will usually recover after 2 or 3 weeks, if the ration is changed and they are fed good alfalfa hay for roughage or put on green pasture. These trials indicate that for 60 days lambs can usually be fed 1 lb. cottonseed meal per head daily with cottonseed hulls as the only roughage without trouble.

V. SUCCULENT FEEDS

1215. Value of succulent feeds.—Silage, roots, pasture, and other succulent feeds are very beneficial to sheep, because of their appetizing and regulating effects. Breeding sheep are more readily kept in the desired thrifty condition when silage or some other succulent feed is fed in addition to good legume hay. Likewise, fattening lambs will make slightly more rapid gains when silage or roots are added to an excellent ration made up of dry feeds.

In Great Britain roots are universally fed in large amounts to sheep, and to this fact may be attributed much of the reputation of the British shepherd for producing mutton of the highest quality. In this country, however, numerous experiments have shown that silage from corn or other crops is a thoroughly satisfactory substitute for roots and very much more economical in most sections.

1216. Corn silage.—Corn silage is the most widely used succulent feed for the winter feeding of sheep in the United States. (**426**) This is due both to its cheapness and to its high value for breeding sheep and fattening animals. As is pointed out in the next chapter, good corn silage aids greatly in maintaining breeding ewes in the desired thrifty condition during winter. (**1238**) Not only does it furnish palatable nutrients, but also it aids in preventing constipation. Only silage of good quality should be fed to sheep, for they are much more susceptible than are cattle to injurious effects from eating spoiled or moldy silage. Also, silage which is unduly sour is apt to cause colic and scours.

The value of corn silage for fattening lambs is shown in the following table, which summarizes the results of 39 experiments in which lambs were fattened on shelled corn and alfalfa or clover hay, in comparison with others fed good corn silage in addition.[92] In 14 of the experiments a small amount of linseed meal or cottonseed meal or cake was added to the silage ration. As is pointed out in the next article, under usual conditions such addition of a supplement to a silage ration for lambs is profitable, as it balances it more completely. In these trials a total of 2,042 lambs, averaging 61 lbs. in weight, were fed for an average of 91 days.

Value of silage added to corn and legume hay

Average ration	Daily gain Lbs.	Corn Lbs.	Supplement Lbs.	Hay Lbs.	Silage Lbs.
			Feed for 100 lbs. gain		
Silage-fed lambs					
Corn silage, 1.23 lbs.					
Legume hay, 1.22 lbs.					
Shelled corn, 1.09 lbs.					
Supplement, 0.07 lb.	0.347	321	19	363	360
Lambs fed no silage					
Legume hay, 1.72 lbs.					
Shelled corn, 1.12 lbs.	0.321	355	..	550	...

Adding silage to the already excellent ration of corn and legume hay increased the average daily gain from 0.321 lb. to 0.347 lb. However, the gain was not increased in all the trials by the addition of silage, for in 11 of the experiments there was no difference, or the lambs fed no silage made the larger gains. On account of slightly better finish, the silage-fed lambs sold for a trifle more in some of the tests, but the average difference in the selling price was only 7 cents per hundredweight.

The great advantage in favor of silage feeding lies in the saving of corn and hay required per 100 lbs. of gain. In these trials 1 ton of corn silage plus 106 lbs. supplement saved 1,038 lbs. legume hay and 190 lbs. shelled corn. From these data, one can readily compute the value of corn silage, with other feeds at his local prices. For example, with shelled corn at $20, supplement at $40, and legume hay at $10 a ton, corn silage would have a value of $4.97 a ton, or about half the price of legume hay per ton, not taking into consideration the more rapid gains on silage and the slightly higher average selling price.

Considering all these factors, it may be concluded that under usual conditions 1 ton of good corn silage is worth slightly more than half as much as a ton of legume hay for fattening lambs. Silage therefore has a higher relative value for lambs than would be expected from its content of total digestible nutrients, for it supplies only about one-third as much total digestible nutrients per pound as does legume hay.

In most of the other experiments in which corn silage has been added to somewhat different rations the results have been similar.[93] In certain western tests corn silage has had a somewhat lower value when it has been added, usually in very limited amounts, to grain and excellent alfalfa hay.[94]

It has been shown in the previous chapter that for fattening lambs it is generally profitable to add a protein supplement to a ration of corn or sorghum silage, legume hay, and corn or other grain. (1165) If little or no legume forage is fed, then it is essential that a sufficient amount of protein supplement be used to balance the ration. Otherwise, slow and uneconomical gains will result.

When fattening lambs are fed either corn or sorghum silage and also legume hay for roughage, it is best to let them have all the silage they will clean up, in addition to what legume hay they will take. This usually produces more rapid and cheaper gains than if the allowance of silage is limited.[95] In very cold weather care must be taken not to feed more silage than will be eaten before it freezes.

It is interesting to note that lambs given all the silage they desire will still eat nearly as many pounds of hay as of silage, while steers fed the same feeds may eat 5 to 7 times as many pounds of silage as hay.

1217. Silage as the only roughage.—Corn silage and sorghum silage are low not only in protein, but also they may be low in calcium and in vitamin A, while well-cured legume hay is rich in all these nutrients. Therefore, when legume hay can be provided economically for sheep, such silage should be fed in combination with legume hay. If it is necessary to feed silage as the only roughage, or a combination of silage and hay from the grasses, care should be taken to provide a sufficient amount of a protein supplement and also to feed a calcium supplement, such as ground limestone. (**1167**)

In the winter feeding of breeding ewes it is best not to use silage as the only roughage, but to feed it along with good legume hay or mixed hay. A common recommendation is that ewes be fed no more than 2 lbs. of silage daily per 100 lbs. live weight before lambing. After lambing they can be allowed all the silage they will take.

A larger allowance of silage than this can probably be fed safely, if it is of good quality and if the ewes have in addition good legume hay or mixed hay containing considerable legumes. Recent Illinois trials indicate that corn silage can even be used successfully as the only roughage for breeding ewes if a sufficient amount of protein supplement is fed and a calcium supplement is also provided.[96] In these tests satisfactory results were secured when pregnant ewes were fed during the winter a ration of 4.8 to 5.0 lbs. corn silage, 0.2 lb. soybean oil meal, 0.6 ounce salt, and 0.6 ounce of either ground limestone or steamed bone meal.

Recent experiments have shown that good corn or sorghum silage can be successfully used as the only roughage for fattening lambs, provided that care is taken to use a large enough amount of a suitable protein supplement to balance the ration and also to feed a sufficient amount of calcium supplement.[97] Unless both of these additions are made to the ration, poor results will be secured.

In these recent trials lambs have been fed 0.25 to 0.40 ounce of ground limestone per head daily, with a ration of corn or sorghum silage, corn or other grain, and a protein supplement, in comparison with others receiving legume hay in their ration. The results with silage as the only roughage have usually, though not always, been nearly as good as when legume hay has been fed in addition. The results of these recent experiments with breeding ewes and with fattening lambs are of much practical importance in those districts where legume hay cannot be provided economically for sheep.

In earlier experiments in which fattening lambs were fed corn silage as the only roughage with corn grain and a protein supplement, but without a calcium supplement, the results were decidedly poorer than when legume hay was fed in addition.[98] In most of such trials it was necessary to feed a little legume hay at times in order to keep the lambs on feed. Feeding legume hay only once or twice a week helped somewhat, but was not so successful as feeding it daily. Supplying oat straw in addition to the silage did not take the place of legume hay, which is not surprising, for it is low in calcium and also in vitamins.

1218. Sorghum silage.—Silage from the sweet sorghums or the grain sorghums is of great importance for sheep feeding in those districts where the sorghums surpass corn for forage. (**443**) Care should be taken not to ensile sorghum when too immature, or the silage may be too sour for sheep feeding. When sorghum is cut at the proper stage of maturity, it makes an excellent silage for sheep feeding that is excelled only by well-eared corn silage.[99] Sorghum silage is nearly equal in feeding value per ton to the type of corn silage usually produced in the semi-arid districts, but is probably worth somewhat less per ton than silage from corn containing a large proportion of corn grain.

A higher value for sheep can be secured from a sorghum crop when it is ensiled than when it is fed as dry fodder, even if the fodder is chopped or ground. In Kansas and Texas trials it required only 2.3 tons of sweet sorghum silage to equal 1 ton of ground dry sweet sorghum fodder for fattening lambs.[100]

1219. Other silages.—The composition and value of other silages suited to sheep feeding have been discussed in the chapters of Part II. Among such silages are corn-and-soybean silage, pea-and-oat silage, pea-vine silage (made from pea-cannery waste), and sunflower silage.

Pea-and-oat silage was practically equal to corn silage for fattening lambs in an Idaho trial, and in Oregon tests with fattening lambs in which *pea-and-bald-barley silage* was added to alfalfa hay, a ton of the silage replaced 1,229 lbs. of hay.[101] Pea-and-oat silage was also satisfactory for fattening lambs and breeding sheep at the Wyoming Station.[102]

When advantage can be taken of the high protein content of *pea-vine silage,* it is probably worth 90 per cent as much per ton as well-eared corn silage. (**403**) On the other hand, when plenty of protein is furnished by the other feeds in the ration, the value of pea-vine silage will be slightly lower, in comparison with that of corn silage. In a Wisconsin trial lambs fed barley with pea-vine silage as the only roughage gained only 0.32 lb. per head daily in comparison with 0.45 lb. for a lot fed alfalfa hay as the roughage.[103]

1220. Roots.—Roots are excellent succulent feeds for sheep, but in the United States silage is usually much more economical, except on farms where too little stock is fed to make silage feeding practical. (**470**) In Great Britain roots are widely fed to sheep of all classes. Sometimes fattening lambs are fed as much as 15 to 20 lbs. of rutabagas or other roots per head daily, though much smaller allowances are more common.[104] In this country it is ordinarily not profitable to feed more than 4 to 5 lbs. of roots per head daily to fattening lambs, and even half this allowance, preferably chopped, will furnish enough succulence in the ration. When pregnant ewes are fed too much roots, weak lambs sometimes result, probably due to a lack of protein or minerals in the ration. The allowance of roots had therefore best be restricted to 2 or 3 lbs. per head daily, and good hay should be fed in addition.

It has been believed that mangels and sugar beets, when fed to sheep over long periods, tend to produce calculi, or stones, in the kidneys and bladder, which are dangerous in the case of rams and wethers.[105] Investigators at the Indiana Station question whether roots are the primary cause of this trouble, as calculi occur when sheep are fed no roots.[106]

Roots, particularly rutabagas, turnips, and mangels, are much more watery than corn silage, and therefore their actual feeding value per ton is much lower. In seven experiments roots have been compared directly with corn silage for fattening lambs, when fed with concentrates and legume or mixed hay.[107] The root-fed lambs ate 4.6 lbs. roots, 1.5 lbs. hay, and 1.2 lbs. concentrates, while those fed silage ate only 3.0 lbs. silage and 1.3 lbs. hay, along with the same allowance of concentrates. The root-fed lambs made a trifle more rapid gains, on the average, but the difference in daily gain was only 0.02 lb. in their favor. On the average, 100 lbs. of silage replaced 145 lbs. of roots, so roots had only 69 per cent as high a feeding value as silage.

Many experienced shepherds, who have been prejudiced in favor of roots for feeding pregnant ewes, are surprised to learn that even for them silage is worth much more per ton than roots. In experiments during four winters at the Wisconsin Station ewes were fed alfalfa hay and either rutabagas or corn silage, with one-half pound per head daily of a mixture of corn, oats, and wheat bran for about a month previous to lambing.[108] On account of the lower dry matter content of the rutabagas, it was necessary to feed a larger allowance of roots and hay than of silage and hay, to keep the two lots in similar condition.

The percentage of strong lambs was noticeably higher from the silage-fed ewes, and the weights of the fleeces were about the same for the two lots. In these trials, rutabagas were worth only about two-thirds as much per ton as corn silage, not considering the better lamb crops from the ewes fed silage. For wintering ewe lambs, rutabagas were also less valuable than corn silage in other Wisconsin trials.[109]

The value of roots for fattening lambs when added to a ration containing no succulent feeds is shown by six trials in which roots have been added to rations of grain and legume or mixed hay.[110] The lambs fed roots (3.3 lbs. per head daily) gained 0.06 lb. more daily than those receiving no roots, and each ton of roots, on the average, replaced 170 lbs. of grain and 364 lbs. of hay. This is a considerably lower value per ton than has been obtained in the trials in which corn silage has been added to similar rations. (1216)

Fattening lambs will not make satisfactory gains on roots and legume hay, without concentrates, even on sugar beets, which are much higher in nutrients than mangels or rutabagas.[111]

1221. Wet beet pulp.—This by-product is extensively fed to fattening sheep in the vicinity of the beet-sugar factories in the western states. (643) Because the pulp is a cheap feed, the sheep are often given all they will eat, along with alfalfa hay. This hay admirably supplements the pulp, which is very low both in protein and calcium. Feeding a limited allowance of corn, barley, or other grain in addition is usually advisable, as it will increase the gains greatly.[112]. A common practice is to start the lambs on a full feed of pulp and alfalfa hay and gradually increase the grain until they are receiving 1 lb. or more a day. Although lambs may eat as much as 10 to 11 lbs. of pulp per head daily, 4 to 6 lbs. are more often fed.

The value of wet beet pulp for fattening lambs is shown by the results of 16 trials in which siloed pulp has been added to a ration of grain and alfalfa hay.[113] On the average, the pulp-fed lambs, which received 4.3 lbs. pulp a day, in addition to 0.9 lb. grain and 1.7 lbs. alfalfa hay, gained 0.33 lb. per head daily, while the lambs fed only grain and hay gained 0.28 lb. In these trials each ton of siloed beet pulp was worth 122 lbs. grain plus 381 lbs. hay, not considering the increase in the rate of gain.

Whether fattening lambs should be fed a protein supplement when they are receiving a heavy allowance of wet beet pulp, along with alfalfa hay and grain, will depend on how much hay they are eating. If enough hay is being eaten to balance the ration, it will not pay to add a supplement like cottonseed meal.[114]

When wet beet pulp is fed in limited amounts, along with grain and hay, 100 lbs. of dry matter in the wet pulp have a considerably higher value than the same amount of dry matter in dried beet pulp. Wet beet pulp is especially suitable for fattening aged ewes with poor teeth. In feeding the watery pulp, it is important that the yards be kept dry by proper drainage and the use of bedding.

1222. Other succulent feeds.—In the sugar-beet districts beet tops are often utilized for feeding sheep, especially fattening lambs. Likewise, in the potato-growing areas cull potatoes are frequently fed to sheep or lambs. Cabbage is prized by shepherds in fitting sheep for show, and other succulent feeds, such as cull apples and other fruit, are occasionally fed to sheep. These feeds are discussed in Part II.

Soiling crops are not commonly grown for sheep in the United States, as such crops are much more expensive than pasture, because of the labor required in harvesting them. (355-357)

1223. Pastures.—In most sections permanent pastures furnish the chief pasturage for sheep from spring to autumn, due to the fact that they are cheaper than temporary pasture crops. Many sheep raisers, however, place far too much reliance on permanent pastures, and fail to recognize their limitations. In the humid regions care is always necessary to prevent infestation with internal parasites when permanent pastures are used. Moreover, the flock will often run short of feed in time of midsummer drought, unless temporary pastures are provided in the manner discussed later.

Instead of keeping the sheep on one large pasture for the entire season, it is much better to fence the area in fields of such size that the sheep can be changed from one to another at frequent intervals, after they have grazed an area thoroughly. This will reduce the trouble from internal parasites, and it will also utilize the pasture more fully, since rotational grazing tends to increase the yield of forage. (312)

As sheep relish weeds and browse eagerly on sprouts and brush refused by other stock, small farm flocks can glean much feed from such sources and at the same time help in cleaning up the farm, especially lanes and fence corners. The wise flockmaster will always fully utilize all such feed, including stubble and stalk fields and the aftermath on meadows, in this manner reducing the cost of feed. Sheep prefer reasonably short grass to rank growths, and will eat weeds much better while they are young.

It is a good plan to have the pastures so located that the sheep can return to the barn for night shelter. It is then easier to inspect the sheep daily so that any trouble may be discovered, and it will help protect them from dogs. Shade should be provided in the pasture. If there are no trees, a cheap movable shade should be made. This may be placed on the poorer spots in the field, so the droppings of the sheep will enrich them.

1224. Importance of good pasture.—The high value of good pasture for sheep is well shown by Indiana experiments with ewes and lambs, conducted over a period of 3 years.[115] Unweaned lambs made larger gains and reached better market finish when on good pasture with their mothers, without grain feeding, than when the ewes were fed in a dry lot, without pasture, on an excellent ration of alfalfa hay, corn, and oats. This was true even when the lambs in the dry lot were fed plenty of corn and alfalfa hay in a lamb creep. The cost of feed eaten by lambs and ewes, for each 100 lbs. gain made by the lambs, was only $2.83 for the lambs on pasture, in comparison with the high cost of $16.82 for those in the dry lot.

Whether or not it will pay to feed grain to lambs on pasture is discussed in the next chapter. (**1252**)

1225. Permanent pastures.—Of the permanent pastures, bluegrass is the most common in the upper Mississippi valley and eastward. Timothy furnishes good early pasture, but it is not very palatable after heading out. Farther south, red top is prominent, and in the southern states, Bermuda grass. In the West, the native grasses, especially the grama species, furnish much of the grazing on the ranges, though on the mountain ranges the food may consist mostly of herbs and the leaves and twigs of shrubs.

The clovers furnish valuable pasture, but care is necessary to prevent bloat when sheep are grazed on them. On alfalfa pasture there is more danger from bloat than on red-clover pasture, but except for this, the pasture is so excellent that many use it for sheep in spite of the danger. (**375-376**) The trouble from bloat seems to differ widely in various sections, and therefore in deciding whether to use alfalfa for sheep pasture, one should be governed largely by the experience in his locality.[116] In some sections of the West, alfalfa is used for winter grazing, as it is then so lacking in succulence that danger from bloat is practically absent.

There is much less danger from bloat on sweet-clover pasture than on alfalfa pasture.[117] Mixtures of clover or alfalfa and timothy or other grasses provide much safer pasture for sheep than the legumes alone, and such mixed pasture furnishes better feed, especially for lambs, than bluegrass or timothy pasture.[118]

In pasturing legumes or even rape the precautions emphasized in Chapter XIII should be taken to lessen the danger of bloat. (**376**) Even when care is taken, animals occasionally bloat, especially on sultry days following a rain. Immediate attention is then necessary to save the afflicted ones. The following methods of treatment are suggested:

A drench of one-half ounce of formalin in a pint of water has been found to give quick relief at the Kentucky Station.[119] The formalin stops the rapid fermentation of the green feed which causes the production of gas. For all except the worst cases, a drench of one-half pint of fresh milk, warm from the cow, will give relief.[120] If necessary, in a short time repeat the dose. Cold milk will not absorb the gas as warm milk does. In cases of bloat, others place a stick in the animal's mouth, like a bit, and tie it back of the head with a string. This helps the sheep get rid of the gas. As a last resort, a trocar or knife should be used to puncture the paunch.

1226. Temporary pastures.—Occasionally sheep are grazed chiefly on annual pastures especially sown for them. This system is usually more expensive under American conditions than a combination of permanent pastures and annual grazing crops. The advantages of the system are that it enables the flockmaster to maintain more animals on a given area than otherwise; it lessens trouble from parasites; it favors rapid, continuous gains by providing succulent pasture from spring to fall; it destroys nearly all kinds of weeds; and it uniformly fertilizes the land. In this system grass pasture should be available during wet seasons, especially on heavy soils. Lands newly seeded to grass and clover can be successfully pastured by sheep, provided they are kept off when the ground is soft from rain, and if they are not allowed to crop the young plants too closely.

Commonly, the best system of flock management is to use annual pastures to supplement the permanent pastures. As is pointed out in the next chapter, the greatest need for such additional feed comes when the lambs are weaned. At this time some pasture crop, not infested with parasites, should always be provided to furnish an abundance of palatable, succulent, and nutritious feed.

1227. Rape.—Throughout most of the United States, rape is more widely grown for sheep than any other annual pasture. (**486**) It is used chiefly as a supplement to permanent pastures, especially when the latter become scanty in midsummer and later. As rape may cause bloat in sheep, the same precautions should be taken as in the case of clover. A combination of oats and rape is less apt to cause bloat than rape alone. Allowing lambs to graze on rape when it is wet or too immature may cause scours. It is best to keep sheep, especially lambs, off a field of rape drenched with dew or rain until the leaves are dry. Often shepherds cut rape and feed it as a green soiling crop, instead of using it as a pasture crop. This is safer but takes considerable labor. Rape may be pastured late in the autumn, even after it freezes, though there may be more danger of bloat on rape which has been frozen.

Three methods are commonly used in growing rape for fall feeding: First, it may be seeded as the only crop; second, it may be sown with oats at the rate of 2 lbs. of rape seed to the acre; and third, it may be seeded in corn at the last cultivation at the rate of about 3 lbs. per acre. When there is sufficient moisture, rape sown in oats grows rapidly after the oats are cut and furnishes feed that is ready to be pastured by the first of September. Securing good growth of rape in corn depends on seeding early, on the supply of moisture, and on the density of the corn foliage, but if the corn is to be pastured with sheep, it usually pays to sow rape.

Rape proved superior to bluegrass pasture for lambs in a Wisconsin trial.[121] Rape or a succession of rye, clover, and rape produced somewhat more rapid gains and better finish on lambs than bluegrass pasture in Ohio experiments.[122] The rape pasture was worth 3 to 4 times as much per acre as bluegrass. In Kentucky trials lambs on excellent bluegrass pasture made nearly as rapid gains as those on rape-and-oats or rape pasture, but required somewhat more grain for each pound of gain.[123] It was concluded that where such excellent bluegrass pasture was available, it was doubtful whether the use of the temporary pasture was profitable, on account of the increased cost.

1228. Other annual pasture crops.—The earliest grazing is usually furnished by the cereals, of which winter rye is the best for the northern states. Rye is also grown for fall grazing. Farther south, winter wheat and winter oats are excellent grazing crops for the colder months.[124] The sorghums are useful in the plains region, although not especially relished by sheep. Sudan grass produces much feed but is less valuable for sheep than soybeans, where the latter thrive.[125] Oats-and-peas, oats-and-vetch, and soybeans all furnish excellent grazing for sheep. Cowpeas are much less palatable to sheep than soybeans as a pasture crop, though they are well liked as hay.[126]

Kale provides excellent winter and spring feed in the mild climate of the Pacific coast. In the fall kohlrabi and cabbage may be useful. Both rutabagas and turnips are widely grown in Great Britain for grazing. These various crops are discussed in detail in the respective chapters of Part II. It is pointed out in the next chapter that the fattening of lambs in corn fields is often practiced in the corn belt. (1267)

1229. Grazing field peas.—The fattening of lambs by grazing them upon field peas is of importance in certain localities in the West, especially in the San Luis Valley, Colorado. The peas are sown at the rate of 30 to 50 lbs. per acre, with a small quantity of oats or barley to support the vines and furnish additional feed. About November 1, as soon as most of the peas have matured, lambs or sheep are turned into the field, and without other feed are fattened in from 70 to 120 days. An acre of such peas will fatten from 8 to 15 lambs, each making a gain of from 6 to 8 lbs. per month. This system is economical, because there is no expense for harvesting the crop. Confining the lambs to small areas by hurdles gives better results than allowing them to roam over the entire field. Sometimes the peas are cut, stacked, and fed to the lambs in yards.

Sometimes serious death losses occur among lambs grazed on field peas, due to digestive disturbances caused by eating too much of the rich seed.[127] Feeding such feeds as alfalfa hay and cull potatoes to lambs on field peas reduced the losses in a Colorado trial, probably because the lambs filled up partly on these feeds and did not gorge so much on the peas.[128]

QUESTIONS

1. Discuss the merits and limitations of corn for sheep feeding.
2. In what forms should corn be fed to sheep?
3. What is the value of hominy feed for sheep?
4. Discuss the value of barley for sheep.
5. For what purposes are oats most commonly used in sheep feeding?
6. Discuss the use and relative value in comparison with corn of any of the following that are important for sheep feeding in your district: (a) Wheat; (b) grain sorghums; (c) rye; (d) beet molasses; (e) cane molasses; (f) dried beet pulp or dried molasses-beet pulp.
7. Discuss the use and the relative value of linseed meal and cottonseed meal for sheep.
8. How is wheat bran used in sheep feeding?
9. Compare the value for sheep of soybeans and of soybean oil meal with that of linseed meal.
10. State the most important facts with reference to the use for sheep feeding of any of the following that are important in your district: (a) Corn gluten feed; (b) corn gluten meal; (c) meat scraps or tankage; (d) fish meal.
11. Discuss the importance of legume hay for sheep.
12. Compare the value of alfalfa hay and of red clover hay for sheep.
13. State the value for sheep of any of the following kinds of legume hay that are important in your district: (a) Sweet clover hay; (b) soybean hay; (c) cowpea hay; (d) field pea hay or pea-and-oat hay.
14. Discuss the use of grass hay for sheep.
15. Tell how any of the following that are important in your district should be used in sheep feeding: (a) Timothy hay; (b) mixed clover-and-timothy hay; (c) prairie hay; (d) marsh hay; (e) millet hay.
16. How should the following be used in sheep feeding: (a) Corn fodder or shock corn; (b) corn stover; (c) sorghum fodder; (d) straw; (e) cottonseed hulls?
17. Discuss the value of corn silage for sheep. What is its value per ton for fattening lambs in comparison with good hay?
18. State the way in which corn silage can be fed successfully as the only roughage to breeding ewes or to fattening lambs.
19. What other kinds of silage are used for sheep feeding in your district and how do they compare with corn silage in value?

20. What is the approximate value of roots per 100 lbs. for sheep feeding in comparison with that of corn silage?

21. If wet beet pulp is used for sheep feeding in your district, tell how it is used for fattening lambs.

22. Discuss the importance of good pasturage for sheep.

23. What kinds of pasture are commonly used for sheep in your district? What improvements can you suggest in the usual provision of pasturage for sheep in your district?

REFERENCES

1. Skinner and King, Ind. Bul. 162; Burnett, Nebr. Bul. 66; Emery, Wyo. Bul. 51; Morton, Wyo. Bul. 73; Faville, Wyo. Bul. 85.
2. Skinner and King, Ind. Bul. 162; Hays, Minn. Bul. 31; Carmichael and Hammond, Ohio Bul. 245.
3. Coffey, Productive Sheep Husbandry, pp. 375-6; Evvard, Shearer, Culbertson, and Wallace, Iowa Bul. 299; Paterson, Kan. Cir. 88; Brown, Mich. Quar. Bul., 16, 1933, No. 1 and mimeo. rpt.; Jordan and Peters, Minn. Bul. 306; Hackedorn, Mo. Bul. 147; Weber and Loeffel, Nebr. Bul. 257.
4. Coffey, Productive Sheep Husbandry, pp. 375-6; Skinner and King, Ind. Buls. 273, 282, 296; Evvard, Shearer, Culbertson, and Wallace, Iowa Bul. 299; Jordan and Peters, Minn. Bul. 306.
5. Coffey, Productive Sheep Husbandry, pp. 375-6.
6. Brown, Mich. Spec. Bul. 233.
7. Blakeslee, Mich. Quar. Bul., 17, 1935, No. 4.
8. Skinner, Vestal, and Starr, Ind. Buls. 221, 234; Harper, Ind. Bul. 304; Evvard, Dunn, and Culbertson, Iowa Bul. 210; Paterson, Kan. Cir. 79; Gramlich, Nebr. Bul. 173.
9. Buffum and Griffith, Colo. Bul. 75; Morton, Colo. Bul. 187; Maynard, Morton, and Osland, Colo. Bul. 379; Morton, Maynard, and Fairbanks, Colo. Press Bul. 76; Morton and Fairbanks, Colo. Press Bul. 79; Hickman, Rinehart, and Johnson, Id. Bul. 194; Kammlade, Ill. Bul. 338; Fox, Nebr. Bul. 211; Holden, Nebr. Bul. 216; Darlow, Okla. Bul. 196; Potter and Dean, Ore. Bul. 198; Maynard, Esplin, and Boswell, Utah Bul. 238; Hackedorn, Sotola, and Singleton, Wash. Bul. 258; Faville, Wyo. Buls. 81, 103.
10. Evvard, Dunn, and Culbertson, Iowa Bul. 210; Paterson and Winchester, Kan. Cir. 88; Brown, Mich. Spec. Bul. 233; Holden, Nebr. Bul. 268; Maynard, Esplin, and Boswell, Utah Bul. 238.
11. Jordan and Peters, Minn. Bul. 306; Holden, Nebr. Bul. 268; Darlow, Okla. Bul. 146; Quayle, Wyo. Bul. 191.
12. Evvard, Dunn, and Culbertson, Iowa Bul. 210; Gramlich, Nebr. Sta., mimeo. rpt.; Fox, Nebr. Bul. 211.
13. Kammlade, Ill. Bul. 338.
14. Miller, Cal. Sta., mimeo. rpt.; Maynard, Morton, and Osland, Colo. Bul. 379; Johnson, Rinehart, and Hickman, Id. Bul. 176; Jordan and Peters, Minn. Bul. 306; Maynard, Esplin, and Boswell, Utah Bul. 238; Hackedorn, Sotola, and Singleton, Wash. Buls. 258, 275; Faville, Wyo. Buls. 89, 103.
15. Harper, Ind. Buls. 312, 325, 333; King and Harper, Ind. Bul. 360.
16. Evvard, Dunn, and Culbertson, Iowa Bul. 210; Brown, Mich. Spec. Bul. 233; Jordan and Peters, Minn. Bul. 306; Potter and Dean, Ore. Bul. 198; Hackedorn, Sotola, and Singleton, Wash. Bul. 258.
17. Dickson and Hansen, Mont. Sta., mimeo. rpt.; Linfield, Mont. Buls. 47, 49; Joseph, Mont. Sta., mimeo. rpt.
18. Evvard, Dunn, and Culbertson, Iowa, Bul. 210; Kammlade, Ill. Rpt. 1930; Skinner and King, Ind. Buls. 168, 179, 184; King and Harper, Ind. Bul. 360; Jordan and Peters, Minn. Bul. 306; Gramlich, Nebr. Sta., mimeo. rpt.; Wilson, Wright, and Fenn, S. D. Bul. 278; Quayle, Wyo. Rpts. 1929, 1930.
19. King and Harper, Ind. Bul. 360; Jordan and Peters, Minn. Bul. 272; Hackedorn, Sotola, and Singleton, Wash. Buls. 258, 275.
20. Morton and Fairbanks, Colo. Press Bul. 79; Johnson, Rinehart, Hickman, Id. Bul. 194; Kammlade, Ill. Sta., mimeo. rpt; Mumford, Mich. Bul. 128; Brown, Mich. Spec. Bul. 233; Baker, Nebr. Bul. 256 and information to the author; Weber and Loeffel, Nebr. Bul. 257; Darlow, Okla. Bul. 213; Potter and Dean, Ore. Bul. 198; Maynard, Esplin, and Boswell, Utah Bul. 238; Hackedorn, Sotola, and Singleton, Wash. Bul. 258.
21. Morton and Fairbanks, Colo. Press Bul. 79; Johnson, Rinehart, and Hickman, Id. Bul. 194; Jordan and Peters, Minn. Bul. 306; Potter and Dean, Ore. Bul. 198; Maynard, Esplin, and Boswell, Utah Bul. 238; Hackedorn, Sotola, and Singleton, Wash. Bul. 258.
22. Rinehart, Hickman, and Johnson, Id. Bul. 194; Saunderson and Vinke, Mont. Bul. 249; Holden, Scottsbluff, Nebr. Substa., mimeo. rpt.; Mackey and Jones, Tex. Bul. 465.
23. Kammlade, Ill. Rpt. 1931; Darlow, Okla. Bul. 213; Weber and Loeffel, Nebr. Bul. 257; Hackedorn, Sotola, and Singleton, Wash. Buls. 258, 275.
24. Jones and Dickson, Tex. Bul. 379.
25. Paterson and Marston, Kan. Cir. 109; Reed and Marston, Kan. Cir. 123; Cox and Connell, Kan. Rpt. 1932-34; Darlow, Okla. Buls. 146, 196.
26. Cochel, Kan. Sta., information to the author; Paterson and Marston, Kan. Cir. 109; Darlow, Okla. Buls. 146, 196; Jones and Dickson, Tex. Bul. 379; Mackey and Jones, Tex. Bul. 465.

27. Paterson and Marston, Kan. Cir. 109; Darlow and Craft, Okla. Bul. 196; Jones and Dickson, Tex. Bul. 379; J. M. Jones, McDowell, and J. H. Jones, Tex. Rpt. 1933.
28. Jones and Dickson, Tex. Bul. 379; Cox, Kan. Sta., mimeo. rpt.
29. Jordan and Peters, Minn. Bul. 306; Baker, Nebr. Bul. 256 and information to the author.
30. Morton, Maynard, and Fairbanks, Colo. Press Bul. 76; Evvard, Culbertson, and Wallace, Iowa Bul. 215.
31. Maynard, Morton, and Osland, Colo. Bul. 379; Jordan and Peters, Minn. Bul. 306; Maynard, Esplin, and Boswell, Utah Bul. 238 and mimeo. rpt.; Hackedorn, Bean, and Sotola, Wash. Bul. 185; Quayle, Wyo. Bul. 191; see also: Bell, Ohio Bul. 497.
32. Bohstedt et al., Wis. Buls. 428, 430, and information to the author.
33. Skinner and King, Ind. Bul. 192.
34. Jordan and Peters, Minn. Bul. 306; Shaw, Mich. Bul. 220; Humphrey and Kleinheinz, Wis. Rpt. 1906.
35. Maynard, Morton, and Osland, Colo. Bul. 379; Holden, Nebr. Bul. 194 and mimeo. rpt.; Quayle, Wyo. Bul. 191.
36. Dickson and Hansen, Mont. Sta., mimeo. rpt.; Maynard, Utah, Sta., mimeo. rpt.
37. Miller, Cal. Sta., mimeo. rpt.
38. Holden, Nebr. Buls. 194, 216, 268; Quayle, Wyo. Bul. 191.
39. Morrison and Kleinheinz, Wis. Buls. 275, 323.
40. Jordan and Peters, Bul. 306; Gramlich, Nebr. Bul. 173 and mimeo. rpts.; Alexander, Nebr. Sta., mimeo. rpts.; Holden, Nebr. Bul. 216.
41. Skinner, Vestal, King, and Starr, Ind. Buls. 221, 256, 263; Paterson and Winchester, Kan. Cirs. 79, 96; see also: Kammlade, Ill. Sta., mimeo. rpt.; Ind. Rpt. 1933.
42. Skinner, Vestal, and King, Ind. Buls. 256, 263.
43. Maynard, Morton, and Osland, Colo. Bul. 379; Morton and Fairbanks, Colo. Press Bul. 79; Rinehart, Hickman, and Johnson, Id. Bul. 194; Holden, Nebr. Bul. 216.
44. Cox, New Mex. Bul. 179; Neale, New Mex. Bul. 222; Magee and Darlow, Okla. Bul. 133; Quayle, Wyo. Bul. 191.
45. Iddings, Id. Bul. 89.
46. Griswold, N. D. Bul. 217.
47. Morton and Fairbanks, Colo. Press Bul. 79.
48. Morton, Osland, and Brandon, Colo. Press Bul. 80; Id. Bul. 205; Kammlade and Mackey, Ill. Bul. 260; Harper, Ind. Sta., information to the author; Skinner, King and Starr, Ind. Buls. 192, 202, 221, 273, 282, 296; Bell, Ohio Buls. 373, 392.
49. Kammlade and Mackey, Ill. Bul. 260; Skinner and King, Ind. Buls. 273, 282, 296.
50. Kammlade and Mackey, Ill. Bul. 260; Bell, Ohio Buls. 373, 392.
51. Skinner and King, Ind. Buls. 273, 282, 296.
52. Jordan and Peters, Minn. Bul. 306; Alexander and Weber, Nebr. Sta., mimeo. rpt.
53. Paterson, Kan. Cirs. 79, 88; Morrison and Kleinheinz, Wis. Bul. 323.
54. Evvard, Dunn, and Culbertson, Iowa Buls. 185, 210.
55. Gramlich and Savin, Nebr. Sta., mimeo. rpt.
56. Miller, Cal. Sta., mimeo. rpt.; Harper, Ind. Sta., mimeo. rpt.; Jordan and Peters, Minn. Sta., mimeo. rpt.; Fox, Nebr. Bul. 211; Alexander, Nebr. Sta., mimeo. rpt.; Morrison and Kleinheinz, Wis. Sta., unpublished data.
57. Miller, Cal. Sta., mimeo. rpts.
58. Jordan and Peters, Minn. Bul. 306; Alexander and Weber, Nebr. Sta., mimeo. rpt.
59. Bell, Ohio Bul. 532 and mimeo. rpt.
60. Morton, Colo. Bul. 73; Skinner and King, Ind. Bul. 162; Burnett, Nebr. Bul. 66; Gramlich, Nebr. Sta., mimeo. rpt.; Fox, Nebr. Bul. 204; McDonald and Malone, Okla. Bul. 78.
61. Hickman, Id. Sta., information to the author; Holden, Nebr. Bul. 194; Fleming, Nev. Bul. 106.
62. Weber and Fox, Nebr. Bul. 259.
63. Hickman, Rinehart, and Johnson, Id. Cir. 19.
64. Fox, Nebr. Buls. 204 and 211.
65. Savin, Nebr. Bul. 197.
66. Skinner and King, Ind. Bul. 179, 184, 192, 202; Carmichael and Hammond, Ohio Bul. 245; Humphrey and Kleinheinz, Wis. Sta., information to the author.
67. Shaw, Mont. Bul. 21.
68. Jordan and Peters, Minn. Bul. 306; Hackedorn, Bean, and Sotola, Wash. Bul. 170.
69. Paterson and Marston, Kan. Cir. 109; Reed and Marston, Kan. Cir. 123; Wilson, S. D. Bul. 143; Hackedorn, Bean, and Sotola, Wash. Bul. 185; Quayle, Wyo. Rpt. 1930.
70. Kammlade, Ill., Buls. 260, 338.
71. Skinner and King, Ind. Buls. 282, 296; Harper, Ind. Buls. 304, 333; Evvard, Culbertson, Hammond, and Henness, Iowa Bul. 234.
72. Kammlade, Ill. Bul. 338, Ill. Cir. 369; Hammond, Evvard, and Culbertson, Iowa Bul. 282; Horlacher, Ky. Rpt. 1926; Leveck, Miss. Rpt. 1928; Md. Rpt. 1928; Ruffner, N. C. Rpt. 1927; Bell, Ohio Buls. 373, 382.
73. Reed and Marston, Kan. Cir. 123; McDonald and Malone, Okla. Bul. 78; Darlow, Okla. Buls. 196, 213.
74. Wilson, S. D. Bul. 143; Quayle, Wyo. Rpts. 1929, 1930.
75. Bell, Thatcher, Hunt, and Kick, Ohio Buls. 470, 479, 516, 548.
76. Bell, Thatcher, and Hunt, Ohio Bul. 516.
77. Jordan and Peters, Minn. Sta., mimeo. rpt.
78. Jordan and Peters, Minn. Bul. 306; Gramlich; Nebr. Sta., mimeo. rpt.
79. Bowstead and Sackville, Alberta, Canada, Col. of Agr. Bul. 19.

80. Morton, Maynard, Brandon, and Osland, Colo. Bul. 395, Colo. Press Bul. 80 ; H. W. Mumford, Mich. Bul. 136.
81. Maynard, Morton, and Osland, Colo. Bul. 379.
82. Neale, New Mex. Bul. 222.
83. Jordan and Peters, Minn. Bul. 306.
84. Brown, Mich. Spec. Bul. 233 ; see also : Cox, New Mex. Bul. 179.
85. Skinner and King, Ind. Bul. 273.
86. Morton, Maynard, and Brandon, Colo. Bul. 395 ; Darlow, Okla. Bul. 213 ; see also Neale, New Mex. Bul. 222.
87. Reed, Kan. Sta., mimeo. rpt. ; Cox and Connell, Kan. Bul. 264 ; Jones, Stangel, and Dickson, Tex. Rpts. 1929, 1930, 1931, 1932.
88. Cox, N. Mex. Bul. 179.
89. Kammlade and Mackey, Ill. Bul. 260 ; Skinner and Vestal, Ind. Buls. 234, 256 ; Skinner and King, Ind. Bul. 263 ; Paterson and Winchester, Kan. Cir. 96 ; Ikeler, Utah Bul. 220 ; see also : Alexander, Nebr. Sta., mimeo. rpt.
90. Miller, Cal. Rpt. 1923 ; see also : Wyo. Rpt. 1934.
91. Neale, N. Mex. Bul. 200 ; Jones and Dickson, Tex. Bul. 379.
92. Maynard, Morton, and Osland, Colo. Bul. 379 ; Coffey, Ill. Sta., information to the author ; Skinner and King, Ind. Buls. 162, 168, 179, 184, 192, 202 ; Evvard, et al., Iowa Bul. 299 ; Paterson and Winchester, Kan. Cir. 88 ; Brown, Mich. Spec. Bul. 233 ; Gramlich, Nebr. Bul. 173 and information to the author ; Savin, Nebr. Bul. 197 ; Fox, Nebr. Bul. 211 ; Holden, Nebr. Bul. 268 ; Morrison and Willman, N. Y. (Cornell) Sta., mimeo. rpts. ; Maynard, Esplin, and Boswell, Utah Bul. 238 ; Hackedorn, Bean, and Sotola, Wash. Bul. 185.
93. Jordan and Peters, Minn. Sta., mimeo. rpt. ; Holden, Nebr. Bul. 268 ; Bell, Ohio Sta., mimeo. rpt. ; see, however : Keith and Henning, Penn. Bul. 288.
94. Hickman, Rinehart, and Johnson, Id. Bul. 194 and mimeo. rpt. ; Vinke and Hansen, Montana Sta., mimeo. rpt.
95. Coffey, Ill. Sta., information to the author ; Skinner and King, Ind. Buls. 162, 168, 179 ; Hackedorn, Bean, and Sotola, Wash. Bul. 185.
96. Kammlade, Ill. Rpts. 1933, 1934.
97. Kammlade, Ill. Rpt. 1934 ; Harper, Ind. Sta., mimeo. rpt. ; Cox, Connell, and Reed, Kan. Sta., mimeo. rpts. ; Alexander, Nebr. Sta., mimeo. rpt. ; Morrison and Willman, N. Y. (Cornell) Rpt. 1934 and mimeo. rpts. ; Stangel, Jones and Mackey, Tex. Rpt. 1933 and mimeo. rpt. ; see also : Neale, New Mex. Bul. 222.
98. Skinner, King, Vestal, and Starr, Ind. Buls. 168, 179, 184, 192, 202, 221, 234 ; Evvard et al., Iowa Bul. 299 ; Kans. Bien. Rpt. 1924-26 ; Jordan and Peters, Minn. Sta., mimeo. rpt.
99. Stanley and Scott, Ariz. Bul. 109 ; Miller, Cal. Rpt. 1919 ; Cox and Connell, Kan. Bul. 264 ; Stangel, Jones, and Mackey, Tex. Rpt. 1933 and mimeo. rpt.
100. Cox and Connell, Kan. Bul. 264 and mimeo. rpt. ; Stangel and Jones, Tex. Sta., mimeo. rpt.
101. Iddings and Hickman, Id. Sta., information to the author ; Potter and Dean, Ore. Bul. 198.
102. Faville, Wyo. Bul. 109 ; Hays, Wyo. Bul. 130.
103. Rupel, Roche, and Bohstedt, Wis. Bul. 420.
104. Ingle, Trans. Highl. and Agr. Soc. of Scotland, 1910.
105. Michael, Iowa Bul. 112.
106. Pontius, Carr, and Doyle, Jour. Agr. Res., 42, 1931, pp. 433-446.
107. Grisdale, Ottawa, Canada, Expt. Farms Rpt. 1910, 1911, 1912 ; Kennedy, Robbins, and Kildee, Iowa, Bul. 110 ; F. B. Mumford, Mich. Buls. 84, 107.
108. Morrison and Kleinheinz, Wis. Buls. 388, 396 ; Roche, Morrison, Bohstedt, and Kleinheinz, Wis. Bul. 410.
109. Humphrey and Kleinheinz, Wis. Bul. 275.
110. Kennedy, Robbins, and Kildee, Iowa Bul. 110 ; Smith and Mumford, Mich. Bul. 113, Arkell, N. H. Bul. 152 ; Hackedorn, Sotola, and Singleton, Wash., Bul. 258.
111. Holden, Nebr. Bul. 194 ; Farmer and Stock-Breeder and Agr. Gaz., England, 42, 1928, No. 1996, p. 67.
112. Linfield, Utah Bul. 78 ; Quayle, Mont. Rpts. 1928, 1930.
113. Maynard, Morton, and Osland, Colo. Bul. 379 ; Maynard, Morton, and Fairbanks, Colo. Press Bul. 76 ; Hickman, Rinehart, and Johnson, Id. Cir. 40 ; Vinke, Bergstedt, and Hansen, Mont. Cir. 29 and mimeo. rpts.
114. Morton, Maynard, Osland, and Fairbanks, Colo. Press Buls. 73, 76.
115. Harper, Ind. Bul. 344.
116. Kammlade, Ill. Rpt. 1933 ; Dorrance, Brown, and Rather, Mich. Quar. Bul., 15, No. 2, 1932 ; Fleming, Nev. Rpt. 1922 ; Ore. Bien. Rpt. 1926-8 ; Aune, U. S. Dept. Agr. Cir. 417 ; Bowstead and Sackville, Alberta, Canada, Col. of Agr., Bul. 19.
117. Horlacher, Sheep Production, p. 243 ; Bowstead and Sackville, Alberta, Canada, Col. of Agr., Bul. 19.
118. Harper, Ind. Rpt. 1933.
119. Horlacher, Sheep Production, p. 243.
120. Kleinheinz, Sheep Management, Breeds, and Judging, pp. 120-1.
121. Craig, Wis. Rpt. 1897.
122. Hammond, Ohio Bul. 340.
123. Horlacher, Ky. Cir. 38.
124. Marshall and Potts, U. S. Dept. Agr., Farmers' Bul. 1181.
125. Hostetler, N. C. Rpts. 1929, 1930.
126. McCampbell, Kan. Bien, Rpt. 1922-24 ; Marshall and Potts, U. S. Dept. Agr., Farmers' Bul. 1181.
127. Newsom and Cross, Colo. Bul. 305.
128. Morton, Colo. Rpt. 1927.

CHAPTER XXXIV

FEEDING AND CARING FOR SHEEP AND LAMBS—
FATTENING—HOT-HOUSE AND SPRING LAMBS—GOATS

I. The Breeding Flock; Raising the Lambs

1230. Essentials of successful flock management.—Intelligent management and proper care are even more necessary for success in sheep production than with the other classes of livestock. Yet sheep are not hard to raise, once their relatively simple requirements are understood. Some of the most important points in successful flock management are: (1) Proper feed and care of the ewes during winter, before and after lambing; (2) plenty of good pasture during the growing season; (3) control of parasites; (4) producing the kinds of lambs that are in demand and having the lambs ready for market at the time of the year when prices are high.

Order, regularity, and quiet are of prime importance in the management of sheep. The flock should always be cared for by the same attendant, who moves among them quietly, giving notice of his approach by speaking in a low voice and closing doors and gates gently. Dogs and strangers should be kept from the pens. Cleanliness is essential, for sheep are the most dainty and particular of all farm animals.

1231. The ewe flock.—Profits from sheep depend largely upon having a flock of ewes that are carefully selected and properly culled. The ewes should be healthy and vigorous, with deep, wide, roomy bodies, good teeth, sound udders, and high-quality, dense fleeces. They should be good milk producers and also be of good size for their breed, for under-sized ewes produce less wool and less weight of lambs per year.[1] However, they should not be too large or coarse, or their lambs may be too large to meet the market demands, before they are fat enough for slaughter.

Before the breeding season in the fall, the flock should be carefully culled, and all ewes should be discarded which are non-breeders or poor milkers or which are otherwise unprofitable. These should be replaced by the most promising individuals raised in the flock. The ewes retained should not be selected by looks alone, for the thinnest ones may have been brought to this condition by a heavy milk flow. The only business-like method is to keep a simple flock record in which are recorded the ear-tag or ear-notch number of each ewe, the weight of fleece produced, the number of lambs raised, and their weights at weaning time or when marketed. As a rule, good ewes should be retained as long as they are productive. In farm flocks most of the ewes are disposed of when 6 to 7 years of age.

Most authorities advise against breeding ewe lambs, which will usually come in heat at 6 to 9 months of age; they recommend that breeding be delayed until the ewes are yearlings. It is believed that if ewes are bred as lambs they are likely to have trouble in lambing, to lack maternal instinct, and to be stunted themselves.

Recent studies indicate that under favorable conditions by breeding mutton-type ewes as lambs a partial extra lamb crop may be secured at little added cost and without injury to the flock, provided that the first crop of lambs from such early-bred ewes is not retained for breeding purposes.[2] Ewes bred as lambs seem to reach as large a size as those first bred as yearlings, and to produce fully as many and as large lambs in later gestations. Usually only 75 to 85 per cent of the ewes can be successfully bred as lambs, and the first lambs from ewes thus bred are not so thrifty as those from older ewes. In purebred flocks it is certainly not advisable to breed ewes as lambs.

1232. Date of lambing; gestation period.—To secure the best prices for farm-raised fat lambs, they should be ready for market either before or after the rush of grass-fat lambs from the western range states. If warm quarters and plenty of good legume hay and grain are available, early lambs, dropped before April first and marketed not later than July, are usually most profitable, for they commonly sell at a higher price than later lambs. Such lambs are less troubled with internal parasites, and another advantage is that the lambing season comes before the rush of spring work.

Ewes which lamb early need plenty of good feed in winter and the lambs should be fed grain before pasture is available in the spring. The production of "hot-house lambs" and "spring lambs" is discussed later in this chapter.

In sections where grain and good hay are expensive or if the shelter is not suitable for early lambs, it is best to have the lambs born in April or May and to market them in autumn after the rush of western lambs.

The average length of the gestation period of ewes is 145 to 147 days, according to various authorities.[3] It is longer for Merino and Rambouillet ewes than for ewes of the mutton breeds, averaging about 152 days for the former. For Southdowns and Shropshires it is usually slightly shorter than for the larger mutton breeds.

1233. Breeding time; flushing the ewes.—The natural breeding season for most breeds of sheep is during the late summer and the autumn. Ewes will usually begin to come in heat after the first cool nights, and the periods of heat recur approximately every 16 days unless the ewes conceive.

It is generally believed that ewes which are "flushed" at breeding time, or fed so that they are gaining in weight, are more apt to produce twins and triplets than those which are in poor flesh, and that they also breed earlier and more nearly at the same time and produce more vigorous lambs.[4] Accordingly, with the farm flock, it is advisable to "flush" the ewes for 2 or 3 weeks before the desired date of breeding; i. e., to supply an abundance of palatable, nutritious feed, such as rape, cabbage, good pasture, or grain.

Liberal feeding before breeding time is especially needed if the ewes have run down in flesh during summer, as is common with ewes having large milk flows, even though they have had good care and pasture. If ewes have been fed inadequately after their lambs were weaned, and have consequently run down in condition, many of them will fail to come in heat or they may fail to conceive.

Where the ewes and lambs are well fed, twin lambs will make nearly as rapid gains in weight as single lambs.[5] Therefore twins are certainly advantageous under favorable farm conditions. On the western range, where less attention can be given to the individual ewes, single lambs have usually been preferred. However, recent studies indicate that even under range conditions, twin lambs are desirable if pasture and feed conditions are average or better, except for aged or for immature ewes.[6] A decidedly larger total weight of lambs was produced by ewes with twins, on the average, than by ewes having single lambs.

1234. The ram.—A well-built, vigorous purebred ram of good breeding should be chosen and then be so fed and cared for that he will remain potent. He needs no grain while on good pasture during summer, but beginning at least a month before breeding time some concentrates should be fed. During the breeding season he should be kept in good condition by feeding at least 1 lb. a day of a mixture fairly rich in protein, such as 3 parts of oats and 1 of wheat bran. This amount is for a ram of average size.

The ram should never be allowed to run down in the breeding season through insufficient feed or over use. On the other hand, he should never become fat. In purchasing a ram, avoid one that has been highly fitted for shows, for this may result in impotence.

During the breeding season the ram should run with the ewes but a short time daily, or at night only, unless he is of very nervous temperament and frets all the time when away from the flock. Where "hand coupling" is not practiced, to determine whether a ewe has been bred and at what time, the ram should be painted on the brisket with some compound which will leave a mark on the wool of the ewe.

A vigorous ram will serve 25 to 50 ewes a season, if allowed to run with them all the time. Where "hand coupling" is practiced or the ram is turned with the ewes only a short time daily, 50 to 75 ewes may be bred to one ram. Ewes are most likely to conceive if bred during the latter part of the heat period, instead of during the early hours.[7] If a ram lamb is used for breeding, he should not serve more than 15 to 20 ewes.

After the breeding season the ram may be kept in thrifty condition on good roughage, such as legume hay and perhaps silage, with a small allowance of concentrates, if needed. Some succulent food is desirable, but mangels and sugar beets should be avoided as they may tend to produce urinary calculi, or "stones." Ram lambs need a liberal ration containing plenty of protein but should not be allowed to become fat. Lack of exercise injures the ram's breeding powers. Except during mating time the ram should be kept away from the ewe flock, so that he cannot annoy them.

1235. Feeding the ewes in the fall.—Plenty of good pasturage should be provided for the ewes in the fall, and where the winters are mild considerable of their winter feed can come from winter rye or wheat pasture or from grass pasture which has been allowed to grow up in the fall. Often they can get much of their fall feed by cleaning up stalk and stubble fields, thus using feed that would otherwise be wasted.

It is best to use such forage early, before fall rains and frosts have lessened its value, and to leave the grass or legume pasture for later grazing. If there is a shortage of pasture in the fall, care should be taken to supply sufficient hay or grain to keep the ewes in thrifty condition. Rape furnishes excellent feed late in the fall.

1236. The flock in winter.—For winter shelter, dry, well-ventilated quarters should be provided, with wide doorways and convenient feed racks. **(1173-1174)** It is best to divide large flocks into groups of sheep of similar size and condition, so that the ration can be suited to the needs of each group. For example, yearling ewes will need a little more feed than mature ewes, as they are still growing. Exercise in winter is essential for breeding ewes, as has been emphasized previously. **(1175)**

The ewes should be wintered so that they will gain 15 to 25 lbs. during pregnancy, and at lambing time be in medium flesh and vigorous condition. Insufficient feed or an unbalanced ration will result in weak lambs and a scanty flow of milk, and therefore reduce the profits.[8] This does not mean, however, that expensive rations are needed, containing a large proportion of concentrates. On the contrary, ewes should be wintered, up to lambing time, chiefly on good roughage, including plenty of legume hay, if possible.

If the ewes go into the winter in good condition and are then fed what legume hay they will eat, with or without silage or roots in addition, they will usually need no grain or other concentrates at all until 4 to 6 weeks before they lamb. Then not more than 0.5 lb. per head daily is commonly required. An experienced shepherd knows that the only safe way to determine the condition of a sheep is by feeling of its back. If he finds that the ewes are not thriving, he will feed them more liberally.

It is not only unnecessarily expensive but also unwise to feed breeding ewes so liberally that they are really fat at lambing time.[9] They are then apt to have more difficulty in lambing and may also produce weak lambs.

Both ram lambs and ewe lambs intended for the breeding flock should be so fed the first winter that they will grow steadily, but they should never receive a fattening ration. Within the limits set by heredity, the size lambs will reach when mature depends very largely upon the development the first year.

1237. Rations for ewes.—As a guide in selecting satisfactory and economical balanced rations for breeding ewes, several example rations are given in Appendix Table VII that are adapted to conditions in various sections. These rations meet the nutritive requirements of ewes as stated in the Morrison feeding standards, and should produce satisfactory results.

The amounts of roughage stated in these rations are the amounts actually eaten, after deducting the wastage. Ewes wintered in the open in the northern range states, without shelter, may require somewhat larger amounts of feed than stated, due to the exposure.

Salt and plenty of good water should always be provided for the flock. **(1166, 1170)**

1238. Hay and other dry roughage for ewes.—The various roughages suitable for feeding ewes have been discussed in the previous chapter. Whenever possible, the ewes should be fed a liberal amount of legume hay or mixed hay high in legumes. Such hay is rich not only in protein, calcium, and vitamins, but it is also laxative. Moreover, it is usually more economical to supply the necessary protein for the ewes by feeding legume hay than by purchasing considerable amounts of protein supplements.

Alfalfa and clover hay are unexcelled among legume hays for feeding the breeding flock. Soybean hay is a satisfactory substitute for these, but there is apt to be more refuse in feeding it, on account of the coarse stems. Cowpeas, vetch, sweet clover, and such a mixture as peas-and-oats, all furnish good hay for the ewe flock. Well-preserved pea or bean straw or alfalfa or clover chaff is a fair substitute for part of the legume hay.

Timothy hay cut at the usual stage of maturity and marsh hay are unsatisfactory for ewes, for not only are they unpalatable but also they may cause serious constipation.[10] Moreover, the heads of timothy work into the wool, irritating the skin and lowering the quality of the wool. As has been pointed out in the preceding chapter, early-cut timothy is much better than that cut late, though not equal to alfalfa or clover. (**1208**) Bright corn fodder or corn stover, cut while the leaves are still green, is preferable to ordinary timothy hay,[11] and early-cut bluegrass hay, prairie hay, or oat hay, or even bright oat straw may often be used satisfactorily as part of the roughage, when fed with legume hay.[12] Straw alone or straw and silage is unsatisfactory as the roughage for ewes.[13]

When no legume hay is fed, it will be necessary to feed more concentrates, and these should furnish plenty of protein. If it is necessary to winter ewes with little or no legume hay, 0.25 to 0.50 ounce per head daily of ground limestone or oyster shell should be fed, or a mineral mixture furnishing calcium should be provided where the ewes can have access to it. (**181**)

1239. Succulent feeds for ewes.—Silage, roots, or other succulent feeds aid greatly in preventing constipation and in keeping the ewes thrifty in winter, especially when little or no legume hay is available. Adding silage to an abundance of good alfalfa hay does not usually make much difference in the thrift of the ewes or the vigor of the lambs.[14] The economy of using silage under such conditions will depend on the relative cost of silage and of alfalfa hay, good corn silage being worth about one-half as much per ton as such hay. (**1216**) Though roots are excellent for ewes, silage is a much more economical feed under conditions in the United States.

It is commonly recommended that pregnant ewes be fed no more than about 2 lbs. of silage daily per 100 lbs. live weight. However, larger allowances can be used satisfactorily when silage of excellent quality is fed with plenty of good legume hay.[15] As has been mentioned in the previous chapter, good corn silage has even been used successfully as the only roughage for pregnant ewes, when a sufficient amount of protein supplement has been fed and also a calcium supplement. (**1217**)

1240. Concentrates for ewes.—Not only the amount but also the kind of concentrates required by breeding ewes will depend on the sort of roughages that are used. If a liberal amount of legume hay is fed, the concentrates may be chiefly or entirely grains, such as oats, corn, barley, or the grain sorghums.

Oats are highly esteemed as a feed for ewes and are often fed as the only concentrate with legume hay. Corn is considered too fattening by many shepherds to be used as the chief concentrate. They prefer bulky mixtures containing considerable oats or wheat bran. However, when plenty of protein is furnished by legume hay or other protein-rich feeds and the ewes are not over-fed on corn so that they become unduly fat, corn can be used satisfactorily as the chief grain.[16] Barley, wheat, and the grain sorghums are all satisfactory for breeding ewes when fed in suitable mixtures.

Unless a liberal amount of legume hay is fed to the ewes, it will be necessary to include a sufficient amount of a protein supplement in the concentrate or grain mixture to balance the ration. Several concentrate mixtures that are suitable for feeding with various combinations of roughage are given in Appendix Table VII. The values of the various protein supplements have been discussed in the previous chapter. Wheat bran and linseed meal are probably most widely used for the breeding flock in the United States, but other supplements are satisfactory when more economical.

Under unusual conditions when hay is high in price in comparison with grain, it may be economical to restrict somewhat the amount of hay fed to ewes and to increase the grain or other concentrates. In Montana trials it was found that each pound of corn replaced 2.5 lbs. of alfalfa hay in wintering ewes, when 0.3 lb. corn was fed in place of part of the hay.[17]

1241. Pregnancy disease of ewes.—This disease is one of the most common causes of death of pregnant ewes in the late winter and early spring, within a month before lambing. It is apparently due to conditions of feeding and management, but the exact cause is still in doubt, although the disease has been studied by several investigators.[18] It occurs in ewes that are well-fed, but in such cases there has usually been a lack of exercise. It also affects ewes that have had an inadequate ration with roughage of poor quality, even when they have had plenty of exercise. The disease is most apt to affect ewes carrying twins or triplets, and also affects older ewes more often than yearlings.

The disease seems to be associated with a deranged metabolism of carbohydrates in the body, and seems in certain respects to resemble acetonemia in dairy cows. (927) Though the exact cause of the disease is not yet known, it is fortunate that there is generally but little trouble from it when the ewes before lambing are fed and cared for as has been advised in this chapter. It is believed that the following factors will aid in preventing the disease: The feeding of an ample amount of good legume hay; the use of sufficient grain or other concentrates to keep the ewes in satisfactory condition; preventing constipation; and seeing that the ewes get sufficient exercise.

1242. Stiff lamb disease.—This is a strange disease of young suckling lambs, which usually becomes apparent when lambs are 1 to 5 weeks old. The lambs that are affected become characteristically stiff and in advanced cases they may be unable to get up or to walk any great distance. Some stiff lambs stagger around for several days and then gradually improve, but many become so stiff that they are unable to walk or to nurse without assistance. It is doubtful that death is due to the disease itself, but owing to starvation the lambs become so thin and weak that they die or are killed by the owner.

Post-mortem examination of stiff lambs shows that certain of the muscles have undergone degeneration, becoming whitish in color.[19] Almost invariably the disease affects the same muscles on the two sides of the body. The trouble seems to be due entirely to feed or management and not to infection.

In experiments during 5 years at the New York (Cornell) Station stiff lambs were produced experimentally each year when the ewes were wintered on a ration of oats, barley, cull beans, and second-cutting alfalfa hay.[20] It was thought at first that liberal feeding of the ewes so that they became too fat and also a lack of exercise tended to cause the disease, but ewes which were fed this ration produced stiff lambs, even when exercised abundantly and fed only a moderate amount.

In contrast to the results on this ration, not a single stiff lamb was produced by ewes which were fed a ration of oats, wheat bran, corn silage, and mixed clover-and-timothy hay. In many cases, the ewes fed the latter ration had previously produced stiff lambs in farm flocks or when fed the experimental ration first mentioned, but none produced stiff lambs when fed this "good" ration.

The exact cause of the trouble is still in doubt, but it is fortunate that apparently it can usually be prevented by feeding a simple ration consisting of grain, wheat bran, corn silage, and mixed hay. Farmers who had previously suffered severe losses from the disease have reported much better results after changing to this ration or one which is similar.

1243. Lambing time.—Profits in sheep raising often depend largely on skillful attention at lambing time, for heavy losses of lambs frequently occur in farm flocks when such care is lacking. The shepherd should therefore be close at hand to give assistance to any ewes or lambs that need it. In order to know when the ewes are due to lamb, it is wise to keep a breeding record, showing when each was bred. Just before lambing little grain or other concentrates should be fed, so as to reduce the danger of milk fever. All tags of long and loose wool about the rear and the udder of each ewe should be removed at this time.

It is best to put each ewe in a "holding" or "lambing" pen immediately after lambing or shortly before, and this should be kept bedded with clean straw. The ewe should remain here for 3 or 4 days after lambing, until the mother and her offspring become thoroughly accustomed to each other and the lambs are strong enough to look out for themselves among the flock. The lambing pens may be made by setting up panels 4 feet long, hinged in pairs, along a warm side of the stable. In very cold weather burlap sacks hung on the panels will help keep new-born lambs warm.

During lambing the ewe should not be disturbed unless assistance is needed. Weak lambs often need special attention to save them. The mucus should be cleaned from the nostrils and mouth of any weakling, and if it is unable to nurse within a half hour after birth it should have patient assistance. A chilled, new-born lamb is best warmed by immersing all but the head in water as hot as the elbow can bear. When well warmed, it should be wiped dry, taken to its mother, and helped to nurse. Some advise wrapping it in thick woolen cloths that have been warmed on a stove, and renewing these as often as they become cool. A lamb born almost lifeless may often be restored by alternately blowing gently into the mouth to start breathing, and laying it on its belly and slapping the body smartly on each side of the heart.

One twin is often weaker than the other, and frequently the mother cares only for the stronger one. In such cases the weakling should be helped to its full share of food. If the navel cord has not broken off, it should be broken off 4 or 5 inches from the body soon after birth. Tincture of iodine should always be applied to the stump of the cord to prevent infection.

A ewe that refuses her lamb will usually accept it if they are kept together in a lambing pen and the lamb helped to suckle a few times. The stubborn ewe may be tied so that she cannot prevent the lamb nursing. In case a ewe loses her lamb, she may often be induced to adopt a twin by first sprinkling some of her own milk over it. Still more effective is tying the skin from the dead lamb upon the back of the one to be adopted.

1244. Breeding studies; weights of lambs at birth.—The number of lambs raised per 100 ewes of breeding age, or the percentage of increase, will vary widely depending on the conditions under which the sheep are kept and also depending on the breed. Fine-wool sheep are less prolific than the mutton breeds, and the percentage of increase can be made much greater with farm flocks than under range conditions.

In the western range states the average number of lambs raised to market age in the different states for each 100 breeding ewes is estimated at 57.7 to 92.5, the average of 11 states being 75.[21] In certain fine-wool flocks in Ohio, an average of 80 to 82 lambs were raised per 100 bred ewes.[22] With ewes of the mutton breeds, kept under excellent conditions, the percentage of increase can be much greater than this. For example, during 24 years at the Wisconsin Station the average number of live lambs born per 100 ewes of various mutton breeds was 161.[23]

In these studies the average birth weights of single lambs were as follows for the various breeds: Shropshire, 9.5 lbs.; Southdown, 9.2 lbs.; Hampshire, 10.6 lbs.; Cheviot, 9.5 lbs.; Dorset, 10.2 lbs.; and Oxford, 10.4 lbs. The average birth weights of the twin lambs were: Shropshire, 7.7 lbs.; Southdown, 7.7 lbs.; Hampshire, 8.2 lbs.; Cheviot, 7.7 lbs.; Dorset, 8.5 lbs.; and Oxford, 8.2 lbs. The triplet lambs were somewhat smaller than the twins. In California studies the average birth weight of Rambouillets was 9.9 lbs.; of Hampshires, 9.3 lbs.; of Shropshires, 8.6 lbs.; of Southdowns, 8.7 lbs.; and of Romneys, 9.0 lbs.[24] In the Wisconsin studies the ram lambs averaged 0.5 lb. heavier at birth than the ewe lambs.

The percentage of increase of ewes tends to grow greater until they reach the fifth or sixth year, as shown by the Wisconsin studies and studies by Roberts of purebred Shropshires.[25] This is doubtless due somewhat to discarding the poorer breeders as 3-year-olds. The larger ewes of a given breed tend to have a greater percentage of increase and their lambs tend to be larger. The gestation period tends to be slightly longer for the larger lambs.

1245. After lambing.—Soon after lambing, the ewe should be given water with the chill removed but should not be allowed to drink too much at a time. To avoid udder trouble, but little grain should be fed for the first 2 or 3 days, although she may have all the dry roughage she wishes. Close attention must be given for a few days to see that the lamb is taking milk from both sides of the udder. All surplus milk should be drawn, or better, a needy lamb helped to an extra meal. Caked udders and sore teats should receive prompt treatment.

With the demand for more milk by the lamb, it pays to increase the ewe's ration, for lambs make the most economical gains when suckling. It must be borne in mind that the ewe is not only producing milk and maintaining her body, but that she is also growing wool, which is protein in character. If there is not sufficient roughage of high quality for the entire winter, the most palatable portion should be reserved until after the lambing period. Plenty of legume hay should be fed, if possible, and also silage or other succulent feed, if it is available. After lambing, the ewes can safely be allowed all the succulent feed they will eat in addition to what hay they want.

If there is, unfortunately, little or no legume hay for the ewes at this time, it will be necessary to include more of such feeds as linseed meal, cottonseed meal, and wheat bran in the concentrate mixture. Rations meeting the requirements of the Morrison feeding standards for ewes nursing lambs will provide enough protein and total digestible nutrients for good results. (Appendix Table III.)

An allowance of 1 lb. of concentrates a head daily, or slightly more in some cases, should be enough with satisfactory roughage to produce a good flow of milk. Ewes that are in thin condition at lambing time will need more concentrates than those in good flesh.

The same concentrate mixtures may be used for ewes nursing lambs as for pregnant ewes, except that some protein supplement should always be included in the ration unless good legume hay is fed as the only roughage. Oats are excellent for ewes that are nursing lambs, and many experienced shepherds prefer to use a concentrate mixture including a considerable proportion of oats.[26]

1246. Ewe's milk.—In America the milk of sheep is seldom used by man, but abroad, especially in the mountain regions of continental Europe, it is extensively employed, both for direct consumption and for the manufacture of cheese. The average composition of ewe's milk, compared with cow's milk, is shown in Appendix Table I. It will be noted that ewe's milk is much richer in protein (casein and albumin) and fat, and also higher than cow's milk in ash. Ewe's milk has a peculiar, somewhat unpleasant odor and taste; it is thicker, and sours more slowly than cow's milk. The fat content is extremely variable, ranging from 2 to 12 per cent. The butter is pale yellow, less firm than cow's butter, and becomes rancid much quicker.

The yield of milk by sheep will vary greatly, according to breed and feed. The East Friesian milk sheep in Germany at 2 to 3 years of age yield from 3 to 4 quarts of milk daily for 2 months after weaning their lambs, and keep up an excellent flow during the autumn months. These sheep are prolific, dropping 2 or 3 lambs and some individuals lambing twice a year. Three sheep are estimated to consume as much feed as 1 cow. Ordinary sheep yield from 100 to 150 lbs. of milk per year, while the milk breeds produce 300 lbs. or more.

1247. Milking qualities of ewes.—In building up a profitable flock it is highly important to select ewes on the basis of their milk production and nursing qualities, as well as on type and conformation. The rate of gain made by a lamb during the suckling period depends more largely on the amount of milk the dam produces than on any other factor.

In studies at the New Hampshire Station there was a difference of 79 per cent in the gains during the suckling period of lambs from heavy-milking ewes and poor-milking ewes.[27] The amount of milk was much more important than its richness in fat.

But relatively little information is available concerning the composition and yield of milk from the various common breeds of sheep. In studies at the Wisconsin, New Hampshire, and Idaho Stations the daily yield of milk by ewes of various breeds ranged from less than 2 lbs. to

7.5 lbs., and the fat content from 3.8 to 12.1 per cent.[28]   There was a much greater range in fat percentage for the milk of ewes of the same breed than difference between the average composition for the various breeds.

In a trial at the Wisconsin Station ewes consumed 113 lbs. of dry matter for each 100 lbs. of milk produced.[29]   Considering that ewes are growing fleeces and that their milk is richer in fat and protein than cow's milk, such ewes compare favorably with cows in economy of production.   In this trial lambs consumed 640 lbs. of their dam's milk for each 100 lbs. they gained.

1248. Orphan lambs.—If possible, a foster mother should be found for any orphan lamb. However, in case this cannot be done, the orphan can be successfully raised on cow's milk, though close attention is necessary the first month.[30]

For the first week the lamb should have some colostrum ewe's milk, if possible, by letting it nurse ewes whose lambs are not yet old enough to take all of the milk. The cow's milk should be from a cow giving milk rich in fat, since ewe's milk is high in fat, or cream may be added. For the first 3 or 4 weeks the lamb should be given milk from the same cow, if possible. For the first day or two after birth only 2 to 4 tablespoonfuls of milk should be given at a time, and the lamb should be fed at least 4 times each 24 hours.

The milk should be fed from a bottle with a medium-sized nipple attached and should always be warmed to approximately 100° F. by immersing the bottle in water of this temperature or slightly above. The bottle and nipple should be carefully washed after each feeding. After the lamb is 2 to 3 weeks old, it is not necessary to feed it more than 3 times a day. Cow's milk may also be used to supply additional feed to lambs in case a ewe with a scanty milk supply has twins.

1249. The young lambs.—During the suckling period of about 4 months, well-fed lambs will make about two-thirds of the growth and gain in weight they will make during the entire first year.[31] Furthermore, the most economical gains are made at this time. It is thus very important that lambs in farm flocks be well fed during this period. During the summer a lamb on pasture will consume nearly as much feed as a dry ewe, according to Nevada trials, and a ewe and her lamb will consume twice as much feed as a dry ewe.[32]

At least until pasture is ready in the spring, early lambs should be fed both grain and hay in a "creep" as soon they show a desire for feed in addition to the milk of their dams.[33] This will be when they are about 2 weeks old. The creep is made by fencing off a corner of the barn with panels in which there are openings just wide enough to allow the lambs to pass through, while keeping the ewes back. Within the creep there should be a hay rack and a low, shallow grain trough with a board lengthwise above the trough to prevent the lambs jumping into it. In this trough a suitable concentrate mixture is fed, only a little being sprinkled at first. Fresh feed should be put in twice a day, and all the refuse should be fed to the ewes.

An excellent concentrate mixture for young lambs is: 20 lbs. coarsely ground or cracked corn, 20 lbs. coarsely ground or crushed oats, 10 lbs. wheat bran, and 10 lbs. linseed meal or cake or soybean oil meal. If the lambs are all to be fattened for market, most of the concentrates may be corn or other grain, for the milk will furnish ample protein. A mixture of half corn and half oats is often used.

Corn alone will give satisfactory results if the lambs have choice legume hay, though it is not liked quite so well by lambs as the mixtures mentioned and usually will not produce quite as rapid gains.[34] Most experienced shepherds prefer not to use more than half corn in a mixture for lambs to be retained for the breeding flock. After the lambs are 5 to 6 weeks old, there is no advantage in grinding the grain.

Fine alfalfa or second-crop clover hay should also be provided in the creep, and silage or roots will be appreciated. All feed should be fresh— that which is left over can be given to the ewes or other stock. Care should be taken to provide fresh, clean water.

1250. Docking and castration.—All the lambs should be docked and the ram lambs not intended for breeding should be castrated when 1 to 2 weeks old, with the possible exceptions noted later. Some advise docking the ewe lambs when 8 to 14 days old and the rams 5 to 7 days after castration; others recommend docking at the same time the ram lambs are castrated.

Recent experiments have shown that ram lambs may make as rapid or even more rapid gains than wether lambs until after 4 or 5 months of age.[35] Also up to this age there is but little difference in the carcasses of ram and wether lambs. However, on the large markets, long-tailed and uncastrated lambs, even when no older than this, often sell at a discount of $1.00 per hundred pounds. This makes castration and docking highly advisable. On certain local markets there is apparently little discrimination against ram lambs up to this age.

When older than 4 or 5 months, ram lambs yield carcasses of distinctly lower value than wethers, being heavy in the fore quarters and containing a smaller proportion of valuable cuts. In hot-house lamb production the ram lambs are not commonly castrated.

1251. Turning to pasture.—Good pasture should be provided for the ewes and lambs as early in spring as possible. This not only lessens the cost but also aids in keeping them thrifty. At first they should be turned to pasture for only a short time, 2 to 4 hours, during the warm part of the day. The ewes and lambs should then be brought back to their shelter, where a full feed awaits them. In the North winter rye provides excellent early grazing, and farther south winter oats and wheat furnish pasturage during the colder months.

When the forage has become ample, stable feeding may be discontinued for the ewes, or for both ewes and lambs, according to the plan followed. With good pasture, breeding ewes need no grain. Shade and plenty of fresh water should always be provided for ewes and lambs on pasture.

1252. Feeding concentrates to lambs on grass.—Whether or not it will pay in the case of suckling lambs intended for slaughter, to feed grain or other concentrates by means of a creep when they are on pasture depends on several conditions. Unless the grazing is excellent, lambs fed grain will make somewhat more rapid gains and therefore be ready for market earlier. Sometimes this will make the grain feeding profitable, as it will make it possible to market the lambs early, before a fall in price. Also, when there is trouble from stomach worms and other internal parasites, a liberal supply of feed helps keep the lambs thrifty. It has been previously pointed out that early lambs should be fed grain in addition to their mothers' milk before they are turned to pasture.

If care is taken to provide good pasture for the ewes and lambs, it may be most profitable to feed no grain or other concentrates to lambs on pasture. For example, in trials during 4 years at the Indiana Station, suckling lambs fed no grain on good pasture gained 0.61 lb. per head daily, in comparison with 0.62 lb. for others fed corn or a suitable concentrate mixture in a creep.[36] On the average, the lambs fed no grain were worth only 10 cents less per hundredweight than those given grain on pasture, and they returned a greater profit.

Similar results were secured in Tennessee and Wisconsin trials.[37] In 5 Alabama experiments grain-fed lambs returned only 24 cents more per head over the cost of feed than did lambs fed no grain on pasture.[38] If the pasturage is good, it is not necessary to feed grain to suckling lambs on pasture which are intended for the breeding flock, unless it is desired to force valuable purebred lambs to maximum growth.

Corn or a mixture of corn and oats is satisfactory for feeding to suckling lambs on pasture, as the milk provides sufficient protein to balance these grains. Heavy feeding of corn in hot weather may cause the lambs to go off feed, however. Many prefer such mixtures as corn, 2 or 3 lbs.; oats, 2 or 3 lbs.; bran, 1 lb., and linseed meal, 1 lb.

1253. Marketing lambs early; weaning lambs.—Where farm lambs are raised under good conditions and with plenty of feed, it is often most profitable to sell before weaning those that are intended for market. This is especially the case with early lambs. Lambs thus marketed early, before the western lambs reach the market, usually bring a considerably higher price per 100 lbs. than if they are marketed in late fall or in winter.

Lambs of the mutton breeds which are to be retained in the flock, or those which do not have sufficient weight and finish to be marketed, should be weaned at about 4 months of age. This should be done for their own good as well as to allow their dams a rest before another breeding period. If possible, advantage should be taken of a cool spell in summer to wean the lambs, as they will then be more comfortable during this trying period.

The lambs should be so far separated from their dams that neither can hear the bleating of the other. For a few days the ewes should be held on short pasture or kept on dry feed in the yard, so as to reduce their milk flow. The udders must be examined, and, if necessary, as is often the case with the best mothers, they should be milked out a few times, so inflammation will not result.

It is especially important to provide fresh pasture, free from parasites, for the lambs after weaning. Profitable gains cannot be expected if the lambs are taken from their mothers and left on a bluegrass pasture infested with parasites and where the feed is scanty because of heat and drought. This practice is the chief cause of the large number of thin, scrawny lambs which reach the central livestock markets each year. The various pasture crops which are suitable for lambs are discussed in the preceding chapter.

Whether or not to feed grain to lambs after weaning will depend on the relative prices of grain and pasture and on the premium paid for well-finished lambs. From trials at the Ohio Station it was concluded that the feeding of grain after weaning is not necessary for the economical production of well-finished lambs, if an abundance of good pasture is provided.[39] Ewe lambs to be retained in the flock need no grain when grazing is good. Ram lambs require grain during the fall to secure proper development, whether they are to be sold as lambs or retained till yearlings.

1254. Cost of maintaining ewes.—The cost of maintaining ewes will vary quite widely in different parts of the country, and will differ considerably depending on whether the flock can get any important part of their fall and winter feed by grazing on stalk and stubble fields, thus utilizing feed that might otherwise be wasted.

Where no such grazing is available, it will require 400 to 600 lbs. or more of hay or other dry roughages (deducting the amount wasted) to carry a breeding ewe of average size, weighing 100 to 150 lbs., through the winter period of 5 to 6 months. Also, for the best results about 20 lbs. of concentrates per ewe should be fed prior to lambing and perhaps additional concentrates for flushing the ewes at the breeding season. In the case of ewes lambing early, additional concentrates will be needed for the ewes and lambs before the pasture season.

In addition to the cost of winter feed and of pasture, in estimating the total cost of keeping ewes there must be included the man and horse labor, the interest, depreciation, and mortality risk on the ewes, the housing charge, and any miscellaneous expenses. On the credit side are the wool and lambs produced and the value of the manure from the flock.

In 70 Ohio fine-wool flocks containing an average of 116 sheep the average amounts of feed required per head during the year for the 3-year period, 1930-1932, were 218 lbs. of dry roughage (42 per cent of which was legume hay) and 51 lbs. grain, in addition to the feed furnished by pasture and other grazing. In these flocks 61 ewes were bred, on the average, each year, and 82 lambs were raised for each 100 ewes bred. The mortality of mature sheep was 4.7 per cent a year, and the amount of man labor per sheep a year was 2.6 hours. The cost of feed, including pasture, was $2.57; and the total cost per sheep, $3.98.[40] The average yield of wool per sheep was 9.44 lbs.

The average amounts of feed required yearly per head in 103 flocks in western New York, containing an average of 58 sheep, were 46 lbs. of concentrates, 486 lbs. of hay, and 190 lbs. of other roughage, including silage, fodder, and stover.[41] On the average, 7.8 lbs. of wool were sold per head, 97 lambs were raised per 100 ewes, and 6.1 hours of man labor were required a year per sheep. Under 1933 conditions, the average yearly costs per sheep were as follows: Feed, except pasture, $2.54; pasture, $1.29; bedding, $0.17; man labor, $0.95; building charges, $1.14; equipment costs, $0.04; interest, $0.31; other costs, $0.14; total cost per head, $6.58.

Detailed records were secured over a term of years at the Pennsylvania Station on the cost of maintaining purebred Shropshire and Delaine-Merino ewes fed various rations.[42] The most economical winter ration tested was an allowance for the Shropshires, which averaged 172 lbs. in weight, of 2.50 lbs. alfalfa hay, 3.07 lbs. corn silage, and 0.22 lb. concentrates. The Delaine-Merino ewes, averaging 122 lbs. in weight, ate 2.30 lbs. alfalfa hay, 2.95 lbs. corn silage, and 0.27 lb. concentrates per head daily.

An average of 85 lbs. bedding was required per ewe during the winter, and 735 lbs. manure were produced per ewe. The Shropshires sheared 7.66 lbs., on the average, and the average weight of the lambs at weaning was 59.0 lbs. The Delaine-Merinos sheared 11.1 lbs. and their lambs averaged 53.1 lbs. at weaning.

1255. Factors affecting the net income from sheep.—The various cost-accounting studies that have been made of sheep and wool production show clearly that some of the most important factors affecting the net income are the following: (1) A flock of sufficient size to make possible the efficient use of labor, buildings, equipment, and ram. (2) A flock that has been selected to produce a high yield of wool per ewe and a high percentage of lambs as well. (3) Proper feed and care of the ewes, so that they will produce vigorous lambs and furnish plenty of milk for them. (4) Plenty of good pasture, preferably rotated so as to aid in the control of parasites. (5) Thorough control of stomach worms and other internal parasites, and also control of ticks and lice.

1256. Stomach worms and other parasites.—In the humid districts of the United States, stomach worms, *Haemonchus contortus,* and also other internal parasites are a serious tax upon sheep raising. For success it is necessary to use effective methods of controlling these parasites.

The stomach worms not only draw nourishment from the blood, but it is also believed that poisonous secretions from the worms reduce the number of red blood cells and the hemoglobin content of the blood of the infested animals. Badly affected sheep may have only one-quarter the normal number of red blood cells. Lambs are usually affected more seriously than older sheep.

The eggs of the stomach worms pass out in the droppings of the sheep and are scattered about the pastures, where they soon hatch and develop to the larval stage. Sheep become infested only by swallowing the worms at this stage while grazing.

Fields on which no sheep, cattle, or goats have grazed for a year, and those that have been freshly plowed and cultivated since sheep grazed thereon, are practically free from infestation. Old bluegrass pastures are especially to be avoided. It is also dangerous to allow sheep to drink from stagnant pools. During warm weather, otherwise clean pastures may become infested in 10 to 20 days of grazing.

To remove the worms from the intestinal tract of sheep various drenches are recommended, the most common probably being the 1 per cent solution of copper sulfate in water.[43] The dose depends on the size of the sheep. A good rule is to use 1 ounce of the solution for each 30 to 35 lbs. of sheep or lamb and never give more than 5 ounces to any sheep.[44] The dose for an average ewe is from 3.5 to 4.0 ounces.

As copper sulfate is poisonous, the solution must be carefully made up and accurately administered for safety. So the drench will control some of the common tape worms as well, 1 ounce of a 40 per cent solution of nicotine sulfate may be added to 3 to 4 quarts of copper sulfate solution. Feed and water should be withheld from the sheep for about 18 hours before drenching and for 5 or 6 hours after drenching, to increase the effectiveness. Other drenches sometimes used are carbon tetrachloride, tetrachlorethylene, and Lugol's iodine solution.

If sheep are severely infested with stomach worms, a second treatment should be given after 10 days. It is a good plan to drench sheep at regular intervals throughout the grazing season. In the northern states once a month from the time they go on pasture will usually give effective control. In the South more frequent drenching may be necessary. Early lambs are ordinarily given the first treatment at weaning time.

Where it is possible to rotate on various pasture plots at intervals of 2 weeks, trouble from stomach worms and other parasites may be largely prevented without drenching. Temporary pastures, such as rape or clover, are well adapted to this system, for it requires 3 or more separate, clean pasture lots. Where permanent pastures are used, this plan is often difficult to follow.

The first essential in control of stomach worms and other intestinal parasites is to protect the lambs, for they are much more seriously affected than older sheep. Thorough drenching of the ewes in the spring with some vermifuge will remove most of the worms and aid in keeping the lambs free from them. Immediately after weaning, the lambs should always be turned on fresh, clean pasture, on which no sheep have grazed previously that season.

In a plan of rotating pastures so as to prevent serious trouble from stomach worms, advantage should be taken of the uninfested grazing furnished by stubble fields, aftermath in meadows, and corn fields. In the northern states worm-free and infested sheep may graze together from the last of September until May with but little danger. Well-fed, thrifty sheep and lambs can resist parasites much better than those getting poor feed and care.

To eradicate ticks or lice, both mature sheep and lambs should be dipped with a suitable preparation in the spring as soon as the cuts have healed on the sheep that have been shorn. If badly infested, the sheep should be dipped a second time to kill any parasites that were in the egg stage before. The second dipping should be 24 to 28 days later for ticks and 14 to 16 days later for lice. The sheep should be dipped on a clear, warm morning, so they will dry during the day. In fall the flock should be dipped again, if necessary. In case of scab, prompt and thorough dipping is necessary.

1257. Range sheep production.—About two-thirds of the sheep in the United States are in the 11 western states and in Texas. Here most of them are kept under range conditions.[45] The ranges grazed by sheep are usually the rougher areas of the plains, foothills, and mountains.

The high mountain ranges furnish excellent forage for sheep during the summer months, for there is usually an abundance of water and good pasturage, and the days are cool. The plains and the semi-desert ranges, which are too hot and dry in summer, furnish excellent winter range, and during the spring and fall the foothills are used to good advantage. Sheep do well on sagebrush and salt-sage browse, neither of which is palatable to cattle, and cattle can browse on the higher growing species which sheep cannot reach. For grazing throughout the year, commonly 4 to 20 acres of range are needed for a mature sheep.

The unit, or band, of range sheep may vary considerably in size, but it usually contains 2,000 to 2,500 sheep. From lambing time to weaning about 1,200 ewes and their lambs are usually kept in one band, and after the lambs are weaned, two bands of ewes are combined for the breeding and winter period.

Most of the western sheep producers use the same general method in handling their sheep. A band is put in charge of one herder, who with his dogs, stays with the sheep, day and night, throughout the season. The herder is quartered in a covered wagon, equipped for his needs, except when he is near headquarters or in summer when the sheep are on a high mountain range where the wagon cannot follow. A tent is then used for shelter.

A camp tender, with a wagon or pack animals, supplies the herder with food and moves his camp, as the sheep need new grazing ground. One camp tender may take care of two or more herders, and in large enterprises a range foreman is usually in charge of several bands. Additional help is needed during lambing and shearing. In Texas, a common method is to keep the range sheep in fenced pastures, where they can graze undisturbed. Under this system one man can care for a larger number of sheep, and the sheep can make better utilization of the feed than on an unfenced range.

On the ranges the sheep receive no feed except the pasturage during the growing season, and often a range at low altitude furnishes most of the winter feed, especially in the southern districts. Usually, however, it is necessary to make provision for additional feed during the winter, such as alfalfa and other hay, or cottonseed cake or meal.

Where early lambs are produced, as in certain valleys of California, Oregon, and Arizona, the ewes lamb in sheds from late in January to early in March. The lambs are raised on the valley and foothill ranges and are marketed as fat "spring lambs" in spring or early in summer, before the low-lying ranges dry up. In this system aged ewes are frequently used, which would not thrive under the usual range system.

The more general range practice is to have the ewes drop their lambs on the range, usually in May. After the ewes are sheared, the bands are gradually moved to the high mountain ranges, where they graze during the summer. The wether lambs and also the ewe lambs which are not needed for replacements in the ewe flocks are marketed in the fall, generally in September and October. Some are fat enough for immediate slaughter, especially if the summer forage has been abundant, but most of them are fattened for market by men who make this a specialty.

II. Fattening Lambs and Sheep

1258. Fattening feeder lambs.—Relatively few of the lambs raised on the western ranges become fat enough on the range forage to meet the demands of the large markets for slaughter lambs. Therefore they are commonly sold as feeders and then fattened in districts where grain and other concentrates are cheaper than in the range sections.

At one time most of the western lambs were fattened by large operators who each fed thousands of lambs a year. Now most of the lambs are fattened by farmers who finish one or more carloads. They raise most of their own feed and usually consider that enough fertility is returned to their land through the feed lot to pay the labor cost of feeding.

Just as is the case in the fattening of feeder steers, good judgment in purchasing the feeder animals and in selling them at the right time plays an exceedingly important part in determining whether there will be a profit or a loss in the feeding operations. The cost of the feeder lambs forms more than half the cost of the fattened animals. Also, the cost per 100 lbs. of the gains made in the feed lot is usually greater than the selling price per 100 lbs. of the lambs when fat. Therefore, to make a profit the fat lambs must sell at a higher price per hundredweight than their cost as feeders. In other words, a margin is required between the initial cost and the selling price. (1007)

During recent years many men have fattened lambs under the "contract" system. In this system they do not buy the lambs, but furnish the feeds and fatten the lambs under a definite contract with the grower, receiving a specified price per pound for the gains made.[46]

In fattening lambs it must be borne in mind at all times that the object is to convert a thin animal into a finished product—a lamb fat enough to meet the market demands. Each year many farmers lose money because they dump half-fattened lambs on the market, where they again are sold as feeders, to be finished for the market by someone else who is better acquainted with the market demands.

Usually men who feed lambs only occasionally make less of a financial success of the undertaking than those who feed each year. The latter may lose money in the unprofitable years, but this will be offset by good returns the rest of the time. Just as important, they gain experience in this business, where good judgment is of great value.

The discussions which follow deal chiefly with the fattening of lambs, owing to the fact that lambs constitute about 75 per cent of the sheep sold for slaughter. Also they deal largely with lambs from the western ranges. In general the same suggestions apply to farm-raised lambs which are not sold at weaning time but are fattened in the fall or winter.

1259. Types of lamb fattening.—Large numbers of lambs are fattened in the vicinity of the western beet-sugar factories, where the beet by-products—beet pulp, beet tops, and molasses—are fed, along with alfalfa hay and usually some grain in addition. In these districts and in general west of the Missouri River, most of the lambs are fed in open yards, with no shelter except a wind break. (1173)

The hay is usually fed in lanes which extend between 2 rows of feed lots, each of which accommodates 400 to 500 lambs. The low fences bordering the lanes have a 7- or 8-inch space between the first and second boards, through which the lambs feed on the hay. About 1 running foot of lane fencing and feed troughs is allowed each sheep. The hay from the stacks is hauled down the lanes and piled along the fences, being pushed up to them 2 or 3 times a day as it is eaten away. Sometimes racks or self-feeders are used for the hay. The grain is fed in flat-bottomed troughs.

In the corn belt many farmers fatten western lambs in late fall and winter on harvested feeds, sheltering them in a barn or an open shed, with or without an exercise lot. Usually all or nearly all the feed is raised on the farm, with the exception of protein supplements. Other systems that are followed are the grazing of lambs in the fall and the fattening in corn fields, which are discussed later. Often lambs are grazed in stubble fields or on aftermath in meadows and then finished

Exercise Is Essential for the Ewe Flock

If the ewes do not secure plenty of exercise, they are apt to have weak lambs. In winter the ewes may be forced to exercise by scattering roughage over a nearby field. (From Wisconsin Station.)

Meal Time for the Lambs

Note the lamb creep in the foreground at the right, thru which the lambs have access to the grain trough, while the ewes are kept out.

A Band of Western Lambs Fattening in the Corn-Belt

Many corn-belt farmers make a practice of fattening one or more carloads of western lambs in the fall on aftermath, stubblefields, or standing corn.

Angora Goats Clearing Land of Brush

Goats are especially fond of the leaves and twigs of brush, and if pastured closely enough, will effectively kill the brush.

n a dry lot. Many lambs are fattened largely on pea-vine silage in the vicinity of pea canneries, especially in Wisconsin.

In Michigan and eastward the lambs are generally not turned out from the barn or shed for exercise. Often a forced feeding system is followed, the lambs being brought to full feed as quickly as possible and then being given all the grain they will clean up. Often they are self-fed, as is discussed later. (**1254**)

Several large feeding yards are located near Chicago and other large markets on the main railroads from the West. Here lambs which have been fattened in the western states are often fed and rested for a few days, so they will reach the market in good condition and without heavy shrinkage. Also, lambs may be carried through the entire fattening period at such yards.

Some men usually fatten two lots of lambs each season, marketing the first in early winter and the second late in the spring. Should the weather grow warm before the lambs are finished, they are often shorn so they will make better gains. (**1178**)

Others who market their lambs in the spring, when prices are usually higher than in the winter, use a deferred system of fattening. They buy small lambs in the fall, when it is easier to get thrifty feeders than it is in winter. Then they feed them on only hay or other roughage until 60 to 80 days before the time they are to be marketed, when grain feeding is started and the lambs are finished on a liberal feed of grain. During the preliminary period on roughage alone, the lambs will make very little gain, but experiments by the Oregon Station show that the total cost of fattening will be less than if a half allowance of grain is fed throughout the entire feeding period.[47]

Nebraska trials show that lambs thus fattened will make less expensive gains and reach a more desirable and more uniform finish than if they are full fed at first until nearly fat, and then are maintained in this fat condition for a month or two, making only small gains on roughage with a little grain.[48]

A larger margin between the initial cost and the selling price per hundred pounds is needed for profit in a deferred system of fattening than under the usual method, as the gains are usually more expensive and such costs as labor and interest are also higher.[49]

1260. Selecting feeder lambs.—The best feeder lambs, which will make the cheapest gains and develop into high-grade fat lambs, are thrifty, deep-bodied, broad, compact, and low-set, with smooth skin, free from wrinkles. Such feeder lambs naturally command the highest prices, and therefore the net returns are not always largest from the best grade of lambs.[50]

Some men specialize in fattening light-weight lambs, or "pewees," sorted out from the shipments of feeder lambs from the ranges. These can usually be bought at a considerably lower price than the larger ones. Though some of these "pewees" are apt to be unthrifty, most of them are merely younger than the rest or are small because their mothers were poor milkers.

Experiments show that, if they are thrifty, such lambs, weighing 50 lbs. or less, will make nearly as rapid gains as the larger ones and that their gains will be cheaper.[51] This is because they will require less feed for each pound of gain, due to their younger age. Naturally, such lambs require a longer feeding period to reach a certain market weight or degree of fatness, and good shelter and more care are necessary in feeding them. Also, they should be fed apart from larger and stronger lambs.

In purchasing "pewees," lambs should be avoided that are small due to unthriftiness. This is especially important in buying small "native" lambs raised in the humid districts, where such lambs are apt to be small because they have been stunted by a serious infestation with stomach worms or other parasites. A considerable proportion of such cull, or "skip" lambs may make fairly satisfactory gains if fed expertly and treated for internal parasites and ticks,[52] but the salvaging of such products of poor management should be undertaken only by experts.

Feeder lambs produced in the humid districts are more apt to be infested with stomach worms and other parasites than western feeder lambs, especially those from the northern range, and therefore often make less rapid and more expensive gains.[53] However, if the lambs are thrifty and are thoroughly drenched before being placed on feed, they may make as good gains as western lambs.[54]

There is not enough difference in the gains made by ewe lambs and by wether lambs in the feed lot, or in the market value when fat, to cause any decided preference among experienced men. However, wether lambs usually make slightly more rapid gains than do ewe lambs.[55]

Some have believed that lambs with heavy pelts make smaller gains and produce less desirable carcasses than those with lighter pelts. In a test by the United States Department of Agriculture there was, however, no marked difference.[56] Heavy-pelted lambs may, however, sell at a lower price, when fat, on the central markets.

1261. Hints on fattening lambs.—Feeder lambs that are not used to grain or silage must be accustomed to these feeds gradually, or scouring and other digestive troubles will result, and perhaps even severe death losses. Especial care is necessary with lambs from the western ranges, which have undergone the hardship of shipment for a long distance and which were probably not weaned from their mothers until they were separated for shipment. When feeder lambs are received on the farm, they should be given only a feed of hay for their first meal, and this should be preferably mixed hay or grass hay, as alfalfa hay may be too laxative for this first feed. It is risky to turn hungry feeder lambs that have just arrived, onto abundant pasture, as this may cause bloating or scours.

After the lambs have rested from shipment, they may be fed as much hay or other dry roughage as they will clean up, but only a small amount of grain (not over 0.1 to 0.2 lb. per head daily) should be fed at first and only a little silage. The grain should be sprinkled along the trough, so none can get too much. The allowance of grain should be increased gradually, until in 4 to 5 weeks the lambs are receiving 1.0 to 1.25 lbs. of grain per head daily. If silage is fed, the amount should also be increased gradually until the lambs are getting all the silage they will eat twice a day. During none of this time should more grain be fed than will be cleaned up in about 15 minutes.

If it is desired to fatten the lambs as rapidly as possible by feeding them all the grain they will eat, further increases should be made cautiously and only if all the lambs are cleaning up their feed regularly. The maximum amount of grain that should be fed is discussed later in this chapter.

In no case should the getting of the lambs on feed be hurried, for this is apt to cause serious digestive trouble. It is a good practice to start the lambs on a mixture consisting chiefly of a bulky feed, like oats or wheat bran. The proportion of corn or other concentrated feed is then gradually increased. When on full feed, the lambs may be given only corn with a small amount of protein supplement, if this is needed to balance the ration. On warm days in winter it is often necessary to reduce the grain allowance slightly, or the lambs may go off feed.

Sheep feeders do not begin operations at an early hour in winter, preferring not to disturb the animals until after daybreak. The lambs are usually fed twice a day, grain being given first, followed by silage, if this is used, with the hay last. The trough in which grain is fed should be kept clean at all times, and there should be ample space, so that each animal may get its share of grain.

Plenty of salt and fresh water should always be supplied fattening sheep. Regularity and quiet are of especial importance in securing good results. In all cases before sheep are put on feed, they should be dipped in a thorough manner, if any evidence of lice, ticks, or scab is found. When necessary, they should be drenched to eradicate stomach worms, but this is not usually needed in the case of western range lambs.

1262. Death losses; overeating disease.—In the commercial fattening of lambs some death losses are unavoidable, and these must be considered in estimating the financial outcome of the enterprise. When healthy lambs are fed by expert feeders, the mortality should not exceed 3 to 4 per cent, but much higher losses often occur if the lambs are not thrifty or if they are fed carelessly. The greatest danger comes at two times. The first is during the first few days while the lambs are recovering from shipment and are being started on feed. Severe losses sometimes also occur later, due to the so-called "overeating disease." This usually affects lambs which have been on full feed for some time and which are being crowded on a heavy allowance of grain, so they will make as rapid gains as is possible.

The lambs affected by this overeating disease are almost invariably the largest, fattest, most vigorous, and greediest in the lot. Sometimes the disease causes very sudden death, the lamb throwing back its head, staggering, falling to the ground, and dying in convulsions, as though from an apoplectic stroke. For this reason the disease is often called "apoplexy," but it is really not apoplexy at all. More commonly, the lambs live a few hours, showing typical brain symptoms, such as the head being thrown back or the lamb running in a circle or pushing against a fence. In many instances lambs which have appeared thrifty the previous day are merely found dead in the morning. In only a few cases do the lambs recover.

After extensive investigations of this disease Newsom and Cross of the Colorado Station conclude that it is probably due to indigestion produced by feeding a large amount of rich concentrates, which causes inflammation of the walls of the intestines.[57] This produces a condition in which poisonous products contained in the intestines pass through the walls and are absorbed into the circulation. If large quantities of concentrates are fed, this inflammation is continued and illness or death results.

The deaths from this disease in a lot of fattening lambs can usually be stopped practically overnight by withholding the grain. However, it is necessary to feed grain liberally to fatten lambs rapidly, and they must be fattened rapidly, or they will become too large before they get fat enough to meet the market demands. In these facts lie the difficulty and the danger.

To reduce the losses as much as possible when lambs are fattened rapidly, the following precautions must be observed. The utmost care must be taken to get the lambs on feed without producing digestive disturbances. All possible measures should be taken to prevent gorging. The grain must be distributed in the troughs so no lamb can get more than its share. If lambs are self-fed, it is best to mix the grain with some bulky feed, as is pointed out later in this chapter. Even when they are hand-fed, it may be wise to mix the grain with cut or ground hay if they are being forced on all the grain they will eat. The lambs should always be fed all the roughage they will clean up, and if a mixture of grain and ground or cut hay is self-fed, with no other roughage, the proportion of grain must not be too high.

It is often possible to sort out the fattest lambs and market them before the rest are ready, thus keeping down the death loss. If this is done, the amount of grain must be reduced accordingly and it must be borne in mind that the lambs which were ready first were the heartiest eaters.

1263. Rations for fattening lambs; cost of gains.—From the many trials reviewed in the preceding chapter, the feeder can readily determine the best combination of feeds to employ under his local conditions. The information on the amount of feed required for 100 lbs. gain will enable him to compute the approximate cost of gains with feeds at market prices. It should be remembered that the results presented were secured with thrifty lambs, fed by skilled feeders and under good conditions. The feed required for a given gain will therefore often exceed the amount stated. Comparing the cost of gains, it will be found that lambs give better returns for the feed supplied than do steers. The gains of mature sheep will cost from 25 to 30 per cent more than those of lambs.

When on full feed, thrifty western lambs, then usually weighing 60 to 70 lbs., will eat 1.25 to 1.50 lbs. or more of grain and other concentrates per head daily, if fed all they will clean up. In addition, they will eat 1.00 to 1.50 lbs. of legume hay. If both legume hay and corn silage are fed for roughage, the consumption of concentrates will be about the same, and they will eat in addition 0.75 to 1.00 lb. or more of hay and 1.00 lb. or more of silage per head daily. During the first part of the fattening period, while they are being gotten on feed, their consumption of concentrates will be much less and the amount of roughage correspondingly greater.

1264. Length of feeding period.—Usually 75 to 100 days or longer are required to produce the desired finish on western lambs, less time being needed for yearlings. During this period the lambs should gain 20 to 30 lbs. per head. This gain, added to a lamb weighing originally 55 to 65 lbs., brings it to the size desired by the market. The demand is now for well-fattened lambs weighing from 80 to 90 lbs. or even less. Lambs heavier than 90 lbs. at the market often sell at a discount, even though they are of good quality.

1265. Amounts and proportions of concentrates and roughage.— Under conditions throughout the corn belt and the eastern states it is usually most profitable to give fattening lambs a liberal allowance of grain after they have been brought onto feed, except when it is desired to fatten them slowly for a later market. If lambs are fed about as much grain as they will clean up twice a day, in addition to what good hay or other roughage they will eat, they will make rapid gains at a minimum cost, reach a good market finish, and sell at a higher price than if less thoroughly fattened.

Even with corn at the high prices during 1917 to 1919, in Indiana trials feeding a liberal amount of corn to fattening lambs was more profitable than feeding a half allowance of corn, or than feeding no corn the first 50 days and then full-feeding corn thereafter.[58] The lambs in each lot were fed all the corn silage and clover hay they would clean up, and enough cottonseed meal to balance the ration. Though the cost of gains was less in some instances when the allowance of corn was restricted, this was more than offset by the fact that the lambs were not so well finished and hence brought a lower price. Similar results have been secured in most of the other experiments conducted to study this subject.[59]

In the West, where hay is usually cheap in comparison with grain, the allowance of grain is often restricted somewhat. However, if the lambs are to be sold on a market that pays a satisfactory premium for well-fattened animals, it will generally pay to feed 1.0 lb. or more of grain per head daily.[60] Lambs will not reach a satisfactory degree of fatness unless fed at least about 0.75 lb. of grain or other concentrates per head daily after they have been brought on feed. On hay alone or even on hay and good corn silage they will usually gain only 0.03 to 0.17 lb. per head daily and will grow rather than fatten to any marked extent.[61]

If it is desired to limit severely the amount of grain fed fattening lambs, it is best during the first half of the fattening period to feed them only hay or hay and silage, or else only a very small amount of grain, and then to finish them on a full feed of grain. This produces more rapid and cheaper gains than feeding half the usual amount of grain throughout the fattening period.[62]

Under usual conditions, fattening lambs should be given all the good hay or other roughage they will clean up satisfactorily. When hay is exceptionally high in price in comparison with grain and hence is a more expensive source of digestible nutrients, it may be wise to restrict the hay allowance somewhat.[63] However, lambs should have at least 0.5 lb. hay per head daily, and on as small an allowance of hay as this with an unlimited amount of grain there is more apt to be trouble from serious digestive disturbances than when 0.75 to 1.00 lb. or more of hay is fed.

1266. Self-feeding.—Many men who fatten large numbers of western lambs for the market use self-feeders for feeding the concentrates, or a mixture of concentrates and chopped or ground hay or other roughage. This method has the advantage of saving some labor and of producing more rapid gains, but it has the disadvantage of often resulting in much larger death losses, due to digestive troubles and "apoplexy." Self-fed lambs usually require more grain and less hay per 100 lbs. gain than those which are hand-fed, and therefore they utilize less farm-grown roughage. For example, in 5 Michigan trials self-fed lambs required 413 lbs. shelled corn and 315 lbs. alfalfa hay for each 100 lbs. gain, while hand-fed lambs required 367 lbs. corn and 437 lbs. hay.[64]

The danger from self-feeding is greatest when a heavy concentrate, like corn or barley, is fed alone in a self-feeder. Even when the lambs are brought on feed by careful hand-feeding and only then turned to self-feeders filled with such grain, heavy losses may occur. For example, in an Illinois trial lambs were hand-fed shelled corn and alfalfa hay for 3 weeks, during which time they were brought up to a consumption of 0.75 lb. corn per head daily.[65] They were then self-fed corn and hay separately, but half of them died. On the other hand, there were no losses in another lot which was self-fed a mixture of ground corn and ground hay. Similar results were secured in Michigan and Ohio trials.[66]

There is less danger when the lambs, after being brought on feed by hand-feeding, are first self-fed such a bulky mixture as 3 parts oats and 1 part corn, and then are gradually changed to corn alone or corn and supplement. Lambs thus self-fed in Indiana trials gained 0.05 lb. more per head daily than hand-fed lambs, with no death losses and at a slightly lower cost of feed per pound of gain.[67] However, sometimes heavy death losses occur even after lambs have been self-fed for several weeks on corn or other heavy feeds alone, with hay fed separately.

The safest method of self-feeding lambs is to feed, throughout the self-feeding period, a mixture of grain and some bulky feed, such as chopped or ground hay, chaffy screenings, or oat feed. Often the proportion of the bulky material is reduced somewhat as the feeding period progresses. In 6 trials lambs self-fed a mixture of corn and ground alfalfa hay ate 1.4 lbs. corn and 1.7 lbs. hay, on the average, and gained 0.37 lb. per head daily.[68] Hand-fed lambs, fed in comparison, ate 1.1 lbs. corn and 1.6 lbs. hay and gained 0.32 lb. per day. (A small amount of cottonseed meal was fed in addition in one of the trials.) The self-fed lambs required 380 lbs. corn and 470 lbs. hay for 100 lbs. gain, in comparison with 352 lbs. corn and 484 lbs. hay for the hand-fed lots. With feeds at usual prices the gains were somewhat cheaper, on the average, for the hand-fed lambs.

In 3 Wisconsin trials in which lambs were self-fed a mixture of cracked barley and chopped alfalfa hay in comparison with others handfed these feeds separately, the cost of feed per 100 lbs. gain was 54 cents more for the self-fed lots.[69] Likewise, in 2 Minnesota trials lambs self-fed a mixture of whole oats and barley, with alfalfa hay fed separately, made somewhat more expensive gains than hand-fed lambs.[70] The use of chaffy screenings in place of chopped hay in self-feeding lambs is advisable only if such low-grade material can be secured very cheaply. Often the price is higher than the actual feeding value.[71]

In cost-accounting surveys on farms in Michigan and New York where Western lambs were fattened for market, the farmers who hand-fed their lambs made more profit per lamb in the majority of cases than those who used the self-feeding method.[72] When grain is cheap in price, the self-feeding method may return the greater profit.

Lambs cannot be trusted to balance their ration if they are self-fed separately corn or other grain and a protein supplement like linseed meal or cottonseed meal. Sometimes they will eat about the proper amount of the supplement, but at other times they will take much more than is needed to balance the ration.[73]   The supplement should therefore be mixed with the grain in the proper proportion.

1267. Fattening lambs in the fall.—Finishing lambs for market in the fall is a common practice with farmers who raise their own lambs and with many who buy western feeder lambs. Until cold weather sets in, the lambs may be grazed on stubble fields, aftermath in meadows, or rape or other pasture, with or without grain in addition. Thrifty lambs placed on feed in the fall should be ready for sale in December or early in January. There is then usually a scarcity of good lambs on the market, since the grass-fed lambs have been marketed and those in winter feed lots are not yet finished.

Often rape is seeded in small grain to increase the fall feed for lambs, the seeding not taking place until the small grain is well above ground, lest the rape grow so large as to injure the grain crop. After the stubble fields are well cleaned, the lambs may be finished by turning them into fields of standing corn.

1268. Fattening in the corn field.—In certain sections of the corn belt many farmers fatten western lambs in the corn field. When proper methods are followed good results are secured, but the experience of farmers and the results of experimental trials have shown that care is necessary to provide the proper conditions.[74] When conditions are favorable, lambs fattened in the corn field with supplemental feed have made nearly as rapid gains as others fattened on corn and legume hay in the dry lot, but the death losses are apt to be higher.

Lambs make poor gains on a corn field alone, as there is a serious lack of protein. Such supplemental crops as rape or soybeans should be grown in the corn. The lambs will usually clean up such forage long before they finish the corn, and it is then especially necessary to provide them either with good legume hay or with one-quarter pound per head daily of a supplement like linseed meal or cottonseed cake or meal. The best results are usually secured when such supplements are fed from the start, and the gains are most rapid when both legume hay and 0.15 lb. of protein supplement are supplied in addition to the feed in the corn field.

The lambs should have plenty of feed available without traveling too far, and they should have shelter from bad storms. It is the best plan to divide a large field into suitable areas by hurdles or by temporary woven-wire fencing. The lambs should be strong and healthy and should have dense fleeces which will shed water well. They should be accustomed to the corn field gradually by giving them a feed of hay in the morning the first few days before turning them on the field. At first the lambs will clean up the other vegetation in the corn field, including most of the weeds. Then they will begin eating the corn leaves and finally will learn how to husk out the corn ears and eat the grain from the cobs.

Plenty of hay and other feed should be available for periods of bad weather or if the lambs clean up the corn field before they are fat. Severe financial losses will be incurred if one is forced to dump half-fat lambs on the market. The lambs should be inspected daily to see that all are thriving. Muddy fields are hard on their feet, as the mud cakes between their toes.

1269. Costs and returns in commercial lamb fattening.—To indicate the results secured in the commercial fattening of lambs, the following data are of interest. They were secured in studies during 4 seasons, 1930-1934, on Michigan farms where a total of over 93,000 lambs, chiefly western, were fattened.[75] On the average 733 lambs were fattened per farm. The lambs averaged 65.0 lbs. in weight at the start and were fed for an average of 109 days. The gain per lamb, or the difference between the purchase weight at the market and the sale weight at the market, deducting all shrinkage and death loss, was 20.8 lbs., or 0.19 lb. per head daily. The average cost of the feeder lambs at the farms was $5.94 per hundredweight, and the average sale value of the fat lambs at the farms was $7.17 per hundredweight; leaving a net margin at the farm of $1.23 per hundredweight.

The mortality averaged 3.8 per cent. On the average 653 lbs. of concentrates and 575 lbs. roughage were required per 100 lbs. gain; the feed cost per 100 lbs. gain was $7.25; and the total cost per 100 lbs. gain, $9.23. The costs per head were as follows: Purchase price of lambs, $4.02; cost of feed, $1.51; labor, $0.11; use of buildings and equipment, $0.14; other costs, $0.17; making the total cost per head, $5.95. The returns were $6.23 per head for lambs sold and slaughtered; $0.34 for wool and pelts; and $0.22 for manure credit. This made a total credit of $6.79 per head. For the 4-year period the average profit per head was $0.84.

III. Hot-House and Spring Lambs; Goats

1270. Hot-house or winter lambs.—In certain sections of the eastern states there is a profitable market for "hot house" or winter lambs. The term "hot house" lambs does not mean that they are raised in artificially warmed quarters, but is used because they are produced at an unusual season and are therefore comparable to the out-of-season products of hot houses. The market for winter lambs is confined mostly to the large eastern cities, where they are consumed chiefly in high-class hotels, restaurants, and clubs. This specialty in sheep production should be undertaken only by experts who have nearby markets that will pay the high prices such products must command.

The demand for winter lambs comes from December, or even earlier, up to Easter, the prices usually being best early in this season. Winter lambs must be fat, for the condition of the carcass is more important than its size. Lambs that are not well finished or that have poor conformation bring unsatisfactory prices. The lambs must therefore be forced ahead rapidly by feeding them a suitable concentrate or grain mixture in a creep. Thus fed, they should be fat at 40 to 60 lbs., live weight, and some markets will pay top prices for lambs weighing considerably less than 40 lbs., if they are well-finished. The lambs are dressed on the farm, according to the demands of the market to which they are to be shipped.

For the production of winter lambs, the ewes must be bred in the spring instead of at the usual season in the fall. The ewes best suited for winter-lamb production are purebreds, grades, or crossbreds of the Dorset, Tunis, Merino, or Rambouillet breeds, for the other breeds will not usually breed at the right season.[76] Pennsylvania trials show that first generation cross-bred Dorset-Merino ewes are excellent for the purpose, especially when bred to a good Southdown ram.[77]

The ewes should be "flushed" before the breeding season, so that more of them will breed at the desired time and so that the percentage of twins will be greater.

They should have abundant pasture during the summer and fall, so they will be in condition to provide a liberal milk flow for their lambs. After lambing, the ewes should be fed liberally on a good concentrate mixture and legume hay, with silage in addition, if available. As has been pointed out, the lambs should receive additional feed in a creep, so they will be ready for market as soon as possible.

1271. Spring lambs.—A less intensive system than the preceding is the production of spring lambs, which are marketed from April into June, at a time of the year when there is a good demand. They should be well-finished at 3 to 5 months of age and weighing 55 to 70 lbs. Raising spring lambs is of especial importance in Tennessee, Kentucky, Virginia, and states to the southward, and also in certain valleys of California, Arizona, and Oregon.[78] In these warmer districts the ewes may be maintained chiefly on pasture throughout the year, greatly reducing the cost of feed. Also, no expensive shelter is necessary.

The native ewes of the southeastern states are well adapted to spring lamb production, as they lamb early and are good milkers, but they should be bred to good mutton rams to produce the desired type of lambs. Unless the ewes and lambs have excellent pasture, the lambs should be fed grain in a creep, so they will be ready for market when the prices are best. Also, the lambs should be sold as soon as they are fat, for they are seldom at their prime for more than a week or two.

Some farmers, especially in the plains states, follow the plan of purchasing in the fall aged western ewes, discarded from range flocks on account of age or poor teeth, and breeding them for the production of one crop of early lambs, which are usually sold at weaning time.

Such ewes must be fed good rations, including plenty of grain both before and after lambing, so they will be fat enough to sell well when their lambs are marketed.[79] The profitableness of this enterprise depends primarily on whether the fat ewes will sell for as much a pound in the spring as they cost as aged breeding ewes in the fall. Usually the prices for such fat ewes decline rapidly and steadily after early May.

1272. Milk goats.—Milk goats are of considerable importance in continental Europe, many families, especially of the poorer classes, relying on goats for their daily supply of milk. Much goats' milk is also used in Europe for the manufacture of certain types of cheese. Though milk goats have never become important in the United States, there are limited numbers in many states, the greatest number being in California. They are especially well suited for furnishing the milk supply for families living in small towns and the suburbs of large cities, or on fruit and truck farms where there is not enough feed available for a cow. Often a milk doe can secure much of her feed by grazing in the waste areas, such as vacant lots and rocky hillsides. In such places as some of the western mining towns, goats have a decided advantage over cows, for they always come home at night from wherever they have been grazing.

Good purebred or high-grade milk goats should give 800 to 1,000 lbs. of milk a year, and exceptional does yield 2,000 lbs. or more. A good doe should yield 2 quarts or more of milk a day and continue in milk for 7 months or more. A herd of high-producing grade milk goats can be developed by using purebred, bred-for-production bucks on ordinary milk goats, just as in the case of dairy cows.[80] The milk of most breeds averages 4.0 per cent or more in fat. The fat globules are much smaller in size than those of cows' milk and goats' milk forms a fine, soft curd during digestion. For these reasons, it commands a high price in some localities for feeding to infants and invalids.

One should always be sure that the goats are free from the infection causing Malta fever in humans. Goats' milk produced under sanitary conditions and when the buck is kept separate from the does, will not have an unpleasant "goat" flavor and odor, though the flavor is somewhat different from that of cows' milk.

On the basis of body weight and of amount of feed consumed, good milk goats are about as efficient milk producers as are good cows. In studies at the New York (Cornell) Station it was found that, as would be expected, the maintenance requirements for goats per 100 lbs. live weight are considerably higher than for cows, on account of their much smaller size and consequent greater body surface in proportion to live weight.[81] Also, for the production of each pound of milk of a given fat content, goats apparently require slightly more digestible nutrients above maintenance requirements than do cows.

However, they are able to consume much more feed per 100 lbs. live weight than do cows, even those of high productive capacity. Therefore, they have left after their maintenance requirements are met a sufficiently larger proportion of the nutrients furnished by their feed to overcome the two handicaps mentioned. The cost of producing goats' milk on a commercial basis is higher than in the case of cows' milk, due chiefly to the greater amount of labor required per quart of milk produced.

In general, the same feeds and the same care and management that are successful with dairy cows and sheep are suitable for milk goats.[82] From 6 to 8 goats can be kept on the feed required by a cow. A suitable ration is 1 to 2 lbs. of good concentrate mixture, with 3 lbs. hay or with 2 lbs. alfalfa or clover hay and 1.5 lbs. silage or roots. On pasture 1 to 1.5 lbs. concentrates daily are usually needed by high producers. The concentrate mixture should be similar to those used for dairy cows. Often the use of refuse from the kitchen or garden or of lawn clippings will considerably reduce the feed bill. At prices in 1912 to 1914 the cost of feeding a goat a year was found to be $11.05 at the New York (Geneva) Station and $11.24 at the California Station.[83]

1273. Angora goats.—The raising of Angora goats for their mohair is an industry of considerable importance in certain districts of the United States. In 1934 over 3,300,000 goats were clipped in this country, of which 2,795,000 were in Texas.[84] The average amount of mohair produced per animal was 4.0 lbs. The meat from the surplus goats is sold under the name of "chevon" and is appetizing if from a well-fattened young goat.

In the western states the goats are usually kept under range conditions, often grazing on rough land and utilizing browse that even sheep would refuse.[85] In the cut-over districts of the North, Angora goats are sometimes used for clearing land of brush, but the area must be heavily stocked and closely grazed to subdue the brush.

QUESTIONS

1. State 4 essentials of successful flock management.
2. On what basis would you cull a flock of ewes?
3. Discuss the breeding of ewe lambs.
4. What factors determine the best date for lambing?
5. Discuss the flushing of ewes.
6. State the most important points in feeding and caring for the ram.
7. How should ewes be fed in the fall?
8. Discuss the feeding of pregnant ewes in winter.
9. How may pregnancy disease of ewes be largely avoided?
10. Describe the care of ewes at lambing time.
11. State the most important points concerning the feed and care of ewes after lambing.
12. How much milk a day do ewes of the common breeds yield?
13. State the important points concerning the feeding of young lambs.
14. Discuss the docking and castration of lambs.
15. Discuss the feeding of lambs on pasture.
16. What are the best times to market farm-raised lambs in your district?
17. Approximately how much hay and concentrates does it require to carry a breeding ewe through the winter?
18. State 5 important factors affecting the net income from sheep.
19. Describe the methods by which stomach worms and other internal parasites can be controlled.

20. How are sheep handled on the western ranges?
21. Describe any methods of fattening western lambs that are used in your district.
22. Describe the kind of feeder lambs you would purchase to fatten for the market.
23. How should fattening lambs be started on feed?
24. How may the losses from overeating disease be avoided?
25. About how much grain and hay will fattening lambs eat when on full feed?
26. Discuss the proportion of concentrates to feed fattening lambs.
27. State the advantages and disadvantages of the self-feeding method of fattening lambs.
28. Describe any of the following phases of sheep production that are important in your district: (a) Fattening lambs in the fall; (b) fattening lambs in the corn field; (c) production of hot-house lambs; (d) production of spring lambs.
29. State the most important facts concerning the feeding of milk goats.
30. In what districts of this country are Angora goats important?

REFERENCES

1. Joseph, Mont. Bul. 242.
2. Bowstead, Scientific Agr. (Can.), 10, 1930, pp. 429-59; Griswold, Amer. Soc. Anim. Prod., Proc. 1932, and mimeo. rpt.; Jacob, Tenn. Rpt. 1933; Hicks, Can. Expt. Farms, Agassiz Farm, Rpt. Supt. 1923; Fortier, Can. Expt. Farms, LaFerne Sta., Rpt. Supt. 1923; Phillips, Welsh Jour. Agr., 4, 1928, pp. 121-41.
3. Humphrey and Kleinheinz, Wis. Sta., information to the author; Wilson, Cal. Rpt. 1921; McKenzie and Phillips, Mo. Bul. 310; Coleman, Sheep of Great Britain; Coffey, Productive Sheep Husbandry, p. 66.
4. Darlow and Hawkins, Okla. Rpts. 1930-32, 1932-34; Marshall and Potts, U. S. Dept. Agr. Bul. 996; Rpt. of Chief of Bur. Anim. Indus., U. S. Dept. Agr., 1932; also see McKenzie and Phillips, Mo. Bul. 328.
5. Fleming, Nev. Rpt. 1926; Fleming and Young, Nev. Rpt. 1930; Ritzman, N. H. Tech. Bul. 14, N. H. Bul. 232; Craig, Wis. Rpt. 1899.
6. Joseph, Natl. Wool Grower, 16, 1926, No. 4, pp. 19-21; Fleming, Nev. Rpt. 1933.
7. McKenzie and Phillips, Amer. Soc. Anim. Prod., Proc. 1930.
8. Bell, Ohio Spec. Cir. 21 and Ohio Bimo. Bul. 118; Snell, Amer. Soc. Anim. Prod., Proc. 1933.
9. Blakeslee, Mich. Spec. Bul. 255; Weber and Loeffel, Nebr. Bul. 250; Jennings, N. D. Bul. 186.
10. Kammlade, Mitchell, and Graham, Ill. Rpt. 1928; Horlacher, Sheep Production, pp. 217-8; Hackedorn, Mo. Bul. 120.
11. Hackedorn, Mo. Bul. 120.
12. Horlacher, Ky. Rpt. 1924; Joseph, Mont. Bul. 164.
13. Putnam and Blakeslee, Mich. Quar. Bul. 15, 1932, No. 2.
14. Fleming, Nev. Rpt. 1923; Hammond, Ohio Bul. 358; Withycombe, Edwards, and Potter, Ore. Cir. 101.
15. Weber and Loeffel, Nebr. Bul. 250.
16. Carlyle and Kleinheinz, Wis. Rpt. 1903.
17. Joseph, Mont. Bul. 247.
18. Dimock, Healy, and Hull, Ky. Cir. 39; Elder and Uren, Mo. Bul. 345; Sampson and Hayden, Jour. Amer. Vet. Med. Assoc., 86, 1935, pp. 12-23; Roderick and Harshfield, N. D. Bul. 261.
19. Metzger and Hagan, Cornell Veterinarian 17, 1927, pp. 35-44.
20. Willman, Asdell, and Olafson, N. Y. (Cornell) Bul. 603 and Rpt. 1934.
21. Report of U. S. Tariff Commission, 1921.
22. Bell, Ohio Spec. Cir. 21; Utz, Ohio Bimo. Bul. 119.
23. Kleinheinz, Wis. Rpts. 1902, 1907, and information to the author.
24. Wilson, Cal. Rpt. 1922.
25. Roberts, Jour. Agr. Res., 22, 1921, pp. 231-234.
26. Harper, Ind. Rpt. 1930.
27. Ritzman and Davenport, N. H. Bul. 232.
28. Carlyle, Fuller, and Kleinheinz, Wis. Rpt. 1904; Ritzman, Jour. Agr. Res. 8, 1917, pp. 29-36; Ritzman, N. H. Tech. Bul. 14; Neidig and Iddings, Jour. Agr. Res., 17, 1919, pp. 19-32.
29. Shepperd, Agr. Science, VI, p. 397.
30. Coffey, Productive Sheep Husbandry, p. 262; Kleinheinz, Sheep Management, Breeds, and Judging, p. 71; Carroll, Utah, Cir. 33.
31. Fleming and Young, Nev. Rpts. 1930, 1931; Ritzman and Benedict, N. H. Tech. Bul. 43; Phillips, Welsh Jour. Agr. 4, 1928, pp. 121-141.
32. Fleming, Miller, and Young, Nev. Rpts. 1931, 1933.
33. Harper, Ind. Rpt. 1933.
34. Harper, Ind. Sta. mimeo. rpt.; Willman, N. Y. (Cornell) Rpt. 1934.
35. Grimes, Sewell, and Cottier, Ala. Cir. 69; Horlacher, Ky. Rpt. 1926; Hinman, Willman, and Schutt, N. Y. (Cornell) Rpts. 1930, 1931, 1932; Bell, Ohio Bul. 402; Ont. Agr. Coll. Rpt. 1919.
36. Harper, Ind. Bul. 344; King and Harper, Ind. Bul. 353; Harper, Am. Soc. Anim. Prod., Proc. 1933.
37. Jacob, Tenn. Rpt. 1932; Bohstedt and Darlow, Wis. Bul. 420.
38. Grimes, Sewell, and Cottier, Ala. Cir. 69.

39. Hammond, Ohio Bul. 340.
40. Morison, Ohio Bimo. Bul. 163; Ohio Bul. 532.
41. Kepner, N. Y. (Cornell) Sta., mimeo. rpt.
42. Severson, Penn. Bul. 144; see also: Curtis and Meacham, N. C. Bul. 253; Jennings, N. D. Bul. 186; Bell, Ohio Spec. Cir. 21; Utz, Ohio Bimo. Bul. 119; S. C. Rpt. 1929.
43. Hall, U. S. Dept. Agr., Farmers' Bul. 1330; Nighbert, U. S. Dept. Agr., Leaflet 89.
44. J. P. Willman and Grams, N. Y. (Cornell) Exten. Bul. 283.
45. For detailed discussions of range sheep production, see: Hultz and Hill, Range Sheep and Wool; Sampson, Live Stock Husbandry on Range and Pasture; Cooper, U. S. Dept. Agr., Farmers' Bul. 1710; Pickrell and Stanley, Ariz. Bul. 134; Walker, Lantow, and Pickrell, New Mex. Bul. 204; Moles, Koogler, and Neale, New Mex. Exten. Cir. 80; Potter and Lindgren, Ore. Bul. 219; Esplin et al., Utah Bul. 204; Vass and Pearson, Wyo. Bul. 156; Kindt, Canada Dept. Agr., Agr. Econ. Branch and Expt. Farms Branch, 1933 Rpt.
46. Thalman, Nebr. Bul. 274.
47. Dean and Potter, Ore. Bul. 218.
48. Weber, Loeffel, and Peters, Nebr. Bul. 262.
49. Willman and Morrison, N. Y. (Cornell) Rpts. 1932, 1933.
50. Lantow and Snell, N. Mex. Bul. 138.
51. Maynard, Morton, and Osland, Col. Bul. 379; Rinehart, Hickman, and Johnson, Id. Buls. 194, 205; Jordan and Peters, Minn. Bul. 272; Mackey and Jones, Tex. Bul. 465; Maynard, Esplin, and Boswell, Utah Bul. 238.
52. Kammlade and McCulloch, Ill. Rpt. 1928; Bell, Ohio Bimo. Bul. 12, 1927, No. 5; Ohio Spec. Cir. 16; see also: Peters and Jordan, Amer. Soc. Anim. Prod., Proc. 1928.
53. Keith and Henning, Penn. Bul. 288.
54. Brown, Mich. Spec. Bul. 233; Bell, Ohio Bul. 402, Ohio Spec. Cir. 16.
55. Morton, Colo. Rpt. 1931; Foster, Colo. Tech. Bul. 10; Coffey, Ill. Bul. 167; King, Am. Soc. Anim. Prod., Proc. 1925-1926; Ky. Rpt. 1926; J. M. Jones et al., Tex. Rpt. 1933.
56. Spencer, Am. Soc. Anim. Prod., Proc. 1930, pp. 192-195.
57. Newson and Cross, Colo. Bul. 409.
58. Skinner, King, Starr, and Vestal, Ind. Buls. 221, 234, 256, 263.
59. Coffey, Ill. Bul. 167; Cox and Connel, Kan. Bul. 264; Gramlich, Nebr. Bul. 170; Blakeslee, Mich. Quar. Bul., 17, 1935, No. 4; Alexander, Nebr. Sta., mimeo. rpt.
60. Fleming, Nev. Bul. 106; Simpson, New Mex. Bul. 79; Hackedorn, Bean, and Sotola, Wash. Bul. 185.
61. Hickman, Id. Sta., mimeo. rpt.; King and Harper, Ind. Bul. 360; Holden, Nebr. Bul. 194; Fleming, Nev. Bul. 106; U. S. Dept. Agr., Rpt. Bur. Anim. Indus., 1933.
62. Skinner, Vestal, and King, Ind. Buls. 234, 256, 263.
63. Reed and Marston, Kan. Cir. 131.
64. Brown, Mich. Quar. Bul. 16, 1934, No. 3.
65. Kammlade, Ill. Bul. 338.
66. Brown, Mich. Quar. Bul. 16, 1933, No. 1; Bell, Ohio Mo. Bul. 151.
67. Skinner and King, Ind. Buls. 273, 282, 296.
68. Maynard, Morton, and Osland, Colo. Bul. 379; Kammlade, Ill. Bul. 338 and Ill. Rpt. 1930; see also: Blakeslee, Mich. Quar. Bul., 17, 1935, No. 4; Alexander, Nebr. Sta., mimeo. rpt.; Darlow, Okla. Rpt. 1932-34.
69. Bohstedt, Wis. Bul. 421.
70. Jordan and Peters, Minn. Bul. 272.
71. Willman and Morrison, N. Y. (Cornell) Rpts. 1932, 1933.
72. LaVoi and Wright, Mich. Quar. Bul. 14, 1932, No. 4; Aylesworth, Mich. Quar. Bul. 16, 1933, No. 1; 17, 1934. No. 1; Kepner, New York (Cornell) Sta., mimeo. rpts.
73. Skinner and King, Ind. Buls. 273, 282, 296; Paterson, Kan. Cir. 108; Brown, Mich. Quar. Bul. 16, 1933, No. 1.
74. Kammlade, Ill. Bul. 338; Foster, Mo. Bul. 244; Gramlich, Nebr. Buls. 167, 170; Bell, Ohio Buls. 382, 402; Bell and Thatcher, Ohio Bi-mo. Bul. 128; Wilson and Kuhlman, S. D. Bul. 207.
75. Aylesworth, Mich. Quar. Bul. 17, 1934, No. 1; see also: Kepner, N. Y. (Cornell) Station, mimeo. rpts.
76. Minn. Bul. 78; Wing, Savage, and Tailby, N. Y. (Cornell) Bul. 309.
77. Henning, Ziegler, and McKenzie, Penn. Buls. 255, 293.
78. Kellogg, Ga. Agr. Coll. Ext. Bul. 372; Miss. Bul. 260; Weber, Nebr. Bul. 250; Lindgren and Potter, Ore. Bul. 265; Willson, Tenn. Buls. 84, 114, Tenn. Agr. Coll. Ext. Pub. 109.
79. Weber and Loeffel, Nebr. Buls. 250 and 276.
80. Cunningham, New Mex. Bul. 154.
81. Brooks, Cornell University, New York, Ph.D. thesis.
82. Voorhies, Cal. Exten. Cir. 6; Matthews and Weaver, Iowa Cir. 111; Mich. Exten. Bul. 85; U. S. Dept. Agr., Farmer's Bul. 920; Richards, Modern Milk Goats; Davies, Goat Keeping for Milk Production; Holmes-Pegler, The Book of the Goat.
83. Jordan and Smith, N. Y. (Geneva) Bul. 429; Voorhies, Cal. Bul. 285.
84. U. S. Dept. Agr. Yearbook 1935.
85. Willingmyer et al., U. S. Dept. Agr., Misc. Cir. 50; Williams, U. S. Dept. Agr., Farmers' Bul. 1203; Nelson, Ore. Bul. 289; Lush and Jones, Tex. Bul. 320; Hamilton, Tex. Bul. 444.

CHAPTER XXXV

GENERAL PROBLEMS IN SWINE HUSBANDRY

I. Economy of Pork Production

1274. Efficiency of pigs as meat producers.—Pigs excel all other farm animals in the economy with which they convert feed into edible flesh, as has been shown in Chapter VII. (**231**) When fed efficient rations, pigs marketed at the usual weights frequently require less than 400 lbs. of concentrates or other air-dry feeds to produce each 100 lbs. of gain, and rarely require much over 450 lbs. In comparison with these amounts, fattening calves and lambs require 800 lbs. or more of grain, hay, and other air-dry feeds per 100 lbs. gain, even when fed excellent rations.

Pigs have a greater capacity to consume feed in proportion to their live weights than do calves or lambs. Due to this and also to a greater efficiency in the utilization of food nutrients, they make much more rapid gains in proportion to their live weight than calves or lambs. From weaning time to market weights, well-fed pigs should make an average gain of 1.0 lb. per head daily or more. This is more than twice as great a gain per 100 lbs. live weight as is made by fattening calves and three times as much as is made by fattening lambs.

The efficiency of pigs as producers of human food is shown in a striking manner by the fact that they are able to store in their bodies 35 per cent of the gross energy in the feed they eat.[1] In comparison with this high efficiency, fattening cattle can store in their bodies only about 10 per cent of the gross energy furnished by their feed. (**1018**)

The great superiority of pigs in the amount of feed required per 100 lbs. gain and in the percentage of food energy they can convert into meat is due partly, but not chiefly, to the fact that their rations consist mostly of grains and other concentrates. Because of this, each pound of dry matter they eat furnishes a larger amount of total digestible nutrients and of net energy than in the case of cattle or sheep.

In addition to their superiority in the utilization of feed, swine also excel in the percentage of dressed carcass they yield, in the proportion of the carcass that is edible, and in the energy content of the meat per pound. Swine yield 65 to 80 per cent of their live weight as dressed carcass, when dressed "packer style" with head, leaf fat, kidneys, and ham facings removed, while cattle dress only 50 to 60 per cent and sheep even less. Because of the small proportion of bone in the dressed carcass of swine, the percentage of the carcass that is edible is decidedly higher than in the case of cattle or sheep. Also, the energy value of pork is usually higher per pound than that of beef or mutton, due to the higher content of fat and the slightly lower content of water. However, beef and mutton furnish a higher percentage of protein, on the average, than does pork.

Further important merits of swine are their great prolificacy and the fact that they do not require expensive buildings. Also, they are especially suited to utilize much feed that might otherwise be wasted, such as dairy by-products, garbage, and garden waste. For this reason alone, practically every farmer should raise enough pigs to furnish his own supply of pork.

Because of the several advantages of swine as meat producers, they are of great importance in most grain-producing countries where the population is dense. Since they must be fed chiefly on grain or other concentrates, they are of only minor importance in sections where but little grain is grown.

1275. Rate and economy of gain by pigs of various weights.—Several studies have been conducted to determine the rate and economy of gain by pigs at various stages of growth and fattening. The following table presents the results secured in Ohio experiments, in which pigs were hand-fed well-balanced rations in dry lots from birth to a weight of 500 lbs.[2] At each 100-lb. stage, representative animals were slaughtered to determine the dressing percentage at that weight. The amount of feed shown for the first period includes the feed eaten by both sows and pigs up to weaning time.

Economy of gain of pigs at different stages of growth

Wt. of pigs	No. of pigs	Feed per head daily	Feed daily per 100 lbs. live wt.	Daily gain	Feed for 100 lbs. gain*	Dressing percentage†
		Lbs.	Lbs.	Lbs.	Lbs.	Per cent
Birth to 100 lbs..	37	2.2	4.2	0.81	304	77.7
100 to 200 lbs....	30	6.1	4.0	1.70	359	83.4
200 to 300 lbs....	23	7.6	3.0	1.83	415	86.4
300 to 400 lbs....	16	7.8	2.8	1.71	470	88.1
400 to 500 lbs....	7	8.0	1.6	1.58	510	88.2

*6 lbs. of skimmilk, fed to some of pigs in first period, considered equal to 1 lb. of concentrates.
†Average for 2 experiments.

This table points out several facts of great importance to the pork producer. While the amount of feed eaten per head daily increased as the pigs grew older, the amount consumed per 100 lbs. live weight decreased. In other words, young pigs have a greater capacity for consuming feed in proportion to their weight than do older ones. The average daily gain was only 0.81 lb. up to the weight of 100 lbs., in comparison with 1.70 lbs. for the period from 100 lbs. to 200 lbs. in weight. During the third period the rate of gain was slightly more rapid than during the second period, but after this the gains became less rapid.

The most important results from the financial standpoint are given in the next to the last column. From birth to 100 lbs. in weight, only 304 lbs. of feed were required per 100 lbs. gain. As the pigs grew older and became fatter the feed consumed per 100 lbs. gain steadily increased, until 510 lbs. were required during the last period. Due to this greater feed requirement, the gains became more expensive as growth and fattening progressed. The last column, which gives the dressing percentage of the pigs slaughtered at the end of each period, shows that the percentage of dressed carcass to live weight increased gradually as the pigs became older and fatter.

The greater economy of young pigs in producing gain in weight is due to the factors that have been discussed in detail in Chapter VII. (**206**) First of all, the gain made during the early stages of growth or fattening contains more water and much less fat than when the animal becomes older and fatter. Less energy is therefore required to produce these early gains in weight. Also, since young animals eat considerably more feed per 100 lbs. live weight than do older ones, they may have available for meat production a greater surplus of nutrients after their maintenance requirements are met.

As has been stated previously, these factors fully account for the lower cost of the gains made by young animals. Though they require less feed per 100 lbs. gain and therefore make cheaper gains, young animals do not utilize any more efficiently the feed consumed beyond the amount they need to maintain their bodies. As a matter of fact, in Missouri experiments where the entire carcasses of pigs were analyzed at various stages of growth up to 300 lbs. live weight, the older pigs apparently required slightly less feed than the younger ones per therm of energy in the gains they made.[3]

It will be noted that in the Ohio experiments the pigs made remarkably rapid and economical gains during the latter periods, considering the heavy weights to which they were carried and the further fact that they were not on pasture during the trials. Such results are possible only with carefully selected animals, fed efficient rations under expert supervision.

Under average conditions appreciably more feed will generally be required per 100 lbs. gain than was needed by the pigs in these trials. In a compilation made by Henry of the results of over 500 feeding experiments at American experiment stations before the big-type swine were developed, the following amounts of feed were required per 100 lbs. gain by pigs of various weights: From 50-100 lbs. live weight, 400 lbs. feed per 100 lbs. gain; 100-150 lbs., 437 lbs. feed; 150-200 lbs., 482 lbs. feed; 200-250 lbs., 498 lbs. feed; 250-300 lbs., 511 lbs. feed; 300-350 lbs., 535 lbs. feed.[4]

In Missouri experiments with big-type Poland-China pigs and with large Yorkshire pigs the amounts of feed consumed per 100 lbs. gain were as follows: From 100-150 lbs. live weight, 425 lbs. feed per 100 lbs. gain; 150-200 lbs., 424 lbs. feed; 200-250 lbs., 546 lbs. feed; 250-300 lbs., 631 lbs. feed.[3]

In cost accounting investigations on Illinois farms that are summarized in Chapter XXXVII it was found that the following amounts of feed, in addition to pasture, were required in producing each 100 lbs. of marketable live hogs; 473 lbs. grain and other concentrates (including 400 lbs. of corn) ; 2.0 lbs. of hay or other dry roughage; 1.5 lbs. of salt and other minerals; and 7.7 lbs. of miscellaneous feeds. This includes not only the feed eaten by the pigs but also that consumed by the breeding herd. (**1443**) These data show the amounts of feed that are required to produce each 100 lbs. of live hogs under farm conditions in the corn belt and with modern-type swine. The cost will usually be somewhat less under the best systems of feeding and management.

1276. Economy of gain on pasture.—The following table shows the average results secured during 6 years with pigs self-fed corn and tankage on good pasture at the Wisconsin Station.[5] In these trials a total of 320 pigs were fed from weights of 50 or 60 lbs. to market weights of 200 lbs. or more. The pasture crops included alfalfa, red clover, sweet clover, rape, and such mixtures as oats-peas-and-rape.

Gains of pigs of various ages on good pasture

Wt. of pigs	Actual av. wt.	Concentrates per head daily	Daily gain	Concentrates for 100 lbs. gain	
				Corn	Tankage
	Lbs.	Lbs.	Lbs.	Lbs.	Lbs.
50 to 75 lbs........	64.5	3.2	0.90	333	26
75 to 100 lbs........	88.5	4.2	1.15	340	29
100 to 150 lbs........	127.1	5.7	1.50	363	26
150 to 200 lbs........	175.8	6.9	1.55	443	20

This table shows about what may be expected of pigs self-fed well-balanced rations on good pasture. It will be noted that the amount of feed required for 100 lbs. gain increased in each period, but that there was no very rapid increase until the weight of 150 lbs. was reached.

1277. Weight at which to market pigs.—Most pigs are now marketed in this country when weighing 225 lbs. or less. This is due not only to the greater cost of gain as the pigs become fatter, but also because American consumers have a decided preference for small cuts of pork that do not carry too much fat. Under present conditions, well-finished pigs that are not over 200 to 225 lbs. in live weight usually command a premium over those that are heavier and fatter.

Ordinarily one should raise enough pigs to dispose of the available feed by the time they reach these market weights. If the number of pigs is limited in comparison with the amount of feed one desires to market through them, and if the price of heavy hogs is high compared with the price of grain, then it may be more profitable to carry the pigs to heavier weights.

1278. Dressing percentage.—Hogs dressed "packer style" with the head off, and also the leaf fat, kidneys, and ham facings removed, will range in dressing percentage from 65 to 80 per cent of the live weight. According to the Census, the average weight of hogs slaughtered at wholesale slaughtering and meat packing plants in the United States was 225.2 lbs. for the period 1923-29 and the average yield of dressed carcass was 167.8 lbs., the average dressing percentage thus being 74.5 per cent. When hogs are dressed "shipper style," with heads on and without the leaf fat, kidneys, and ham facings being removed, the dressing percentage will be about 8 per cent higher than for those dressed "packer style."

The chief factor affecting the dressing percentage is the degree of fatness. **(1275)** Very fat barrows weighing 400 lbs. or more that have been fitted for shows may have a dressing percentage of 89 per cent, or even more when dressed "shipper style."

Studies by the Ohio Station show that the ration on which pigs have been finished has but little influence on the dressing percentage.[6]

Also, in these tests there was no difference between the dressing percentage of purebred, grade, and cross-bred hogs. There was a low point in dressing percentage in September and October, probably due to the marketing of pigs that were not very well finished. The dressing percentage then increased gradually and reached a high point in January and February.

II. Nutrient Requirements of Swine

1279. Nutrient requirements of swine.—Swine are fed largely on grain, and they eat relatively little roughage, except when on pasture. Moreover, they grow more rapidly than cattle, horses, or sheep, and produce young when less mature. As a result, swine suffer much more frequently than these other classes of livestock from inadequate rations. It is therefore especially necessary, if maximum profits are to be secured from pork production, that their nutrient requirements be clearly understood.

In no field of animal husbandry have the recent discoveries in stock feeding had a more important bearing than upon practical pork production. These experiments show that the nutrient requirements of swine are relatively simple, when once understood, and that it is not necessary to feed complicated or expensive rations in order to secure the best results. The following are the chief nutritive deficiencies that are apt to occur in swine feeding.

Because swine are fed chiefly on grain, particular care is necessary to provide in their rations a sufficient amount of protein and also protein of the right kind or quality.

Since the grains are all low in calcium, it is necessary to feed swine a mineral supplement supplying this essential, unless an adequate amount of calcium is furnished by the other feeds in the ration. A phosphorus supplement must also be added to certain swine rations, because the cereal grains are not rich in this mineral. In some districts brood sows must be fed an iodine supplement to prevent disaster from goiter, or "hairlessness," in the new-born pigs. When young suckling pigs are confined without contact with the soil, a source of iron and copper must be provided, or heavy losses will occur from anemia. Except possibly when tankage or fish meal is used as the only or the chief protein supplement, swine should be supplied with salt.

The vitamin requirements of swine are met adequately when they are on good pasture, but under other conditions they may suffer seriously from deficiencies of vitamin A or vitamin D, unless well-cured legume hay or some other vitamin supplement is fed.

The requirements of swine for these and other nutrients are discussed in detail in the following pages.

1280. Importance of good pasture or legume hay.—Wherever possible, all swine should be provided with good pasture during the growing season and with well-cured legume hay when pasture is not available. Nothing is more important than this in reducing the cost of pork production.

It is exceedingly fortunate that either good pasture or well-cured legume hay will prevent any deficiency of vitamins A and D in swine feeding. These feeds also aid greatly in meeting the protein requirements of swine. This is because actively-growing pasture crops and also legume hay are fairly rich in protein, and the proteins in these forages are of such kind that they help to correct the deficiencies in the proteins of the cereal grains. Legume hay and legume pasture crops are also very rich in calcium, and other good swine pasture crops supply much more calcium than do any of the grains or the grain by-products.

Pigs cannot consume a large amount of dry roughage, even of excellent legume hay. Therefore when they are fed liberally on corn or other low-protein grain, they cannot eat enough of such roughage to balance the ration completely in protein content. In order to secure rapid and economical gains a sufficient amount of an efficient concentrated protein supplement must hence be added to furnish the proper amount of protein and also to supply protein of excellent quality. (**1399**)

Good pasture should be provided for swine during the growing season, because green forage and pasture conditions are definitely superior to legume hay in meeting their nutritive essentials. It is shown in Chapter XXXVII that in Kansas and Missouri experiments brood sows did not raise satisfactory litters when confined to small exercise lots throughout the year, although fed good rations, even including well-cured legume hay. (**1406**) These rations would have produced excellent results if the sows had been on pasture during the growing season.

1281. Protein of good quality essential.—In swine feeding fully as much attention must be given to providing protein of good quality as to supplying a sufficient amount of this nutrient. (**142-153**) This is of especial importance for growing and fattening pigs and also for brood sows that are nursing litters, because their requirements for protein are much greater than those of other swine.

None of the cereal grains furnishes proteins of good quality. Since swine are ordinarily fed chiefly on the grains, it is necessary to correct the deficiencies of the cereal-grain proteins by the use of efficient protein supplements that are rich in those essential animo acids which are provided in too small amounts by the grains. (**142**) Detailed information is presented in the next chapter on the quality of the protein in each of the common supplements used in swine feeding, and on the values of these supplements when used in various rations.

Skimmilk, other dairy by-products, fish meal, digester tankage, and meat scraps all provide proteins that admirably correct the deficiencies of the proteins in the cereal grains. Therefore any one of these feeds of animal origin is satisfactory as the only protein supplement to the grains. (For pigs not on pasture legume hay should be included in the ration to provide an ample amount of vitamins.)

Part of the protein needed to balance a ration for swine may be provided by a protein supplement that would not be satisfactory if used as the only supplement to cereal grains. For example, linseed meal, cottonseed meal, or wheat middlings are unsatisfactory when used as the only protein supplement for young pigs. However, when any one of these supplements is used in combination with a limited amount of tankage, fish meal, or dairy by-products, excellent results are produced.

It is shown in the next chapter that even better results are secured when pigs are fed certain combinations of tankage or fish meal and of protein supplements of plant origin, than when the tankage or fish meal is used as the only supplement. Thus, for pigs not on pasture the trio or Wisconsin supplemental mixture (consisting of tankage, alfalfa hay, and linseed meal) is definitely more efficient than tankage alone as a supplement to corn, and it is slightly superior to a combination of tankage and alfalfa hay. (**1341-1343**) Certain modifications can be made in this combination, without decreasing its effectiveness. For example, cottonseed meal can be substituted for the linseed meal, fish meal can replace the tankage, and other well-cured legume hay can be used instead of the alfalfa hay.

It is likewise shown in the next chapter that even for pigs on good pasture, certain combinations of tankage and protein supplements of plant origin may be more efficient or more economical than tankage as the only supplement to grain. Thus, pigs self-fed on good pasture make slightly more rapid gains when self-fed a mixture of one-half linseed meal and one-half tankage than when self-fed tankage as the only supplement. (**1345**)

Among the protein supplements of plant origin, proteins of good quality are provided by soybean oil meal that has been thoroughly cooked in the manufacturing process, by cooked soybeans, by peanut oil meal, and by peanuts. When fed as the only protein supplement to young pigs, these supplements do not generally produce quite such rapid gains as do protein supplements of animal origin, or supplemental mixtures including animal by-products. Unfortunately, the usefulness of soybeans and of peanuts in swine feeding is seriously limited, because they both produce soft pork when fed in too large amounts or for too long a time. (**1321**) Raw soybeans and soybean oil meal that has not been thoroughly cooked are much less efficient for swine than well-cooked products. (**1367, 1368**)

1282. Certain feeds unsatisfactory as sole supplements.—It is shown in the next chapter that any ration made up of only grain and grain by-products is very unsatisfactory for pigs, even when a mineral mixture is supplied to furnish plenty of calcium and phosphorus and when there is no lack of vitamins A or D. For example, if pigs are fed yellow corn supplemented by wheat middlings, corn gluten feed, corn gluten meal, rye feed, brewers' dried grains, or distillers' dried grains, they will make poor and expensive gains, even if they are out in the sunlight (which will supply vitamin D) and if they are fed a suitable mineral mixture to provide additional calcium and phosphorus.

The results will still be poor if pigs are fed a mixture of various grains supplemented by a combination of two or more of these protein-rich grain by-products. Thus, a combination of corn, barley, oats, wheat middlings, and corn gluten meal furnishes protein of unsatisfactory quality for swine.

Linseed meal is no more effective than wheat middlings as the only protein supplement to grain in swine feeding. Likewise, none of the following produces good results when used as the sole protein supplement to corn or other grain in swine feeding: Cottonseed meal, field peas, cowpeas, field beans, coconut meal, or buckwheat middlings. If the pigs are fed choice legume hay in addition to corn or other grain, these protein supplements will produce better results than without the legume hay. However, especially in the case of young pigs, the gains will be much more rapid and economical if these protein supplements are combined with such supplements as tankage, fish meal, or dairy by-products.

Excellent pasture, such as alfalfa, clover, or rape, furnishes a considerable amount of protein of good quality. On such pasture, even young pigs make fairly good gains on a ration consisting of grain, a suitable mineral mixture, and such a protein supplement as linseed meal or wheat middlings. However, the results are generally enough better when a more efficient protein supplement is included in the ration to make such an addition profitable. If protein supplements of animal origin are unusually high in price, then it is best to use such a combination as linseed meal and wheat middlings; or cottonseed meal, linseed meal, and wheat middlings, instead of only one of these supplements.[7] The addition of soybean oil meal to such mixtures is beneficial.

1283. Amounts of protein required by swine.—Because of their rapid growth, pigs need rations containing liberal proportions of protein. Unless care is taken to meet this requirement, they will make slow and expensive gains.

The exact proportion of protein that is needed in the ration for pigs will depend on their stage of growth. It has been shown in Chapter VII that the rate of protein storage in the body is most rapid at early ages. (**204**) Young pigs therefore require a much greater proportion of protein in their rations than do those which are older and are therefore storing less protein and more fat in their bodies.

Often this fundamental fact is overlooked and pigs are fed the same proportion of protein supplement from weaning time to market. If enough protein supplement is included in the mixture to produce good growth when the pigs are young, there will be considerably more than is needed after they reach weights of 100 to 125 lbs. On the other hand, if only a small proportion of supplement is used throughout the entire period, the pigs will have too little protein while they are young to make rapid and efficient gains.

The amounts of digestible protein and the nutritive ratios advised by the author for pigs of various stages of growth and also for brood sows are stated in the Morrison feeding standards. (Appendix Table III.) These recommendations are based on the experiments which have been conducted to study the protein requirements of pigs, especially investigations by Fargo at the Wisconsin Station.[8]

In the Wisconsin experiments pigs have been fed various proportions of corn and the trio supplemental mixture from shortly after weaning until they were ready for market. It was found in these studies that pigs from 40 to 75 lbs. in weight made slightly more rapid gains when fed a ration having a nutritive ratio of 1:4.5 than when the nutritive ratio was 1:5.0. However, the gains were more expensive on the larger proportion of protein. It was therefore concluded that it does not pay to feed the larger proportion of protein except when a materially higher price is anticipated in an early market, or in the case of purebred animals which are being developed for show or for sale at an early age.

For pigs over 100 lbs. in weight, a ration having a nutritive ratio of 1:6.2 provided ample protein in these experiments. Feeding a ration having a nutritive ratio of 1:5.0 until the pigs reached a weight of about 100 lbs., and then changing to a ration having a nutritive ratio of 1:6.2, produced excellent results. This method was just as satisfactory as starting them on a nutritive ratio of 1:4.5 and then decreasing the proportion of protein as the pigs reached weights of 75 lbs., 100 lbs., and 150 lbs., so as to provide nutritive ratios of 1:5.4, 1:5.9, and 1:6.5, respectively.

The amounts of digestible protein required by pigs undoubtedly depend somewhat on the quality of the protein supplied by the ration. If the quality of protein is unusually good, less protein will be needed for maximum gains than when the protein is not so excellent in character. For this reason, a somewhat smaller amount of protein is necessary when skimmilk or other dairy by-products are used as the chief protein supplements than is required in other rations. In the case of an inefficient protein supplement, however, poor results cannot be prevented by feeding an unusually large proportion of the supplement.

1284. Self-feeding supplements separately.—Most fortunately, pigs show a remarkable ability to balance their own rations in protein content when they are self-fed corn or other low-protein grains and also self-fed separately *certain* single protein supplements or *certain* supplemental mixtures. At early ages they eat enough supplement to balance their ration, and then gradually eat a smaller proportion of the supplement as they grow older and their requirements for protein become less.

This free-choice plan of self-feeding usually works excellently with pigs on pasture or in dry lot which receive tankage or fish meal as a single supplement to corn or the grain sorghums, or when the trio mixture or a similar combination is self-fed as the supplement to these grains.

Occasionally, the pigs may eat somewhat more supplement than they need, and once in a while they may not consume as much of the supplement as they should. However, the results from the free-choice method of feeding these supplements with corn will average fully as good or better than when time is taken to mix the proper proportion of supplement with ground corn or to hand-feed the supplement.

The free-choice plan of self-feeding grain and protein supplement is not so satisfactory with barley, oats, rye, or kafir. With these grains less of the protein supplement is needed than with corn, for they contain somewhat more protein. However, the pigs often eat fully as much of the supplement with these grains as when they are self-fed corn. To avoid wastage of the protein supplement it is therefore necessary to mix the proper proportion of the supplement with the ground grain, or else to hand-feed the amount of supplement that is actually needed to balance the ration. Wheat is so palatable to pigs that they generally do not eat more of such a protein supplement as tankage or fish meal, when they are self-fed wheat and the supplement, free-choice.

Even when self-fed corn and certain supplements or supplemental mixtures, the pigs are apt to eat much more of the supplement than they need, especially if they are on good pasture. Thus, pigs will eat a much greater amount of roasted soybeans than they need to balance their rations. Sometimes they also eat much more than they need of soybean oil meal or of such a mixture as one-half tankage or fish meal and one-half soybean oil meal. In any such case, the expense can be reduced by hand-feeding just enough of the supplement to balance the ration.

1285. When is the use of a supplement advisable?—None of the cereal grains provides a sufficient amount of protein or protein of proper quality to permit growing and fattening pigs to make rapid or economical gains when they are fed the grain without any protein supplement. The trials summarized in the next chapter show that when pigs not on pasture are fed corn alone or corn and a mineral supplement, the gains are slow and expensive. (**1327**)   Sometimes the pigs will become runts or even die as a result of protein and vitamin deficiencies.   Balancing the ration by the addition of a good supplement, such as tankage, will double the rate of gain in the case of young pigs.   Also, each 100 lbs. of tankage will save 500 to 600 lbs. or more of corn, without considering the advantage of the more rapid gains.

After pigs have reached a weight of 175 to 200 lbs., they may make fair gains on corn alone, because their requirements for protein are then not high.   However, the gains are usually much more rapid and also somewhat more economical when the use of a good supplement is continued until the pigs are marketed.[9] Adding alfalfa hay or other legume hay to corn for pigs not on pasture will permit fair gains and will generally prevent serious nutritional trouble.   However, as is shown in the next chapter, the gains on corn and alfalfa hay are much less rapid and usually are more expensive than when such a supplement as tankage is also provided. (**1399**)

On barley, wheat, or oats as the only feeds, or on these grains plus a mineral supplement, the gains may be somewhat better than on corn alone, because these grains supply more protein and protein of somewhat better quality than does corn.[10] However, in the case of pigs not on pasture, the gains are greatly increased by the addition of a sufficient amount of a good protein supplement to balance the ration.

Because of the higher protein content of these grains, alfalfa hay produces somewhat better results when fed as the only protein supplement to them, than it does when used as the only protein supplement with corn.   However, unless tankage and other efficient protein supplements are unusually high in price, it generally pays to add a limited amount of such a supplement to a ration of any of these grains and good-quality alfalfa hay, especially for pigs under 100 to 125 lbs. in weight.[11]

1286. Feeding a supplement on pasture.—When pigs are on good pasture, a considerable amount of protein is provided by the green forage they eat.   Therefore pigs will make fairly good gains when full-fed corn on such pasture, without any other protein supplement, especially if a mineral mixture is provided to furnish additional calcium and phosphorus.

Pigs will not eat enough pasturage in addition to a full-feed of corn to balance their ration completely.   The rate of gain will therefore be considerably increased by the addition of a good protein supplement, such as tankage, fish meal, or a dairy by-product.   However, each 100 lbs. of the supplement will save a much smaller amount of corn than when fed to pigs not on pasture.

In the case of early spring pigs, the increase in the rate of gain produced by the supplement is more important than the saving of corn.   If such pigs are full-fed on corn plus a good supplement, they can be brought to market weights before the severe slump in hog prices which usually occurs in late autumn. (**1302**) On the other hand, if no supplement is fed it will take at least 2 to 4 weeks longer to get them to the same weights, and during this time the price may decline 50 cents or more per hundred weight. Because of the difference in selling price, it will usually be most profitable to feed a supplement if pigs can thereby be hurried to market early in the fall.

Whether or not to feed a supplement to later pigs will depend on the age of the pigs, on the rate of gain that is desired, and on the relative price of corn and of supplements. Except when supplements are high in price in comparison with corn, it is probably best to feed a supplement until the pigs reach a weight of at least 100 lbs. Unless the pasture is excellent, good gains cannot be secured without a supplement. Thus, there is more advantage in feeding a supplement to pigs on grass pasture (such as bluegrass, timothy, or Sudan grass) than to pigs on excellent legume or rape pasture.[12]

The results that are secured from using a supplement for pigs that are full-fed corn and also supplied with a mineral mixture on good pasture are shown by 15 experiments summarized in the following table.[13] In each of these tests one lot of pigs was full-fed corn on legume or rape pasture, while another lot received tankage in addition. All the pigs were provided with a mineral mixture which supplied calcium and phosphorus. In these experiments pigs weighing an average of 61 lbs. were fed until they reached market weights.

Adding a supplement to corn and good pasture

	Daily gain Lbs.	Concentrates for 100 lbs. gain		
Average ration		Corn Lbs.	Tankage Lbs.	Minerals Lbs.
Lot I, no protein supplement				
Corn, 4.5 lbs.				
Minerals, 0.06 lb. Pasture...............	1.29	352.4	...	4.8
Lot II, fed protein supplement				
Corn, 4.6 lbs.				
Tankage, 0.33 lb.				
Minerals, 0.04 lb. Pasture...............	1.47	314.5	23.1	2.6

The pigs fed only corn and minerals on good pasture in these experiments made surprisingly rapid gains. This was undoubtedly due to the excellence of the pasture. Adding tankage to the ration increased the daily gain from 1.29 to 1.47 lbs. With this difference in rate of gain it would take 17 days longer to get 40-lb. pigs to a market weight of 225 lbs. when they were fed no supplement, than it would for pigs fed tankage. In these trials each 100 lbs. of tankage saved only 164 lbs. of corn plus 10 lbs. of mineral mixture, if no value is placed on the difference in rate of gain. The pigs fed tankage also undoubtedly ate a little less of the pasturage, though no exact record of this difference could be made in these trials.

When no mineral mixture is provided for pigs full-fed corn on good pasture, there is a somewhat greater advantage in adding a protein supplement. For example, adding tankage to this ration for pigs averaging 60 lbs. in weight at the start increased the daily gain from 1.13 lbs. to

1.46 lbs., on the average, in 27 experiments.[14] In these numerous trials each 100 lbs. of tankage saved an average of 282 lbs. corn, not considering the difference in rate of gain.

Experiments have shown that in the case of pigs on good pasture that are fed barley, wheat, oats, or rye (which grains contain somewhat more protein than does corn) there is less benefit from adding a protein supplement.[15] After pigs fed these grains reach a weight of about 100 lbs., it does not usually pay to add a supplement, unless maximum gains are desired. Up to this weight, it is generally best to feed a small amount of supplement, unless the pasture is unusually good or protein supplements are high in price. With these grains, pigs on pasture will eat too much of the supplement if it is self-fed, free-choice. Therefore the proper proportion should be mixed with the ground grain, or a small amount of the supplement should be hand-fed daily.

When the pasture is good, 4 lbs. of tankage or fish meal of usual grades are enough per 100 lbs. of these grains for pigs under 100 lbs. in weight. If a supplement is fed to older pigs, not over 2 to 3 lbs. of tankage or fish meal per 100 lbs. of grain are advisable. When the supplement is hand-fed to pigs fed barley, oats, wheat, or rye on good pasture, 0.2 lb. per head daily of tankage or fish meal is sufficient.

If pigs are fed only a limited amount of grain on good pasture, they will eat more of the green forage than when full-fed on grain. There will therefore be less benefit from adding a protein concentrate to the ration, and under usual conditions it will not pay to use a supplement, even when the grain is corn. For example, in 4 Ohio experiments pigs averaging 50 lbs. in weight at the start gained 0.95 lb. per head daily when fed 3.0 lbs. of corn a day on rape pasture.[16] Others fed an average of 0.23 lb. tankage in addition to corn gained 1.09 lbs. a day. In these trials each 100 lbs. of tankage saved only 127 lbs. of corn.

1287. Feeding standards; digestibility of feeds by swine.—The Morrison feeding standards for swine are stated in terms of dry matter, digestible protein, total digestible nutrients, and nutritive ratios, the same as for the other classes of farm animals. (Appendix Table III.) For those desiring to compute rations according to the net energy system, recommendations are also made of amounts of net energy, stated in therms. The standards for growing and fattening pigs are for pigs that are full-fed, so as to make rapid gains in weight.

These standards are designed for use with the values for digestible nutrients in various feeds that are given in Appendix Table I. Relatively few digestion trials have been conducted with swine, in comparison with the large number that have been carried on with ruminants. It has therefore seemed wiser to the author to use in computing rations for swine the digestible nutrient values in Appendix Table I, than to use a separate set of values, computed from the limited data obtained in digestion trials with swine.

There is not much difference in the ability of swine and of ruminants to digest concentrates that are not high in fiber.[17] Because they do not have the four-compartment stomach of ruminants or the large caecum of horses, swine digest a considerably smaller percentage of the fiber in feeds than do cattle and sheep, or even horses.

This difference is not important in the case of most concentrates, for they are relatively low in fiber. However, swine digest hay and other roughages much less completely than do ruminants. It is for this reason, as well as because of the limited capacity of their digestive tracts, that swine are not able to make so much use of roughage as do cattle, sheep, or horses. Pigs have much less ability to utilize roughage than do older swine, such as brood sows.

Evvard has proposed for use in computing rations for growing and fattening pigs, standards based, not on digestible nutrients, but upon dry matter, total protein (not digestible protein), and "fiberless carbohydrate equivalent;" the latter being the total nitrogen-free extract plus 2.2 times the total fat.[18] For the sake of simplicity and uniformity, the author prefers standards expressed in the same terms that are used for cattle, sheep, and horses.

1288. Fiber content of swine rations.—Since pigs do not digest the fiber of feeds well, it is necessary to give attention to the fiber content of the ration when rapid gains in weight are desired. If any large part of the ration is made up of feeds high in fiber, the ration will be so bulky that pigs cannot eat enough of it to provide sufficient nutrients for rapid gains.

It is highly advantageous to include about 5 per cent of good-quality legume hay in the rations of pigs which are not on pasture, in order to furnish sufficient amounts of vitamins A and D. However, if legume hay forms a much greater part of the ration for pigs, the rate of gain will usually be decreased. Likewise, the gains are lessened if oats form too large a part of a ration for pigs. In the case of brood sows, such feeds as legume hay and oats can form a considerably larger proportion of the ration.

Growing and fattening pigs usually make the most rapid and economical gains when their rations do not contain more than about 5 per cent of fiber.[19] It is therefore not generally economical to use rations having a higher percentage of fiber for such pigs, unless the prices of corn, barley, wheat, or other feeds low in fiber are very high in comparison with the prices of feeds higher in fiber, such as oats, oat mill feed, or legume hay.

1289. Salt—Though swine require less salt than cattle, horses, or sheep, they should be supplied with it regularly, unless plenty is otherwise provided by the feeds in their ration. The best plan is to provide free access to salt in a suitable box or trough, so the pigs can take as much as they desire. When salt is thus fed, pigs will eat from 0.03 to 0.12 ounce per head daily, depending on the ration they are receiving. If pigs have not previously been fed salt for a considerable time, the allowance should be limited at first, or they may overeat, causing indigestion.

When salt is mixed with the concentrates or with a mixture of protein supplements, instead of being fed separately, too much should not be used. In case salt is added to a combination of grain and protein supplements, not over one-quarter pound of salt should be added to each 100 lbs. of feed. If the salt is included in a mixture of protein supplements, 2 to 3 lbs. of salt to each 100 lbs. of supplement are sufficient.

It is especially necessary to provide salt for swine fed grain and protein supplements that are entirely or largely of plant origin. The benefit from salt with such rations is shown by an Iowa experiment in which pigs were fed corn and protein supplements of plant origin (wheat middlings, linseed meal, alfalfa meal, cottonseed meal, and corn oil cake meal).[20] The pigs fed salt in addition gained 1.47 lbs. per head daily and required 467 lbs. feed per 100 lbs. gain, while those that had no salt gained only 1.07 lbs. and consumed 574 lbs. feed per 100 lbs. gain. In other Iowa tests there was a decided advantage from supplying salt when tankage formed as much as one-half of the supplemental mixture fed with corn.

When tankage, blood meal, or fish meal is fed as the only or the chief supplement to corn or other grain, there may be little or no benefit from supplying salt. For example, in a Nebraska trial there was no advantage from adding salt to a ration of corn and tankage for fattening pigs, while there was a decided benefit from adding salt to a ration of corn and alfalfa hay.[21] Similarly, in Texas experiments there was no need of providing salt for pigs fed milo grain and tankage, but there was a benefit from adding salt to a ration of milo and cottonseed meal.[22]

1290. Calcium; phosphorus.—With the exception of salt, calcium is the mineral nutrient that is most apt to be lacking in swine rations. This is because all the grains and their by-products and also practically all protein-rich concentrates of plant origin are low in this mineral, as has been shown in Chapter VI. (**160**) Fortunately, skimmilk, buttermilk, tankage, meat scraps, fish meal, legume forage (pasturage and hay), and rape forage all are rich in calcium. Dried blood and meat products including no bone are, however, low in calcium. Whether or not there will be any need of supplying swine with a calcium supplement will therefore depend entirely on the ration that they are fed.

There is much less apt to be a lack of phosphorus in swine rations than of calcium, because most protein-rich concentrates are rich in phosphorus, as has been emphasized in Chapter VI. (**160-161**) Also, though the cereal grains are not rich in phosphorus, they contain much more phosphorus than calcium. Skimmilk, buttermilk, tankage, meat scraps, and fish meal are especially rich in this mineral, and wheat middlings, wheat bran, linseed meal, and cottonseed meal are also high in phosphorus. Soybeans, soybean oil meal, peanuts, and peanut oil meal contain much more than do the cereal grains.

It is evident from the preceding statements that when swine are fed a well-balanced ration consisting of grain with skimmilk, tankage, meat scraps, or fish meal as the chief supplement, they will receive considerable amounts of both calcium and phosphorus, even when they are not on pasture. If they are fed such a ration on legume or rape pasture, their calcium supply will be further increased. It is not surprising therefore that numerous experiments have proved that there is no great advantage in adding calcium or phosphorus supplements to such rations.[23] In some cases pigs have made slightly more rapid or economical gains when fed the mineral supplements in addition to salt, but in other tests there has been no benefit whatsoever from the calcium or phosphorus supplements. Similar results have been secured in experiments with brood sows and with gilts being raised for the breeding herd.

Since there has been a slight benefit from these mineral supplements in some cases, it may be wise to provide a suitable mineral mixture where swine can have access to it, even when they are fed such good rations. However, it should be understood thoroughly that under such conditions excellent results will be secured without the calcium and phosphorus supplements, and often there will be no advantage from their use.

There is more apt to be a slight benefit from the addition of such mineral supplements to efficient rations for swine that are not on good pasture. Also, there is probably more advantage from adding such mineral supplements to good rations for brood sows and for young pigs than for fattening pigs.

When there is a definite lack of calcium or phosphorus in the ration, then the mineral need must be met, or unsatisfactory results will be secured. If the lack is pronounced, rickets will be caused and disaster may follow. Brood sows suffering from a serious lack of either of these minerals are unable to produce thrifty offspring. Many pigs will be born dead or weak, and the sows may be unable to provide an adequate supply of milk for those that appear normal at birth. (**1407**)

Numerous experiments have been conducted to determine the effect of supplying a calcium supplement or else supplements providing both calcium and phosphorus, when swine are fed little or none of the supplements of animal origin that are rich both in calcium and in phosphorus.[24] These experiments have shown conclusively that swine fed such rations without good pasture should always be supplied with a calcium supplement or else with a mineral supplement which furnishes both calcium and phosphorus. When swine are on excellent legume or rape pasture, there is less need of a supplement, but even then the use of a mineral supplement has generally produced more rapid and economical gains. It is especially important that brood sows be fed a calcium or a calcium and phosphorus supplement, whenever there is any danger of a lack of these minerals.

When the ration includes a reasonable amount of wheat middlings, linseed meal, or cottonseed meal (all of which are rich in phosphorus) there will not be any great need of additional phosphorus, but the lack of calcium will be just as pronounced. The chief lack is calcium rather than phosphorus even when grain is supplemented by soybeans, soybean oil meal, peanuts, or peanut oil meal, none of which is as rich in phosphorus as wheat middlings, linseed meal, or cottonseed meal. Therefore a mineral supplement which provides only calcium may give just as good results, particularly in the case of pigs on good pasture, as a supplement such as bone meal, which furnishes both calcium and phosphorus. In some of the experiments, however, there has been a distinct benefit from supplying not only calcium, but also phosphorus. It would therefore seem wise to use a mineral supplement or a mineral mixture that has both these minerals.

A supplement such as bone meal, that furnishes both phosphorus and calcium, should be provided when pigs on pasture are fed only corn or other grain, without any protein-rich concentrate, or when pigs in dry lot are fed only corn or grain sorghum with alfalfa or other legume hay.[25] A mineral supplement is less advantageous in the case of barley, wheat, or rye, as these grains contain somewhat more of these minerals.[26]

1291. Sources of calcium and phosphorus; amounts required.—
Steamed bone meal is the mineral supplement used most commonly in
swine feeding when both calcium and phosphorus are needed, and it
is excellent for this purpose. It is shown in Chapter VI that other
satisfactory supplements supplying both of these mineral nutrients are
bone black and raw bone meal. (**166-171**) Raw rock phosphate (lime
phosphate), phosphorized limestone, and superphosphate are less desirable, as they all contain appreciable amounts of fluorine. These supplements should not be fed to breeding stock for long periods, as fluorine
is a cumulative poison. However, phosphates of rock origin from which
practically all of the fluorine has been removed by special treatment
are entirely suitable for use as mineral supplements.

Ground limestone, ground oyster shell, ground chalk, and high-
calcium marl are all excellent calcium supplements, as is stated in Chapter VI.[27] (**165**) Wood ashes, especially hardwood ashes, may also be
used as a calcium supplement.[28] Even gypsum or other forms of calcium sulfate are satisfactory as a source of calcium.[29]

There is as yet but little information on the minimum amounts of
calcium and phosphorus required by swine. From Illinois studies Carroll, Hunt, and Mitchell concluded that growing pigs need about 5
grams of calcium per head daily.[30] For a full-fed 100-lb. pig this amount
of calcium would be about 0.3 per cent of the ration. From Missouri
investigations Hogan decided that the rations for brood sows should
contain not less than 0.4 per cent of calcium.[31]

There is but little information available concerning the minimum
amounts of phosphorus required by swine. In a recent Illinois experiment it was concluded that a ration containing 0.3 per cent phosphorus
supplied enough of this mineral for growing pigs.[32]

1292. Iodine, prevention of goiter or hairlessness in pigs.—It has
been shown in Chapter VI that goiter in new-born pigs and other farm
animals is due to a lack of iodine in the feed and water consumed by
the dams during pregnancy. (**172**) In localities where goiter occurs it
can readily be prevented by supplying the dams with small amounts of
iodine during the pregnancy period.

For reasons that are not well understood, the prevalence of goiter
varies widely from year to year in the iodine-deficient regions. Therefore, where one has once had trouble from it, or where there has been
any considerable occurrence of the disease in the vicinity, the pregnant
sows should be supplied with iodine as insurance against goiter. The
simplest method of administering iodine is to supply iodized stock salt
where the sows can have access to it during at least the latter 12 weeks
of pregnancy.

If the sows are fed a mineral mixture which includes salt, instead
of feeding them salt separately, one-third ounce of potassium iodide
should be added to each 100 lbs. of the mineral mixture.

In localities where there is a definite lack of iodine and frequent
cases of goiter in livestock, it is probably wise to use iodized stock salt
instead of common salt for brood sows throughout the year and also
to use this salt for growing and fattening pigs. It is doubtful whether
there will generally be any appreciable benefit from thus supplying
iodine to swine in districts where there has been no trouble from hair-

less pigs. In Illinois and Pennsylvania experiments there was no advantage in adding iodine to well-balanced rations for pigs, while there was a slight benefit in Iowa and Ohio trials.[33]

1293. Anemia in suckling pigs.—If suckling pigs are confined to pens or paved lots, away from contact with soil or sod, serious losses will occur from anemia (lack of red blood cells), unless special precautions are taken to prevent the disease. It was first recognized by McGowan and Crichton in 1923 that this disease was due to the deficiency of iron in milk.[34] As is stated in the discussion of anemia in Chapter VI, it is now known that not only iron, but also traces of copper, are necessary for the formation of blood hemoglobin and red blood cells. (**173-174**)

The young are born with a sufficient store of iron and copper to last until, under normal conditions, they begin to consume other food than the milk from their dam. This food generally furnishes plenty of iron and the necessary traces of copper. If the pigs have access to pasture or even to the soil in an exercise plot, they begin to eat forage or to nibble at lumps of dirt within a few days after birth and thus get the small amounts of these minerals necessary to prevent anemia.

When they do not have access to pasture or dirt, however, the number of red blood cells and the amount of hemoglobin in the blood decline rapidly, and often death results at from 3 to 6 weeks of age. In white pigs the anemic condition is clearly visible in the lack of a healthy pink color of such parts as the ears and nose. Anemic pigs usually have little appetite, are weak and inactive, and in severe cases breathe in the labored manner commonly described as "thumps." If they survive for 6 weeks, they usually recover from the anemia, because they then eat considerable food other than milk. However, pigs that have had anemia generally do not make good gains for a considerable period.

Anemia is especially apt to occur with pigs farrowed in the winter or early spring in the northern states, because the weather is then usually so cold that the young pigs do not get outdoors to any great extent. Also, they usually have no access to pasture, and the dirt in exercise paddocks may be covered with snow. In the McLean County system of round worm control, described later, there may be serious losses from anemia unless the necessary precautions are taken, because the sows and their litters are confined to carefully cleaned pens to avoid infestation with worms and other parasites. (**1440**)

Many experiments have been conducted during recent years to find methods of preventing anemia in suckling pigs. It was first shown by Hart and associates at the Wisconsin Station that anemia could be prevented in confined pigs by administering doses of a solution of an iron salt which also carried a trace of copper.[35] (All commercial grades of iron salts contain small amounts of copper.) Other investigations have supplied further information concerning the most convenient methods of preventing anemia.[36]

When the sows and litters are confined to a central hog house or to enclosures with concrete or wooden floors so that the pigs do not have access to soil, anemia may be prevented by any one of the following methods:

1. Swabbing the udder of the sow regularly once daily with a satu-

rated solution of ferrous sulfate or other soluble iron salt until the pigs are 4 to 6 weeks old, and allowing them access to a palatable concentrate mixture to each 100 lbs. of which has been added 0.1 lb. of the iron salt. The iron solution may be prepared by dissolving as completely as possible 1 lb. of ferrous sulfate in a quart of hot water. The solution may be put on the udder by means of a paint brush or a swab made by tying cloth to a stick.

2. Another method is administering a dose of the saturated iron solution to each pig at least once a week until the pigs are not less than 4 and preferably 6 weeks old. The solution can readily be given with a spoon. The dose should be one-third of a teaspoonful for pigs under a week of age, this being increased to 1 teaspoonful by the time the pigs are 3 to 4 weeks old.

3. A third method is to put in the pen at frequent intervals fresh sod or soil. The pigs will usually root about this and nibble at it, thus getting traces of the necessary minerals. This method does not always prevent the trouble, however, for the pigs sometimes do not eat sufficient of the sod or soil. Care should be taken to get the sod or soil from a spot where swine have not grazed for more than a year, to make sure that it does not carry the eggs of round worms or other parasites. Extremely sandy soil that is very low in iron should not be used. Putting sod or soil in the pen tends to prevent anemia more than giving the pigs access to a good concentrate mixture to which an iron salt has been added.

The investigations on this problem have proved that anemia cannot be prevented by any method of feeding or caring for the sows, because it is impossible to increase the amount of iron in milk by any known method. If an iron salt is added to the concentrate mixture fed the sows, the pigs may eat a little of this feed, or they may, pig fashion, eat some of the iron-rich feces. However, such a method often does not prevent anemia in the pigs.

It was formerly thought anemia was prevented by exercising the pigs; for example, by letting them play in the alley of the hog barn. When this helps, it is due, not to the exercise itself, but to particles of feed or other matter that the pigs eat in their characteristic curiosity. Exposure to sunlight or ultraviolet light has no effect in preventing anemia.

1294. Iron and copper for other swine.—After the suckling period pigs generally get sufficient iron and copper in their usual rations and do not show symptoms of anemia. Therefore it is not necessary to supply any additional source of these minerals, except perhaps in the few sections where there is an unusual deficiency of iron in the soil. (**173**)

In some of the experiments in which growing or fattening pigs have been supplied with an iron salt in addition to a good ration there has apparently been a slight benefit from the iron supplement, but in other trials there has been no such effect.[37] It therefore seems doubtful whether such an addition will generally be profitable.

1295. Other minerals; simple vs. complex mineral mixtures.— Whenever swine are fed a ration that is definitely lacking in one or more of the essential mineral nutrients which have been discussed, the best way of correcting the deficiency is to allow them access to a mineral mixture that supplies the specific minerals that are lacking. The formulas for various simple mineral mixtures which are well suited for swine are given in Chapter VI. (**181**)

If calcium is the only mineral that is lacking, there is no need of including in the mineral mixture bone meal or other supplements supplying phosphorus in addition to calcium. These are much more expensive than the calcium supplements, such as ground limestone, ground oyster shell, etc. Merely such a mixture as ground limestone and salt will be satisfactory.

On the other hand, when there is a lack of both calcium and phosphorus, then a mineral mixture should obviously be used that supplies both of these nutrients. Whether to add potassium iodide or another source of iodine to the mineral mixture will depend on whether or not there is a definite lack of iodine in the feed and water in the particular locality. Adding iron oxide or another iron supplement to a mineral mixture is not generally of any decided benefit, and perhaps not advantageous under most conditions.

The excellent results that have been secured in experiment station tests and on farms when mineral supplements have been used that supply only these mineral constituents show definitely that there is no need of using more complex mineral mixtures. As is stated in greater detail in Chapter VI, the author therefore recommends the use of simple mineral mixtures, when they are advantageous, instead of complex mineral mixtures, containing such additional ingredients as sulfur, charcoal, coal, sodium carbonate, Glauber's salts, Epsom salts, etc.[38] (**182, 669-670**)

The results of trials in which dried kelp has been added to rations for pigs or for brood sows indicate that there is little or no benefit from its use, and that such an addition is not generally economical.[39]

1296. Vitamin requirements.—Vitamin A and vitamin D are of great importance in swine feeding, as is shown in the following paragraphs. The other vitamins are apparently provided in sufficient amounts by all usual swine rations, or are not required by swine.

Swine that are on good pasture have their vitamin A and D requirements amply met through the high vitamin A value (carotene content) of the green forage and the anti-rachitic effect of sunlight. In the case of swine not on pasture, there may be a serious lack of vitamin A or vitamin D unless well-cured legume hay or some other feed or supplement rich in these vitamins is included in the ration.

1297. Vitamin A and vitamin D.—The symptoms of rickets and other bone diseases produced by a lack of vitamin D or a deficiency of calcium or phosphorus have been described fully in Chapter VI.[40] (**163-164**) The most characteristic symptom of rickets in pigs is stiffness of the legs, especially of the hind legs. In severe case, the hind legs are often paralyzed, because of which condition the disease is sometimes called "posterior paralysis."

For a detailed discussion of the effects of vitamin A deficiency, the reader is likewise referred to Chapter VI.[41] (**186**) Sometimes vitamin A deficiency in swine may be confused with rickets, for both produce difficulty in walking, including stiffness. In severe cases of both diseases pigs may become paralyzed so that they cannot rise to their feet. In vitamin A deficiency the condition is brought about by degeneration of the nervous system, and the result is a failure to control the legs, instead of inability to move them. In walking, the pigs have a peculiar jerky gait, in which the rear legs are thrown out to the side. One of the first symptoms of vitamin A deficiency is often marked restlessness. Later, the pigs may have severe spasms and also show characteristic impairment of vision.

If pigs are fed a ration that is excellent, except for a lack of vitamin A, they may make excellent gains for several weeks, and then die from pneumonia, brought on by a lack of the vitamin. Brood sows fed rations seriously deficient in vitamin A may fail to come in heat or may not conceive when bred, and if they do become pregnant, the pigs are apt to be born dead or very weak.

Of all the seeds and their by-products that are commonly used for swine feeding, yellow corn is the only one that furnishes any significant amount of vitamin A. Likewise the vitamin is deficient in tankage, meat scraps, and skimmilk and other dairy by-products that contain only a trace of butter fat. Fish meal that has been dried at a low temperature may supply some vitamin A and also vitamin D, but the vitamin content is highly variable, depending on the raw material used and the process of manufacture. It is therefore often not safe to rely on fish meal as a source of these vitamins.

It is evident from the foregoing that when swine not on pasture are fed grain and other concentrates alone, their rations are apt to be seriously deficient in vitamin A, unless the grain is yellow corn. This deficiency can readily be prevented by including well-cured legume hay in the ration in the manner stated later in this discussion.

None of the grains or the by-product concentrates of plant origin supply appreciable amounts of vitamin D, nor do tankage, meat scraps, skimmilk, buttermilk, or whey. Fish meal may provide vitamin D, but cannot be relied on as a source of the vitamin, unless one is certain of the method of manufacture and of the kind of raw material used. These statements show that practically all common concentrates used for swine feeding are deficient in vitamin D.

Exposure to plenty of direct sunlight in summer will protect pigs against a lack of vitamin D, even when they are not on pasture. On the other hand, during winter in the northern states, swine, especially young pigs, are apt to suffer seriously from a lack of vitamin D, unless care is taken to include a source of it in the ration. As has been explained in Chapter VI, winter sunlight has far less anti-rachitic effect than summer sunlight, and also in many sections of the country there is much cloudy weather during winter. (**191**)

Pigs that are making very rapid growth require more liberal amounts of vitamin A and vitamin D than those that are so fed that their gains are slow. For example, an abundant supply of nothing but white corn and skimmilk is especially apt to cause disaster because of a lack of these vitamins. (**1329**) This is because the ration is excellent, except for the vitamin deficiency, and it therefore produces rapid gains until the pigs begin to suffer from the lack of vitamins. If a ration is well supplied with calcium and phosphorus, somewhat less vitamin D is needed for normal bone development than when the supply of one or both of these minerals is scanty.

PIGS NOT ON PASTURE NEED SOURCE OF VITAMINS A AND D

Tankage and grain (even yellow corn) is not an efficient ration for young pigs not on pasture. These pigs, weighing 65 lbs. at the start, gained 1.04 lbs. per head daily on yellow corn and tankage. (From Wisconsin Station.)

TRIO MIXTURE PROVIDES VITAMINS A AND D

These pigs, which were of the same age as those above, were fed corn and the trio or Wisconsin supplemental mixture (tankage, linseed meal, and alfalfa hay). They were more thrifty, gained 1.36 lbs. per head daily, and made cheaper gains than the first lot.

WHITE CORN AND TANKAGE WERE INEFFICIENT IN DRY LOT

These pigs were fed corn and tankage in dry lot, without pasture, from a weight of 65 lbs. Due to the lack of vitamins, they gained only 0.77 lb. a head daily. Compare them with the pigs of the same age in the two previous lots.

GOOD PASTURE PROVIDES VITAMINS, PROTEIN, AND MINERALS

These young pigs and their mothers, which are on good alfalfa pasture, will be amply provided with vitamin A and calcium. The alfalfa forage will also aid in furnishing protein to balance the ration. The sunlight will supply vitamin D.

SWINE NOT ON PASTURE SHOULD HAVE LEGUME HAY

With the few exceptions pointed out in this chapter, all swine not on pasture should be supplied with well-cured legume hay to protect them against a lack of vitamin A or vitamin D. These sows are provided with good alfalfa hay in the rack. (From J. P. Willman, New York, Cornell, Station.)

1298. Protecting swine against lack of vitamins A and D.—Fortunately, legume hay cured with ordinary exposure to sunlight is so rich in vitamin D that only a small amount of it will protect swine against a deficiency. Still more fortunately, the legume hay will also provide an ample supply of vitamin A in rations that would otherwise be deficient in this vitamin.[42]

To make sure that brood sows have plenty of vitamin D as well as sufficient vitamin A, their rations during the winter when they are not on pasture should include at least 10 to 15 per cent of well-cured legume hay. The methods of feeding legume hay to sows are discussed in Chapter XXXVII. (**1408**)

For pigs not on pasture about 4 to 5 per cent of excellent-quality legume hay should be included in the ration, wherever it is possible to do so, in order to supply the necessary amounts of vitamins A and D. Numerous experiments have shown that disaster is apt to result if young pigs having no green pasture are fed throughout the winter on grain with protein supplements lacking these vitamins.[43]

In experiments in which young pigs have been fed such rations for considerable periods of time they have generally failed to thrive and eventually many have become stiff or paralyzed from rickets or they have suffered severely from the deficiency of vitamin A. If the grain in such rations is yellow corn, there will be probably a fair supply of vitamin A, but there will still be a decided benefit from adding legume hay to the ration, especially for pigs weighing less than 100 lbs. at the start. This is commonly the case even when pigs during the winter are exposed to considerable direct sunlight in outside exercise lots to which they have access.

When pigs have been previously grown to a weight of 100 lbs. or more on good pasture, they may have a sufficient store of vitamins A and D in their bodies to enable them to make satisfactory gains up to the usual market weights on a vitamin-deficient ration. However, it is best to include legume hay in the ration, even for such pigs that are not on pasture, as a cheap insurance against vitamin deficiencies.

If the pigs follow cattle in the barnyard and work over the manure, they may secure a limited amount of these vitamins in this manner. Also, kitchen garbage may help provide a supply. For these reasons, pigs may not suffer from vitamin deficiencies under farm conditions when the feeds that they are regularly given would produce disaster if fed under controlled, experimental conditions.

When choice-quality alfalfa hay is supplied in a rack so pigs can help themselves to it, they will usually (but not always) eat sufficient to provide the necessary amounts of vitamins. If the hay is not of first-class quality, the pigs may not eat enough of it to protect them against vitamin deficiencies. Also, they are much less apt to eat a sufficient amount of red clover hay, sweet clover hay, soybean hay, or cowpea hay from a rack than of alfalfa hay.

The safest plan in feeding pigs not on pasture is therefore to include a definite amount of legume hay in the ration. This can conveniently be done by using such a protein supplemental mixture as the trio mixture, which contains 25 per cent of ground or chopped legume hay of good quality. When a mixture of ground grain and other concentrates is fed, 5 lbs. of chopped or ground legume hay can be included in each 100 lbs. of the entire mixture. As is shown in the next chapter, almost any kind of well-cured legume hay is satisfactory for these purposes. (**1401**)

When it is impossible to feed young pigs during the winter either legume hay or fish meal that contains vitamins A and D, it is wise to include 0.125 to 0.25 per cent of cod-liver oil concentrate or 0.50 to 1.00 per cent of cod-liver oil in the ration, especially for pigs that are fed little or no yellow corn.[44] On the other hand, if legume hay is supplied as has been here advised, there will probably be no benefit from the use of cod-liver oil or a cod-liver oil concentrate.[45]

1299. Vitamin B complex; yeast; vitamin C.—There is evidently no deficiency of the vitamin B complex (including vitamins B and G) in ordinary swine rations. (**195-197**) In Arkansas experiments there was not even any benefit from adding rice polish, which is rich in vitamin B, to a ration very low in these vitamins.[46]

In numerous experiments the effect has been tested of adding yeast (which is rich in vitamins B and G) to rations for pigs.[47] In some of the trials the yeast has been added to a dry concentrate mixture and in others the yeast has been added to the moistened feed several hours before it was fed, and fermentation allowed to take place. No matter what method of yeast feeding has been used, the addition of yeast to ordinary rations has not been profitable. Generally the rate of gain has not been improved and the cost of the gains has been increased. (**198**)

Swine apparently do not require vitamin C, or else they can synthesize the vitamin in their bodies. (**199**) In a North Dakota test sprouting barley (which causes the development of vitamin C in the grain) did not increase its value for pigs.[48]

1300. Water.—Swine, like all other classes of stock, should always be supplied with plenty of water. The amount of water consumed by pigs ranges from about 12 lbs. daily per 100 lbs. of animal at weaning time down to 4 lbs. or less per 100 lbs. live weight during the fattening period.[49]

In an Iowa test yearling brood sows drank 7.5 lbs. of water per head daily during the winter previous to farrowing.[50] Sows suckling litters require somewhat more water.

Water should commonly be provided for swine twice a day in a trough, or an automatic waterer should be used. If swine get an abundance of water in such watery feeds as dairy by-products or slop, there may be no need of furnishing water separately. In very cold winter weather, swine may not drink enough water for the best results unless it is warmed sufficiently to keep it from freezing soon after it is put in a trough.

Watering pigs during the summer by means of an automatic waterer did not produce any more rapid or economical gains in Iowa and Minnesota tests than providing plenty of water in a trough two or three times a day.[51] However, when pigs are watered by hand, they are too often not given all the water they will drink.

1301. Stock foods or tonics; vitamin and mineral preparations.— Various stock foods or stock tonics have been tested in several experiments to find whether there was any benefit from feeding such preparations to swine, when used according to the directions supplied by the manufacturers.[52] In practically all cases these products have proved uneconomical. Pigs fed well-balanced rations without any stock food or tonic have made just as rapid or even more rapid gains than those fed such a product. Still more important is the fact that the cost of the gains has been increased by the feeding of the stock food or tonic. (**669**)

Before paying out money for highly advertised mineral mixtures or vitamin preparations, the wise stockman will first secure unprejudiced advice from the experiment station in his state or from his county agricultural agent. (**670**)

III. General Problems in Pork Production

1302. Prices of hogs during the year.—In deciding upon the best plan of pork production to follow, one should consider the average prices of hogs on his own market for various months in the year. By having pigs ready for market at the time when the price is usually highest, the profit can commonly be increased decidedly.

The number of pigs farrowed in the spring in this country is much greater than of those born in the fall, and the bulk of these spring-farrowed pigs reach the market from late October to February. During this period the supply of hogs on the central markets is therefore the heaviest, and as a result the price is considerably lower than during the rest of the year. This is shown in the following table, which gives the average number of hogs received each month at all public stockyards in the United States for the 20-year period, 1915-1934, and the average monthly price per hundredweight of hogs on the Chicago market for the same period.[53]

*Monthly receipts of hogs and average Chicago price**

	Monthly receipts at public stockyards Million head	Av. price per cwt. at Chicago Dollars		Monthly receipts at public stockyards Million head	Av. price per cwt. at Chicago Dollars
January	4,839,000	9.32	July	2,911,000	10.31
February	3,923,000	9.68	August	2,610,000	10.37
March	3,605,000	10.25	September	2,611,000	10.51
April	3,250,000	10.23	October	3,329,000	9.81
May	3,462,000	10.15	November	3,932,000	9.22
June	3,347,000	10.05	December	4,465,000	8.92

*Compiled from reports of packer and shipper purchases, which do not include pigs, boars, stags, extremely rough sows, or cripples.

The table shows that the highest average prices during the year occur in August and September, when the receipts of hogs at the central markets are lowest. In October the average price begins to drop sharply as the spring-pig crop then starts to come on the market in large quantity. The average price reaches the lowest levels from November to January, when the marketings are heaviest. The price then begins to recover, and the price is uniformly good during the spring months. A slight drop occurs in June, due to the large number of sows then sold after they have weaned their spring litters.

It is evident from these data that the farmer who has facilities for taking proper care of early spring litters can usually secure the highest price in the year by having them ready for market before October. This means, however, that the pigs must be liberally fed on efficient rations and must have the best of care, or they will not reach a market weight of 200 lbs. or more by that time. Instead, they will get to market in November or December, when prices are low.

The farmer who raises early spring litters for marketing before the slump in price occurs in the fall, usually finds it most profitable to breed as many sows as possible for fall litters, as well. These should be far-rowed before October first, and if properly fed and cared for, they will be ready for market from April to May, when prices are again high.

The various systems of pork production are discussed in detail in Chapter XXXVII.

1303. Limited-feeding vs. full-feeding of pigs.—One of the most important questions that every hog raiser must decide is how much grain he will feed his growing, fattening pigs. He knows that the larger the amount of grain or other concentrates he feeds, the faster they will gain, no matter whether in dry lot or on pasture, but he wonders whether or not he will make more profit if he restricts the amount of concentrates.

It has been shown previously that animals fed liberal rations tend to digest and utilize their feed with slightly less efficiency than those that receive limited rations. (**113**) However, if a growing and fattening animal, such as a pig, is fed a limited ration, a longer period will be required before it reaches the desired market weight and the proper degree of fatness. Other factors being the same, this will increase the amount of feed required for mere body maintenance during the growing and fattening period, and therefore reduce the proportion of feed available for producing gain in weight.

These two factors therefore tend to have an opposite effect on the relative amounts of feed required per 100 lbs. gain by pigs that are full-fed and by those that are fed limited rations. The only way to determine which factor is of more importance is by experiments in which pigs are full-fed in direct comparison with others that receive limited amounts of the same feeds. It is important that such tests be continued until the limited-fed pigs have reached market weights, which has not been done in some of the experiments on this problem.

1304. Limited-feeding vs. full-feeding in dry lot.—There will first be considered the full-feeding versus the limited-feeding of pigs that are not on pasture. Since all spring pigs should be on good pasture during the growing season, this phase of the problem is limited primarily to fall pigs being fed during winter in the northern states.

When the feed of pigs in dry lot is restricted very much, they commonly make slow gains and require a large amount of feed per 100 lbs. gain. This is because they then need most of their feed for maintaining their bodies. For example, in 2 New York tests pigs fed only a half ration from an average weight of 62 lbs. to market weights of 200 or 225 lbs. gained only 0.65 lb. per head daily and required 428 lbs. of feed per 100 lbs. gain.[54] Others full-fed the same well-balanced mixture gained 1.39 lbs. a day (over twice as much) and required only 391 lbs. of feed per 100 lbs. gain. The pigs receiving the half ration took 224 days to reach market weights. The labor was therefore practically doubled by the limited feeding, and the miscellaneous expenses were also increased.

In a Michigan trial pigs self-fed a well-balanced mixture of ground corn, tankage, and ground alfalfa hay gained 1.13 lbs. from a weight of 56 lbs. to market weight.[55] Others fed only two-thirds as much of the same mixture gained but 0.66 lb. per head daily and required 50 lbs. more feed per 100 lbs. gain, when carried to the same market weight. Still poorer results were secured with pigs fed less than half of a normal ration. In Ohio experiments the results were also unfavorable to such scanty feeding of pigs in dry lot.[56] On the other hand, in tests by the United States Department of Agriculture, though pigs fed a half-ration made very slow gains, they required less feed per 100 lbs. gain than others fed liberally.[57]

If the feed of pigs is but slightly restricted and they are fed about three-fourths of a full ration until ready for market, they may require a trifle less feed per 100 lbs. gain than when full-fed. However, their gains will be considerably slower, and therefore any saving in feed will generally be more than offset by the greater expense for labor and miscellaneous charges. In the New York trials pigs fed about a three-fourths ration gained only 1.02 lbs. per day in comparison with 1.39 lbs. for others that were full-fed. The limited-fed pigs required 12 lbs. less feed per 100 lbs. gain, but this was more than offset by the fact that it required an average of 35 days longer to get them to market weights.

In a similar Michigan trial pigs fed 3.5 lbs. of feed daily per 100 lbs. live weight gained 1.08 lbs. a day, while self-fed pigs gained 1.47 lbs. a day.[55] There was a saving of 6 lbs. feed per 100 lbs. gain by limited feeding, but it took 40 days longer for the limited-fed pigs to reach the same market weight. There was also a slight saving of feed in Oregon trials, when pigs were fed a three-fourths ration instead of a full ration.[58] In the tests by the United States Department of Agriculture there was a somewhat greater saving in feed when pigs were fed a ration that was slightly limited.[57]

When pigs receive a limited amount of a well-balanced ration up to market weights, there will be a tendency for their carcasses to be less fat and to contain a larger proportion of lean meat than in the case of full-fed pigs. However, this advantage is offset by the fact that the dressing percentage is slightly less for the limited-fed pigs, and also there is more tendency for the fat of the carcass to be undesirably soft.

1305. Limited-feeding followed by full-feeding.—Those who favor the limited-feeding of pigs commonly advocate that the pigs should get a limited amount of concentrates until they reach a weight of 100 to 150 lbs., and that they should then be full-fed until they are ready for market. In 2 Minnesota trials 64-lb. pigs were fed a half ration for 90 days, and then full-fed to a weight of 200 lbs., in comparison with others that were full-fed throughout the entire period.[59] The full-fed pigs gained 1.33 lbs. a day and required 404 lbs. of feed per 100 lbs. gain, while those whose feed was limited at first gained only 0.91 lb. daily for the entire period and required 480 lbs. of feed per 100 lbs. gain. This method of severely limiting the feed at first and then full-feeding during the finishing period was also uneconomical in the Michigan and New York experiments previously mentioned, and also in a South Dakota test.[60]

Ohio tests indicate that when one wishes to limit the amount of grain fed to pigs in dry lot, it is a good plan to supply them with plenty of well-cured legume hay in a rack, so they can get their fill of some feed, even hay.[61]

1306. Conclusions concerning limited-feeding in dry lot.—Considering all the data, it is recommended that under usual conditions fall pigs in dry lot and other pigs not on pasture be full-fed from weaning time and hurried to market as soon as possible. Any saving in the amount of feed required per 100 lbs. gain that can be made by slightly limiting the feed will usually be too small to offset the additional labor required on account of the slower gains, and also the increase in overhead expenses.

If one is raising fall pigs to follow fattening cattle, then it may be desirable to limit their feed slightly. Also, some farmers feed fall pigs a limited amount of concentrates during the winter, and then finish them on pasture in the spring. Ohio tests indicate that this is doubtful economy, unless grain is very high in price in comparison with the expense for pasture.[61] Too often such fall pigs are fed so little during the winter that their gains are exceedingly expensive and they may even become unthrifty because of stingy feeding.

1307. Limited-feeding vs. full-feeding on pasture.—Whether it will be more profitable to full-feed pigs on good pasture or to give them only a limited amount of grain and other concentrates will depend on several factors. Full-feeding is generally much more profitable, if the pigs are farrowed early enough in the spring so they can be fattened for marketing early in the fall, before the usual slump in price occurs. (**1302**)

In the case of late spring pigs, the net returns may be greater if only enough concentrates are fed to keep them growing well during the summer and if the pigs are then fattened on the new corn crop in the fall and early winter for marketing in January or February, after the price recovers somewhat. Pigs to be used in the fall for hogging-down corn or for following fattening cattle should also be fed a limited amount of grain in the summer, so they will be in thrifty feeder condition in the fall.

Many trials have been conducted to compare full-feeding of pigs on pasture throughout the season with the plan in which the pigs are fed only a limited amount of grain during the pasture season, and then fattened on a full feed of grain and other concentrates in the fall. The following table summarizes the results of 28 such experiments in each of which one lot of pigs averaging 56 lbs. in weight has been full-fed (usually self-fed) on good pasture, while another lot has been fed a limited amount of concentrates until fall and then full-fed until they reached approximately the same weight as the first lot.[62] In most of the trials the ration was shelled corn and tankage, and in the others it was corn supplemented by a combination of tankage and either linseed meal or wheat middlings.

The pigs full-fed from the start gained 1.44 lbs. a day and reached an average market weight of 214 lbs. in 110 days. It took the pigs that at first received a limited allowance of corn 141 days to reach the same weight. A fact that will be surprising to many is that the limited-feeding made no appreciable saving in the amount of concentrates required

Limiting the concentrates during the summer for pigs on good pasture

Average ration	Daily gain Lbs.	Time to reach market weight Days	Concentrates for 100 lbs. gain	
			Corn Lbs.	Supplement Lbs.
Lot I, full-fed entire time				
Corn, 4.9 lbs. Supplement, 0.43 lb....... 1.44		110	339	30
Lot II, limited ration in summer				
Corn, 3.9 lbs. Supplement, 0.33 lb....... 1.12		141	338	27

per 100 lbs. gain. Limited-fed pigs eat considerably more pasturage than those that are full-fed. The total feed cost per 100 lbs. gain in these trials was therefore fully as high for the limited-fed pigs as for those that were full-fed. These data show clearly that under conditions in the corn belt it will commonly be most profitable to full-feed early spring pigs on pasture, so that they can be sent to market before the rush begins and the price declines severely.

This is also proved by a study of the net returns from early-spring litters on 43 Indiana farms where the pigs were fed limited amounts of grain during the first 3 months after weaning and on 24 farms where the full-feeding method was used.[63] The full-fed pigs were ready for market on September 27, on the average, and sold for $10.12 per hundredweight. The limited-fed pigs were not marketed until December 10, and brought only $9.15 per hundredweight. For each 100 lbs. gain the full-fed pigs required only 6.1 bushels corn and 8.2 lbs. tankage, while the limited-fed pigs needed 8.7 bushels corn and 6.6 lbs. tankage. The death loss after weaning was also in favor of the full-fed pigs, being only 2.5 per cent, in comparison with 7.5 per cent for the other pigs.

The total cost of 100 lbs. gain, including not only feed cost but also all other expenses, was only $6.32 for the full-fed pigs, while it was $7.51 for those fed a limited ration at first. The profit was therefore much greater from full-feeding, for the average cost of 100 lbs. gain was $1.19 less and the average selling price per hundredweight $0.97 greater.

If for any reason it seems desirable to limit the feed of pigs on pasture, it will generally be advisable to finish them on a liberal amount of grain, rather than to continue the scanty feeding until they are finally ready for market.[64]

In the alfalfa districts of the West it is often most profitable to limit the allowance of grain for pigs during the summer, for pasture is very cheap in comparison with grain.[65] This method is commonly used in the sections that specialize in the production of feeder pigs for shipment to the corn belt. Even when the pasture is excellent, it is necessary to feed 1.0 to 1.5 lbs. of grain per head daily to growing pigs, in order to keep them growing thriftily and making the desired gain in weight. Whether or not to feed a protein supplement to pigs receiving a limited amount of grain on first-class pasture has been discussed earlier in this chapter. (**1286**)

1308. Self-feeding.—Numerous experiments have proved that the feeding of fattening pigs by means of a self-feeder is an efficient and economical method of pork production. Pigs that are self-fed suitable rations not only make slightly more rapid gains than those that are hand-fed two or three times a day, but also they usually require slightly

less feed per 100 lbs. gain.   In addition to these advantages, considerable labor is saved.

The self-feeding method gives excellent results with growing-fat-
tening pigs, with well-grown shotes, and with old sows that are being
fattened. Self-feeding is also a good method of feeding brood sows and
their litters, as is pointed out in Chapter XXXVII.

The self-feeder should not be used when rapid gains are not desired,
as when one wishes to force pigs to make the maximum use of pasturage
by limiting the grain allowance. Many swine breeders prefer not to
use a self-feeder for pigs that are being raised for the breeding herd,
as they fear that they will then get too fat. However, pigs of big or
intermediate type can be self-fed on suitable rations up to weights of
175 to 225 lbs. without injuring their usefulness in the breeding herd.

The use of the self-feeder for pregnant sows is discussed in Chapter
XXXVII. (1417) It is there shown that sows will get too fat when
self-fed, unless considerable bulky feed is included in the mixture. Even
then, care is often needed to keep the feeds so proportioned that the
sows do not gain too much or too little. Therefore, hand-feeding pregnant sows is a much more common practice than self-feeding them.

In self-feeding swine, grain and protein-rich supplements may be
fed, free choice, in separate compartments of the self-feeder, or the pigs
may be self-fed a properly balanced mixture of grain and protein-rich
supplements. The merits of these two methods have been discussed previously. (1284)

1309. Self-feeding vs. hand-feeding fattening pigs.—The excellent
results secured when the self-feeder is used for fattening pigs are shown
in the following table. This summarizes the results of 24 experiments
in each of which one lot of pigs, not on pasture, was self-fed, free-choice,
on corn and tankage, or else corn, tankage and either wheat middlings
or alfalfa, each feed being supplied in a separate compartment of the
self-feeder.[66] Another lot in each trial was hand-fed a well-balanced
ration of the same feeds, being given all they would clean up twice a
day. In these trials a total of 480 pigs, averaging 95 lbs. in weight at
the start, were fed for an average of 88 days.

Self-feeding vs. hand-feeding pigs in dry lot

Average ration	Daily gain Lbs.	Corn Lbs.	Supplement Lbs.	Total Lbs.
Lot I, self-fed Corn, 5.6 lbs. Supplement, 0.94 lb.	1.59	355	59	414
Lot II, hand-fed Corn, 5.1 lbs. Supplement, 0.93 lb.	1.42	359	66	425

It will be noted, first of all, that the self-fed pigs ate 0.6 lb. more
corn per head daily than those which were hand-fed twice daily all they
would clean up. This is the usual result and is due to the fact that
self-fed pigs help themselves many times a day and even during the
night, thus being "full-fed" at all times. Naturally they gained a trifle
more rapidly than those which were hand-fed. Most important of all,
is the fact that 11 lbs. less concentrates were required for 100 lbs. gain
by the self-fed pigs This is not a large saving in itself, but to it are

added the advantages of the more rapid gains and the saving of labor by self-feeding. It will be noted furthermore that these self-fed pigs in dry lot ate less protein-rich supplement than the hand-fed pigs were given.

Self-feeding is also an economical method of feeding pigs on pasture. This is shown by the following table, which summarizes 9 trials in each of which one lot of spring pigs has been self-fed corn and tankage, free choice, on good pasture, while another lot has been hand-fed the same feeds.[67] In these trials a total of 170 pigs, averaging 58 lbs. in weight at the start, were fed for 112 days on the average.

Self-feeding vs. hand-feeding pigs on pasture

Average ration	Daily gain Lbs.	Concentrates for 100 lbs. gain		
		Corn Lbs.	Tankage Lbs.	Total Lbs.
Lot I, self-fed				
Corn, 4.6 lbs. Tankage, 0.38 lb.......... 1.32		340	27	367
Lot II, hand-fed				
Corn, 4.2 lbs. Tankage, 0.28 lb.......... 1.20		341	23	364

Just as in the trials in dry lot, the self-fed pigs ate more corn than those which were hand-fed, and made somewhat more rapid gains. On the average the self-fed pigs ate 4 lbs. more tankage per 100 lbs. gain, but took 1 lb. less corn. This slight difference of 3 lbs. total feed per 100 lbs. gain in favor of the hand-fed pigs would, however, ordinarily be more than offset by the saving in labor through self-feeding and by the greater rapidity of the gains.

It should be pointed out that in all of these trials the hand-fed pigs were under the supervision of an expert feeder   Under average conditions there would be a greater advantage in favor of self-feeding.

1310. Free-choice method of self-feeding.—In the free-choice method of self-feeding, grain is fed in one compartment and the protein supplement or supplemental mixture is fed in another compartment, the pigs being allowed to eat as much as they wish of each. Occasionally more than one protein supplement is fed, each in a separate compartment of the feeder.

It has been pointed out in the discussion previously given in this chapter of the free-choice method of feeding protein supplements that it gives very satisfactory results when corn or other grain low in protein is fed with tankage, meat scraps, or fish meal as the only supplement. (**1284**) The results are also excellent when the grain is fed with certain supplemental mixtures, such as the trio mixture or modifications of it. With such combinations of feeds, pigs show a surprising ability to balance their rations. On the other hand, when pigs are self-fed, free-choice, on certain other combinations of feeds, they may eat so much protein supplement that their gains are unduly expensive. Also, when a protein supplement is used that is not very palatable, they may fail to eat a sufficient amount of it to balance the ration adequately, and therefore may make poor gains.

In the following chapter the advisability of using the free-choice plan of self-feeding is discussed under the various feeds, where data are available.

1311. Grinding grain for swine.—Whether or not it will pay to grind any particular grain for swine will depend on the completeness with which they chew it when unground. In the discussion of the various grains in the next chapter, information is given as to whether or not it pays to grind each grain for swine.

In general, it does not pay to grind corn for pigs up to the usual market weights, or for brood sows. Instead, ear corn or shelled corn is commonly fed. There is generally enough saving through grinding barley, oats, or millet to make such preparation decidedly profitable. If wheat and the grain sorghums are fed in self-feeders, pigs usually chew the grain with sufficient thoroughness so that grinding does not pay. On the other hand, when these grains are hand-fed, there is a considerably greater saving through grinding.

1312. Soaking grain; feeding slop.—If corn becomes very hard in the spring or summer, it may pay to soak it before feeding, though the increase in value is not usually very marked. (**1330**) Also, when barley or oats cannot be conveniently ground or rolled, it may pay to soak the grain, but soaking is a rather poor substitute for grinding. (**1333, 1334**) When grain is soaked for pigs, it should be soaked for only about 12 hours, and it should not be allowed to sour or ferment. It does not generally pay to soak ground grain or a mixture of concentrates for swine.[68] (**103**)

Some years ago it was a common practice to feed concentrate mixtures to swine in the form of slop or swill. Experiments have shown, however, that with the following exceptions this method offers no advantage over dry-feeding, or at least insufficient advantage to warrant the additional labor.[69]

Slop-feeding may be advisable when a finely-ground concentrate mixture is fed outdoors in a windy location, merely to prevent feed from being blown from the trough and wasted. Also, in very cold weather it may be advisable to feed a warm slop, so the hogs will get enough water. If ground wheat tends to form a sticky mass when swine are chewing it, this may be obviated by feeding the wheat in a fairly thin slop. However, if the wheat is not ground too finely, there is usually no difficulty of this kind.

1313. Cooking feed.—Early agricultural writers strongly advocated cooking feed for swine, but numerous experiments many years ago proved conclusively that, instead of a gain from cooking, there is in nearly every case a loss. In 26 trials in which pigs were fed either cooked or uncooked grain (corn, barley, rye, peas, or wheat shorts, fed separately or in combination), 89.4 lbs. of uncooked grain were as valuable, on the average, as 100 lbs. of the same grain when cooked.[70] There was thus a loss of over 10 per cent by cooking. A few feeds, such as potatoes, soybeans, field beans, and velvet beans, are improved by cooking.

1314. Feeding floors.—If ear corn is fed on the ground, there may be considerable wastage in muddy weather, for the pigs will be unable to get all the grain. Thus, in a Kentucky test during the fall the feed cost of 100 lbs. gain was $10.80 when ear corn was fed in the mud, and only $9.31 when it was fed on a platform.[71] Therefore, it pays well to have feeding platforms in hog lots where feeding is done during the rainy season. This not only saves feed, but also is much more sanitary and reduces trouble from parasites and infections.

When ear corn is fed during the summer on "clean" pasture lots that are free from infestation with parasites, there may be no appreciable advantage in the use of feeding platforms.[72] It is advisable, however, to place self-feeders on platforms in the pasture or outside lot, so that the pigs may salvage any feed that may be nosed out of the self-feeder.

1315. Shelter.—Even in the northern states, where the winters are cold, inexpensive shelter is all that is necessary for swine. The essentials for healthful winter shelter are freedom from dampness, good ventilation without drafts on the animals, sunlight, reasonable warmth, and a moderate amount of dry bedding. The quarters should be located on well-drained ground and should be so arranged that they may be easily and thoroughly cleaned and disinfected.

Swine may be housed in a central hog house with a number of pens or in small portable houses, or colony houses. Many use a combination of the two systems, for in the northern states the central house is well suited for winter shelter and early spring farrowing, while the portable houses are particularly useful for housing pigs on pasture. Portable houses may also be used for winter shelter, and will be fairly warm if corn stalks, horse manure, or other litter is banked against the sides of the houses. A strong sack may be hung in the doorway to keep out the cold and yet allow the hogs to go back and forth at will.

Even in the North, brood sows wintered in cheap portable houses do not require much more feed than those housed in a central house, especially if the houses are well protected. In trials during 4 winters at the Wisconsin Station, pregnant gilts were wintered in shed-roof colony houses made of a single thickness of boards.[73] The opening through which the sows entered was left open at all times so they could come and go at will, and no litter was banked up against the houses to make them warmer. At farrowing time the sows were removed to farrowing pens in the central barn.

The feed cost of wintering these sows was 16 per cent higher than for sows kept in a central hog barn and allowed to run at will in an exercise paddock during the day. However, this greater feed cost was offset by the fact that 88 per cent of the pigs from the sows in the portable houses were vigorous, and only 74 per cent of the pigs from the sows wintered in the central house. This was probably due to the following reasons: The sows in the portable houses took more exercise; they were out in the sunlight a greater part of the time; and they had an opportunity to get a small amount of green grass from the paddocks in which the houses were located. All of these factors are important in enabling sows to produce thrifty litters.

For very young pigs there is much more advantage from warmer shelter. It is not, therefore, wise in the northern states to have sows farrow very early in the spring or in late winter, unless suitable quarters can be provided. For such litters a well-ventilated central hog house is best. However, many farmers raise early pigs successfully in well-protected portable houses, even in the northern part of the corn belt. In the coldest weather a lantern hung in the portable house will usually keep the temperature comfortable.

Fall pigs that get a good start before cold weather comes on will do well in portable houses during northern winters. For instance, in 3 Michigan trials fall pigs averaging 50 lbs. in weight at the start were housed during the winter in portable houses, while others were kept in a central hog house with access to an outside paved exercise lot.[74] The pigs in the portable house made fully as rapid gains as those in the central house and required no more feed per 100 lbs. gain.

Where the winters are more severe, a considerable saving in feed may be made by providing warmer shelter. Thus, at the Ottawa, Ontario, Station pigs weighing 70 lbs. at the start that were housed in portable houses during the winter required 44 per cent more feed than others in a well-built central house.[75] Brood sows in the portable houses required only 25 per cent more feed than those in the warmer quarters, showing that large animals can withstand severe cold better than small ones. The health of the animals was good under both conditions. In a Kansas test during a winter in which the temperature at 8 a. m. ranged from 31° F. to —12° F., large hogs in warm quarters required 25 per cent less feed than those in a yard protected only by a high board fence on the north.[76]

1316. Exercise.—For breeding swine and growing pigs ample exercise is of the utmost importance. Even for fattening pigs limited exercise is preferable to close confinement.

In addition to the benefits from the exercise itself, when swine are out-of-doors in outside paddocks a considerable part of the day, they are protected against a deficiency of vitamin D, through the anti-rachitic effect of direct sunlight. Also, swine exercising in outside pasture lots of ample size usually get some green feed, even during the winter. Though the amount of green forage they eat may be small, it is often of much value in keeping them thrifty. It is shown in Chapter XXXVII that this is especially important in the case of pregnant sows. (**1406**) Sows closely confined without access to green forage or access to the dirt may have unsatisfactory litters, even when fed rations that produce excellent results with sows that have ample exercise in pasture paddocks.

To induce brood sows to take plenty of exercise in winter, it is advisable to feed them at the end of the exercise paddock opposite from their sleeping quarters. Here there should be a rack filled with choice legume hay, as has been emphasized before. (**1298**) The sows will thus not only secure needed vitamins, calcium, and protein, but also they will be kept on their feet, getting considerable exercise, instead of lying in their pens most of the time.

1317. Types of swine.—The principal breeds of swine are of two distinct types—the lard type and the bacon type. In this country the leading breeds of the lard type are the Poland-China, Duroc-Jersey, Chester-White, Berkshire, and Hampshire breeds. The two leading breeds of the bacon type are the Large Yorkshire and the Tamworth breeds. In the United States there are but few swine of the bacon breeds, while bacon hogs are of especial importance in Canada, Great Britain, and Denmark.

In the effort to produce pigs that would fatten early and furnish a large amount of lard, the lard-type breeds had been developed to an undesirable extreme in these respects prior to 1908. These swine were rather small, weighing only 300 to 400 lbs. when mature and in breeding condition. They had bodies of only medium length, were short-legged, had small bones, and became very fat at weights of 200 to 225 lbs. When carried to heavier weights, their gains were very expensive. In the development of these characteristics the prolificacy had been seriously decreased, the sows tending to have too few pigs in their litters to make economical pork production possible.

To overcome these serious defects, swine breeders then developed the big-type strains of the lard breeds, and this development was likewise later carried to an extreme. About 1922 the popular hogs in the show rings were extremely rangy, long-bodied, long-legged, and late-maturing. At maturity such hogs weighed 700 to 1,000 lbs. They were so rangy in conformation and so slow-maturing that they did not become well fattened until they reached a weight of 275 lbs. or more. At lighter weights their carcasses were undesirably soft, and the bacon thin and flabby.

Most American consumers now show a decided preference for small, lean, firm and tender hams, loins, and shoulders. They wish bacon made from small, but firm and well-fattened bellies, and desire a minimum amount of lard and fat cuts. Recent investigations, especially those at the Illinois, Indiana, and Iowa Stations show that the intermediate type of pig most nearly meets these demands.[77]

To best meet the present demand for small cuts of pork, pigs should be marketed at not over 200 to 225 lbs. in weight. At this weight pigs that are rangy, or of decidedly big-type, are so immature that their carcasses tend to be soft, and the bacon is especially lacking in firmness and the desired degree of fatness. On the other hand, the old-fashioned type of "chuffy" or "very chuffy" lard pigs are apt to be too fat, even at this weight, and to have too small a proportion of lean meat. At a weight of 200 lbs. pigs of the intermediate type well meet the present demand, except that there is a tendency for the carcasses to be a trifle soft and for the bellies to lack slightly in the finish and firmness desired for the production of the best bacon.

In the experiments that have been conducted to compare the rate and economy of gain of the various types of lard pigs, the old-fashioned "chuffy" pigs have usually made smaller gains and required more feed per 100 lbs. gain than those of intermediate or rangy type.[78] The difference is especially marked when the "chuffy" pigs are carried much beyond 200 lbs. in weight. The difference in economy of gain is due chiefly to the fact that the lard-type pigs store a higher proportion of fat in their carcasses than do pigs of the intermediate type or of the rangy type.

There have been no appreciable differences in rate or economy of gain by pigs of the intermediate type and by those of the rangy or very rangy types, when carried to usual market weights. Since pigs of the intermediate type better meet present market demands than those which are more rangy, and since they make just as cheap gains, they are to be preferred decidedly for efficient modern pork production.

1318. Breed comparisons.—Tests have been conducted at several stations to find whether or not there is any difference in the economy of meat production by the various breeds of swine.[79] In these trials there have been no consistent and uniform differences in gains or economy of production, a breed which ranged high in some of the tests being surpassed by other breeds in the rest of the trials. On the whole, the bacon breeds made as economical gains as those of the lard type.

We may conclude that there is no best breed of swine so far as rate and economy of gains are concerned. There are far greater differences between individuals of the same breed than between the different breeds. One should select the breed which seems best adapted to his conditions and suits his fancy, and then be sure to secure and to maintain vigorous, well-bred animals of that breed.

In most comparisons that have been made of purebred or high-grade swine and of cross-breds between two pure breeds, the cross-bred pigs have produced a trifle more rapid and economical gains.[80] For this reason, many large-scale pork producers use a definite system of cross-breeding for the production of market hogs. Such cross-breds should not be retained for the breeding herd.

In modern domestic hogs the length of the intestines is apparently longer, in proportion to body length, than in wild hogs. This indicates that the improved hog can digest his food more thoroughly than his ancestors, and also that he can eat a larger quantity of food for his size. Cuvier reported many years ago that the total length of the intestines of the wild boar was 9 times the body length; in the domestic boar, 13.5 times; and in the Siam boar 16 times the body length.[81] Henry found the average length of the intestines of 39 fattening hogs to be about 21 times the body length.[82]

1319. Swine improvement; production records.—In order to secure the best returns from swine it is necessary to have well-bred breeding stock. The sows and boar should be carefully selected from strains of swine that excel in the following characteristics: (1) They produce good-sized litters of thrifty pigs; (2) their pigs make rapid gains and therefore usually economical gains; (3) their pigs yield carcasses that meet the present market demands. Disposition and milk yield are also important factors to consider in selecting sows to retain in the herd. If a sow has a mean disposition or if she is careless, she may crush or injure a considerable percentage of the pigs she farrows. If the sow does not have a good flow of milk, her pigs will fail to make good gains.

A simple herd record should be kept in which the number of pigs farrowed and the number raised by each sow are recorded, with notations as to whether the pigs make good gains. Only gilts from the best sows, as shown by this record, should be retained for the breeding herd. To identify the pigs, they should be ear-notched or otherwise marked at birth.

Alabama experiments show the improvement that can be made by using good purebred boars on scrub sows in successive generations.[83] Scrub pigs required 244 days to reach a weight of 200 lbs., while it took only 201 days for pigs out of scrub sows and a purebred boar to reach the same weight, and but 187 days for pigs carrying seven-eighths of the improved blood. Perhaps even more important than the difference in rate of gain was the difference in cost of gain. The scrub pigs required 465 lbs. of feed per 100 lbs. gain; the half-bloods, 403 lbs.; and the seven-eighths bloods, only 382 lbs.

Through the swine extension projects carried on by the agricultural colleges in various states, the factors that are essential for economical pork production have been called prominently to the attention of farmers. One of the popular projects has been the "ton litter" project, in which prizes are offered or recognition given for litters from single sows that reach a total weight of one ton in 180 days. More recently various types of pork-production contests and demonstrations have been conducted, in which the most effective methods of breeding, feeding, and management are shown.

Outstanding progress has been made in Denmark and certain other European countries in using production records for swine improvement. In Denmark herds of swine of approved type are designated as breeding centers. To ascertain the strains which are superior in these herds, 4 pigs are selected from a litter and fed to market weights on a standard ration at a central feeding station, where a careful record is kept of feed consumed and gains made. Representative pigs from each litter are slaughtered in order to secure data on the desirability of the carcasses.

Since rapid-gaining pigs usually make the most economical gains, pig-recording systems have been developed in Sweden, Great Britain, and some other countries. These are often combined with the milk-recording service for dairy herds. Under these systems the pigs are ear-notched and weighed at a definite age by an inspector. These records are used as a basis for the selection of breeding stock. Largely through studies and tests made by the Iowa and Minnesota Stations and the United States Department of Agriculture, interest in these methods of swine improvement has been aroused among pork producers in this country. It is to be hoped that some plan of pig-recording can be generally adopted here that is well adapted to our conditions.

1320. Barrows vs. sows.—It is commonly believed that barrows will make slightly more rapid and economical gains than open sows, due to the restlessness of the sows during the oestrum periods. Up to the usual market weights there is, however, apparently no appreciable difference in the gains of gilts and barrows. This is indicated in experiments carried on during several years by Morrison, Bohstedt, and colleagues at the Wisconsin Station.[85] In these trials pigs were fed well-balanced rations, either in dry lot or on pasture. The trials were usually begun when the pigs weighed 50 to 70 lbs., and the pigs were carried to market weights of 200 lbs. to 225 lbs.

In these experiments 601 barrows gained on the average 1.28 lbs. a head daily, while the average gain of 469 gilts was 1.26 lbs. The slightly more rapid gains of the barrows were probably due to the fact that somewhat more gilts than barrows were retained for breeding stock and not fattened for market in the experiments. Thus, the barrows in the trials tended to average a trifle better in quality than the gilts.

In experiments where the yields of dressed carcass and of the various cuts from barrows and from unbred gilts have been determined, there has been no consistent difference in the dressing percentage.[86] In some tests the yield of dressed carcass has been slightly lower from the gilts, but in other trials the dressing percentage for the gilts has been as high as for the barrows, or even higher. The yield of hams is generally slightly higher for gilts, and the yield of bacon and of fat slightly less. The fact that gilts have slightly less fat at a given weight than do barrows is opposite to the condition in cattle, for heifers are fatter at a given weight than steers. In an Illinois test the meat from barrows was slightly tougher, on the average, than from gilts.[87]

Spaying sows before fattening them is of no advantage, for unspayed sows make just as good gains.[88]

1321. Soft pork.—It has long been known that certain feeds, especially soybeans, peanuts, rice bran, rice polish, and chufas, tend to produce soft pork when fed to pigs in considerable amounts. The products from hog carcasses that are soft are undesirable from the standpoint of both the processor and the consumer, and therefore sell at a decided discount.

Lard from soft hogs does not harden at ordinary temperatures. The bacon is soft and flabby, and is difficult to slice, even with a machine. The loins are smeary and unattractive. The hams are less affected, as they have a smaller proportion of fat. When the pork is very soft, oil will drip from hams or bacon in the smoke house, thus increasing the shrinkage. Unless the carcass is extremely soft, the meat after cooking may be just as attractive and palatable as that from a firm carcass. However, there will be more wastage of the cuts in cooking, due to loss of fat.

It is impossible to determine whether or not hogs will have soft carcasses by handling them when alive, as the fat is fluid at body temperature even in the case of hogs that yield hard carcasses. In sections where there is considerable trouble from soft pork, the packer usually protects himself against loss by paying a lower price for all hogs, or buys them subject to a discount if they kill soft.

Extensive experiments have been conducted during recent years by the United States Department of Agriculture in co-operation with several experiment stations to study the soft pork problem.[89] Similar tests have also been made by other stations. An especial object of these studies has been to determine the extent to which softening feeds can be used without injuring the carcasses of hogs.

These investigations have shown that the body fat which swine make from carbohydrates or protein in their food has a melting point sufficiently high to be hard and firm at ordinary air temperatures. However, fat in the feed may be converted into body fat with but little change. Therefore, when swine receive such feeds as soybeans and peanuts, that are high in fat, much of the fat deposited in their bodies comes from this source. Since the fat in these feeds is liquid at ordinary temperatures soft pork results if much of the body fat comes from this source.

The grains also contain fat which is liquid at ordinary temperatures, and which will produce soft pork if fed in large enough amounts. However, the percentage of fat in the grains is relatively low. When pigs are fed on grain and supplements that are not high in fat, most of the body fat is therefore made from the carbohydrates, and not from the fat in the feed. Such rations hence produce firm pork. Corn and oats have a greater tendency to soften pork than do barley, wheat, rye, or the grain sorghums, because corn and oats are both higher in fat.

When pigs are well fattened on corn and such supplements as tankage, meat scraps, fish meal, or dairy by-products, their carcasses are sufficiently firm and hard to meet the requirements of the markets in the United States. However, for the production of the type of bacon that commands a premium in England, a harder carcass is necessary. Therefore, as is pointed out later, corn should not form too large a part of the ration when such bacon is to be produced. (**1323**)

Much of the trouble from soft pork during recent years in this country has been due to the fact that pigs of the extreme big-type are not sufficiently fat at the weights when they are usually marketed. Even if fed a ration that normally produces hard pork, pigs of decidedly rangy conformation yield soft carcasses if slaughtered at live weights below 250 to 275 lbs.

While pigs are young, they store a much smaller proportion of fat in the gains they make, than during the later stages of fattening. Therefore a large part of the body fat can then come from the fat in their feed. Later, when they are storing fat rapidly, most of it must be made from the carbohydrates in the ration, and this manufactured fat is hard in character. This fact also explains why pigs that have made rapid gains usually yield firmer carcasses than those of the same degree of fatness that have gained more slowly on the same combination of feeds.[90]

1322. Extent to which softening feeds can be used.—It was formerly believed that after pigs had been fed for 6 to 8 weeks on a ration that produced soft pork, their fat could be hardened satisfactorily by feeding them for an equal period on such a ration as corn and tankage. The extensive experiments on this problem have shown, however, that soft pork cannot be prevented in this manner.

When pigs weighing 85 lbs. or more were grazed on peanuts or were fed only peanuts in dry lot for 8 weeks, they did not yield firm carcasses, even after a period on corn and tankage during which they each gained 120 lbs. in weight. Therefore, to avoid soft pork, peanuts should be used only for young pigs up to a weight of about 85 lbs., which are finished, after they reach this weight, on a ration that produces hard pork.

If pigs weighing 85 lbs. or more are grazed for 6 to 8 weeks on soybeans, receiving 2.5 lbs. daily of corn per 100 lbs. live weight in addition, they will not yield hard carcasses, even when they make an equal total gain during a finishing period on corn and tankage. On the other hand, when young pigs weighing less than about 85 lbs. make a gain of 40 to 75 lbs. while grazing on soybeans with corn in addition, they can usually be hardened satisfactorily if they later gain 125 lbs. or more on such a ration as corn and tankage.

When soybeans are used as a supplement to corn for pigs on pasture, care must be taken that the proportion of soybeans eaten is not too large, or soft pork will result. In Indiana tests satisfactory carcasses were usually produced from pigs self-fed corn and soybeans, free choice, with a mineral supplement in addition, if they weighed about 125 lbs.

when started on this ration in dry lot or 75 lbs. on pasture. On the other hand, in some of the other tests soybeans have produced soft carcasses when forming more than about 10 per cent of the ration. As a greater proportion of soybeans than this is often needed to balance the ration, the soybeans should then be fed in combination with tankage or some other non-softening supplement.

Rice bran and rice polish have a decidedly softening effect, and therefore much use cannot be made of them in fattening pigs, without producing soft pork. For example, pigs weighing 50 to 114 lbs., that were fed for 8 weeks on rice polish and tankage, did not yield hard carcasses even after making 1.8 times as much total gain on corn and tankage as they had made on rice polish. However, satisfactory carcasses were produced when such pigs were finished on brewers' rice, if they made twice as much gain on brewers' rice as they had on rice polish.

Certain feeds have much more of a hardening effect than a ration of corn and tankage. Brewers' rice has such an effect, due to its very low content of fat. Sweet potatoes also belong to this class. Cottonseed oil has a softening effect, if any considerable amount is fed to pigs, but cottonseed meal has a pronounced hardening effect. An excellent ration for hardening the carcasses of pigs is therefore corn supplemented by a combination of one-half cottonseed meal and one-half tankage or fish meal. (**1365**)

1323. Bacon production.—Most consumers prefer bacon that has a good "streak" of lean meat, but which is firm and of fair thickness. In the United States most of the best bacon is made from the leaner pigs of the lard breeds, for there are but few swine of the true bacon breeds in this country.

In England there has been for many years a demand for a very superior quality of bacon, marketed under the name of "Wiltshire sides." This demand is met by pigs produced there and by importation, chiefly from Denmark, Ireland, and Canada. A Wiltshire side comprises the entire half of the dressed pig, minus the head, shank, shoulder bone, and hip bone. All of the side, except the ham and the shoulder, is sold as "bacon." Wiltshire sides are made exclusively from choice pigs that have proper length of body, a high proportion of lean meat, a medium covering of fat on the back (preferably 1.0 to 1.5 inches thick) and bellies smoothly finished with firm fat.

It was formerly believed that pigs of the bacon breeds or crosses between the bacon and the lard breeds were the only ones well suited to the production of Wiltshire bacon. However, investigations by the North Dakota and Minnesota Stations and by the United States Department of Agriculture show that the lard-type swine now produced in the United States can be selected so that, at the proper weight, they will be satisfactory for the preparation of Wiltshire sides.[91]

Even a slight degree of softness of fat, that would not be very objectionable in a lard hog, will disqualify a carcass for high-quality Wiltshire sides. Canadian and Danish experiments have shown that the chief causes of soft bacon are: Lack of maturity and lack of finish (degree of fatness); unthriftiness of the pigs; the feeding of an unbalanced ration composed almost entirely of grain; too large a proportion of corn in the ration; and a lack of exercise.[92] It is often stated that pigs produce less desirable Wiltshire sides when self-fed than when hand-fed slightly less than a full ration.   However, in tests at the Alberta, Canada, College of Agriculture, self-feeding produced a larger proportion of carcasses grading as "select" for Wiltshire sides than did limited hand-feeding.

Barley ranks first for bacon production, followed by oats and peas. Skimmilk and whey in combination with the cereal grains, including corn in limited amount, make good bacon.   Good pasture, such as alfalfa, clover, or rape, is very helpful in producing good bacon carcasses.

QUESTIONS

1. Compare the efficiency of pigs and other classes of stock as meat producers.
2. Discuss the rate and economy of gain by pigs of various weights.
3. At what weights should pigs commonly be marketed in the United States?
4. Approximately what is the average dressing percentage of hogs slaughtered at the large plants in this country?
5. Why do swine suffer from nutritive deficiencies more frequently than do cattle, sheep, or horses?
6. Discuss the importance of good pasture or legume hay for swine.
7. Name 7 protein supplements that provide protein of good quality for swine.
8. Name 10 protein supplements that are unsatisfactory when fed as the only supplements to swine not on pasture.
9. Discuss the amounts of protein required by swine.
10. State a combination of feeds that is well adapted to self-feeding by the free-choice plan.   State a combination of feeds which is not suited to free-choice feeding.
11. Discuss the use of protein supplements with the cereal grains for pigs not on pasture.
12. Under what conditions would you feed a protein supplement to pigs fed grain on good pasture?   When is it more economical not to use a supplement?
13. Compare the ability of swine and of ruminants to digest various classes of feeds.
14. Discuss the importance of the fiber content of the ration for pigs.
15. Discuss the requirements of swine for salt.
16. State in detail the kind of rations for swine: (a) That require a calcium supplement; (b) that require a phosphorus supplement; (c) that need no calcium or phosphorus supplement.
17. Name 5 suitable calcium supplements for swine; 3 safe phosphorus supplements.
18. How can goiter or hairlessness in new-born pigs be prevented?
19. State 3 methods of preventing anemia in suckling pigs.
20. Should iron and copper be added to the rations of older swine?
21. Discuss the use of simple versus complex mineral mixtures for swine.
22. How could you tell whether a pig was suffering from a deficiency of vitamin A or a lack of vitamin D?
23. State the conditions under which swine will be amply supplied with vitamins A and D.
24. State the conditions under which there will be a deficiency of vitamin A for swine; a deficiency of vitamin D.
25. How would you protect brood sows not on pasture against a lack of vitamin A or vitamin D?   How would you protect pigs not on pasture against these deficiencies?
26. Discuss the requirements of swine for vitamins B and G; for vitamin C.
27. Discuss the water requirements of swine.
28. Is it profitable to feed stock foods or tonics to swine?
29. At what times during the year should pigs be marketed to bring the highest prices, on the average?

30. Discuss limited-feeding vs. full-feeding of pigs not on pasture.
31. Discuss the limited-feeding of pigs on pasture.
32. Why has the self-feeding of pigs become so popular?
33. What results have been secured in experiments in which self-feeding of pigs has been compared with hand-feeding: (a) In dry lot; (b) on pasture?
34. What grains should commonly be ground for swine?
35. What feeds for swine may be improved by soaking?
36. Under what conditions may it be desirable to feed concentrates to pigs in the form of a slop?
37. Discuss the following: (a) Cooking feeds for swine; (b) feeding floors; (c) shelter for swine; (d) exercise.
38. What type of swine best meets present consumer demands?
39. What methods have been used in Europe for improving the quality of swine carcasses and increasing the efficiency of production?
40. Compare barrows and sows for pork production.
41. Discuss the soft pork problem, stating the feeds that produce soft pork and describing the extent to which soybeans can be safely fed to pigs.
42. Discuss the especial requirements for the production of choice bacon to be marketed as "Wiltshire sides."

REFERENCES

1. Armsby and Moulton, The Animal as a Converter of Matter and Energy, pp. 219-220; see also: Hogan, Weaver, Edinger, and Trowbridge, Mo. Res. Bul. 73.
2. Robison, Ohio Bul. 335.
3. Hogan, Weaver, Edinger, and Trowbridge, Mo. Res. Bul. 73.
4. Henry, Feeds and Feeding, 1st ed., 1898.
5. Morrison, Bohstedt, and Fargo, Wis. Sta.; data compiled by McKay.
6. Henning and Stout, Ohio Bul. 505.
7. Aubel and McConnell, Kan. Sta., mimeo. rpt.; Loeffel and Lewis, Nebr. Rpt. 1934 and mimeo. rpt.; Bohstedt and Fargo, Wis. Bul. 428.
8. Fargo, Wis. Bul. 420; Fargo, Amer. Soc. Anim. Prod., Proc. 1927, and information to the author; Carroll, Garrigus, Mitchell, and Hamilton, Ill. Rpt. 1934; Mitchell, rpt. at meeting of Amer. Soc. Anim. Prod., 1935; Grimes and Salmon, Ala. Bul. 224; Baker, Del. Bul. 133; Joseph, Mont. Bul. 169.
9. Aubel and Connell, Kan. Rpt. 1932-34.
10. Hughes, Lindsay, and Smith, Amer. Soc. Anim. Prod., Proc. 1930; Hughes, Jour. Agr. Res., 47, 1933, pp. 487-494; Carmichael, Md. Bul. 336; Joseph, Mont. Bul. 169; S. D. Rpt. 1931; Smith and Maynard, Utah Bul. 254; Sinclair, Col. of Agr., Univ. of Alberta, Canada, mimeo. rpt.
11. Joseph, Mont. Bul. 169; Vinke and Bergstedt, Mont. Bul. 284; Dickson and Bergstedt, Mont. Sta., mimeo. rpt.; S. D. Rpt. 1931; Smith and Maynard, Utah Bul. 254.
12. Weaver, Mo. Bul. 285; Loeffel, Nebr. Rpts. 1928, 1929, 1930, 1934, and mimeo. rpts.
13. Vestal, Ind. Sta., mimeo. rpts.; Evvard, Culbertson, et al., Iowa Sta., mimeo. rpts.; Culbertson, Thomas, Hammond, and Beard, Iowa Sta., mimeo. rpts.; Robison, Ohio Bul. 552; Godbey, S. C. Bul. 274; Wilson and Wright, S. D. Bul. 262; see also: Martin, Ark. Bul. 321; Carmichael, Md. Bul. 376.
14. Vestal, Ind. Bul. 300 and mimeo. rpt.; Evvard and Culbertson, Iowa Sta., mimeo. rpt.; Aubel and Connell, Kan. Sta., mimeo. rpt.; Loeffel, Nebr. Sta., mimeo. rpt.; Robison, Ohio Bul. 552; see also: Tomhave, Del. Bul. 152; Carroll and Garrigus, Ill. Rpts. 1933, 1934; Weber, Anderson, and Marston, Kan. Cir. 138; Miller, Minn. Sta., Morris Substa., Rpts. 1921, 1922, 1923; Weaver, Mo. Bul. 256; Wyo. Rpt. 1929.
15. Thompson and Voorhies, Cal. Bul. 342; Osland and Morton, Colo. Bul. 381; Freeman, Mich. Quar. Bul., 15, 1933, No. 4; Joseph, Mont. Bul. 236; Wilson and Wright, S. D. Bul. 262; Smith and Maynard, Utah Bul. 254.
16. Robison, Ohio Bul. 552; see also: Freeman, Mich. Quar. Bul., 17, 1935, No. 3; Loeffel, Nebr. Sta., mimeo. rpt.
17. Fraps, Tex. Bul. 454.
18. Evvard, Iowa Res. Bul. 118.
19. Evvard, Iowa Res. Bul. 118; Headley, Nev. Bul. 125; Robison, Ohio Bimo. Bul. 145; Oliver and Potter, Ore. Bul. 269; Bohstedt and Fargo, Wis. Bul. 425.
20. Evvard, Culbertson, et al., Iowa Leaflet 9 and mimeo. rpts.; see also: Nebr. Rpt. 1924; Hale, Tex. Rpt. 1926; Sinclair and Sackville, Sci. Agr., Canada, 6, 1926, pp. 373-379.
21. Loeffel, Nebr. Rpt. 1924.
22. Hale, Tex. Rpts. 1925, 1926.
23. Rice and Mitchell, Ill. Bul. 250; Vestal, Ind. Rpts. 1930, 1931; Evvard, Culbertson, and Hammond, Iowa Sta., mimeo. rpts.; Kan. Rpt. 1923-24; Vinke and Bergstedt, Mont. Bul. 284; Loeffel, Nebr. Rpt. 1924; Hostetler et al., N. C. Rpts. 1929, 1930, 1932; Robison, Ohio Buls. 402, 417, 470, 532, 552; Ohio Spec. Cir. 17; Thompson, Okla. Rpts. 1926-1930, 1930-1932; Hale, Tex. Rpt. 1925; Morrison and Fargo, Wis. Buls. 396, 405; Bohstedt, Amer. Soc. Anim. Prod., Proc. 1930; Sinclair and Sackville, Sci. Agr., 6, 1926, pp. 373-379; Paterson, West of Scotland Agr. Col., Bul. 102.

24. Grimes, and Salmon, Ala. Bul. 222; Salmon, Breeder's Gazette, 85, 1924, p. 765;
    Hughes, Cal. Rpt. 1928, and Amer. Soc. Anim. Prod., Proc. 1930; Palmer, Del.
    Bul. 135; Rice and Mitchell, Ill. Bul. 250; Carroll, Hunt, and Mitchell, Ill. Rpt.
    1930; Vestal, Ind. Rpt. 1927 and mimeo. rpts.; Evvard, Culbertson, and Ham-
    mond, Iowa Rpts. 1922, 1923, 1924; Evvard, Culbertson and Hammond, Amer.
    Soc. Anim. Prod., Proc. 1922, and mimeo. rpts.; Weaver, Mo. Bul. 256; Maynard,
    Goldberg, and Miller, N. Y. (Cornell) Memoir 86; Maynard and Miller, Amer.
    Jour. Physiol., 86, 1925, pp. 3-34; Gray and Hostetler, Bul. N. C. Dept. Agr., 41,
    1920, No. 6; Bohstedt, Robison, Bethke, and Edgington, Ohio Bul. 395; Robison,
    Ohio Buls. 373, 552, and mimeo. rpt.; Thompson, Okla. Rpt. 1926-1930; Hale,
    Tex. Rpt. 1926; May, Puerto Rico Sta. Rpt. 1929; Shaw, Jour. Min. Agr., Great
    Britain, 35, 1928, pp. 342-347; Evans, Jour. Agr. Sci., England, 20, 1930, pp.
    117-125; Sheehy and Senior, Irish Free State, Dept. Agr. Jour. 30, 1931, No. 1,
    pp. 1-63; Crowther and Wright, Jour. Min. Agr., Great Britain, 39, 1932, pp.
    201-207.
25. Culbertson, Hammond, and Thomas, Iowa Sta., mimeo. rpt.; Robison, Ohio Buls.
    470, 532; see also: Nebr. 1924.
26. Joseph, Mont. Bul. 169; Vinke and Bergstedt, Mont. Bul. 284; Mont. Rpts. 1925,
    1929.
27. Evvard, Culbertson, Hammond, and Wallace, Iowa Sta., mimeo. rpt.; Culbertson
    and Thomas, Iowa Rpt. 1933; Hostetler and Nance, N. C. Rpt. 1932; Ohio Bul.
    417.
28. Ind. Rpt. 1927.
29. Fraser, Sci. Agr., 12, 1931, pp. 57-80; McCampbell and Aubel, Kan. Rpt. 1932-34.
30. Carroll, Hunt, and Mitchell, Ill. Rpt. 1930.
31. Hughes, Mo. Res. Bul. 167.
32. Carroll, Garrigus, Mitchell, and Hamilton, Ill. Rpt. 1934.
33. Carroll, Mitchell, and Hunt, Jour. Agr. Res., 41, 1931, pp. 65-77; McClure and
    Mitchell, Jour. Agr. Res., 41, 1931, pp. 79-87; Forbes et al., Jour. Agr. Res., 45,
    1932, pp. 113-128; Evvard and Culbertson, Iowa Res. Bul. 86; Robison, Ohio
    Buls. 402, 417; see also: Kelly, Biochem. Jour. 19, 1925, pp. 559-568.
34. McGowan and Crichton, Biochem. Jour., 17, 1923, pp. 204-207; 18, 1924, pp.
    265-272.
35. Hart, Elvehjem, Steenbock, Bohstedt, and Fargo, Wis. Buls. 409, 410; Hart, Kem-
    merer, Fargo, and Bohstedt, Wis. Bul. 420.
36. Carroll, Hunt, and Mitchell, Ill. Rpt. 1929; Hamilton, Hunt, Mitchell, and Carroll,
    Jour. Agr. Res., 40, 1930, pp. 927-938; 47, 1933, pp. 543-563; Doyle, Mathews,
    and Whiting, Ind. Bul. 313; Doyle, Ind. Cir. 188; Willman, McCay, and Gormel,
    N. Y. (Cornell) Rpts. 1930, 1931, 1932, 1933; Willman, McCay, and Morrison,
    Amer. Soc. Anim. Prod., Proc. 1932; Moe, Craft, and Thompson, Okla. Rpt.
    1932-34; Fargo, Beeson, and Deobald, Wis. Bul. 430; Schofield, Ontario Vet. Col.,
    Canada, Rpt. 1929.
37. Carroll, Hunt, and Mitchell, Ill. Rpts. 1928, 1929; Culbertson, Edward, et al., Iowa
    Rpt. 1929 and mimeo. rpts.; Bohstedt, Bethke, and Edgington, Ohio Bul. 395;
    Robison, Ohio Buls. 417, 488; Hart, Elvehjem, Bohstedt, and Fargo, Wis.
    Bul. 420.
38. Carroll, Hunt, Mitchell, and Hamilton, Ill. Rpt. 1931; Evvard and Culbertson, et
    al. Iowa Leaflets 5, 12, 13, 17, and mimeo. rpts.; Culbertson, Iowa Rpt. 1931;
    Anderson, Culbertson, Evvard, and Hammond, Amer. Soc. Anim. Prod., Proc.
    1932; Robison, Ohio Buls. 488, 532; Thompson, Okla. Rpt. 1930-32 and mimeo.
    rpt.; Morrison and Fargo, Wis. Bul. 405; Bohstedt, Amer. Soc. Anim. Prod.,
    Proc. 1930.
39. Vestal, Ind. Rpts. 1929, 1930, and mimeo. rpts.; Hostetler, N. C. Sta., information
    to the author; Robison, Ohio Sta., mimeo. rpt.
40. Kernkamp, Minn. Tech. Bul. 31; Loeffel, Thalman, F. C. Olson, and F. A. Olson,
    Nebr. Res. Bul. 58; Maynard, Goldberg, and Miller, N. Y. (Cornell) Memoir 86;
    Bohstedt, Robison, Bethke, and Edgington, Ohio Bul. 395; Hart and Steenbock,
    Wis. Buls. 339, 352, 362.
41. E. H. Hughes, Cal. Rpt. 1931, and Jour. Agr. Res. 49, 1934, pp. 943-953; J. S.
    Hughes, Aubel, and Lienhardt, Kan. Tech. Bul. 23; Morrison and Fargo, Wis.
    Buls. 339, 352; Hale, Jour. Heredity, 24, 1933, pp. 105-106; Dunlop. Jour. Agr.
    Sci., England, 24, 1934, pp. 435-456.
42. Hart and Steenbock, Wis. Buls. 339, 352, 362; Morrison and Fargo, Wis. Buls.
    339, 352, 373; Bohstedt, Robison, Bethke, and Edgington, Ohio Bul. 395; see also:
    Martin, Ark. Buls. 231, 246; Tomhave, Del. Bul. 147.
43. See the publications listed under the previous three references, and also: Hughes,
    Cal. Rpts. 1928, 1930; Joseph, Mont. Bul. 169; Halverson and Hostetler, N. C.
    Rpt. 1930; Longwell, West. Va. Bul. 244, and Amer. Soc. Anim. Prod., Proc. 1932.
44. Loeffel, Thalman, F. C. Olson, and F. A. Olson, Nebr. Res. Bul. 58; Maynard,
    Goldberg, and Miller, N. Y. (Cornell) Memoir 86; Robison, Ohio Bul. 488;
    Bohstedt, Robison, Bethke, and Edgington, Ohio Bul. 395; Hart and Steenbock,
    Wis. Bul. 362, 388; Golding, Zilva, Drummond, and Coward, Biochem. Jour. 16,
    1922, pp. 394-402; Zilva, Golding, Drummond, and Korenchevsky, Biochem. Jour.,
    18, 1924, pp. 872-880; Paterson, West of Scotland Agr. Col. Bul. 102; Sinclair,
    Sci. Agr., 13, 1933, pp. 489-502.
45. Morrison, Willman, and Briggs, N. Y. (Cornell) Sta., unpublished data.
46. Martin, Ark. Buls. 257, 268.
47. Culbertson, Iowa Rpt. 1932; Culbertson and Thomas, Iowa Rpt. 1933; Brown and
    Edwards, Mich. Quar. Bul., 7, 1924, No. 1; Edwards and Brown, Mich. Quar.
    Bul. 8, 1925, No. 2; Weaver, Mo. Bul. 228; Robison, Ohio Buls. 392, 402;
    Thompson, Okla. Bul. 165; Wash. Bul. 187; Livesay and Stillwell, West Va.
    Bul. 213; Morrison, Fargo, and Thomas, Wis. Bul. 488; Shrewsbury, Vestal, and
    Hauge, Jour. Agr. Res., 44, 1932, pp. 267-274.
48. Christensen, N. D. Bul. 174.

49. Dietrich, Swine, p. 156; Ferrin and Johnson, Minn. Sta., mimeo. rpt.
50. Evvard, Wallace, and Culbertson, Iowa Bul. 245.
51. Culbertson, Evvard, et al., Iowa Leaflet 18; Ferrin and McCarty, Minn. Sta., mimeo. rpt.
52. Michaels and Kennedy, Iowa Bul. 113; Culbertson, Evvard, et al., Iowa Leaflet 18 and mimeo. rpts.; Kinzer and Wheeler, Kan. Bul. 192; Grisdale, Ottawa, Canada, Expt. Farms, Rpt. 1904.
53. U. S. Dept. Agr. Yearbooks.
54. Morrison, Willman, and St. Pierre, N. Y. (Cornell) Rpt. 1934; St. Pierre, Morrison, and Willman, Amer. Soc. Anim. Prod., Proc. 1934.
55. Freeman, Mich. Quar. Bul., 17, 1935, No. 3.
56. Robison, Ohio Monthly Buls. 59-60.
57. Ellis and Zeller, U. S. Dept. Agr. Tech. Bul. 413.
58. Lindgren, Oliver, and Potter, Ore. Bul. 297.
59. Ferrin and McCarty, Minn. Bul. 248.
60. S. D. Bul. 1926; see also: Hostetler, N. C. Rpt. 1931.
61. Robison, Ohio Mo. Buls. 59-60.
62. Vestal, Ind. Bul. 279; Evvard, Iowa Sta., mimeo. rpts.; Bell, Winchester, and Marston, Kan. Cir. 98; Edwards, Mich. Spec. Bul. 199; Ferrin and McCarty, Minn. Bul. 248; Weaver, Mo. Bul. 247 and information to the author; Robison, Ohio Sta., Amer. Soc. Anim. Prod., Proc. 1931; Morrison, Bohstedt, and Fargo, Wis. Sta., mimeo. rpts. and unpublished data; see also: Grimes, Sewell, and Taylor, Ala. Bul. 233; Nordby, Id. Cir. 57; Kan. Rpt. 1924-1926; Weaver, Mo. Bul. 285; Loeffel, Nebr. Rpt. 1934 and mimeo. rpts.; Peters and Geiken, N. D. Bul. 127; Shepperd, N. D. Bul. 156; Godbey, Kyzer, and Clyburn, S. C. Bul. 289.
63. Lloyd and Young, Ind. Bul. 310.
64. Robison, Ohio Sta., Amer. Soc. Anim. Prod., Proc. 1931.
65. Vaughan, Joseph, and Vinke, Mont. Rpts. 1925, 1927, 1929; Arnett and Joseph, Mont. Bul. 128; Joseph, Mont. Bul. 236; Ore. Rpt. 1920-1922; S. D. Rpt. 1928; Schaefer and Smith, Wash. Bul. 198; Hansen, U. S. Dept. Agr. Cir. 204; Russell, U. S. Dept. Agr. Tech. Bul. 17.
66. Dvorachek and Sandhouse, Ark. Bul. 191; Rice and Liable, Ill. Sta., information to the author; McCampbell, Kan. Cir. 78; Weaver, Mo. Bul. 144 and information to the author; Snyder, Nebr. Bul. 214; Loeffel, Nebr. Sta., mimeo. rpts.; Robison, Ohio Bul. 355; Ashbrook and Gongwer, U. S. Dept. Agr., Farmers' Bul. 906; see also: Weaver, Mo. Bul. 328, Penn. Buls. 170, 176; Godbey, S. C. Bul. 277.
67. Evvard, Iowa Sta., Corn Belt Meat Producers' Assoc., Rpt. 1914, and mimeo. rpt.; Snyder, Nebr. Bul. 165; Robison, Ohio Buls. 343, 355; see also: Godbey, S. C. Bul. 277.
68. Culbertson and Thomas, Iowa Rpt. 1933; Edwards and Brown, Mich. Quar. Bul., 8, 1925, No. 2.
69. Thompson and Voorhies, Cal. Bul. 342; Vestal, Ind. Sta., mimeo. rpt.; Culbertson and Thomas, Iowa Rpt. 1933; Ky. Rpt. 1932; Ferrin and Johnson, Minn. Sta., mimeo. rpt.; Weaver, Mo. Bul. 163; Penn. Bul. 293; Wyo. Rpt. 1921; Garrido, Philippine Agr., 19, 1930, pp. 397-409.
70. Me. State Col. Agr., Rpt. Trustees, 1876; Ontario School of Agr., Rpt. 1876; Kan. Agr. Col. Rpt. 1885; Iowa Agr. Col. Rpt. 1891; Wis. Rpt. 1886; Coburn, Swine in America.
71. Wilford, Ky. Rpts. 1928, 1929; Amer. Soc. Anim. Prod., Proc. 1930.
72. Anderson and Marston, Kan. Cir. 112.
73. Morrison, Bohstedt, and Scott, mimeo. rpts.
74. Edwards and Freeman, Mich. Rpt. 1928-1930.
75. Grisdale, Ottawa, Canada, Expt. Farms, Rpt. 1904.
76. Shelton, Kan. Agr. Col., Rpt. Prof. Agr., 1883.
77. Bull and Longwell, Ill. Bul. 322; Bull, Olson, Hunt, and Carroll, Ill. Bul. 415; Scott, Ind. Bul. 340; Evvard and Culbertson, Iowa Rpt. 1924 and mimeo. rpts.; see also: Nordby, Id. Bul. 190; Lindgren, Oliver, and Potter, Ore. Bul. 297.
78. Carroll, Bull, et al., Ill. Bul. 321; Bull, Olson, Hunt, and Carroll, Ill. Bul. 415; Scott, Ind. Bul. 340; Evvard and Culbertson, Iowa Rpts. 1918, 1919, 1920, 1921, 1922, 1924, 1925, 1928; Lindgren, Oliver, and Potter, Ore. Bul. 297.
79. Rommel, U. S. Dept. Agr., Bur. Anim. Indus., Bul. 47; Ferrin and McCarty, Minn. Sta., mimeo. rpt.; Hogan, Weaver, Edinger, and Trowbridge, Mo. Res. Bul. 73; Christensen, Thompson, and Jorgenson, N. D. Bul. 194; Robison, Amer. Soc. Anim. Prod., Proc. 1928; Wyo. Rpt. 1929.
80. Roberts and Carroll, Ill. Rpt. 1926; Shearer, Evvard, Culbertson, et al., Iowa Leaflet 20; Iowa Rpt. 1928; Mont. Rpt. 1931; Craft, Okla. Rpt. 1926-1930; Winters, Jordan, and Kiser, Amer. Soc. Anim. Prod., Proc. 1934; Jour. Min. Agr., England, 29, 1923, pp. 939-941; Schmidt, Lauprecht, and Vogel, Züchtungskunde, 1, 1926, pp. 242-256.
81. Darwin, Animals and Plants under Domestication.
82. Henry, Wis. Rpt. 1889.
83. Grimes, Sewell, and Taylor, Ala. Bul. 234.
84. Culbertson, Evvard, Kildee, Helser, et al., Iowa Bul. 277 and Iowa Leaflet 26; Culbertson, Kildee, Helser, and Hammond, Iowa Leaflets 28, 30; Ferrin, Anderson, and Johnson, Minn. Sta., mimeo. rpts.; Ferrin, Amer. Soc. Anim. Prod., Proc. 1932, 1934.
85. Morrison, Bohstedt, and Fargo, Wis. Sta., unpublished data; see also: Ariz. Rpt. 1923; Ky. Rpt. 1926.
86. Bull and Olson, Ill. Rpt. 1931; Scott, Ind. Bul. 340; Ind. Rpt. 1927; Robison, Ohio Bul. 497; Mohler, U. S. Dept. Agr., Ann. Rpt. Chief of Bur. of Anim. Indus., 1928; Park, National Provisioner, 82, 1930, p. 25; Warner, Ellis, and Howe, Jour. Agr. Res., 48, 1934, pp. 251-252.
87. Mitchell, Hamilton, Bull, and Longwell, Ill. Rpt. 1927.
88. Foster and Merrill, Utah Bul. 70.

89. Hankins and Ellis, U. S. Dept. Agr. Bul. 1407; Hankins, Ellis, and Zeller, U. S. Dept. Agr. Bul. 1492; Ellis, U. S. Dept. Agr. Tech. Bul. 368; Ellis and Hankins, Jour. Biol. Chem., 66, 1925, pp. 101-122 Ellis and Isbell, Jour. Biol. Chem., 69, 1926, pp. 219-248; Ellis and Zeller, Jour. Biol. Chem., 89, 1930, pp. 185-197; Ellis, Rothwell, and Pool, Jour. Biol. Chem., 92, 1931, pp. 385-398; Martin, Ark. Buls. 246, 268; Tomhave and Mumford, Del. Bul. 179; Edwards, Ga. Rpt. 1927; Bull, Carroll, et al., Ill. Bul. 366; Bull, Ill. Rpt. 1933; Scott, Ind. Bul. 340; Vestal and Shrewsbury, Amer. Soc. Anim. Prod., Proc. 1932, 1933; Culbertson, Helser, Beard, and Thomas, Iowa Rpt. 1933; Hostetler and Halvorsen, N. C. Rpts. 1929, 1930, 1931; Robison, Ohio Buls. 452, 516; Robison, Ohio Bimo. Bul. 152; Godbey, S. C. Rpt. 1930; Wilson, S. D. Rpts. 1931, 1933; Jacob, Tenn. Rpt. 1930.
90. Helmrich, Amer. Soc. Anim. Prod., Proc. 1929; Fargo and Coyner, Wis. Bul. 420.
91. Shepperd and Severson, N. D. Bul. 263; Ferrin and McCarty, Minn. Sta., mimeo. rpt.; Hankins, U. S. Dept. Agr., Amer. Soc. Anim. Prod., Proc. 1931.
92. Day, Productive Swine Husbandry, 5th ed., pp. 269-270; Sinclair and Sackville, Alberta Univ., Canada, Col. of Agr. Bul. 15; Fjord and Friis, Copenhagen, Denmark, Station, Rpts. 1884 et seq.

CHAPTER XXXVI

FEEDS FOR SWINE

I. Grains and Other Concentrates Low in Protein

1324. Efficient rations necessary for economical pork production.—It has been shown in the preceding chapter that swine are much more apt to suffer from nutritive deficiencies in their rations than are the other farm animals, except poultry. A thorough knowledge concerning the use and value of the various feeding stuffs is hence especially necessary for success in pork production.

We shall learn in this chapter that many rations which were formerly considered satisfactory have been shown by careful experiments to be strikingly inefficient under certain conditions. In order to secure maximum profits from hogs, it is therefore necessary not only to feed "balanced rations," which supply enough digestible crude protein, but also to supply combinations of feeds which provide protein of the proper quality and which furnish ample vitamins and minerals. Fortunately, investigations have shown that for success in pork production it is not necessary to feed complicated or expensive rations. All that is necessary are common feeding stuffs properly combined in the manner pointed out later.

1325. The cereal grains.—In this and all other main pork-producing countries swine are commonly fed chiefly on the cereal grains. It is therefore especially important that the merits and also the deficiencies of the cereals be fully understood.

The grains excel in content of total digestible nutrients and net energy, due primarily to the large percentage of starch and their high digestibility. Since swine cannot make any large use of roughage, the cereals commonly supply digestible nutrients in rations for pork production more cheaply than do other feeds.

Though differing materially in protein content, all of the cereals are low in percentage of this nutrient. While barley, oats, wheat, rye, and kafir contain somewhat more protein than corn, milo, rice, or feterita, even the former grains do not supply enough protein for efficient results, except possibly for well-grown pigs on excellent pasture. (**1285-1286**)

Fully as important as this low protein content is the fact that the proteins of the cereals are unbalanced in composition. As has been shown in the preceding chapter, to produce pork economically this deficiency in quality of protein must be corrected. (**1281-1282**) This can be done by the use of such protein supplements as tankage, meat scraps, fish meal, and dairy by-products, that furnish ample amounts of the amino acids in which the cereals and their by-products are lacking.

The facts that all the cereal grains are very low in calcium and only fair in phosphorus content must also be borne in mind in swine feeding. It has been emphasized in the previous chapter that suitable mineral supplements should be added to any rations that do not already have enough of these important mineral nutrients. (**1290-1291**)

The cereals are also all deficient in vitamin D, and none of them, with the single exception of yellow corn, supplies appreciable amounts of vitamin A. The methods of correcting these deficiencies have been discussed in detail in the previous chapter. (**1297-1298**)

Fortunately, pasture crops do much to supply the nutritive essentials in which the cereals are lacking. Swine fed grain when grazing on green forage crops are amply provided with vitamins. All the good pasture crops, such as alfalfa, clover, or rape, also aid in making good the lack of protein in the grains and in improving the quality of protein in the ration. In addition, legume pasture provides an abundance of calcium, and other good pastures help to overcome the lack of this mineral in the grains.

For swine that are not on pasture well-cured legume hay is the best substitute for green forage, especially in correcting the vitamin deficiencies of the cereals. It is therefore important that swine that are not on pasture, especially young pigs and brood sows, be provided with good legume hay in the manner stated elsewhere. (**1280, 1298**)

1326. Indian corn.—Corn is the most common swine feed in the great pork-producing districts of this country. Not only is it the cheapest carbohydrate feed in the corn belt, but also it is exceedingly palatable to swine and it produces excellent results with all classes of swine when fed in properly-balanced rations. (**512**)

Corn is unsurpassed as a feed for growing and fattening pigs and therefore is commonly taken as the standard with which other grains are compared. It is also entirely satisfactory for brood sows and other breeding stock when its deficiencies in proteins, minerals, and vitamins are corrected, and when the amount of this concentrated grain is so limited that such swine do not become too fat.

1327. Correcting the deficiencies of corn.—No single fact in stock feeding has been more clearly demonstrated by numerous feeding trials than that corn alone gives exceedingly poor results when fed to growing and fattening pigs. A glance at the following table should convince any farmer of the folly of feeding such an inefficient ration. This summarizes the results of 7 trials in which corn alone, without pasture, has been fed to young pigs, averaging 69 lbs. in weight, in comparison with a balanced ration of corn and tankage. The results are also given for 22 similar comparisons of corn alone versus corn and tankage for older pigs, averaging 136 lbs. in weight when the experiments began.

The table shows that in the trials with young pigs the average daily gain on corn alone was only 0.59 lb. and that 642 lbs. corn were required per 100 lbs. gain. This was a poor showing, indeed, but the results would have been even worse if the pigs had been started on this inadequate ration when still younger. When corn was balanced with tankage, the gains were doubled, and only 387 lbs. corn and 42 lbs. tankage were consumed for each 100 lbs. gain. Furthermore, at the end of the trials the pigs fed corn alone were usually stunted and averaged only 141 lbs. in weight, while those fed tankage in addition weighed over 200 lbs. and were ready for market.

The older pigs averaged 136 lbs. in weight when the experiments began, and hence could stand the ration of corn alone somewhat better. Nevertheless, they gained only 0.97 lb. a head daily, while those fed tankage in addition gained 1.56 lbs. There was also nearly as great a difference in the feed required for 100 lbs. gain as in the case of the younger pigs. The folly of feeding such an unbalanced ration as corn alone is shown by the fact that in these trials 100 lbs. of tankage saved 607 lbs. of corn with the younger pigs and 538 lbs. of corn with the older ones.

Corn alone vs. corn and tankage for growing, fattening pigs

Average ration	Average length of trials, days	Daily gain Lbs.	Feed for 100 lbs. gain Corn Lbs.	Tankage Lbs.
Trials with young pigs				
Lot I, corn alone				
Corn, 3.5 lbs............................	122	0.59	642	..
Lot II, corn and tankage				
Corn, 4.4 lbs.				
Tankage, 0.48 lb..........................	122	1.18	387	42
Trials with older pigs				
Lot I, corn alone				
Corn, 5.4 lbs............................	78	0.97	628	..
Lot II, corn and tankage				
Corn, 6.0 lbs.				
Tankage, 0.65 lb.........................	75	1.56	402	42

It has been shown in the previous chapter that even when pigs have good pasture in addition to a full feed of corn, better results are secured when some protein-rich concentrate is added to the ration, to balance it more completely. (**1286**) Corn alone is fairly satisfactory for fattening old sows, for they have completed their growth and hence need less protein. However, even here the use of a limited amount of supplement will usually produce cheaper gains.

From the fact that the value of tankage as a supplement to corn has been emphasized in this discussion, it must not be concluded that tankage is superior to other protein-rich supplements. Skimmilk, buttermilk, fish meal, and combinations of other feeds will give fully as good results, as is pointed out later in this chapter. In fact, for pigs not on pasture, tankage fed as the only supplement to corn is inferior to such combinations as the trio mixture. (**1281, 1298**)

Corn alone is just as unsatisfactory for pregnant sows as it is for young pigs, as is pointed out in the next chapter. (**1407**) Farmers who persist in wintering their sows on this poor ration have no basis for complaint if their pig crop is a failure. On account of the poor results whch have been secured with corn improperly fed, many breeders recommend that not over one-third to one-half the ration for brood sows consist of this grain. However, excellent results have been secured in numerous trials where corn has been the chief feed, but where the allowance was restricted so that the sows did not become too fat and the ration was properly balanced by furnishing such feeds as legume hay and tankage, fish meal, or dairy by-products. (**1412**)

1328. Minerals alone do not supplement corn adequately.—Corn is particularly deficient in calcium and also contains less phosphorus than the other grains. It might therefore be thought that the poor results on corn alone that have just been summarized were due largely to a lack of these minerals, instead of to deficiencies in quantity and quality of protein.

However, experiments have clearly proved that the results are not greatly improved when there is added to corn for pigs in dry lot only a mineral supplement which furnishes an abundance of calcium and phosphorus.[1] For proper growth and economical fattening the ration must be fully balanced by the addition of a sufficient amount of an efficient protein supplement.

1329. Yellow vs. white corn.—The discovery made by Steenbock at the Wisconsin Station in 1920 that yellow corn supplies considerable vitamin A, while white corn has little or none, is of particular importance in swine feeding. (**511**) Following this discovery, experiments were conducted by the author and associates at the Wisconsin Station and also by other investigators to find what effect this difference in vitamin A content would have on the value of the two kinds of corn for swine under various conditions.[2]

These experiments have shown that white corn produces poor results when fed for any extended period to pigs not on pasture, unless care is taken to include in the ration some supplement that provides an adequate amount of vitamin A. For example, in 5 Wisconsin tests young pigs not on pasture were fed from a weight of 50 to 60 lbs. to a market weight of 200 lbs. on either white corn or yellow corn, supplemented by tankage, skimmilk, or whey and linseed meal (all of which supply little or no vitamin A). The pigs fed yellow corn made decidedly more rapid and economical gains than those fed white corn, and on the latter ration many pigs became runts or died because of the vitamin deficiency.

On the other hand, for pigs on good pasture there is no difference in the value of the two kinds of corn, because green forage supplies an abundance of vitamin A. Adding a small amount of leafy, well-cured legume hay to the ration entirely corrects the deficiency of vitamin A in white corn and in the small grains, as has been emphasized in the previous chapter. (**1298**)

It should be borne in mind that although yellow corn is rich in vitamin A, it is deficient in vitamin D, just as is the case with white corn and the small grains. Therefore when swine fed yellow corn or any other grain are not exposed to enough sunshine to prevent rickets, legume hay or some other vitamin D supplement should be included in the ration. For example, this is generally advisable with pigs and also with brood sows during winter in the northern states, especially where the weather is such that they do not spend much time in direct sunshine.

1330. Forms in which to feed corn; types of corn.—The question as to the most economical form in which to feed corn to swine was one of the first to be studied by the American experiment stations. For example, up to 1906 Henry and Henry and Otis had conducted 18 experiments at the Wisconsin Station to find whether it paid to grind corn for fattening pigs.[3] Many trials have since been conducted by the various experiment stations to determine what is the most economical method of feeding corn to pigs of various ages.[4]

These experiments have shown in general that pigs up to about 150 lbs. in weight chew corn grain thoroughly, and therefore there is generally not enough saving through grinding corn to warrant the expense. Ear corn usually produces as good results as shelled corn or ground corn. After pigs reach a weight of about 150 lbs. they chew the grain somewhat less completely. Hence, grinding the corn or soaking it will make a larger saving in the amount of feed required per 100 lbs. gain. Whether this saving (which will probably not average more than 6 to 7 per cent) will cover the cost of preparation, will depend on the price of corn and on the cost of grinding it. Soaking corn that has become hard through storage will increase its value nearly as much as grinding it.

There is probably a somewhat greater advantage in grinding flint corn than in the case of dent corn, for flint corn is much harder. Except for this difference, the values of the two types of corn are equal. In an Iowa test there was no significant difference in the value for pigs of shelled dent corn which was rather hard and that which was softer.[5]

Similar to the condition with wheat and the grain sorghums, there is probably less saving through grinding corn for pigs that are self-fed the grain than for those that are hand-fed. (**1336**) When pigs were self-fed either shelled corn or ground corn with a protein supplemental mixture in Wisconsin tests to a market weight of 200 lbs., there was no saving whatsoever through grinding corn for fall pigs fed in dry lot.[6] For spring pigs on pasture the saving amounted to only 5 per cent.

In the early trials by Henry and Otis at the Wisconsin Station pigs averaging 175 lbs. in weight at the start were hand-fed a mixture of two-thirds corn (either shelled or ground) and one-third wheat middlings. Grinding the corn for these heavy-weight pigs increased its value about 10 per cent, on the average. In recent Pennsylvania experiments in which pigs weighing 60 to 100 lbs. at the start have been carried to a market weight of about 200 lbs. on a hand-fed mixture of corn, flour wheat middlings, tankage, linseed meal, and minerals, the saving through grinding the corn was even larger than this.[7]

For feeding to brood sows, ear corn and shelled corn are the most economical forms. If the sows do not chew all the kernels, they will be commonly sorted out of the droppings and thus finally utilized, for brood sows are not generally fed all the grain they will eat. In an Iowa experiment brood sows were fed during winter on the same amounts of corn grain in the form of ear corn, shelled corn, corn-and-cob meal, and ground shelled corn.[8] There was no appreciable difference in the gains produced, and ear corn or shelled corn was more economical than ground corn or corn-and-cob meal.

When shelled corn is ground for pigs, it should be ground to a medium degree of fineness. Pennsylvania and Wisconsin tests show that grinding to a fine meal does not increase the value of the grain over medium grinding, and the cost of labor and power for such grinding is much greater.[9] However, medium-fine grinding is preferable to merely cracking the grain.

1331. Hogging down corn.—In the corn belt the practice of turning pigs into standing corn to harvest the crop has become common during recent years. This method has certain very definite merits and also certain disadvantages.   It saves labor at a busy season of the year, conserves fertility, and provides for the pigs a fresh field which is not contaminated by parasites.

When pigs are thus fattened on the new corn crop in the corn belt, they cannot be marketed before the usual sharp decline in price occurs in the fall.   Therefore they generally sell at a decidedly lower price per hundredweight than early spring pigs that are self-fed a well-balanced ration on good pasture during the summer and are ready for market in September or early October.   In the South, where the corn crop matures earlier, there is not this disadvantage.

Many experiments have been conducted to determine the economy of hogging down corn and to find the best methods of supplementing the corn to produce rapid and economical gains.[10]   In 11 of these experiments one lot of pigs hogged down corn in which soybeans, rape, or rye had been grown as a supplemental crop, while a similar lot of pigs was fed ear corn in a dry lot.   In addition, all the pigs were fed tankage or another protein supplement   The corn consumed by the pigs in the corn field was estimated by husking out representative rows.   The pigs hogging down corn gained 1.51 lbs. per head daily on the average and required 460 lbs. of corn and supplement per 100 lbs. gain.   Those fed ear corn and supplement in dry lot gained 1.48 lbs. a day and required 479 lbs. of corn and supplement per 100 lbs. gain.   Thus, hogging down produced slightly more rapid and more economical gains in these tests.

This comparison perhaps is unduly favorable to the hogging-down method, for the pigs receiving the harvested corn were fed in dry lot, without pasture.   This is generally an uneconomical method of feeding pigs during the pasture season.   In 7 similar trials hogging down corn was compared with the feeding of ear corn and tankage or other supplement to pigs on good pasture.   In these tests the pigs fed ear corn gained 0.17 lb. more per head daily than those which hogged down standing corn and required 39 lbs. less corn and supplement per 100 lbs. gain.

The trials at various experiment stations have shown that it is generally advisable to grow some supplemental crop with the corn, or else to allow the pigs access to good alfalfa, clover, or rape pasture in addition.   The crops most commonly grown in the corn belt are soybeans and rape.   In most of the comparisons that have been made of these crops for this purpose, the results have been slightly better with soybeans than with rape.   Soybeans have the further advantage that they add nitrogen to the soil, if they are properly inoculated.   A large-seeded variety of soybeans should be used for hogging-down.   Soybeans are planted with the corn at the regular planting time, while rape is usually seeded at the time of the last cultivation.   If there is a mid-summer drought, or if there is a heavy crop of corn, the rape may not make much growth.   Therefore, a separate strip of rape is sometimes grown at one side of the cornfield.

Growing either soybeans or rape in corn reduces the yield of corn slightly, but this is generally more than offset by the protein-rich feed they furnish.   Even when one of these crops is grown in the corn, it is usually most profitable to feed in addition 0.2 to 0.3 lb. per head daily of tankage or an equivalent amount of some other efficient protein supplement. Linseed meal, wheat middlings, or corn gluten meal is not satisfactory for this purpose, and it is best to use soybeans or soybean oil meal in combination with tankage, meat scraps, or fish meal.

If protein supplements are unusually high in price and there is a considerable amount of soybean or rape forage in the corn field, it may be most economical not to use any additional protein supplement. In this case it is very important to let the pigs have access to a mineral mixture supplying calcium and phosphorus. (**181**)

When no supplemental forage is grown with the corn, 0.3 to 0.4 lb. per head daily of tankage should be fed, or the equivalent amount of other suitable supplements. Though choice alfalfa hay used as a supplement does not produce such rapid gains as tankage, it is much better than no protein supplement for pigs hogging down corn. There is little or no advantage from supplying any minerals other than salt, when proper amounts of tankage, meat scraps, fish meal or skimmilk are used as the supplements for pigs hogging-down corn.

Spring shotes, well grown on pasture and weighing 75 to 130 lbs. at the start, are best for hogging down. Lighter pigs may be used if a few heavy hogs are put with them to break down the corn. Breeding stock should not be used to hog down corn, as they will get too fat. However, brood sows and their pigs can be turned into the field after the fattened pigs have been removed, to clean up what little corn is left.

It is often recommended that the pigs be confined by a temporary fence to an area of the corn field that they can clean up in 2 or 3 weeks. This may reduce the wastage of corn, but it adds to the expense and its advisability is questionable, except in the case of heavy hogs and in very wet seasons. When desired, the field may be divided by means of a woven wire fence that is tied to corn stalks and further supported by posts or stakes where necessary.

Hogging down corn is most successful when the weather is reasonably dry. In wet seasons the pigs will waste corn and may injure the land. The crop should not be used for hogging down until the corn has reached the glazing stage, due to the great storage of nutrients which occurs after this time. It is doubtful whether it is advisable to grow very early varieties of corn so as to have the crop ready sooner. Such varieties generally yield much less than the standard grain varieties in any locality.

The area of corn required for a given number of pigs may be computed from the estimated yield and from the following data secured in Ohio experiments:[11] When tankage or other protein supplement is fed to pigs hogging down corn, about 1 bushel of corn will be eaten a day during the hogging-down period by each 9 to 10 pigs which weigh 75 to 100 lbs. at the start. About 1 bushel of corn will likewise be eaten daily by 7 to 8 pigs weighing 100 to 150 lbs. at the beginning, or by 5 to 6 pigs weighing 150 to 200 lbs. at the start.

If a protein supplement is not fed, it will usually take a given number of pigs somewhat longer to harvest a field of corn, for they will eat less per head daily and make correspondingly slower gains.

1332. New corn; soft corn.—If pigs are to hog down immature corn in the fall or are to be fed such grain in the yard, the change should always be made gradually, or digestive disturbances are apt to result. Immature corn is **more**

fermentable than mature grain and is apt to cause scours unless this precaution is taken. The statement is still sometimes heard that new corn causes hog cholera. This is untrue, though pigs which have become unthrifty due to improper feeding of new corn may be more susceptible to this and other diseases when exposed to infection.

Soft corn from a crop that is killed by frost before it matures can often be utilized best by feeding it to swine. (516) Experiments have shown that when soft corn is of good quality and not damaged by mold or rot, the dry matter in it is about equal to that in mature corn.[12] Of course, the feeding value per acre is lower, due to the reduced yield of dry matter from the immature crop. Soft corn that is damaged to some extent will be worth less than that of good quality, but will not injure hogs unless it is very moldy or rotten. It can therefore be fed to swine with much greater safety than to sheep or horses.

Ear-corn silage, which is very satisfactory for fattening cattle, gave poor results when fed to pigs in an Illinois trial and caused digestive trouble in an Iowa test.[13]

1333. Barley.—Barley is widely used for swine feeding in those sections of the northern states where corn is not an important grain crop, and in Canada and northern Europe it is the most common grain for swine. (551) Barley produces pork and bacon of excellent quality, the fat being hard and firm. Because of the hulls of ordinary barley, it is less concentrated than corn, and therefore is worth somewhat less per 100 lbs., as is shown in the experiments summarized later.

Due to the small size and the hardness of the barley kernels, the grain should be ground or rolled for the best results in swine feeding. It is best to grind barley to at least a medium degree of fineness, instead of merely cracking it.[14] Very fine grinding does not probably cause sufficient additional increase in value to warrant the greater cost. In Oregon tests steam-rolled barley was worth a trifle more than finely-ground barley.[15]

Many experiments have been conducted to compare the value of whole and ground barley for fattening pigs. While the savings made by grinding differed considerably in the various tests, in nearly all cases it paid to grind the grain. In 25 experiments grinding barley has increased its value 17 per cent, on the average.[16] On whole barley the gain is less rapid and considerably more feed is required per 100 lbs. gain.

When barley cannot conveniently be ground, it is often soaked for 12 hours or more before feeding it, but this is a poor substitute for grinding. Soaking the grain may produce somewhat more rapid gains, but usually there is little or no saving in the amount of feed required per 100 lbs. gain.[17]

Since barley is richer than corn in protein, less protein supplement is needed to balance the ration with barley. Pigs that are self-fed, free-choice, on barley and tankage or other protein supplements often eat decidedly more of the supplement than is needed to balance the ration. Therefore, it is best to mix the proper proportion of supplement with the ground barley and then self-feed the mixture, instead of self-feeding the grain and supplement separately. Suitable mixtures for dry lot and pasture feeding are shown in Appendix Table VII. The use of a protein supplement for pigs fed barley on pasture has been discussed in the previous chapter. (1286)

Barley has the same deficiencies as all the other small grains, having proteins of rather poor quality, being low in calcium, and lacking vitamins A and D. (**1325**)

The value of ground barley for swine feeding has been compared with that of corn and other grains in many experiments. The following table gives the results of 17 trials in which good-quality ground barley has been compared with corn, when self-fed to pigs in dry lot with tankage or a combination of tankage and alfalfa hay or alfalfa hay and linseed meal.[18] In these trials pigs averaging 79 lbs. in weight at the start were fed for an average of 75 days.

Experiments have not been included in this summary where the pigs ate an excess of supplement when it was fed free-choice, or where the experimenters fed considerably more supplement than was needed to balance the ration. When just as much supplement is fed with barley as with corn, advantage is not taken of the fact that barley contains more protein than corn.

Ground barley vs. corn for fattening pigs

Average ration	Daily gain Lbs.	Feed for 100 lbs. gain Grain Lbs.	Supplement Lbs.
Lot I. Barley, 6.6 lbs. Supplement, 0.4 lb..............	1.55	428	27
Lot II. Corn, 6.2 lbs. Supplement, 0.6 lb..............	1.66	373	36

The barley-fed pigs made gains that were good, though not quite so rapid as those of the pigs fed corn. For 100 lbs. gain they required 55 lbs. more grain than the corn-fed pigs, but 9 lbs. less supplement (nearly all of which was tankage). In these trials 100 lbs. of ground barley was equal in value to 87.1 lbs. corn plus 2.1 lbs. tankage. With corn at $20 per ton and tankage at $60, ground barley would be worth 93 per cent as much as corn, so far as amount of feed required per 100 lbs. gain was concerned.

In 10 similar trials in which good-quality ground barley has been compared with corn for pigs on pasture, the results have been similar.[19] In these tests the pigs fed barley likewise gained slightly less than those fed corn, and each 100 lbs. of ground barley was equal in value to 83 lbs. corn plus 4 lbs. supplement (tankage and linseed meal). With feeds at representative prices, ground barley was worth about 91 per cent as much as corn in these tests. Light-weight barley is worth less than heavy grain, the value depending on the proportion of kernels to hulls.

Barley should be ground for pigs, while this is not necessary with corn. Therefore the cost of grinding must be deducted from the relative value of ground barley, in order to find how much whole barley which is to be ground before being fed is worth. With usual prices for grinding, this will make whole barley worth about 81 to 85 per cent as much per ton as corn. There is no appreciable difference between the value of Trebi barley and the Manchurian varieties of barley for swine feeding.[20] Hull-less barley resembles wheat in feeding value.[21] Barley which is badly affected with scab is unsuited for feeding to swine. (**503**)

1334. Oats.—Oats are very satisfactory to use as a limited part of the ration for swine, but they are too bulky and too high in fiber to be fed as the chief concentrate. (**528**) While oats may be worth fully as

THE SCOOP SHOVEL METHOD OF PREPARING CORN FOR PIGS

For pigs under 150 lbs. in weight, shelling or grinding corn does not increase its value. For older pigs the saving by grinding is only 6 to 7 per ct. (From Iowa Station.)

SELF-FEEDING IS AN ECONOMICAL METHOD OF FATTENING PIGS

This labor-saving method of feeding gives excellent results with growing, fattening pigs, with well-grown shotes, and with old sows which are being fattened. (From Wisconsin Station.)

WHEAT MIDDLINGS OR LINSEED MEAL ARE FAIR ON PASTURE

On good pasture, such as this, wheat middlings or linseed meal are fair as supplements to corn or other grains. Still better results are secured when a small amount of tankage, fish meal, or dairy by-products is fed in addition. On the other hand, they are inefficient when used as the only supplement for feeding young pigs in dry lot.

BLUEGRASS PROVIDES EXCELLENT SPRING AND FALL PASTURE

Bluegrass furnishes cheap pasture for early spring and late fall, but it makes little growth in midsummer. Then such crops as alfalfa, clover, or rape should be provided.

much as corn per 100 lbs. when they form only a relatively small part of the ration, their value is much less than that of corn, barley, or wheat when fed in large amounts.

Oats vary considerably in weight per bushel and in proportion of hulls. Heavy-weight oats, containing a large percentage of kernels and a small percentage of hulls, are much better for swine than light-weight oats, and may satisfactorily form a somewhat larger proportion of the ration.

For growing and fattening pigs oats should generally not form more than one-third and preferably not more than one-fourth of the ration. If a larger proportion of oats is fed, the rate of gain will be reduced, and the value of the oats per 100 lbs. will be considerably less than when a smaller amount is used. For brood sows before their litters are farrowed, oats can form one-half of the grain without appreciably reducing the efficiency of the ration. This proportion of oats can also be continued until the pigs are 2 to 3 weeks old. They will then need a large flow of milk, and the sow's ration should therefore be more concentrated, containing not over one-fourth to one-third oats.

Extensive experiments have been conducted, especially by the Illinois, Indiana, Iowa, Minnesota, and Ohio Stations, to determine the best ways of using oats for growing and fattening pigs.[22] It has been found in these studies that oats have the highest value when ground oats are used to replace not more than one-fourth of the corn in a ration.

In 10 experiments pigs fed approximately 3 parts by weight of shelled corn and 1 part of ground oats with tankage or other efficient protein supplements gained an average of 1.23 lbs. per head daily, which was a trifle more than the average of 1.21 lbs. for others fed shelled corn as the only grain with the same supplements. Since oats have somewhat more protein than does corn, less protein supplement was needed when oats were included in the ration, but the oat-fed pigs required slightly more grain per 100 lbs. gain. In these experiments 100 lbs. of ground oats were equal to 88.8 lbs. corn plus 5.1 lbs. of tankage or tankage equivalent. With shelled corn at $20 and tankage at $60 a ton, this would give ground oats a value of $20.82 a ton, or 4 per cent more than that of shelled corn.

When forming more than 25 per cent of the ration for pigs, oats usually decrease the rate of gain and are worth decidedly less than corn per 100 lbs. Pigs fed oats as the only grain with good protein supplements gain much less rapidly than when a more concentrated ration is fed. Without considering the difference in rate of gain, ground oats fed as the only grain in 14 trials have been worth only 75 per cent as much as corn per 100 lbs.

Occasionally, when pigs are self-fed corn and tankage or some other protein supplement, free-choice, ground oats are also provided in a compartment of the self-feeder. When this is done, the pigs generally eat very little of the oats. Therefore, if one desires to use oats for pigs, it is best to mix the proper proportion of ground oats with the corn or other grain.

Oats should be ground to a medium fineness for swine, as grinding generally increases the value of the grain 25 per cent or more. Soaking whole oats does not increase their value appreciably.

1335. Hulled oats.—Sometimes oats for swine feeding are run through hulling machines which grind the grain and remove most of the hulls. Generally not over 85 to 90 per cent of the kernels are recovered in the hulled oats, the rest going with the hulls. It takes about 155 to 165 lbs. of whole oats to produce 100 lbs. of hulled oats.

Hulled oats are an excellent feed for swine, but they are usually much more expensive than corn or barley. Except perhaps for very young pigs, ground oats are a more economical feed than hulled oats. In 9 experiments with growing and fattening pigs, the addition of a limited amount of hulled oats to a ration of corn and protein supplement has increased the rate of gain slightly.[23] Each 100 lbs. of hulled oats (made from 155 to 165 lbs. of whole oats) has saved enough corn and protein supplement to equal about 140 lbs. of corn in value. In these trials the oats before hulling were therefore worth decidedly less than corn per pound.

Hulled oats are commonly too expensive to be fed as the only grain to swine.

1336. Wheat.—Except in certain districts of the Northwest, wheat is commonly too high in price, in comparison with the other grains, to be used in swine feeding. (537) As is shown later, wheat of good quality is even slightly superior to corn for swine. Wheat of poor quality that is unsuited for milling may be nearly equal to high-grade wheat in feeding value.[24] The value of salvage wheat, which has been damaged in elevator fires, will depend on the extent of injury by charring or smoke.

Many trials have been conducted by the experiment stations to compare the value of wheat with that of corn or barley for swine feeding. In 16 experiments in which ground wheat has been directly compared with shelled corn as the only grain for growing and fattening pigs, the pigs fed ground wheat with tankage or some other efficient protein supplement gained 1.39 lbs. per head daily on the average.[25] Others fed shelled corn in place of ground wheat gained 1.27 lbs. Because wheat contains more protein than does corn, a little less tankage or other protein supplement was required with wheat, but the wheat-fed pigs consumed a trifle more grain per 100 lbs. gain. In these trials 100 lbs. of ground wheat were equal in value to 97.7 lbs. shelled corn plus 3.2 lbs. tankage or tankage equivalent. With shelled corn at $20 a ton and tankage at $60 a ton, this would make wheat worth 7 per cent more than shelled corn.

Ground wheat has been compared with ground barley in 15 simliar experiments.[26] The pigs fed ground wheat gained 1.41 lbs. per head daily, in comparison with 1.31 lbs. for those fed ground barley. Somewhat less grain and supplement were required per 100 lbs. gain by the wheat-fed pigs than by those fed barley, and 100 lbs. ground wheat were equal in feeding value to 111.0 lbs. ground barley plus 2.5 lbs. tankage or tankage equivalent.

In these trials excellent results were secured when wheat was fed as the only grain to pigs on pasture and also to those in dry lot. Occasionally, pigs fed wheat as the only grain may show a little more tendency than those fed corn or barley to go off feed. In such cases, it is well to mix other grain with the wheat, for such combinations produce very satisfactory results.[27]   When wheat or corn is improperly used as the only feed for pigs not on pasture, wheat will produce somewhat better results than white corn, because wheat has more protein and minerals.

Though wheat is somewhat richer than corn in protein, nevertheless it requires the addition of an efficient protein supplement to produce rapid and economical gains, except for pigs on excellent pasture. Wheat is so palatable to pigs that when they are self-fed free-choice on wheat and either tankage or fish meal, they do not generally take more of the supplement than they need. Like the other grains, the quality of protein in wheat is not satisfactory for swine, and the grain lacks vitamins A and D. These deficiencies must be accordingly borne in mind and corrected. (**1325**)

When wheat is fed in self-feeders, pigs chew the grain so thoroughly that grinding increases its value only about 6 per cent, on the average.[28]   This saving is not usually sufficient to warrant the expense of grinding. If whole wheat is hand-fed, the pigs are so eager to get their share that they chew the grain less thoroughly. As a result, grinding wheat is probably advisable when the grain is hand-fed.[29]   Whole wheat should not be soaked as a substitute for grinding, as it is not so well utilized as the dry whole grain.[30]

1337. Rye.—The results that have been secured in experiments in which rye has been fed as the only or the chief grain to swine have differed widely. In some trials good results have been secured with rye, even when fed as the only grain to pigs from weights of 50 or 60 lbs. to market weights. However, in other experiments poor results have been secured with rye when it has formed most of the ration. (561)

These unsatisfactory results may have been due in some instances to the rye containing ergot, but investigators have reported poor results even when the rye was not appreciably contaminated with ergot. (502)   Minnesota investigations show that swine have a pronounced dislike for rye containing any marked amount of ergot, and will consume much less feed than they would otherwise.[31] Especial care should be taken not to feed rye containing ergot to breeding swine.

In experiments at several stations ground rye has been unsatisfactory when fed as the only grain for more than 30 to 60 days, even when combined with tankage or tankage and alfalfa hay.[32]   In Minnesota trials the results were not improved when the rye was cooked, or when there was added to a ration of rye, tankage, and minerals, either a vitamin A supplement or milk casein (which supplies excellent protein).[33]

In strong contrast with these results, rye has been satisfactory as the only grain in other trials. In 7 Montana trials pigs fed ground rye with alfalfa hay or alfalfa hay and tankage gained nearly as rapidly as others fed ground barley in place of the rye, and they required 7 per cent less grain per 100 lbs. gain.[34]

In 7 experiments where ground rye was compared with shelled corn for pigs in dry lot, when fed with tankage or a good supplemental mixture, the average daily gain was 1.11 lbs. on rye and 1.38 lbs. on corn.[35]   Not considering the less rapid gains on rye, 100 lbs. of ground rye were equal to 91.0 lbs. corn plus 0.8 lb. of supplement (chiefly tankage). When pigs do well on rye, the quality of the carcasses is good.

Due to the poor results that are often secured when rye is fed as the only grain, it had best be mixed with at least an equal weight and preferably a larger amount of other grain, such as corn, barley, oats, or wheat.[36]   Rye gives more uniformly good results when fed to pigs on pasture than to those in dry lot. Adding well-cured alfalfa hay to the ration of rye-fed pigs in dry lot is beneficial. A protein supplement should be added to balance the ration when rye is the chief grain, except perhaps for pigs over 75 to 100 lbs. in weight which are on good pasture. Unless the cost of grinding is unusually high, it pays to grind rye for swine.[37]

1338. Grain sorghums; sweet sorghums.—Throughout the sorghum belt the grain sorghums are of outstanding importance in pork production. (565) These grains are similar to corn in composition, though containing less fat. Kafir and feterita have about as much digestible protein as barley, while milo and darso supply but little more than corn. In swine feeding all the grain sorghums are excellent substitutes for corn, both for growing and fattening pigs and for breeding stock.

Kafir, milo, and feterita, when ground, are all worth fully 91 per cent as much as shelled corn for swine. The value of kaoliang and of sweet sorghum seed is lower, as is shown later. The grain of the various sorghums differs somewhat in palatability for swine, as shown in Kansas tests.[38] Probably this is due chiefly to differences in the amount of tannin in the seed. Red kafir, Wheatland milo, dwarf milo, and Atlas sorghum were more palatable than Blackhull kafir or Kalo, and Sumac sorghum seed was least liked.

Grain from the various sorghums has the same nutritive deficiencies as the other small grains and also white corn. Unless these lacks, which have been emphasized previously, are corrected, unsatisfactory results will be secured. (1325) For example, brood sows are unable to produce thrifty pigs when fed only grain sorghum, without a proper supply of protein, minerals, and vitamins.[39]

The sorghums should be threshed for swine, instead of being fed in the head. In Oklahoma tests threshing kafir and darso increased the value of the grain one-third or more.[40] Grinding sorghum heads is a disadvantage, as it forces the swine to eat the fibrous stems of the heads. Soaking the heads is also inadvisable.

It has been shown in recent Texas and Oklahoma experiments that when threshed grain sorghum is self-fed, grinding the grain does not increase its value enough to justify the expense.[41] On the other hand, when the grain is hand-fed the pigs are in such haste to get their shares that they do not chew it thoroughly. Therefore, grinding the grain is usually advisable. In a Texas test, for example, only 2 per cent of the milo grain passed through pigs unchewed when self-fed, while the loss was 10 per cent when the grain was hand-fed.

There is no advantage in soaking either whole or ground grain sorghum for swine.[42]

Kafir has been directly compared with corn in 7 experiments in which fattening pigs were fed grain supplemented with tankage, tankage and shorts, or alfalfa hay.[43] In the trials in which the daily gain was reported, it was practically as rapid on ground kafir as on corn. A little more feed was required per 100 lbs. gain on the kafir rations, and on the average 100 lbs. of ground kafir were equal in value to 91 lbs. of corn.

Milo was likewise worth about 91 per cent as much as corn in 6 similar tests in which ground milo was compared with corn for fattening pigs.[44]

Feterita was fully equal to milo for swine feeding in tests at the Kansas Station, and in an Arkansas test ground feterita was slightly superior to ground kafir.[45]

Kaoliang is apparently somewhat less valuable for swine feeding than kafir, milo, or feterita. In a South Dakota trial ground kaoliang was worth only about four-fifths as much as ground corn per 100 lbs., either when fed with alfalfa hay or when the grains were fed without any supplement.[46]

Seed from the sweet sorghums is not so palatable to swine as grain sorghum and has a lower value. When fed as the only grain, ground sweet sorghum seed has produced much less rapid gains than corn in 6 tests, and considerably more feed has been required per 100 lbs. gain on the sweet-sorghum-seed ration.[47] On the average 100 lbs. of ground sweet sorghum seed have been worth only as much as 68 lbs. of corn. Due to the small size of the seeds, sweet sorghum grain should be ground for swine.

Darso, a hybrid which has some of the characteristics of both the sweet sorghums and the grain sorghums, was worth about 88 per cent as much as corn in 3 Oklahoma tests in which pigs were fed either ground darso or ground corn, with tankage as the supplement.[48]

Seed from Atlas sorghum, another hybrid, produced nearly as rapid gains as corn in a Kansas trial in which pigs were fed ground Atlas seed or ground corn with tankage and alfalfa hay.[49] The ground Atlas grain was worth 94 per cent as much as ground corn in this test.

1339. Hominy feed.—Hominy feed is a satisfactory substitute for corn in swine feeding, and can be used for all classes of swine. However, it is worth only 95 per cent as much as corn per 100 lbs. for this purpose, while it is equal to corn for dairy cattle, beef cattle, and sheep. The slightly lower value of hominy feed for swine is probably due to the facts that hominy feed is somewhat higher than corn in fiber and that swine have but little ability to digest fiber.

In 14 experiments where hominy feed has been compared with corn when fed either with tankage or a supplemental mixture containing tankage, the gains have usually been a little less rapid on hominy feed.[50] Also, slightly more feed was required per 100 lbs. gain. On the average, hominy feed was worth 95 per cent as much as corn in these trials. Perhaps due to a difference in the milling process then employed, hominy feed was apparently worth more than corn for pigs in certain early experiments in which these feeds were compared.[51] Yellow hominy feed supplies vitamin A, while white hominy feed lacks the vitamin. (188)

When pigs are self-fed hominy feed and tankage or other palatable protein supplements by the free-choice method, they sometimes eat considerably more supplement than is needed. In such cases the supplement had best be mixed with the hominy feed in the proper proportion, or else be hand-fed.

1340. Minor grains; miscellaneous carbohydrate-rich feeds.—In addition to the grains that have been discussed in this chapter, emmer, spelt, millet seed, rice, and rice by-products are all used for swine feeding. Detailed information on the composition and values of these grains is given in Chapter XVII.

Emmer should be used in the same manner as oats, which it resembles in composition. Because of the hulls, emmer is worth much less than corn when fed as the only grain, but ground emmer is satisfactory when forming not more than one-half and preferably not more than one-third of the ration.[52] (574)

Finely-ground *hog millet seed* was worth 97 per cent as much as shelled corn for pigs in 3 Colorado trials, and finely-ground *hay millet seed* (from Kursk millet, a fox-tail variety) was worth about 92 per cent as much as corn.[53] (575)

Ground *rough rice* and *brewers' rice* produce firm pork of good quality, but *rice polish* and *rice bran* tend to produce soft pork. (568-572)

Ground *buckwheat* may be used like oats in swine feeding. It is too high in fiber to give good results when it forms a large part of the ration, and it also produces soft pork when too much is fed. (576)

Oat mill feed was worth about one-half as much per 100 lbs. as corn or hominy feed for pigs in Wisconsin tests, if not more than 16 per cent of it was included in the ration.[54] (530) *Oat hulls* were without value for growing and fattening pigs in an Ohio test in which 8 per cent of oat hulls was added to corn and the trio supplemental mixture.[55] (531) On the other hand, including the same percentage of *oat middlings* in the ration increased the gain slightly, and the oat middlings were worth 29 per cent more than corn. (529)

Molasses, either beet or cane, is used less commonly for swine feeding than for cattle, sheep, or horses.   However, when considerably cheaper than corn or other grain, molasses may well be substituted for a part of the grain in rations for swine.

Including 10 per cent of *cane molasses* in a ration of rolled barley, tankage, linseed meal and minerals in 4 tests at the Hawaii Station did not affect the average rate of gain of pigs and the molasses was worth slightly more than rolled barley per 100 lbs.[56] In Wisconsin tests cane molasses was generally worth somewhat less than corn when not to exceed 10 per cent of molasses was included in the rations of pigs fed corn and the trio supplemental mixture.[57]   When molasses is added to the ration, it is better to mix it with the grain than to mix the molasses with the protein supplement. (641)

Beet molasses is apt to cause scours in pigs unless they are started on it very gradually and only limited amounts are fed. (642)

The use of *garbage* in swine feeding has been discussed in Chapter XIX. (663) During the winter in the northern states, garbage-fed pigs may suffer from deficiencies of vitamin A or vitamin D, unless they are provided with well-cured legume hay or some other source of these vitamins.[58]

Many *commercial mixed feeds* for swine are available on the market. Some of these are intended as complete rations, while others are protein-rich mixtures to be used as supplements to the farm grains.   Several experiments have been conducted to compare various commercial mixed feeds with simple rations composed of corn or other grain supplemented by tankage or other efficient protein supplements.[59]   In these trials the simple rations have produced fully as good or even better results than the commercial mixed feeds, showing that there is no need of great variety in swine feeding, providing the nutritive requirements are met.

II. Protein Supplements

1341. Advantages of certain mixtures of supplements.—It has been shown in the previous chapter that pigs not on pasture are apt to suffer from a deficiency of vitamin A or of vitamin D if they are fed a ration consisting of only cereal grain and any of the most common protein-rich concentrates. (**1297**) If the grain is chiefly yellow corn, there will be an adequate supply of vitamin A, but there will still be a lack of vitamin D, unless the pigs receive more exposure to sunlight than is often possible during winter in the northern states.   Fish meal may or may not supply sufficient amounts of these vitamins, depending on the process of manufacture and the kind of raw material used. (**635**)

Numerous experiments have shown that tankage, meat scraps, skim-milk, or buttermilk produce excellent results when any one of these feeds is used as the only protein supplement for pigs on pasture.   On the other hand, young fall pigs often become unthrifty when fed grain and one of these supplements during the winter without pasture, especially under the climatic conditions in the northern states.   If the pigs have been raised on excellent pasture in the fall and if they are not too young when placed in dry lot, they may make satisfactory gains on such a ration until they reach the usual market weights.   This is because they will then have considerable stores of vitamin A and vitamin D in their bodies.   As has been emphasized previously, very poor results are secured when such a feed as linseed meal or wheat middlings is used as the only protein supplement to grain for young pigs in dry lot, even when a mineral supplement is added to provide an abundance of calcium and phosphorus. (**1282**)

These facts had been revealed even before vitamin D was discovered, and when but little was yet known concerning the importance of vitamin A in swine feeding. Investigations were therefore undertaken at various experiment stations in an endeavor to find some combination of protein supplements to use with corn or other grains, which would enable fall pigs to thrive under winter conditions like spring pigs do on good pasture.

As has been mentioned earlier in this chapter, it was found by the author and associates, Bohstedt and Fargo, at the Wisconsin Station that the addition of only 5 per cent of good-quality alfalfa hay to a ration of white corn and either skimmilk or tankage would fully protect the pigs against disaster from a lack of vitamin A. (**1329**) In these and other experiments that are discussed later in this chapter it was also learned that such an addition of alfalfa hay would very appreciably improve a ration of yellow corn and tankage or a ration of yellow corn and skimmilk. (**1396, 1397**)

Finally, mixtures of protein supplements were developed in these investigations which are safer and more efficient for young pigs not on pasture than any common single supplement. Probably the first of these mixtures was the combination of 50 lbs. tankage, 25 lbs. ground or chopped alfalfa hay or other legume hay, and 25 lbs. linseed meal, which was developed by the author with Bohstedt and Fargo at the Wisconsin Station.[60] This combination is now generally called the "trio mixture," the "Wisconsin mixture," or the "trinity mixture." It is commonly designated as the trio mixture in this volume.

As is mentioned later, it has been found in experiments at other stations that certain substitutions can be made satisfactorily in this combination. For example, fish meal is a trifle superior to tankage in the trio mixture, and soybean oil meal or cottonseed meal is a good substitute for the linseed meal.

1342. Results secured with the trio mixture.—To determine definitely whether or not the trio mixture was generally superior to tankage as the protein supplement to yellow corn for young pigs not on pasture, 10 experiments were conducted by the author and associates at the Wisconsin Station.[61] In these trials the pigs fed yellow corn and tankage gained 0.96 lb. per head daily, on the average, while those fed corn and the trio mixture gained 1.14 lbs. a day. This difference in daily gain means that 40-lb. pigs fed this ration would reach a market weight of 200 lbs. about 26 days before those fed the ration of corn and tankage.

Still more important was the fact that practically all of the pigs remained uniformly thrifty on corn and the trio mixture, and continued to make efficient gains even under winter conditions. On the other hand, several pigs fed only yellow corn and tankage did not thrive, and some showed definite symptoms of rickets. This was in spite of the fact that the pigs were provided with outdoor exercise lots, where they could get out in the sunlight when the weather was suitable. In these experiments the pigs fed corn and the trio mixture required 16.7 lbs. less feed for each 100 lbs. gain than did those fed corn and tankage. This may at first not seem to be an important saving, but it must be borne in mind that the improvement was made over the ration of yellow corn and tankage, which had long been considered the standard of excellence.

The trio mixture has been compared with tankage as the supplement to yellow corn for young pigs not on pasture in 21 experiments at other stations with similar results.[62] In these trials the average daily gain for the pigs fed yellow corn and the trio mixture was 1.35 lbs., and for those fed corn and tankage 1.17 lbs. Combining the results of the 31 separate experiments, pigs fed yellow corn and the trio mixture gained 1.28 lbs. per head daily from an average weight of 53 lbs. until they reached market weights. Those fed yellow corn and tankage gained an average of 1.10 lbs.

On the trio mixture an average of 351 lbs. corn and 63 lbs. trio mixture were required per 100 lbs. gain, while on tankage as the only supplement there were required 384 lbs. corn and 44 lbs. tankage. In these experiments each 100 lbs. of the trio mixture saved 70 lbs. tankage and 52 lbs. corn, without placing any value on the increase in rate of gain. With corn at $20, tankage at $60, linseed meal at $40, and ground or chopped alfalfa hay at $20 a ton, the feed cost per 100 lbs. gain would be $5.16 for the pigs fed yellow corn and tankage and only $4.93 for those fed corn and the trio mixture.

It should be borne in mind that the most important advantage of the trio mixture over tankage as a supplement to grain for pigs not on pasture is not the slight increase in rate of gain or the slight saving in feed required per 100 lbs. gain. The chief merit of the trio mixture and similar combinations is the insurance against some of the pigs being made unthrifty or even becoming runts, because of a lack of vitamins. It is fortunate, indeed, that this insurance against vitamin deficiency can be gained, not only without added expense, but at an actual saving in cost, through the use of these cheap combinations.

The trio mixture is relatively simple, being composed of only 3 feeds. Nevertheless, there seems to be no advantage in making the mixture more complex by including other ingredients, at least for pigs that are past the weaning stage. For pigs at weaning time it is advantageous to add dairy by-products to the ration, when they are available on the farm.

The advantages secured from the trio mixture can mostly be gained by adding merely alfalfa hay to such a ration as grain and tankage. However, experiments at the Kansas, Ohio, South Dakota, and Wisconsin Stations show that the gains are slightly more rapid and also more economical when corn and the trio mixture are fed to young pigs in dry lot, instead of a ration of corn, tankage, and alfalfa hay.[63]

If pigs are well grown on pasture or on grain and such a supplement as the trio mixture until they reach a weight of 100 lbs., they can usually be fed safely on only grain and tankage until they reach the usual market weights. Sometimes the cost of gains may even be a trifle less after this time on a ration of yellow corn and tankage than on yellow corn and the trio mixture.[64] Especially in the case of fall pigs fed in dry lot during the winter conditions in the northern states, it is the safest plan to continue to use the trio mixture or a similar combination until the pigs are marketed. The trio mixture and similar combinations are satisfactory for feeding to pigs on pasture, but if the pasture is really good, there is no need of including legume hay in the combination of supplements.[65]

In 3 Ohio experiments with young pigs in dry lot, the combination of corn and the trio mixture was superior to a ration of corn, tankage, and a small amount of cod-liver oil (fed as a vitamin supplement).[66] The pigs fed corn and the trio mixture gained 1.14 lbs. per head daily, on the average, at a feed cost per 100 lbs. gain of $6.80. Those fed corn, tankage, and cod-liver oil gained 1.03 lbs. a day at a feed cost per 100 lbs. gain of $7.11.

1343. Methods of feeding trio mixtures.—The trio mixture and similar supplemental combinations produce excellent results when self-fed, free-choice, as the supplement to shelled corn, also self-fed, or to ear corn that is full-fed. In 3 Wisconsin tests the gains were about as rapid and were slightly more economical when pigs were thus self-fed, free-choice, on shelled corn and the trio mixture, than when a mixture was self-fed which consisted of ground corn and the proper proportion of the trio mixture to balance the ration.[61]

When pigs are fed the grains that are richer in protein than corn (including barley, oats, kafir, and rye) they may eat a larger amount of the trio mixture or similar mixtures if the mixture is self-fed, free-choice. With such grains, except in the case of wheat, it is generally more economical to mix the proper proportion of supplement with the grain and then self-feed the mixture. (**1284**)

1344. Other supplemental mixtures for dry lot feeding.—Numerous experiments have been conducted during recent years to determine the value of different combinations of protein supplements as supplements to corn and the other grains for pigs in dry lot and for those on pasture. Only the briefest summary can be given here of some of the most important of the results secured in these studies.

It is shown later in this chapter that soybean oil meal is about equal to linseed meal when used as a substitute for the latter in the trio mixture. (**1369**) In a Delaware test raw soybeans were not a satisfactory substitute for linseed meal in the trio mixture.[67] Cottonseed meal can be used to replace linseed meal in the trio mixture, but the cottonseed-meal combination is slightly inferior to the original trio mixture. (**1366**)

In 3 Wisconsin experiments the results were not quite so good when either corn germ meal or wheat standard middlings were substituted for the linseed meal in the trio mixture.[68] However, the corn germ meal combination and the middlings combination were both slightly superior to tankage as the supplement to corn for young pigs not on pasture. As stated later in this chapter, other legume hay of good quality can be used in place of alfalfa hay in the trio mixture. (**1401**)

Meat scraps are probably deficient in vitamin A and vitamin D, the same as is digester tankage. For young pigs in dry lot it is therefore advisable to use a trio mixture including meat scraps, instead of feeding meat scraps as the only protein supplement. In an Ohio trial there was a decided improvement in rate and economy of gain when the meat scraps trio mixture was fed to young pigs in dry lot instead of meat scraps as the only supplement.[69] On the other hand, there was no benefit from the use of the trio mixture in Minnesota trials.[70] Perhaps in the latter the pigs had an unusually good store of vitamins in their bodies when the experiments began.

Trials at the New York (Cornell) Station which are reviewed later show that when menhaden fish meal is substituted for the tankage in the trio mixture, the results are even a trifle better than when the tankage trio mixture is used. (1358) If the fish meal contains goodly amounts of vitamin A and vitamin D, just as good results may be secured when it is fed as the only protein supplement to pigs in dry lot as when a trio combination is used (including legume hay).[71] However, unless one is sure that the fish meal has plenty of these vitamins, it is wise to use a trio combination for young pigs in dry lot, or at least to supply them with legume hay.

The "big ten" supplemental mixture, developed by Evvard and Culbertson at the Iowa Station, is probably about equal to the trio mixture.[72] This consists of 40 lbs. tankage; 20 lbs. cottonseed meal; 15 lbs. linseed meal; 12.8 lbs. ground alfalfa hay; 9 lbs. peanut oil meal; 1 lb. salt; 1.5 lbs. ground limestone; 0.198 lb. iron oxide, commercial grade; 0.5 lb. hardwood ashes; and 0.002 lb. potassium oxide. It will be noted that this combination is much more complex than the relatively simple trio mixture or its various modifications.

Such a combination as tankage and linseed meal may produce slightly more rapid and economical gains than tankage when used as the only supplement to grain for pigs not on pasture.[73] However, especially in the case of pigs under 100 to 125 lbs. in weight, it is advisable to include good legume hay in the ration to insure an adequate supply of vitamins A and D.

1345. Supplemental mixtures for pasture feeding.—A mixture of one-half by weight of linseed meal and one-half of tankage is excellent for self-feeding, free-choice, to pigs that are self-fed corn on pasture. In 6 Wisconsin trials pigs self-fed this mixture and yellow corn on good pasture made an average daily gain of 1.36 lbs., while others self-fed tankage and corn gained 1.31 lbs.[74] Though the difference in gains was but slight, there was also a slight saving in the amount of feed required per 100 lbs. gain. The feed cost of 100 lbs. gain was $6.59 for the pigs fed the mixed supplement and $6.71 for those fed tankage. In these trials each 100 lbs. of linseed meal replaced 51 lbs. of tankage plus 80 lbs. of corn.

In other experiments in which mixtures of various proportions of linseed meal and tankage have been self-fed in comparison with tankage as the supplement to corn or barley for pigs on good pasture, the gains have, on the average, been slightly more rapid and also a trifle cheaper, with the mixed supplement.[75] In some of the trials, however, tankage has been just as efficient as the mixed supplement. On the other hand, there has been no benefit from adding linseed meal to the ration in experiments in which corn, linseed meal, and tankage have been self-fed separately to pigs on pasture, in comparison with corn and tankage, or in trials in which the entire ration or the supplements have been hand fed.[76]

After a study of all the available data, the author prefers a mixture of one-half tankage and one-half linseed meal to tankage for self-feeding, free-choice, to pigs fed corn on pasture, if the cost of linseed meal per ton is not over two-thirds that of tankage.   It is shown later in this chapter that a combination of one-half cottonseed meal and one-half of either tankage or meat scraps is even slightly superior to a combination of linseed meal and tankage or meat scraps. (**1366**)

The "all-purpose protein supplement" developed by Gerlaugh and associates in Ohio is an excellent supplemental mixture for swine on pasture. (**629**)   This consists of a combination of 30 lbs. meat scraps, 30 lbs. soybean oil meal, 20 lbs. cottonseed meal, 15 lbs. linseed meal, and 5 lbs. minerals (equal parts of steamed bone meal, ground limestone, and salt).   For young pigs not on pasture, it would be advisable to add 30 lbs. of chopped or ground legume hay to each 100 lbs. of this mixture, in order to provide vitamins A and D.

Pigs on pasture will generally make as rapid gains when fish meal is the only supplement to corn or other grain, as when a combination is used of fish meal and either linseed meal, cottonseed meal, or soybean oil meal. (**1358**) Whether or not there will be any advantage from the use of such a combination, will depend on the relative prices of the various supplements.

1346. Skimmilk; buttermilk.—Both skimmilk and buttermilk are ideal protein supplements to the farm grains in swine feeding, for these dairy by-products are rich in protein of the highest quality and they are also high in calcium and phosphorus. (**618-619**) Skimmilk and buttermilk are of especially high value for young pigs before weaning and also for several weeks after weaning.   When either of these dairy by-products is used as the supplement to corn or other grain for pigs, the gains will generally be slightly more rapid than when other excellent protein supplements are used, such as tankage or fish meal.   Skimmilk and buttermilk are also excellent protein supplements for breeding swine.

In feeding skimmilk, buttermilk, or whey to swine, it must be borne in mind that they are all very low in vitamin A and that they have but traces of vitamin D. (**188, 192**) A ration made up only of grain and one of these dairy by-products will be deficient in vitamin D, and unless the grain is yellow corn, there will be a serious lack of vitamin A.

A combination of grain and skimmilk or buttermilk produces excellent results when fed to pigs on good pasture, for the green forage provides an abundance of vitamin A, and the exposure to direct sunlight meets their vitamin D requirements.   For all swine not on pasture, legume hay should, if possible, be supplied in addition to grain and these dairy by-products, so as to provide an adequate supply of these vitamins. (**1298**) Legume hay is especially necessary when little or no yellow corn is fed, and also for young pigs during winter when they are not protected from rickets by abundant exposure to sunlight.

For pigs before and soon after weaning, skimmilk is best if fed fresh, though even for young pigs skimmilk which has soured under sanitary conditions is satisfactory.   However, if sour milk is to be used, it should always be fed sour.   Feeding the milk sweet at one feeding and sour at the next is apt to cause scours.

Buttermilk which has not been diluted by the addition of churn washings has practically the same chemical composition as skimmilk. Experiments have shown that it is of approximately the same value for swine.[77] Contrary to certain claims that have been made, the lactic acid in buttermilk does not give buttermilk any higher value than sweet skimmilk for swine.[78] Storage of buttermilk for a few days under sanitary conditions does not apparently injure its value.[79]

In order to prevent the introduction of disease on the farm, dairy by-products should be pasteurized at the creamery or cheese factory before being returned to the farm. (621)

1347. Value of skimmilk or buttermilk.—To determine the real value of skimmilk or buttermilk for swine feeding we must compare it with another efficient protein supplement, such as tankage. Also, no more of either supplement should be fed than is needed to balance the ration. If an excess is used, the value of the supplement will be reduced, as full use will then not be made of the protein it provides.

In many of the early experiments to study the value of these dairy by-products, a ration of grain and skimmilk or buttermilk was compared with a ration of grain alone. This is obviously not a fair basis for determining the value of these dairy by-products, for no progressive farmer now feeds his pigs such an inefficient ration as grain alone when they are not on pasture.

The value of skimmilk as a protein supplement to corn for pigs not on pasture is shown in 12 experiments in each of which one lot of pigs was fed a ration of skimmilk and corn (yellow corn in nearly all cases) in the proper proportion to make a well-balanced ration, and another lot was fed proper proportions of corn and tankage.[80] In these trials pigs averaging 75 lbs. in weight at the start were fed for an average of 97 days with the results shown in the following table.

Skimmilk vs. tankage as supplement to corn for fattening pigs

Average ration	Daily gain Lbs.	Corn Lbs.	Skim-milk Lbs.	Tankage Lbs.
Lot I, fed skimmilk				
Skimmilk, 7.1 lbs.				
Corn, 4.6 lbs............................	1.36	346	535	..
Lot II, fed tankage				
Tankage, 0.47 lb.				
Corn, 4.9 lbs............................	1.24	404	...	39

The pigs fed skimmilk and corn in these extensive trials gained 1.36 lbs. a head daily, which was 0.12 lb. more than those fed tankage and corn. On skimmilk and corn there were required only 346 lbs. corn and 535 lbs. skimmilk for 100 lbs. gain, while the pigs on tankage and corn consumed 404 lbs. corn and 39 lbs. tankage for each 100 lbs. gain.

In these trials each 100 lbs. of skimmilk saved 7.3 lbs. tankage, plus 10.9 lbs. corn, without giving any credit for the more rapid gains produced by feeding skimmilk. The high value of the dry matter in skimmilk is shown by the fact that 100 lbs. of skimmilk, containing only 9.9 lbs. dry matter, replaced 15.7 lbs. of dry matter in corn and tankage.

It has been emphasized previously that grain supplemented either by tankage or by skimmilk is not an ideal ration for pigs not on pasture, due to the lack of vitamin D and also to a deficiency of vitamin A unless the grain is yellow corn. One of the best possible rations that does not include dairy by-products is the combination of corn and the trio supplemental mixture (consisting of tankage, linseed meal, and alfalfa or other legume hay). (**1341**) It is therefore important to know the value of skimmilk when it is substituted for tankage in this efficient and popular ration.

In 3 Wisconsin tests pigs self-fed corn and the trio mixture from shortly after weaning up to market weights gained an average of 1.07 lbs., while others fed corn, supplemented by 5.9 lbs. skimmilk, 0.21 lb. linseed meal, and 0.21 lb. alfalfa hay gained 1.14 lbs.[81] In these experiments each 100 lbs. of skimmilk saved 7.4 lbs. tankage plus 13.1 lbs. corn and 1.1 lbs. linseed meal.

Skimmilk was compared with tankage in 3 Michigan and Nebraska trials, which were similar except that linseed meal was not included in the rations.[82] In these tests each 100 lbs. of skimmilk was equal in value to 6.7 lbs. tankage plus 7.5 lbs. corn and 1.3 lbs. alfalfa hay.

Skimmilk or buttermilk will have an even higher value than shown in these experiments for very young pigs up to 50 to 60 lbs. in weight. Also, the value of these dairy by-products per 100 lbs. will be greatest when only a very limited amount of skimmilk or buttermilk is used, and a sufficient amount of some other protein supplement is fed to balance the ration fully. Only 2 to 4 lbs. of skimmilk or buttermilk per head daily will produce excellent gains on young pigs, when the rest of the protein needed to balance the ration is supplied by another supplement. This supplement may be a small amount of tankage or fish meal, or it may also be wheat middlings or linseed meal, both of which are inefficient when fed as the only protein supplement to pigs. (**1282**)

The high value of skimmilk when only a limited amount is fed with a small amount of another supplement is shown in 3 Ohio trials in which pigs were fed from a weight of 45 lbs. to a market weight of about 200 lbs.[83] On a ration of 3.2 lbs. skimmilk, 0.22 lb. tankage, and 3.8 lbs. corn, pigs gained 1.19 lbs. per head daily, in comparison with 0.96 lb. for others fed corn and tankage, a mineral mixture being included in both rations. When this small amount of skimmilk was fed as a partial substitute for tankage, each 100 lbs. of skimmilk replaced 7.4 lbs. tankage plus 22.5 lbs. corn.

As is pointed out later, skimmilk and buttermilk have a lower value if more is fed than is needed to balance the ration. As a supplement to other grains, these dairy by-products have about the same value as when fed with corn. The value of skimmilk or buttermilk in comparison with tankage and other protein supplements will in general be somewhat less for pigs on pasture than for those in dry lot.[84] This is because good pasturage aids in furnishing some of the nutritive factors which make milk such a superlative feed for young pigs.

If a ration already contains a sufficient amount of tankage, fish meal, or other efficient protein supplement to balance it properly, it is uneconomical to add skimmilk or buttermilk to it.[85] The other protein supplements should be omitted, or else reduced in amount if there is not enough milk to balance the ration completely.

1348. Amount of skimmilk or buttermilk to feed.—Skimmilk and buttermilk are too rich in protein and also too watery to produce economical gains when fed alone. They should therefore always be fed with cereal grains or other carbohydrate-rich concentrates. These dairy by-products have the greatest value when no more is fed than is needed to balance the ration. Much larger amounts can, however, be fed when there is a surplus available, after the dairy calves and poultry have been provided with a sufficient amount of these efficient protein supplements. Any additional amounts of skimmilk or buttermilk that may be used beyond the amounts needed to balance the rations for pigs will, of course, be worth much less than the portion that is actually needed as a protein supplement. This is because the pigs will be able to use the excess amount only as a source of energy and not as a source of high-quality protein to make good the deficiencies of protein in the rest of the ration.

Various experiments have shown clearly the lessened value of skim-milk or buttermilk when more is fed than is needed to balance the ration. For example, in 2 Ohio tests pigs were fed from weights of 33 to 45 lbs. until they were ready for market on various proportions of skimmilk and corn, in comparison with pigs fed corn and tankage in proper amounts.[86] With corn at 56 cents a bushel and tankage at $60 a ton, skimmilk was worth 51 cents per 100 lbs. when 1 lb. of skimmilk was fed with each 1 lb. of corn. When 3 lbs. of milk were fed per pound of corn, the value of 100 lbs. of skimmilk was reduced to 30 cents, and when the pigs were allowed to drink all the skimmilk they would take in addition to a full feed of corn, each 100 lbs. of the milk was worth only 21 cents.

Due to the high efficiency of the milk proteins as supplements to the cereal grains, pigs fed grain and either skimmilk or buttermilk do not require quite as much protein as is generally advised in the feeding standards. In computing balanced rations for pigs of various weights with skimmilk or buttermilk as the chief supplement, the amount of protein may even fall a trifle below the amounts advised in the Morrison feeding standards. (Appendix Table III.)

The proportion of skimmilk or buttermilk that is needed to balance corn or other grain will depend on the age of the pigs. Just after weaning, pigs require so much protein that 4 to 6 lbs. of skimmilk or butter-milk are needed to balance each pound of corn. This is a larger proportion of milk than pigs will usually take when they are full-fed on corn. Therefore milk should preferably be used at this time in combination with a limited amount of other protein supplements. An excellent combination is corn, skimmilk, and a small amount of wheat middlings or linseed meal (with legume hay in addition for pigs not on pasture).

As the pigs grow older, the proportion of skimmilk or buttermilk needed to balance the ration decreases as follows: Pigs weighing 50 to 100 lbs., 2.5 to 3 lbs. milk to 1 lb. corn; pigs weighing 100 to 150 lbs., 2 to 2.5 lbs. milk to 1 lb. corn; pigs weighing 150 to 200 lbs., 1.5 to 2.0 lbs. per pound of corn; and pigs weighing over 200 lbs., only 1.0 to 1.5 lbs. of milk for each pound of corn. Where barley or wheat is fed in place of corn, only about one-half to two-thirds as much milk is needed for each pound of grain as with corn.

Pigs fed corn on good pasture will need only about one-half as much milk for each pound of grain. If the above amounts of milk are available, there is no use of adding any other protein-rich feed. But if sufficient skimmilk or buttermilk is not on hand, it will pay to feed a small amount of some other supplement, like tankage, linseed meal, or wheat middlings, to balance the ration properly.

Pigs need a large proportion of skimmilk to each pound of corn when they are young, but they consume more grain per head daily as they grow older. Therefore after pigs reach a weight of 40 to 50 lbs., the weight of milk that is needed per head daily to balance the ration remains about constant. For pigs not on pasture that are full-fed corn and are supplied with legume hay in addition, 6 lbs. of skimmilk or buttermilk per head daily will produce rapid and economical gains.[87] The rate of gain may be a trifle more rapid when more milk is fed, but generally the value of the milk per 100 lbs. will be less.

For pigs full-fed corn on good pasture a daily allowance of only 3 lbs. of milk per head is satisfactory.[88] If an abundance of milk is available, the gains can be increased slightly by feeding 4 to 6 lbs. of milk a day, but the milk will then have a somewhat lower value per 100 lbs.

1349. Money value of skimmilk or buttermilk.—It is evident from the preceding discussion that the actual value of skimmilk or buttermilk per 100 lbs. in comparison with that of tankage depends somewhat on the ration that is fed. It seems safe to conclude that when no more of one of these dairy by-products is used than is needed to balance the ration, each 100 lbs. will be equal in value to approximately 7.3 lbs. tankage plus 10.9 lbs. corn. The money value of skimmilk or buttermilk thus depends on the prices both of tankage and of corn.

For convenience, the money value of 100 lbs. of skimmilk or buttermilk with corn and tankage at various prices (based on this valuation) is shown in the following table. It should be borne clearly in mind that these values will be secured only when no more milk is fed than is needed to balance the ration.

Money value of skimmilk or buttermilk per 100 lbs., for pigs

	Price of corn per bushel				
	$.40	$.56	$.70	$.85	$1.00
Value of 100 lbs. skimmilk or buttermilk	Cents	Cents	Cents	Cents	Cents
With tankage at $40 a ton...........	22	25	..	..	..
With tankage at $50 a ton...........	26	29	32	..	..
With tankage at $60 a ton...........	30	33	35	38	..
With tankage at $70 a ton...........	33	36	39	42	45
With tankage at $80 a ton...........	..	40	43	46	48
With tankage at $100 a ton..........	..	..	50	53	56

When only a very limited amount of skimmilk or buttermilk is fed to pigs in combination with grain and a small amount of other protein supplements, the value of the milk will be even higher than shown in this table. On the other hand, for pigs on excellent pasture the value will generally be less than here shown. When the pigs are given considerably more milk than is needed to balance their rations, the value of the milk per 100 lbs. is correspondingly lessened.

1350. Whole milk.—Because of the high value of butter fat for human food, it is not profitable to feed whole milk to pigs, except perhaps in the case of orphan pigs raised by hand. **(1428)** Indeed, it was found in a Utah trial that whole milk is worth only about twice as much per 100 lbs. as skimmilk for pigs.[89] Cow's milk rich in fat is not so good as milk lower in fat for young pigs, as it is apt to cause digestive disturbances on account of the high fat content. **(209)**

1351. Dried skimmilk; dried buttermilk.—Dried skimmilk and dried buttermilk are generally too expensive to be economical protein supplements for swine feeding. They have a considerably higher value in comparison with tankage or fish meal for dairy calves being raised on a minimum amount of milk and for poultry than they do for pigs. **(622)** One pound of dried skimmilk or dried buttermilk is equal in amount of nutrients and in feeding value to 10 lbs. of fluid skimmilk or buttermilk.

Where no fluid skimmilk or buttermilk is available these dried dairy by-products are excellent protein supplements for pigs, particularly at weaning time and during a few weeks afterward. The gains at this time will usually be a trifle greater when some dairy by-product is included in the ration. However, the cost of the gains is nearly always less when such a protein supplement as the trio mixture is used, without dried skimmilk or dried buttermilk.

These feeds have only 33 to 35 per cent protein, in comparison with 50 to 60 per cent protein in high-grade tankage, meat scraps, or fish meal. Considerably more dried skimmilk or dried buttermilk than of tankage or fish meal is therefore needed to balance the ration. Because of this, these dried dairy by-products have been worth only about 90 per cent as much per ton in experiments in which they have been fed as the only protein supplements to growing and fattening pigs.[90]

Even when only a small amount of dried skimmilk or dried buttermilk has been used in combination with a reduced amount of tankage or some other supplement, the dried skimmilk or buttermilk has been worth only a little more per ton than tankage.[91] These dried dairy by-products generally cost much more per ton than tankage, meat scraps, or fish meal.

When maximum growth of purebred pigs is desired, regardless of the expense, and no fluid skimmilk or buttermilk is available, excellent results are secured when 5 to 10 per cent of dried skimmilk or dried buttermilk is included in the ration, at least until the pigs reach a weight of 50 to 75 lbs. These dairy by-products should not be self-fed separately, free-choice, for they are so palatable that the pigs will eat much more than they need.

1352. Condensed or evaporated buttermilk.—Condensed buttermilk, also called "evaporated buttermilk" and "semi-solid buttermilk," usually contains over 60 per cent water, and it takes about 3 lbs. of condensed buttermilk to equal 1 lb. of dried buttermilk in feeding value. The expense for freight is high in transporting condensed buttermilk, considering the amount of dry matter it contains. Also, it must be shipped in water-tight containers. For these reasons it is necessarily high in price for the amount of nutrients it actually provides, and consequently it has been largely replaced by dried buttermilk in stock feeding.

Numerous experiments have been conducted to determine the value of condensed buttermilk for pigs, either as a substitute for tankage or other common protein supplements, or when a small amount has been added to a good ration.[92] In these trials pigs fed condensed buttermilk have made slightly more rapid gains than others receiving no dairy by-products, but the gains have been unduly expensive. While the price of the condensed buttermilk per ton was nearly as high as that of tankage, it was generally worth no more than one-third to two-thirds as much per ton as tankage.

Some years ago claims were made that even when condensed buttermilk was fed in very diluted form as a "sour drink," it would have a highly beneficial effect on the health of pigs. In 3 Wisconsin tests, however, there was no benefit whatsoever from adding 0.15 lb. of condensed buttermilk per head daily (diluted with about 30 parts of water to each part of buttermilk) to a ration consisting of corn and the trio supplemental mixture.[93]

1353. Whey.—Whey has only 0.9 per cent protein, but the protein it does contain (which is nearly all milk albumin) is especially effective in making good the deficiencies of the proteins in the cereal grains. (**620**) Because of this high quality of the protein in whey, well-grown pigs weighing over 100 lbs. will make excellent gains on a ration of only whey and barley or wheat, without the addition of any other supplement.

For example, in 2 Wisconsin trials such pigs gained even more rapidly on a ration of 7.8 lbs. barley plus what whey they would drink (an average of 18.4 lbs. a day) than others did on barley and tankage.[94] Likewise, in 2 California experiments pigs fed barley and whey gained nearly as rapidly as those fed barley and skimmilk.[95]

It was found in the Wisconsin tests that for younger pigs some protein-rich feed, such as linseed meal or wheat middlings, should be added to barley and whey to balance the ration more completely. With corn and whey, a supplement should be fed even to pigs over 150 lbs. in weight, for corn contains considerably less protein than does barley. An important fact brought out in these trials is that if pigs are given what whey they will drink, there is no further need, even for young pigs in dry lot, of supplying protein-rich feeds of animal origin. Entirely satisfactory results are secured when the ration is balanced by the protein-rich concentrates of plant origin, like linseed meal or wheat middlings.

For pigs not on pasture, legume hay should be provided in addition to grain and whey, in order to provide ample amounts of vitamins A and D. This is especially important in the case of pigs under 100 to 125 lbs. in weight.

In the Wisconsin trials skimmed whey was worth about one-half as much per 100 lbs. as skimmilk. Unskimmed whey from American or Cheddar cheese factories, which contains about 0.3 per cent fat, will be worth a trifle more; and unskimmed whey from Swiss factories, which may contain 0.8 to 1.0 per cent fat, will have a correspondingly higher value than skimmed whey.

In the California trials whey was worth more than one-half as much as skimmilk per 100 lbs. For pigs on good pasture whey has been worth somewhat less than one-half as much as skimmilk per 100 lbs.[96]

Whey should always be pasteurized at the factory to prevent the spread of disease and should be fed under sanitary conditions. Whey soured in clean containers is as valuable as sweet whey, but that from a filthy whey tank may be an unsatisfactory feed.

1354. Tankage; meat scraps.—For many years digester tankage (or wet-rendered tankage) has been the high-protein supplement most extensively used for swine feeding in this country. (**626**) Not only are tankage and meat scraps excellent supplements for growing and fattening pigs, but they also have the same high rank for feeding breeding swine.

In the feeding experiments conducted by the experiment stations, digester tankage has generally been selected as the standard with which other protein supplements have been compared. This has been done on account of the excellent results that are secured when tankage is properly used, and also because tankage of high grade could often be more readily obtained than a constant supply of skimmilk or buttermilk. In this chapter the values of the other protein supplements are therefore generally compared with that of tankage.

As has been stated previously, the digester process of producing tankage is now being largely replaced by the dry-rendering process, in which the product called meat scraps, or dry-rendered tankage, is produced. (**627**) It is shown later that meat scraps are even slightly superior to digester tankage for swine feeding.

Digester tankage and meat scraps are both rich in protein that effectively corrects the deficiencies in the proteins of the cereal grains. (**1281**) These supplements are likewise very rich in calcium and phosphorus. The only respect in which digester tankage and meat scraps fail to be complete supplements to the grains is that they lack vitamins A and D. While these meat by-products are complete supplements to the grains for swine on good pasture, in the case of swine not on pasture legume hay should be included in the ration to provide an abundant supply of these vitamins. (**1298**) This is especially important for both young pigs and brood sows during winter or whenever they are not out in direct sunlight much of the time.

As single protein supplements for swine, digester tankage and meat scraps are excelled only by skimmilk, buttermilk, and fish meal. When tankage or meat scraps are used in such protein supplemental mixtures as the trio mixture for pigs not on pasture, then the results are well-nigh ideal. Though excellent results are secured when tankage is used as the only supplement to grain for pigs on good pasture, it is shown elsewhere that combinations of tankage and other supplements may produce a trifle more rapid and economical gains, especially when self-fed by the free-choice method. Thus, a mixture of one-half tankage and one-half linseed meal or cottonseed meal is slightly superior for feeding in this manner as a supplement to corn for pigs on pasture. (**1345**)

The results of trials in which well-proportioned rations of corn and tankage have been compared with corn alone for pigs not on pasture have been given on previous pages. (**1327**) It is there pointed out that on corn alone young pigs made exceedingly poor gains, and that compared with this inefficient ration, 100 lbs. of tankage are worth more than 600 lbs. of corn. Well-grown pigs which were started on corn alone at an average weight of 150 lbs. stood this poor ration somewhat better, but even for feeding such older pigs, each 100 lbs. of tankage saved 538 lbs. of corn. These figures cannot be taken as showing the actual money value of tankage, for several protein-rich supplements are usually available for swine feeding, and the actual feeding value of tankage will depend on the prices of the other supplements available.

1355. Grades of tankage and meat scraps.—High-grade digester tankage is generally guaranteed to contain 60 per cent protein, and this is the grade that has commonly been used in the feeding experiments summarized in this chapter. Meat scraps, or dry-rendered tankage, is usually guaranteed to contain either 50 or 55 per cent protein. Sometimes, however, meat scraps are produced that have 60 per cent protein or more. Tankage or meat scraps containing only 50 per cent protein or less commonly contains so much bone that it must be sold as a meat-and-bone product to conform to the definitions of the American Association of Feed Control Officials.

Tankages containing only 30 to 45 per cent protein are produced by some small plants, and especially by rendering plants which render dead animals and scrap meat and bones from butcher shops for soap grease and other inedible fat. Tankages of this kind are usually so high in bone that they should be sold as *digester tankage with bone,* or *meat and bone scraps.* (**628**) The dead-animal tankage, or reduction tankage, is used chiefly for fertilizer. Some is fed to stock, and it is satisfactory for this purpose if not made from material that has begun to decompose before it is processed. (**630**)

In tests at the Indiana and Ohio Stations very satisfactory results have been secured with low-protein tankages having 35 to 45 per cent protein, these tankages being worth more per unit of protein than high-grade digester tankage or meat scraps.[97] On the other hand, in Alabama and Iowa tests tankage containing 40 per cent protein was a much less satisfactory supplement to corn when self-fed, free-choice, than high-grade tankage containing 60 per cent protein.[98] Quite possibly these differences in results were due to differences in the character of the raw materials used in making the low-protein tankages.

1356. Meat scraps vs. digester tankage.—Several experiments have been conducted recently to compare the 60-per-cent-protein grade of digester tankage with meat scraps as the supplement for pigs. These trials have shown that although there is less protein in the usual grade of meat scraps (which contains about 50 per cent protein), such meat scraps are worth fully as much or slightly more for swine feeding than digester tankage having 60 per cent protein. Meat scraps containing 55 per cent protein are worth correspondingly more than the product containing 50 per cent protein, and meat scraps having 60 per cent protein are still more valuable.

In 14 recent experiments pigs on pasture fed meat scraps of 50 to 55-per-cent-protein grade as the supplement to corn gained 1.61 lbs. per head daily, in comparison with 1.56 lbs. for others fed digester tankage of the 60-per-cent-protein grade as the supplement to corn.[99] The pigs fed meat scraps required 3.8 lbs. less corn but 0.5 lb. more supplement per 100 lbs. gain. In these trials 100 lbs. of meat scraps were equal in value to 98.0 lbs. digester tankage plus 15.0 lbs. corn. With corn at $20 and digester tankage at $60 a ton, this would give meat scraps a value of $61.80 per ton, without considering the difference in rate of gain.

In experiments where meat scraps and digester tankage have been compared as the supplement to corn or other grain for pigs not on pasture, meat scraps have likewise been superior to high-grade digester tankage.[100]

1357. Important points in feeding tankage.—On account of their richness in protein, ordinarily tankage and meat scraps sell at a much higher price per ton than the grains or than other protein supplements which contain less protein. To avoid wasting these rich feeds it is important to know just how much tankage or meat scraps is required to balance a ration.

The example rations given in Appendix Table VII show the amounts of these supplements needed in different combinations of feeds for various classes of swine. The amount required to balance other rations can readily be found by computing rations that are balanced according to the Morrison feeding standards, which are given in Appendix Table III.

It has been pointed out previously that pigs self-fed corn and tankage, free-choice, in separate compartments of a self-feeder usually eat about the correct proportions of these feeds to make a well-balanced ration, no matter whether they are in dry lot or on pasture. (1284) Due to the convenience of this method of feeding and the saving of labor, it has become very popular throughout the corn belt. Though good results are commonly secured when corn and tankage are thus self-fed, free-choice, occasionally the pigs either overeat on tankage, or else they fail to take enough to balance their ration properly. In such cases it may be necessary to discontinue free-choice feeding and either self-feed them a mixture of ground corn and tankage in the proper proportions, or else self-feed the shelled corn and hand-feed the tankage.

When pigs are self-fed such combinations as barley and tankage or wheat and tankage, free-choice, they frequently overeat on tankage to such an extent as to increase the cost of the gains materially. Free-choice feeding of such combinations is not, therefore, to be recommended generally. Instead, a mixture of the proper proportions of ground grain and tankage should be fed, or the grain may be self-fed and the necessary amount of tankage hand-fed twice daily.

When pigs are hand-fed their rations, it makes no difference whether the tankage is mixed with the other feed in suitable proportions or whether the proper amount to balance the ration is fed separately. There is no advantage in feeding the tankage in the form of a slop or in soaking it.

1358. Fish meal.—Numerous experiments have shown that fish meal of good quality is even superior to tankage or meat scraps as a protein supplement for swine. (634-636) When fish meal of good quality is properly used, it does not produce any fishy flavor in pork. If considerably more fish meal is fed than is needed to balance the ration, it may injure the flavor of pork, especially if the fish meal is higher than normal in fat content. Only a few comparisons have yet been made of the relative values of the different kinds of fish meal, but they are all apparently very satisfactory when made from raw material of suitable quality for stock feeding.

In 18 experiments fish meal was compared with high-grade digester tankage as the only protein supplement for pigs averaging 76 lbs. in weight at the start, which were not on pasture.[101] The pigs fed fish meal in these trials gained 1.68 lbs. per head daily, on the average, and required 349 lbs. corn and 35 lbs. fish meal per 100 lbs. gain. Those fed tankage gained 1.46 lbs. a day and required 381 lbs. corn and 37 lbs. tankage per 100 lbs. gain. In these trials each 100 lbs. of fish meal was equal in value to 106 lbs. digester tankage plus 91 lbs. corn, without considering the advantage of the more rapid gains.

Fish meal has also been superior to digester tankage when fed as the only supplement to corn for pigs on pasture, but the difference in value of the two supplements has not been so great as for pigs in dry lot. In 5 experiments with pigs on pasture the average daily gain has been 1.55 lbs. on fish meal and corn, in comparison with 1.47 lbs. on tankage and corn.[102] In these trials each 100 lbs. of fish meal has been equal in value to 107 lbs. tankage plus 25 lbs. corn.

As has been stated previously, fish meal dried in a partial vacuum is of higher nutritive value than flame-dried fish meal made from the same material. Because of the lower temperature during the process, the vacuum-dried product will contain more vitamin A and vitamin D, and also the protein will be more digestible. However, vacuum drying will not make a good fish meal from unsuitable raw material.

Though fish meal of good quality is worth more than tankage for swine feeding, occasionally fish meal produces unsatisfactory results. Thus, as has been mentioned previously, on two different occasions in New York experiments on fish meals, pigs fed vacuum-dried white fish meal of supposedly excellent quality failed to thrive, while similar pigs fed other supplements made excellent gains. (**635**) Likewise, very unsatisfactory results were secured with fish meal as a supplement to corn in one New Jersey trial.[103]

Unless one is sure that the fish meal he is using contains an adequate supply of vitamin A and vitamin D, it is best to add alfalfa or other legume hay to a ration of grain and fish meal for swine not on pasture, especially during the winter for young pigs and for brood sows. (**1298**) An excellent combination for growing and fattening pigs not on pasture is a trio supplemental mixture of 50 lbs. fish meal, 25 lbs. linseed meal or cottonseed meal, and 25 lbs. chopped or ground legume hay.

In 6 comparisons with fall pigs fed during the winter at the New York (Cornell) Station, a fish meal trio mixture (consisting of menhaden fish meal, linseed meal, and ground alfalfa hay) was compared with the trio mixture made up of digester tankage, linseed meal, and alfalfa hay.[104] In 3 comparisons the trio mixture was self-fed, free-choice, as the supplement to yellow shelled corn, also self-fed. In the 3 other comparisons a mixture of ground corn and the proper proportion of the trio mixture was self-fed. On the average, the pigs fed the fish meal trio mixture gained 0.06 lb. more per head daily than those fed the tankage trio mixture, but there was no appreciable difference in the amount of feed required per 100 lbs. gain on the two supplemental mixtures. When fed in this highly efficient combination, menhaden fish meal was worth only 9 per cent more a ton than digester tankage. A fish meal trio supplemental mixture was likewise slightly superior to the tankage trio mixture for pigs in dry lot in 2 experiments at the West Virginia Station.[105]

It is of interest to note that in the New York trials there was practically no difference in the rate of gain by the pigs self-fed shelled corn and the trio mixtures, free-choice, and those self-fed the mixtures of ground corn and supplements. The average feed cost per 100 lbs. gain was, however, 35 cents less for the pigs self-fed shelled corn and the trio mixtures separately, free-choice.

In experiments during 4 years at the New York (Cornell) Station a mixture of one-half menhaden fish meal and one-half linseed meal was compared with a combination of one-half digester tankage and one-half linseed meal for self-feeding free-choice as the supplement to shelled corn, also self-fed, for pigs on pasture.[104] Also, each year another lot was self-fed menhaden fish meal as the only protein supplement to corn for similar pigs. The pigs fed either menhaden fish meal as the only supplement or the combination of fish meal and linseed meal gained 0.1 lb. more per head daily than those fed the combination of tankage and linseed meal and also required 21 lbs. less feed per 100 lbs. gain. This difference in feed requirement per 100 lbs. gain gave menhaden fish meal a decidedly higher value per ton than tankage.

In these trials the results were practically the same on menhaden fish meal fed as the only protein supplement and on the mixture of fish meal and linseed meal. Vacuum-dried white fish meal was also tested in each of these New York trials, both on pasture and during the winter in dry lot. Except for the two occasions, previously mentioned, in which this fish meal produced unsatisfactory results, it was even superior to menhaden fish meal in value.

1359. Wheat standard middlings; brown shorts.—Wheat standard middlings and brown shorts rank among the most popular feeds for all classes of swine. (543) These wheat by-products produce excellent results when fed in combination with such protein supplements as dairy by-products, tankage, or fish meal, which furnish protein that makes good the deficiencies in the proteins of the cereal grains.

Standard middlings and brown shorts are similar in composition and about equal in feeding value. Standard middlings are slightly higher than brown shorts in fiber, but this is more than offset by the fact that they contain 0.8 per cent more fat. Therefore standard middlings furnish a slightly larger amount of total digestible nutrients. Both of these feeds are high in phosphorus, but they are low in calcium. They also lack vitamin A and vitamin D, which facts, as well as the incomplete nature of their proteins, must be borne in mind in using them efficiently. Since standard middlings and shorts contain only 14.4 to 15.1 per cent digestible protein, a much larger proportion is needed to balance a ration than in the case of either tankage or fish meal.

Standard middlings or brown shorts should not be used as the only supplement to grain for young pigs or breeding swine that are not on pasture. (1282) On such a ration the results will generally be unsatisfactory, due to the poor quality of protein, the lack of calcium, and the deficiency of vitamins.

In the fattening of well-grown pigs, middlings or shorts will produce fair results as the only protein supplement to the grains, if a calcium supplement is provided. However, more rapid gains and generally much cheaper gains will be secured when a more efficient ration is used. This is shown by 6 trials in which pigs that averaged 119 lbs. in weight were fattened on either middlings and corn or tankage and corn, without pasture.[106] The pigs fed middlings and corn gained 1.33 lbs. per head daily and required 201 lbs. middlings and 266 lbs. corn per 100 lbs. gain. Those fed tankage and corn gained one-quarter pound more a day and consumed 42 lbs. tankage and 376 lbs. corn per 100 lbs. gain.

In these trials each 100 lbs. of middlings replaced 21 lbs. tankage plus 55 lbs. corn, considering only the feed required per 100 lbs. gain and not taking into account the slower gains on middlings. Because of the difference in rate of gain, middlings were worth somewhat less per ton than corn in these trials. If the pigs had not been well-grown when placed on the ration of corn and middlings, the results would have been very poor.[107]

Even for pigs not on pasture which are fed alfalfa hay in addition to grain, middlings are not very efficient as the protein supplement, in comparison with tankage. In 3 Missouri and Nebraska tests pigs fed middlings, alfalfa hay, and corn gained only 0.91 lb. a day, while others fed corn and tankage, with or without alfalfa hay, gained 1.30 lbs.[108]

Middlings give better results when used as the only supplement to grain for pigs on good pasture than in dry lot feeding. In 4 Ohio and Wisconsin experiments pigs self-fed middlings and corn, free-choice, on good pasture gained 1.21 lbs. per head daily, in comparison with 1.32 lbs. for other pigs self-fed tankage as the supplement to corn.[109] If the slower gain on middlings is not taken into consideration, middlings were worth 75 per cent more per ton than corn in these tests. Better results are secured when corn and middlings are self-fed separately, free-choice, to pigs on pasture than when such a mixture as one-half middlings and one-half corn is fed.[110]

Occasionally, middlings are considerably lower in price per ton than corn or other grain. They may then be used as a substitute for corn or other grain, but as they are a less concentrated feed than corn, they produce less rapid gains and are worth only about 85 per cent as much as corn for fattening pigs. In 3 Iowa and Wisconsin experiments pigs self-fed standard middlings as the only feed on rape pasture gained only 0.82 lb. per head daily.[111] Others self-fed corn and tankage gained 1.31 lbs. and required considerably less feed per 100 lbs. gain. Middlings are more satisfactory as the only feed for pigs that are being fed a limited ration on pasture than for those that are being fattened.[112] They are very inefficient as the only feed for young pigs not on pasture.

1360. Adding middlings to grain and tankage.—Middlings have a higher value when added to such a ration as grain and either tankage or dairy by-products than when fed as the only protein supplement to grain for pigs not on pasture. This is shown clearly by the results of 11 trials with pigs averaging 63 lbs. in weight at the start.[113] Pigs fed about 1 lb. per head daily of middlings in addition to corn and tankage gained 0.07 lb. more a day than others fed only corn and tankage. In these trials each 100 lbs. of middlings replaced 72 lbs. of corn plus 9 lbs. of tankage. With corn at $20 and tankage at $60 a ton this would make the middlings worth just about as much as corn per ton. Better results would have undoubtedly been secured in these trials if legume hay had been added to both rations.

In 9 trials with well-grown pigs averaging 140 lbs. in weight at the start, the addition of middlings to a fattening ration of corn and tankage increased the daily gain 0.15 lb.[114] Each 100 lbs. of middlings replaced 108 lbs. of corn plus 11 lbs. of tankage in these trials. For these older pigs the addition of middlings was therefore of slightly greater benefit than for the younger ones.

The addition of middlings or shorts to a ration of corn, tankage, and alfalfa hay for pigs not on pasture does not generally increase the rate of gain. In 3 experiments each 100 lbs. of shorts added to this ration has equalled 114 lbs. of corn in value.[115]

Unless middlings are much cheaper than corn, it does not pay to add them to a ration of corn and tankage for growing and fattening pigs on pasture. In 6 experiments the addition of middlings to this ration has increased the daily gain 0.08 lb., on the average, but each 100 lbs. of middlings has replaced only 66 lbs. corn plus 4 lbs. tankage.[116]

1361. Wheat flour middlings; gray shorts.—Wheat flour middlings and gray shorts are preferred to standard middlings and brown shorts for young pigs, because of their lower fiber content. (543) In 2 Minnesota trials with pigs on pasture flour middlings were compared with standard middlings when forming 30 per cent of the ration until the pigs reached a weight of 100 lbs., and 23 per cent after that time.[117] In these tests flour middlings were worth 18 per cent more than standard middlings. In a similar Ohio trial with pigs in dry lot flour middlings were worth 12 per cent more than standard middlings.[118]

1362. Wheat red dog flour; white shorts.—Wheat red dog flour and white shorts are excellent feeds for young pigs, as they are palatable, highly digestible, and contain but little fiber. (544) In Minnesota tests wheat red dog flour was worth no more than flour middlings when forming part of the ration for pigs weighing 66 to 77 lbs. at the start.[117] In South Carolina tests wheat red dog flour was worth 21 per cent more than standard middlings when fed with corn and tankage to young pigs.[119]

1363. Wheat bran; wheat mixed feed.—Wheat bran and wheat mixed feed are too bulky to be very useful for growing and fattening pigs, middlings being worth much more.[119] (542, 546) These feeds are satisfactory as part of the ration for brood sows, and are especially useful, because of their bulk and their laxative effect, when no legume hay is available for the sows. It is an excellent plan to include one-third by weight of wheat bran in the rations for brood sows shortly before farrowing and for a few days afterward.

1364. Linseed meal.—Linseed meal is an excellent protein supplement for swine when it is fed in combination with such animal by-products as tankage, fish meal or skimmilk. Thus, it forms part of the well-known trio supplemental mixture, or Wisconsin mixture, developed by the author and associates at the Wisconsin Station. (1341) This mixture consists of 50 lbs. tankage or fish meal, 25 lbs. linseed meal, and 25 lbs. ground or chopped alfalfa hay or other legume hay. As has been shown previously, this combination is one of the most efficient supplemental mixtures that has been developed for growing or fattening pigs which are not on pasture.

The experiments reviewed before have proved that for pigs which are on pasture a mixture of 50 lbs. linseed meal and 50 lbs. tankage is highly efficient for self-feeding, free-choice, as a supplement to corn, also self-fed. (1345) Thus fed, this combination produces a trifle more rapid and economical gains than when tankage is used as the only supplement. This combination of only linseed meal and tankage is also very satisfactory for pigs not on pasture, if they are supplied with choice legume hay in a rack to provide the vitamins that linseed meal and tankage both lack.[120] Where possible, it is best, however, to include ground or chopped legume hay in the supplemental mixture so as to be sure that the pigs will eat a sufficient amount of the hay to provide ample amounts of vitamins. The proportions of the feeds in these supplemental mixtures may be varied somewhat, if one desires, but the author prefers the proportions here stated.

Because of its laxative effect, linseed meal is an excellent protein supplement for brood sows, if fed in combination with supplements of animal origin and with legume hay or pasture to provide vitamins and calcium.

If used as the only protein supplement in swine feeding, linseed meal is much less efficient than tankage, fish meal, or dairy by-products. When thus fed to swine, the proteins in linseed meal do not effectively make good the deficiencies of the proteins in the cereal grains. (1282) Linseed meal is particularly inefficient when fed as the only supplement to grain for pigs not on pasture. Not only is the quality of protein unsatisfactory, but also the ration is low in calcium and it lacks vitamin D. (Vitamin A is also deficient unless the grain is yellow corn.) If fed for a long period of time, such a ration is apt to produce rickets or other serious nutritional trouble.

Even if a calcium supplement is provided to correct the lack of this mineral in linseed meal and grain, this ration is decidedly unsatisfactory for young pigs not on pasture. This is shown by the results of 5 experiments in which the pigs averaged 57 lbs. in weight at the beginning of the trials.[121] Pigs fed corn and linseed meal, with a calcium supplement in addition, gained only 1.08 lbs. per head daily and required 409 lbs. corn and 50 lbs. linseed meal per 100 lbs. gain. Others fed corn and tankage gained 1.37 lbs. a day, and required only 359 lbs. corn and 33 lbs. tankage per 100 lbs. gain. In these trials 100 lbs. of linseed meal was worth only as much as 66 lbs. tankage minus 100 lbs. corn. With corn at $20 and tankage at $60 per ton, this would give linseed meal, fed in this improper manner, a value of only $19.60 per ton.

For well-grown, thrifty pigs weighing more than 100 lbs. at the start, the results from using linseed meal as the only supplement to grain for dry-lot feeding are not quite so unsatisfactory. However, it is much more economical to use a more efficient protein supplement. For example, in 14 trials with well-grown pigs averaging 117 lbs. in weight at the beginning, the daily gain on a ration of corn and linseed meal was 1.35 lbs. in comparison with 1.51 lbs. on a ration of corn and tankage.[122] With corn and tankage at the prices stated previously, linseed meal was worth about $28 a ton, not taking into consideration the difference in rate of gain on the two rations.

Where no animal by-products, like tankage, fish meal, or dairy by-products, are available to feed with linseed meal and grain to pigs not on pasture, much better results will generally be secured if legume hay is added to the ration, even when the grain is yellow corn. For example, in 4 trials pigs which ate 0.3 lb. alfalfa hay per head daily in addition to corn and linseed meal gained 0.34 lb. more daily than others receiving no alfalfa hay.[123]   In these trials each 100 lbs. of hay actually saved an average of 65 lbs. of linseed meal and 467 lbs. corn, in comparison with the inefficient ration of only corn and linseed meal.

In the case of young pigs, however, the gains will be much less rapid on a ration of corn, linseed meal, and alfalfa hay than when tankage or some other animal by-product is included in the ration. Thus, in a Kansas test 70-lb. pigs gained only 0.96 lb. a day on the former ration, while similar pigs receiving tankage in addition gained 1.63 lbs.[124]

Linseed meal produces fairly satisfactory results when fed as the only protein supplement to growing and fattening pigs on good pasture, but the gains are less rapid than when a more efficient supplement is used.   In 9 experiments 59-lb. pigs fed corn and linseed meal on alfalfa pasture or rape pasture gained 1.29 lbs. per head daily, while others fed corn and tankage gained 1.34 lbs.[125]   With corn and tankage at the prices given previously, linseed meal was worth about $34 per ton in these trials.

1365. Cottonseed meal.—Recent investigations have proved that excellent results are secured under certain conditions when cottonseed meal is used as part of the protein supplements in swine feeding, both for growing and fattening pigs and for brood sows.   These investigations, especially experiments at the Ohio and Texas Stations, have shown that the ration should not contain more than about 9 to 10 per cent of cottonseed meal and it should provide protein of good quality and plenty of vitamins and calcium.[126] **(581-584)**

When cottonseed meal is properly fed in a suitable combination, not only does the ration produce excellent gains on growing and fattening pigs, but also cottonseed meal has a much more pronounced hardening effect on the carcass than does either tankage or fish meal when fed as the only supplement to corn or other grain.[127]

The numerous experiments that have been conducted have shown clearly that when too much cottonseed meal is fed, disaster may result from the effect of gossypol contained in the cottonseed meal, even when other feeds in the ration supply an abundance of vitamin A and also ample calcium.   The condition in swine feeding is thus much different than with cattle, for cattle may safely be fed large amounts of cottonseed meal, if care is taken to provide an abundance of vitamins and an ample supply of calcium.

Cottonseed meal may vary considerably in the amount of gossypol it contains, depending on the amount present in the cottonseed before it is processed and also depending on the temperature reached in the process of manufacture. **(582)**   This fact accounts for the great difference in the results that have been secured when cottonseed meal has been used as the only protein supplement for swine.   In some cases no injury has resulted when it has been thus fed, especially when the pigs have been on pasture or when they have been well grown when the feeding of cottonseed meal was begun.   However, in other tests the pigs have been injured or even killed by the effects of gossypol when cottonseed meal has been used as the only supplement, even though there has been no lack of vitamins or minerals in the ration.

A combination of one-half to two-thirds cottonseed meal and the remainder tankage, meat scraps, or fish meal is an excellent supplement to the cereal grains for pigs or brood sows that are on pasture. When no more of such a mixture is fed than is needed to balance the ration, the proportion of cottonseed meal is kept within limits that are safe, and the animal by-products make good the deficiencies in the quality of the proteins in the grains and in such supplements as cottonseed meal, linseed meal, and the wheat by-products.

Unless the mixture contains at least one-half tankage or fish meal, a calcium supplement should be fed, since cottonseed meal is low in this mineral. For swine that are not on pasture, some legume hay should be added to a ration of grain, cottonseed meal, and tankage or fish meal, in order to provide an abundant supply of vitamins. This is especially necessary when little or no yellow corn is fed. It is also particularly advantageous for young pigs and for brood sows during winter in the northern states, where the winter sunlight cannot be depended upon to protect swine against rickets. (**191**)

When cottonseed meal is fed in combination with such a protein supplement as tankage or fish meal, not only is the amount of cottonseed meal reduced that is needed to balance the ration, but also these other supplements seem to have a specific effect in preventing any injury from the cottonseed meal. Robison of the Ohio Station has suggested that this may be due to the gossypol in the cottonseed meal combining with the proteins of tankage, fish meal, or similar feeds in the digestive tract, to form an insoluble, and therefore harmless, compound.[128]

As has been stated previously, by special heating of dampened cottonseed meal under steam pressure, the gossypol can be destroyed so completely that the product can be safely fed to swine in much larger amounts than would otherwise be safe. (**582**) Feeding a solution of iron salts with cottonseed meal also tends to prevent injury from the meal when large amounts are fed, but may not always avoid trouble.

1366. Value of cottonseed meal in efficient combinations.—The excellent results that are secured when cottonseed meal is fed in combination with tankage to supplement grain for growing and fattening pigs are shown by 10 experiments with pigs in dry lot and 15 with pigs on pasture.[129] In these trials the pigs averaged 73 lbs. in weight at the start and were usually fed to market weights of 200 lbs. or more. Both in the trials in dry lot and in those on pasture, the gain was a trifle more rapid on the combination of cottonseed meal and tankage as the supplement to corn than when tankage was fed as the only supplement. For the 25 comparisons, the average daily gain was 1.52 lbs. for the pigs fed the combination of supplements and 1.44 lbs. for those fed tankage. In these experiments 100 lbs. of cottonseed meal were equal in value to 65 lbs. of corn plus 43 lbs. of tankage. With corn at $20 and tankage at $60 a ton, this would give cottonseed meal a value of $38.80 a ton, without placing any valuation on the slight increase in rate of gain on the combined supplements.

In 13 similar experiments pigs in dry lot fed a combination of cottonseed meal and fish meal as the supplement to corn gained an average of 1.45 lbs., while others fed fish meal as the only supplement gained 1.57 lbs.[130] Each 100 lbs. of cottonseed meal saved 89 lbs. of corn plus 34 lbs. of fish meal in these trials, without taking into consideration the more rapid gains on the cottonseed meal combination. With corn at $20 and fish meal at $60 a ton, this would give cottonseed meal a value of $38.20 per ton, merely from the amount of feed saved.

In feeding a combination of cottonseed meal and either tankage or fish meal, it is safest not to use more than one-half or two-thirds of cottonseed meal in the mixture. Combinations of three-fourths cottonseed meal and one-fourth fish meal have been satisfactory in North Carolina tests.[131] However, in the case of young pigs not on pasture, the amount of cottonseed meal in such a mixture may be a little too high for safety under all conditions.

Experiments have shown that a combination of cottonseed meal and tankage or meat scraps is generally slightly superior, as a supplement for corn or other grain, to a similar combination of linseed meal and tankage or meat scraps. This is true both for pigs on pasture and for pigs in dry lot.[132] For pigs not on pasture it is best to add legume hay to such rations, in order to provide an abundance of vitamins A and D.

Cottonseed meal is a satisfactory substitute for linseed meal in the trio supplemental mixture for pigs not on pasture, which consists of 50 lbs. tankage or meat scraps, 25 lbs. linseed meal, and 25 lbs. chopped or ground legume hay. (1341)   However, in 10 experiments in which the cottonseed trio mixture has been directly compared with the linseed meal trio mixture for young pigs in dry lot the results have been slightly better on the latter.[133]   On the average, the pigs fed corn and the linseed trio mixture gained 1.42 lbs. per head daily and required a total of 384 lbs. feed per 100 lbs gain. Those fed corn and the cottonseed meal mixture gained 1.34 lbs. a day and required a total of 392 lbs. feed per 100 lbs. gain. With corn at $20, tankage at $60, ground alfalfa hay at $20, and linseed meal at $40 per ton, cottonseed meal was worth only $28 a ton, on the average, in these experiments.

It should be pointed out that although the difference in amount of feed required per 100 lbs. gain on the two rations was relatively small, this difference was the result of substituting only a small amount of cottonseed meal for a similar amount of linseed meal. Therefore the difference in value per ton of these feeds was considerable.

1367. Soybeans.—Because of the great increase in the production of soybeans in the corn belt during the past few years, there has been widespread interest in the use of soybeans as a home-grown supplement for swine feeding. The numerous experiments that have been conducted to study the use of soybeans for pork production have shown that they have very definite limitations for this purpose.

First of all, if growing and fattening pigs are fed soybeans as the only protein supplement and a sufficient amount of the soybeans is fed to balance the ration, the carcasses are apt to be soft and therefore undesirable from the market standpoint. It is shown in the previous chapter that the tendency for the carcasses to be soft is lessened (but not always entirely prevented) if pigs in dry lot weigh at least 125 lbs. and pigs on pasture at least 75 lbs. before soybean feeding is begun. (1322) No greater amount of soybeans should be fed than is needed to balance the ration. If the ration does not contain more than about 10 per cent of soybeans, satisfactory carcasses will usually be produced under these conditions.

In addition to the fact that soybeans produce soft pork unless thus fed, there is the further limitation that uncooked soybeans are not utilized so well by swine, especially by young pigs, as are soybean oil meal and cooked soybeans. (**150, 594**) Cooked soybeans and soybean oil meal that has been well cooked in the manufacturing process produce excellent gains when fed as the only protein supplement, even to young pigs. On the other hand, if raw soybeans are fed to young pigs as the only protein supplement, the gains are decidedly inferior to those produced by tankage, fish meal, or dairy by-products. Also, in an Indiana test raw soybeans were not so satisfactory as tankage or cooked soybeans as the protein supplement for brood sows and their litters.[134] On the other hand, good results were secured in an Illinois trial when raw soybeans were used as the only protein supplement to corn for brood sows during the winter, both before and after farrowing.[135]

Because of these limitations to the use of soybeans, it is wise for soybean growers to exchange soybeans for soybean oil meal for use in swine feeding, if a ton of the soybean oil meal can be secured for not much more than a ton of soybeans. Raw soybeans can be used satisfactorily as the protein supplement for sows prior to farrowing and also for well-grown fattening pigs. Care should be taken not to feed pregnant sows a much greater amount of soybeans than is needed to balance the ration, for there have been reports that sows have produced unsatisfactory litters when grazed on mature soybeans, without much other feed.

In using soybeans as a protein supplement in swine feeding, it should be borne in mind that they are low in calcium and that they contain much less phosphorus than tankage, fish meal, or skimmilk. A mineral mixture supplying these minerals should therefore be provided, even for pigs on good pasture. Also, in the case of young pigs not on pasture, legume hay should be included in the ration in order to supply ample amounts of vitamins A and D. For very young pigs, however, a ration of corn, raw soybeans, alfalfa hay, and a mineral mixture is much less satisfactory than a ration that includes some animal by-product.[136] There is no need of grinding soybeans for swine.[137]

The unsatisfactory results that are produced when young pigs not on pasture are fed corn and raw soybeans, even with a mineral supplement furnishing calcium and phosphorus, are shown by 6 Ohio trials.[138] In these experiments pigs averaging 49 lbs. in weight at the start gained only 0.74 lb. per head daily on this ration, in comparison with 1.06 lbs. for similar pigs fed corn and tankage. In some of the trials it was necessary to add ground alfalfa hay to the ration to save the pigs from disaster because of the lack of vitamins.

In the case of pigs on good pasture which weigh 60 to 75 lbs. at the start, or of pigs not on pasture which weigh 100 to 125 lbs. or more, satisfactory gains are produced on a ration of corn, soybeans, and a mineral supplement supplying calcium and phosphorus. Thus, in 9 experiments pigs averaging 110 lbs. in weight at the start gained 1.53 lbs. per head daily on this ration, and required 349 lbs. corn, 58 lbs. soybeans, and 6 lbs. mineral mixture per 100 lbs. gain.[139] Similar pigs fed corn and tankage gained 1.75 lbs., and required 361 lbs. corn, 26 lbs. tankage, and 3 lbs. minerals per 100 lbs. gain. In these trials 100 lbs.

of soybeans and 5 lbs. of mineral mixture replaced 21 lbs. of corn plus 45 lbs. of tankage, not taking into consideration the difference in rate of gain or any softening effect of soybeans on the carcasses.

When soybeans have been fed without a suitable mineral supplement, the results have been considerably poorer, even in the case of well-grown pigs.[140]

Except for the danger of producing soft pork, the results are satisfactory when pigs weighing 60 lbs. or over which are on good pasture are self-fed or hand-fed soybeans and a calcium and phosphorus supplement, with a full feed of corn. In 17 trials pigs averaging 64 lbs. in weight at the start gained an average of 1.37 lbs. per head daily on this ration and required 337 lbs. corn, 32 lbs. soybeans, and 5 lbs. mineral mixture per 100 lbs. gain.[141] Similar pigs that were fed corn, tankage, and the mineral supplement gained 1.49 lbs. daily and consumed 341 lbs. corn, 23 lbs. tankage, and 2 lbs. mineral mixture per 100 lbs. gain. In these trials, 100 lbs. of soybeans and 10 lbs. mineral mixture replaced 13 lbs. of corn and 73 lbs. of tankage, not considering the difference in rate of gain on the two rations, and the danger of producing soft pork on the soybean ration. For pigs on good pasture which are older at the start, soybeans produce better results than with young pigs, and there is less danger of softening the carcasses.

Soybeans that have been thoroughly roasted or otherwise cooked have produced excellent gains when fed with corn and a calcium and phosphorus supplement, even to pigs not on pasture.[142] However, cooking the soybeans does not prevent the softening effect on the carcass. Also, roasted soybeans are so palatable to pigs that when the soybeans are self-fed, the pigs will eat much greater amounts than are needed to balance the ration. If a mixture of shelled corn and the proper proportion of roasted soybeans is fed, the pigs will sort out the soybeans from the corn. Therefore it is necessary to hand-feed the roasted soybeans, or to self-feed a mixture of suitable amounts of ground corn and ground soybeans.

Various types of special equipment for roasting soybeans have been developed. Soybeans may also be cooked satisfactorily by boiling them in water for a sufficient length of time.

The tendency to produce soft pork is greatly lessened if pigs are self-fed a combination of soybeans and a non-softening supplement, such as tankage or fish meal. Even in such a combination, however, raw soybeans are apt to produce a trifle less rapid gains than when tankage or fish meal is used as the only supplement. For example, in 5 tests pigs averaging 50 lbs. in weight which were fed corn, soybeans, tankage, and a mineral mixture on alfalfa or rape pasture gained 1.12 lbs. per head daily, in comparison with 1.22 lbs. for pigs fed tankage in place of the combination of soybeans and tankage.[143] In these trials the value of the soybeans was very low, with corn and tankage at usual prices.

1368. Soybean oil meal.—Soybean oil meal that has been heated sufficiently in the process of manufacture is an excellent protein supplement to the cereal grains for swine feeding, both for growing and fattening pigs and for breeding swine. Except for young pigs up to a weight of 50 to 75 lbs., it is very satisfactory as the only protein supplement, if a mineral supplement is supplied to furnish additional calcium and phosphorus. For swine not on pasture, legume hay should be included in the ration to supply vitamins A and D.

Young pigs will do fairly well on a ration of grain, soybean oil meal, a suitable mineral mixture, and either pasture or legume hay. However, still better results will generally be secured when a small amount of some protein supplement of animal origin (such as tankage, fish meal, or dairy by-products) is included in the ration until the pigs reach a weight of 50 to 75 lbs. The advantage of this addition is more marked in the case of pigs in dry lot than in the case of those on pasture.

The following table shows the excellent results that are secured when well-cooked soybean oil meal and a mineral mixture are fed as the only supplements to corn for pigs on good pasture which weigh more than 50 lbs. at the start. This table summarizes the results of 8 experiments in each of which one lot of pigs on pasture was fed corn supplemented by soybean oil meal, while another lot was fed corn and tankage.[144] A mineral mixture supplying calcium and phosphorus was provided for all the pigs. This was much more necessary for the pigs fed soybean oil meal than for those fed tankage, as has been shown previously. (**1290**)

Soybean oil meal vs. tankage as a supplement to corn

| | | Feed for 100 lbs. gain | | |
| | Daily gain Lbs. | Corn Lbs. | Protein supple- ment Lbs. | Mineral mixture Lbs. |
Average ration				
Lot I. Soybean oil meal and minerals				
Soybean oil meal, 0.75 lb.				
Mineral mixture, 0.04 lb.				
Corn, 4.7 lbs.............................	1.55	305	48	2.6
Lot II. Tankage and minerals				
Tankage, 0.37 lb.				
Mineral mixture, 0.02 lb.				
Corn, 4.9 lbs.............................	1.52	320	24	1.3

The pigs fed soybean oil meal and a mineral mixture as the supplements to corn gained fully as rapidly as those fed tankage in these trials, and they also made very economical gains. On the average 100 lbs. of soybean oil meal was equal in value to 50 lbs. of tankage plus 31 lbs. corn and minus 3 lbs. of mineral mixture. With corn at $20, tankage at $60, and mineral mixture at $40 a ton, this would give soybean oil meal a value of $35 a ton.

In 16 similar experiments with pigs not on pasture the average daily gain has been 1.28 lbs. on the soybean oil meal ration and 1.35 lbs. on the tankage ration.[145] To prevent poor results from a deficiency of vitamins it was necessary to add a small amount of alfalfa hay to both rations in certain of the tests. On the average, the value of soybean oil meal in comparison with tankage was even higher in these dry-lot tests than in the trials with pigs on pasture. If the difference in rate of gain is not considered, 100 lbs. of soybean oil meal were equal to 71 lbs. of tankage plus 18 lbs. of corn and minus 9 lbs. of mineral mixture.

Soybean oil meal has a great advantage over soybeans as a supplement for fattening pigs because it does not tend to produce soft pork when fed in any ordinary amount. Also, well-cooked soybean oil meal is decidedly superior to raw soybeans for young pigs, either in dry lot or on pasture. For pigs on pasture that have reached a weight of 60 lbs. or more and for pigs over 100 lbs. in weight that are not on pasture, there is not so much difference in the value of these supplements, except for the effect of soybeans on the carcass.

In 4 experiments pigs averaging 63 lbs. in weight, which were on alfalfa or rape pasture, gained 1.55 lbs. per head daily when self-fed, free-choice, on shelled corn, soybean oil meal, and a mineral mixture supplying calcium and phosphorus.[146] Others fed raw soybeans in place of the soybean oil meal gained 1.41 lbs. a day, not a large difference. On the average, 100 lbs. of soybean oil meal equalled 95 lbs. of soybeans plus 17 lbs. corn and 2 lbs. of mineral mixture in these trials, without considering the difference in rate of gain.

Often well-cooked soybean oil meal is liked so well by pigs that they will eat much more than they need to balance the ration when it is self-fed, free-choice, in addition to corn, also self-fed. In such cases the soybean oil meal should be hand-fed, or else mixed with ground legume hay, with ground oats, with other ground grain, or with mineral mixture so that the pigs will take less of the soybean oil meal.

Soybean oil meal that has not been thoroughly cooked in the manufacturing process is decidedly inferior to well-cooked soybean oil meal for swine feeding.[147] Expeller-process soybean oil meal, hydraulic-process meal, and solvent-process meal are all satisfactory for swine, if they have been heated sufficiently in the manufacturing process to cook them thoroughly. A sufficient number of comparisons of the different types of soybean oil meal have not yet been made to warrant final conclusions concerning their relative values.[148] Expeller-process soybean oil meal that has a light brownish color and a decidedly nutty taste is most excellent for swine, while raw-tasting expeller-process meal should be avoided. Hydraulic-process soybean oil meal that has been thoroughly cooked and that has a nutty taste is also a first-rate feed for swine. Solvent-process meal may equal the best expeller-process meal if it has been cooked sufficiently and if all traces of the solvent have been removed.

As has been previously stated, soybean oil meal made by the expeller process or by the hydraulic process will have a nutty taste instead of a raw, beany taste, if it has been thoroughly cooked. Well-cooked solvent-process meal does not have a raw taste, but may not have any appreciable nutty flavor. (595)

1369. Soybean oil meal combinations.—Particularly good results are secured when soybean oil meal is used in combination with tankage, meat scraps, or fish meal. For pigs not on pasture soybean oil meal is an excellent substitute for linseed meal in the trio mixture (which consists of 50 lbs. tankage, meat scraps, or fish meal; 25 lbs. linseed meal; and 25 lbs. chopped or ground legume hay). In most of the comparisons of these two trio mixtures, the soybean oil meal combination has been equal or practically equal to the original linseed meal trio mixture in value for pigs.[149] The soybean oil meal trio mixture was also equal to the linseed meal trio mixture for brood sows in Iowa trials.[150]

Soybean oil meal fed in combination with alfalfa hay or other legume hay is decidedly superior to soybean oil meal without legume

Pigs Make Cheaper Gains Under Such Conditions

Pigs fed well-balanced rations on good pasture and in sanitary quarters can be expected to make economical gains.

Under These Conditions Profits Should Not Be Expected

Pigs which have no pasture and are in filthy, unsanitary quarters make expensive gains. Many become runts or die because of disease or infection with worms.

COLONY HOUSES BANKED WITH STRAW FOR WINTER

Colony houses thus protected provide comfortable winter quarters for all but small pigs, even in the northern states.

BROOD SOWS HOUSED IN COLONY HOUSES AT WISCONSIN STATION

Brood sows housed in these unprotected colony houses required 16 per ct. more feed than those kept in a central hog house, but the percentage of vigorous pigs they farrowed was higher, because they took more exercise.

hay to supplement grain for swine not on pasture.[151] For young pigs this combination, however, may not produce as good gains as the soybean oil meal trio mixture (which includes tankage in addition).

For swine on pasture excellent supplemental mixtures are combinations of one-half soybean oil meal and one-half tankage, meat scraps, or fish meal. These combinations are fully as good as the mixture of one-half linseed meal and one-half tankage, except that when pigs are self-fed corn and the soybean oil meal combinations, free-choice, they may eat much more of the supplemental mixture than they need.[152]

1370. Peanuts.—Except for the fact that they produce soft pork when forming too large a part of the ration, peanuts are an excellent feed for swine. In spite of the softening effect of peanuts on the carcass, over one-third of the peanut acreage in the United States has commonly been hogged down (swine being turned into the field to root out the nuts). **(597)** Even when the peanuts are harvested for sale, hogs are usually turned into the field to utilize the nuts that still remain after harvesting is completed.

In the peanut-growing districts pigs are generally bought by the packing plants subject to a deduction of $1.00 or more per hundred-weight if their carcasses are soft. The experiments reviewed in the previous chapter have shown that to avoid soft pork, peanuts should be used only for young pigs up to a weight of about 85 lbs., which are then finished (after reaching this weight), on a ration that produces hard pork. **(1322)** For this reason, where pigs must be sold subject to a considerable reduction in price if their carcasses are soft, only brood sows and young pigs are used to hog down peanuts.

North Carolina tests show the economical gains that are made by pigs that hog-down peanuts.[153] In 4 trials pigs hogging down peanuts and fed corn or corn and shorts in addition gained 1.25 lbs. a day on the average, and required only 104 lbs. corn and shorts plus 0.45 acre of peanuts for 100 lbs. gain. Compared with this, pigs fed similarly on soybean pasture gained only 0.74 lb. a day and required 187 lbs. corn and shorts plus 0.55 acre soybeans for 100 lbs. gain. The feed cost for 100 lbs. gain was less than three-fourths as much on peanuts as on soybeans.

In an Alabama trial a crop yielding 39.5 bushels of peanuts per acre produced 668.2 lbs. pork, and in another test a crop of 30.2 bushels per acre produced 416 lbs. of pork.[154] On the average, 184 lbs. of peanuts, plus the forage furnished by the peanuts and any other vegetation in the field, produced 100 lbs. of pork. Peanuts can be grazed during only a relatively short season, for after a time the nuts will sprout or rot if left in the ground, especially in wet weather.

In experiments at the North Carolina Station young pigs in dry lot made satisfactory gains when fed nothing but peanuts plus a small amount of alfalfa hay and a mineral mixture supplying calcium.[155]

1371. Peanut oil meal; peanut oil feed.—Peanut oil meal is an excellent protein supplement for swine feeding, as has been shown in Chapter XVIII. (598) Peanut oil meal is satisfactory as the only protein supplement for pigs on good pasture or for well-grown pigs in dry lot, but for very young pigs in dry lot it is best to use peanut oil meal in combination with tankage, fish meal, or dairy by-products. A mixture of one-half peanut oil meal and one-half tankage or fish meal produces excellent results, either for pigs in dry lot or for those on pasture.[156]   When peanut oil meal is fed as the only supplement, a calcium supplement should be supplied, since peanuts are low in this mineral.[157]

Peanut oil feed, made from unhulled nuts or nuts only partially hulled, is, of course, worth less than peanut oil meal made from well-hulled nuts. The exact difference in value will depend on the proportion of hulls in the peanut oil feed, for the hulls are of little or no value as a feed. In Alabama trials 100 lbs. of peanut oil meal from well-hulled nuts was equal in value to 104 lbs. of peanut oil feed from unhulled nuts plus 33 lbs. corn.[158]

1372. Corn gluten feed.—Corn gluten feed is not commonly fed to swine, for it is worth much more for cattle than for swine. (523)   The protein in gluten feed does not make good the deficiencies in the proteins of the cereal grains. Also, gluten feed is rather bulky for swine and it is not very palatable. However, swine will readily eat a mixture containing 10 to 15 per cent of the feed.

Gluten feed is not an economical addition to rations for growing and fattening pigs unless the price per ton is less than that of the cereal grains. Gluten feed has generally been worth less than corn in experiments in which it has been added to such a ration as corn and tankage, with or without alfalfa hay or wheat shorts in addition.[159] If gluten feed is so cheap in price that it may be used economically as part of the ration for swine, it should be fed in combination with protein supplements of animal origin, such as tankage, fish meal, or dairy by-products. When fed as the only supplement to corn, gluten feed has not produced good results, either in dry-lot feeding or on pasture.[160]

1373. Corn gluten meal.—Corn gluten meal has the same general limitations as gluten feed for swine feeding, except that it is less bulky and much higher in protein. (524) Kansas experiments show that it is very unsatisfactory as the protein supplement to corn for pigs not on pasture, even when alfalfa hay is included in the ration to provide vitamins and calcium and to aid in improving the quality of protein.[161] Fair results were secured when gluten meal was used as the only supplement to corn for pigs on alfalfa pasture, although the daily gain was 0.14 lb. less than on corn and tankage. A supplemental mixture of one-half gluten meal and one-half tankage produced nearly as rapid gains as were made on tankage as the only supplement.

The rate of gain of pigs not on pasture was slightly decreased in a Nebraska test when gluten meal was substituted for linseed meal in the trio supplemental mixture (50 lbs. tankage, 25 lbs. linseed meal, and 25 lbs. alfalfa hay).[162] Also, the pigs fed the gluten meal combination and corn required more feed per 100 lbs. gain than those fed the regular trio mixture and corn, or a cottonseed meal trio mixture and corn.

1374. Corn oil meal; corn germ meal.—These corn-germ by-products, from which the greater part of the fat has been removed, are much better for swine feeding than gluten feed or gluten meal, for they furnish protein of somewhat better quality. (522, 525) Corn oil meal and corn germ meal are similar in composition and value, corn germ meal being slightly lower in protein and higher in nitrogen-free extract than corn oil meal. These feeds contain only about one-third as much protein as high-grade digester tankage.

Experiments at the Indiana, Iowa, and Ohio Stations have shown that corn oil meal or corn germ meal should not be fed as the only protein supplement to the grains.[163] Instead, these feeds should be used in combination with protein supplements such as tankage, fish meal, or dairy by-products, which supply protein of better quality. When corn oil meal or corn germ meal is fed as the only supplement to corn for pigs on good pasture, the gains are fairly good, but when thus fed these feeds have been worth little or no more than corn, ton for ton.

In 6 experiments at the Iowa and Wisconsin Stations a mixture of corn germ meal and tankage has been compared with tankage for self-feeding, free-choice, as the supplement to corn for pigs on pasture.[164] The pigs fed the corn-germ-meal combination gained an average of 1.35 lbs. per head daily, in comparison with 1.39 lbs. for those given tankage as the only supplement. In these trials each 100 lbs. of corn germ meal replaced 46 lbs. tankage and 13 lbs. corn. With corn at $20 and tankage at $60 per ton, the value of corn germ meal on this basis would be $30.20 per ton. When a mixture of tankage and corn germ meal or corn oil meal is used as the supplement to grain, the best results are secured when tankage forms at least one-half of the mixture.

The results have differed rather widely in 7 experiments where corn germ meal or corn oil meal has been added to a ration of corn and tankage for pigs in dry lot.[165] On the average, the gain has not been increased by the addition. In these trials each 100 lbs. of corn germ meal or corn oil meal has replaced 42 lbs. tankage plus 45 lbs. corn. For pigs not on pasture, it is best to add legume hay to such a ration as grain, tankage, and either corn germ meal or corn oil meal, in order to provide plenty of vitamins A and D. In 3 Wisconsin experiments the gains of pigs in dry lot were slightly decreased and more feed was required per 100 lbs. gain when corn germ meal was substituted for linseed meal in the trio supplemental mixture (50 lbs. tankage, 25 lbs. linseed meal, and 25 lbs. ground alfalfa hay).[166]

When corn germ meal and corn oil meal have been lower in price per ton than corn, as has occasionally happened, these feeds have been used as a substitute for part of the corn in swine feeding. However, when thus used as a grain substitute, corn germ meal or corn oil meal is not equal to corn in value per ton. In an Ohio trial the results were unsatisfactory when pigs on rape pasture were fed a mixture of one-half corn oil meal and one-half corn, with a small amount of tankage in addition.[167] If fed in too large amounts, corn germ meal or corn oil meal may cause scours, and too large a proportion in the ration may reduce the palatability.

1375. Distillers' dried grains.—Distillers' dried grains are not usually fed to swine, since they are much better suited for feeding to cattle, especially to dairy cows. (648) They are not relished by pigs when forming a large part of a concentrate mixture, and are also too bulky to form any considerable portion of the ration for fattening pigs. In an Ohio trial 85-lb. pigs fed a mixture of 22.5 lbs. distillers' corn dried grains, 67.5 lbs. ground corn, 3.0 lbs. meat scraps, 4.0 lbs. ground alfalfa hay, and 3.0 lbs. mineral mixture gained 0.97 lb. per head daily and required 523 lbs. feed per 100 lbs. gain.[168] Other pigs that were fed a similar mixture, except that the distillers' grains were omitted and the proportion of meat scraps was increased, gained 1.31 lbs. a day and required only 419 lbs. of feed per 100 lbs. gain.

In a Kentucky trial pigs fed 3.3 lbs. ground corn and 0.66 lb. distillers' dried grains per head daily in dry lot gained 0.88 lb. and required 444 lbs. concentrates for 100 lbs. gain.[169] Others fed corn and 0.51 lb. distillers' dried grains on good pasture gained 1.03 lbs. a head daily and consumed only 300 lbs. concentrates for 100 lbs. gain.

1376. Distillery slop.—Strained distillery slop (the by-product left after the distillers' grains are removed) is exceedingly watery, having only 5 per cent or less of dry matter. Recent tests at the Kentucky Station show that for use in swine feeding this thin or strained slop should be allowed to settle for several hours and the top portion, consisting of clear liquid, should be removed by dipping or allowing it to run off.[170] This will remove about one-third the volume. The remaining "settled slop" will contain an appreciably higher percentage of dry matter than the thin slop.

For fattening pigs the thin slop should be fed in addition to a liberal feed of corn or other grain, and tankage or fish meal should also be added to provide protein of better quality than is furnished by the combination of merely grain and distillers' slop.

Well-grown pigs given all the settled distillers' slop they would drink, in addition to shelled corn and tankage, self-fed, gained 1.89 lbs. per head daily and required 322 lbs. corn, 34 lbs. tankage, and 97 gallons of distillery slop per 100 lbs. gain. Similar pigs self-fed shelled corn and tankage gained 1.81 lbs. a day and consumed

372 lbs. corn and 42 lbs. tankage per 100 lbs. gain. Each 100 gallons of the settled distillers' slop (somewhat over 800 lbs.) saved 5 lbs. corn plus 8 lbs. tankage.

Pigs fed only corn and distillers' slop, without tankage, failed to make satisfactory gains, probably because of the poor quality of protein in this ration. On settled distillery slop alone pigs gained only 0.29 lb. a day.

III. Pasture and Forage Crops; Other Succulent Feeds

1377. Importance of pasture and forage crops.—Few facts in swine feeding have been so clearly proved, both by scientific experiments and by the common experience of successful farmers, as the importance of good pasture for all classes of swine.

Pasture is of especial value for growing pigs, because good pasture crops are rich in the nutritive essentials that are lacking in the cereal grains. Such crops are rich in protein and, moreover, the protein is of the right kind or quality to aid in supplementing the proteins of the grains. The best pasture crops are also rich in mineral matter, particularly calcium, which is deficient in all the grains. Last, but not least important, green pasture crops provide large amounts of vitamin A, through their high content of carotene. (**187**) Pasture crops are not rich in vitamin D, but swine on pasture receive an abundant supply of vitamin D through the anti-rachitic effect of sunlight.

Because good pastures furnish a large amount of feed of excellent character, pigs on such pasture require much less grain or other concentrates for each 100 lbs. gain than those not provided with pasture. Moreover, only about one-half as much expensive protein supplements are needed by pigs on pasture. They therefore make much cheaper gains than pigs fed in dry lot.

Pigs on pasture not only make cheaper gains, but the green, succulent feed and the exercise they get aid greatly in keeping them thrifty. Merely from a sanitary standpoint, it is highly important that swine, and especially young pigs, be on pasture free from parasites all through the growing season, instead of being kept in filthy hog lots. Nothing is more important than this in preventing serious trouble from worms and filth-borne diseases. (**1239-1240**)

Another important advantage of having swine on pasture is the fact that then the manure is evenly distributed over the field and none is wasted, as is the case when pigs are fed in dry lot.

Because of the many virtues and economies of pasture for swine, everyone who expects a profit from pork production should provide an abundance of good forage for all his swine during as much of the year as is possible. In the southern states good pasture can even be provided during all or most of the winter. In the North there should be pasture for the brood sows and their litters in the spring; pasture for the growing, fattening pigs from weaning time until market or until frost kills the crop; pasture for the brood sows and boar throughout the growing season; and good pasture for any fall litters.

The choice of pasture crops for any particular section will depend primarily on the soil and climatic conditions. The following pages, which set forth the merits of many pasture crops, show that alfalfa, the clovers, rape, soybeans, peanuts, the cereals, Sudan grass, bluegrass, and several other crops all have decided merits and provide valuable swine pastures in various sections of the country or for certain seasons of the year. In general, those pasture crops are best in a given locality which give high yields of palatable, nutritious forage over a long season, at a low cost for growing the crop. The crop should be rich in protein and also in mineral matter, especially in calcium and phosphorus. It should also endure grazing well, and not merely furnish pasture for a few weeks of the season. As will be noted in the following pages, over much of the country most of these essentials are possessed by alfalfa, the clovers, and rape, or mixtures such as oats-peas-and-rape or oats-and-rape.

The high value of pasture crops in pork production is clearly shown in the following table. This summarizes the results of 30 experiments in each of which one lot of pigs averaging 62 lbs. in weight has been fed until they reached market weights on a well-balanced ration of corn (nearly all yellow corn) and tankage in dry lot, without pasture, while another lot has been full-fed corn and tankage on alfalfa, clover, or rape pasture.[171] In some of the trials the pigs were self-fed and in others the pigs were hand-fed all they would eat, both in dry lot and on pasture. In these experiments an average of 21.7 pigs were pastured per acre.

In several of the early trials of this nature, the pigs on pasture were fed just as large a proportion of tankage or other supplement as those in dry lot. The results of such trials are not included in these averages, for one of the advantages of pasture crops is that pigs on good pasture need only about one-half as much protein supplement to balance their rations as those fed in dry lot.

Value of pasture for growing, fattening pigs

Average ration	Daily gain Lbs.	Concentrates per 100 lbs. gain	
		Corn Lbs.	Tankage Lbs.
Lot I, pigs on pasture			
Corn, 4.8 lbs.			
Tankage, 0.36 lb. Pasture............................	1.41	343	25
Lot II, no pasture			
Corn, 4.4 lbs.			
Tankage, 0.48 lb..................................	1.16	376	42

The table shows that the pigs fed corn and tankage on good pasture gained 1.41 lbs. per head daily and required only 343 lbs. corn and 25 lbs. tankage for 100 lbs. gain. Compared with these excellent results, those fed corn and tankage in dry lot gained only 1.16 lbs. a day and required 33 lbs. more corn and 17 lbs. more tankage for each 100 lbs. gain.

When spring pigs are carried on pasture from weaning time until they are ready for market or until the end of the pasture season, each acre of good pasture should save approximately 800 to 1,000 lbs. of corn plus 500 lbs. or more of tankage, in comparison with dry lot feeding. With corn at $20 and tankage at $60 per ton, this saving of feed per acre of pasture would amount to $23 or more, without including the value of the hay cut on alfalfa or clover pastures. Many of these trials did not begin until some weeks after the pigs were weaned, and therefore complete use was not made of the pasture throughout the season. In this computation of the value of pasture, no credit is given for the more rapid gains of the pigs on pasture, which would often permit their being sold early in the fall, before prices slump. Also, no credit is included for the fertility added to the soil through the growth of legumes and through the manure produced from the corn and tankage fed on pasture, practically all of which is saved when pigs are fed on pasture instead of in dry lot.

Furthermore, in some of the experiments the pasture-fed pigs and the dry-lot pigs were removed from the tests at the time when the pasture-fed pigs were ready for market. At that time the dry-lot pigs had not yet reached market weights, and therefore they still had to make their most expensive gains. (1275) If the dry-lot pigs had all been continued on the experiments until they reached the same weights as the pasture-fed pigs, the saving in feed through the use of pasture would have been somewhat greater.

It has been shown previously that a ration of yellow corn and tankage is not ideal for pigs not on pasture, even when they get plenty of sunlight. (1341) Slightly more rapid and more economical gains are secured when alfalfa hay is added to this ration, or when such a supplement as the trio combination (tankage, linseed meal, and legume hay) is fed instead of tankage.

In each of 3 Michigan trials one lot of 43-lb. pigs was self-fed yellow corn and tankage on alfalfa pasture until they reached an average market weight of 209 lbs.[172] Another lot in each trial was self-fed, free-choice, in a sanitary dry lot on shelled corn and a mixture of equal parts by weight of tankage and linseed meal. In addition, alfalfa hay was provided in a rack for the dry-lot pigs. On this ideal dry-lot ration the pigs gained fully as rapidly as did those on pasture, but they required 49 lbs. more concentrates plus hay per 100 lbs. gain. On the average, each acre of pasture saved 747 lbs. supplemental mixture, 309 lbs. corn, and 172 lbs. alfalfa hay. In addition, an average of 2,827 lbs. hay per acre was cut from the pasture each year. With corn at $20, tankage at $60, linseed meal at $40, and alfalfa hay at $15 a ton, the saving of feed per acre of pasture would amount to $23.05, without including any credit for the hay cut from the pasture.

1378. Methods of feeding pigs on pasture.—After providing plenty of good pasture for all of his swine, the next question which arises in the mind of a farmer is whether he should full-feed grain or other concentrates to growing and fattening pigs on pasture, or whether it will be more profitable to limit the amount of concentrates. This matter has been fully discussed in the previous chapter, where it has been pointed out that the answer will depend primarily on the relative price of grain and pasture and on whether or not it is the desire to finish the pigs for an early fall market. (1307)

To keep pigs on pasture growing thriftily it is usually necessary to feed them at least 1.0 to 1.5 lbs. of concentrates daily per 100 lbs. live weight. Many young pigs are stunted because they are forced to live on pasture alone, or on pasture with too scanty a supply of grain. Such a diet is decidedly unsuited to the digestive tracts of young pigs.

Self-feeding growing and fattening pigs on pasture is an economical and labor-saving method of pork production, when the pigs are to be finished for an early market. The merits of self-feeding versus hand-feeding have been discussed in the preceding chapter. (**1309**)

Pigs on pasture should be provided with shade and with an abundant supply of fresh water. Automatic waterers are convenient, labor-saving devices, which give excellent satisfaction when properly adjusted. Salt should be supplied at all times, except possibly when tankage, meat scraps, or fish meal are fed as the only supplement. (**1289**)

Pigs which are fed well-balanced rations on pasture are much less apt to root than dissatisfied pigs fed an inefficient ration, such as corn alone. It is often not necessary to ring spring pigs which will be sold in the fall at the close of the pasture season, for they are less apt to root than are older hogs. However, the pasture lots must be watched closely, and if the pigs start to root badly, it will be necessary to ring them at once, especially if they are on a permanent pasture, such as alfalfa or bluegrass. Even if fed good rations, pigs are apt to begin rooting after hard summer or fall rains, in order to get the earth worms which then come close to the surface of the ground. This is not surprising, for in a state of nature the hog gained his living largely by rooting. On annual crops, such as rape, it is not usually necessary to ring pigs if they are fed well-balanced rations.

1379. Feeding a supplement with grain on pasture.—All forage crops at the immature stages when commonly used for pasture are much richer in protein than the same crops when nearly mature. (**295**) It will be noted in Appendix Table I that at the stages of growth when pastured most of the forage crops used for swine have even narrower nutritive ratios than does standard wheat middlings. This means that they are richer in digestible protein than standard middlings, on the dry basis.

Due to the richness of the common pasture crops in protein and also because of their other virtues, young pigs fed only corn on good pasture will usually make fair gains. However, as has been shown in the preceding chapter, the addition of an efficient protein supplement will considerably increase the rate of gain. (**1286**) Whether or not it will pay to add a supplement will depend upon the various factors that have been pointed out in the previous discussion. It will usually pay to feed a supplement to early spring pigs that are full-fed corn on good pasture. The rapid gains resulting from the use of the supplement will make it possible to finish the pigs for market before the severe decline in hog prices that usually occurs in late autumn.

It has been emphasized in the previous discussion that there is less need of adding a protein supplement when pigs are fed barley, wheat, oats, or rye on good pasture, than when the grain is corn. After pigs fed chiefly on these grains reach a weight of about 100 lbs., it does not usually pay to add a supplement, unless maximum gains are desired. Until they reach this weight, it is generally best to feed a small amount of supplement, unless the pasture is particularly good or unless protein supplements are high in price.

1380. Alfalfa pasture.—Wherever it thrives, alfalfa ranks first as a pasture crop for swine. (**375**) It provides pasturage during a longer season than most other forage crops, starting early in the spring and remaining green and succulent in the late summer when bluegrass has dried up and even clover grows hard and woody. Since continuous close grazing of alfalfa injures the stand, the number of pigs should be restricted and the plants should be allowed to grow up, being cut for hay once or twice during the season. This is especially important where it is desired to retain the stand as long as possible.

Except in the best alfalfa districts of the West, no more than 17 to 20 spring pigs per acre should usually be grazed on alfalfa, even when they are full-fed grain in addition. If the amount of grain is limited, then fewer pigs should be carried per acre. Where the winters are severe, care must be taken not to pasture alfalfa too late in the fall, for there is danger of its being killed out unless sufficient growth is left standing to protect the plants. With swine there is no danger from bloat on alfalfa pasture.

It is of interest to compare the results from alfalfa pasture with those from rape, which is the best single temporary pasture crop for swine, where it thrives. In each of 14 experiments one lot of spring pigs, averaging 50 lbs. in weight at the start, has been full-fed corn and either tankage or a mixture of one-half tankage and one-half linseed meal on alfalfa pasture, in comparison with another lot of similar pigs on rape pasture.[173] The gains were a trifle more rapid on the alfalfa pasture, averaging 1.27 lbs. per head daily, in comparison with 1.21 lbs. for the pigs on rape pasture. Also, slightly less feed was required per 100 lbs. gain on alfalfa pasture, the average being 344 lbs. corn and 24 lbs. supplement. On rape pasture the pigs required 347 lbs. corn and 31 lbs. supplement per 100 lbs. gain.

In addition to these slight advantages in rate of gain and in feed requirement per 100 lbs. gain, a considerable amount of hay was secured from the alfalfa plot, the average yield being 2,142 lbs. per acre. A further advantage of alfalfa over rape is that rape is not a legume, and therefore does not add nitrogen to the soil. Also, it is an annual, and the cost of growing it is therefore somewhat higher than the cost of alfalfa pasture in sections where a seeding of alfalfa will last for 3 years or more.

There was not much difference in the number of pigs carried per acre on these two pasture crops, the average being 17.2 pigs per acre for alfalfa and 16.8 for rape. In any particular section, the relative carrying capacity of these forages will depend upon which crop thrives better in the particular locality.

Since alfalfa forage is fairly rich in protein and is high in calcium, pigs fed only corn and salt on alfalfa pasture will make satisfactory gains. However, when rapid gains are desired, a protein supplement should be fed in addition, as has been shown in the previous chapter. (1286)

1381. Clover pasture.—In the northern and central states *red clover* is one of the most valuable pasture crops for swine, being surpassed only by alfalfa. (383) Red clover cannot generally be grazed quite as early in the spring as alfalfa, and it provides somewhat less forage per acre. When the rainfall is ample, clover will provide good pasture throughout the growing season, if it is not overgrazed, but yet is not allowed to go to seed or become too mature. In dry seasons, it does not furnish as constant a supply of forage as does alfalfa. Clover pasture should be clipped with a mower when necessary, to induce new growth and to prevent it from going to seed.

It is fortunate that red clover closely approaches alfalfa in value as a pasture crop for swine, for it can be grown on soils that are not sufficiently well drained for alfalfa. Red clover is particularly adapted to growing in a short crop rotation to provide pasture free from infestation with swine parasites and filth-borne diseases. (**1239-1240**) That red clover pasture rivals alfalfa pasture for swine is shown by the results of 7 experiments, in each of which one lot of pigs averaging 52 lbs. in weight at the start was fed corn and tankage on alfalfa pasture, while another lot of pigs was fed similarly on red clover pasture.[174] On both kinds of pasture the average daily gain was the same, 1.24 lbs. There was a slight advantage in amount of feed required per 100 lbs. gain in favor of the alfalfa pasture, 8 lbs. less corn and 2 lbs. less tankage being consumed for each 100 lbs. gain by the pigs on alfalfa than was required by those on clover pasture. Somewhat more hay was also cut from the alfalfa pasture lots than from the clover pastures.

In sections where both red clover and rape thrive, clover is very slightly superior to rape as a swine pasture. In 12 experiments at the Ohio, Wisconsin, and Iowa stations pigs fed corn and tankage on red clover pasture gained an average of 1.25 lbs. per head daily, while others similarly fed on rape pasture gained 1.18 lbs.[175] A trifle less feed was also required per 100 lbs. gain on the clover pasture. However, the difference was too small to be significant, as it only amounted to 3 lbs. corn and 1 lb. tankage.

The difference between these two excellent pasture crops is so small that the choice between them should be based on the adaptability of each to the local soil and climatic conditions. In considering the merits of these crops, it must be borne in mind that clover improves the soil, while rape does not.

There is somewhat more advantage in feeding pigs on clover pasture a protein supplement in addition to corn or other grain, than there is in the case of alfalfa pasture, for clover is not so rich as alfalfa in protein.

Alsike clover is an excellent pasture crop for swine on soils too wet or too acid for red clover. (**386**) Ohio tests show that where the soil is adapted to red clover, it is preferable to alsike clover for swine pasture, for red clover provides good grazing over a longer season.[176] On sandy soil, *mammoth clover* may yield more pasturage than red clover. (**385**)

White clover is not commonly grown alone for swine pasture, but it is important in mixed and native pastures in many districts. A mixture of white clover and bluegrass makes a much better pasture than bluegrass alone, especially in mid-summer. (**387**) Particularly in the southeastern states, *crimson clover*, sown as a winter annual, furnishes valuable spring pasturage for pigs. (**394**) *Lespedeza* is one of the most valuable pasture crops in the South. (**405**)

1382. Sweet clover.—On soils not well adapted to alfalfa or red clover, sweet clover may often be used to advantage as a pasture for swine. (**390**) Experiments at various stations have shown that alfalfa or red clover is usually preferable to sweet clover where these crops thrive.[177] It is sometimes difficult to get swine to eat sweet clover, but they will usually become accustomed to it after a time.

Biennial sweet clover, sown in the spring, is much better for swine pasture during the first season of its growth than during the second season. The first year it will provide forage throughout the summer. On the other hand, the second year it will rapidly grow up rank and coarse. Even if the crop is cut for hay to prevent it from going to seed, the pasture may be none too good thereafter, and the plants will usually die by mid-August.

1383. Rape pasture.—Over the greater part of the northern and central portion of the United States, rape is the best single annual forage crop for swine. (486) Rape provides excellent forage over a long season; it is easily grown and requires no cultivation; it thrives on any fertile soil adapted to corn; and the seed is cheap. Since the young plants are not injured by light frosts, rape may be seeded in early spring and should be 8 to 10 inches high and ready for grazing in 7 or 8 weeks after seeding. If not pastured too heavily, the crop will provide pasturage until late in the fall, for the plants are not killed by ordinary frosts.

Although rape commonly produces the best yield when sown early in the spring, it will make a satisfactory crop when seeded as late as June or early in July, if sufficient moisture is available. If rape is pastured heavily, the pigs must be removed when it has been grazed down to 4 or 5 leaves to the plant, in order to give the crop a chance to recover. A much better plan is not to overstock the pasture. If spring pigs are full-fed concentrates on pasture, spring-sown rape on good soil should furnish good grazing throughout the season for 16 to 20 pigs, or even more, per acre.

The opinion is sometimes expressed that rape is not palatable to swine, and that they fail to eat it as they should. In the numerous experiment station tests of this pasture crop, there has been no difficulty of the kind, and excellent results have practically always been secured from good crops of rape. The idea that pigs do not eat much rape is probably explained by the fact that it grows so rapidly under favorable conditions that the pigs do not make much of an impression on the crop.

Rape occasionally is damaged by aphis or plant lice, especially if it is not on a fertile soil. Also, it sometimes causes blistering or sunscalding of swine. White pigs and those with very thin hair or white belts or spots are most apt to suffer from sunscald, although no breed is immune. Usually the ears and the back are the parts affected. Sunscalding is caused by pigs grazing in the rape when it is wet and then getting into the hot sunshine. It is therefore more apt to occur in rainy periods than during dry weather. Care should be taken to rub crude oil, vaseline, or lard on any blistered spot. Generally very little sunscalding is experienced, even with white pigs. This characteristic of rape should therefore not deter one from using it as a pasture crop. Sometimes sunscalding occurs to a lesser extent on alfalfa and other forages.

The experiments which have been previously summarized in this chapter show that rape closely approaches alfalfa or red clover in value as swine pasture.[178] (**1380, 1381**) Where alfalfa thrives, it slightly excels rape, chiefly because it need not be reseeded each year and also because it is a legume and thus builds up the soil. The portion of the rape plant eaten by pigs is nearly as rich as alfalfa in protein. However, pigs self-fed, free-choice, corn and tankage or such a mixture as one-half tankage and one-half linseed meal, generally eat a somewhat greater amount of supplement on rape pasture than when on alfalfa or clover pasture. In the South rape is an excellent winter forage crop for fertile soils.

1384. Combinations including rape.—In the northern-most states of this country rape is often seeded for swine pasture in combination with oats and peas, or with only oats or barley. In localities particularly well adapted to field peas, the combination of oats, peas, and rape may be sufficiently superior to rape alone to warrant the additional cost of the oat and pea seed. Pigs self-fed corn and tankage on oat-pea-and-rape pasture in 5 Wisconsin trials gained no more rapidly than others on rape pasture, but each year they required a little less concentrates for 100 lbs. gain.[179] This saving amounted to 17 lbs. corn and 2 lbs. tankage for each 100 lbs. gain, on the average, which usually more than covered the additional cost of growing the mixture over seeding rape alone. Farther South, or in other sections where field peas do not thrive so well, rape is superior to the mixture of oats, peas, and rape.

A combination of oats and rape was slightly superior to rape alone in 2 Wisconsin tests, but in trials at the Ohio and Pennsylvania Stations rape alone was better.[180] In seeding one of these combination crops, the rate at which the oats and peas or the oats is seeded should not be too heavy. Otherwise the rape may be crowded out in the early stages of growth.

1385. Field peas for pasture.—Field peas or a mixture of field peas and oats are sometimes grown for swine pasture in the northern states. (**402**) These crops provide excellent pasture for a short period, but cannot compete with alfalfa, clover, or rape as long-season forages.[181] By sowing rape with oats-and-peas, excellent pasture may easily be provided until late fall, for the rape will come on after the oats and the peas are grazed off. Austrian winter peas are sometimes grown in combination with winter oats or other winter grain for winter and early spring pasture in the southern states and in certain sections of the Pacific-Coast district.[182]

In certain districts of the northwest where field peas thrive and grain is high in price, pigs are sometimes fattened by allowing them to "hog down" field peas, into which they are turned from the time the pods begin to form until they ripen. Sometimes the crop is not hogged down until the peas have matured and the vines have died. Fairly good gains are made by pigs hogging down peas if the vines are still green. In North Dakota tests over a period of 10 years, 385 lbs. of pork were produced per acre of peas hogged down, and in Idaho tests over a 3-year period, 406 lbs. of pork were produced per acre.[183] More rapid gains are made when the pigs are fed a limited amount of grain in addition to the peas. Whether or not it will be economical to add grain, will depend on its cost. It may also be advisable to feed a small amount of protein supplement, such as tankage, that supplies protein of high quality, for the protein in field peas is not of a very complete nature.

Colorado tests show that poor results may be secured when pigs hog down ripe field peas, unless supplementary feed is given.[184] In these trials excellent gains were made when pigs hogging down peas were fed barley and either tankage, alfalfa meal, or skimmilk in addition. Cull potatoes were a good addition to such a ration.

1386. Soybean pasture.—Green soybean plants provide good pasturage for swine, but only during a rather short season. Soybeans cannot be seeded in the spring until danger of frost is over, and therefore they do not furnish feed as early as do alfalfa, clover, and rape. Also, when soybean plants are grazed off, the growth is not renewed, as it is in the case of the long-season pasture crops. For these reasons soybeans are inferior to alfalfa, clover, or rape where the latter crops thrive.[185]

In some sections of the South, soybeans produce larger yields of good forage than any other summer pasture crop suited for swine.[186] In using soybeans for fattening pigs, however, care must be taken to avoid the production of soft pork. This difficulty may be largely prevented by using a late variety of soybeans that will not mature seed until after spring pigs are ready for market.

Well-grown pigs make satisfactory gains when they hog down a field of soybeans after the beans have developed, if they receive a limited amount of corn or other grain in addition.[187] Unfortunately, however, this method of feeding produces soft pork. The growing of soybeans in a corn field that is to be hogged down has been discussed earlier in this chapter. (**1331**)

1387. Cowpea pasture.—On the poorer soils in the southern states cowpeas are useful as a forage crop for swine, as they flourish where other legumes will not produce good crops. (**401**)[188] On the better soils, however, soybeans are superior to cowpeas.[189]

1388. Velvet bean pasture.—In the South velvet beans are sometimes grown with corn and the crop hogged down, part of the corn ears often being picked first. The gains may be satisfactory as long as the corn lasts, but later they are often poor. This is due to the fact, pointed out in Chapter XVIII, that velvet beans are unsatisfactory for swine when forming any considerable part of the ration. (605)

When a crop of corn and velvet beans is to be hogged down, the pigs should be fed a limited amount of some efficient protein supplement, such as tankage. In an Alabama trial pigs were turned into a field where velvet beans had been grown with corn but the good corn ears had been already removed.[190] In addition, they were given a half ration of a mixture of 9 parts corn meal and 1 part tankage. Another lot of pigs was fed corn and tankage in a dry lot. The pigs foraging on velvet beans gained 1.23 lbs. per head daily and required 0.38 acre of velvet beans and only 170 lbs. concentrates for 100 lbs. gain, while those in dry lot consumed 400 lbs. concentrates per 100 lbs. gain.

1389. Permanent pasture.—Among the permanent grasses, *bluegrass* generally provides the best pasture throughout the humid area of the northern states. In this district it forms the chief part of the native pasture, often in combination with white clover. The value of native pasture will depend largely upon the proportion of clover and other legumes present, for the pasture will provide a much more uniform supply of feed throughout the season when there is a goodly proportion of legumes.

Bluegrass furnishes excellent early spring and late fall pasturage, being ready even before alfalfa or the clovers. However, it makes little growth during mid-summer, so other crops should be provided at this season. The cost per acre of bluegrass and other permanent pasture is usually very low, for there is little or no expense for seeding, and areas not suited to cultivation can be used for this purpose. If the same permanent pasture lot is used for swine during successive years, it will become badly infested with round worms and other parasites. (**1439**)

In the several trials in which bluegrass pasture or native pasture consisting chiefly of bluegrass has been compared with rape pasture for growing and fattening pigs, the rate of gain has generally been distinctly less on the grass pasture. Even more important, 90 lbs. more concentrates have been required, on the average, for each 100 lbs. gain.[191] In addition to these advantages of the rape pasture, it will commonly carry more pigs per acre than bluegrass or other permanent grass pasture. In certain tests where there was a high proportion of white clover in the pasture, bluegrass more closely approached rape in value.

Since bluegrass and other grasses are lower in protein than alfalfa, clover, or rape, a somewhat larger amount of protein supplement is needed to balance the ration for pigs full-fed grain on such pastures. Also, it is much more necessary to add a protein supplement to the ration than in the case of the better forage crops. (**1286**)

Throughout much of the southern states *Bermuda grass* furnishes the best permanent pasture for swine. (**461**) *Orchard grass* is also a good grass for permanent swine pasture in sections where it thrives better than bluegrass. (**453**) In 4 tests at the North Carolina Station pigs full-fed a mixture of corn, wheat shorts, and fish meal on orchard-grass pasture gained 0.10 lb. per head more daily than those fed this excellent ration in dry lot.[192] The pasture-fed pigs also required 6 lbs. less concentrates per 100 lbs. gain. When only one-half as large a proportion of protein supplements was fed to the pigs on this pasture as was included in the ration for the pigs in dry lot, the gains were a trifle slower and also decidedly more expensive.

1390. The cereals.—Winter rye and winter wheat provide excellent late fall and early spring pasture in the northern states, rivalling or excelling bluegrass in this respect. In the central states these winter grains will also furnish considerable forage during the winter, if there has been a good growth by the time cold weather comes on in the fall. In the South winter cereals will provide good pasture from fall until spring, thus greatly decreasing the cost of maintaining brood sows and raising fall pigs.

At the pasture stage of growth green rye and other cereals are richer than alfalfa hay in protein, on the dry basis.[193] (**295**) Therefore cereal pasture saves protein supplements in the same manner as does alfalfa, clover, or rape pasture. However, the feeding of a small amount of an efficient protein supplement to pigs fed grain on cereal pasture, even of the best quality, will increase the rate of gain considerably and will generally reduce the cost of producing pork.

For fall, winter, and spring pasture the cereal should be chosen that produces the best yield of forage in the particular locality.[194] In the North rye is generally superior to wheat, because it is more hardy.

Farther South, wheat is preferable in some sections. In the southern states winter barley or winter oats may be better than rye or wheat for winter pasture.

For seeding in the spring to provide pasture in summer, the cereals are generally much inferior to such crops as alfalfa, clover, or rape, for they soon ripen and die. Sometimes winter wheat or winter rye is seeded in the spring in order to secure a longer pasture season than is possible with the spring varieties of grain.

1391. Hogging down ripe grain; gleaning stubble fields.—Ripe grain, especially rye, wheat, or bald barley, is sometimes hogged down, pigs being turned into the field when the crop is nearly ripe. The method may give satisfactory results when the season is dry, and for this reason it is used most in the wheat-growing districts of the Northwest.[195] Experiments have shown that in the corn belt and other humid districts a grain crop generally produces much less pork when hogged down than when it is harvested and the threshed grain fed instead.

For example, in recent Ohio experiments pigs hogging down ripe wheat and fed tankage in addition made an average gain of only 0.57 lb. per head daily.[196] Other pigs fed harvested wheat from the same field, with tankage as the protein supplement gained 1.25 lbs. daily. When the wheat was hogged down, the gross return per bushel of wheat was only 49 cents, after deducting the cost of the tankage. The gross return from the harvested and threshed wheat was 73 cents per bushel, after deducting the cost of the tankage, but not the cost of harvesting and threshing. Similar results were secured when rye was hogged down.

It has been shown previously in this chapter that hogging down corn is a thoroughly successful method of harvesting the crop. (1331)

Especially on the grain farms of the West, stubble fields are an important factor in economical pork production. Where the grain is harvested by means of a header or a combine thresher, a considerable amount may be left ungarnered, and this was formerly wasted. Many farmers have hog fenced their fields and turn pigs on the stubble to glean the scattered heads of grain. Gains made on such waste are almost clear profit.

1392. Sudan grass; sorghum; Japanese cane.—*Sudan grass* is a very satisfactory pasture crop for swine in districts where it thrives and where the climate is too dry or is otherwise unsuited for such forages as alfalfa, red clover, or rape. (457) It is therefore especially adapted to the drier portions of the Great Plains, often providing more feed than alfalfa.[197] On the other hand, in the corn belt and eastward and in the south central and southeastern states, Sudan grass is generally excelled very decidedly by other pasture crops.[198]

Where alfalfa, clover, or rape thrives, these crops provide pasture over a longer season than does Sudan grass, for the latter is readily killed by frosts. It therefore cannot be seeded until corn planting time, and it does not provide forage late in the fall. Sudan grass is a better pasture crop for pigs over 50 to 75 lbs. in weight than for very young pigs. However, even for the latter it is much better than no pasture at all.

Since Sudan grass pasture is decidedly lower in protein than alfalfa, red clover, or rape, pigs will not make good gains on it unless an efficient protein supplement is provided.

Sorghum is too high in fiber to excel as a pasture for young pigs, though it is useful in the South for providing succulence when other crops are not available. For older pigs fed considerable grain it gives somewhat better results.[199] (444)

In a Florida test, *Japanese cane* fed alone would not maintain young pigs.[200] For pigs fed grain, this forage should have about the same value as sorghum. (465)

1393. Soiling crops.—It is not ordinarily profitable to cut and haul green crops for pigs, for they can better do their own harvesting. If for any reason any of the hogs cannot be provided with pasture, it will help to cut a little green feed for them, but it will save labor to fence off a plot in some nearby field and turn them in.[201] (355-357)

1394. Roots.—Roots were formerly esteemed by many swine raisers, especially for feeding brood sows. (470-471) In several trials carried on years ago roots were added to rations which were then considered satisfactory for pigs, but which we now know to be inefficient. For example, pigs were fed grain alone or grain and shorts alone in comparison with others fed roots in addition. In 8 trials pigs fed concentrates alone gained 1.2 lbs. a head daily and required 499 lbs. concentrates for 100 lbs. gain.[202] Others fed roots in addition (sugar beets in most of the trials) gained 1.0 lb. a head daily, and required 358 lbs. concentrates plus 631 lbs. roots for 100 lbs. gain. In these trials 448 lbs. of roots saved 100 lbs. of concentrates. If such a value as this could usually be secured from roots, when added to modern, efficient rations, they would perhaps be economical winter feeds for swine, for with concentrates at $25.00 a ton, roots would be worth $5.50 a ton.

However, when roots were added to efficient rations for brood sows or fattening pigs in trials by the author and Bohstedt at the Wisconsin Station, the roots had so low a value that they were decidedly uneconomical.[203] In these trials alfalfa or clover hay was a much more efficient addition than roots to the rations of brood sows or fall pigs. We might expect this, since legume hay is rich in good-quality protein, in calcium, and in vitamins A and D, and it has a desirable laxative effect. Roots are palatable, succulent, and laxative, but they are low in protein and in calcium. Moreover, roots are lacking in vitamin D, and most roots have little or no vitamin A, though yellow carrots are rich in it. Roots should be chopped before being fed to swine.

1395. Other succulent feeds.—In the potato-growing districts *cull potatoes* are often an economical feed for swine, if they are fed after thorough cooking, as has been explained previously. (480)

In the South sweet potatoes are often used for swine feeding. The manner in which they can be best utilized has been shown previously. (482)

Corn silage and *sorghum silage* are not useful feeds for swine. They are bulky and high in fiber, and they do not have the nutritive qualities that make legume hay so valuable for swine not on pasture. In strong contrast to legume hay, corn silage and sorghum silage are low in protein and in calcium, and they provide much less vitamin A and vitamin D than does well-cured legume hay.

Wet beet pulp is not so commonly fed to swine as to cattle or sheep, but limited amounts can be thus used. (643) In a Utah trial 130-lb. pigs, fed 3.3 lbs. wheat shorts and 12.3 lbs. wet beet pulp a head daily, gained 1.2 lbs. per day and required 275 lbs. shorts and 1,030 lbs. beet pulp for 100 lbs. gain.[204] Compared with pigs fed shorts alone, 609 lbs. of beet pulp replaced 100 lbs. of shorts.

IV. LEGUME HAY

1396. Importance of legume hay for swine not on pasture.—It has already been emphasized that swine which are not on pasture should be provided with legume hay whenever possible. (1280, 1298) Such hay aids in supplying the necessary amount of protein and also protein of a kind that will help to make good the deficiencies in the proteins of the cereal grains. It also is rich in calcium and fair in phosphorus content. Still more important, such hay is the only rich source of both vitamin A and vitamin D among all the feeds commonly used in feeding swine in dry lot.

It is especially advantageous to include legume hay in the rations of young pigs and brood sows during the winter when they are not on pasture. Indeed, this may often make all the difference between profit and loss in pork production, for it will prevent unthriftiness and possible disaster due to a lack of vitamins. Many experiments have shown that a ration is unsafe for feeding to swine for a long period of time which consists only of any grain except yellow corn, supplemented by minerals and any of the most common protein supplements.[205] Such a ration will be seriously deficient in vitamin A and will also lack vitamin D.

Even when swine are fed yellow corn (which is a good source of vitamin A) there is still a decided benefit from adding well-cured legume hay to the ration for swine not on pasture.[206] The hay provides an even more liberal supply of vitamin A and, still more important, is a protection against any lack of vitamin D.

Pigs or brood sows fed a ration of yellow corn supplemented by tankage, meat scraps, or dairy by-products may remain thrifty during the winter when not on pasture, provided the climate is such that they are outdoors and exposed to direct sunlight during much of the daytime. Though winter sunlight is relatively weak in anti-rachitic effect, swine may then be protected against rickets. (**191**) However, the only safe plan is to supply them with well-cured legume hay during the winter.

Even when fish meal is fed as the supplement to grain, it is advisable to supply legume hay in addition, unless one is sure that the fish meal is rich in vitamin A and vitamin D. When it is impossible to provide legume hay for swine in dry lot during the winter, it may be advisable to feed a cod-liver oil concentrate or some other vitamin A and D supplement. However, this should be done only when legume hay is not available. (**1298**)

1397. Amount of legume hay to use.—As has been stated in the previous chapter, at least 10 to 15 per cent of legume hay should be included in the rations of brood sows that are not on pasture. (**1298**) If the legume hay is of good quality, sows will generally eat enough of it when it is fed, uncut, in a rack.

The proportion of legume hay should be less for pigs, because their digestive tracts cannot utilize as large a proportion of hay as the digestive systems of more mature swine. No more than 4 to 5 per cent of good legume hay need be included in the rations of pigs not on pasture to protect them amply against vitamin deficiencies. If pigs are forced to eat a much larger proportion of hay than this the rate of gain will generally be decreased and the gains will be less economical.[207] Pigs can, however, be allowed to eat as much legume hay as they will take if it is fed separately in a rack.

When pigs are fed a mixture of ground grain and protein supplements, 4 to 5 lbs. of the chopped or ground legume hay should be included in each 100 lbs. of the mixture. If the pigs are self-fed shelled corn or hand-fed all the ear corn they will eat, the safest way of supplying the legume hay is to self-feed them the trio mixture developed by the author and associates at the Wisconsin Station, or to use one of the modifications of this mixture. (**1341**) The trio mixture consists of 50 lbs. tankage, 25 lbs. linseed meal, and 25 lbs. legume hay. (As has been pointed out previously, various changes can be made in this mixture. For example, fish meal may be substituted for the tankage, and soybean oil meal or cottonseed meal for the linseed meal.)

Sometimes supplemental mixtures are used which contain less than 25 per cent of legume hay, but the author believes this is unwise. The primary purpose of using the legume hay is to make sure that there will be no deficiency of vitamin A or vitamin D. Since legume hay varies rather widely in vitamin content, the only safe plan is to include sufficient hay in the mixture to provide ample protection under any usual conditions.

If alfalfa hay of excellent quality is available (preferably second or third cutting), even young pigs will generally eat a sufficient amount of the hay to protect them against vitamin deficiency when it is fed uncut in a rack.[208] However, unless the hay is really of first quality, they will often take an insufficient amount of it.[209] The author therefore prefers to include 4 to 5 per cent of chopped or ground hay in the rations of pigs fed in dry lot during the winter, for there will then be no danger of the pigs consuming an insufficient proportion of the hay to protect them against disaster.

In the case of other legume hay, such as red clover or soybean, it is more necessary to mix the proper proportion of chopped or ground hay with other feeds, for pigs will often eat but little of it when it is fed in a rack.

If there are no facilities on the farm for chopping or grinding legume hay, the leaves and chaff which accumulate where the hay is pitched from the mow may be used instead. Such material usually contains some long stems, and it is therefore not very satisfactory for use in a concentrate mixture that is to be self-fed, for these stems may clog the self-feeder.

1398. Adding alfalfa hay to grain and tankage.—That it is highly advantageous to add alfalfa hay to such a ration as grain and tankage for young pigs not on pasture is clearly shown by the following table.

Adding alfalfa hay to yellow corn and tankage in dry lot

Average ration	Daily gain Lbs.	Corn Lbs.	Tankage Lbs.	Alfalfa hay Lbs.
Lot I, no hay				
Tankage, 0.46 lb. Corn, 4.40 lbs.............	1.16	383	41	..
Lot II, fed alfalfa hay				
Alfalfa hay, 0.21 lb.				
Tankage, 0.45 lb. Corn, 4.57 lbs.............	1.26	365	36	16

This table gives the results of 8 experiments in each of which one lot of pigs has been self-fed yellow corn and tankage while another lot has received alfalfa hay in addition.[210] In these trials the pigs were fed in dry lot from an average weight of 62 lbs. until they reached market weights of approximately 200 lbs. The alfalfa hay fed to Lot II in these experiments formed 4 per cent of the total ration, on the average.

The addition of alfalfa hay to the ration of yellow corn and tankage increased the average daily gain from 1.16 lbs. to 1.26 lbs. and also reduced the amount of feed required per 100 lbs. gain. In these trials each 100 lbs. of alfalfa hay saved 112 lbs. corn plus 31 lbs. tankage, which is really a remarkable showing. With corn at $20 and tankage at $60 a ton, alfalfa hay would have a value of $41 per ton, without giving it any credit for the increase in rate of gain. This well shows that one cannot afford to fail to provide legume hay for pigs fed such a ration as yellow corn and tankage in dry lot.

If any other grain than yellow corn had been fed in these experiments, the addition of alfalfa hay would have been even more beneficial, for many of the pigs fed grain and tankage, without alfalfa hay, would have been injured by the deficiency of vitamin A. Also, if the pigs had been started on the trials immediately after weaning, those fed yellow corn and tankage would not have made as creditable gains as were made by these 62-lb. pigs. The younger the pigs are when they are put in dry lot, without fresh, green feed, the greater will be the advantage in supplying them with good legume hay.

It should, however, not be concluded from these statements that it is not advantageous to add alfalfa hay to corn and tankage for pigs in dry lot that are already well-grown when put on this ration. The contrary is shown by the results of 8 similar experiments with pigs that averaged 110 lbs. in weight at the start.[211] In these tests the well-grown pigs fed corn (chiefly yellow corn) and tankage in dry lot gained an average of 1.37 lbs. per head daily while those fed alfalfa hay in addition gained 1.50 lbs. Each 100 lbs. of alfalfa hay actually saved 211 lbs. corn (but no tankage) in these trials, giving the hay fully as high a value per ton as in the experiments with younger pigs that have been previously summarized.

It should be emphasized that even a ration of corn, tankage, and alfalfa hay is not quite ideal for young pigs in dry lot. As has been shown previously in this chapter, still better results will be secured from the trio supplemental mixture or similar combinations of protein supplements. (1342)

There is the same general advantage in adding legume hay to rations of grain and other supplements that there is in the case of corn and tankage, except when corn is fed with a kind of fish meal which has goodly amounts of vitamin A and vitamin D. For example, when any grain except yellow corn is fed with skimmilk, buttermilk, or whey to young pigs not on pasture, disaster may occur from a lack of vitamin A. Such trouble can readily be prevented by the use of well-cured legume hay.

It was found in 3 Wisconsin trials that it was even beneficial to add legume hay to a ration of yellow corn and skimmilk.[212] In these tests pigs fed yellow corn and skimmilk from shortly after weaning up to market weights gained an average of 1.03 lbs. per head daily. Others fed 0.20 lb. alfalfa hay a day gained 1.11 lbs. Pigs in a third lot, fed not only alfalfa hay but also 0.21 lb. linseed meal in addition to the yellow corn and skimmilk, gained 1.14 lbs. a day, with a feed cost per 100 lbs. gain of 24 cents less than for the pigs fed only corn and skimmilk.

1399. Alfalfa hay as the only supplement to grain.—Alfalfa hay is fairly rich in protein, and the protein is also of such quality that it helps to correct the deficiencies in the proteins of the grains. The question therefore arises as to whether alfalfa hay is satisfactory when used as the only protein supplement to the grains in swine feeding. It is shown in the following chapter that a ration consisting only of legume hay and grain is satisfactory for wintering pregnant sows a year of age or more, if the hay is of excellent quality. (**1409**) For younger sows during pregnancy and also for all sows when they are suckling their pigs, a small amount of a more concentrated protein supplement should be added to the ration.

Growing and fattening pigs have less capacity to consume hay than do older swine. Also, their needs for protein are relatively large. While the addition of alfalfa hay to a full feed of corn for pigs will produce much better results than corn alone, the gains are much less rapid and also less economical than when a more concentrated and more efficient protein supplement is fed in addition.

For example, in 14 experiments well-grown pigs, averaging 102 lbs. in weight at the start gained but 1.08 lbs. per head daily on a full feed of corn supplemented by only alfalfa hay.[213] Others fed corn and tankage, with no alfalfa hay, gained 1.51 lbs. a day and required considerably less feed per 100 lbs. gain. In these trials each 100 lbs. of tankage replaced 194 lbs. corn plus 174 lbs. of hay, without considering the large increase in rate of gain.

As has just been shown, still better results would have been secured with these pigs fed in dry lot, if alfalfa hay had been added to the ration of corn and tankage. Also, if the pigs fed only corn and alfalfa hay had not been well-grown when placed on this ration the results would not have been nearly so good as were secured in these tests.[214] Young pigs need very much more protein than is provided by a ration consisting only of corn and excellent alfalfa hay.

It has been shown in the previous chapter that alfalfa hay produces somewhat better results when fed as the only protein supplement to the grains that are higher than corn in protein. (**1285**) However, unless efficient protein supplements are unusually high in price in comparison with grain and hay, it is usually economical to add such a supplement to a ration of alfalfa hay and a full-feed of barley, wheat, oats, kafir, or rye, especially for pigs under 100 to 125 lbs. in weight.[215]

1400. Alfalfa leaf meal; alfalfa stem meal.—There is no need of going to the expense of using *alfalfa leaf* meal instead of alfalfa hay or alfalfa meal (ground alfalfa hay) as a vitamin supplement for pigs in dry lot. Alfalfa leaf meal has a somewhat higher value per ton than alfalfa meal or alfalfa hay, but there is not usually sufficient difference in the value for pigs to offset the higher cost of the alfalfa leaf meal.[216]

Alfalfa stem meal should not be used as a substitute for alfalfa hay or alfalfa meal in protecting swine in dry lot against vitamin deficiencies.[217] Since it is composed chiefly of alfalfa stems, it is much lower than leafy alfalfa hay in vitamins and protein.

1401. Other legume hay.—When alfalfa hay is not available, other legume hay of good quality may be substituted for it in swine feeding. However, most other kinds of legume hay are somewhat less palatable to swine than good alfalfa hay. When such hay is fed separately in a rack, swine are therefore less apt to eat a sufficient amount of it to protect them against a lack of vitamin A or vitamin D. It is therefore more frequently necessary with other legume hay to mix the chopped or ground hay with other feeds, so as to make sure that enough is consumed.

Red clover hay of good quality is a satisfactory substitute for alfalfa hay for pigs or for brood sows. In 5 Wisconsin experiments with pigs fed in dry lot excellent results were secured when chopped clover hay was substituted for chopped alfalfa hay in the trio or Wisconsin supplemental mixture.[218] On the average, the gains were even a trifle more rapid and economical on the clover-hay mixture. In an Ohio test clover hay was likewise a satisfactory substitute for alfalfa hay in the trio mixture.[219]

When used as the only supplement to grain for swine, clover hay is less efficient than alfalfa hay, for it is less palatable and lower in protein and in calcium.

Sweet clover hay of excellent quality was a satisfactory substitute for alfalfa hay in a Kansas test.[220] Excellent results were secured both when pigs in dry lot were self-fed corn, tankage, and sweet clover hay, free-choice, and when a supplemental mixture was self-fed which consisted of 75 lbs. tankage and 25 lbs. ground sweet clover hay.

Soybean hay and *cowpea hay* were both satisfactory for brood sows in Arkansas trials, and soybean hay produced good results when added as a vitamin supplement to a ration of white corn and tankage in Alabama experiments.[221] Chopped soybean hay was a good substitute for alfalfa hay in the trio supplemental mixture in Wisconsin tests with pigs in dry lot.[222]

Field pea hay was a good substitute for alfalfa hay in a Wyoming trial with brood sows, though not quite equal to alfalfa in value.[223] The sows consumed 1.9 lbs. of the field pea hay per head daily when it was fed uncut in a rack.

Ground kudzu hay produced excellent results in an Alabama trial, when used for pigs in dry lot in a trio supplemental mixture consisting of 50 lbs. tankage, 25 lbs. cottonseed meal, and 25 lbs. of the ground kudzu hay.[224]

QUESTIONS

1. State the merits and the deficiencies of the cereal grains for swine feeding.
2. Discuss the results of the experiments in which corn alone has been compared with corn and tankage for growing and fattening pigs.
3. Under what conditions is white corn equal to yellow corn for swine feeding?
4. What are the most economical forms in which to feed corn to growing and fattening pigs; to brood sows?
5. Discuss the hogging down of corn.
6. What is the relative value for swine of the dry matter in soft corn and in mature corn?
7. How does barley compare with corn in value for pigs? How should barley be prepared for swine?
8. Discuss the use of oats in swine feeding, stating the manner in which oats should be fed to have the highest value.
9. Is it generally advisable to hull oats for swine feeding?

10. Compare the values of wheat and corn for swine feeding. Should wheat be ground for swine?

11. Discuss the use and value of any of the following that are important for swine in your district: (a) Rye; (b) grain sorghums; (c) hominy feed; (d) emmer; (e) rice, rice polish, and rice bran; (f) buckwheat; (g) oat mill feed; (h) molasses.

12. What is the trio mixture? Why are the trio mixture and similar combinations superior to tankage or fish meal as the supplement to grain for young pigs in dry lot?

13. In what different ways may the trio mixture and similar combinations be fed?

14. State 2 combinations of protein supplements that are superior to tankage for pigs on pasture.

15. Discuss the value of skimmilk and buttermilk for swine feeding. How should these dairy by-products be fed to secure the highest value from them?

16. Why are not dried skimmilk, dried buttermilk, and condensed buttermilk used more often for swine feeding?

17. Compare the composition of whey and skimmilk and their values for swine feeding.

18. Discuss the use of tankage and meat scraps for swine feeding.

19. Under what conditions would you use low-protein tankage for swine feeding?

20. What is the relative value of meat scraps containing 50 to 55 per cent protein in comparison with that of digester tankage of 60-per-cent-protein grade?

21. Compare the value of fish meal for swine feeding with that of tankage.

22. State in detail how wheat standard middlings or brown shorts should be used in swine feeding.

23. State the approximate value of the following for pigs in comparison with wheat standard middlings: (a) Wheat flour middlings or gray shorts; (b) wheat red dog flour or white shorts.

24. How should wheat bran and wheat mixed feed be used in swine feeding?

25. Discuss the use of linseed meal for swine.

26. State in detail how cottonseed meal may be fed safely to swine.

27. Under what conditions are raw soybeans satisfactory for swine feeding? What are the limitations to the use of cooked soybeans for pigs?

28. Compare the usefulness and value of soybean oil meal and soybeans for swine. What characteristics should soybean oil meal possess to be desirable for swine feeding?

29. If any of the following are of importance for swine feeding in your section, discuss their use and value: (a) Peanuts; (b) peanut oil meal; (c) corn gluten feed; (d) corn gluten meal; (e) corn oil meal and corn germ meal; (f) distillers' dried grains; (g) distillery slop.

30. State the merits of good pasture for swine.

31. Summarize the most important facts concerning the feeding of protein supplements with grain to pigs on good pasture.

32. What pasture crops would you use in your district to provide pasturage for swine over as great a part of the year as possible?

33. State the merits and limitations of any of the following crops for swine pasture which are important in your district: (a) Alfalfa; (b) red clover; (c) sweet clover; (d) rape; (e) combinations including rape; (f) field peas; (g) soybeans; (h) cowpeas; (i) velvet beans; (j) permanent pasture; (k) the cereals; (l) Sudan grass.

34. Why are not roots used to any appreciable extent for swine feeding in the United States?

35. Discuss the importance of legume hay for swine not on pasture.

36. How much legume hay should be included in the rations of pigs not on pasture; in the rations of brood sows not on pasture?

37. What results have been secured in experiments where alfalfa hay has been added to a ration of corn and tankage for growing and fattening pigs?

38. Discuss the use of alfalfa hay as the only protein supplement to grain for swine feeding.
39. Which would you purchase for use as a vitamin supplement in swine feeding, alfalfa meal, alfalfa leaf meal, or alfalfa stem meal?
40. In addition to alfalfa hay, what other kinds of legume hay are suitable for swine feeding?

REFERENCES

1. Hogan, Kan. Sta., Jour. Biol. Chem., 29, 1917, pp. 485-493; Vestal, Ind. Sta., mimeo. rpt.; Robison, Ohio Buls. 316, 349.
2. Morrison, Bohstedt, and Fargo, Wis. Buls. 323, 339, 352; Grimes and Sewell, Ala. Rpts. 1929, 1930, 1931; Martin, Ark. Bul. 321; Tomhave, Del. Bul. 147; Rice, Mitchell, and Laible, Ill. Bul. 281; Lamb and Evvard, Iowa Sta., Amer. Soc. Anim. Prod., Proc. 1923; Snyder, Nebr. Bul. 214; Loeffel, Nebr. Rpt. 1921 and information to the author; Nebr. Rpt. 1934; Hostetler, N. C. Rpts. 1929, 1931; Halvorsen, N. C. Rpt. 1931; Livesay and Stillwell, West. Va. Bul. 213.
3. Henry and Otis, Wis. Bul. 145 and Wis. Rpt. 1906.
4. Garrigus and Mitchell, Ill. Rpt. 1934, and Jour. Agr. Res., 50, 1935, pp. 731-735; King, Ind. Sta., Amer. Soc. Anim. Prod., Proc. 1913; Vestal, Ind. Sta., mimeo. rpt.; Kennedy and Robbins, Iowa Bul. 106; Evvard, Iowa Sta., mimeo. rpt.; Aubel and Connell, Kan. Sta., mimeo. rpt.; Weaver, Mo. Sta., mimeo. rpt.; Loeffel, Nebr. Sta., mimeo. rpt.; Robison, Ohio Buls. 362, 516, 552, and Ohio Spec. Cir. 39; Penn. Bul. 147; Wilson and Wright, S. D. Bul. 252; Wyo. Rpt. 1933.
5. Culbertson, Evvard, and Hammond, Iowa Sta., mimeo. rpt.
6. Bohstedt, Roche, Fargo, Rupel, and Duffee, Amer. Soc. Anim. Prod., Proc. 1931.
7. McCarty and Nicholas, Penn. Buls. 279, 293, 308.
8. Evvard, Wallace, and Culbertson, Iowa Bul. 245.
9. McCarty, Nicholas, and Keith, Penn. Buls. 279, 308, and Amer. Soc. Anim. Prod., Proc. 1932, 1933; Bohstedt, Roche, Fargo, Rupel, and Duffee, Amer. Soc. Anim. Prod., Proc. 1931.
10. Martin, Ark. Sta., information to the author; Carroll et al., Ill. Rpt. 1927; Vestal, Ind. Rpts. 1922, 1927, and mimeo. rpt.; Evvard, Iowa Bul. 143; Evvard, Culbertson, et al., Iowa Rpts. 1924, 1926, 1927, and mimeo. rpts.; Anderson and Marston, Kan. Cir. 118; Good, Ky. Rpts. 1918, 1919, 1920, 1921, 1922, 1923, 1924, 1925, 1926; Bray and Francioni, La. Bul. 236; Edwards, Mich. Spec. Bul. 200 and Mich. Quar. Bul. 7, 1924, No. 1; Gaumnitz, Wilson, and Bassett, Minn. Bul. 104; Selvig and Kiser, Minn. Sta., Crookston Substa., Rpt. 1923; Ferrin and Jessup, Minn. Sta., mimeo. rpt.; Weaver, Mo. Bul. 224; Hansen, Mont. Bul. 193; Vinke and Morgan, Mont. Bul. 257; Holden, Nebr. Bul. 159; Loeffel, Nebr. Sta., mimeo. rpt.; N. J. Rpts. 1924, 1926; N. C. Rpt. 1927; Shepperd, N. D. Bul. 174; Robison, Ohio Bul. 398 and Amer. Soc. Anim. Prod., Proc. 1921; Wilson and Kuhlman, S. D. Bul. 192; Seamans and Hutton, U. S. Dept. Agr. Cir. 330.
11. Robison, Ohio Bul. 398.
12. Laible and Smith, Ill. Rpt. 1925; Evvard, Culbertson, Wallace, and Maynard, Iowa Bul. 273; Robison, Ohio Bul. 362.
13. Laible and Smith, Ill. Rpt. 1925; Evvard, Culbertson, Wallace and Maynard, Iowa Bul. 273.
14. Oliver, Ore. Cir. 104; Bohstedt, Roche, Fargo, and Duffee, Wis. Bul. 421.
15. Oliver, Ore. Cir. 104.
16. Freeman, Mich. Sta., Am. Soc. Anim. Prod., Proc. 1932; Arnett, Mont. Rpts. 1922, 1923, Joseph, Mont. Rpt. 1924; Nebr. Rpt. 1934; Oliver, Ore. Cir. 104; Thompson, Okla. Bul. 198; Wilson and Kuhlman, S. D. Bul. 192; Wilson and Wright, S. D. Bul. 252; Hale, Tex. Rpts. 1931, 1932, 1933; Bohstedt, Roche, Fargo, Rupel, and Duffee, Wis. Bul. 421, and Amer. Soc. Anim. Prod., Proc. 1931; see also: Ore. Rpt. 1924-1926; Wyo. Rpt. 1929; Sinclair, Univ. of Alberta, Canada, mimeo. rpt.
17. Good, Ky. Rpt. 1923; Loeffel, Nebr. Bul. 251; Arnett, Mont. Rpts. 1922, 1923; Joseph, Mont. Rpt. 1924; Ore. Rpt. 1924-1926; Thompson, Okla. Bul. 198; Wilson and Kuhlman, S. D. Bul. 192; Morrison and Bohstedt, Wis. Bul. 319.
18. Brown, Mich. Rpt. 1922; Carnes, Minn. Sta., Duroc Digest, Nov. 1, 1921; Ferrin and McCarty, Minn. Sta., mimeo. rpt.; Wilson and Kuhlman, S. D. Bul. 192; Wilson and Wright, S. D. Bul. 262 and mimeo. rpt.; Morrison and Bohstedt, Wis. Bul. 319; see also: Maynard and Brandon, Colo. Press Bul. 69; Id. Bul. 131; Bull, Carroll, et al., Ill. Bul. 366; Vestal, Ind. Sta., mimeo. rpt.; Peters, Ferrin, and Johnson, Minn. Sta., mimeo. rpt.; Weaver, Mo. Bul. 172; Hansen, Mont. Rpt. 1921; Joseph, Mont. Bul. 169; Quesenberry et al., Mont., Rpt. 1927; Loeffel, Nebr. Bul. 251; Robison, Ohio Spec. Cir. 10; Thompson, Okla. Bul. 198; McCarty, Penn. Buls. 266, 279; Carroll, Utah Bul. 192; Willard, Wyo. Rpt. 1931.
19. Ferrin and Winchester, Kan. Cir. 89; Edwards, Mich. Spec. Bul. 199; Wilson and Wright, S. D. Bul. 262; Morrison and Bohstedt, Wis. Sta., mimeo. rpt.; see also: Evvard, Iowa Sta., mimeo. rpt.; Freeman, Mich. Quar. Bul., 15, 1933, No. 4; Miller, Minn. Sta., Morris Substa., Rpt. 1923.
20. Ferrin and Peters, Minn. Sta., mimeo. rpt.; Severson, N. D. Bul. 264.
21. Joseph, Mont. Bul. 169; see also: Wright, S. D. Sta., Am. Soc. Anim. Prod., Proc. 1934.
22. Carroll et al. Ill. Rpt. 1928; Carroll, Ill. Cir. 414; Vestal, Ind. Sta., mimeo. rpts.; Evvard, Culbertson, et al., Iowa Leaflet 15 and mimeo. rpts.; Ferrin, Minn. Pamphlet 21; Joseph, Mont. Bul. 169; Robison, Ohio Buls. 488, 516, and Ohio

Spec. Cirs. 17, 32, 39; Robison, Ohio Bimo. Bul. 134; Thompson, Okla. Rpt. 1919; McCarty, Penn. Buls. 258, 266; S. D. Rpt. 1926; Henry, Wis. Rpt. 1889; McCarty, Amer. Soc. Anim. Prod., Proc. 1927; Dowell and Latimer, Univ. of Alberta, Canada, mimeo. rpt.; Sinclair, Univ. of Alberta, Canada, mimeo. rpt.; Woodman, Evans, and Kitchen, Jour. Agr. Sci., England, 22, 1932, pp. 657-669; Blissett, Scot. Jour. Agr., 16, 1933; pp. 335-339.

23. Carroll, Ill. Cir. 414; Carroll and Garrigus, Ill. Rpt. 1933; Evvard, Culbertson, and Hammond, Iowa Sta., mimeo. rpt.; Robison, Ohio Bul. 488; see also Ferrin, Minn. Pamphlet 21; Weaver, Mo. Bul. 247; Robison, Ohio Bimo. Bul. 134.

24. Ferrin and Winchester, Kan. Cir. 89; Clark, Mont. Bul. 89; Day, Ontario, Canada, Agr. Col. Rpt. 1908; Grisdale, Ottawa, Canada, Expt. Farms Rpt. 1908.

25. Vestal, Ind. Sta., mimeo. rpts.; Aubel and Connell, Kan. Sta., mimeo. rpts.; Carmichael, Md. Bul. 336; Freeman, Mich. Quar. Bul., 13, 1931, No. 3; Peters, Ferrin, and Johnson, Minn. Sta., mimeo. rpt., Weaver, Mo. Bul. 328; Loeffel, Nebr. Bul. 261 and mimeo. rpt.; Loeffel and Lewis, Nebr. Sta., mimeo. rpt.; Wilson and Wright, S. D. Sta., mimeo. rpt.; see also: Ky. Rpt. 1930; Weaver, Mo. Bul. 136; Eastwood, Ohio Bul. 268.

26. Peters, Ferrin, and Johnson, Minn. Sta., mimeo. rpt.; Minn. Sta., Crookston Substa., Rpt. 1924; Vinke and Bergstedt, Mont. Bul. 284; Mont. Rpt. 1931; Smith and Young, Utah Bul. 254.

27. Sinclair, Univ. of Alberta, Canada, mimeo. rpt.

28. Aubel and Connell, Kan. Sta., mimeo. rpts.; Loeffel and Lewis, Nebr. Sta., mimeo. rpt.; Thompson, Okla. Rpt. 1930-32; Hale, Tex. Rpts. 1932, 1933.

29. Bliss and Lee, Nebr. Bul. 144; Snyder, Nebr. Bul. 147; Loeffel, Nebr. Sta., mimeo. rpt.; Withycombe, Ore. Bul. 80.

30. Thompson, Okla. Bul. 165 and Okla. Rpt. 1930-32.

31. Johnson and Palmer, Jour. Agr. Res. 50, 1935, pp. 39-45.

32. Ferrin, Minn. Sta., Amer. Soc. Anim. Prod., Proc. 1925-1926; Vinke and Bergstedt, Mont. Bul. 284; Nebr. Rpt. 1932; Ore. Rpt. 1924-1926; Wilson and Wright, S. D. Bul. 271; Willard, Wyo. Rpt. 1931.

33. Ferrin, Minn. Sta., Amer. Soc. Anim. Prod., Proc. 1925-1926, and mimeo. rpts.

34. Morgan and Arnett, Mont. Bul. 192.

35. Brown, Mich. Rpt. 1922; Peters, Ferrin and Johnson, Minn. Sta., mimeo. rpt.; Wilson and Wright, S. D. Bul. 271; see also: Nebr. Rpts. 1932, 1934.

36. Vinke and Bergstedt, Mont. Bul. 284; Nebr. Rpt. 1932; McCarty, Penn. Buls. 279, 293; Willard, Wyo. Rpt. 1931.

37. Hays, Del. Bul. 124; Md. Rpt. 1933; Nebr. Rpts. 1932, 1934.

38. Aubel and Connell, Kan. Rpt. 1932-34.

39. Williams and Stanley, Ariz. Rpt. 1922; Williams, Burns, and Smith, Ariz. Rpt. 1923; Thompson, Okla. Bul. 144.

40. C. P. Thompson, Okla. Bul. 165, Okla. Rpt. 1926-1930; see also: J. I. Thompson and Voorhies, Cal. Bul. 342.

41. Hale, Tex. Rpts. 1929, 1930, 1932; Thompson, Okla. Bul. 165 and mimeo. rpt.; Thompson, Amer. Soc. Anim. Prod., Proc. 1930; see also Cochel, Kan. Industrialist, May 1, 1915.

42. Thompson, Okla. Bul. 165; Hale, Tex. Rpt. 1930.

43. Dvorachek and Sandhouse, Ark. Cir. 34; Cochel, Kan. Industrialist, May 1, 1915; Waters et al., Kan. Bul. 192; Ferrin and Winchester, Kan. Cir. 89; Malone, Okla. Bul. 120; see also: Hale, Tex. Sta., mimeo. rpt.

44. Cochel, Kan. Industrialist, May 1, 1915; Waters et al., Kan. Bul. 192; Ferrin and Winchester, Kan. Cir. 89; Warren, Tex. Bul. 305.

45. Cochel, Kan. Industrialist, May 1, 1915; Ferrin and Winchester, Kan. Cir. 89; Dvorachek and Sandhouse, Ark. Cir. 34.

46. Wilson, S. D. Bul. 157.

47. Waters, et al., Kan. Bul. 192; Bell, Winchester, and Marston, Kan. Cir. 128; Snyder, Nebr. Bul. 124; Okla. Rpt. 1921.

48. Malone, Okla. Bul. 120; Okla. Rpt. 1921.

49. Kan. Rpt. 1928-1930.

50. Skinner and Starr, Ind. Bul. 219; Evvard, Dunn, and Culbertson, Iowa Sta., mimeo. rpts.; Gramlich and Jenkins, Nebr. Bul. 175; Gramlich, Nebr. Bul. 176; Gramlich and Loeffel, Nebr. Sta., mimeo. rpt.; Robison, Ohio Mo. Bul. 57 and mimeo. rpt.

51. Skinner and King, Ind. Bul. 158; Eastwood, Ohio Bul. 268.

52. Burnett and Snyder, Nebr. Bul. 99; Wilson and Wright, S. D. Rpt. 1931 and mimeo. rpt.; Wyo. Rpt. 1930.

53. Maynard, Osland, and Brandon, Colo. Bul. 396.

54. Bohstedt, Lathrop, Wolberg, and Sell, Wis. Bul. 421; see also: Culbertson, Evvard, et al., Iowa Leaflet 18.

55. Robison, Ohio Bul. 548.

56. Henke, Hawaii Bul. 69.

57. Bohstedt, Roche, Fargo, et al. Wis. Buls. 428, 430; see also: Barnett and Goodell, Miss. Bul. 218; Robison, Ohio Sta., mimeo. rpt.; Fjeldsted and Potter, Ore. Bul. 165; Burns, Tex. Bul. 131; Hackedorn and Sotola, Wash. Bul. 169.

58. Duck and Gilmore, Syracuse University, N. Y., mimeo. rpt.

59. Ala. Rpt. 1931; Skinner and Starr, Ind. Bul. 219; Evvard et al., Iowa Sta., mimeo. rpts.; Brown, Mich. Quar. Bul. 13, 1930, No. 1; Weaver, Mo. Buls. 247, 285; Tenn. Rpt. 1929; Hislop, Wash. Rpt. 1916.

60. Morrison, Bohstedt, and Fargo, Wis. Spec. Cir., Dec. 1922; Morrison and Fargo, Wis. Bul. 352.

61. Morrison and Fargo, Wis. Bul. 352; Fargo and Bohstedt, Amer. Soc. Anim. Prod., Proc. 1929.

62. Evvard, Culbertson, Hammond, et al., Iowa Sta., mimeo. rpts.; Johnson, Minn. Sta., mimeo. rpt.; Robison, Ohio Bul. 488; Kuhlman and Wilson, S. D. Bul. 216.

63. Aubel and Connell, Kan. Rpt. 1930-32; Robison, Ohio Bul. 488; Kuhlman and Wilson, S. D. Bul. 216; Morrison and Fargo, Wis. Bul. 352; Fargo and Bohstedt, Amer. Soc. Anim. Prod., Proc. 1929; see also: Wilson and Wright, S. D. Bul. 262.
64. Morrison and Fargo, Wis. Bul. 396; Loeffel, Nebr. Rpt. 1932; see also Weaver, Mo. Sta., mimeo. rpt.
65. Evvard, Culbertson, et al., Iowa Sta., mimeo. rpts.
66. Robison, Ohio Bul. 488.
67. Tomhave, Del. Bul. 167.
68. Morrison, Fargo, and Thomas, Wis. Bul. 388; Fargo and Bohstedt, Amer. Soc. Anim. Prod., Proc. 1929.
69. Robison, Ohio Bul. 488.
70. Johnson, Minn. Sta., mimeo. rpt.
71. Evvard, Culbertson, et al., Iowa Sta., mimeo. rpt.; Robison, Ohio Spec. Cir. 17.
72. Evvard, Culbertson, et al., mimeo. rpt.
73. Weber, Anderson, and Marston, Kan. Cir. 138; Ferrin and McCarty, Minn. Sta., mimeo. rpt.; Loeffel, Nebr. Sta., mimeo. rpts.; Snyder, Nebr. Bul. 243; Robison, Ohio Bul. 488; Longwell, West Va. Sta., information to the author; Morrison and Fargo, Wis. Bul. 362; Fargo and Bohstedt, Amer. Soc. Anim. Prod., Proc. 1929.
74. Morrison and Fargo, Wis. Bul. 323; Fargo and Bohstedt, Amer. Soc. Anim. Prod., Proc. 1929, and unpublished data.
75. Martin, Ark. Sta., mimeo. rpt.; Vestal, Ind. Sta., mimeo. rpts.; Evvard, Culbertson, et al., Iowa Sta., mimeo. rpt.; Aubel and McConnell, Kan. Sta., mimeo. rpt.; Wilson and Wright, S. D. Bul. 262.
76. Weber, Anderson, and Marston, Kan. Cir. 138; Weaver, Mo. Bul. 266 and mimeo. rpt.; Loeffel, Nebr. Bul. 243 and mimeo. rpts.; Robison, Ohio Spec. Cirs. 26, 32.
77. Hughes and Feldmiller, Cal. Exten. Cir. 15; Goesmann, Mass. Rpts. 1884, 1885; Wilson, S. D. Bul. 136; see also: Dvorachek, Ark. Cir. 38; Skinner and Cochel, Ind. Bul. 137; Vestal, Ind. Sta., mimeo. rpt.; Ferrin and McCarty, Minn. Bul. 221; Peters and McCarty, Minn. Sta., mimeo. rpt.; Kuhlman and Wilson, S. D. Bul. 216.
78. Lindsey and Beals, Mass. Bul. 217.
79. Horlacher, Ky. Rpts. 1921, 1922, and Poland China Jour., Feb. 10, 1922.
80. Dvorachek, Ark. Cir. 38; Skinner and Cochel, Ind. Bul. 137; Robison, Ohio Buls. 316, 349; Morrison, Fargo, and Bohstedt, Wis. Sta., mimeo. rpts. and unpublished data; see also: Thompson and Voorhies, Cal. Bul. 342; Hughes, Cal. Sta., mimeo. rpt.; Osland and Morton, Colo. Bul. 381; Ferrin and McCarty, Minn. Sta., mimeo. rpts.; Joseph, Mont. Bul. 169; Headley, Nev. Buls. 114, 125; Headley and Wilber, Nev. Rpt. 1934; Loeffel, Nebr. Sta., mimeo. rpt.
81. Morrison and Fargo, Wis. Sta., mimeo. rpts. and unpublished data.
82. Brown, Mich. Sta., Amer. Soc. Anim. Prod., Proc. 1930; Freeman, Mich. Cir. 53; Loeffel, Nebr. Sta., mimeo. rpt.
83. Robison, Ohio. Bul. 488; see also: Ferrin and McCarty, Minn. Sta., mimeo. rpt.; Bohstedt, Fargo, and Beeson, Wis. Bul. 425.
84. Ferrin and McCarty, Minn. Sta., mimeo. rpt.; Weaver, Mo. Bul. 247; McCarty, Penn. Bul. 179; Morrison and Fargo, Wis. Bul. 373.
85. Culbertson and Evvard, Iowa Sta., Amer. Soc. Anim. Prod., Proc. 1924; Kuhlman and Wilson, S. D. Bul. 216.
86. Robison, Ohio Bul. 316; see also: Ferrin and Johnson, Minn. Sta., mimeo. rpts.; Ellenberger and Aplin, Vt. Bul. 273; Henry, Wis. Rpt. 1895.
87. Freeman, Mich. Cir. 53; Bohstedt, Fargo, and Beeson, Wis. Bul. 425; see also: Ferrin and Johnson, Minn. Sta., mimeo. rpt.
88. Freeman, Mich. Quar. Bul. 16, 1933, No. 2; McCarty, Penn. Bul. 179; Bohstedt and Fargo, Wis. Bul. 428.
89. Linfield, Utah Bul. 94.
90. Evvard, Culbertson, and Wallace, Iowa Bul. 278; Brown, Mich. Rpt. 1923; Ferrin and McCarty, Minn. Bul. 221 and mimeo. rpt.; Ferrin and Engebretson, Minn. Sta., mimeo. rpt.; Weaver, Mo. Bul. 247; Smith and Maynard, Utah Bul. 254; Bohstedt, Fargo, and Ries, Wis. Bul. 428; see also: Fla. Rpt. 1925; Williams and Warren, Tex. Bul. 305.
91. Evvard, Culbertson, and Wallace, Iowa Bul. 278; Bohstedt, Fargo, and Ries, Wis. Bul. 428; Crampton, Sci. Agr., Canada, 11, 1931, pp. 347-350.
92. Thompson and Voorhies, Cal. Bul. 342; Evvard and Culbertson, Iowa Sta., mimeo. rpt.; Vestal, Ind. Sta., mimeo. rpt.; McCampbell, Kan. Cir. 78; Aubel and Connell, Kan. Sta., mimeo. rpt.; Ferrin and McCarty, Minn. Buls. 213, 221; Weaver, Mo. Bul. 247; Gramlich, Nebr. Bul. 176; Gramlich and Loeffel, Nebr. Sta. mimeo. rpt.; Helyar, N. J. Rpt. 1921; Grimes, Penn. Bul. 168.
93. Morrison, Fargo, and Thomas, Wis. Bul. 388; see also: Helyar, N. J. Rpt. 1921.
94. Morrison and Bohstedt, Wis. Buls. 319, 323.
95. Thompson and Voorhies, Cal. Bul. 342; Hughes, Cal. Bul. 440; see also: Miss. Rpt. 1924; Loeffel, Nebr. Sta., mimeo. rpt.
96. Bohstedt and Fargo, Wis. Bul. 428.
97. Vestal, Ind. Rpt. 1930 and mimeo. rpts.; Robison and Beatty, Ohio Sta., mimeo. rpt.
98. Grimes, Sewell, and Cottier, Ala. Rpt. 1931-32; Evvard and Culbertson, Iowa Sta., mimeo. rpt.
99. Vestal, Ind. Sta., mimeo. rpts.; Aubel and Connell, Kan. Sta., mimeo. rpts.; Ferrin, Minn. Sta., mimeo. rpt.; Loeffel, Nebr. Sta., mimeo. rpt.; Robison, Ohio Bul. 552; see also: Culbertson and Hammond, Iowa Sta., mimeo. rpt.
100. Maynard, Osland, and Brandon, Colo. Bul. 396; Bray, Francioni, and Gregory, La. Bul. 228; Loeffel, Nebr. Sta., mimeo. rpt.; Robison, Ohio Bul. 488.
101. Edwards, Ga. Cir. 84; Vestal, Ind. Sta., mimeo. rpts.; Evvard, Culbertson, et al., Iowa Sta., mimeo. rpts., and Amer. Soc. Anim. Prod., Proc. 1924; Hostetler,

N. C. Sta., information to the author; Robison, Ohio Bul. 349; Godbey and Durant, S. C. Bul. 234; Wilson and Kuhlman, S. D. Bul. 192; Morrison and Bohstedt, Wis. Sta., mimeo. rpt.; Ala. and Tenn. Stations, data from U. S. Dept. of Agr.; see also: Thompson and Voorhies, Cal. Bul. 342; Palmer, Del. Buls. 135, 141; N. J. Rpts. 1925, 1928; 1931; N. J. Agr. 15, 1933, No. 1; Hostetler and Foster, N. C. Rpt. 1932; McCarty, Penn. Sta., mimeo. rpt.; Hackedorn and Sotola, Wash. Bul. 169; Longwell, West Va. Sta., information to the author.

102. Evvard, Culbertson, et al., Iowa Sta., mimeo. rpt.; Culbertson and Hammond, Iowa Sta., mimeo. rpt.; Robison, Ohio Spec. Cir. 32; Grimes, Penn. Bul. 168.

103. N. J. Rpt. 1935.

104. Morrison, Willman, and Gormel, N. Y. (Cornell) Rpt. 1933; Morrison and Willman, N. Y. (Cornell) Rpt. 1934 and mimeo. rpts.

105. Longwell, West Va. Sta., information to the author.

106. Skinner and Cochel, Ind. Bul. 137; Erf and Wheeler, Kan. Bul. 192; Loeffel, Nebr. Sta., mimeo. rpt.; Snyder, Nebr. Bul. 147; Carmichael, Ohio Bul. 209; Forbes, Ohio Bul. 213; see also: Warren, Tex. Bul. 305.

107. Evvard, Iowa Sta., mimeo. rpt.; Morrison, Bohstedt, and Fargo, Wis. Bul. 323 and unpublished data.

108. Gramlich and Jenkins, Nebr. Bul. 175; Robison, Ohio Bul. 349.

109. Robison, Ohio Bul. 349; Morrison and Bohstedt, Wis. Sta., mimeo. rpt.

110. Weaver, Mo. Bul. 247; Loeffel, Nebr. Sta., mimeo. rpt.

111. Evvard, Iowa Sta., mimeo. rpt.; Morrison and Bohstedt, Wis. Bul. 323 and mimeo. rpt.

112. Loeffel, Nebr. Sta., mimeo. rpt.

113. Rice and Laible, Ill. Sta., mimeo. rpt.; Ferrin and Winchester, Kan. Cir. 78; Loeffel, Nebr. Sta., mimeo. rpt.; Robison, Ohio Bul. 355; Grimes, Penn. Bul. 215.

114. Waters, Kinzer, Wheeler, and Wright, Kan. Bul. 192; Weaver, Mo. Bul. 144; Loeffel, Nebr. Sta., mimeo. rpt.

115. Aubel and Alexander, Kan. Sta., mimeo. rpt.; Gramlich and Jenkins, Nebr. Bul. 175.

116. Martin, Ark. Sta., mimeo. rpt.; Rice, Ill. Bul. 247; Ferrin and McCarty, Minn. Bul. 219; Loeffel, Nebr. Sta., mimeo. rpt.

117. Ferrin and McCarty, Minn. Bul. 219.

118. Robison, Ohio Bul. 488.

119. Starkey and Salmon, S. C. Bul. 213.

120. Robison, Ohio Bul. 488; Kuhlman and Wilson, S. D. Bul. 216.

121. Robison, Ohio Bul. 349 and information to the author; Morrison and Bohstedt, Wis. Sta., mimeo. rpt.; see also: Ferrin and Winchester, Kan. Cir. 78; Snyder, Nebr. Bul. 243; Hackedorn and Sotola, Wash. Bul. 169.

122. Dvorachek, Sandhouse, and Hunt, Ark. Bul. 198; Hays, Del. Bul. 124; Skinner and Cochel, Ind. Bul. 126; McCampbell, Ferrin, and Winchester, Kan. Cir. 78; Snyder, Nebr. Buls. 147, 243; Forbes, Ohio Bul. 213; Robison, Ohio Buls. 316, 349; Tomhave, Penn. Bul. 147.

123. Gramlich, Nebr. Bul. 175; Robison, Ohio Bul. 349; Morrison and Bohstedt, Wis. Sta., unpublished data.

124. Weber, Anderson, and Marston, Kan. Cir. 138.

125. Weber, Alexander, and Marston, Kan. Cir. 138 and mimeo. rpt.; Weaver, Mo. Sta., mimeo. rpt.; Robison, Ohio Bul. 349; Grimes, Penn. Bul. 168; Morrison, Bohstedt and Fargo, Wis. Bul. 323; see also: Evvard, Iowa Sta., mimeo. rpt.

126. Robison, Ohio Bul. 534; Hale, Tex. Bul. 410. References to the reports of numerous other investigations on the use of cottonseed meal in swine feeding are given in these bulletins.

127. Halverson, N. C. Rpt. 1932.

128. Robison, Ohio Bul. 534.

129. Martin, Ark. Sta., mimeo. rpt.; Evvard, Culbertson, Hammond, and Bassett, Iowa Sta., mimeo. rpt.; Aubel and Connell, Kan. Sta., mimeo. rpt., Bray, Francioni, and Gregory, La. Bul. 228; Snyder, Nebr. Bul. 243; Loeffel, Nebr. Sta., mimeo. rpts., Robison, Ohio Spec. Cirs. 26, 32; see also: Grimes, Sewell, and Cottier, Ala. Rpt. 1933; Maynard, Osland, and Brandon, Colo. Bul. 396; Thompson, Okla. Rpts. 1930-32, 1932-34; Williams and Warren, Tex. Bul. 305; Hale, Texas Bul. 410.

130. Hostetler, N. C. Rpts. 1926, 1927, 1929, 1930; Hostetler and Foster, N. C. Sta., mimeo. rpts. and information to the author; Godbey and Starkey, S. C. Bul. 281.

131. Hostetler and Foster, N. C. Sta., information to the author.

132. Martin, Ark. Sta., mimeo. rpt.; Vestal, Ind. Sta., mimeo. rpt.; Evvard, Culbertson, et al., Iowa Sta., mimeo. rpt.; Aubel and Connell, Kan. Sta., mimeo. rpt.; Snyder, Nebr. Bul. 243; Loeffel, Nebr. Sta., mimeo. rpt.; Robison, Ohio Spec. Cir. 32.

133. Carroll and Smith, Ill. Rpt. 1927 and mimeo. rpt.; Vestal, Ind. Sta., mimeo. rpts.; Evvard, Culbertson, et al., Iowa Sta., mimeo. rpt.; Aubel and Connell, Kan. Sta., mimeo. rpt.; Ferrin and Johnson, Minn. Sta., mimeo. rpt.; Robison, Ohio Bul. 488; Longwell, W. Va. Sta., information to the author; see also: Weaver, Mo. Sta., mimeo. rpts.; Loeffel, Nebr. Sta., mimeo. rpts.

134. Vestal, Ind. Sta., mimeo. rpt.

135. Carroll and Hunt, Ill. Rpt. 1930.

136. Palmer, Del. Bul. 135; Carroll, Bull, et al., Ill. Rpt. 1930; Vestal, Ind. Bul. 341; Robison, Ohio Bul. 452.

137. Tomhave and Mumford, Del. Bul. 179; Carroll, Bull, et al., Ill. Rpt. 1930; Vestal, Ind. Rpt. 1924; Robison, Ohio Bul. 452.

138. Robison, Ohio Bul. 452; see also: Vestal, Ind. Sta., mimeo. rpts.

139. Dvorachek, Sandhouse, and Hunt, Ark. Bul. 198; Vestal, Ind. Sta., mimeo rpt.; Bedenbaugh, Miss. Bul. 283; Robinson, Ohio Bul. 452; see also: Barnett and Goodell, Miss. Bul. 218; Loeffel, Nebr. Sta. mimeo. rpt. Jacob, Tenn. Rpt. 1929.

140. Dvorachek, Sandhouse, and Hunt, Ark. Bul. 198; Skinner and Cochel, Ind. Bul. 137; Wheeler, Kan. Bul. 192; Good, Ky. Bul. 175; Robison, Ohio Bul. 452.
141. Tomhave, Del. Bul. 170, Vestal, Ind. Sta., mimeo. rpt.; Culbertson, Thomas, Hammond, and Beard, Iowa Sta., mimeo. rpts.; Robison, Ohio Bul. 452; see also: Tomhave and Mumford, Del. Bul. 179; Miss. Sta., mimeo. rpt.; Weaver Mo. Bul. 266; Loeffel and Lewis, Nebr. Sta., mimeo. rpt.
142. Vestal, Ind. Rpt. 1934 and mimeo. rpts., Robison, Ohio Bul. 452; Wilson, S. D. Rpt. 1933; Shrewsbury, Vestal, and Hauge, Jour. Agr. Res., 44, 1932, pp. 267-274.
143. Tomhave, Del. Bul. 170; Culbertson et al., Iowa Sta., mimeo. rpt.; Weaver, Mo. Bul. 266.
144. Vestal, Ind. Sta., mimeo. rpts.; Evvard, Culbertson, et al, Iowa Sta., mimeo. rpt.; Culbertson, Thomas, Hammond, and Beard, Iowa Sta., mimeo. rpts.; Robison, Ohio Bul. 452.
145. Vestal, Ind. Sta., mimeo. rpts.; Robison, Ohio Bul. 452; Godbey and Durant, S. C. Bul. 234.
146. Vestal, Ind. Sta., mimeo. rpt.; Culbertson, Thomas, Hammond, and Beard, Iowa Sta., mimeo. rpts.; Robison, Ohio Bul. 452; see also: Evvard, Culbertson, et al., Iowa Sta., mimeo. rpt.; Hostetler, N. C. Bul. 259.
147. Robison, Ohio Bul. 452; Bohstedt, Fargo, and Hayward, Wis. Bul. 430.
148. Ferrin, Minn. Sta., mimeo. rpts.; Robison, Ohio Bul. 452 and information to the author; Bohstedt, Fargo, and Hayward, Wis. Bul. 430 and information to the author.
149. Carroll, Mitchell, Hamilton, and Garrigus, Ill. Sta., mimeo. rpt.; Loeffel, Nebr. Sta., mimeo. rpt.; Bohstedt, Fargo, and Hayward, Wis. Bul. 430 and information to the author.
150. Culbertson, Iowa Rpt. 1933.
151. Bull, Carroll, et al., Ill. Bul. 366; Carroll, Garrigus, Mitchell, and Hamilton, Ill. Rpt. 1933; Carroll, Ill. Sta., mimeo. rpt.; Ferrin, Minn. Sta., mimeo. rpt.; Robison, Ohio Spec. Cir. 10.
152. Vestal, Ind. Sta., mimeo. rpts.; Culbertson, Thomas, Hammond, and Beard, Iowa Sta., mimeo. rpt.; Weaver, Mo. Sta., mimeo. rpt.; Loeffel, Nebr. Rpt. 1934 and mimeo. rpt.; Hostetler, N. C. Bul. 259; Godbey and Durant, S. C. Bul. 234; Godbey and Starkey, S. C. Bul. 281.
153. Hostetler, N. C. Sta., information to the author.
154. Templeton, Ala. Bul. 206.
155. Halverson, Hostetler, and Sherwood, N. C. Tech. Bul. 41; see also: Grimes and Salmon, Ala. Bul. 223.
156. Godbey and Durant, S. C. Bul. 234; Godbey and Starkey, S. C. Bul. 281.
157. Salmon, Ala. Rpt. 1924.
158. Grimes and Salmon, Ala. Bul. 224.
159. Evvard and Culbertson, Iowa Leaflet 11; Evvard, Hammond, and Bassett, Iowa Leaflet 18; Ashby, Minn. Rpt. 1918; Loeffel, Nebr. Sta., mimeo. rpt.
160. Hays, Del. Bul. 124; Evvard, Iowa Sta., mimeo. rpt.
161. Aubel and Alexander, Kan. Rpt. 1928-30 and mimeo. rpts.
162. Loeffel, Nebr. Sta., mimeo. rpt.
163. Skinner and Starr, Ind. Bul. 219; Evvard, Iowa Sta., mimeo. rpts.; Robison, Ohio Bul. 349.
164. Evvard, Iowa Sta., mimeo. rpts.; Morrison and Fargo, Wis. Bul. 373.
165. Skinner and Starr, Ind. Bul. 219; Evvard, Live Stock Health Jour., Nov. 1, 1920; Loeffel, Nebr. Sta., mimeo. rpts.; Robison, Ohio, Mo. Bul. 57.
166. Morrison, Fargo, and Thomas, Wis. Bul. 388; Fargo and Bohstedt, Amer. Soc. Anim. Prod., Proc. 1929.
167. Robison, Ohio, Mo. Bul. 57.
168. Robison, Ohio Sta., information to the author.
169. Good and Smith, Ky. Bul. 190.
170. Wilford, Ky. Sta., mimeo. rpt. and information to the author.
171. Evvard, Iowa Bul. 136; Snyder, Nebr. Bul. 243; Loeffel, Nebr. Sta., mimeo. rpts.; Robison, Ohio Bul. 552; Grimes, Penn. Bul. 168; Morrison and Bohstedt, Wis. Bul. 323 and mimeo. rpts.; Morrison, Fargo, and Brant, Wis. Cir. 213; see also: Martin, Ark. Bul. 321; Bray, La. Sta., mimeo. rpt.
172. Edwards, Mich. Spec. Bul. 199.
173. Evvard, Iowa Bul. 136 and Iowa Cir. 53; Evvard, Amer. Soc. Anim. Prod., Proc. 1913; Edwards, Mich. Spec. Bul. 199; Robison, Ohio Bul. 552; Morrison and Bohstedt, Wis. Bul. 323 and mimeo. rpts.; Morrison, Fargo, and Brant, Wis. Cir. 213; see also: Weaver, Mo. Bul. 247; Joseph, Mont. Bul. 236; Loeffel, Nebr. Sta., mimeo. rpt.; McCarty and Grimes, Penn. Bul. 254; S. D. Rpt. 1925; Longwell, West Va. Bul. 244.
174. Evvard, Iowa. Bul. 136; Robison, Ohio Bul. 552; Morrison and Bohstedt, Wis. Bul. 323 and mimeo. rpts.; Morrison, Fargo, and Brant, Wis. Cir. 213; see also: Vestal, Ind. Sta., mimeo. rpt.; Weaver, Mo. Bul. 247; Joseph, Mont. Bul. 236.
175. Robison, Ohio Bul. 552; Morrison and Bohstedt, Wis. Bul. 323 and mimeo. rpts.; Morrison, Fargo, and Brant, Wis. Cir. 213; Evvard, Iowa Bul. 136.
176. Robison, Ohio Bul. 552.
177. Rice, Ill. Bul. 247; Evvard, Iowa Bul. 136; Weber, Anderson, and Marston, Kan. Cir. 138; Ferrin and McCarty, Minn. Sta., mimeo. rpt.; Arnett and Joseph, Mont. Bul. 128; Nebr. Rpt. 1926; Shepperd, N. D. Bul. 174; Robison, Ohio Bul. 552; S. D. Rpt. 1930; Smith, Wash. Bul. 187; Morrison and Bohstedt, Wis. Bul. 323; Morrison, Fargo, and Brant, Wis. Cir. 213.
178. See also: Gray, Summers, and Shook, Ala. Bul. 168; Tomhave, Del. Buls. 158, 170; Weaver, Mo. Bul. 247; Ore. Rpt. 1928-30.
179. Morrison and Bohstedt, Wis. Bul. 323.

180. Morrison and Bohstedt, Wis. Bul. 323; Robison, Ohio Bul. 552; McCarty and Grimes, Penn. Bul. 254.
181. Mont. Rpt. 1923; Robison, Ohio Bul. 552; Ore. Rpts. 1920-22, 1922-24; McCarty and Grimes, Penn. Bul. 270; Hackedorn, Wash. Bul. 158; Morrison and Bohstedt, Wis. Bul. 323.
182. Grimes, Sewell, and Taylor, Ala. Bul. 233.
183. Thompson, N. D. Bul. 217; Gongwer and Hickman, Id. Bul. 125; see also: Nordby and Gildow, Id. Exten. Bul. 89; Mont. Rpt. 1929; Shepperd, N. D. Bul. 230; Hackedorn and Sotola, Wash. Bul. 169; Faville, Wyo. Bul. 107.
184. Osland and Morton, Colo. Bul. 381.
185. Weaver, Mo. Bul. 247; Ohio Bul. 552.
186. Godbey, Kyzer, and Clyburn, S. C. Bul. 289; Tomhave, Del. Bul. 179; Carmichael, Md. Bul. 376; Miss. Sta., mimeo. rpt.
187. Gray, Ridgeway, and Eudaly, Ala. Bul. 154; Good and Smith, Ky. Bul. 201; Bedenbaugh, Miss. Bul. 283; Hostetler, N. C. Sta., mimeo. rpt.; Godbey, S. C. Bul. 274.
188. Gray, Summers, and Shook, Ala. Bul. 168; Barnett and Goodell, Miss. Bul. 218.
189. Del. Bul. 147; Weaver, Mo. Bul. 247.
190. Gray, Summers, and Shook, Ala. Bul. 168; see also: Templeton, Ferguson, and Gibbens, Ala. Bul. 198; S. C. Rpt. 1923.
191. Evvard, Iowa. Sta., mimeo. rpt.; Weaver, Mo. Bul. 247; McCarty and Grimes, Penn. Bul. 254; Morrison and Bohstedt, Wis. Bul. 323.
192. Hostetler and Foster, N. C. Bul. 286.
193. Good, Ky. Bul. 175.
194. Martin, Ark. Bul. 321; Tomhave, Del. Bul. 179; N. C. Rpt. 1929; Kyzer and Clyburn, S. C. Rpt. 1931; Godbey, S. C. Rpts. 1932, 1933; Seamans, U. S. Dept. Agr. Bul. 1143.
195. Nordby and Gildow, Id. Exten. Bul. 89; Hunter, U. S. Dept. Agr., Farmers' Bul. 599.
196. Robison and Jones, Ohio Bul. 516 and information to the author; see also: Vestal, Ind. Rpt. 1932 and mimeo. rpt.; Evvard, Iowa Bul. 136; Ferrin and Johnson, Minn. Sta., mimeo. rpt.; S. D. Rpt. 1931.
197. Bell, Winchester, and Marston, Kan. Cir. 98; Anderson and Marston, Kan. Cir. 112; Mont. Rpt. 1927; Nebr. Rpts. 1924, 1926; Hale, Tex. Rpt. 1933.
198. Martin, Ark. Bul. 321; Evvard and Culbertson, Iowa Sta., mimeo. rpt.; McCarty and Grimes, Penn. Buls. 254, 276; S. C. Rpt. 1926; Tenn. Rpts. 1931, 1932.
199. Gray, Duggar, and Ridgway, Ala. Bul. 143; Martin, Ark. Bul. 321; Scott, Fla. Bul. 113; Hansen, Seamans, and Mosley, Mont. Rpt. 1927.
200. Scott, Fla. Bul. 113.
201. Aubel, and Connell, Kan. Sta., mimeo. rpt.
202. Plumb, Ind. Buls. 79, 82; Shaw, Mont. Bul. 27; Lazenby, Ohio Rpt. 1884; Sanborn, Utah Rpt. 1891; Clark, Utah Bul. 101; Robertson, Ottawa, Canada, Expt. Farms, Rpt. 1891.
203. Morrison, Bohstedt, and Fargo, Wis. Bul. 362 and mimeo. rpts.
204. Clark, Utah Bul. 101.
205. Joseph, Mont. Bul. 169; Robison, Ohio Bimo. Bul. 145; Powell, Amer. Soc. Anim. Prod., Proc. 1931; Morrison and Fargo, Wis. Buls. 339, 352.
206. Loeffel, Nebr. Sta., mimeo. rpt.; Carroll, Utah Sta., Amer. Soc. Anim. Prod., Proc. 1922; Morrison and Fargo, Wis. Bul. 352.
207. Georgia Col. of Agr., Rpt. 1932; Vestal, Ind. Sta., Amer. Soc. Anim. Prod., Proc. 1921; Aubel and Connell, Kan. Rpt. 1930-32; Freeman, Mich. Sta., mimeo. rpt.
208. Weber, Anderson, and Marston, Kan. Cir. 138; Aubel and Connell, Kan. Sta., mimeo. rpt.; Snyder, Nebr. Bul. 147; Loeffel, Nebr. Sta., mimeo. rpt.
209. Kuhlman and Wilson, S. D. Bul. 216; Morrison, Bohstedt, and Fargo, Wis. Sta., mimeo. rpts. and unpublished data.
210. Loeffel, Nebr. Sta., mimeo. rpt.; Robison, Ohio Bul. 488; Kuhlman and Wilson, S. D. Bul. 216; Morrison, Bohstedt, and Fargo, Wis. Sta., mimeo. rpts. and unpublished data; see also: Nordby, Id. Cir. 56; Ferrin and McCarty, Minn. Sta., mimeo. rpt.; Weaver, Mo. Bul. 272; Thompson, Okla. Rpt. 1930-32.
211. Weber, Anderson, and Marston, Kan. Cir. 138; Snyder, Nebr. Bul. 147; Gramlich and Jenkins, Nebr. Bul. 175; Loeffel, Nebr. Sta., mimeo. rpts.; see also: Aubel and Connell, Kan. Sta., mimeo. rpt.
212. Morrison and Fargo, Wis. Bul. 373 and unpublished data.
213. Wheeler, Kan. Bul. 192; McCampbell, Kan. Cir. 78; Snyder, Nebr. Bul. 147; Gramlich and Jenkins, Nebr. Bul. 175; Loeffel, Nebr. Sta., mimeo. rpts.; see also: Barnett and Goodell, Miss. Bul. 218; Penn. Bul. 147.
214. Freeman, Mich. Quar. Bul. 17, 1935, No. 3.
215. Joseph, Mont. Bul. 169; Vinke and Bergstedt, Mont. Bul. 284; Carroll, Utah Bul. 192; Sinclair, Univ. of Alberta, Canada, mimeo. rpt.
216. Evvard, Culbertson, et al., Iowa Sta., mimeo. rpt.; Aubel and Connell, Kan. Rpt. 1932-34 and mimeo. rpt.
217. Evvard, Culbertson, et al., Iowa Sta., mimeo. rpt.
218. Morrison, Fargo, and Thomas, Wis. Bul. 488 and unpublished data.
219. Robison, Ohio Bul. 488.
220. Aubel and Connell, Kan. Rpt. 1932-34 and mimeo. rpt.
221. Dvorachek, Ark. Buls. 181, 203, 215; Grimes and Sewell, Ala. Rpts. 1930, 1931.
222. Morrison, Fargo, and Thomas, Wis. Bul. 488 and unpublished data.
223. Faville, Wyo. Bul. 107.
224. Grimes, Sewell, and Cottier, Ala. Rpt. 1931.

CHAPTER XXXVII

FEEDING AND CARE OF SWINE

I. THE BREEDING HERD

1402. Selecting the brood sows and boar.—For efficiency in pork production, it is necessary, first of all, to have breeding stock of the right kind. The sows and boar should be of the proper type and conformation to produce finished hogs that meet the present market demands. Also, they should be selected from strains of swine that excel in rapidity and economy of gains. Fully as important as these essentials, is the prolificacy of the sows and their ability to raise good-sized litters of pigs.

It costs nearly as much to feed and care for a sow that raises a litter of only 3 to 5 pigs to weaning age as for one that raises 7 or 8 pigs or more. Therefore to reduce the cost per pig at weaning time the sows must have large litters of thrifty pigs and also be good mothers, so they will raise nearly all of the pigs that they farrow.

To build up an efficient herd it is necessary that the pigs be earnotched or otherwise marked and that breeding records be kept. The unproductive sows can then be culled from the herd and replaced by gilts from the best sows. These will be the ones that are good mothers and raise large litters of pigs of good type which make rapid gains in weight. Such pigs generally produce pork much more economically than those which gain slowly.

1403. Proper feed and care necessary for profits.—In securing a good profit from hogs nothing is of greater importance than proper feeding and care of the brood sows and boars. Every year thousands of farmers are grievously disappointed at farrowing time by seeing their possible profits vanish when the sows produce unsatisfactory litters.

Either the number of pigs in the litters is small, or the pigs are so weak that many die or survive only to become unprofitable runts. In most cases such results are due to a lack of proper feed and care of the sows. Yet the needs of brood sows are relatively simple and easily met.

The most important essentials in the feeding and care of brood sows are: (1) Efficient rations that fully meet their nutrient requirements; (2) rations that are laxative, instead of constipating; (3) the right amount of feed—not too much or the sows will get too fat; (4) plenty of exercise; (5) comfortable, sanitary quarters, with proper guard rails in the pens to protect the young pigs; (6) freedom from lice and worms.

1404. Efficient rations necessary.—In order to produce thrifty pigs brood sows must receive rations that provide a sufficient amount of protein and protein of the right quality, for developing the bodies of the unborn pigs in addition to meeting the needs of the sow. An adequate amount of minerals, especially of calcium and phosphorus, is also

918

essential, as well as a plentiful supply of vitamins A and D. These nutritive requirements have been discussed in detail in Chapter XXXV. If sows are not properly fed, they cannot be expected to produce large litters of vigorous pigs. Also, when sows are fed inadequately during pregnancy, there is sometimes a tendency for them to kill and eat their young pigs.

The supply of total digestible nutrients in the rations of sows during pregnancy should be ample to meet the needs for maintaining their own bodies and for the storage of nutrients in the fetuses. Therefore they must be fed amounts of grain or other concentrates sufficient to keep them in thrifty, vigorous condition. On the other hand, care must be taken not to feed them too liberally during this period, or they will become over-fat, which will tend to increase the difficulties at farrowing time. Also, fat sows are so clumsy that they are much more apt to kill some of their pigs by carelessly lying on them.

During the suckling period, brood sows must be fed more liberally than during pregnancy, for they then need additional nutrients for the production of a good flow of milk. Not only should they receive more grain, to furnish the necessary total digestible nutrients and energy, but also the supply of protein, calcium, phosphorus, and vitamins must be considerably greater, since milk is rich in these nutrients.

Because of the large amounts of nutrients needed in milk production, sows that are good milk producers will lose much weight while nursing their litters, even when they are fed liberally. This means that the amount of nutrients they can assimilate from their feed is insufficient to furnish the nutrients in the milk, and therefore they draw temporarily on the store in their bodies.

1405. Rations for pregnant sows.—Corn or other grain ordinarily forms the chief part of the ration for sows during pregnancy and also during the suckling period. In addition, they should be fed adequate amounts of suitable supplements to provide the needed protein, calcium, phosphorus, vitamin A and vitamin D.

In the proper feeding of brood sows nothing is more important than providing good pasture during just as much of the year as possible, and furnishing them with an abundance of well-cured legume hay when pasture is not available. Good pasture and legume hay not only aid in supplying protein of good quality, as well as calcium and phosphorus, but, still more important, these feeds amply take care of the vitamin requirements. In addition, as is mentioned later, green forage and pasture apparently provide other essentials concerning which but little is yet known.

In addition to grain and either pasture or legume hay, it is advisable to provide pregnant sows with a small amount of an efficient protein supplement. This is particularly beneficial in the case of young sows. Sows that are suckling pigs should always be fed a protein supplement in addition to grain and either pasture or legume hay, as they need a considerably larger proportion of protein. A supplement should be used that provides protein of proper quality to correct the deficiencies in the proteins of the cereal grains. As has been shown previously, such supplements as dairy by-products, tankage or meat scraps, fish meal, or soybean oil meal are excellent for this purpose. **(1281)** Mixtures of the animal by-products with such feeds as wheat middlings, wheat bran, linseed meal, or cottonseed meal are also excellent.

The vitamin requirements of brood sows will generally be met fully if they are on good pasture or if they are fed sufficient well-cured legume hay. The use of mineral supplements is discussed in later paragraphs. (1415)

In Appendix Table VII will be found examples of well-balanced, efficient rations for pregnant sows and also for those that are nursing litters. These will serve as a guide in feeding brood sows under conditions in various districts. In case of doubt as to whether any ration meets the requirements of brood sows for digestible protein and total digestible nutrients, it should be checked with the recommendations given in the Morrison feeding standards. (Appendix Table III.)

Brood sows, as well as all other swine, should always be provided with plenty of clean, fresh water, as has been emphasized in Chapter XXXV. Where the winter climate is so cold that water soon freezes in a trough, a heated waterer should be provided or else water should be supplied by feeding a warm slop or pouring warm water over the concentrate mixture after it is distributed in the trough.

1406. Importance of pasture for brood sows.—The great importance of good pasture for brood sows is strikingly shown by recent investigations at the Kansas and Missouri Stations. In these experiments sows produced pigs that were weak or they failed to provide an adequate supply of milk for their young when they were fed good rations but confined to the barn and paved outside exercise pens, so they had no green forage and no access to the soil.[1]

For example, in the Kansas experiments sows thus confined were fed a mixture of 75 lbs. yellow corn, 10 lbs. tankage, 10 lbs. alfalfa leaf meal, and 5 lbs. bone meal during pregnancy and when nursing their litters. Though this ration will produce excellent results under usual farm conditions where the sows have some pasture during most of the year, it was very unsatisfactory in these tests. Only 59 per cent of the live pigs that were farrowed lived to weaning time, most of the deaths occurring before the pigs were 10 days old.

In the Missouri experiments green forage was very beneficial when added to such a ration. Including 20 per cent of wheat shorts in the ration, in addition to alfalfa meal, also improved the results decidedly.

1407. Grain alone unsatisfactory for sows.—Experiments have proved that a ration of grain alone may be very unsatisfactory for pregnant sows, even when the grain is yellow corn, which supplies vitamin A. In the case of gilts, the results from such a ration are apt to be disastrous, for the pigs are often weak and unthrifty and some may even be dead at birth. Supplementing the grain with bone meal helps somewhat, but does not make the ration adequate, especially for gilts.

For instance, gilts fed only yellow corn and bone meal at the Indiana Station farrowed pigs that were dead or were so weak that they died within a day.[2] The results were somewhat better on a combination of yellow corn, oats, and bone meal, but 36 per cent of the pigs were dead at birth or died within 3 days. On the other hand when 5 per cent of meat scraps was added to the ration, the sows farrowed twice as many pigs, with only 13 per cent that were born dead or died within 3 days. This ration would have been still further improved by the addition of legume hay.

In experiments at the Iowa and Kansas Stations corn alone was likewise inadequate for pregnant sows.[3] Similarly, investigations at the California Station have shown that barley must be supplemented with protein of good quality and with calcium and vitamins A and D, or the results will be disastrous.[4] Likewise, in Oklahoma tests, sows fed kafir grain alone produced no strong pigs, and only half the pigs were strong when the sows were fed kafir and wheat shorts.[5] On the other hand, 81 per cent of the pigs were strong from sows fed a combination of kafir, oats, and tankage.

Indiana experiments have shown that under certain conditions mature sows may produce fairly satisfactory litters when wintered on only yellow corn or a combination of two-thirds yellow corn and one-third oats.[6] In these tests the sows had been on good pasture during the summer, and hence had stores of vitamins and minerals in their bodies when the pasture season ended. Also, they were forced to take plenty of outdoor exercise and therefore were protected from a lack of vitamin D by exposure to sunlight. Finally, they were not allowed to become too fat by overfeeding of corn. In these experiments the sows were fed a well-balanced ration including tankage and wheat shorts after farrowing. Otherwise, they would have been unable to produce sufficient milk for their pigs. Under usual conditions it is advisable to provide legume hay in winter, even for mature sows, in order to protect them against a lack of vitamins and to aid in supplying protein and calcium.

1408. Legume hay.—Legume hay excels in so many respects as a feed for pregnant sows, and furthermore, is so economical that a special effort should be made to supply it in winter when the sows are not on pasture. (**1396**) When choice, leafy alfalfa hay is used, the sows will usually eat a sufficient amount to produce the desired results if it is fed uncut in a simple slatted rack, preferably with a cover to keep out snow and rain. This, together with the feed troughs, should be put in the paddock at some distance from the hog barn or the colony house, so the sows will secure needed exercise in going to and fro.

Clover hay is usually less palatable to sows than alfalfa, and consequently they will often eat relatively little of it when fed uncut in a rack, even if the allowance of concentrates is restricted. Whenever the sows fail to eat enough of the legume hay, it should, if possible, be chopped or ground and mixed with the concentrates. The hay may be chopped at small expense by running it through a silage or hay cutter, preferably equipped with an alfalfa screen. If no cutter is available, the leaves and chaff which accumulate where the hay is pitched from the mow may be gathered up and mixed with the concentrates. To get the sows to clean up such chaff it may be necessary to feed the mixture as a slop.

A safe rule is to see that legume hay forms at least 10 to 15 per cent of the ration for sows in winter, and they may well be fed all they will eat in addition to a limited allowance of grain.

But little study has been given to the relative value of the different kinds of legume hay for brood sows. In general, the value will depend on the leafiness and palatability. Alfalfa hay exceis clover, because it is richer in both protein and calcium, as well as being liked better by swine. Soybean hay, cowpea hay, and other kinds of legume hay may also be used instead of alfalfa hay. (1401)

Mature sows are sometimes wintered on alfalfa hay without any grain or other concentrates, but this is inadvisable, for they will then not make the desired gains in weight during pregnancy. Also, although the cost for feed up to farrowing time will be low, Pennsylvania experiments show that it will later be necessary to feed them with great liberality on concentrates to provide even a fair milk flow for their pigs.[7] This will offset the saving in concentrates before farrowing.

1409. Legume hay and grain for brood sows.—For wintering pregnant sows a year old or more, a ration consisting of only grain and legume hay is satisfactory, providing the hay is of excellent quality. When leafy, palatable alfalfa hay is fed to old sows, they will generally eat a pound or more per head daily, if the allowance of grain is strictly limited. Under such conditions there may be little advantage in adding tankage or similar protein supplements to the ration throughout the winter.[8] When the sows do not eat so much hay or if it is of only fair quality, then a protein supplement should be added.[9] This is especially important during the last 2 or 3 weeks before farrowing, when the growth of the unborn pigs is most rapid.

In the case of pregnant gilts a small amount of a protein supplement, such as tankage, skimmilk, fish meal, or soybeans, had best be added to a ration of legume hay and grain. Because they are still making considerable growth, they need a larger proportion of protein in their ration than do older sows.

The benefit from feeding such a supplement is shown by trials during 4 winters by the author and Bohstedt at the Wisconsin Station.[10] Each winter one lot of gilts, averaging 206 lbs. in weight at the start, was allowed access to good alfalfa hay in a rack and fed in addition enough ear corn to make the desired gains. Another lot was fed similarly, except that they were given one-quarter to one-third pound of tankage per head daily, as shown in the following table:

Alfalfa hay as only supplement vs. alfalfa plus tankage

	Daily gain Lbs.	No. of pigs farrowed	Av. wt. of pigs Lbs.	Proportion of vigorous pigs Per cent	Feed cost per head daily Cents
Lot I					
Alfalfa hay, 0.50 lb.					
Ear corn, 5.2 lbs.*........	0.93	7.12	2.25	80.8	5.6
Lot II					
Tankage, 0.30 lb.					
Alfalfa hay, 0.48 lb.					
Ear corn, 4.7 lbs.*........	1.00	7.90	2.34	89.2	5.5**

*Ear corn reduced to basis of No. 3 shelled corn.
**Crediting excess gain of Lot II over Lot I at 7 cents per lb.

On the average, the gilts fed 0.3 lb. tankage in addition to ear corn and alfalfa hay made somewhat larger gains. Also, the average weight of the pigs at birth and the proportion of vigorous pigs were greater with this ration. When the additional gains of the gilts fed tankage

FARROWING PEN EQUIPPED WITH FENDERS

Every farrowing pen should be supplied with fenders to prevent the sow from crushing the little pigs against the wall or lying on them. See Page 696. (From Wisconsin Station.)

YOUNG PIGS FEEDING IN A CREEP

It is important to supply young pigs feed in addition to their mother's milk after they are 2 to 3 weeks old. (From Wisconsin Station.)

EVERY LITTER NEEDS GOOD PASTURE

Nothing is more important in swine raising than furnishing good pasture just as early as possible for the brood sows and their litters.

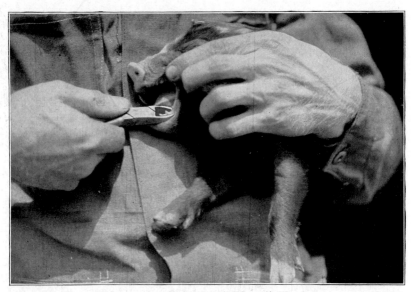

BREAKING OFF THE "WOLF" TEETH

Commonly the most experienced breeders break off the "wolf" teeth, or temporary tusks, which pigs have at birth, to prevent lacerating the udder of the sow or wounding the other pigs. See Page 697. (From Wisconsin Station.)

are credited at 7 cents per pound, the feed cost per head daily was a little less on this ration, with ear corn at 56 cents a bushel and with tankage at $60 and alfalfa hay at $15 a ton. Thus, from all standpoints it was advisable under corn-belt conditions to add a small amount of a protein concentrate to the ration of corn and alfalfa hay.

When much of the grain is barley, wheat, kafir, or oats instead of corn, there will be somewhat less advantage in adding a supplement such as tankage to a ration of grain and legume hay.[11] This is because these grains are considerably higher in protein content.

If sows will eat a reasonable amount of legume hay when it is fed uncut in a rack, there is no advantage in chopping or grinding the hay and mixing it with the grain in order to get them to consume a larger proportion of hay. In a Nebraska trial it was found that even where alfalfa is cheap, the cost of wintering brood sows fed a mixture of half ground corn and half chopped alfalfa is greater than for sows fed shelled corn with alfalfa hay in racks.[12]

1410. Protein supplements for brood sows.—Protein supplements of animal origin, such as tankage, meat scraps, dairy by-products, and fish meal, are of especially high value for brood sows, just as they are for pigs. (**1281**) Next to these feeds in quality of proteins come the legume hays and also soybean oil meal, peanuts, and peanut oil meal. Ideal winter rations for brood sows are furnished by combinations of grain and legume hay, along with small amounts of these efficient protein supplements.

If skimmilk or buttermilk is available for the sows, there is no better ration than grain and legume hay, plus 4 to 6 lbs. of either of these dairy by-products per head daily. There is no need whatsoever of adding purchased concentrates to such a ration, unless perhaps a little wheat bran or linseed meal shortly before farrowing, to ensure the sows being kept in a laxative condition.

Whey is relatively low in protein, but nevertheless the protein it does contain is of such high efficiency that a ration of whey, grain, and legume hay will be satisfactory for sows. If legume hay is not fed, a small amount of a feed like linseed meal, wheat middlings, or wheat bran should be added to a ration of grain and whey, especially if the grain is corn.

Such supplements as wheat middlings, wheat bran, and linseed meal are fairly satisfactory when the sows eat a considerable amount of good legume hay.[13] However, it is best to add to these rations a small allowance of one of the more efficient protein supplements.

A ration consisting only of grain and grain by-products, with or without linseed meal, is unsafe for feeding over long periods to brood sows, even when a mineral supplement is fed to make good the lack of calcium. Such a ration is seriously deficient in quality of protein and in vitamin D. Also, it will lack vitamin A unless the grain is yellow corn.

The poor results secured on a ration of this kind are well shown by Wisconsin experiments.[14] In these trials sows were maintained for many months on corn, oats, or barley, supplemented by only such protein-rich feeds as linseed meal, wheat middlings, or field peas, and with salt in addition and water rather high in calcium to drink. On such rations the offspring tended to be small and weak, and when sows were kept on such feeds for successive gestation periods many of the pigs were born dead. Even when a mineral supplement supplying calcium and phosphorus was added to a ration of yellow corn, linseed meal, and salt, to supply more calcium, the results were still poor. However, when 15 to 25 per cent of alfalfa hay was included in the ration, normal litters were produced.

If sows have been on excellent pasture during the summer, they will have a considerable store of vitamins and minerals in their bodies when winter begins. This may enable them to produce normal litters when fed only grain and such protein supplements as wheat middlings or linseed meal during the winter. However, feeding such a ration is an unsafe practice, for the results may be poor, even under these conditions.

1411. Animal by-products as the only supplements.—Except from the standpoint of vitamins, such animal by-products as tankage, fish meal, and skimmilk are ideal for brood sows. Therefore, if the sows have been on good pasture during the summer and fall, and if they are out in the sunshine during the winter, they can usually produce satisfactory litters when fed only grain and such supplements during the winter.

However, it is much safer and usually also cheaper to feed sows some well-cured legume hay in addition.[15] This will ensure their receiving sufficient vitamins A and D and will help to prevent constipation. As a result, the pigs will often be stronger and more thrifty than when no legume hay is supplied. Also, the addition of legume hay to the ration will generally reduce the feed bill for wintering the sows.

1412. Grains for brood sows.—On account of its cheapness, corn is the chief grain fed to sows throughout the corn belt. Due undoubtedly to the poor results secured when corn is unwisely fed to brood sows without proper supplements, the statement is sometimes made that corn should not form over one-third to one-half the ration for brood sows, as it is "too fattening." However, experiments have shown clearly that excellent results are secured when corn is the only grain, if it is properly supplemented, and provided the allowance is strictly limited to the amount needed to keep the sows in thrifty condition without becoming too fat.

For example, in 3 trials with gilts at the Wisconsin Station a concentrate mixture which many breeders would consider about ideal was compared with the more simple ration of ear corn, alfalfa hay fed in a rack, and 0.3 lb. tankage per head daily in addition.[16] The concentrate mixture consisted of 35 lbs. ground corn, 30 lbs. ground oats, 30 lbs. wheat middlings, and 5 lbs. tankage. On the average, the gilts required 5.5 lbs. of this mixture per head daily to keep them making the desired gain of about 0.9 lb. per head daily, while the other lot made a trifle larger gains on 4.5 lbs. corn (reduced to the basis of shelled corn), 0.3 lb. tankage, and 0.4 lb. alfalfa hay.

Thus, the gilts fed ear corn properly supplemented required 0.3 lb. less feed per head daily, which would be expected from the fact that corn is a more concentrated feed and richer in net energy than oats or middlings. With feeds at usual corn-belt prices, the daily cost of feed per sow was 30 per cent less on this ration. Still more important was the fact that the farrowing results were even a trifle better than on the ration which contained 35 per cent of corn.

Where other cereals are cheaper than corn, pound for pound, they may often be used economically for brood sows. With the possible exception of ground wheat, none of them is quite equal to corn in feeding value.

In an Iowa trial ground barley, fed dry, was worth about 95 per cent as much as shelled corn per pound, when supplemented with alfalfa meal and a small amount of tankage.[17] Dry whole barley or soaked whole barley was worth only about 80 per cent as much as shelled corn.

Ground oats is excellent when used as part of the grain for brood sows, but it is worth less than corn per 100 lbs., due to the lower content of digestible nutrients.[18] It has the highest value when it forms not more than one-third to one-half of the grain allowance. Oats are too bulky to be satisfactory as the only grain for gilts, but can be fed thus to older sows, along with legume hay.

1413. Succulent feeds for brood sows.—The importance of pasture for brood sows has already been emphasized in this chapter, and the fact has been stressed that well-cured legume hay is the best and most economical substitute for pasture.

Formerly, roots and tubers were widely advocated for the feeding of brood sows. We now know, however, that roots and tubers do not have the nutritive merits of legume hay. They are low in protein, calcium, and phosphorus; they supply little or no vitamin D; and with the exception of carrots, sweet potatoes, and yellow rutabagas, they are deficient in vitamin A. It is evident, therefore, that roots or tubers are poor substitutes for pasture or for legume hay. **(1394)**

To find whether there was any advantage in adding roots to well-balanced rations including alfalfa or clover hay, experiments were conducted during 4 winters at the Wisconsin Station.[19] Either sugar-mangels or yellow carrots were added to a ration of corn, tankage, and alfalfa hay, or to a ration consisting of clover hay and a concentrate mixture of barley, oats, wheat middlings, and linseed meal. Gilts, yearlings, and aged sows were used in the various trials. Contrary to what some swine breeders would have predicted, in no case did the addition of roots to these rations result in larger or more thrifty pigs. Furthermore, roots proved to be decidedly uneconomical under corn belt conditions, for in no case was their actual feeding value as high as $4.00 per ton, with corn at 56 cents a bushel and other feeds at corresponding prices.

In a Montana trial sugar beets were worth slightly less than half as much as alfalfa hay when sows were fed hull-less barley and either sugar beets or hay.[20]

Silage is not a satisfactory feed for brood sows, for they will usually eat only the corn grain, leaving most of the forage.

1414. Salt.—Brood sows should always be provided regularly with salt. **(1289)** The best plan is to let them have access to it in a suitable box, where they can take what they wish.

In an Iowa test the rock salt consumption was determined of yearling gilts fed during the winter on various forms of corn with wheat standard middlings, linseed meal, and tankage.[21] The average amount of salt ranged from one-twentieth ounce per head daily for the sows fed shelled corn to one-fourth ounce for those fed ear corn.

1415. Other mineral supplements.—Whether or not it will be beneficial to supply any mineral supplement other than salt for brood sows will depend entirely on the ration that is fed, as has been emphasized in Chapter XXXV. (1290) In sections where there is trouble from goiter, or hairlessness, in new-born pigs, iodine should always be supplied the sows during at least the last 12 weeks of pregnancy. (1292)

When sows are fed such animal by-products as skimmilk, tankage, meat scraps, or fish meal and in addition are on pasture or are supplied with plenty of well-cured legume hay, there is generally no need to add other mineral supplements to provide calcium and phosphorus. This is shown by Wisconsin experiments in which gilts were started on the trials in early summer when weighing 60 to 70 lbs. and were continued on the experiments during the summer and the following winter and spring.[22]

Each year one lot of gilts was fed a well-balanced concentrate mixture of corn, oats, wheat middlings, linseed meal and tankage, with no mineral supplement except salt. During the summer the gilts were on good pasture and during the winter they had access to well-cured alfalfa hay in a rack. This check lot was thus fed merely a modern efficient ration, made of ordinary feeds. Another lot of gilts was similarly fed each year, except that 2 lbs. of steamed bone meal were mixed with each 100 lbs. of the concentrate mixture. A third lot received ground limestone instead of bone meal.

Neither during the pasture season nor during the winter period was there any advantage, so far as rate or economy of gains was concerned, from the addition of the bone meal or the ground limestone. Also, the pigs from the gilts fed no mineral supplement except salt were just as large and just as thrifty as those from the gilts fed bone meal or ground limestone. There was hence no benefit from adding these mineral supplements to this excellent, well-balanced ration, which already contained plenty of calcium and phosphorus.

Likewise, in an Iowa experiment a mineral mixture supplying calcium and phosphorus produced no benefit when added to a ration of corn, oats, and 0.3 lb. tankage per head daily for young gilts being raised on good pasture.[23]

When less complete rations than these are fed it is wise to allow sows access to a mineral mixture supplying calcium and phosphorus. One of the simple mineral mixtures recommended previously will probably give just as good results as a more complex and expensive mixture. (181-182, 1295) If a ration is used which is low either in calcium or phosphorus, it is very important to add a supplement that will correct this lack. Unless this is done, the sows may suffer themselves from the deficiency and are apt to produce unsatisfactory litters.[24] (1291)

1416. Amount of concentrates to feed pregnant sows.—It is just as important not to overfeed pregnant sows as it is to feed them a well-balanced ration. If they become too fat, they are apt to have weak pigs, and they may be restless and clumsy at farrowing time and then kill their pigs. When sows are too fat at breeding time, they may even fail to conceive.[25] On the other hand, a sow which is too thin lacks the reserve energy necessary to nourish her pigs properly before and after birth.

A mature sow which is in vigorous, active condition at the beginning of the breeding season in the fall should be fed so as to gain 75 to 85 lbs. by farrowing time in the spring. This will about cover the loss in weight which will occur at farrowing and while she is nursing her pigs. More of this gain should be made during the last 4 to 6 weeks of the gestation period than during the first part, for most of the growth of the unborn litter occurs then.

If mature sows are fed plenty of legume hay, about 0.8 to 1 lb. of concentrates daily per 100 lbs. of live weight will be sufficient during the first 10 to 12 weeks, and from 1.2 to 1.3 lbs. during the last 4 to 6 weeks of the gestation period.[26] Sows will eat much more feed than this if it is supplied, and they will usually squeal lustily for a more liberal allowance. One must therefore not pay any attention to their desires, but feed only enough to keep them at the proper weights and in the desired condition. It pleases an experienced hog raiser to see his sows industriously hunting for the last grains of corn, for he knows that they are securing the exercise which is so essential for a good pig crop. Furthermore, he knows that his feed bill will be much less than if he had allowed mistaken generosity to rule in feeding the sows.

Yearlings and especially gilts should receive more concentrates in proportion to their live weight, in order to provide for their growth. As a rule an average allowance of 1.4 to 1.6 lbs. concentrates daily per 100 lbs. live weight in addition to legume hay will be plenty for yearlings, and 1.6 to 1.7 lbs. daily per 100 lbs. live weight for gilts.

When a number of sows are kept on the farm, it pays to sort them into two or more lots, depending on age, condition, and disposition. The amount of feed for each lot can then be regulated so that all the sows are kept in the proper condition.

1417. Methods of feeding brood sows.—Pregnant brood sows are ordinarily hand-fed the amount of concentrates they need. Occasionally, they are fed by means of a self-feeder. Chopped or ground legume hay or other bulky feeds such as oat mill feed then must be mixed with the grain or other concentrates, so that the sows will not eat too much concentrates and get too fat.

In some experiments satisfactory results have been secured when pregnant sows have been self-fed such mixtures, but in other tests hand feeding has been decidedly preferable. It is shown later that self-feeding is a very satisfactory method for feeding sows with litters, because the sows then need a liberal amount of concentrates. (**1431**)

In Nebraska trials mature pregnant sows were successfully wintered by self-feeding a mixture of 3 parts by weight of chopped alfalfa hay and 1 part of ground corn.[27] However, in 3 Wisconsin trials feeding gilts ear corn with a little tankage and with alfalfa hay in a rack proved decidedly preferable to self-feeding a mixture of chopped alfalfa and ground corn, with tankage self-fed separately.[28] The sows did not over eat on tankage, but there was much difficulty in shifting the proportions of alfalfa and corn to keep them in the desired condition. As a rule 30 to 40 per cent of the mixture consisted of chopped alfalfa. For older sows the proportion of hay should be larger.

In Texas experiments in which various methods of feeding brood sows were compared, excellent results were secured when sows were fed the entire daily allowance in the morning at one feeding, instead of feeding them twice a day, as is usual.[29]

It is often recommended that brood sows be fed their concentrates in the form of a slop. In certain cases there may be some advantage in this. For example, sometimes sows waste much of a fine concentrate mixture when fed in a trough. This may be avoided by slop feeding or by the more sanitary and convenient plan of first putting the concentrate mixture in the trough and then pouring in some water. In very cold weather pouring warm water on the concentrate mixture in this manner or feeding warm slop induces the sows to take more water than they would otherwise. (1312)

Some years ago the slop or swill feeding of hogs was very common, and too often the barrel in which the slop was mixed was far from sanitary. Progressive pork producers have found that the results are just as good or even better when they use a more cleanly and more convenient method of feeding.

1418. Exercise; shelter.—It has already been stressed in this chapter that sows should be on good pasture during as much of the year as possible. When pasture is not available, they should be induced to take plenty of exercise. In the corn belt a common practice in the fall is to turn the brood sows into the corn fields after the corn has been gathered, to pick up any scattered ears. This not only provides an abundance of exercise but also utilizes feed that would otherwise be wasted.

During the winter it is a good plan to feed the sows at some distance from their sleeping quarters. If there is at this place a rack with choice legume hay, the sows will make many trips back and forth each day. When sows are fed ear corn and the allowance is properly limited, they will spend considerable time searching for the last kernels, and the longer they can be kept on their feet, the better it is for their health. If a ground concentrate mixture is fed, it is often a good plan to scatter a little shelled corn, whole oats, or sheaf oats on the ground for the sows to work over. Sows heavy in pig should not be compelled to plow through snowdrifts, but paths should be made for them. Ashes or sand should be sprinkled on icy places, else they may slip and wrench themselves, which may result in abortion.

The benefits from outdoor exercise for brood sows during the winter are shown by Indiana and Kansas tests.[30] In an Indiana trial the pigs from gilts that had been allowed to roam in a pasture field were more vigorous than those from gilts that had been kept in a small lot. In the Kansas test when sows were fed corn alone and were confined without exercise several pigs were born dead and the others were weak. On the other hand, the results were much better from sows fed similarly, but allowed exercise and access to dirt, which undoubtedly helped correct the mineral deficiencies in corn. Liberal exercise was also decidedly beneficial to sows fed grain alone in Indiana trials.

Recent Kansas and Missouri investigations indicate that the beneficial effect of outdoor exercise for sows may be largely due to the dirt or green forage they get and to the exposure to the sunlight, rather than to the actual exercise they take.[31]

The shelter requirements for the various classes of swine are discussed in Chapter XXXV. (1315)

1419. Summer care of brood sows.—If good pasture is provided, the problem of feeding brood sows in summer after the spring litters are weaned is easily solved. Where sows raise but one litter of pigs a year, they need little or no concentrates in summer, if they are on such first-class pasture as alfalfa, clover, or rape. Enough grain should be given to keep the sows in thrifty condition, and in any event they should get some grain for two or three weeks before breeding time in the fall.

On such protein-rich pasture only a small amount of protein supplement is needed to balance the ration, even when corn or milo grain, both of which are lower in protein than the other common cereals, is fed. For example, dry sows on alfalfa, clover, or rape pasture will do well on corn with no more than 4 to 5 per cent by weight of tankage, or on equal weights of corn and either skimmilk or buttermilk. When barley, oats, or wheat is fed, little supplement, if any, is needed when the pasture is first class.

Where sows raise two litters a year, they will need more concentrates in addition to pasture, due to the added draft on their bodies. They should be fed so as to make about the same gains as recommended for sows in winter.

1420. The sows at breeding time.—Sows are in the best condition for breeding when they are not fat, but are gaining in weight. About two weeks before breeding starts, the sows should be "flushed," just as in the case of ewes. (1233) This means increasing their feed so they will gain 0.50 to 0.75 lb. a day. Sows thus treated are more apt to have large litters, and they also come in heat more promptly and are more apt to become pregnant from the first breeding.

The ration at this time should be similar to that fed during the gestation period and should contain a protein supplement. If possible, the sows should always be on pasture at this season.

Sows usually remain in heat about 3 to 4 days, and if not bred will return in heat at intervals of about 21 days. In Missouri trials larger litters were produced when sows were bred about 30 hours after the beginning of heat than when they were bred either when they first came in heat or at the end of the period.[32]

1421. The boar.—The feed and care of the boar do not differ materially from that of the sows. The boar should be kept in thrifty condition, neither too fat nor run down in flesh, as either extreme may injure his breeding powers. In summer he should be kept in a lot where there is good pasture, and in winter he should have the freedom of a paddock of sufficient size so that he will get abundant exercise. A good plan is to have a small colony house for shelter at one end of the lot, and to feed the boar at the other end.

The most common mistake made in feeding boars is to overfeed them and get them so fat that their breeding powers are seriously injured. Except during the breeding season when more feed is required, about 1 lb. of concentrates daily per 100 lbs. live weight is sufficient in summer for fairly mature boars on good pasture. A little more concentrates will be needed in winter. Young boars should be fed sufficient to keep them growing thriftily.

Two weeks before the breeding season starts, the ration should be increased somewhat, so the boar will be gaining in weight when service begins. The amount of concentrates to be fed during the breeding season will depend on how much the boar is used. In general, he should be fed enough to prevent his losing much weight. Many breeders prefer not to feed much corn to boars at this time, but to use instead concentrate mixtures made up of farm grains and a considerable proportion of protein supplements, such as wheat middlings or bran, linseed meal, tankage, and chopped legume hay.

A boar should not be used for breeding until he is 8 months of age, and then he should preferably not breed more than one sow a day and 12 to 15 in a season. When a boar is allowed to serve each sow only once, as is by far the best practice, a yearling boar can breed 25 to 30 sows in the breeding season, if the services are well distributed. A 2-year-old can take care of 50 to 60 sows, if properly cared for. In breeding gilts or small sows to a mature boar, a breeding crate can be used to advantage.

1422. Gestation period; breeding studies.—The average gestation period of sows is given as 112 to 115 days. The average period was 114.6 days for sows of various breeds in Illinois studies and 115 days in North Dakota tests.[33] About three-fourths of the Illinois sows farrowed between the 113th and 117th day.

In these studies and also in Missouri trials the length of the gestation period was not affected by the age of the sow.[34] Also, in the Missouri experiments the size of the sow or liberal or scanty feeding did not affect the length of gestation.

The proportion of male pigs is slightly greater than of females. In the Illinois studies 51.9 per cent were males, and in the North Dakota tests 52.3 per cent. The average number of pigs per litter was 8.1 in the Illinois records, which were obtained before the development of the large-type lard hogs, while there were 9.6 pigs per litter in the North Dakota records, which were largely obtained with the modern types of swine.

The boar probably does not have any appreciable influence on the number of pigs in the litter, unless he is approaching sterility.[35] On the other hand, he does have an influence on the number of pigs his daughters produce.

A sow that produces a small number of pigs in her first and second litters will tend to have a small number in subsequent litters.[36] The second litter is a somewhat better basis of selection than the first litter, in which the number of pigs is more variable.

The light pigs in a litter usually make less rapid and less economical gains than those that are of average size or heavier.[37] If there are runts in a large litter, it is best to kill them rather than to waste feed and care upon them.

1423. Gilts vs. older sows.—It is well known that gilts have fewer pigs in their litters than do older sows. For instance, in tests at the

North Dakota Station 210 gilts farrowed an average of 8.6 pigs in their first litters, and raised an average of 5.8 pigs while 319 older sows farrowed an average of 10.9 pigs and raised an average of 8.0.[38] In these tests the percentage that was raised of the live pigs farrowed was slightly higher for the older sows than for the gilts. This may have been due to wise culling of the sows that proved to be poor mothers when they were gilts.

The pigs from gilts average slightly smaller in weight at birth than those from older sows and also tend to make somewhat less rapid gains. Thus, in Wisconsin studies the average birth weight of 972 pigs farrowed by gilts was 2.35 lbs. and of 1,344 pigs farrowed by older sows 2.55 lbs.[39] When the pigs were 98 days old there was a difference of 9.4 lbs. in weight in favor of the pigs from the older sows.

Practical hog men differ widely in their opinions concerning the relative economy of proven older sows and of gilts for pork production. All admit that older sows raise somewhat larger litters of pigs and that their pigs tend to make slightly more rapid gains. However, gilts have certain advantages, as well. Their chief superiority is that they are continuing to grow and appreciate in value for pork while they are producing their pigs. Also, due to their greater smoothness and lighter weight after raising one litter of pigs, they usually sell at a higher price on the market than do older sows.

In a study on central Illinois farms of the cost of producing pork, it was concluded that there was little choice between gilts and tried older sows except when the price of pork was sufficiently favorable so that the gain in weight of the gilts could be sold at a decided profit.[40] It should be borne in mind, however, that even young fat sows, after raising their first litters, commonly sell at a considerable discount from the price of fat pigs.

The Illinois studies show clearly that when spring-farrowing sows are retained in the breeding herd for further litters, it is unprofitable to raise only one litter a year from them. As many of them as possible should be bred for fall litters in the two-litter method of pork production described later. (**1436**)

The breeder of purebred swine should certainly not rely chiefly on gilts for his breeding herd. Sows which produce especially good litters and which are good milkers and careful mothers should be retained as long as they are useful. Only the offspring from such proven mothers should be chosen for replacements. By such selection much can be done to build up a herd which is much more profitable than the average. Unless there is some very good reason to expect better returns in the future, one should discard a sow raising a litter of less than 5 pigs, or one which is vicious with her pigs, in spite of being properly fed and cared for. A sow that can save and raise 8 good pigs is an excellent producer and should be retained.

1424. Preparations for farrowing.—Even if the sows have been properly fed and cared for during pregnancy, heavy losses may occur among the young pigs at farrowing time, unless attention is given to certain necessary details. Lack of care at this critical time results in many pigs being lost through disease or parasites, or from being lain on by the sows. It has been estimated that in some seasons 40 per cent of the pigs farrowed in the corn belt perish from these causes, all of which may largely be prevented by the right care and management.

At least 3 days before she is to farrow, each sow should be removed from the herd and placed in a separate farrowing pen. This allows her to become accustomed to her surroundings and to the presence of the herdsman, so she will be more quiet when farrowing. If the breeding dates have not been recorded, the sows should be watched closely as the farrowing season approaches, and each sow should be put in a farrowing pen as soon as the udder and teats begin to fill. After a sow starts to arrange her nest, she may be expected to farrow within 12 hours. Recording the breeding date is highly important where the litters come before the weather is warm, for otherwise sows will often farrow before they are expected, and their litters may perish from cold or lack of proper care.

The farrowing pen should be dry, well ventilated, free from drafts and well lighted. If possible, it should be exposed for a part of each day to direct sunlight, so it will be warmer, and also because of the germicidal action of sunlight.

Before the sow is placed in the farrowing pen, it should previously have been thoroughly cleaned and also scrubbed with a hot lye solution, as is described later, to kill round worm eggs and to prevent infections. (1440) For the same reason all filth should have been removed from the sow and her udder washed thoroughly with soap and warm water. After the clean sow has been put into the scrubbed pen she should not be allowed to go out of the pen where she will have contact with the sources of infection in the hog lots about the barn. Otherwise, all the labor spent in the sanitary measures may be wasted. It is beneficial, however, if the sow can get exercise in a thoroughly cleaned, paved outside pen, adjacent to the farrowing pen.

When a sow farrows during the pasture season, it may be most convenient to have her farrow in a colony house located in a pasture that is free from round worms and other parasites. However, it is then difficult to aid her in case she has difficulty in farrowing.

Each farrowing pen should have guard rails, or fenders, to protect the little pigs during and after farrowing. These can be made by fastening planks edgewise, like shelves, 8 to 10 inches from the floor, along both sides of the corner in which the sow makes her bed. Guard rails largely prevent the sow from squeezing the pigs against the wall or lying on them while they are small. If the farrowing pen has a concrete floor, a wood overlay in the nest corner makes the sow's bed warmer, drier, and cleaner.

The farrowing place should be sufficiently warm so that a deep nest is not necessary to prevent the new-born pigs being chilled, for they may be crushed in a deep, bird-like nest. Cut straw or hay, shredded stover, chaff, or leaves are the best for bedding, provided they are reasonably free from dust. Only about a bushel of bedding should be used, for too much bedding or straw or hay that is too long may entangle the pigs so they will be crushed when the sow lies down.

As soon as the sow is put in the farrowing pen, her ration should be reduced and also be made more laxative. A good rule is to feed only two-thirds as much concentrates as previously, with wheat bran forming one-third of the ration by weight. Linseed meal is also a helpful addition at this time, and the feeding of legume hay should be continued. Some breeders prefer to feed the concentrates as a thin, warm slop. This may satisfy the sow better and aid in getting her to take plenty of water.

1425. Farrowing time.—At farrowing time the herdsman should be on hand to render assistance, if necessary, but should otherwise not disturb the sow. In large herds it has been found exceedingly profitable to have an experienced man near during the night at this time to inspect the sows every three hours. The farmer with only a few sows will find that a few night trips to the hog house at farrowing time will save many a litter, and prove a wise investment of his time and energy.

When farrowing occurs in very cold weather, it is a good plan, as the pigs arrive, to dry them thoroughly and put them in a basket or box which is lined with sacks or other cloth. A jug of hot water or warm bricks wrapped in cloth can be placed in the center to keep the pigs warm, and the receptacle lightly covered to hold the heat. Separating the pigs thus from the sow as they are farrowed is also wise in the case of heavy, clumsy sows, or those which are very restless. Sows properly handled before farrowing will not usually resent such separation.

The pigs should be kept in this box or basket until farrowing is over, provided the time is not more than 2 or 3 hours. When they are returned to the sow, each pig should be placed at a nipple, and the litter should be watched until their safety is assured. In the case of a very cross sow it may be advisable to keep the pigs away from her for a day or so, returning them to nurse every 3 or 4 hours.

To prevent losses due to navel infection it is wise to dip the navel of each pig in tincture of iodine as soon as possible after birth. Some herdsmen tie the navel cord with a string about an inch from the body, cut the end of the cord off, and then disinfect the stump with iodine.

A pig that is apparently born dead can sometimes be saved by removing all mucus from the nose and then giving it a few gentle slaps on the side with the hand. A chilled pig may be revived by immersing it up to the head in water as warm as the elbow will bear.

At birth, pigs have long, sharp "wolf" teeth, which are also called "needle" teeth or "black" teeth. These temporary tusk-like teeth are of no benefit to the pigs and are apt to lacerate the udder of the sow and also to wound the other pigs as they tussle among themselves. Therefore experienced hogmen commonly break off these teeth close to the gums with nippers made for the purpose. Care must be taken to make a clean break, without leaving jagged edges, and at the same time without injuring the jaw or gums of the pig.

It is, of course, necessary to mark purebred pigs that are to be registered, and the ear-notching system is perhaps the most convenient. Its main advantage is that pigs can be marked within a few hours after birth, avoiding danger of mistakes, while a small pig's ear is too small and tender to permit marking by buttons or labels until the pigs are several weeks of age. Marking the pigs is also highly advisable even in grade herds, to permit selecting gilts for the breeding herd from the best litters and out of the best dams.

If brood sows have been kept thrifty by feeding them well-balanced rations and by inducing them to take plenty of exercise, and if constipation is prevented, little trouble will be experienced from sows failing to furnish enough milk for their pigs or from being restless and irritable, which may lead to their eating the young. If a sow has a feverish udder, which often is a result of constipation, a light application of kerosene and lard, well rubbed in, will reduce the congestion and relieve the pain.

1426. After farrowing.—A sow should receive no feed for 12 to 24 hours after farrowing, but should have plenty of water. In very cold weather it is wise to take the chill off the water. If the sow frets for feed, a handful of wheat bran may be put on top of the water to quiet her.

For the first feed she should get only a double handful of a laxative mixture, preferably containing considerable wheat bran. The amount of concentrates should be increased very gradually or the milk flow may be stimulated too soon. This may result in the sow having milk fever or suffering from a caked udder, or in the pigs getting scours. For the second day 2 or 3 lbs. of feed, divided into 2 meals, are sufficient.

During the first few days it is best to use a bulky concentrate mixture containing at least one-third ground oats or wheat bran. Such a mixture may then be changed to the one that is to be fed during the suckling period.

After 10 to 14 days the sows should be getting all the feed they will clean up. By this time, the sows and litters should, whenever possible, be put on clean pasture, free from infestation with round worms or other parasites. As described later, they should be hauled to the pasture, and should not be driven down a lane that may infest the pigs with parasites as they stop to nibble at grass or other material on their way. (1440)

1427. Sows as milk producers.—The amounts of milk produced by sows have been determined by keeping the pigs away from the sows except at nursing time, when the pigs have been weighed immediately before and after nursing. The amount of milk produced by sows per pig in their litters varies widely, ranging from 0.18 to 0.65 lb. in Oklahoma tests.[41] The pigs securing the most milk made the most rapid gains both during the suckling period and during the first 2 months after weaning.

In these and other experiments the average total amount of milk yielded daily by sows ranged from 4.9 to 10.3 lbs.[42] During the 60 to 85 days that most sows nurse their litters, a good dam should produce a total of 400 to 500 lbs. of milk or more. Since the gains made by suckling pigs depend largely on whether their dams are good milk producers, it is important to select gilts for replacements in the herd from good milk-producing ancestors.

In tests at the North Dakota Station it was found that the average interval between the nursings by pigs was 62 minutes, and the longest interval recorded was 175 minutes.[43] There was no marked difference between the intervals in the daytime and at night.

It is shown in Appendix Table I that sow's milk is richer than cow's milk in all nutrients, and especially in fat, for it contains on the average 6.7 per cent fat. Woll found that the fat globules of sow's milk were only one-fourth as large as those of cow's milk, but 8 times as numerous.[44]

1428. Orphan pigs; "evening up" number in litters.—If a sow dies shortly after farrowing a litter or becomes seriously sick, the problem arises as to how the pigs may be reared. The best plan is to induce sows which have litters of about the same age to adopt the orphans. This same method may be used to "even up" the number of pigs in various litters, pigs being taken from a sow that has too many pigs to nurse adequately and added to a small litter of the same age.

A sow should be taken out of the pen when the orphans are added to her litter, and the pigs should be allowed to run together for 10 to 20 minutes before the sow is returned to the pen. Sprinkling a weak solution of stock dip over all the pigs will make it difficult for the sow to distinguish the new arrivals by smell.

Where no sows with litters of about the same age are available for raising orphan pigs, they may usually be raised successfully by hand, if the herdsman has enough patience. It is best to feed the pigs whole sweet cow's milk 5 to 6 times daily until they are 3 to 4 weeks old, when the number of feedings may be reduced to 3 a day. However, in Iowa tests satisfactory results were secured when the pigs were fed only 3 times daily from the beginning.[45] Some use a nursing bottle at the start, but with patience even the youngest pigs can be taught to drink milk from a shallow dish. The pig's mouth and nose are pushed into the milk, care being taken not to continue the process so long that the pig is strangled.

A maximum of one quart of milk a day is enough per pig, if they are supplied with a suitable concentrate mixture as soon as they can be taught to eat solid food. Care should be taken to supply fresh water at all times. If whole milk is not available, fresh skimmilk or even buttermilk can be substituted, according to the Iowa tests. It is not advisable to add cream or sugar to whole milk for orphan pigs.

If young pigs do not get the colostrum milk from a sow, it is more difficult to rear them, as the colostrum protects them against various infections. **(210)**

II. RAISING THE PIGS

1429. Feeding sows suckling litters.—Sows suckling their litters have the same general nutrient requirements as dairy cows. They need a liberal allowance of concentrates rich in protein, calcium, phosphorus and vitamins. To supply vitamins A and D, when the sows are not on pasture 5 to 10 per cent of chopped or ground legume hay should be included in the concentrate mixture, or choice legume hay should be supplied in a rack.

It is essential that sows with litters be fed suitable rations containing a sufficient amount of concentrates so that they will have a good milk flow. Otherwise, the young pigs will not get a good start in life. At no other time do pigs make as economical gains as when suckling their dams.

When on full feed, a 400-lb. sow nursing a litter will need 8 to 12 lbs. of concentrates a day, the exact amount depending on her condition and on the number of pigs in the litter. The concentrates may consist chiefly of corn and other grains, but plenty of protein supplements should be added to balance the ration. A sufficient amount of such supplements as dairy by-products, tankage, meat scraps, or fish meal should be fed to provide the proper quality of protein in the ration. This is especially important when the sows are not on pasture or have no legume hay. These supplements may be combined with wheat shorts, wheat bran, linseed meal, soybeans, soybean oil meal, etc.

For sows on pasture or for those supplied with good legume hay such simple combinations as grain and either tankage or fish meal, or grain and skimmilk, are satisfactory, but many breeders prefer mixtures containing more variety and including some bulky feed. Corn may be fed as ear corn or shelled corn (preferably soaked if it is hard and dry) or it may be ground and mixed with the other concentrates. The smaller cereals should always be ground for sows, if possible.

Several example rations for brood sows suckling litters are given in Appendix Table VII. These will serve as guides in making up a ration that will be most economical under one's local conditions. As is shown in Appendix Table III, rations for brood sows with litters should contain sufficient protein so that the nutritive ratio will not be wider than 1:6.0 to 1:7.0.

1430. Prevention of anemia; mineral mixtures.—One of the methods of preventing anemia in suckling pigs that have been described in Chapter XXXV should always be used when sows and pigs cannot be gotten on pasture by the time the pigs are 2 weeks of age, but are confined to pens and paved lots, away from contact with the soil. (**1293**) For sows and pigs not on pasture, it is also wise to supply a suitable mineral mixture, in addition to common salt, unless one is sure there is no lack of calcium or phosphorus in the ration.

1431. Methods of feeding brood sows and litters.—Brood sows with litters may be hand-fed 2 or 3 times a day, or they may be self-fed. Until recently, the self-feeding method has not been used extensively, but experiments and also the experience of farmers have shown it to be convenient and successful. In this method both sows and pigs have access to a suitable concentrate mixture at all times in a self-feeder, after the pigs are about 2 weeks old.

Self-feeding is especially desirable where more than one sow is in the same lot, as there is no quarreling at the feed trough, and each pig can get all it wants to eat. A self-feeder should not, however, be used for sows that are nursing only 2 to 4 pigs, as the sows are apt to become too fat.

Self-feeding sows and litters proved preferable to hand-feeding in experiments by the United States Department of Agriculture and also in a Kansas test.[46] In the former trials self-fed sows gained an average of 12.8 lbs. and their pigs an average of 20.4 lbs. during 41 days, while hand-fed sows lost an average of 11.6 lbs. and their pigs gained an average of 17.0 lbs. during 44 days. The self-fed pigs also continued to make more rapid gains after weaning. For 100 lbs. gain of sows and litters combined only 441 lbs. of feed were required by the self-fed lot, in comparison with 603 lbs. for the hand-fed lot. Also, when the sows were bred before their pigs were weaned, 81 per cent of the self-fed sows settled at the first service and only 47 per cent of those that were hand-fed. It has been shown previously that the self-feeding method is not well suited to pregnant sows.

When the sows are hand-fed, additional feed should be supplied the pigs by means of a creep, as soon as they are 2 to 3 weeks old. This is an enclosure in a corner of the pasture or paddock, with openings of such size that the pigs can run in and out, while the sows are excluded. Here the pigs are supplied a suitable mixture of concentrates, either in a small trough or in a self-feeder. For creep-feeding suckling pigs any of the concentrate mixtures suggested in Appendix Table VII for brood sows and their litters are excellent. For suckling pigs and particularly for pigs at weaning time, skimmilk and buttermilk are the best of all protein supplements. Nothing else aids so greatly in keeping them growing lustily.

Most of the concentrates for suckling pigs can be ground grain. If there is an abundance of skimmilk or buttermilk for the pigs, relatively little of other protein supplements need be used. Where these dairy by-products are not available, some tankage, meat scraps, or fish meal should be included in the concentrate mixture. Good pasture is especially beneficial to young pigs, due to the protein, minerals, and vitamins it provides, and also because pigs get an abundance of exercise when on pasture.

If the pigs show a tendency to become too fat the first few weeks, the dam's ration should be reduced gradually, so she will give a little less milk. Scours should be avoided by keeping the quarters dry and clean and the troughs sanitary. Overfeeding the sows or letting the pigs run out in a cold rain are other frequent causes of this trouble.

Boar pigs not to be kept for the breeding herd should be castrated when 3 to 6 weeks old. This should be done on a clear, cool day, and the pigs should be kept in dry, clean quarters afterwards. Before the operation the pigs should receive only a light feed.

1432. Weaning time.—When only one litter of pigs is raised a year, the pigs may run with their dams 10 to 12 weeks, or the sow may be allowed to wean the pigs herself. However, when 2 litters are raised yearly the pigs must be weaned at the age of 7 or 8 weeks, as the sows do not commonly come in heat until after their pigs are weaned.

When the litters are to be weaned at this age, the amount of concentrates fed the sows should be reduced for a few days before weaning, in order to check the milk flow. If the sows and litters have been self-fed on pasture, it is best to shut the sows away from the self-feeder by means of a creep 3 or 4 days before weaning. For this short period the sows will get enough nourishment from the pasture.

After the sow is taken away from her pigs it may be necessary to return her to the pigs for a few minutes the second day if her udder becomes unduly distended with milk. In the case of very persistent milkers, the process should be repeated at two-day intervals, as needed.

It is especially important that clean pasture, free from contamination with round worms and other parasites, be provided for the pigs after weaning. If there is much difference in the ages of the various litters, it is best to group them according to size, subdividing a pasture, if necessary. Pigs will do best if there are not over about 20 in a group, as there is then less crowding in the colony house on cold nights.

However, a much greater number may be successfully kept in a large pasture, if self-feeders and colony houses are well distributed, instead of all being located at one point.

Since the pigs no longer get their mother's milk, the ration after weaning should contain a somewhat larger proportion of protein-rich feeds than before. An abundance of skimmilk or buttermilk with grain is excellent. In the absence of this, the proportion of tankage or other protein supplements should be large enough to provide a nutritive ratio of 1:4.0 or 1:4.5 for pigs not on pasture and of 1:5.0 or 1:6.0 for those having good forage.

Several rations for pigs after weaning and also at later ages are given in Appendix Table VII. These will serve as convenient guides in selecting suitable combinations under the conditions in any particular locality.

1433. Growing and fattening pigs.—In the preceding chapter the various rations which are satisfactory for growing and fattening pigs have been discussed in detail. A study of the trials there reported will show which combinations of feed are most economical under various conditions. Further suggestions are given in the example rations included in Appendix Table VII.

The importance of good pasture for all swine throughout the entire growing season cannot be too strongly emphasized. (**1377**) Pasture is especially important for young pigs, as it keeps them growing thriftily, and also greatly reduces the cost of the gains made. In fact, no one should expect the best profits from his pigs if he fails to provide this nutritious and economical feed. In addition to such pasture as alfalfa, clover, or rape, at least 2 lbs. of concentrates daily per 100 lbs. live weight should be fed, except where pasture is unusually cheap compared with grain, and the allowance of concentrates should never be less than 1.0 to 1.5 lbs. daily per 100 lbs. live weight. (**1307**) Pigs should gain at least one-half to three-fourths pound a day, even when they are being raised on pasture plus a limited amount of grain, for fattening in the fall.

In most sections of the United States self-feeding pigs on pasture has become a common practice, except for breeding stock. The use of the self-feeder for growing and fattening pigs has been discussed fully in a preceding chapter. (**1308-1309**) Where the amount of concentrates fed in summer on pasture is limited, the pigs should be finished in the fall on all the concentrates they will eat, hand-fed or self-fed. In the corn belt when new corn is ready, pigs are commonly fattened on new ear corn, along with a suitable protein-rich supplement. As has been pointed out previously, turning pigs into standing corn to "hog down" the crop has become a common practice in the corn belt. (**1331**)

Whether to fatten spring pigs for market early in the fall by self-feeding them concentrates on pasture, or to force them to consume more pasture by restricting their concentrate allowance, will depend on the relative prices of grain and pasture, and the prices for pork at the various times in the fall and winter, as has been discussed in Chapter XXXV. (**1307**) It is practically always advisable to feed fall pigs liberally during the winter and get them to market as soon as possible. The only exception is when it seems probable that prices for hogs will be better somewhat later. **(1303-1306**)

Pigs should always be provided with an abundance of fresh water in a trough or an automatic waterer. If self-feeders and automatic waterers are used, it should be borne in mind that even with these labor-saving devices one cannot expect success if he does not give the proper attention to his pigs. One should see daily that the feeders and waterers are working properly and should clean them out when necessary.

If the pigs are on first-class pasture and are fed such supplements as skimmilk, tankage, or fish meal, there is probably little or no advantage in feeding any other mineral supplement than salt. However, for pigs not on good pasture, feeding a simple mineral mixture, such as has been recommended before, may be advisable, even when protein supplements of animal origin are used.

1434. Raising breeding stock.—Pigs selected for the breeding herd, both sows and boars, should be fed so they will develop good size and strong bone, but should not be allowed to become so fat as pigs that are being finished for market. If the spring pigs are fed a limited allowance of concentrates on good pasture and receive a well-balanced ration, it may not be necessary to separate the gilts to be retained for breeding from the other pigs until full feeding is started in the fall.

On the other hand, if the pigs intended for the market are being fattened as they grow by self-feeding or by hand-feeding a full fattening ration, it is best to separate the breeding stock soon after weaning, so they may be fed a ration suited to their needs. However, if gilts are of the intermediate or big type, they may be safely fed with the market pigs until they reach a weight of 175 to 225 lbs., even when the pigs are self-fed.

Especial care should be taken that the ration for pigs being raised for breeding stock contains sufficient protein and protein of good quality, and that there is an abundant supply of calcium, phosphorus, vitamin A, and vitamin D. Such pigs should be on good pasture during just as much of the year as is possible. This is the best insurance against any lack of vitamins. When pasture is not available, legume hay should be included in the ration.

Breeding swine may be raised with success on grain (even corn) as the chief concentrate, provided the grain is properly supplemented and also provided the amount is limited so that the pigs do not get too fat. However, most breeders prefer concentrate mixtures containing a reasonable proportion of rather bulky feeds, such as ground oats, wheat bran, or standard middlings. If possible, some protein-rich feed of animal origin should be included in the ration, such as dairy by-products, tankage, or fish meal. This is especially important if the pigs are not on first-class pasture.

Though simple concentrate mixtures are satisfactory, such a mixture as the following may be considered ideal for such stock: Corn, barley, or grain sorghum, 40 lbs.; ground oats, 30 lbs.; standard middlings, 20 lbs.; linseed meal or cottonseed meal, 5 lbs.; tankage or fish meal, 5 lbs. If plenty of skimmilk or buttermilk is available, a mixture of one-half corn, barley, or grain sorghum and one-half oats or standard middlings should be entirely satisfactory.

Sows and boars of the larger breeds should reach a weight of 350 lbs. or over at one year of age, if properly fed and managed.

1435. Age to breed gilts.—Commonly, spring gilts not intended for showing at fairs are bred in the fall and farrow when they are about a year old. Those intended for a show herd are usually not bred until they are a year old, in order that they may mature earlier and reach a larger size. Thus, under general farm conditions gilts are bred when very immature.

Extensive experiments were conducted by Mumford and associates at the Missouri Station over a period of 18 years to study the effects of continued early breeding of sows during successive generations.[47] The special objects of the investigations were to find whether this would retard their growth and diminish their mature size, and also to determine whether early breeding would result in offspring that were smaller or less thrifty.

In these experiments some sows and their offspring in several generations were bred to farrow the first time at less than a year of age, and then bred as frequently as possible thereafter. Other sows and their offspring were bred the first time at 18 months of age, and still others not until they were 30 months of age. These groups of sows were all liberally fed, but other lots of early-bred sows were kept on a moderate plane of nutrition and still others were scantily fed.

The mature weight of sows was not reduced when they were well fed and bred during 11 to 16 successive generations to farrow their first litters at slightly less than a year of age and then bred as frequently as possible thereafter. Such sows were only slightly smaller at 20 months of age than the later-bred sows. They continued to grow for a longer time and finally became fully as large.

The pigs in the first litters of young sows are slightly smaller at birth than those from older sows, and also make a trifle less rapid gain. In commercial pork production this is much more than offset by the additional cost of maintaining a later-bred sow for a longer period before she produces her first litter.

When early and frequent breeding was combined with scanty feeding, the sows did not reach normal size. This checking of growth was due to the heavy drain on the sows when they were fed scantily during lactation.

1436. Two litters vs. one litter a year.—Whether to follow the two-litter-a-year or the one-litter method of pork production is a problem of great importance that every swine raiser must decide. The answer should depend on the local conditions, especially on the winter climate, the shelter that can be furnished, and the feeds that are available.

When the one-litter system is followed, the pigs are nearly all farrowed in the spring and few or no sows are bred for fall pigs. Commonly, gilts are used chiefly or entirely in this system, and in the summer after they have weaned their first litters they are fattened for market. This plan is followed because it does not pay to maintain a sow an entire year to raise only one litter of pigs.

Under the two-litter system the sows are bred to farrow sufficiently early in the spring so that the fall litters can get a good start before cold weather comes on. Sows usually come in heat a few days after their litters are weaned, but not during the suckling period. Since the fall litters should be farrowed by September, this means that the spring litters must come not later than March. Raising two litters a year should therefore not be attempted in the North unless these early pigs can be given proper shelter and care.

Even when an endeavor is made to raise two litters a year from all the sows possible, there will usually be more spring litters than fall litters. Often some of the spring-farrowing sows will not become pregnant from the first service, and then it may be too late in the season to breed them again for fall litters. Under this system, however, it is easily possible to raise an average of three litters every two years.

Where the climate is mild, the two-litter system is usually more profitable than the one-litter method. In such sections the fall litters should prove as satisfactory as the spring pigs, for they can be furnished pasture until late in the fall and in the southern states also during the winter. Even in the North, excellent results can be secured from fall pigs when they are properly fed and cared for.

In the corn belt the two-litter system has several advantages, as well as certain disadvantages. The chief advantages are:[48] (1) A maximum use is made of capital invested in equipment; (2) the breeding herd may be improved more readily by retaining sows that produce large litters of pigs that prove efficient in the feed lot; (3) there is a better distribution of labor under the two-litter system; (4) under this system pigs can be marketed at the two times of the year when the prices are usually highest—in early fall and in spring; (5) there is a better distribution of farm income; and (6) the danger of loss through a drop in the market price is reduced, since the pigs are marketed at two different seasons.

These advantages are offset to some extent by the fact that the death losses are usually higher in pigs farrowed early in the spring, as is necessary in the two-litter system, than they are in litters farrowed later when the weather is more favorable. In cost studies on farms in central Illinois during 3 years there was practically no difference in the average total cost of producing each 100 lbs. of pork under the one-litter system and the two-litter system.[49] However, the selling price of the pigs per hundredweight commonly averages higher under the two-litter system, when it is properly carried out.

1437. Fall vs. spring pigs.—In the South where pasture can be provided during all or most of the winter, there should be but little difference in the rate or in the economy of gains made by pigs in summer or winter. Winter-fed pigs in Texas trials gained even more rapidly than summer-fed pigs, but required 4 to 6 per cent more feed per 100 lbs. gain.[50] In these tests the average winter temperature was 53°F. and the average summer temperature 83°F.

In the North there will also be but little difference in the cost of producing 100 lbs. of pork from fall pigs and from spring pigs, if the fall pigs are farrowed early enough to get a good start on pasture and if they have proper feed and care. More concentrates will be required per 100 lbs. gain than in the case of spring pigs raised on good pasture, but this will be offset to some extent by the lower price of grain in the fall and winter. Also, fall pigs that are efficiently raised reach the

market in the spring when the price is usually higher than at the time
in the fall when most spring pigs are marketed. Therefore under favorable conditions even better net returns can often be secured from fall
litters than from spring pigs.

The excellent results that can be secured from fall pigs under suitable conditions are well shown by tests at the Minnesota Station.[51]
During 2 years fall pigs were fed efficient rations in dry lots from
weights of 50 to 60 lbs. to market weights. In comparison, spring pigs
were fed the same rations during the summer in dry lots, and still
other spring pigs were fed on alfalfa pasture. The average daily gains
were practically the same for the three systems. The fall pigs required
404 lbs. of concentrates per 100 lbs. gain; the spring pigs fed in dry
lot, 402 lbs.; and the spring pigs on pasture, 390 lbs. Due to a higher
selling price, the net return over the cost of feed and the initial cost
of pigs was considerably higher than for the spring pigs, even when
no charge was made for their pasture.

Fall pigs were also compared with spring pigs in Delaware tests
during 3 years.[52] Both fall and spring pigs were on rye pasture before
weaning, but after weaning, the fall pigs were fed in dry lot during
the late fall and winter, while the spring pigs had good pasture during
the summers. The average daily gain from birth to a weight of 100
lbs. was 0.56 lb. for the fall pigs and 0.72 lb. for the spring pigs. The
fall pigs required 398 lbs. concentrates per 100 lbs. gain during this
period, while the spring pigs consumed only 319 lbs., largely due to the
greater amount of feed they secured from pasture.

1438. Essentials in raising fall pigs.—Unless fall pigs are given
proper feed and care, they will be a disappointment where the winter
climate is cold. As emphasized previously, they should be farrowed early
enough to get a good start before cold weather. It is important that
clean pasture be provided for sows with fall litters, as this aids greatly
in keeping the pigs thrifty. Where the climate is suitable, the pigs
should also be on good pasture at weaning time and for as long a period
afterward as possible. On pasture the pigs will be able to build up
a store of vitamins in their bodies to help overcome any shortage during
the winter.

To secure rapid and economical gains with fall pigs after the
pasture season, it is essential that their rations furnish not only sufficient protein, but also protein of excellent quality. In addition,
especial care is needed to ensure that the rations provide sufficient
vitamin A, vitamin D, calcium, and phosphorus. Several example rations
are given in Appendix Table VII, which will serve as guides in deciding
upon a ration adapted to local conditions.

The investigations summarized in the previous chapter show conclusively the importance of including a small proportion of well-cured
legume hay in the rations of growing pigs when they are not on pasture.
(**1396-1398**) Such legume hay not only provides vitamin A and vitamin
D, but also helps balance the ration in protein and supplies calcium.
For information on the manner in which the hay should be fed to pigs,
the reader is referred to this discussion.

An excellent supplemental mixture for pigs in dry lot is the trio
mixture, or Wisconsin mixture, discussed in the preceding chapter.

(**1341**) This consists of 50 lbs. tankage, meat scraps, or fish meal; 25 lbs. chopped or ground legume hay; and 25 lbs. linseed meal. As has been previously shown, several modifications can be made in this combination without reducing its efficiency.

If plenty of skimmilk or buttermilk is available, the ration for fall pigs may consist of only grain and the dairy by-product with a little legume hay. For pigs under 75 lbs. in weight it is advisable to add to a ration of corn, skimmilk, and legume hay a small amount of some other protein supplement, as young pigs full-fed on corn will often not drink enough milk to balance the ration completely.

Suitable, well-ventilated quarters must be provided for fall pigs, where they can be kept comfortable during cold, wet weather. They should be supplied with sufficient bedding, and this should be replaced when it becomes damp.

III. OTHER FACTORS IN PORK PRODUCTION

1439. Sanitation and disease prevention.—Sanitation is fully as important in pork production as is proper feeding. If hogs are raised on the same ground year after year with little or no regard for proper sanitation, there will be heavy losses from round worms and other parasites and also from filth-borne diseases. Many pigs will die before they get to market as a result of these conditions, and others will become unprofitable. On the other hand, under an efficient system of swine sanitation, including the use of clean, uncontaminated pasture for the young pigs, such losses can be largely prevented.

The common round worm of swine *(Ascaris suum* or *Ascaris lumbricoides)* is one of the chief causes of death or lack of thrift among young pigs, and also is one of the most injurious parasites in older swine. Under usual conditions probably one-third of the hogs of breeding age are infested to a greater or less extent with these parasites.

It is difficult to control round worms, because the eggs, which are voided in the feces from infested swine, are resistant to freezing, thawing, or drying and also are not killed by most chemical disinfectants. However they live only a short time if exposed to sunlight in a dry place.

An efficient method of control of round worms has been developed by the United States Department of Agriculture which has become commonly known as the "McLean County System of Swine Sanitation," because it was first tried on a large scale in coöperative tests with farmers in that county of Illinois.[53] This system not only controls round worms but also largely eliminates trouble from other parasites and from filth-borne diseases, such as necrotic enteritis.

To understand the principles upon which the success of the system depends, it is first necessary to know how the round worms develop in swine. Pigs become infested by swallowing the eggs of the parasite, which are of microscopic size and are found in the manure of infested hogs or in the soil of lots contaminated by the droppings from infested hogs. It has been estimated that one full-grown female worm in the intestine of a hog may produce as many as 80,000,000 eggs.

The eggs as they are passed out of the body of the hog in the droppings are not at first infectious, but in a few weeks or months, depending upon the weather and various other conditions, the egg reaches a stage of development at which it contains a tiny worm within the shell, and it is then infectious, if swallowed. These eggs may remain alive in the soil for a year or more.

When an incubated egg is swallowed by a pig, it passes to the small intestine, where it hatches, The young worms, which are too small to be seen by the naked eye, then penetrate the walls of the small intestine and are carried in the blood through the liver to the heart and lungs. In the lungs the small worms migrate through the blood vessels and invade the lung tissues. From the air spaces in the lungs, the worms are coughed up by the pigs into the throat and swallowed. The worms, which are now only one-fifteenth to one-twentieth inch in length, grow to adult size in the intestines in a period of 2 to 3 months.

The greatest injury to young pigs occurs when the worms are in the lungs. In case of a heavy invasion many abcesses are produced, the pigs become unthrifty, and many die from pneumonia. Common indications of infestation are coughing and the difficult breathing, sometimes known as "thumps." In the later intestinal stages, the worms may also be decidedly injurious if many are present. This is especially the case when they invade the gall bladder and the ducts of the liver.

1440. Round-worm control.—The "McLean County System of Swine Sanitation" is as follows:

1. The farrowing pens should be cleaned thoroughly, all dirt, dust, and litter being removed. Then the floors and the walls for 2 feet from the floor should be scrubbed with boiling water, to each 30 gallons of which 1 lb. of lye has been added. After the pen has been scrubbed it is wise to spray it with a reliable disinfectant. The lye does not kill the round worm eggs, but is necessary to loosen the dirt, and thus remove the eggs. The hot water kills some of the eggs and the lye and the disinfectant kill disease germs.

2. Before the sow is put in the farrowing pen, all dirt and litter should be carefully brushed from her sides and legs, and her udder, legs, and feet washed with warm water and soap. A single small chunk of dirt remaining on the sow may contain enough round worm eggs to stunt a pig that swallows it.

3. Until they are taken to "clean" pasture, the sow and pigs must be confined to the farrowing pen, or to the pen and a paved adjacent outside lot which has been similarly scrubbed. The sow and litter should be hauled (not driven) to a pasture where no pigs have been kept for at least a year, and which preferably has been cultivated since last used by hogs. If the pigs are driven over contaminated ground, they may pick up enough worm eggs on the way to lessen greatly the benefits from the system.

4. The pigs should be kept on this "clean" pasture until they are at least 4 months old, after which time they are much less susceptible to injury from round worms or other parasites, or to infection with necrotic enteritis or other filth-borne diseases.

In sections where the soil is sandy and well-drained it may not be necessary to wash the sows before farrowing.[54] Also, when sows farrow during the pasture season, they can be housed in portable colony houses located in the "clean" pasture where they are to remain after farrowing. The floor of the colony house should, of course, be cleaned and scrubbed as advised in the case of the farrowing pen.

The great benefits from following this system of swine sanitation are shown by studies of the cost of pork production on central Illinois farms.[55] On farms where the McLean county system was followed, an average of 5.8 pigs were weaned per litter, the pigs gained an average of 1.31 lbs. daily after weaning and required 466 lbs. of feed per 100 lbs. gain. Where no system of sanitation was followed, only 5.4 pigs were weaned per sow, the pigs gained only 1.21 lbs. per head daily after weaning, and 521 lbs. of feed were required per 100 lbs. gain. With the good system of sanitation the total cost of 100 lbs. of pork was $7.31, while it was $9.00 on the farms with no system of sanitation.

1441. Treatment for worms, lice, or mange.—Much better results are secured when round worms and other parasites are controlled by this method of sanitation than when worm expellents are used after pigs have been allowed to become infested. No worm remedy can reach the worms when they are in the lungs, and it is at this time that they do the most injury to young pigs.

Even when good sanitation is followed, some pigs may become infested with worms. In all such cases a reliable worm expellent should be used, such as tetrachorethylene; or a mixture of oil of chenopodium (oil of wormseed) and castor oil; or combinations including santonin. Before administering a worm remedy, feed should be withheld for 15 to 20 hours.

Lice may readily be eradicated by greasing, spraying, or dipping the pigs with crude oil or waste crank case oil. Mange should be eradicated by treatment with crude oil, or kerosene mixed with lard or cottonseed oil, or lime sulphur solution.[56]

Where hog cholera is common, the only safe plan is to immunize all swine by the double method of vaccination.

1442. Shipment to market; shrinkage.—In order to reduce to a minimum the shrinkage in weight of hogs during shipment to market, certain precautions should be taken. It is sometimes advised that hogs on pasture be confined to a dry lot for a week before shipping. It is doubtful whether this is advisable. It may reduce the shrinkage between home weights and market weights, because some shrinkage will have already occurred in the change from pasture to dry feed. Therefore the practice is probably not advantageous. If hogs have been fed largely on slop, it may be best to use dry feed a few days before shipment.

The recommendation is sometimes made that the regular feed be omitted immediately before shipment, or even that no feed be given during the last 24 hours. Ohio tests show that this is not wise.[57] This practice reduces the shrinkage between home weights and market weights only because considerable shrinkage has already occurred before shipment, due to the lack of feed.

It is doubtful whether it is advisable to make a great change in the regular feeding prior to shipment. It is probably best, however, to give only a light feed of grain immediately before shipment. This is of most importance in hot weather. The hogs will be less apt to overheat if they are not producing a great amount of heat in their bodies due to the digestion of a large amount of feed.

In driving or loading the hogs, care must be taken not to hurry or excite them, and they should not be beaten or bruised. Crippled hogs sell at a severe discount, and bruises also affect the selling price, as they injure the carcass. The hogs should reach the shipping station in ample time for them to become rested and cool before they are loaded. They should not be loaded more than an hour before the train is to depart.

The car should be thoroughly cleaned before loading. Sand is the best material for bedding, for Indiana tests show that it decidedly reduces the death losses and the number of hogs crippled in transit.[58] This is because it furnishes better footing than straw or than no bedding at all. The percentage of shrinkage is higher when a car is loaded too full, as shown by Indiana experiments.[59] On the other hand, if there are not enough hogs to fill it comfortably when they are lying down, the shrinkage will also be increased somewhat, due to greater jostling about. It is best not to load a car much in excess of the usual minimum carload weights (16,500 to 17,000 lbs. for a 36-foot car). In hot weather it is wise to keep the weight about 1,000 lbs. under this limit, in order to prevent excessive shrinkage, even if the freight rate per 100 lbs. is increased a trifle.

In hot weather hogs should be sprayed with a hose before loading and also when possible at stopping points in transit. Suspending from the roof of the car about 6 sacks containing large cakes of ice helps prevent overheating, if it is very hot. In extreme winter weather it is a good plan to protect the hogs from cold winds by nailing a few strips of building paper on the inside of the car.

The average percentage of shrinkage for hogs shipped by rail for various distances in the Indiana studies ranged from 1.35 per cent for those shipped less than 62 miles, to 1.89 per cent for those shipped 263 miles or more. Heavy hogs shrank somewhat more than lighter ones, probably because they cannot handle themselves so well and they tire more easily. Also, they may not fill so well at the market.

The shrinkage increased as the temperature rose, except that the shrinkage was also higher when the temperature was less than 18 to 27°F. The shrinkage was lowest in late fall and in winter when the hogs had been fattened on dry feeds. It was greatest in spring when pasture was lush, and in early fall when a large proportion of the hogs had probably been finished on new corn. The percentage shrinkage of hogs is considerably greater in mixed carloads of hogs and other stock than it is in straight carloads of hogs.[60]

In Illinois studies there was no marked difference in percentage of shrinkage when hogs were shipped the same distance by rail and by truck, though there was a tendency for the shrinkage to be slightly higher for truck shipment.[61] The losses by death and crippling were only about one-half as great in Indiana studies for hogs trucked (usually less than 75 miles) as they were for hogs shipped by rail (usually 75 to 175 miles).[62] Part of this difference was, of course, due to the greater distance of the rail shipments.

1443. Cost of pork production.—The cost of producing pork will vary widely from year to year and also during the same year in various sections, depending chiefly upon the prices of feed. The cost of feed, including pasture, will commonly form 74 to 84 per cent of the total cost of producing each 100 lbs. of marketable hogs. To this cost must be added the cost of labor, both man and horse, and the expenses for equipment and shelter, interest, veterinary services, and miscellaneous items. The latter include death losses, taxes, and insurance on buildings.

The following table summarizes data secured on 34 central Illinois farms on which a total of 2,790,000 lbs. of marketable live hogs were produced during the 3-year period 1924-1926, and on 81 Iowa farms on which total gains of 2,940,000 lbs. were made by hogs during the 3-year period 1922-1924.[63]

Cost of producing 100 lbs. of marketable live hogs

	Illinois farms 1924-26	Iowa farms 1922-24
Feed, including pasture	$7.33	$6.60
Labor, man and horse	.41	.56
Equipment and shelter	.24	.27
Interest	.20	.35
Veterinary services	.14	.14
Other costs	.38	.42
Total costs	$8.70	$8.34

The total cost of feed per 100 lbs. of marketable live hogs was $7.33 in the Illinois studies, with corn at an average farm price of 78 cents per bushel; and $6.60 in the Iowa records. Feed formed 84 per cent of the total cost on the Illinois farms and 79 per cent on the Iowa farms. Of this feed cost approximately 80 per cent was for corn. This shows the importance of swine in serving as a market for this grain in the corn belt. The table shows that the other costs in pork production are relatively low.

On the Illinois farms 473 lbs. of grain and other concentrates (including 400 lbs. of corn) were required in producing 100 lbs. of marketable live hogs. This includes the feed eaten by the pigs and by the breeding herd. Also 2.0 lbs. dry roughage, 1.5 lbs. minerals, and 7.7 lbs. of miscellaneous feeds, in addition to pasture, were consumed per 100 lbs. of marketable hogs produced, and 1.53 hours man labor and 0.33 hour horse labor were required.

In the Illinois studies the total cost of producing each 100 lbs. of marketable hogs was equal to 11.1 times the average farm price of corn per bushel over the 3-year period. This relationship, called the corn-hog ratio, was found to be 12.2 in similar studies by the United States Department of Agriculture during 1922 with corn at an average price of 52 cents per bushel.[64] On the other hand, in 1921 when the average farm price of corn was only 36 cents per bushel, the cost of producing 100 lbs. of hogs was 15.2 times the farm price of corn per bushel. The difference is due to the fact that the other expenses, in addition to the cost of corn, form a much larger part of the total cost when corn is unusually low in price.

On the Illinois farms the sows in the breeding herds consumed an average of 2,075 lbs. of feed in addition to pasture during the 291 days they were in the herd during the year. On many of the farms gilts were used solely or chiefly for breeding, and these were sold as soon as they could be fattened after weaning their first litters.

In these studies approximately 30 per cent of the total cost of producing pork was for the maintenance of the breeding herd and 70 per cent for the growing and fattening pigs. The average net cost per pig at weaning time was $3.53, after deducting credit for the value of the gains in weight made by the sows during the year and the value of the manure produced.

1444. Reducing the cost of pork production.—These cost studies and also similar other investigations show clearly the ways in which the cost of pork production may be reduced on the average farm.[65] On the 15 Iowa farms that produced pork at the lowest cost, the average cost of producing 100 lbs. of live hogs was only $6.16, while it was $14.02 during the same years and in the same county on the 15 high-cost farms.

On the high-cost farms the breeding herd was generally handled less efficiently than were the fattening pigs. This reduced the number of thrifty pigs raised per litter and consequently made a decided increase in the cost of producing each 100 lbs. of marketable hogs. On more than half the Iowa farms in the high-cost group the rations fed the brood sows were deficient in protein. On 7 out of 15 of these farms the ventilation in the hog house was poor. On the efficient farms only 24 per cent of the pigs farrowed were lost before weaning, while the loss on the inefficient farms was 36 per cent. As a result of the difference in methods, only 4.2 pigs were weaned per sow on the inefficient farms, while the average was 6.3 on the efficient farms.

However, even on most of the efficient farms the equipment for farrowing was far from satisfactory. On only 3 out of the 82 farms were the farrowing pens equipped with guard rails. Yet the number of pigs killed by the sows lying on them was greater than the number lost before weaning from all other causes combined.

The most important factor determining the cost per pig at weaning time is the number of pigs weaned in the litter. For example, in the Illinois studies the cost of producing a pig up to weaning time was only $3.56 in spring litters containing 6 to 8 pigs, while it was $5.18 in litters having only 2 to 4 pigs. When the number of pigs weaned per litter is small, the pigs will start into the fattening period with a handicap that cannot be overcome by any system of feeding or care that may be followed later.

To keep the cost of pork production at a minimum, the pigs must obviously be fed so as to make efficient gains from weaning time to market. In the corn belt liberal feeding is commonly most efficient, except when the pigs are purposely fed limited rations during the summer, so that they will be of the proper size for hogging-down corn in the fall or for following fattening cattle.

In the Iowa studies the average rate of gain was 0.9 lb. per head daily. Increasing the rate of gain only 0.1 lb. a day lowered the cost of each 100 lbs. pork by 64 cents, thus considerably increasing the profit. On the average this added one-tenth of a pound gain per day resulted in a greater net return of 5.3 cents from each bushel of corn fed and increased the profit of the hog enterprise per farm by $47.70 a year.

These studies, therefore, show that to produce pork at minimum cost and to secure the largest profit, efficiency is necessary throughout the whole enterprise. The first essential is proper feed and care of the breeding herd. With this must be combined a system of sanitation that will prevent losses from parasites and filth-borne diseases. Finally, the thrifty pigs raised by such methods must be fed modern, efficient rations that fully meet their nutrient requirements.

QUESTIONS

1. What factors should be considered in selecting brood sows and boars?
2. State 6 essentials in the feed and care of brood sows.
3. Discuss the general nutrient requirements of brood sows: (a) During pregnancy; (b) when they are suckling their litters.
4. What have experiments shown concerning the importance of pasture for brood sows?
5. Discuss the feeding of brood sows on grain alone during pregnancy.
6. Discuss the use of legume hay for brood sows.
7. Which protein-rich feeds are satisfactory as the only protein supplements for brood sows? Which protein supplements should be fed in combination with more efficient supplements?
8. Discuss the use of corn for brood sows. How do barley and oats compare with corn in value for sows?
9. Under what conditions should other mineral supplements than salt be fed to brood sows?
10. How would you regulate the amount of grain for pregnant sows? Is it generally advisable to self-feed brood sows?
11. Discuss the importance of exercise for brood sows.
12. How should brood sows be fed during the summer?
13. Why is it advisable to "flush" sows shortly before breeding time?
14. State the most important points concerning the feed and care of the boar.
15. What are the advantages and disadvantages of gilts in comparison with older sows?
16. State briefly how you would feed and care for a sow: (a) Previous to farrowing; (b) at farrowing time; (c) immediately after farrowing.
17. About how much milk does a good sow produce during a lactation period?
18. How can orphan pigs be raised?
19. Discuss the feeding of sows that are suckling litters.
20. Discuss the feeding and care of pigs and sow at weaning time.
21. In what respect should the feeding of pigs which are being raised for breeding stock differ from that of pigs which are being fattened for market?
22. What have experiments shown concerning the effects of breeding gilts at an early age?
23. State the advantages and disadvantages of the two-litter-a-year method of pork production in comparison with the one-litter method.
24. How do fall pigs compare with spring pigs in rate and economy of gains, when properly fed and cared for?
25. What are the essentials for success with fall pigs?
26. Discuss the importance of sanitation and disease prevention in pork production.
27. Describe the McLean County system of round-worm control, stating the facts in the life history of the round worm upon which the effectiveness of the system depends.

28. What precautions would you take to reduce the shrinkage when hogs are shipped to market?
29. Discuss the main factors in the cost of pork production.
30. What are the ways in which the cost of pork production may be reduced on the average farm?

REFERENCES

1. Aubel, Hughes, and Lienhardt, Kan. Tech. Bul. 31; Hogan, Mo. Res. Bul. 168; Hogan, McKenzie, and Casida, Mo. Bul. 285; Hogan and Johnson, Mo. Bul. 340 and Mo. Cir. 187.
2. Vestal, Ind. Rpt. 1933.
3. Evvard, Amer. Soc. Anim. Prod., Proc. 1933; Vestal, Kan. Rpt. 1917.
4. Hughes, Jour. Agr. Res., 49, 1934, pp. 943-953; see also: Dowell, Univ. of Alberta, Canada, Col. Agr. Cir. 1.
5. Thompson, Okla. Bul. 144.
6. Vestal, Ind. Sta., information to the author.
7. Grimes, Penn. Bul. 168.
8. Martin, Ark. Bul. 221; Evvard, Amer. Soc. Anim. Prod., Proc. 1913; Mich. Rpts. 1930-32, 1934; Weaver, Mo. Bul. 340; Snyder, Nebr. Bul. 147; Grimes, Penn. Bul. 168; Penn. Bul. 204.
9. Robison, Ohio Mo. Bul. 48.
10. Morrison and Bohstedt, Wis. Bul. 302; Morrison, Bohstedt, and Fargo, Wis. Bul. 362; Morrison, Fargo, and Bohstedt, Wis. Bul. 400.
11. Mich. Rpt. 1930-32; Weaver, Mo. Bul. 340; Ore. Rpt. 1920-22.
12. Snyder, Nebr. Bul. 147; see also: Ore. Rpt. 1920-22.
13. Wash. Bul. 187.
14. Hart and Steenbock, Wis. Buls. 323, 339, and Jour. Biol. Chem. 39, 1919, pp. 209-233.
15. Tomhave, Del. Bul. 139; Minn. Rpt. 1921; Morrison and Bohstedt, Wis. Sta., mimeo. rpt.
16. Morrison and Bohstedt, Wis. Bul. 302; Morrison, Bohstedt, and Fargo, Wis. Bul. 362; see also: Grimes, Penn. Bul. 168.
17. Evvard, Iowa Sta., mimeo. rpt.
18. Carroll and Smith, Ill. Rpt. 1927; S. D. Rpt. 1926.
19. Morrison, Bohstedt, and Fargo, Wis. Bul. 362.
20. Joseph, Mont. Bul. 165.
21. Evvard, Wallace, and Culbertson, Iowa Bul. 245.
22. Morrison and Fargo, Wis. Bul. 405.
23. Evvard, Culbertson, and Hammond, Amer. Soc. Anim. Prod., Proc. 1922.
24. Evvard, Cox, and Guernsey, Amer. Jour. Physiol., 34, 1914, p. 312; Hart and Steenbock, Jour. Biol. Chem., 39, 1919, pp. 209-233; Baskett, Agr. Progress, England, 3, 1926, pp. 34-36; Evans, Jour. Agr. Sci., England, 19, 1929, p. 752; Davidson, Jour. Agr. Sci., England, 20, 1930, p. 233.
25. Ariz. Rpt. 1923.
26. Smith, Pork Production; Robison, Ohio Mo. Bul. 48.
27. Snyder, Nebr. Bul. 162.
28. Morrison and Bohstedt, Wis. Sta., mimeo. rpts.
29. Hale, Tex. Sta., information to the author.
30. Vestal, Ind. Rpt. 1931 and information to the author; Anderson and Marston, Kan. Cir. 118.
31. Aubel, Hughes, and Lienhardt, Kan. Rpt. 1930-32; Hogan, Mo. Res. Bul. 168.
32. McKenzie and Miller, Mo. Bul. 285.
33. Carmichael and Rice, Ill. Bul. 226; Severson, Amer. Soc. Anim. Prod., Proc. 1925-26.
34. McKenzie, Mo. Res. Bul. 118.
35. Lush and Culbertson, Iowa Rpt. 1932; see also: Krallinger and Schott, Züchtungskunde, 9, 1934, pp. 175-179.
36. Keith, Ill. Sta., Jour. Agr. Res., 41, 1930, pp. 593-600.
37. Headley, Nev. Rpt. 1933; Kraft, Okla. Sta., Amer. Soc. Anim. Prod., Proc. 1929; Kuhlman and Cole, Wis. Bul. 405.
38. Shepperd, N. D. Bul. 230; see also: Iddings, Id. Sta., Breeders' Gazette, 64, 1913, p. 241; Carmichael and Rice, Ill. Bul. 226; Keith, Ill. Sta., Jour. Agr. Res., 41, 1930, pp. 593-600.
39. Kuhlman and Cole, Wis. Bul. 405; see also: Nebr. Rpt. 1926.
40. Wilcox, Carroll, and Hornung, Ill. Bul. 390.
41. Thompson, Amer. Soc. Anim. Prod., Proc. 1931.
42. Carlyle, Wis. Bul. 104; Olofsson and Larsson, Meddel. Centralanst. Försöksv. Jordbruksområdet, Sweden, No. 371, 1930.
43. Shepperd, N. D. Bul. 230.
44. Woll, Wis. Rpt. 1897.
45. Evvard and Glatfelder, Iowa Cir. 80; see also: Evvard, Glatfelder, and Wallace, Iowa Res. Bul. 79; Evvard, Wallace, and Glatfelder, Iowa Res. Bul. 83.
46. Russell and Zeller, U. S. Dept. Agr., Farmers' Bul. 1504; Aubel and Connell, Kan. Rpt. 1930-32.
47. Mumford, Mo. Res. Bul. 45; McKenzie, Mo. Res. Bul. 118.
48. Young, Ind. Bul. 338.
49. Wilcox, Carroll, and Hornung, Ill. Bul. 390.
50. Hale, Tex. Rpts. 1932, 1933.
51. Ferrin and McCarty, Minn. Bul. 213; see also Snyder, Nebr. Bul. 243.
52. Tomhave, Del. Bul. 156.

53. Ransom, U. S. Dept. Agr. Leaflet 5 ; Raffensperger and Connelly, U. S. Dept. Agr. Tech. Bul. 44.
54. Nighbert and Connelly, U. S. Dept. Agr., Tech. Bul. 374.
55. Wilcox, Carroll, and Hornung, Ill. Bul. 390 ; see also: Robbins, Ill. Cir. 306.
56. Ignes, U. S. Dept. Agr., Farmers' Bul. 1085.
57. Robison, Ohio Bul. 497.
58. Wiley, Ind. Bul. 318.
59. Wiley, Ind. Bul. 358.
60. U. S. Dept. Agr., Yearbook, 1922.
61. Ashby, Ill. Bul. 388.
62. Wiley, Ind. Bul. 237.
63. Wilcox, Carroll, and Hornung, Ill. Bul. 390 ; Wilcox, Iowa Bul. 255.
64. Steanson and Wilcox, U. S. Dept. Agr. Bul. 1381.
65. Pope and Wingate, Ala. Bul. 240 ; Grimes, Sewell, and Cottier, Ala. Cir. 68 ; Ky. Rpt. 1933 ; Hostetler, Nance, and Foster, N. C. Bul. 272 ; Smith, Pork Production.

APPENDIX

In this table is presented a new and exhaustive compilation made for this volume of the analyses of American feeding stuffs and of the results of digestion experiments. These data have been compiled by the author and under his supervision from the bulletins and reports of the State Experiment Stations, the United States Department of Agriculture, the Departments of Agriculture of various states, and other publications. Data for a few feeds, for which American analyses are not available, have been taken from foreign sources.

Where the composition of any feeding stuff has changed since the first compilation made by the author was published in 1915, the older data have been discarded, and the averages here given include only recent data. Where there has been no change in the composition of a feed during this period, the averages cover all suitable data.

Where information is available, separate averages are given for the various grades of a feeding stuff. Thus, separate averages are given for the most important forage crops cut at different stages of maturity; for hay of various qualities; for high-grade and lower-grade concentrates of the same name; etc. In this table the scientific names of the various plants are not stated where they are given in the discussion of the particular feeds in the body of the text.

So that all the data concerning the chemical composition and the digestibility of any feed may be conveniently available, the data presented in Appendix Tables I, II, and III of previous editions of Feeds and Feeding have been combined into this single table. For any particular feed, part of the data is given on the left-hand page, and the remainder is immediately across on the right-hand page.

The figures for dry matter, digestible protein, and total digestible nutrients are printed in bold-face type and are given first in this table, since these are the figures commonly used in computing balanced rations. Explanations of the methods of computing digestible protein, total digestible nutrients, and nutritive ratios are given in Chapter III. (73) Where no digestion coefficients are available for a feed, or such data seem unreliable, the digestion coefficients for a similar feed have been used and that fact is indicated by an asterisk.

The figures for digestible nutrients have been computed by means of the digestion coefficients obtained in experiments with cattle and sheep. However, these figures may also be used in computing rations for horses and swine according to the feeding standards given in Appendix Table III. (72)

In using this table it must be borne in mind that individual lots of any particular feeding stuff may differ in composition from the average, as has been shown previously. (105-109) In the case of roughages, the variations are apt to be especially large in the content of calcium and of phosphorus. Also, much less information is available concerning the mineral content of various feeds than concerning the amounts of other nutrients they contain. The figures for calcium and phosphorus therefore merely indicate the approximate percentages that are present in the different feeds when produced on soil reasonably well supplied with these minerals. (160)

The great mass of data utilized in the preparation of these Appendix Tables is evident from the fact that time equivalent to one person working steadily for about six years has been required in the compilation and averaging of the data, not including the supervision of the author.

The author wishes to acknowledge the aid of many investigators who have furnished him with unpublished data for inclusion in this table, especially the co-operation of Mr. H. A. Halvorson of the Minnesota State Department of Agriculture, Dairy, and Food, who has supplied extensive data on the calcium and phosphorus content of various concentrates.

This table and the other tables in the Appendix are fully protected by copyright. These data may not be reproduced in any form without the permission of the publishers of this volume.

TABLE I. Average composition and digestible nutrients.

Feeding stuff	Total dry matter	Dig. protein	Total dig. nutri- ents	Nutri- tive ratio	Average total composition					
					Protein	Fat	Fiber	N-free extract	Mineral matter	No. of anal.
	Per ct.	Per ct.	Per ct.	1:	Per ct.	Per ct.	Per ct.	Per ct.	Per ct.	
Dry Roughages										
Alfalfa hay, all analyses........	90.4	10.6	50.3	3.7	14.7	2.0	29.0	36.4	8.3	632
Alfalfa hay, very leafy (less than 25% fiber).................	90.0	12.4	53.7	3.3	16.5	2.7	22.6	39.5	8.7	108
Alfalfa hay, leafy (25-28% fiber)	90.4	12.0	51.1	3.3	16.0	2.3	27.6	35.8	8.7	166
Alfalfa hay, good (28-31% fiber)	90.4	10.3	50.3	3.9	14.3	1.8	29.6	36.5	8.2	194
Alfalfa hay, fair (31-34% fiber)...	90.4	9.6	49.8	4.2	13.5	1.7	31.6	35.9	7.7	80
Alfalfa hay, stemmy (over 34% fiber)......................	90.4	8.2	47.5	4.8	12.1	1.4	36.0	33.1	7.8	84
Alfalfa hay, before bloom......	90.4	14.2	53.2	2.7	19.0	2.7	22.3	36.6	9.8	12
Alfalfa hay, 1/10 to ½ bloom...	90.6	11.0	50.1	3.6	14.9	1.7	30.1	35.0	8.9	29
Alfalfa hay, ¾ to full bloom....	90.4	9.9	49.7	4.0	14.0	2.0	30.3	35.8	8.3	21
Alfalfa hay, past bloom.......	90.4	8.6	44.9	5.2	12.8	2.1	31.9	36.1	7.5	10
Alfalfa hay, dehydrated*.......	93.5	13.2	54.9	3.2	17.6	3.0	26.0	38.7	8.2	3
Alfalfa hay, brown	89.8	9.9	50.6	4.1	14.6	1.3	24.7	39.9	9.3	1
Alfalfa leaf meal, good*........	91.9	16.2	57.4	2.5	21.1	2.8	16.1	39.8	12.2	116
Alfalfa leaf meal, high in fiber*...	92.0	14.7	57.1	2.9	19.6	2.6	19.8	40.0	10.1	76
Alfalfa leaves.................	89.0	16.9	57.0	2.4	21.9	3.0	14.1	39.8	10.2	43
Alfalfa meal, good.............	91.9	10.8	53.9	4.0	15.2	1.9	28.4	37.9	8.5	551
Alfalfa meal, stemmy..........	92.3	8.8	51.8	4.9	12.4	1.5	35.9	35.3	7.2	33
Alfalfa stem meal*.............	92.4	5.9	43.0	6.3	11.5	1.3	36.2	36.6	6.8	29
Alfalfa stems	88.6	5.1	40.8	7.0	10.0	1.2	36.6	34.2	6.6	40
Alfalfa straw*.................	92.6	4.5	42.6	8.5	8.8	1.5	40.4	35.1	6.8	4
Alfalfa and timothy hay*.......	92.4	6.8	50.2	6.4	11.6	1.4	32.2	41.8	5.4	7
Alfilaria, dry (*Erodium cicu- tarium*)*....................	89.2	7.8	48.5	5.2	10.9	2.9	23.4	40.2	11.8	6
Barley hay....................	91.9	4.9	54.1	10.0	7.5	2.0	26.6	49.0	6.8	13
Barley hay, heading out, dehy- drated*......................	88.9	8.7	51.4	4.9	13.4	3.0	22.6	41.1	8.8	1
Barley straw..................	90.0	0.9	44.5	48.4	3.7	1.6	37.7	41.0	6.0	97
Bean hay, moth or mat........	90.0	10.9	46.7	3.3	16.2	2.4	16.0	41.4	14.0	2
Bean hay, mung*..............	90.3	7.4	49.3	5.7	9.8	2.2	24.0	46.6	7.7	3
Bean hay, tepary*.............	90.0	12.8	48.8	2.8	17.1	2.9	24.8	34.7	10.5	6
Bean straw, field.............	89.1	3.0	45.2	14.1	6.1	1.4	40.1	34.1	7.4	20
Beggarweed hay*.............	90.9	11.1	49.2	3.4	15.2	2.3	28.4	37.2	7.8	13
Bent grass hay, creeping*.......	90.0	3.6	53.6	13.9	5.8	1.8	26.9	49.9	5.6	1
Bermuda grass hay...........	90.7	3.7	43.0	10.6	7.3	1.8	25.6	48.4	7.6	17
Bermuda grass hay, poor quality*	90.0	2.3	42.1	17.3	5.8	0.9	38.8	37.7	6.8	1
Berseem, or Egyptian clover* ...	91.7	9.8	56.5	4.8	13.4	2.7	21.0	42.7	11.9	4
Black grass hay (*Juncus Gerardi*)*	89.7	5.6	55.0	8.8	7.5	2.5	25.1	47.3	7.3	21
Bluegrass hay, Canada.........	89.3	2.8	53.3	18.0	6.6	2.3	28.2	46.4	5.8	10
Bluegrass hay, Kentucky, all anal.	89.4	4.7	53.3	10.3	8.2	2.8	29.8	42.1	6.5	25
Bluegrass hay, Kentucky, in seed*	87.3	2.2	41.6	17.9	5.5	2.5	31.0	41.9	6.4	3
Bluegrass hay, native western*...	91.9	6.7	52.6	6.9	11.2	3.0	29.8	39.9	8.0	7
Bluejoint hay (*Calamagrostis Ca- nadensis*)*...................	88.5	3.3	45.5	12.8	7.2	2.3	32.9	39.6	6.5	10
Bluestem hay (*Andropogon*, spp.)*	86.6	2.5	48.2	18.3	5.4	2.2	30.2	43.4	5.4	51
Bromegrass hay, all analyses....	88.1	5.0	48.9	8.8	9.9	2.1	28.4	39.5	8.2	74
Bromegrass hay, before bloom ...	89.0	7.4	48.2	5.5	14.5	2.3	24.6	37.9	9.7	15
Broom corn stover*............	90.6	0.9	44.7	48.7	3.9	1.8	36.8	42.4	5.7	1
Brush feed*...................	95.0	0.2	13.3	65.5	5.4	2.4	46.5	37.9	2.8	1
Buckwheat hulls*..............	90.0	0.1	28.0	27.0	4.3	0.9	44.4	38.3	2.1	18
Buckwheat straw*.............	90.1	1.2	32.3	25.9	5.2	1.3	43.0	35.1	5.5	3
Buffalo grass hay (*Bulbilis dacty- loides*)......................	88.7	3.7	47.7	11.9	6.8	1.8	23.8	46.2	10.1	15
Bunch grass hay, misc. var.*....	91.7	2.7	48.7	17.0	5.8	2.0	30.4	44.1	9.4	12

TABLE I. Average composition and digestible nutrients.

Feeding stuff	Mineral and fertilizing constituents				Digestion coefficients				
	Calcium	Phosphorus	Nitrogen	Potassium	Protein	Fat	Fiber	N-free extract	No. of trials
	Per ct.	Per ct.	Per ct.	Per ct.	Per ct.	Per ct.	Per ct.	Per ct.	
Dry Roughages									
Alfalfa hay, all analyses........	1.43	0.21	2.35	2.02	72	32	43	71	242
Alfalfa hay, very leafy (less than 25% fiber)..................	1.69	0.24	2.64	2.20	75	33	41	76	28
Alfalfa hay, leafy (25-28% fiber)	1.27	0.22	2.56	2.17	75	34	42	72	49
Alfalfa hay, good (28-31% fiber)	1.15	0.22	2.29	1.85	72	34	43	71	76
Alfalfa hay, fair (31-34% fiber)	1.15	0.21	2.16	1.81	71	31	44	70	40
Alfalfa hay, stemmy (over 34% fiber)......................	1.01	0.19	1.94	1.70	68	28	45	67	49
Alfalfa hay, before bloom.......	..	..	3.04	..	..	..	..	..	..
Alfalfa hay, 1/10 to ½ bloom...	..	..	2.38	..	..	..	..	..	..
Alfalfa hay, ¾ to full bloom....	..	..	2.24	..	..	..	..	..	..
Alfalfa hay, past bloom........	..	..	2.05	..	67	34	41	60	6
Alfalfa hay, dehydrated........	..	..	2.82	..	..	..	..	..	..
Alfalfa hay, brown.............	..	..	2.34	..	68	0	50	71	5
Alfalfa leaf meal, good........	1.90	0.22	3.38	2.42	..	..	..	..	..
Alfalfa leaf meal, high in fiber...	..	..	3.14	..	..	..	..	..	..
Alfalfa leaves.................	2.25	0.23	3.50	2.46	77	30	56	76	18
Alfalfa meal, good.............	1.31	0.17	2.43	1.91	71	30	50	73	6
Alfalfa meal, stemmy...........	..	..	1.98	..	71	30	50	68	2
Alfalfa stem meal..............	..	..	1.84	..	..	..	..	..	..
Alfalfa stems.................	0.79	0.14	1.60	2.67	51	48	39	59	18
Alfalfa straw.................	..	..	1.41	..	..	..	..	..	..
Alfalfa and timothy hay........	0.73	0.23	1.86	1.76	..	..	..	..	..
Alfilaria, dry (*Erodium cicutarium*)....................	1.57	0.41	1.74	..	..	..	..	..	..
Barley hay....................	0.27	0.29	1.20	1.37	65	41	62	63	4
Barley hay, heading out, dehydrated....................	..	..	2.14	..	..	..	..	..	..
Barley straw..................	0.32	0.09	0.59	1.26	25	39	54	53	7
Bean hay, moth or mat........	..	..	2.59	..	67	11	52	65	2
Bean hay, mung...............	..	..	1.57	..	..	..	..	..	..
Bean hay, tepary.............	..	..	2.74	..	..	..	..	..	..
Bean straw, field.............	1.67	0.13	0.98	1.02	49	57	43	68	5
Beggarweed hay...............	1.05	0.27	2.43	2.32	..	..	..	..	..
Bent grass hay, creeping........	..	..	0.93	..	..	..	..	..	..
Bermuda grass hay............	0.48	0.20	1.17	1.42	51	45	52	52	11
Bermuda grass hay, poor quality	..	..	0.93	..	..	..	..	..	..
Berseem, or Egyptian clover....	3.27	0.28	2.14	2.05	..	..	..	..	..
Black grass hay (*Juncus Gerardi*)	..	0.09	1.20	1.56	..	..	..	..	..
Bluegrass hay, Canada.........	..	0.20	1.06	1.94	43	37	70	62	2
Bluegrass hay, Kentucky, all anal	0.30	0.22	1.31	1.26	57	52	66	61	7
Bluegrass hay, Kentucky, in seed	..	..	0.88	..	..	..	..	..	..
Bluegrass hay, native western...	..	..	1.79	..	..	..	..	..	..
Bluejoint hay (*Calamagrostis Canadensis*)....................	..	..	1.15	..	..	..	..	..	..
Bluestem hay (*Andropogon*, spp.)	..	..	0.86	..	..	..	..	..	..
Bromegrass hay, all analyses....	0.20	0.28	1.58	2.35	51	39	59	64	11
Bromegrass hay, before bloom ..	..	..	2.32	..	..	..	..	..	..
Broom corn stover.............	..	..	0.62	..	..	..	..	..	..
Brush feed...................	..	..	0.86	..	..	..	..	..	..
Buckwheat hulls...............	..	0.02	0.69	0.62	..	..	..	..	..
Buckwheat straw..............	..	0.06	0.83	0.94	..	..	..	..	..
Buffalo grass hay (*Bulbilis dactyloides*)......................	0.70	0.13	1.09	1.36	54	45	61	60	3
Bunch grass hay, misc. var.....	..	..	0.93	..	..	..	..	..	..

TABLE I. Average composition and digestible nutrients—*continued*.

Feeding stuff	Total dry matter	Dig. protein	Total dig. nutrients	Nutritive ratio	Average total composition					No. of anal.
					Protein	Fat	Fiber	N-free extract	Mineral matter	
	Per ct.	Per ct.	Per ct.	1:	Per ct.	Per ct.	Per ct.	Per ct.	Per ct.	
Dry Roughages—Cont.										
Carpet grass hay*.............	92.1	3.1	50.0	15.1	7.0	2.2	31.8	40.9	10.2	1
Cat tail, or tule hay (*Typha augustifolia*)*................	90.8	2.3	36.5	14.9	5.8	1.7	30.8	44.3	8.2	2
Chamiza, leafy twigs (*Atriplex canescens*).................	94.5	15.3	45.0	28.4	20.4	3.3	12.0	34.8	24.0	30
Chess, or cheat hay (*Bromus*, spp.)	91.7	2.9	40.4	12.9	6.9	2.1	29.2	46.1	7.4	12
Clover hay, alsike, all anal......	89.0	7.7	49.0	5.4	12.0	2.2	27.1	39.8	7.9	45
Clover hay, alsike, in bloom....	89.0	8.6	52.7	5.1	13.4	3.2	26.9	37.7	7.8	5
Clover hay, bur...............	92.1	13.4	54.4	3.1	18.4	2.9	22.9	37.8	10.1	14
Clover hay, crimson...........	89.4	9.7	48.8	4.0	14.1	2.3	27.3	36.9	8.8	18
Clover hay, mammoth red*.....	88.0	6.9	51.7	6.5	11.7	3.4	29.2	37.0	6.7	19
Clover hay, red, all analyses...	88.2	7.0	51.9	6.4	11.8	2.6	27.3	40.1	6.4	183
Clover hay, red, leafy (less than 25% fiber)..................	88.2	8.6	54.5	5.3	13.4	3.1	23.6	40.9	7.2	52
Clover hay, red, good quality 25 to 31% fiber.............	88.8	6.8	53.9	6.9	11.5	2.6	27.4	41.1	6.2	104
Clover hay, red, stemmy (over 31% fiber)*.................	88.2	6.0	50.9	7.5	10.1	2.1	34.1	36.0	5.9	27
Clover hay, red, before bloom*...	89.6	12.0	56.4	3.7	18.7	3.6	18.3	41.8	7.2	2
Clover hay, red, in bloom.......	88.2	7.8	53.4	5.8	12.6	3.6	26.2	39.6	6.2	45
Clover hay, red, past full bloom*.	88.2	7.3	51.7	6.1	12.3	3.6	28.1	36.8	7.4	9
Clover hay, red, second cutting..	89.9	8.8	50.6	4.8	13.5	3.0	25.1	41.3	7.0	15
Clover hay, sweet, first year*....	93.3	14.6	53.5	2.7	19.5	2.9	21.0	41.2	8.7	9
Clover hay, sweet, second year...	92.0	10.5	49.9	3.8	14.0	2.0	29.8	38.7	7.5	28
Clover hay, white...........	88.0	10.5	55.6	4.3	14.4	2.4	22.5	40.9	7.8	11
Clover leaves, sweet*..........	92.2	20.5	59.8	1.9	26.6	3.2	9.5	41.9	11.0	10
Clover stems, sweet*..........	92.7	5.4	42.4	6.9	10.6	1.1	38.0	35.6	7.4	10
Clover straw, crimson*........	87.7	1.7	41.8	23.6	7.5	1.5	38.8	32.9	7.0	3
Clover and mixed grass hay, high in clover*...................	89.7	5.2	50.5	8.7	9.6	2.7	28.8	42.4	6.2	40
Clover and mixed grass hay, second crop*...............	89.0	7.9	53.6	5.8	12.1	3.0	28.5	39.5	5.9	11
Clover and timothy hay, all anal.*.....................	88.0	4.4	48.0	9.9	8.6	2.3	30.1	41.0	6.0	57
Clover and timothy hay, 30 to 50% clover*.................	91.9	4.8	51.4	9.7	9.2	2.2	31.9	43.6	5.0	5
Corn cobs, ground.............	90.4	0.4	46.2	114.5	2.3	0.4	32.0	54.1	1.6	58
Corn fodder, well-eared, very dry (from barn or in arid districts)	91.1	4.1	59.4	13.5	7.8	2.2	27.1	47.6	6.4	59
Corn fodder, medium in water...	82.5	3.5	54.6	14.6	6.7	2.1	21.7	46.9	5.1	69
Corn fodder, high in water......	60.7	2.5	40.1	15.0	4.8	1.4	16.7	34.2	3.6	23
Corn fodder, sweet corn........	87.7	5.9	56.5	8.6	9.2	1.8	26.4	41.3	9.0	6
Corn husks, dried.............	76.3	0.4	34.9	86.3	3.1	0.8	25.3	44.5	2.6	18
Corn leaves, dried*...........	82.8	4.2	50.7	11.1	7.7	1.9	23.9	42.6	6.7	28
Corn stalks, dried*...........	82.8	1.0	39.9	38.9	4.7	1.5	28.0	43.3	5.3	20
Corn stover (ears removed), very dry.....................	90.6	2.2	52.2	22.7	5.9	1.6	30.8	46.5	5.8	186
Corn stover, medium in water....	81.0	2.1	46.2	21.0	5.7	1.2	27.7	40.9	5.5	97
Corn stover, high in water.......	59.0	1.4	33.9	23.2	3.9	1.0	20.1	30.2	3.8	247
Corn tops, dried..............	82.1	3.1	51.0	15.5	5.6	1.5	27.4	42.0	5.6	8
Cotton bolls, dried...........	90.8	2.3	42.5	17.5	8.7	2.4	30.8	42.0	6.9	16
Cotton leaves, dried*..........	91.7	8.4	53.6	5.4	15.3	6.8	10.3	43.5	15.8	17
Cotton stems, dried*..........	92.4	1.3	37.8	28.1	5.8	0.9	44.0	37.5	4.2	12
Cottonseed hulls..............	90.6	0.1	43.7	436.0	3.9	0.9	46.6	36.7	2.5	38
Cottonseed hull bran*.........	91.6	0.1	44.7	446.0	3.4	1.2	34.8	49.7	2.5	9

TABLE I. Average composition and digestible nutrients—*continued*.

Feeding stuff	Mineral and fertilizing constituents				Digestion coefficients				
	Calcium	Phosphorus	Nitrogen	Potassium	Protein	Fat	Fiber	N-free extract	No. of trials
Dry Roughages—Cont.	Per ct.	Per ct.	Per ct.	Per ct.	Per ct.	Per ct.	Per ct.	Per ct.	
Carpet grass hay..............	..	..	1.12	..	..	..	..	..	..
Cat tail, or tule hay (*Typha augustifolia*).................	..	..	0.93	..	..	..	..	..	..
Chamiza, leafy twigs (*Atriplex canescens*)..................	..	..	3.26	..	75	..	..	71	4
Chess, or cheat hay(*Bromus*, spp.)	0.33	0.25	1.10	1.47	42	32	46	49	1
Clover hay, alsike, all anal......	0.76	0.23	1.92	1.44	64	43	49	65	12
Clover hay, alsike, in bloom....	..	..	2.14	..	..	..	..	..	..
Clover hay, bur...............	1.32	0.45	2.94	2.96	73	42	53	69	12
Clover hay, crimson...........	1.31	0.20	2.26	1.86	69	44	47	65	13
Clover hay, mammoth red......	..	0.24	1.87	..					
Clover hay, red, all analyses....	1.21	0.18	1.89	1.58	59	58	51	69	33
Clover hay, red, leafy (less than 25% fiber).................	..	..	2.14	..	..	..	..	..	..
Clover hay, red, good quality (25 to 31% fiber)............	..	..	1.84	..	59	59	56	69	22
Clover hay, red, stemmy (over 31% fiber)..................	0.99	0.15	1.62	1.77	..	..	..	..	..
Clover hay, red, before bloom...	..	0.32	2.99	1.85	..	..	..	..	..
Clover hay, red, in bloom.......	..	0.25	2.02	1.28	62	54	53	69	4
Clover hay, red, past full bloom.	..	0.17	1.97	0.91	..	..	..	..	..
Clover hay, red, second cutting..	..	..	2.16	..	65	60	47	63	4
Clover hay, sweet, first year....	1.47	0.22	3.12	1.56	..	..	..	..	..
Clover hay, sweet, second year..	0.95	0.19	2.24	1.79	75	31	34	72	3
Clover hay, white.............	1.22	0.26	2.30	1.66	73	51	61	70	1
Clover leaves, sweet...........	..	..	4.26	..	..	..	..	..	..
Clover stems, sweet...........	..	..	1.70	..	..	..	..	..	..
Clover straw, crimson..........	..	..	1.20	..	..	..	..	..	..
Clover and mixed grass hay, high in clover.................	0.83	0.17	1.54	1.49	..	..	..	..	..
Clover and mixed grass hay, second crop.................	..	..	1.94	..	..	..	..	..	..
Clover and timothy hay, all anal......................	0.65	0.17	1.38	1.45	..	..	..	..	..
Clover and timothy hay, 30 to 50% clover.................	0.74	0.17	1.47	1.47	..	..	..	..	..
Corn cobs, ground.............	..	0.02	0.37	0.37	19	25	56	51	9
Corn fodder, well eared, very dry, (from barn or in arid districts)	0.24	0.16	1.25	0.82	52	73	66	71	15
Corn fodder, medium in water...	0.21	0.14	1.07	0.74	..	..	..	..	..
Corn fodder, high in water......	0.16	0.11	0.77	0.55	..	..	..	..	..
Corn fodder, sweet corn........	..	0.17	1.47	0.98	64	74	74	68	6
Corn husks, dried.............	0.14	0.11	0.50	0.50	13	26	52	47	7
Corn leaves, dried.............	..	..	1.23	..	..	..	..	..	..
Corn stalks, dried.............	..	..	0.75	0.75	..	..	..	..	..
Corn stover (ears removed), very dry.........................	0.46	0.09	0.94	1.67	37	62	66	59	35
Corn stover, medium in water...	0.41	0.08	0.91	1.50	..	..	..	..	..
Corn stover, high in water......	0.30	0.06	0.62	1.09	..	..	..	..	..
Corn tops, dried..............	..	..	0.90	..	55	71	71	62	2
Cotton bolls, dried............	..	..	1.39	..	26	64	39	59	4
Cotton leaves, dried...........	4.58	0.18	2.45	1.36	..	..	..	..	..
Cotton stems, dried...........	..	..	0.93	..	..	..	..	..	..
Cottonseed hulls..............	0.13	0.10	0.62	0.94	2	76	51	50	33
Cottonseed hull bran..........	..	..	0.54	..	..	..	..	..	..

TABLE I. Average composition and digestible nutrients—*continued*.

Feeding stuff	Total dry matter	Dig. protein	Total dig. nutrients	Nutritive ratio	Average total composition					No. of anal.
					Protein	Fat	Fiber	N-free extract	Mineral matter	
Dry Roughages—Cont.	Per ct.	Per ct.	Per ct.	1:	Per ct.	Per ct.	Per ct.	Per ct.	Per ct.	
Cowpea hay, all analyses.......	90.4	12.6	49.4	2.9	18.6	2.6	23.3	34.6	11.3	41
Cowpea hay, before bloom......	90.4	17.5	46.2	1.6	25.7	2.5	20.2	25.0	17.0	13
Cowpea hay, in bloom to early pod	89.9	12.3	50.3	3.1	18.1	3.2	21.8	36.7	10.1	7
Cowpea hay, ripe..............	90.0	6.9	51.2	6.4	10.1	2.5	29.2	41.8	6.4	3
Cowpea straw*.................	91.5	1.6	36.1	21.6	6.8	1.2	44.5	33.6	5.4	1
Cowpea and millet hay*........	90.3	8.8	46.4	4.3	13.7	2.2	27.6	32.0	14.8	2
Crab grass hay.................	90.5	3.5	45.8	12.1	8.0	2.4	28.7	42.9	8.5	9
Crowfoot grass hay (*Eleusine*, spp.)*.......................	90.5	3.8	45.9	11.1	8.6	2.2	27.4	44.4	7.9	10
Dolichos lablab hay..............	90.2	10.7	52.6	3.9	14.8	1.4	33.6	33.6	6.8	1
Durra fodder*..................	89.9	3.3	53.9	15.3	6.4	2.8	24.1	51.4	5.2	3
Emmer hay*....................	90.0	5.2	45.4	7.7	9.7	2.0	32.8	36.4	9.1	4
Fescue hay, meadow*..........	89.2	4.3	52.3	11.2	7.0	1.9	30.3	43.2	6.8	25
Fescue hay, native western (*Festuca*, spp.)*..................	90.0	5.3	53.5	9.1	8.5	2.0	31.0	42.8	5.7	13
Feterita stover*...............	86.3	1.8	49.3	26.4	5.2	1.7	29.2	41.9	8.3	1
Flax plant by-product..........	92.4	0.3	12.0	39.0	6.3	1.2	45.8	32.4	6.7	2
Flax straw....................	92.8	5.8	38.1	5.6	7.2	3.2	42.5	32.9	7.0	11
Fowl meadow grass hay*.......	87.4	5.4	51.1	8.5	8.7	2.3	29.7	39.5	7.2	8
Foxtail hay, miscellaneous*.....	90.0	5.4	51.4	8.5	8.7	2.4	28.1	41.3	9.5	17
Furze, dried*..................	94.5	8.6	36.1	3.2	11.6	2.0	38.5	35.4	7.0	1
Gama grass hay (*Tripsacum dactyloides*)*...................	88.2	4.0	51.2	11.8	6.7	1.8	30.4	43.1	6.2	3
Grama grass hay (*Bouteloua*, spp.)*.......................	89.8	3.5	51.1	13.6	5.8	1.6	28.9	45.6	7.9	59
Grass hay, mixed, eastern states, good quality................	89.0	3.5	51.7	13.8	7.0	2.5	30.9	43.1	5.5	39
Grass hay, mixed, second cutting*	89.0	8.0	53.4	5.7	12.3	3.3	24.8	41.7	6.9	67
Grass straw....................	85.0	1.8	40.0	21.2	4.5	2.0	35.0	37.8	5.7	...
Greasewood, dried*............	95.4	14.7	39.7	1.7	19.8	2.4	24.5	34.3	14.4	1
Guar hay.....................	90.7	12.4	51.6	3.2	16.5	1.3	19.3	41.2	12.4	1
Hair grass hay, miscellaneous*...	90.0	3.5	46.6	12.3	8.0	2.1	30.1	43.3	6.5	17
Harding grass hay (*Phalaris tuberosa*, var. *stenoptera*)*.....	90.0	2.8	50.6	17.1	6.3	1.5	31.7	43.9	6.6	1
Hegari stover*................	72.1	1.1	39.1	34.5	3.3	1.6	22.9	33.3	11.0	1
Hops, dried, spent.............	93.8	6.7	29.0	3.3	23.0	3.6	24.5	37.4	5.3	...
Horse bean hay*...............	91.5	9.1	54.0	4.9	13.4	0.8	22.0	49.8	5.5	1
Horse bean straw..............	87.9	4.2	44.2	9.5	8.6	1.4	36.4	33.1	8.4	2
Johnson grass hay.............	90.1	2.9	50.3	16.3	6.5	2.1	30.4	43.7	7.4	37
June grass hay, western, (*Koeleria cristata*)*...............	88.3	4.9	51.0	9.4	8.1	2.5	30.4	40.5	6.8	17
Kafir fodder, dry..............	91.1	4.6	54.1	10.8	8.9	2.8	26.8	43.2	9.4	21
Kafir fodder, high in water......	71.7	3.4	45.7	12.4	6.5	2.7	21.6	37.6	3.3	2
Kafir stover, medium in water ...	83.7	1.7	47.7	27.1	5.1	1.7	27.4	41.2	8.3	3
Kafir stover, high in water......	72.7	1.3	41.3	30.8	3.8	1.3	23.7	36.6	7.3	4
Kudzu vine hay*...............	90.0	12.0	50.8	3.2	17.7	2.8	29.1	33.3	7.1	2
Lespedeza hay, annual, all anal.*.	89.1	9.2	52.2	4.7	12.8	2.3	26.2	42.4	5.4	38
Lespedeza hay, annual, before bloom*......................	89.0	10.7	55.5	4.2	14.2	2.6	20.8	45.2	6.2	3
Lespedeza hay, annual, in bloom*	89.0	10.1	53.1	4.3	13.4	1.8	25.8	42.8	5.2	6
Lespedeza hay, annual, after bloom*......................	89.0	8.9	51.1	4.7	12.5	1.6	31.3	39.1	4.5	6
Lespedeza hay, perennial*.......	89.0	10.7	51.9	3.9	14.9	1.4	27.8	39.6	5.3	6
Lespedeza leaves, annual*......	89.0	13.1	58.9	3.5	17.0	2.7	19.7	43.3	6.3	13
Lespedeza stems, annual*........	89.0	4.4	42.4	8.6	8.6	0.9	38.0	37.7	3.8	13

TABLE I. Average composition and digestible nutrients—*continued*.

Feeding stuff	Mineral and fertilizing constituents				Digestion coefficients				
	Calcium	Phosphorus	Nitrogen	Potassium	Protein	Fat	Fiber	N-free extract	No. of trials
	Per ct.	Per ct.	Per ct.	Per ct.	Per ct.	Per ct.	Per ct.	Per ct.	
Dry Roughages—Cont.									
Cowpea hay, all analyses.......	1.13	0.25	2.98	1.45	68	39	47	68	4
Cowpea hay, before bloom......	..	..	4.11	..	..	..	..	..	..
Cowpea hay, in bloom to early pod	..	..	2.90	..	..	..	..	..	..
Cowpea hay, ripe..............	..	..	1.62	..	..	..	..	..	..
Cowpea straw..................	..	..	1.09	...	..	..	..	..	..
Cowpea and millet hay.........	..	..	2.19	..	..	..	..	..	..
Crab grass hay................	..	..	1.28	..	44	43	60	53	8
Crowfoot grass hay (*Eleusine,* spp.).....................	..	..	1.38	..	..	..	..	..	..
Dolichos lablab hay.............	..	..	2.37	..	72	52	55	65	2
Durra fodder..................	..	..	1.02	..	..	..	..	..	..
Emmer hay....................	..	..	1.55	..	..	..	..	..	..
Fescue hay, meadow...........	..	0.20	1.12	1.43	..	..	..	..	..
Fescue hay, native western (*Festuca,* spp.)..................	..	..	1.36	..	..	..	..	..	..
Feterita stover.................	..	..	0.83	..	..	..	..	..	..
Flax plant by-product..........	..	..	1.01	..	5	25	5	27	3
Flax straw....................	0.45	0.07	1.15	0.68	81	93	26	44	2
Fowl meadow grass hay........	..	..	1.39	..	..	..	..	..	..
Foxtail hay, miscellaneous......	..	..	1.39	..	..	..	..	..	..
Furze, dried..................	..	..	1.86	..	..	..	..	..	..
Gama grass hay (*Tripsacum dactyloides*).....................	..	..	1.07	..	..	..	..	..	..
Grama grass hay (*Bouteloua,* spp.).....................	..	..	0.93	..	..	..	..	..	..
Grass hay, mixed, eastern states, good quality................	0.48	0.17	1.12	1.36	50	47	61	62	31
Grass hay, mixed, second cutting	0.79	0.33	1.97	2.24	..	..	..	..	..
Grass straw...................	..	..	0.72	..	40	40	50	50	..
Greasewood, dried.............	..	0.24	3.17	2.40	..	..	..	..	..
Guar hay.....................	..	..	2.64	..	75	16	45	73	2
Hair grass hay, miscellaneous...	..	0.20	1.28	1.44	..	..	..	..	..
Harding grass hay (*Phalaris tuberosa,* var. *stenoptera*)......	..	..	1.01	..	..	..	..	..	..
Hegari stover..................	..	..	0.53	..	..	..	..	..	..
Hops, dried, spent.............	..	..	3.68	..	29	26	23	39	..
Horse bean hay................	..	..	2.14	..	..	..	..	..	..
Horse bean straw..............	..	..	1.38	..	49	57	43	68	5
Johnson grass hay.............	0.87	0.26	1.04	1.22	44	46	67	57	9
June grass hay, western (*Koeleria cristata*)................	..	..	1.30	..	..	..	..	..	..
Kafir fodder, dry..............	0.47	0.17	1.42	1.54	52	59	61	68	12
Kafir fodder, medium in water..	0.37	0.13	1.04	1.22	..	..	..	..	..
Kafir stover, dry..............	..	..	0.82	..	34	75	67	60	5
Kafir stover, high in water......	..	..	0.61	..	..	..	..	..	..
Kudzu vine hay................	..	0.27	2.83	..	..	..	..	..	..
Lespedeza hay, annual, all anal..	0.99	0.19	2.05	0.84	..	..	..	..	..
Lespedeza hay, annual, before bloom.....................	1.24	0.17	2.27	0.82	..	..	..	..	..
Lespedeza hay, annual, in bloom	1.09	0.18	2.14	0.90	..	..	..	..	..
Lespedeza hay, annual, after bloom.....................	0.87	0.15	2.00	0.78	..	..	..	..	..
Lespedeza hay, perennial.......	1.01	0.24	2.38	0.91	..	..	..	..	..
Lespedeza leaves, annual.......	1.34	0.20	2.72	0.86	..	..	..	..	..
Lespedeza stems, annual.......	0.64	0.13	1.38	0.80	..	..	..	..	..

TABLE I. Average composition and digestible nutrients—*continued*.

Feeding stuff	Total dry matter	Dig. protein	Total dig. nutrients	Nutritive ratio	Protein	Fat	Fiber	N-free extract	Mineral matter	No. of anal.
	Per ct.	Per ct.	Per ct.	1:	Per ct.	Per ct.	Per ct.	Per ct.	Per ct.	
Dry Roughages—Cont.										
Lespedeza straw, excellent*.....	90.0	3.5	45.1	11.9	6.8	2.3	29.2	47.1	4.6	1
Marsh or swamp hay, fair quality	90.2	2.9	40.6	13.0	7.7	2.3	28.2	44.3	7.7	37
Mesquite grass hay............	90.0	2.3	31.5	12.7	4.9	1.6	26.9	40.8	15.8	1
Millet hay, common or Hungarian......................	90.0	5.2	51.5	8.9	8.7	2.8	25.5	46.4	6.6	59
Millet hay, common, heading out, dehydrated*............	88.5	7.3	61.0	7.4	11.4	2.4	17.9	48.3	8.5	3
Millet hay, German*...........	91.3	4.8	52.0	9.8	8.0	2.6	27.3	46.5	6.9	22
Millet hay, hog or broom-corn*..	90.7	5.3	51.8	8.8	8.8	2.5	21.3	52.2	5.9	5
Millet hay, Japanese...........	86.5	5.1	47.3	8.3	8.3	1.6	27.6	40.8	8.2	14
Millet hay, pearl, or cat-tail....	87.2	4.2	49.8	10.9	6.7	1.7	33.0	36.8	9.0	6
Millet straw*.................	90.0	1.5	42.5	27.3	3.8	1.6	37.5	41.6	5.5	6
Milo fodder, dry...............	88.9	4.3	53.0	11.3	8.2	3.9	22.5	47.6	6.7	12
Milo stover, dry*.............	91.0	1.1	48.8	43.4	3.2	1.1	29.1	48.1	9.5	1
Napier grass hay, mature*......	89.1	3.3	44.1	12.4	8.2	1.8	34.0	34.6	10.5	1
Napier grass hay, immature*....	88.4	8.2	45.4	4.5	18.2	1.3	26.6	28.5	13.8	1
Natal grass hay*..............	90.2	3.0	47.9	15.0	7.4	1.8	36.8	39.2	5.0	...
Natal grass hay, in seed........	90.0	1.4	48.1	33.4	3.6	1.4	38.4	41.9	4.7	1
Native hay, western mt. states, good quality................	90.0	4.9	52.0	9.6	8.1	2.1	29.8	43.3	6.7	42
Native hay, western mt. states, matured and weathered......	90.0	1.6	36.6	21.9	3.9	1.4	33.6	43.6	7.5	46
Needle grass hay (*Stipa*, spp.)*...	88.1	4.3	51.1	10.9	7.2	2.0	30.8	41.9	6.2	38
Nerved manna grass hay (*Panicularia nervata*)*.............	90.0	4.6	51.0	10.9	7.7	1.8	27.4	44.9	8.2	4
Oak leaves (live oak)...........	93.8	0.0	17.0	...	9.3	2.7	29.9	45.3	6.6	2
Oat chaff*....................	91.8	1.3	40.9	30.5	5.9	2.4	25.7	46.3	11.5	4
Oat hay......................	88.0	4.5	46.3	9.3	8.3	2.7	28.4	41.7	6.9	88
Oat hay, heading out, dehydrated*...................	87.7	9.5	60.8	5.4	14.9	3.5	20.2	40.7	8.4	23
Oat hay wild (*Avena fatua*)*....	92.5	3.6	48.7	12.5	6.6	2.6	32.5	44.0	6.8	11
Oat hulls....................	93.5	0.8	38.3	46.9	3.8	1.2	30.6	51.2	6.7	16
Oat straw....................	89.6	0.9	44.1	48.0	4.0	2.3	36.1	41.2	6.0	67
Oat grass hay, downy (*Danthonia spicatum*)..................	89.0	6.1	56.5	8.3	10.5	2.3	29.0	42.6	4.6	4
Oat grass hay, tall, or meadow grass.......................	88.7	3.8	48.2	11.7	7.5	2.4	30.1	42.7	6.0	15
Orchard grass hay, early cut.....	88.6	4.6	49.6	9.8	7.7	2.9	30.5	40.7	6.8	50
Panic grass hay (*Panicum*, spp.)*	92.1	5.0	53.1	9.6	8.3	2.3	29.5	44.9	7.1	21
Para grass hay................	90.2	2.1	41.7	18.9	4.6	0.9	33.6	44.5	6.6	3
Pasture grasses and clovers, mixed, from closely-grazed, fertile pasture, dried.........	90.0	13.1	64.7	3.9	18.0	3.5	20.1	40.1	8.3	262
Pasture grasses, mixed, from poor to fair pasture, before heading out, dried*.:..................	90.0	9.9	58.3	4.9	14.1	2.3	19.4	43.2	11.0	40
Pasture grass, dried, western plains, clipped frequently*....	90.0	18.5	61.8	2.3	25.3	3.3	19.9	30.2	11.3	33
Pasture grass, dried, western plains, autumn*..............	90.0	6.3	60.0	8.5	9.0	3.9	27.6	40.1	9.4	5
Pasture grass, dried, western mt. states, growing actively*......	90.0	8.6	59.3	5.9	12.3	2.4	26.2	40.0	9.1	9
Pea hay, field................	89.2	11.6	56.9	3.9	14.9	3.2	24.5	38.9	7.7	34
Pea hay, Tangier*.............	89.0	8.3	57.7	6.0	10.6	1.1	26.1	44.2	7.0	2
Pea hulls*...................	92.4	1.6	46.0	27.8	7.3	1.0	42.4	38.1	3.6	4

TABLE I. Average composition and digestible nutrients—*continued*.

Feeding stuff	Mineral and fertilizing constituents				Digestion coefficients				
	Calcium	Phos-phorus	Nitro-gen	Potas-sium	Protein	Fat	Fiber	N-free extract	No. of trials
Dry Roughages—Cont.	Per ct.	Per ct.	Per ct.	Per ct.	Per ct.	Per ct.	Per ct.	Per ct.	
Lespedeza straw, excellent......	..	..	1.09	..	..	..	..	..	..
Marsh or swamp hay, fair quality	..	..	1.23	..	38	49	46	50	4
Mesquite grass hay............	..	..	0.78	..	..	68	45	36	2
Millet hay, common or Hungarian..................	0.30	0.17	1.39	1.75	60	64	62	57	..
Millet, hay, common, heading out, dehydrated............	..	..	1.82	..	..	..	..	..	..
Millet hay, German............	..	0.15	1.28	1.20	..	..	..	..	..
Millet hay, hog or broom-corn..	..	0.19	1.41	1.76	..	..	..	..	..
Millet hay, Japanese...........	..	0.20	1.33	2.10	61	47	64	56	4
Millet hay, pearl, or cat-tail....	..	..	1.07	..	63	46	67	59	2
Millet straw.................	..	0.08	0.61	1.44	..	..	..	..	..
Milo fodder, dry.............	..	..	1.31	..	..	63	61	62	7
Milo stover, dry.............	..	..	0.51	..	..	..	..	..	..
Napier grass hay, mature.......	..	..	1.31	..	..	..	..	..	..
Napier grass hay, immature....	..	..	2.91	..	..	..	..	..	..
Natal grass hay..............	0.45	0.29	1.18	..	..	..	..	..	..
Natal grass hay, in seed........	..	..	0.58	..	..	69	59	52	4
Native hay, western mt. states, good quality..............	..	..	1.30	..	60	39	62	62	22
Native hay, western mt. states, mature and weathered.......	0.26	0.21	0.62	..	40	25	46	43	19
Needle grass hay (*Stipa*, spp.)...	..	..	1.15	..	..	..	..	..	..
Nerved manna grass hay (*Panicularia nervata*).............	..	..	1.23	..	..	..	..	..	..
Oak leaves (live oak)..........	..	..	1.49	..	0	30	10	27	1
Oat chaff...................	0.80	0.30	0.94	0.86	..	..	..	..	..
Oat hay....................	0.22	0.17	1.33	1.09	54	61	52	56	22
Oat hay, heading out, dehydrated....................	..	..	2.38	..	..	..	..	..	..
Oat hay, wild (*Avena fatua*).....	0.22	0.25	1.06	..	..	..	..	..	..
Oat hulls...................	0.20	0.10	0.61	0.48	21	30	53	40	3
Oat straw...................	0.36	0.13	0.64	1.66	22	33	59	49	30
Oat grass hay, downy (*Danthonia spicatum*).................	..	..	1.68	..	58	51	68	66	2
Oat grass hay, tall, or meadow grass......................	..	0.14	1.20	1.36	51	56	55	58	2
Orchard grass hay, early cut....	..	0.17	1.23	1.61	60	55	61	56	3
Panic grass hay (*Panicum*, spp.).	..	..	1.33	..	..	..	..	..	..
Para grass hay...............	0.42	0.16	0.74	0.64	..	45	53	47	3
Pasture grasses and clovers, mixed, from closely-grazed, fertile pasture, dried.........	0.66	0.29	2.88	1.94	73	59	76	79	20
Pasture grass, dried, from poor to fair pasture, before heading out, dried.................	0.45	0.12	2.26	..	..	..	..	..	..
Pasture grass, dried, western plains, clipped frequently.....	..	..	4.05	..	..	..	..	..	..
Pasture grass, dried, western plains, autumn..............	..	..	1.44	..	..	..	..	..	..
Pasture grass, dried, western mt. states, growing actively......	..	..	1.97	..	..	..	..	..	..
Pea hay, field.................	1.36	0.22	2.38	1.03	78	50	51	79	3
Pea hay, Tangier..............	..	..	1.70	..	..	..	..	..	..
Pea hulls....................	..	..	1.17	..	..	..	..	..	..

TABLE I. Average composition and digestible nutrients—*continued*.

Feeding stuff	Total dry matter	Dig. protein	Total dig. nutrients	Nutritive ratio	Average total composition					No. of anal.
					Protein	Fat	Fiber	N-free extract	Mineral matter	
	Per ct.	Per ct.	Per ct.	1:	Per ct.	Per ct.	Per ct.	Per ct.	Per ct.	
Dry Roughages—Cont.										
Pea straw, field	90.2	3.2	51.8	15.2	6.1	1.6	33.1	44.0	5.4	22
Peas and oats hay	89.0	8.9	52.2	4.9	12.2	2.8	27.3	38.9	7.8	30
Peas, oats and barley hay*	89.0	9.8	53.3	4.4	13.4	3.2	31.4	34.6	6.4	1
Peanut hay, without nuts or with few nuts	91.4	6.3	57.8	8.2	9.7	3.3	23.3	45.7	9.4	48
Peanut hay, with nuts	92.0	10.2	71.6	6.0	13.4	12.6	23.0	34.9	8.1	11
Peanut hay, mowed	91.4	6.9	58.4	7.5	10.6	5.1	23.8	42.2	9.7	6
Peanut hulls	92.3	3.2	27.3	7.5	6.7	1.2	60.3	19.7	4.4	74
Prairie hay, western, good quality	90.4	2.6	49.2	17.9	5.7	2.4	30.3	44.4	7.6	64
Prairie hay, western, mature or weathered	90.4	0.6	47.1	77.5	3.6	3.4	32.8	43.7	6.9	3
Quack, or couch grass hay*	89.0	2.8	41.9	14.0	6.9	1.9	34.5	38.8	6.9	4
Red top hay, all analyses	91.0	4.5	53.6	10.9	7.2	2.3	29.3	45.3	6.9	49
Red top hay, in bloom	91.1	4.5	52.9	10.8	7.3	2.2	29.6	44.0	8.0	16
Reed canary grass hay*	90.8	3.5	46.6	12.3	7.5	2.4	29.1	44.4	7.4	12
Rescue grass hay*	90.2	4.5	46.3	9.3	9.8	3.2	24.6	44.5	8.1	3
Rhode Island bent grass hay*	88.5	4.1	52.6	11.8	6.6	3.0	29.5	42.8	6.6	2
Rhodes grass hay	91.4	3.1	52.2	15.8	6.8	1.7	31.0	42.4	9.5	5
Rice hulls	92.0	0.1	9.9	98.0	3.0	0.8	40.7	28.4	19.1	39
Rice straw	92.5	0.9	39.4	42.8	3.9	1.4	33.5	39.2	14.5	13
Rush hay, western (*Juncus*, spp.)	90.0	7.0	56.6	7.1	9.4	1.8	29.1	44.3	5.4	46
Ryegrass hay, Italian*	88.6	3.7	45.1	11.2	8.1	1.9	27.8	43.3	7.5	7
Ryegrass hay, perennial*	88.0	4.2	45.1	9.7	9.2	3.1	24.2	43.4	8.1	14
Ryegrass hay, native western*	87.4	3.6	44.7	11.4	7.8	2.1	33.5	37.6	6.4	8
Rye hay, all analyses*	91.3	2.8	44.7	15.0	6.7	2.1	36.5	41.0	5.0	15
Rye hay, heading out, to bloom*	91.8	4.5	47.6	9.6	9.8	2.6	33.9	39.7	5.8	3
Rye straw	92.9	0.7	41.2	57.9	3.0	1.2	38.9	46.6	3.2	7
Sagebrush, dried*	88.6	8.0	43.8	4.5	10.6	4.6	24.9	38.9	9.6	7
Sagebrush leaves, dried*	91.8	11.2	57.8	4.2	15.5	14.5	11.5	44.0	6.3	3
Saltbushes, dried	93.5	10.2	36.6	2.6	13.8	1.6	22.1	38.8	17.2	27
Saltbush leaves, dried*	94.5	10.3	45.2	3.4	14.3	2.0	11.4	41.4	25.4	18
Saltgrass hay, misc. var.*	90.0	3.7	45.9	11.4	8.1	1.8	28.8	39.5	11.8	6
Sanfoin hay (*Onobrychis viciaefolia*)*	84.1	7.6	49.3	5.5	10.5	2.6	19.7	44.2	7.1	5
Sedge hay, eastern (*Carex*, spp.)*	90.7	2.1	34.7	15.5	6.1	1.7	29.2	46.3	7.4	3
Sedge hay, western (*Carex*, spp.)*	90.7	3.5	35.2	9.1	10.2	2.4	27.1	44.3	6.7	68
Serradella hay	90.3	11.8	50.6	3.3	15.7	2.5	19.6	40.2	12.3	5
Sorghum bagasse, dried	89.3	0.6	41.4	68.0	3.1	1.4	31.3	50.0	3.5	3
Sorghum fodder, sweet, dry	89.2	3.6	52.7	13.6	6.4	2.5	25.8	47.3	7.2	47
Sorghum fodder, sweet, high in water	65.2	2.5	39.8	14.9	4.4	2.4	16.6	37.7	4.1	17
Soybean hay, all analyses	90.8	11.1	50.6	3.6	14.8	3.3	28.4	37.0	7.3	77
Soybean hay, in bloom or before	91.5	13.1	51.0	2.9	17.4	3.4	21.4	39.3	10.0	8
Soybean hay, seed developing	90.9	11.2	50.0	3.5	14.9	2.4	28.2	38.0	7.4	22
Soybean hay, seed well developed	90.8	11.9	53.0	3.5	15.8	5.1	27.2	36.6	6.1	16
Soybean hay, seed nearly ripe	90.8	11.8	56.0	3.7	15.7	6.9	24.8	39.3	4.1	2
Soybean hay, poor quality, weathered	90.8	4.5	38.8	7.6	9.6	1.1	44.3	28.1	7.7	4
Soybean hay, immature, dehydrated*	88.0	7.8	61.4	6.9	12.2	2.3	19.0	47.3	7.2	24
Soybean straw	88.8	0.9	36.5	39.6	4.0	1.1	41.1	37.5	5.1	16
Soybean and Sudan grass hay, chiefly Sudan*	89.0	3.6	50.8	13.1	7.4	2.2	31.1	43.4	4.9	1
Spanish moss, dried	89.2	0.0	51.4	...	5.0	2.4	26.6	47.7	7.5	3

TABLE I. Average composition and digestible nutrients—*continued*.

Feeding stuff	Mineral and fertilizing constituents				Digestion coefficients				
	Calcium	Phosphorus	Nitrogen	Potassium	Protein	Fat	Fiber	N-free extract	No. of trials
Dry Roughages—Cont.	Per ct.	Per ct.	Per ct.	Per ct.	Per ct.	Per ct.	Per ct.	Per ct.	
Pea straw, field	1.58	0.10	0.98	1.08	53	56	53	66	5
Peas and oats hay	0.80	0.20	1.95	1.36	73	59	58	61	7
Peas, oats, and barley hay	..	..	2.14	..	..	..	..	..	..
Peanut hay, without nuts or with few nuts	1.13	0.13	1.55	1.26	65	60	51	77	8
Peanut hay, with nuts	1.13	0.15	2.14	0.85	76	92	49	69	7
Peanut hay, mowed	..	..	1.70	..	..	..	..	..	..
Peanut hulls	0.31	0.07	1.07	0.83	48	83	17	59	10
Prairie hay, western, good quality	0.49	0.10	0.91	..	46	40	60	59	17
Prairie hay, western, mature or weathered	0.53	0.05	0.58	0.49	18	42	60	54	24
Quack, or couch grass hay	..	..	1.10	..	..	..	..	..	..
Red top hay, all analyses	..	0.19	1.15	1.56	62	53	61	63	3
Red top hay, in bloom	..	..	1.17	..	..	..	..	..	..
Reed canary grass hay	..	0.23	1.20	1.57	..	..	..	..	..
Rescue grass hay	..	..	1.57	..	..	..	..	..	..
Rhode Island bent grass hay	..	0.18	1.06	1.41	..	..	..	..	..
Rhodes grass hay	0.36	0.28	1.09	1.21	45	49	69	61	4
Rice hulls	0.08	0.08	0.48	0.31	4	47	6	23	4
Rice straw	0.19	0.07	0.62	1.22	22	23	59	46	6
Rush hay, western (*Juncus*, spp.)	..	..	1.50	..	74	49	71	61	2
Ryegrass hay, Italian	..	0.24	1.30	1.00	..	..	..	..	..
Ryegrass hay, perennial	..	0.24	1.47	1.25	..	..	..	..	..
Ryegrass hay, native western	..	..	1.25	..	..	..	..	..	..
Rye hay, all analyses	..	0.18	1.07	1.05	..	..	..	..	..
Rye hay, heading out, to bloom	..	..	1.57	..	..	..	..	..	..
Rye straw	0.28	0.11	0.48	0.86	23	36	55	39	9
Sagebrush, dried	..	..	1.70	..	75	..	..	71	4
Sagebrush leaves, dried	..	..	2.48	..	..	..	..	..	..
Saltbrushes, dried	..	0.59	2.21	4.69	74	41	16	55	5
Saltbrush leaves, dried	..	..	2.29	..	..	..	..	..	..
Saltgrass hay, misc. var	..	..	1.30	..	..	..	..	..	..
Sanfoin hay (*Onobrychis viciaefolia*)	..	..	1.68	..	..	..	..	..	..
Sedge hay, eastern (*Carex*, spp.)	..	0.09	0.98	0.77	..	..	..	..	..
Sedge hay, western (*Carex*, spp.)	..	..	1.63	..	..	..	..	..	..
Serradella hay	..	0.33	2.51	1.25	75	65	50	63	1
Sorghum bagasse, dried	..	..	0.50	..	..	..	53	45	3
Sorghum fodder, sweet, dry	0.49	0.14	1.02	1.30	56	64	61	63	22
Sorghum fodder, sweet, high in water	0.36	0.10	0.70	0.95	..	..	..	..	..
Soybean hay, all analyses	0.96	0.25	2.37	0.82	75	60	44	61	20
Soybean hay, in bloom or before	1.59	0.28	2.78	0.90	..	..	..	..	..
Soybean hay, seed developing	1.42	0.26	2.38	0.78	..	..	..	..	..
Soybean hay, seed well developed	1.18	0.28	2.53	0.73	..	..	..	..	..
Soybean hay, seed nearly ripe	0.89	0.33	2.51	0.84	..	..	..	..	..
Soybean hay, poor quality, weathered	0.96	..	1.54	..	47	32	40	56	..
Soybean hay, immature, dehydrated	..	..	1.95	..	..	..	..	..	..
Soybean straw	..	0.13	0.64	0.62	23	26	33	57	16
Soybean and Sudan grass hay, chiefly Sudan	..	..	1.18	..	..	..	..	..	..
Spanish moss, dried	..	0.04	0.80	0.46	0	16	52	77	2

TABLE I. Average composition and digestible nutrients—*continued*.

Feeding stuff	Total dry matter	Dig. protein	Total dig. nutrients	Nutritive ratio	Average total composition					
					Protein	Fat	Fiber	N-free extract	Mineral matter	No. of anal.
	Per ct.	Per ct.	Per ct.	1:	Per ct.	Per ct.	Per ct.	Per ct.	Per ct.	
Dry Roughages—Cont.										
Spear grass hay (*Poa*, spp.)*....	90.0	4.3	52.8	11.3	7.2	2.0	28.6	46.7	5.5	33
Spurrey, dried..................	92.1	8.1	52.8	5.5	11.3	4.5	19.1	46.8	10.4	7
Sudan grass hay, all analyses...	89.2	4.3	48.5	10.3	8.8	1.6	27.9	42.9	8.0	108
Sudan grass hay, before bloom..	89.6	6.7	45.0	5.7	11.4	1.6	25.9	41.2	9.5	30
Sudan grass hay, in bloom......	89.2	4.7	51.7	10.0	8.4	1 5	30.7	41.7	6.8	2
Sudan grass hay, in seed........	89.5	2.5	50.2	19.1	6.8	1.6	29.9	44.4	6.8	11
Sudan grass, immature, dehydrated.....................	88.0	9.3	59.5	5.4	14.5	2.5	20.4	41.2	9.4	45
Sudan grass straw.............	90.4	3.3	44.6	12.5	7.1	1.5	33.0	42.3	6.5	3
Sugar cane fodder, dried, Japanese*.....................	89.0	0.7	55.8	78.7	1.3	1.8	19.7	64.3	1.9	1
Sugar cane bagasse, dried*......	95.5	0.2	45.9	228.5	1.1	0.4	49.6	42.0	2.4	1
Sugar cane pulp, dried*........	94.2	0.3	44.4	147.0	1.7	0.6	46.0	42.1	3.8	10
Sweet potato vines, dried*......	90.7	8.6	51.4	5.0	12.6	3.3	19.1	45.5	10.2	9
Sweet vernal grass hay (*Anthoxanthum oderatum*)*.......	90.6	2.5	47.7	18.1	5.5	1.9	28.7	49.1	5.4	2
Switch grass hay (*Panicum virgatum*)*.....................	90.0	2.4	43.1	17.0	5.9	2.0	30.4	46.0	5.7	18
Teosinte fodder, dried*.........	89.4	4.7	54.9	10.7	9.1	1.9	26.4	41.7	10.3	4
Thistle hay, Russian*..........	91.8	1.7	43.1	24.4	7.9	0.9	41.5	33.1	8.4	2
Timothy hay, all analyses......	88.7	2.9	46.9	15.2	6.2	2.4	30.1	45.0	5.0	266
Timothy hay, before bloom*....	88.7	5.6	50.2	8.0	10.1	2.7	27.5	41.8	6.6	8
Timothy hay, early bloom......	88.7	4.2	51.6	11.3	7.6	2.4	29.7	44.6	4.4	25
Timothy hay, full bloom.......	88.7	3.2	48.0	14.0	6.2	2.6	30.3	44.8	4.8	47
Timothy hay, in bloom, nitrogen-fertilized..................	88.7	4.8	51.8	9.8	8.8	2.1	31.5	42.4	3.9	17
Timothy hay, late bloom to early seed......................	88.7	2.4	44.4	17.5	5.8	2.9	29.6	45.7	4.7	23
Timothy hay, late seed.........	87.7	2.1	42.8	19.4	5.2	2.2	30.7	45.2	4.4	32
Timothy hay, second cutting*...	88.7	8.3	50.3	5.1	15.0	4.6	25.4	36.5	7.2	3
Trefoil hay, yellow, or black medic (*Medicago lupulina*)*...	88.8	12.7	53.8	3.2	16.9	3.0	14.8	43.2	10.9	2
Velvet bean hay*..............	92.8	12.3	52.0	3.2	16.4	3.1	27.5	38.4	7.4	4
Vetch hay, common............	91.8	9.1	57.8	5.4	13.6	1.1	26.0	44.8	6.3	39
Vetch hay, hairy.............	87.9	15.3	57.0	2.7	19.4	2.6	24.8	32.6	8.5	16
Vetch hay, Hungarian*.........	90.9	9.6	56.3	4.9	14.4	1.8	29.0	38.2	7.5	1
Vetch and oats hay, mostly vetch*...................	90.0	9.1	52.5	4.8	12.5	2.5	29.3	38.1	7.6	5
Vetch and oats hay, mostly oats.	89.8	4.8	53.0	10.0	6.6	2.9	29.4	45.1	5.8	9
Vetch and wheat hay..........	90.0	11.4	58.0	4.1	15.4	2.2	28.8	36.4	7.2	4
Wheat chaff..................	90.0	1.3	38.5	28.6	4.4	1.5	29.4	47.1	7.6	1
Wheat hay*..................	89.0	3.2	46.5	13.5	5.9	1.7	26.1	48.9	6.4	18
Wheat hay, heading out, dehydrated*..................	88.1	7.1	50.7	6.1	12.7	2.6	21.1	43.9	7.8	1
Wheat straw..................	90.1	0.8	35.7	43.6	3.8	1.5	35.7	40.9	8.2	73
Wheat grass hay, crested (*Agropyron cristatum*)*............	87.9	6.9	50.3	6.3	11.5	2.1	29.4	37.7	7.2	25
Wheat grass hay, slender, or western rye grass*..........	89.1	5.4	51.3	8.5	9.0	2.1	31.0	40.0	7.0	43
Wheat grass hay, misc. (*Agropyron*, spp.)*................	90.1	4.9	52.1	9.6	8.2	2.5	30.2	42.3	6.9	54
Winter fat, or white sage, dried (*Eurotia lanata*)*............	92.6	7.7	51.7	5.7	12.9	1.9	27.4	40.8	9.6	8
Wire grass hay, southern, (*Aristida*, spp.)*.................	90.0	1.9	35.8	17.8	5.5	1.4	31.8	47.9	3.4	50

TABLE I. Average composition and digestible nutrients—*continued*.

Feeding stuff	Mineral and fertilizing constituents				Digestion coefficients				
	Calcium	Phosphorus	Nitrogen	Potassium	Protein	Fat	Fiber	N-free extract	No. of trials
	Per ct.	Per ct.	Per ct.	Per ct.	Per ct.	Per ct.	Per ct.	Per ct.	
Dry Roughages—Cont.									
Spear grass hay (*Poa*, spp.).....	..	..	1.15	..	..	..	..	..	..
Spurrey, dried..................	..	..	1.81	..	..	..	..	..	..
Sudan grass hay, all analyses....	..	..	1.41	..	49	52	64	57	16
Sudan grass hay, before bloom..	..	..	1.82	..	59	40	66	48	4
Sudan grass hay, in bloom......	..	..	1.34	..	56	60	65	60	4
Sudan grass hay, in seed.......	..	..	1.09	..	37	52	64	60	5
Sudan grass, immature, dehydrated.....................	0.76	0.30	2.32	..	64	71	71	77	6
Sudan grass straw..............	..	..	1.14	..	46	35	60	48	2
Sugar cane fodder, dried, Japanese...................	0.32	0.14	0.25	0.59	..	..	..	..	..
Sugar cane bagasse, dried.......	..	..	0.18	..	..	..	..	..	..
Sugar cane pulp, dried.........	..	..	0.27	..	..	..	..	..	..
Sweet potato vines, dried.......	..	..	2.02	..	..	..	..	..	..
Sweet vernal grass hay (*Anthoxanthum oderatum*)........	..	..	0.88	..	..	..	..	..	..
Switch grass hay (*Panicum virgatum*)......................	..	..	0.94	..	..	..	..	..	..
Teosinte fodder, dried..........	..	0.17	1.46	0.88	..	..	..	..	..
Thistle hay, Russian...........	..	..	1.26	..	..	..	..	..	..
Timothy hay, all analyses......	0.27	0.16	0.99	1.36	46	48	51	58	92
Timothy hay, before bloom.....	..	..	1.62	..	..	..	..	..	..
Timothy hay, early bloom......	0.41	0.21	1.22	..	55	44	63	59	8
Timothy hay, full bloom.......	0.27	0.16	0.99	1.36	51	45	55	57	15
Timothy hay, in bloom, nitrogenfertilized....................	0.40	0.21	1.41	..	..	..	..	..	..
Timothy hay, late bloom to early seed........................	..	..	0.93	..	42	49	49	53	25
Timothy hay, late seed..........	..	..	0.83	..	40	40	51	51	13
Timothy hay, second cutting....	..	..	2.40	..	..	..	..	..	..
Trefoil hay, yellow, or black medic (*Medicago lupulina*)....	..	0.25	2.70	..	..	..	..	..	..
Velvet bean hay................	..	0.24	2.62	2.20	..	..	..	..	..
Vetch hay, common............	0.86	0.29	2.18	1.83	67	64	57	72	5
Vetch hay, hairy...............	..	0.45	3.10	2.18	79	67	59	71	8
Vetch hay, Hungarian..........	..	..	2.30	..	..	..	..	..	..
Vetch and oats hay, mostly vetch......................	0.62	0.22	2.00	1.69	..	..	..	..	..
Vetch and oats hay, mostly oats.	..	..	1.06	..	73	62	58	60	11
Vetch and wheat hay..........	..	..	2.46	..	74	64	65	68	6
Wheat chaff...................	0.21	0.14	0.70	0.50	30	55	48	45	..
Wheat hay....................	0.18	0.21	0.94	1.47	..	..	..	..	..
Wheat hay, heading out, dehydrated.....................	..	..	2.03	..	..	..	..	..	..
Wheat straw...................	0.22	0.07	0.61	0.80	20	55	40	46	14
Wheat grass hay, crested (*Agropyron cristatum*)...........	..	..	1.84	..	..	..	..	..	..
Wheat grass hay, slender, or western rye grass............	0.29	0.24	1.44	2.38	..	..	..	..	..
Wheat grass hay, misc. (*Agropyron*, spp.).................	0.24	0.22	1.31	2.08	..	..	..	..	..
Winter fat, or white sage, dried (*Eurotia lanata*).............	..	..	2.06	..	..	..	..	..	..
Wire grass hay, southern, (*Aristida*, spp.)..................	0.15	0.14	0.88	..	..	..	..	..	..

TABLE I. Average composition and digestible nutrients—*continued*.

Feeding stuff	Total dry matter	Dig. protein	Total dig. nutrients	Nutritive ratio	Average total composition					
					Protein	Fat	Fiber	N-free extract	Mineral matter	No. of anal.
	Per ct.	Per ct.	Per ct.	1:	Per ct.	Per ct.	Per ct.	Per ct.	Per ct.	
Dry Roughages—Cont.										
Wire grass hay, western, (*Aristida*, spp.)*............	90.0	2.4	40.1	15.7	6.4	1.3	34.1	41.0	7.2	6
Yucca (bear grass), dried.......	92.6	2.4	51.2	20.3	6.6	2.2	38.6	38.3	6.9	4
Green Roughages, Roots, Etc.										
Alfalfa, green, all analyses......	25.4	3.4	14.7	3.3	4.6	1.0	7.0	10.4	2.4	146
Alfalfa, immature, to 10 in. high.	20.0	4.0	11.7	1.9	5.4	0.9	3.8	7.4	2.5	4
Alfalfa, before bloom..........	19.9	3.2	11.5	2.6	4.3	0.7	4.4	8.2	2.3	7
Alfalfa, in bloom..............	25.9	3.3	14.7	3.5	4.4	0.8	7.8	10.4	2.5	27
Alfalfa, after bloom*..........	29.8	1.9	14.4	6.6	2.9	0.6	12.8	11.3	2.2	6
Alfilaria (*Erodium cicutarium*)*..	16.3	2.4	8.8	2.7	3.2	0.4	2.9	6.8	3.0	2
Apples*.....................	17.9	0.2	14.4	71.0	0.5	0.4	1.3	15.3	0.4	10
Artichoke tubers*.............	20.5	1.0	16.1	15.1	2.0	0.1	0.8	15.9	1.7	22
Artichoke tops*...............	27.2	0.5	15.1	29.2	1.4	0.3	4.9	18.5	2.1	1
Barley fodder.................	22.6	2.3	14.4	5.3	3.3	0.8	5.6	10.8	2.1	17
Beet leaves, sugar*...........	11.6	1.4	7.7	4.5	1.9	0.3	1.1	6.5	1.8	5
Beet tops, sugar..............	11.4	1.9	7.4	2.9	2.6	0.3	1.2	5.3	2.0	4
Beets, roots, common*........	13.0	1.2	10.2	7.5	1.6	0.1	0.9	8.9	1.5	23
Beets, roots, sugar............	16.4	1.2	13.8	10.5	1.6	0.1	1.0	12.6	1.1	86
Beggarweed*.................	27.1	3.2	14.3	3.5	4.2	0.5	7.5	11.7	3.2	3
Bermuda grass*...............	34.2	2.8	25.0	7.9	3.5	1.0	8.7	18.3	2.7	4
Berseem*....................	18.4	1.8	11.1	5.2	2.5	0.6	3.8	8.6	2.9	2
Bluegrass, Canada*...........	33.2	1.3	19.5	14.0	3.0	1.2	10.3	16.1	2.6	9
Bluegrass, Kentucky, all anal.*..	31.8	2.4	18.6	6.8	4.2	1.2	8.7	14.9	2.8	34
Bluegrass, Ky., before heading*..	24.8	4.4	17.7	3.0	5.6	1.3	5.3	9.8	2.8	8
Bluegrass, Ky., headed out*....	36.4	2.8	21.0	6.5	4.9	1.3	10.9	15.6	3.7	4
Bluegrass, Ky., after bloom*....	43.6	1.4	20.3	13.5	3.4	1.3	13.2	21.6	4.1	2
Bluegrasses, native...........	32.0	1.7	17.2	9.1	2.6	1.0	10.2	16.3	1.9	6
Bluejoint (*Calamagrostis Canadensis*)*.....................	44.6	1.6	20.7	11.9	4.1	1.2	15.2	20.0	4.1	3
Brome grass, smooth, all anal.*..	33.8	2.9	19.7	5.8	4.2	1.4	9.7	15.6	2.9	39
Brome grasses, misc...........	36.3	3.0	20.8	5.9	4.5	1.0	11.9	15.7	3.2	17
Broom-corn fodder*...........	22.9	0.7	13.1	17.7	2.0	0.5	8.6	10.1	1.7	1
Buckwheat...................	36.6	2.9	21.7	6.5	4.6	0.9	8.0	19.5	3.6	1
Bunch grasses, misc.*.........	49.4	2.6	28.2	9.8	4.3	1.2	15.8	23.9	4.2	1
Cabbage, entire..............	9.4	1.9	8.1	3.3	2.2	0.3	1.0	5.0	0.9	6
Cabbage, head, without outer leaves......................	9.7	1.4	9.4	5.7	1.8	0.1	0.9	6.1	0.8	1
Cabbage waste, outer leaves....	15.8	1.7	10.1	4.9	2.6	0.4	2.7	7.1	3.0	3
Cactus, cane, entire plant*......	10.4	0.5	6.5	12.0	0.9	0.2	1.1	6.5	1.7	5
Cactus, cane, fruit*...........	18.6	0.8	11.9	13.9	1.5	0.8	3.2	10.4	2.7	35
Cactus, cane, stems*..........	21.7	0.8	13.2	15.5	1.5	0.4	3.4	12.6	3.8	42
Cactus, prickly pear, all anal....	16.6	0.4	9.9	23.8	0.8	0.3	2.3	9.8	3.4	98
Cactus, prickly pear, old joints*.	16.4	0.3	9.9	32.0	0.6	0.3	2.5	9.8	3.2	4
Cactus, prickly pear, young joints*	12.9	0.5	7.9	14.8	0.9	0.4	1.2	7.8	2.6	5
Carrots, roots................	11.9	0.8	9.6	11.0	1.2	0.2	1.1	8.2	1.2	22
Cassava roots................	32.6	0.3	17.9	58.7	1.1	0.3	1.4	28.8	1.0	3
Chamiza (*Atriplex canescens*)....	29.7	4.8	14.1	1.9	6.4	1.0	3.8	11.0	7.5	30
Chufa tubers*................	20.5	0.3	17.4	57.0	0.7	6.6	2.2	10.5	0.4	..
Clover, alsike*	22.2	2.4	13.2	4.5	3.8	0.6	5.8	9.7	2.3	16
Clover, bur*.................	20.8	3.7	12.8	2.5	5.1	1.7	3.9	7.8	2.3	3
Clover, crimson..............	17.4	2.3	11.3	3.9	3.0	0.6	4.7	7.4	1.7	22
Clover, hop, (*Trifolium procumbens*).....................	25.7	2.9	18.6	5.4	4.6	1.1	5.0	13.3	1.7	10

TABLE I. Average composition and digestible nutrients—*continued*.

Feeding stuff	Mineral and fertilizing constituents				Digestion coefficients				
	Calcium	Phos-phorus	Nitro-gen	Potas-sium	Protein	Fat	Fiber	N-free extract	No. of trials
Dry Roughages—Cont.	Per ct.	Per ct.	Per ct.	Per ct.	Per ct.	Per ct.	Per ct.	Per ct.	
Wire grass hay, western, (*Aristida*, spp.)	..	..	1.02	..	..	..	..	..	..
Yucca (bear grass), dried	..	..	1.06	..	36	0	65	62	2
Green Roughages, Roots, Etc.									
Alfalfa, green, all analyses	0.40	0.06	0.74	0.57	74	38	42	72	2
Alfalfa, immature, to 10 in. high.	..	..	0.86	..	..	..	..	..	..
Alfalfa, before bloom	..	..	0.69	..	..	..	..	..	..
Alfalfa, in bloom	..	..	0.70	..	..	..	..	..	..
Alfalfa, after bloom	..	..	0.46	..	..	..	..	..	..
Alfilaria (*Erodium cicutarium*)	0.29	0.07	0.51	..	..	..	..	..	..
Apples	0.01	0.01	0.08	0.14	..	..	..	..	..
Artichoke tubers	..	0.06	0.32	0.41	..	..	..	..	..
Artichoke tops	0.44	0.03	0.22	0.37	..	..	..	..	..
Barley fodder	0.07	0.08	0.53	0.35	71	56	59	72	6
Beet leaves, sugar	0.26	0.05	0.30	0.80	..	..	..	..	..
Beet tops, sugar	0.15	0.04	0.42	0.53	74	55	70	80	4
Beets, roots, common	0.03	0.04	0.26	0.42	..	..	..	..	..
Beets, roots, sugar	0.03	0.04	0.26	0.27	72	..	34	97	30
Beggarweed	..	0.12	0.67	0.47	..	..	..	..	..
Bermuda grass	..	0.07	0.56	0.61	..	..	..	..	..
Berseem	..	..	0.40	..	73	52	57	74	9
Bluegrass, Canada	..	0.08	0.48	0.57	..	..	..	..	..
Bluegrass, Kentucky, all anal	0.16	0.08	0.67	0.53	..	..	..	..	..
Bluegrass, Ky., before heading	0.12	0.09	0.90	0.53	..	..	..	..	..
Bluegrass, Ky., headed out	..	..	0.78	..	..	..	..	..	..
Bluegrass, Ky., after bloom	..	..	0.54	..	..	..	..	..	..
Bluegrasses, native	..	..	0.42	..	64	50	45	60	2
Bluejoint (*Calamagrostis Canadensis*)	..	..	0.66	..	..	..	..	..	..
Brome grass, smooth, all anal	0.07	0.09	0.67	0.71	..	..	..	..	..
Brome grasses, misc	..	0.10	0.72	0.79	68	39	53	67	2
Broom-corn fodder	..	0.07	0.32	0.58	..	..	..	..	..
Buckwheat	..	0.11	0.74	0.83	64	50	58	67	..
Bunch grasses, misc	..	..	0.69	..	..	..	..	..	..
Cabbage, entire	0.06	0.03	0.35	0.24	86	70	91	96	2
Cabbage, head, without outer leaves	0.05	0.03	0.29	0.25	77	43	100	100	2
Cabbage waste, outer leaves	..	..	0.42	..	64	37	78	84	2
Cactus, cane, entire plant	..	0.01	0.14	0.17	..	..	..	..	..
Cactus, cane, fruit	..	..	0.24	..	..	..	..	..	..
Cactus, cane, stems	..	0.04	0.24	0.40	..	..	..	..	..
Cactus, prickly pear, all anal	..	0.03	0.13	0.36	50	68	47	81	4
Cactus, prickly pear, old joints	..	0.03	0.10	0.33	..	..	..	..	..
Cactus, prickly pear, young joints	..	0.02	0.14	0.27	..	..	..	..	..
Carrots, roots	0.06	0.06	0.19	0.40	68	40	94	92	12
Cassava roots	..	0.04	0.18	0.33	24	59	80	56	1
Chamiza (*Atriplex canescens*)	..	..	1.02	..	75	..	..	71	4
Chufa tubers	..	..	0.11	..	..	..	..	..	..
Clover, alsike	0.34	0.05	0.61	0.56	..	..	..	..	..
Clover, bur	..	..	0.82	..	..	..	..	..	..
Clover, crimson	0.31	0.04	0.48	0.25	77	66	56	74	3
Clover, hop (*Trefolium procumbens*)	..	..	0.74	..	63	51	71	82	1

TABLE I. Average composition and digestible nutrients—*continued*.

Feeding stuff	Total dry matter	Dig. protein	Total dig. nutri- ents	Nutri- tive ratio	Average total composition					
					Protein	Fat	Fiber	N-free extract	Mineral matter	No. of anal.
Green Roughages, Roots, Etc. —Cont.	Per ct.	Per ct.	Per ct.	1:	Per ct.	Per ct.	Per ct.	Per ct.	Per ct.	
Clover, mammoth red*.........	25.1	2.6	14.9	4.7	4.0	0.5	7.3	11.0	2.3	7
Clover, red, all analyses........	25.0	2.6	15.4	4.9	4.0	0.9	6.8	11.2	2.1	124
Clover, red, before bloom.......	18.7	3.2	13.3	3.2	4.3	0.6	2.6	9.2	2.0	1
Clover, red, in bloom..........	27.5	2.6	17.1	5.6	4.1	1.1	8.2	12.1	2.0	36
Clover, red, second crop*.......	34.4	3.4	21.6	5.4	5.3	1.3	9.1	16.2	2.5	7
Clover, sweet.................	22.0	3.0	14.0	3.7	3.9	0.7	6.4	9.2	1.8	20
Clover, sweet, before bloom*....	24.3	3.4	15.6	3.6	4.4	0.9	6.3	10.6	2.1	6
Clover, white*.................	16.2	2.5	9.8	2.9	3.9	0.6	3.0	6.9	1.8	27
Clover and mixed grasses*......	27.3	1.9	17.1	8.0	3.0	0.9	8.5	13.3	1.6	19
Corn ears, sweet, including husk*	37.8	2.4	29.5	11.3	3.8	2.6	4.3	26.2	0.9	3
Corn fodder, dent, all anal......	24.0	1.2	16.3	12.6	2.0	0.6	5.6	14.5	1.3	331
Corn fodder, dent, in tassel.....	15.0	1.0	9.7	8.7	1.6	0.3	4.2	7.8	1.1	19
Corn fodder, dent, in milk......	19.9	0.9	13.7	14.2	1.6	0.5	5.1	11.6	1.1	29
Corn fodder, dent, dough to glaz- ing.........................	26.9	1.2	19.1	14.9	2.1	0.7	6.2	16.6	1.3	62
Corn fodder, dent, kernels ripe..	37.7	1.7	26.0	14.3	3.0	1.0	7.8	24.2	1.7	20
Corn fodder, flint, all anal*.....	22.3	1.2	15.2	11.7	2.0	0.6	4.9	13.6	1.2	139
Corn fodder, flint, in tassel*.....	11.6	0.9	7.4	7.2	1.5	0.3	3.3	5.5	1.0	13
Corn fodder, flint, in milk*.....	17.0	0.9	11.5	11.8	1.6	0.3	4.2	9.8	1.1	12
Corn fodder, flint, dough to glaz- ing*........................	24.7	1.3	17.7	12.6	2.2	0.8	5.1	15.3	1.3	33
Corn fodder, flint, kernels ripe*..	41.2	2.0	28.5	13.3	3.5	1.3	8.1	26.2	2.1	10
Corn fodder, pop*.............	16.9	0.8	11.1	12.9	1.3	0.4	6.0	8.2	1.0	2
Corn fodder, sweet, before milk*.	10.0	0.6	6.4	9.7	1.0	0.3	2.5	5.2	1.0	5
Corn fodder, sweet, roasting ears or later...................	20.3	1.2	14.2	10.8	1.9	0.6	4.4	12.2	1.2	55
Corn leaves and tops*..........	15.9	1.2	10.4	7.7	1.9	0.6	4.4	7.8	1.2	2
Corn stover, green, field corn (ears removed)*.............	22.7	0.5	13.0	25.0	1.3	0.4	6.0	13.6	1.4	18
Corn stover, sweet, (ears re- moved)*....................	21.5	0.6	12.3	19.5	1.6	0.4	5.6	12.6	1.3	3
Cowpeas.....................	16.3	2.3	10.9	3.7	3.0	0.5	3.8	7.0	2.0	147
Cowpeas and corn*...........	20.0	1.4	13.3	8.5	2.1	0.4	5.3	10.4	1.8	1
Cowpeas and oats*............	21.8	3.4	14.1	3.1	4.5	0.9	5.7	8.5	2.2	3
Crab grass*...................	30.9	1.5	16.6	10.1	2.7	1.0	9.1	13.8	4.3	6
Darso fodder, green*..........	29.0	0.7	19.5	26.9	1.3	0.6	7.3	17.7	2.1	..
Durra fodder, green*..........	22.4	1.1	14.8	12.5	2.0	0.6	6.2	11.8	1.8	3
Fescue, meadow*..............	30.5	1.8	17.8	8.9	3.0	1.0	10.1	14.0	2.4	33
Fescues, native (*Festuca*, spp.)*..	36.0	2.1	21.0	9.0	3.5	0.8	12.5	16.7	2.5	10
Flat pea (*Lathyrus silvestris*,var.)*	22.5	4.4	14.2	2.2	5.7	0.8	6.4	8.0	1.6	8
Foxtail, meadow*.............	29.6	2.2	17.2	6.8	3.6	1.2	8.0	14.1	2.7	4
Grama grass (*Bouteloua*, spp.)*..	35.7	2.0	20.6	9.3	3.2	0.8	12.9	16.0	2.8	5
Grasses, mixed, immature......	29.7	3.6	20.2	4.6	5.1	1.5	6.3	13.8	3.0	6
Grasses, mixed, at haying stage..	30.8	1.7	18.2	9.7	3.0	1.3	10.6	14.1	1.8	7
Grasses, mixed, second crop*....	28.2	3.7	20.7	4.6	4.7	1.5	7.3	12.3	2.4	6
Guinea grass*.................	28.5	1.1	16.0	13.5	2.2	0.7	10.9	12.1	2.6	1
Horse bean*..................	17.4	2.7	10.8	3.0	3.5	0.5	4.1	7.6	1.7	8
Jack bean*...................	23.2	4.0	13.8	2.5	5.2	0.5	6.4	8.4	2.7	1
Johnson grass*................	29.1	1.1	16.5	14.0	2.5	0.9	9.3	14.4	2.0	14
Kafir fodder, all anal.*.........	23.6	1.3	15.5	10.9	2.4	0.7	6.6	12.0	1.9	56
Kafir fodder, heads just showing*	19.9	0.9	13.1	13.6	1.6	0.4	6.5	10.1	1.3	5
Kale........................	11.8	1.9	7.8	3.1	2.4	0.5	1.6	5.5	1.8	16
Kohlrabi*....................	9.0	1.6	8.3	4.2	2.0	0.1	1.3	4.3	1.3	2
Kudzu vine*..................	30.6	4.2	19.4	3.6	5.5	1.0	8.3	13.6	2.2	1

TABLE I. Average composition and digestible nutrients—*continued*.

Feeding stuff	Mineral and fertilizing constituents				Digestion coefficients				
	Calcium	Phosphorus	Nitrogen	Potassium	Protein	Fat	Fiber	N-free extract	No. of trials
Green Roughages, Roots, Etc. —Cont.	Per ct.	Per ct.	Per ct.	Per ct.	Per ct.	Per ct.	Per ct.	Per ct.	
Clover, mammoth red..........	..	0.05	0.64	0.33	..	..	..	..	..
Clover, red, all analyses........	0.43	0.07	0.64	0.54	64	63	53	71	4
Clover, red, before bloom.......	0.43	0.09	0.69	0.61	74	65	60	83	2
Clover, red, in bloom..........	0.50	0.08	0.66	0.54	..	..	..	..	..
Clover, red, second crop........	..	0.09	0.85	0.79	..	..	..	..	..
Clover, sweet.................	0.32	0.10	0.62	0.65	78	51	60	69	4
Clover, sweet, before bloom.....	..	..	0.70	..	..	..	..	..	..
Clover, white.................	0.23	0.05	0.62	0.40	..	..	..	..	..
Clover and mixed grasses.......	0.22	0.06	0.48	0.55	..	..	..	..	..
Corn ears, sweet, including husk.	..	..	0.61	..	..	..	..	..	..
Corn fodder, dent, all anal......	0.06	0.05	0.32	0.37	59	74	63	73	48
Corn fodder, dent, in tassel.....	..	..	0.26	..	61	69	64	71	15
Corn fodder, dent, in milk......	..	..	0.26	..	59	73	62	76	10
Corn fodder, dent, dough to glazing.........................	0.07	0.06	0.34	0.35	59	79	62	77	5
Corn fodder, dent, kernels ripe..	..	..	0.48	..	58	78	62	73	18
Corn fodder, flint, all anal......	..	0.04	0.32	0.33	..	..	..	..	..
Corn fodder, flint, in tassel.....	..	..	0.24	..	..	..	..	..	..
Corn fodder, flint, in milk......	..	..	0.26	..	..	..	..	..	..
Corn, fodder, flint, dough to glazing.........................	..	..	0.35	..	..	..	..	..	..
Corn fodder, flint, kernels, ripe..	..	..	0.56	..	..	..	..	..	..
Corn fodder, pop..............	..	..	0.21	..	..	..	..	..	..
Corn fodder, sweet, before milk.	..	0.02	0.16	0.16	..	..	..	..	..
Corn fodder, sweet, roasting ears or later.....................	..	0.04	0.30	0.32	62	75	60	77	12
Corn leaves and tops...........	..	..	0.30	..	..	..	..	..	..
Corn stover, green, field corn (ears removed)..............	..	0.05	0.21	0.28	..	..	..	..	..
Corn stover, sweet (ears removed)....................	..	..	0.26	..	..	..	..	..	..
Cowpeas......................	0.20	0.06	0.48	0.26	76	59	60	81	4
Cowpeas and corn..............	..	..	0.34	..	..	..	..	..	..
Cowpeas and oats..............	..	..	0.72	..	..	..	..	..	..
Crab grass....................	..	0.08	0.43	0.59	..	..	..	..	..
Darso fodder, green............	..	..	0.21	..	..	..	..	..	..
Durra fodder, green............	..	0.08	0.32	0.47	..	..	..	..	..
Fescue, meadow...............	0.15	0.07	0.48	0.69	..	..	..	..	..
Fescues, native (*Festuca*, spp.)..	..	..	0.56	..	..	..	..	..	..
Flat pea (*Lathyrus silvestris*, var.)	..	..	0.91	..	..	..	..	..	..
Foxtail, meadow...............	..	..	0.58	..	..	..	..	..	..
Grama grass (*Bouteloua*, spp.)...	..	..	0.51	..	..	..	..	..	..
Grasses, mixed, immature......	..	0.09	0.82	0.66	70	62	66	75	2
Grasses, mixed, at haying stage..	..	0.11	0.48	0.53	56	46	62	61	4
Grasses, mixed, second crop.....	..	0.09	0.75	0.62	..	..	..	..	..
Guinea grass..................	..	..	0.35	..	..	..	..	..	..
Horse bean...................	0.16	0.05	0.56	0.36	..	..	..	..	..
Jack bean....................	..	..	0.83	..	..	..	..	..	..
Johnson grass.................	..	..	0.40	..	..	..	..	..	..
Kafir fodder, all anal..........	0.06	0.04	0.38	0.40	..	..	..	..	..
Kafir fodder, heads just showing.	..	..	0.26	..	..	..	..	..	..
Kale........................	0.19	0.06	0.38	..	81	66	59	76	4
Kohlrabi.....................	0.08	0.07	0.32	0.37	..	..	..	..	..
Kudzu vine..................	..	..	0.88	..	..	..	..	..	..

TABLE I. Average composition and digestible nutrients—*continued*.

Feeding stuff	Total dry matter	Dig. protein	Total dig. nutrients	Nutritive ratio	Average total composition					No. of anal.
					Protein	Fat	Fiber	N-free extract	Mineral matter	
Green Roughages, Roots, Etc. —Cont.	Per ct.	Per ct.	Per ct.	1:	Per ct.	Per ct.	Per ct.	Per ct.	Per ct.	
Lespedeza, annual*............	36.6	5.0	20.9	3.2	6.7	1.0	10.7	14.7	3.5	1
Lupines......................	17.4	2.6	11.4	3.4	3.4	0.6	4.6	7.2	1.6	9
Mangels, roots................	9.4	1.0	7.3	6.3	1.4	0.1	0.8	6.1	1.0	38
Melons, pie, or stock*.........	6.1	0.5	4.8	8.6	0.7	0.2	1.4	3.4	0.4	3
Millet, foxtail varieties........	29.9	1.9	19.1	9.1	2.9	0.8	9.4	14.3	2.5	34
Millet, Japanese..............	21.7	1.0	14.2	13.2	1.7	0.6	6.8	11.0	1.6	46
Millet, hog, or broom-corn*....	24.7	1.2	16.2	12.5	2.0	0.6	7.4	12.9	1.8	11
Millet, pearl, or cat-tail*......	18.7	1.1	11.9	9.8	1.8	0.3	6.2	8.8	1.6	5
Milo fodder*.................	22.7	1.0	15.1	14.1	1.8	0.4	7.0	12.1	1.4	9
Mustard, white (*Brassica alba*)..	14.0	3.3	9.4	1.8	4.1	0.6	1.7	5.5	2.1	2
Napier grass*.................	24.1	1.4	15.0	9.7	2.5	0.3	9.1	10.0	2.2	4
Oat fodder...................	25.4	2.3	15.4	5.7	3.2	1.1	7.5	11.5	2.1	23
Oat fodder, 8 in. high*........	13.0	3.9	9.2	1.4	4.9	0.8	1.7	4.0	1.6	1
Oat grass, tall, or meadow oat grass*......................	30.3	1.6	17.9	10.2	2.6	0.9	10.5	14.3	2.0	31
Oats, wild (*Avena fatua*)*.......	36.6	1.9	22.3	10.7	2.6	1.4	8.6	21.3	2.7	5
Orchard grass, all anal.........	29.1	1.7	16.0	8.4	2.9	1.1	9.8	12.8	2.5	58
Orchard grass, before heading*..	22.8	3.5	16.1	3.6	4.4	1.2	5.3	9.1	2.8	5
Para grass*..................	27.2	1.0	15.5	14.5	1.7	0.5	9.2	13.4	2.4	2
Parsnips, roots*..............	16.6	1.3	14.3	10.0	1.7	0.4	1.3	11.9	1.3	2
Pasture grasses and clovers, mixed, from closely-grazed, fertile pasture.................	28.7	4.4	20.6	3.7	5.7	1.1	6.4	12.8	2.7	262
Pasture grasses and clovers, mixed, from fertile pasture, southern states*..............	24.4	2.6	16.1	5.2	3.7	0.8	6.5	10.8	2.6	179
Pasture grasses, mixed, from poor to fair pasture, before heading out*........................	30.2	3.3	19.6	4.9	4.7	0.8	6.5	14.5	3.7	40
Peas, field, Canada...........	16.6	2.9	10.6	2.7	3.6	0.5	4.0	6.9	1.6	33
Peas, field, miscellaneous*......	18.8	2.6	11.9	3.6	3.2	0.6	5.3	8.1	1.6	16
Peas and barley..............	20.2	2.7	12.5	3.6	3.6	0.8	5.2	8.9	1.7	11
Peas and oats................	22.1	2.4	14.1	4.9	3.2	0.9	6.2	9.9	1.9	49
Peas, oats, and rape*.........	17.9	2.3	10.7	3.7	3.1	0.8	4.3	7.0	2.7	3
Potatoes, tubers*.............	21.2	1.1	17.3	14.7	2.2	0.1	0.4	17.4	1.1	471
Potato pomace, wet*..........	8.3	0.4	6.9	16.3	0.7	0.1	0.9	6.3	0.3	2
Prickly comfrey*..............	12.8	2.0	8.0	3.0	2.5	0.3	1.8	5.9	2.3	20
Pumpkins, field..............	10.4	1.3	9.0	5.9	1.7	1.0	1.6	5.2	0.9	8
Pumpkins, with seeds and inside tissue removed..............	7.3	1.1	6.9	5.3	1.2	0.2	1.1	4.3	0.5	3
Purslane*....................	10.3	1.8	6.5	2.6	2.2	0.3	1.5	4.4	1.9	3
Quack grass*.................	25.0	1.8	14.1	6.8	3.8	1.2	7.0	10.5	2.5	6
Rape........................	16.4	2.6	13.0	4.0	2.9	0.6	2.6	8.1	2.2	39
Rape, leaves and leaf stalks*....	15.4	3.8	12.6	2.3	4.3	0.6	1.0	7.9	1.6	3
Rescue grass*................	30.6	1.8	17.6	8.8	3.8	1.0	8.6	14.8	2.4	8
Red top.....................	39.3	1.9	23.1	11.2	3.1	1.1	12.2	20.2	2.7	16
Reed canary grass*...........	37.0	1.7	21.4	11.6	3.6	1.1	10.9	18.5	2.9	5
Rhode Island bent grass*.......	32.7	1.4	18.7	12.4	2.9	0.7	10.6	15.9	2.6	3
Rushes, western (*Juncus*, spp.)*.	31.1	1.3	14.0	9.8	3.4	0.6	9.8	15.1	2.2	11
Rutabagas, roots.............	11.1	1.0	9.3	8.3	1.3	0.2	1.4	7.2	1.0	11
Rye fodder, all analyses........	22.3	2.3	16.2	6.0	2.9	0.8	7.3	9.5	1.8	45
Rye fodder, 5 in. high*........	18.1	5.1	12.8	1.5	6.5	0.9	2.0	6.5	2.2	1
Rye fodder, not over 10 in. high*.	17.4	4.4	12.3	1.8	5.6	0.8	2.1	6.8	2.1	2
Rye grass, Italian*............	27.1	1.5	15.7	9.5	3.1	1.3	6.8	13.4	2.5	25

TABLE I. Average composition and digestible nutrients—*continued*.

Feeding stuff	Mineral and fertilizing constituents				Digestion coefficients				
	Calcium	Phosphorus	Nitrogen	Potassium	Protein	Fat	Fiber	N-free extract	No. of trials
Green Roughages, Roots, Etc. —Cont.	Per ct.	Per ct.	Per ct.	Per ct.	Per ct.	Per ct.	Per ct.	Per ct.	
Lespedeza, annual.............	0.41	0.08	1.07	0.35	..	..	..	..	..
Lupines.....................	..	0.04	0.54	0.42	75	57	56	76	2
Mangels, roots................	0.01	0.03	0.22	0.36	70	..	78	94	6
Melons, pie, or stock..........	..	..	0.11	..	..	..	..	..	
Millet, foxtail varieties.........	0.30	0.12	0.46	0.84	64	62	70	67	8
Millet, Japanese...............	0.11	0.07	0.27	0.52	60	62	69	70	9
Millet, hog, or broom-corn......	..	0.05	0.32	0.47	..	..	..	..	
Millet, pearl, or cat-tail........	..	0.07	0.29	0.37	..	..	..	..	
Milo fodder...................	..	0.07	0.29	0.62	..	..	..	..	
Mustard, white (*Brassica alba*)..	..	..	0.66	..	..	..	..	..	
Napier grass..................	..	..	0.40	..	..	..	..	..	
Oat fodder....................	0.12	0.10	0.51	0.71	73	70	55	63	5
Oat fodder, 8 in. high..........	..	..	0.78	..	..	..	..	..	
Oat grass, tall, or meadow oat grass......................	0.16	0.08	0.42	0.68	..	..	..	..	..
Oats, wild (*Avena fatua*)........	0.09	0.10	0.42	..	..	..	..	..	
Orchard grass, all anal.........	0.12	0.09	0.46	0.77	60	54	60	55	3
Orchard grass, before heading...	0.13	0.16	0.70	0.80	..	..	..	..	
Para grass....................	0.13	0.05	0.27	0.19	..	..	..	..	
Parsnips, roots................	0.06	0.08	0.27	0.52	..	..	..	..	
Pasture grasses and clovers, mixed, from closely-grazed, fertile pasture.................	0.21	0.09	0.91	0.62	77	56	76	78	51
Pasture grasses and clovers, mixed, from fertile pasture, southern states..............	0.24	0.19	0.59	..	..	..	..	..	..
Pasture grasses, mixed, from poor to fair pasture, before heading out.......................	0.15	0.04	0.75	..	..	..	..	..	..
Peas, field, Canada...........	0.28	0.06	0.58	0.28	81	54	49	74	8
Peas, field, miscellaneous.......	..	0.05	0.51	0.27	..	..	..	..	
Peas and barley...............	..	0.06	0.58	0.49	75	59	52	68	4
Peas and oats.................	0.07	0.07	0.51	0.42	74	64	59	68	10
Peas, oats, and rape...........	..	0.07	0.50	0.37	..	..	..	..	
Potatoes, tubers..............	0.01	0.05	0.35	0.45	51	..	..	90	30
Potato pomace, wet............	0.01	0.03	0.11	0.11	..	..	..	..	
Prickly comfrey...............	..	0.07	0.40	0.58	..	..	..	..	
Pumpkins, field...............	..	0.04	0.27	0.27	77	92	61	89	7
Pumpkins, with seeds and inside tissue removed...............	0.02	0.03	0.19	0.26	93	93	100	100	2
Purslane.....................	..	0.04	0.35	0.94	..	..	..	..	
Quack grass..................	..	..	0.61	..	..	..	..	..	
Rape........................	0.34	0.07	0.46	0.37	89	49	87	92	4
Rape, leaves and leaf stalks.....	..	..	0.69	..	..	..	..	..	
Rescue grass..................	..	0.08	0.61	0.44	..	..	..	..	
Red top......................	..	0.10	0.50	0.70	61	50	61	62	3
Reed canary grass	0.16	0.09	0.58	0.67	..	..	..	..	
Rhode Island bent grass	..	0.10	0.46	0.71	..	..	..	..	
Rushes, western (*Juncus*, spp.)..	..	..	0.54	..	..	..	..	..	
Rutabagas, roots..............	0.07	0.05	0.21	0.41	78	75	78	95	4
Rye fodder, all analyses........	..	0.07	0.46	0.41	79	74	80	71	2
Rye fodder, 5 in. high..........	..	..	1.04	..	..	..	..	..	
Rye fodder, not over 10 in. high	..	..	0.90	..	..	..	..	..	
Rye grass, Italian..............	..	0.09	0.50	0.62	..	..	..	..	

TABLE I. Average composition and digestible nutrients—*continued*.

Feeding stuff	Total dry matter	Dig. protein	Total dig. nutrients	Nutritive ratio	Average total composition					
					Protein	Fat	Fiber	N-free extract	Mineral matter	No. of anal.
	Per ct.	Per ct.	Per ct.	1:	Per ct.	Per ct.	Per ct.	Per ct.	Per ct.	
Green Roughages, Roots, Etc. **—Cont.**										
Rye grass, perennial*..........	26.6	1.4	15.5	10.1	3.0	1.3	6.7	13.2	2.4	25
Saltbush, Australian*..........	23.3	2.7	9.0	2.3	3.7	0.4	4.4	9.4	5.4	7
Saltbushes, miscellaneous*......	24.3	2.9	9.8	2.4	3.9	0.3	4.2	10.8	5.1	3
Sanfoin (*Onobrychis viciaefolia*)..	25.6	2.8	16.3	4.8	3.8	0.8	6.2	12.4	2.4	4
Sedges, western (*Carex*, spp.)*...	37.9	1.5	17.1	10.4	3.9	1.1	11.3	18.5	3.1	19
Serradella*...................	20.2	2.2	11.1	4.0	2.9	0.7	4.8	8.8	3.0	8
Sorghum fodder, sweet.........	24.9	0.8	17.3	20.6	1.5	1.0	7.0	14.0	1.4	94
Sotol, heads, or bulbs.........	39.7	0.9	24.8	26.6	2.2	0.6	10.4	24.8	1.7	7
Soybeans, all analyses..........	24.4	3.2	15.1	3.7	4.2	1.1	6.7	10.1	2.3	239
Soybeans, before bloom*.......	27.8	3.5	17.2	3.9	4.5	1.4	8.2	11.2	2.5	23
Soybeans, in bloom............	20.8	3.0	12.2	3.1	3.9	0.6	5.8	8.2	2.3	8
Soybeans, in seed.............	24.2	3.1	15.0	3.8	4.0	1.0	6.4	10.4	2.4	21
Soybeans, seed well developed...	29.0	3.6	18.2	4.1	4.7	1.7	8.3	11.7	2.6	22
Soybeans and corn, ⅓ or more soybeans*...................	23.1	1.8	15.3	7.5	2.8	0.8	5.3	12.5	1.7	7
Soybeans and corn, small proportion of soybeans*............	26.7	1.3	18.3	13.1	2.2	0.8	6.3	15.9	1.5	5
Soybeans and kafir*...........	17.1	1.1	10.6	8.6	2.0	0.6	6.2	6.2	2.1	1
Soybeans and millet*..........	23.5	1.5	15.1	9.1	2.3	0.5	7.5	11.4	1.8	7
Soybeans and Sudan grass......	24.2	2.0	16.1	7.1	2.7	0.5	8.3	11.1	1.6	7
Sudan grass, all analyses.......	25.7	1.4	17.7	11.6	2.0	0.6	8.5	12.8	1.8	12
Sudan grass, in bloom or before..	23.2	1.6	16.0	9.0	2.2	0.6	7.5	11.2	1.7	4
Sudan grass, in seed...........	28.5	0.6	16.1	25.8	1.7	0.5	9.6	14.6	2.1	3
Sugar cane*...................	21.7	0.5	15.1	29.2	0.9	1.0	6.2	12.2	1.4	8
Sugar cane, Japanese*..........	28.2	0.4	19.6	48.0	0.7	0.5	7.7	18.2	1.1	3
Sugar cane tops*..............	28.5	0.8	18.7	22.4	1.5	0.4	8.9	15.6	2.1	1
Sunflowers, Russian, whole plant*	16.4	0.7	9.3	12.3	1.4	0.7	5.0	7.6	1.7	38
Sunflowers and corn*..........	18.2	0.7	10.3	13.7	1.4	0.6	6.1	8.5	1.6	2
Sweet potatoes, tubers*........	31.5	0.8	26.7	33.4	1.6	0.4	1.9	26.4	1.2	29
Sweet vernal grass (*Anthoxanthum oderatum*)*..............	31.2	1.2	18.4	14.3	2.6	1.0	9.7	15.9	2.0	6
Teosinte*....................	21.3	1.0	13.7	12.7	1.7	0.5	6.7	10.4	2.0	19
Thistle, Russian*..............	20.4	2.2	8.0	2.6	3.0	0.5	4.8	8.3	3.8	5
Timothy, all analyses..........	31.3	1.8	18.1	9.1	3.8	1.0	8.6	15.5	2.4	160
Timothy, pasture stage*........	22.8	3.7	16.0	3.3	4.7	0.8	4.2	10.4	2.7	68
Timothy, before bloom.........	24.2	1.6	15.9	8.9	2.5	0.7	7.3	12.0	1.7	5
Timothy, in bloom.............	32.1	1.3	18.8	13.5	2.7	0.9	10.4	16.1	2.0	15
Timothy, in seed*.............	46.4	1.2	22.7	17.9	3.1	1.3	15.3	24.4	2.3	13
Tomatoes, whole fruit*.........	5.7	0.8	5.4	5.8	0.9	0.4	0.6	3.3	0.5	24
Tomato waste (skin, seeds, etc.)*	11.1	1.1	6.9	5.3	2.3	1.2	2.8	4.3	0.5	1
Trefoil, yellow, or black medic (*Medicago lupulina*)*.........	22.7	3.3	13.2	3.0	4.5	0.8	5.6	9.5	2.3	2
Turnips......................	9.5	1.3	8.5	5.5	1.4	0.2	1.1	5.9	0.9	20
Turnip tops..................	15.0	2.2	10.9	4.0	2.8	0.4	1.5	7.3	3.0	5
Velvet bean..................	17.9	2.6	12.3	3.7	3.5	0.7	5.1	6.6	2.0	1
Vetch, common...............	20.4	2.7	12.2	3.5	3.8	0.5	5.5	8.5	2.1	14
Vetch, hairy.................	18.2	3.5	12.3	2.5	4.2	0.5	5.0	6.3	2.2	21
Vetch, kidney (*Anthyllis vulneraria*)*......................	27.7	2.6	16.1	5.2	3.7	0.5	8.3	12.0	3.2	5
Vetches, wild*................	24.6	3.6	13.9	2.9	5.1	0.5	6.9	10.0	2.1	6
Vetch and oats...............	26.5	2.9	17.1	4.9	3.8	0.9	7.5	12.0	2.3	15
Vetch and wheat..............	22.7	2.4	15.4	5.4	3.3	0.6	7.1	10.1	1.6	5
Wheat fodder, all analyses*.....	26.0	2.6	15.2	4.8	3.6	0.7	7.0	12.1	2.6	19
Wheat fodder, 5 in. high*.......	24.2	5.1	16.9	2.3	6.5	0.7	3.9	10.1	3.0	1

TABLE I. Average composition and digestible nutrients—*continued*.

Feeding stuff	Mineral and fertilizing constituents				Digestion coefficients				
	Calcium	Phosphorus	Nitrogen	Potassium	Protein	Fat	Fiber	N-free extract	No. of trials
Green Roughages, Roots, Etc.—Cont.	Per ct.	Per ct.	Per ct.	Per ct.	Per ct.	Per ct.	Per ct.	Per ct.	
Rye grass, perennial...........	0.13	0.07	0.48	0.51	..	..	..	..	..
Saltbush, Australian...........	..	0.15	0.59	1.20	..	..	..	..	..
Saltbushes, miscellaneous.......	..	..	0.62	..	..	..	..	..	..
Sanfoin (*Onobrychis viciaefolia*)..	..	..	0.62	..	73	67	42	78	2
Sedges, western (*Carex*, spp.)....	..	..	0.62	..	..	..	..	..	..
Serradella....................	0.28	0.09	0.46	0.43	..	..	..	..	..
Sorghum fodder, sweet.........	0.12	0.05	0.24	0.36	56	70	62	75	6
Sotol, heads, or bulbs..........	..	..	0.35	..	40	3	36	81	..
Soybeans, all analyses..........	0.29	0.09	0.67	0.29	77	53	45	75	23
Soybeans, before bloom.........	..	..	0.72	..	..	..	..	..	..
Soybeans, in bloom.............	..	..	0.62	..	77	50	47	71	2
Soybeans, in seed..............	..	..	0.64	..	..	..	..	..	..
Soybeans, seed well developed...	..	..	0.75	..	..	..	..	..	..
Soybeans and corn, ⅓ or more soybeans......................	0.15	0.07	0.45	0.34	..	..	..	..	..
Soybeans and corn, small proportion of soybeans.............	0.08	0.05	0.35	0.36	..	..	..	..	..
Soybeans and kafir.............	..	..	0.32	..	..	..	..	..	..
Soybeans and millet............	..	..	0.37	..	..	..	..	..	..
Soybeans and Sudan grass......	..	..	0.43	..	..	..	..	..	..
Sudan grass, all analyses........	0.14	0.06	0.32	0.43	72	72	76	69	4
Sudan grass, in bloom or before..	..	..	0.35	..	..	..	..	..	..
Sudan grass, in seed............	..	..	0.27	..	..	..	..	..	..
Sugar cane....................	..	0.04	0.14	0.37	..	..	..	..	..
Sugar cane, Japanese...........	..	..	0.11	..	..	..	..	..	..
Sugar cane tops................	..	..	0.24	..	..	..	..	..	..
Sunflowers, Russian, whole plant	..	..	0.22	..	..	..	..	..	..
Sunflowers and corn............	..	..	0.22	..	..	..	..	..	..
Sweet potatoes, tubers.........	0.03	0.06	0.26	0.38	..	..	..	..	..
Sweet vernal grass (*Anthoxanthum oderatum*)...............	..	..	0.42	..	..	..	..	..	..
Teosinte......................	..	0.04	0.27	0.21	..	..	..	..	..
Thistle, Russian................	..	..	0.48	..	..	..	..	..	..
Timothy, all analyses..........	0.14	0.06	0.61	0.56	48	53	56	66	3
Timothy, pasture stage.........	0.11	0.08	0.75	0.56	..	..	..	..	..
Timothy, before bloom.........	..	..	0.40	..	..	..	..	..	..
Timothy, in bloom.............	..	..	0.43	..	..	..	..	..	..
Timothy, in seed..............	..	..	0.50	..	..	..	..	..	..
Tomatoes, whole fruit..........	..	0.03	0.14	0.30	..	..	..	..	..
Tomato waste (skin, seeds, etc.)	..	..	0.37	..	..	..	..	..	..
Trefoil, yellow, or black medic (*Medicago lupulina*)..........	..	..	0.72	..	..	..	..	..	..
Turnips......................	0.06	0.04	0.22	0.37	90	88	100	97	2
Turnip tops...................	0.39	0.08	0.45	0.46	79	65	86	93	2
Velvet bean...................	..	0.06	0.56	0.37	73	81	60	82	2
Vetch, common................	0.35	0.09	0.61	0.44	71	59	44	76	2
Vetch, hairy..................	..	0.06	0.67	0.42	83	72	64	77	14
Vetch, kidney (*Anthyllis vulneraria*)......................	..	0.04	0.59	0.25	..	..	..	..	..
Vetches, wild.................	..	..	0.82	..	..	..	..	..	..
Vetch and oats................	..	0.07	0.61	0.52	75	47	68	68	3
Vetch and wheat..............	..	..	0.53	..	74	57	68	73	5
Wheat fodder, all analyses......	0.07	0.09	0.58	0.60	..	..	..	..	..
Wheat fodder, 5 in. high.......	..	..	1.04	..	..	..	..	..	..

TABLE I. Average composition and digestible nutrients—*continued*.

Feeding stuff	Total dry matter	Dig. protein	Total dig. nutrients	Nutritive ratio	Average total composition					
					Protein	Fat	Fiber	N-free extract	Mineral matter	No. of anal.
Green Roughages, Roots, Etc.	Per ct.	Per ct.	Per ct.	1:	Per ct.	Per ct.	Per ct.	Per ct.	Per ct.	
—Cont.										
Wheat fodder, not over 10 in. high*	20.8	4.3	13.5	2.1	5.7	0.7	3.1	8.7	2.6	2
Wheat grasses, misc. (*Agropyron* spp.)*	46.9	2.0	27.0	12.5	4.1	1.3	16.5	21.6	3.4	21
Wire grasses, western*	38.9	1.8	22.6	11.6	3.8	0.9	13.3	18.6	2.3	4
Yucca (bear grass)	49.4	1.4	27.5	18.6	3.8	1.0	21.1	20.0	3.5	2
Yucca (soapweed)	44.6	0.9	23.4	25.0	2.4	0.8	14.1	24.0	3.3	22
Yucca (soapweed), leaves*	56.2	1.7	28.4	15.7	4.4	1.7	18.7	27.7	3.7	8
Silages										
Alfalfa, wilted before being ensiled*	54.0	5.1	29.0	4.7	10.0	2.5	14.2	22.0	5.3	4
Alfalfa, high in water*	23.9	1.9	12.7	5.7	3.7	1.4	7.4	8.6	2.8	5
Apple pomace*	20.9	0.6	15.5	24.8	1.6	1.3	4.4	12.6	1.0	15
Artichoke, globe	30.2	0.3	15.7	51.3	2.1	0.5	8.2	13.8	5.6	1
Barley*	25.0	1.7	14.4	7.5	2.6	1.0	9.4	9.4	2.6	2
Bean, mung, nearly mature*	23.3	1.9	13.5	6.1	3.1	1.2	9.8	8.0	1.2	1
Beet tops, sugar*	27.0	1.8	11.8	5.6	3.5	0.7	3.0	11.3	8.5	8
Broom-corn*	20.0	0.7	11.4	15.3	1.3	0.2	6.8	9.8	1.9	1
Clover, red	24.4	2.0	13.4	5.7	3.9	1.3	6.7	10.4	2.1	73
Clover, sweet*	28.0	3.5	16.1	3.6	4.5	0.9	9.6	10.5	2.5	10
Clover, sweet, wilted before being ensiled	40.0	4.9	23.0	3.7	6.4	1.3	13.7	15.0	3.6	10
Corn, dent, well-matured, all analyses	28.3	1.3	18.7	13.4	2.3	0.9	6.9	16.5	1.7	248
Corn, dent, well-matured, well-eared	29.2	1.5	20.6	12.7	2.5	0.9	6.4	17.8	1.6	135
Corn, dent, well-matured, fair in ears	26.7	1.1	17.4	14.8	2.1	0.8	7.1	14.9	1.8	83
Corn, dent, well-matured, few ears	26.6	1.1	16.3	13.8	2.1	0.9	8.6	12.9	2.1	22
Corn, dent, immature, before dough stage	20.4	1.0	13.3	12.3	1.8	0.6	5.8	10.9	1.3	80
Corn, dent, immature, southern-type corn	19.4	0.9	12.1	12.4	1.6	0.5	6.0	10.2	1.1	21
Corn, dent, stover silage (ears removed)	22.6	0.8	13.6	16.0	1.5	0.6	7.7	11.3	1.5	8
Corn, flint, well-matured, well-eared	29.2	1.4	20.6	13.7	2.4	0.9	6.5	17.3	2.1	...
Corn, sweet	24.2	1.5	15.8	9.5	2.3	0.8	6.9	12.2	2.0	14
Corn, sweet, stover silage (ears removed)*	24.0	1.3	13.9	9.7	2.3	0.5	5.6	13.8	1.8	1
Corn and clover*	28.6	1.7	16.4	8.6	3.3	0.9	7.7	14.5	2.2	1
Corn and rye*	19.4	1.1	13.1	10.9	2.1	1.2	7.2	7.5	1.4	1
Corn and soybeans, mostly corn*	28.3	1.5	19.5	12.2	2.5	0.7	7.2	16.2	1.7	9
Corn and soybeans, well-matured, 30% or more soybeans	28.1	2.0	19.5	8.8	3.1	1.1	7.2	14.3	2.4	9
Corn-canning factory waste (husks, cobs, and waste ears)*	22.4	1.1	11.5	9.5	2.0	1.0	5.6	12.8	2.0	2
Cowpea	20.7	1.8	12.2	5.8	3.1	0.8	5.9	8.6	2.3	13
Crotalaria intermedia	27.1	2.1	10.8	4.1	3.3	0.8	12.5	8.3	2.2	1
Darso	26.9	1.0	15.6	14.6	1.9	0.3	6.5	16.7	1.5	1
Durra*	20.3	0.6	11.3	17.8	1.2	0.7	7.0	9.5	1.9	3
Ear corn silage (corn ears and husks, without stalks)*	45.7	2.7	36.3	12.4	4.1	1.7	6.1	32.9	0.9	5

TABLE I. Average composition and digestible nutrients—*continued*.

Feeding stuff	Mineral and fertilizing constituents				Digestion coefficients				
	Calcium	Phosphorus	Nitrogen	Potassium	Protein	Fat	Fiber	N-free extract	No. of trials
Green Roughages, Roots, Etc.—Cont.	Per ct.	Per ct.	Per ct.	Per ct.	Per ct.	Per ct.	Per ct.	Per ct.	
Wheat fodder, not over 10 in. high	..	..	0.91	..	..	..	..	..	..
Wheat grasses, misc. (*Agropyron*, spp.)	..	..	0.66	..	..	..	..	..	..
Wire grasses, western	..	..	0.61	..	..	..	..	..	..
Yucca (bear grass)	..	..	0.61	..	36	0	65	62	2
Yucca (soapweed)	..	..	0.38	..	38	0	35	73	7
Yucca (soapweed), leaves	..	..	0.70	..	..	..	..	..	..
Silages									
Alfalfa, wilted before being ensiled	0.85	0.13	1.60	1.21	..	..	..	..	..
Alfalfa, high in water	0.38	0.06	0.59	0.53	..	..	..	..	..
Apple pomace	0.02	0.02	0.26	0.10	..	..	..	..	..
Artichoke, globe	..	..	0.34	..	16	34	65	70	5
Barley	0.08	0.08	0.42	0.39	..	..	..	..	..
Bean, mung, nearly mature	..	..	0.50	..	..	..	..	..	..
Beet tops, sugar	0.31	0.09	0.56	1.26	..	..	..	..	..
Broom-corn	..	..	0.21	..	..	..	..	..	..
Clover, red	0.42	0.07	0.62	0.53	51	62	49	61	10
Clover, sweet	0.41	0.13	0.72	0.83	..	..	..	..	..
Clover, sweet, wilted before being ensiled	0.58	0.18	1.02	1.18	77	62	44	68	11
Corn, dent, well-matured, all analyses	0.07	0.06	0.37	0.30	54	74	66	69	85
Corn, dent, well-matured, well-eared	0.08	0.06	0.40	0.28	58	80	65	75	18
Corn, dent, well-matured, fair in ears	0.09	0.06	0.34	0.31	53	73	66	69	45
Corn, dent, well-matured, few ears	0.10	0.05	0.34	0.38	50	65	71	61	7
Corn, dent, immature, before dough stage	..	..	0.29	..	52	73	67	66	41
Corn, dent, immature, southern-type corn	0.05	0.04	0.26	0.34	53	73	66	62	15
Corn, dent, stover silage (ears removed)	0.11	0.02	0.24	0.42	56	66	67	59	8
Corn, flint, well-matured, well-eared	..	..	0.38	..	61	81	65	77	5
Corn, sweet	..	..	0.37	..	66	78	73	64	4
Corn, sweet, stover silage (ears removed)	..	..	0.37	..	..	..	..	..	..
Corn and clover	..	..	0.53	..	..	..	..	..	..
Corn and rye	..	..	0.34	..	..	..	..	..	..
Corn and soybeans, mostly corn	0.11	0.06	0.35	0.30	..	..	..	..	..
Corn and soybeans, well-matured, 30% or more soybeans	0.18	0.08	0.50	0.31	63	83	62	77	8
Corn-canning factory waste (husks, cobs, and waste ears)	..	..	0.32	..	..	..	..	..	..
Cowpea	0.26	0.07	0.50	0.31	57	63	52	73	4
Crotalaria intermedia	..	..	0.53	..	63	67	33	41	4
Darso	..	..	0.30	..	..	60	39	70	3
Durra	..	..	0.19	..	..	..	..	..	..
Ear corn silage (corn ears and husks, without stalks)	..	..	0.66	..	..	..	..	..	..

TABLE I. Average composition and digestible nutrients—*continued*.

Feeding stuff	Total dry matter	Dig. protein	Total dig. nutrients	Nutritive ratio	Protein	Fat	Fiber	N-free extract	Mineral matter	No. of anal.
	Per ct.	Per ct.	Per ct.	1:	Per ct.	Per ct.	Per ct.	Per ct.	Per ct.	
Silages—Cont.										
Feterita*.....................	30.0	1.4	17.1	11.2	2.6	0.7	6.0	18.6	2.1	1
Hegari*......................	34.7	0.9	19.5	20.7	1.8	0.8	6.9	22.2	3.0	3
Hegari stover*...............	29.1	0.5	16.3	31.6	0.9	0.6	7.9	16.3	3.4	2
Horse bean*..................	21.2	2.0	12.2	5.1	3.3	0.5	5.7	10.3	1.4	3
Kafir........................	30.2	1.0	17.3	16.3	1.9	1.1	8.7	16.3	2.2	6
Millet*......................	31.1	1.6	17.5	9.9	2.7	1.0	9.6	14.9	2.9	7
Millet, barnyard, and soybeans..	21.0	1.6	12.4	6.8	2.8	1.0	7.2	7.2	2.8	9
Napier grass..................	32.5	0.3	14.3	46.7	1.2	0.7	14.4	14.4	1.8	1
Oat*........................	28.3	1.1	15.4	13.0	2.0	1.3	9.8	13.3	1.9	2
Pea, field*...................	27.9	2.9	18.0	5.2	3.8	1.2	7.8	12.5	2.6	8
Pea and oat..................	30.0	2.7	19.2	6.1	3.6	1.2	9.4	13.0	2.8	18
Pea-vine, from canneries*.....	27.9	2.6	17.8	5.8	3.5	1.0	7.8	13.1	2.5	4
Reed canary grass*...........	30.5	0.8	17.9	21.4	1.5	0.6	11.1	15.3	2.0	1
Rye*........................	30.3	1.4	14.2	9.1	3.5	1.0	10.8	12.5	2.5	7
Sagrain sorghum, well-matured*.	38.1	1.6	23.1	13.4	2.8	1.2	9.1	22.7	2.3	4
Sorghum, grain varieties*.......	31.3	1.1	17.8	15.2	2.1	0.9	7.9	18.1	2.3	19
Sorghum, sweet*..............	25.1	0.8	15.1	17.9	1.5	0.8	7.0	14.2	1.6	94
Sorghum and cowpeas*.........	32.3	1.3	18.4	13.2	2.4	1.0	8.5	18.2	2.2	8
Soybean......................	27.2	2.6	15.0	4.8	4.2	1.5	7.9	10.1	3.5	12
Sudan grass*.................	26.1	1.2	15.1	11.6	2.2	0.9	8.8	11.8	2.4	3
Sugar cane, Japanese*.........	25.2	0.6	14.6	23.3	1.1	0.5	9.3	12.4	1.9	4
Sugar cane tops*..............	29.6	0.8	16.8	20.0	1.5	0.6	10.6	14.1	2.8	3
Sunflower....................	22.2	1.1	12.6	10.5	2.1	1.0	6.8	10.0	2.3	77
Sunflower and corn*...........	23.6	1.5	13.4	7.9	3.0	0.7	7.0	11.1	1.8	2
Thistle, Russian*.............	34.4	1.0	17.3	16.3	2.0	0.9	10.4	14.7	6.4	1
Velvet bean*..................	23.6	2.7	14.0	4.2	4.3	1.2	8.0	9.0	1.1	1
Vetch.......................	30.1	2.0	18.8	8.4	3.5	1.0	9.8	13.4	2.4	6
Vetch and oats*..............	26.4	1.7	16.7	8.8	2.2	0.6	8.8	12.9	1.9	2
Concentrates *(Grains and other seeds and their by-products; miscellaneous concentrates.)*										
Acorn, whole (red oak)*........	50.0	0.6	34.9	57.2	3.2	10.7	9.9	25.0	1.2	1
Acorn, whole, (white and post oaks)	62.4	0.7	30.3	42.3	3.3	3.4	11.3	43.0	1.4	3
Alfalfa-molasses feed*..........	86.0	7.8	56.3	4.9	11.4	1.2	18.5	46.2	8.7	11
Alfalfa seed screenings*........	90.3	18.3	59.7	2.3	31.1	9.9	11.1	33.1	5.1	11
Alcohol by-product feed*.......	92.6	20.1	59.9	2.0	31.4	9.2	9.2	30.9	11.9	1
Apple-pectin pulp, dried*.......	91.2	2.6	55.0	20.2	7.0	7.3	24.2	49.4	3.3	6
Apple pectin pulp, wet*........	16.7	0.6	9.7	15.2	1.5	0.9	5.8	7.9	0.6	4
Apple pomace, dried...........	89.4	1.7	60.5	34.6	4.5	5.0	15.6	62.1	2.2	7
Apple pomace, wet............	21.1	0.5	16.0	31.0	1.3	1.3	3.7	13.9	0.9	29
Babassu oil meal*.............	89.7	18.6	74.7	3.0	22.4	6.4	11.8	44.2	4.9	4
Bakery waste, dried (high in fat)*	91.6	10.0	101.2	9.1	10.9	13.7	0.7	64.7	1.6	3
Barley, common, not including Pacific Coast states...........	90.4	9.3	78.7	7.5	11.8	2.0	5.7	68.0	2.9	98
Barley, Pacific Coast states.....	89.9	6.9	78.8	10.4	8.7	1.9	5.7	71.0	2.6	78
Barley, light weight*...........	89.8	9.7	73.1	6.5	12.3	2.3	8.5	63.7	3.0	18
Barley, hull-less or bald*.......	90.2	9.2	80.4	7.7	11.6	2.0	2.4	72.1	2.1	6
Barley bran, nearly all hulls*....	91.9	4.3	40.8	8.5	5.9	1.3	26.4	51.8	6.4	2
Barley feed, high grade*........	90.1	10.2	67.6	5.6	13.2	3.5	8.4	61.0	4.0	33
Barley feed, low grade........	92.0	9.1	50.2	4.5	12.3	3.5	14.7	56.2	5.3	19
Barley malt*..................	93.4	10.0	82.1	7.2	12.7	2.1	5.4	70.9	2.3	6
Barley screenings*.............	88.6	8.1	60.8	6.5	11.5	2.8	9.5	60.6	4.2	4

TABLE I. Average composition and digestible nutrients—*continued*.

Feeding stuff	Mineral and fertilizing constituents				Digestion coefficients				
	Calcium	Phosphorus	Nitrogen	Potassium	Protein	Fat	Fiber	N-free extract	No. of trials
Silages—Cont.	Per ct.	Per ct.	Per ct.	Per ct.	Per ct.	Per ct.	Per ct.	Per ct.	
Feterita	..	..	0.42	..	..	..	..	..	..
Hegari	..	..	0.29	..	..	..	..	..	..
Hegari stover	..	..	0.14	..	..	..	..	..	..
Horse bean	0.19	0.06	0.53	0.44	..	..	..	..	..
Kafir	0.06	0.05	0.30	0.51	..	50	57	62	3
Millet	0.31	0.12	0.43	0.87	..	..	..	..	..
Millet, Japanese, and soybeans	..	..	0.45	..	57	72	69	59	4
Napier grass	..	..	0.19	..	29	65	50	40	3
Oat	..	..	0.32	..	..	..	..	..	..
Pea, field	..	..	0.61	..	..	..	..	..	..
Pea and oat	0.09	0.07	0.58	0.58	75	75	61	67	2
Pea-vine, from canneries	..	..	0.56	..	..	..	..	..	..
Reed canary grass	..	..	0.24	..	..	..	..	..	..
Rye	..	0.07	0.56	0.56	..	..	..	..	..
Sagrain sorghum, well-matured	..	..	0.45	..	..	..	..	..	..
Sorghum, grain varieties	..	..	0.34	..	..	..	..	..	..
Sorghum, sweet	0.07	0.04	0.24	0.37	..	58	57	65	5
Sorghum and cowpeas	0.14	0.04	0.38	0.30	..	58	49	64	..
Soybean	0.31	0.10	0.45	0.32	62	55	51	64	9
Sudan grass	..	..	0.35	..	..	..	..	..	..
Sugar cane, Japanese	..	..	0.18	..	..	..	..	..	..
Sugar cane tops	..	..	0.24	..	..	..	..	..	..
Sunflower	0.39	0.04	0.34	0.65	50	74	49	66	26
Sunflower and corn	..	..	0.48	..	..	..	..	..	..
Thistle, Russian	..	..	0.32	..	..	..	..	..	..
Velvet bean	..	..	0.69	..	..	..	..	..	..
Vetch	..	..	0.56	..	56	77	63	67	2
Vetch and oats	..	..	0.35	..	..	..	..	..	..
Concentrates (*Grains and other seeds and their by-products; miscellaneous concentrates.*)									
Acorn, whole (red oak)	..	..	0.51	..	..	..	..	..	..
Acorn, whole (white and post oaks)	..	..	0.53	..	20	84	15	50	2
Alfalfa-molasses feed	..	..	1.82	..	..	..	..	..	..
Alfalfa seed screenings	..	..	4.98	..	..	..	..	..	..
Alcohol by-product feed	..	..	5.02	..	..	..	..	..	..
Apple-pectin pulp, dried	..	..	1.12	..	..	..	..	..	..
Apple pectin pulp, wet	..	..	0.24	..	..	..	..	..	..
Apple pomace, dried	0.10	0.09	0.72	0.43	37	35	64	78	7
Apple pomace, wet	0.02	0.02	0.21	0.10	37	46	65	85	6
Babassu oil meal	..	..	3.58	..	..	..	..	..	..
Bakery waste, dried (high in fat)	..	..	1.74	..	..	..	..	..	..
Barley, common, not including Pacific Coast states	0.05	0.38	1.89	0.52	79	80	56	92	16
Barley, Pacific Coast states	..	..	1.39	..	..	..	..	..	..
Barley, light weight	..	..	1.97	..	..	..	..	..	..
Barley, hull-less or bald	..	..	1.86	..	..	..	..	..	..
Barley bran, nearly all hulls	..	..	0.94	..	..	..	..	..	..
Barley feed, high grade	0.03	0.40	2.11	0.60	..	..	..	..	..
Barley feed, low grade	..	..	1.97	..	74	9	38	62	2
Barley malt	0.06	0.42	2.03	0.37	..	..	..	..	..
Barley screenings	..	..	1.84	..	..	..	..	..	..

TABLE I. Average composition and digestible nutrients—*continued*.

| Feeding stuff | Total dry matter | Dig. protein | Total dig. nutri-ents | Nutri-tive ratio | Average total composition | | | | | No. of anal. |
					Protein	Fat	Fiber	N-free extract	Mineral matter	
	Per ct.	Per ct.	Per ct.	1:	Per ct.	Per ct.	Per ct.	Per ct.	Per ct.	
Concentrates—Cont.										
(Grains and other seeds and their by-products; miscella-neous concentrates.)										
Beans, Adzuki (*Phaseolus angularis*)*	86.0	12.4	62.0	4.0	21.0	0.7	4.0	56.7	3.6	2
Beans, field	88.2	19.9	75.6	2.8	22.9	1.4	3.5	56.1	4.3	14
Beans, mat*	90.3	13.6	64.5	3.7	23.0	0.7	4.2	58.1	4.3	6
Beans, pinto	90.9	13.4	64.8	3.8	22.7	1.2	4.5	58.0	4.5	5
Beans, tepary*	90.5	13.1	65.2	4.0	22.2	1.4	3.4	59.3	4.2	1
Beechnuts*	91.4	12.2	84.9	6.0	15.0	30.6	15.0	27.5	3.3	1
Beet pulp, dried	92.0	4.8	71.8	14.0	9.0	0.8	18.8	59.9	3.5	432
Beet pulp, dried, molasses	91.8	6.1	74.3	11.2	9.9	0.7	15.9	60.1	5.2	57
Beet pulp, wet*	11.6	0.8	8.9	10.1	1.5	0.3	3.9	5.4	0.5	28
Beet pulp, wet, pressed*	14.2	0.7	11.0	14.7	1.4	0.4	4.6	7.1	0.7	10
Blood meal, or dried blood	91.2	70.7	75.9	0.7	82.2	1.2	1.3	2.7	3.8	34
Blood, dried, soluble	94.0	85.2	87.5	.03	88.7	0.7	0.6	0.7	3.3	4
Bone flour, or precipitated bone	97.5	...	...	...	7.3	2.6	...	4.6	83.0	1
Bone meal, steamed	96.4	...	...	...	7.1	3.3	0.8	3.9	81.3	64
Bone meal, 10 to 20% protein	96.5	...	...	...	12.5	6.5	0.6	3.1	73.8	19
Bone meal, raw	94.0	...	...	...	25.8	2.9	0.8	2.9	61.6	125
Bread, stale*	66.2	7.3	63.8	7.7	7.9	0.7	0.7	55.4	1.5	2
Bread, stale, dried*	86.8	10.5	83.9	7.0	11.4	1.0	0.4	72.0	2.0	1
Brewers' grains, dried, all anal.	92.8	20.7	65.3	2.2	25.6	6.7	14.8	42.0	3.7	623
Brewers' grains, dried, 25% protein or over	92.6	21.5	65.7	2.1	26.6	6.8	14.6	41.0	3.6	479
Brewers' grains, dried, 23-25% protein	93.9	19.3	65.2	2.4	23.8	6.5	14.9	44.9	3.8	61
Brewers' grains, dried, below 23% protein*	93.0	17.5	63.6	2.6	21.6	6.2	16.1	45.2	3.9	83
Brewers' grains, dried, from California barley*	91.1	16.2	61.3	2.8	20.0	5.7	18.1	43.6	3.7	4
Brewers' grains, wet*	23.9	4.6	16.6	2.6	5.7	1.7	3.6	11.9	1.0	50
Broom corn seed	88.6	4.6	55.7	11.0	10.8	3.5	8.4	62.7	3.2	5
Buckwheat, common	90.4	8.9	64.4	6.2	11.9	2.4	10.3	63.8	2.0	31
Buckwheat, Tartary*	88.9	7.7	61.0	6.9	10.2	2.3	15.2	59.6	1.6	1
Buckwheat feed, good grade*	89.1	14.7	59.1	3.0	18.6	5.0	18.3	43.1	4.1	28
Buckwheat feed, low grade*	88.3	10.4	47.1	3.5	13.3	3.4	28.6	39.8	3.2	31
Buckwheat flour*	87.5	7.9	86.1	9.9	8.6	1.7	0.7	75.3	1.2	20
Buckwheat kernels, without hulls*	89.4	9.7	77.7	7.0	11.2	2.4	0.7	73.6	1.5	4
Buckwheat middlings	88.7	25.8	75.7	1.9	29.7	7.3	7.4	39.4	4.9	25
Buttermilk*	9.4	3.3	9.1	1.8	3.5	0.6	...	4.5	0.8	...
Buttermilk, condensed*	29.9	10.7	27.3	1.6	11.3	1.6	...	13.3	3.7	13
Buttermilk, dried*	92.2	32.1	85.5	1.7	33.8	5.6	0.4	41.9	10.5	130
Carob beans and pods	87.8	1.9	69.4	35.5	5.5	2.6	8.7	68.5	2.5	6
Carob beans pods*	89.5	1.6	71.0	43.4	4.7	2.5	8.7	70.9	2.7	17
Carob bean seeds*	88.5	5.7	63.8	10.2	16.7	2.6	7.6	58.4	3.2	5
Cassava, dried*	94.4	1.5	77.6	50.7	2.8	0.5	5.0	84.1	2.0	6
Cassava meal, or dried starch waste*	88.0	0.4	73.1	181.8	0.8	0.7	6.1	78.8	1.6	1
Chick-peas	90.0	15.8	76.9	3.9	20.3	4.3	8.5	54.0	2.9	...
Clover seed, red, screenings*	90.5	16.6	60.1	2.6	28.2	5.9	10.2	40.3	5.9	1
Clover seed, sweet, screenings*	89.9	8.8	54.6	5.2	21.7	3.7	14.7	41.1	8.9	28
Cocoa shells	95.1	1.7	53.3	30.4	15.4	3.0	16.5	49.9	10.3	21
Cocoa meal	96.0	9.0	60.7	5.7	24.3	17.1	5.1	43.7	5.8	17

TABLE I. Average composition and digestible nutrients—*continued*.

Feeding stuff	Mineral and fertilizing constituents				Digestion coefficients				
	Calcium	Phosphorus	Nitrogen	Potassium	Protein	Fat	Fiber	N-free extract	No. of trials
	Per ct.	Per ct.	Per ct.	Per ct.	Per ct.	Per ct.	Per ct.	Per ct.	
Concentrates—Cont.									
(Grains and other seeds and their by-products: miscellaneous concentrates.)									
Beans, Adzuki (*Phaseolus angularis*)	..	..	3.36		..	..	..	..	..
Beans, field	0.14	0.45	3.66	1.16	87	83	58	91	30
Beans, mat	..	..	3.68	..					
Beans, pinto	..	..	3.63	..	59	38	49	83	14
Beans, tepary	..	..	3.55	..					
Beechnuts	0.58	0.30	2.40	0.62	..	..	..	..	..
Beet pulp, dried	0.68	0.07	1.44	0.18	53	..	81	85	5
Beet pulp, dried, molasses	0.52	0.07	1.58	1.60	62	..	80	91	5
Beet pulp, wet	0.09	0.01	0.24	0.02	..	..	..	..	..
Beet pulp, wet, pressed	..	..	0.22						
Blood meal, or dried blood	0.33	0.26	13.15	0.09	86	100	..	..	1
Blood, dried, soluble	..	..	14.19	..	96	100	..	..	1
Bone flour, or precipitated bone	26.85	17.16	1.17	0.08	..	..	..	..	
Bone meal, steamed	32.61	15.17	1.14	0.18	..	..	..	..	
Bone meal, 10 to 20% protein	26.00	12.66	2.00	..	..	..	..	..	
Bone meal, raw	23.00	10.00	4.13	..	..	..	..	..	
Bread, stale	0.02	0.09	1.26	0.10	..	..	..	..	
Bread, stale, dried	0.03	0.12	1.82	0.13	..	..	..	..	
Brewers' grains, dried, all anal	0.25	0.47	4.10	0.05	81	89	49	57	5
Brewers' grains, dried, 25% protein or over	..	..	4.26	..	..	..	..	..	..
Brewers' grains, dried, 23-25% protein	..	..	3.81	..	..	..	..	..	..
Brewers' grains, dried, below 23% protein	..	..	3.46	..	..	..	..	..	..
Brewers' grains, dried, from California barley	..	..	3.20	..	..	..	..	..	..
Brewers' grains, wet	0.07	0.12	0.91	0.01	..	..	..	..	..
Broom corn seed	..	..	1.73	..	43	86	35	66	4
Buckwheat, common	0.04	0.29	1.90	0.27	75	73	24	77	..
Buckwheat, Tartary	..	..	1.63	..	..	..	..	..	..
Buckwheat feed, good grade	..	0.48	2.98	0.66	..	..	..	..	..
Buckwheat feed, low grade	..	0.37	2.13	0.68	..	..	..	..	..
Buckwheat flour	0.10	0.19	1.38	0.16	..	..	..	..	..
Buckwheat kernels, without hulls	..	..	1.79	..	..	..	..	..	..
Buckwheat middlings	..	1.02	4.75	0.98	87	83	32	86	5
Buttermilk	0.18	0.10	0.56	0.15	..	..	..	..	..
Buttermilk, condensed	0.54	0.30	1.81	0.39	..	..	..	..	..
Buttermilk, dried	1.36	0.74	5.41	0.71	..	..	..	..	..
Carob beans and pods	..	..	0.88	..	34	56	61	86	4
Carob bean pods	..	..	0.75	..	..	..	..	..	..
Carob bean seeds	..	..	2.67	..	..	..	..	..	..
Cassava, dried	..	..	0.45	..	..	..	..	..	..
Cassava meal, or dried starch waste	..	0.03	0.13	0.23	..	..	..	..	..
Chick-peas	..	..	3.25	..	78	88	59	88	2
Clover seed, red, screenings	..	..	4.51	..	..	..	..	..	..
Clover seed, sweet, screenings	..	..	2.38	..	..	..	..	..	..
Cocoa shells	..	0.59	2.46	2.16	11	100	51	73	2
Cocoa meal	..	..	3.89	..	37	89	..	40	5

TABLE I. Average composition and digestible nutrients—*continued*.

Feeding stuff	Total dry matter	Dig. protein	Total dig. nutri- ents	Nutri- tive ratio	Average total composition					
					Protein	Fat	Fiber	N-free extract	Mineral matter	No. of anal.
	Per ct.	Per ct.	Per ct.	1:	Per ct.	Per ct.	Per ct.	Per ct.	Per ct.	
Concentrates—Cont.										
(Grains and other seeds and their by-products; miscella- neous concentrates.)										
Coconut oil meal, old process....	90.7	18.7	80.8	3.3	20.8	8.2	10.4	45.0	6.3	36
Coconut oil meal, high in fat*...	91.7	18.0	86.1	3.8	20.0	11.6	11.5	42.6	6.0	40
Coconut oil meal, solvent process*	91.1	19.3	71.6	2.7	21.4	2.4	13.3	47.4	6.6	7
Cod-liver oil meal.............	94.4	49.4	113.5	1.3	52.5	29.4	1.0	8.4	3.1	3
Corn, dent, well-dried..........	88.5	7.4	83.7	10.3	9.7	4.0	2.3	71.1	1.4	2602
Corn, dent, Grade No. 1.......	87.2	7.3	82.5	10.3	9.6	3.9	2.3	70.0	1.4	...
Corn, dent, Grade No. 2........	85.2	7.1	80.6	10.3	9.4	3.9	2.2	68.4	1.3	...
Corn, dent, Grade No. 3........	83.5	7.0	79.0	10.3	9.2	3.8	2.2	67.0	1.3	...
Corn, dent, Grade No. 4........	81.2	6.8	76.8	10.3	8.9	3.7	2.1	65.2	1.3	...
Corn, dent, Grade No. 5.......	78.5	6.6	74.2	10.3	8.6	3.6	2.0	63.0	1.3	...
Corn, dent, soft or immature*...	69.5	5.6	66.7	10.9	7.4	3.8	1.2	56.0	1.1	159
Corn, flint*...................	88.5	7.4	84.1	10.4	9.8	4.3	1.9	71.0	1.5	450
Corn, pop*....................	90.6	9.2	86.5	8.4	12.1	5.2	2.0	69.7	1.6	7
Corn, sweet, mature*..........	90.7	8.7	89.4	9.3	11.5	7.9	2.3	67.2	1.8	68
Corn ears, including kernels and cobs (corn-and-cob meal)*....	88.5	6.0	75.9	11.2	8.2	3.3	8.2	67.4	1.4	...
Corn ears, soft or immature*....	64.3	4.2	53.4	11.7	5.8	1.9	7.8	47.7	1.1	4
Corn, snapped, or ear-corn chops with husks*.................	91.0	5.9	70.6	11.0	8.7	3.2	10.4	66.8	1.9	390
Corn, snapped, very soft or im- mature*.................	39.9	2.3	30.1	12.1	3.4	1.2	5.0	29.2	1.1	1
Corn bran....................	90.1	5.7	74.4	12.1	9.8	6.4	9.8	61.8	2.3	288
Corn feed meal*..............	89.2	7.6	84.2	10.1	10.0	4.4	3.0	70.1	1.7	385
Corn flour*..................	87.8	7.9	88.7	10.2	8.6	4.0	0.7	73.3	1.2	10
Corn germ meal*.............	93.0	14.5	79.5	4.5	19.8	7.8	8.9	53.2	3.3	14
Corn gluten feed, all analyses...	90.5	22.7	77.4	2.4	26.4	2.5	7.1	48.4	6.1	338
Corn gluten feed, 27% protein, or over......................	90.6	24.1	77.6	2.2	28.0	2.5	6.8	47.4	5.9	118
Corn gluten feed, 24-27% protein.	90.6	22.2	77.6	2.5	25.8	2.5	7.3	48.9	6.1	200
Corn gluten feed, below 24% pro- tein......................	89.8	19.7	76.1	2.9	22.9	2.5	7.5	49.8	7.1	20
Corn gluten feed with molasses*.	88.8	18.7	74.6	3.0	21.8	2.7	7.4	49.0	7.9	3
Corn gluten meal, all analyses...	91.5	36.5	81.8	1.2	42.9	2.3	2.5	42.0	1.8	286
Corn gluten meal, 43% protein, or over..................	91.5	37.7	81.4	1.2	44.4	1.9	2.3	41.2	1.7	118
Corn gluten meal, below 43% protein....................	91.5	35.5	82.0	1.3	41.8	2.5	2.6	42.7	1.9	168
Corn meal, degermed and bolted*	89.8	6.7	84.3	11.6	8.8	2.5	1.1	76.5	0.9	...
Corn oil meal, old process......	91.8	16.7	78.7	3.7	22.9	7.5	10.0	49.1	2.3	19
Corn oil meal, solvent process*..	91.2	17.4	70.5	3.1	23.8	1.8	11.3	52.3	2.4	12
Corn-and-oat feed, good grade*..	89.7	8.4	79.5	8.5	11.0	4.2	5.6	66.6	2.3	274
Corn-and-oat feed, low grade*...	90.5	4.8	60.0	11.5	8.9	3.6	13.7	59.7	4.6	388
Cottonseed, whole.............	92.7	17.0	91.0	4.4	23.0	23.0	16.9	26.3	3.5	65
Cottonseed, whole, immature or bolly*.....................	93.2	15.2	80.6	4.3	20.5	15.9	24.1	29.0	3.7	16
Cottonseed, whole pressed, 28% protein, or over.............	94.7	23.1	70.9	2.1	28.5	6.3	23.8	31.7	4.4	208
Cottonseed, whole pressed, below 28% protein*...............	92.9	21.8	70.8	2.2	26.9	7.2	24.3	30.3	4.2	252
Cottonseed kernel, without hull, Texas*....................	93.6	32.4	118.0	2.6	39.0	33.2	2.2	14.8	4.4	70

Table I. Average composition and digestible nutrients—*continued*.

Feeding stuff	Mineral and fertilizing constituents				Digestion coefficients				
	Calcium	Phos-phorus	Nitro-gen	Potas-sium	Protein	Fat	Fiber	N-free extract	No. of trials
	Per ct.	Per ct.	Per ct.	Per ct.	Per ct.	Per ct.	Per ct.	Per ct.	
Concentrates—Cont. *(Grains and other seeds and their by-products: miscellaneous concentrates.)*									
Coconut oil meal, old process....	0.21	0.62	3.33	1.90	90	100	43	87	3
Coconut oil meal, high in fat....	..	..	3.20	..	..	..	..	..	..
Coconut oil meal, solvent process	..	..	3.42	..	..	..	..	..	..
Cod-liver oil meal.............	0.13	0.75	8.40	..	94	97	..	..	1
Corn, dent, well dried.........	0.01	0.28	1.55	0.33	76	91	57	94	22
Corn, dent, Grade No. 1........	0.01	0.28	1.54	0.32	..	..	..	..	..
Corn, dent, Grade No. 2.......	0.01	0.27	1.50	0.31	..	..	..	..	..
Corn, dent, Grade No. 3........	0.01	0.27	1.47	0.31	..	..	..	..	..
Corn, dent, Grade No. 4........	0.01	0.26	1.42	0.30	..	..	..	..	..
Corn, dent, Grade No. 5........	0.01	0.25	1.38	0.29	..	..	..	..	..
Corn, dent, soft or immature....	..	0.24	1.18	0.26	..	..	..	..	..
Corn, flint...................	..	0.30	1.57	0.32	..	..	..	..	..
Corn, pop....................	..	..	1.94	..	..	..	..	..	..
Corn, sweet, mature...........	..	..	1.84	..	..	..	..	..	..
Corn ears, including kernels and cobs (corn-and-cob meal).....	..	0.23	1.31	0.34	..	..	..	..	..
Corn ears, soft or immature.....	..	..	0.93	..	..	..	..	..	..
Corn, snapped, or ear-corn chops with husks..................	..	..	1.39	..	..	..	..	..	..
Corn, snapped, very soft or immature.....................	..	..	0.54	..	..	..	..	..	..
Corn bran....................	0.03	0.27	1.57	0.56	58	76	72	82	13
Corn feed meal...............	0.04	0.38	1.60	0.28	..	..	..	..	..
Corn flour...................	..	..	1.38	..	..	..	..	..	..
Corn germ meal..............	..	..	3.17	..	..	..	..	..	..
Corn gluten feed, all analyses....	0.14	0.55	4.22	0.54	86	74	92	91	13
Corn gluten feed, 27% protein, or over......................	..	..	4.48	..	..	..	..	..	..
Corn gluten feed, 24-27% protein	..	..	4.13	..	..	..	..	..	..
Corn gluten feed, below 24% protein.......................	..	..	3.66	..	..	..	..	..	..
Corn gluten feed with molasses..	..	..	3.49	..	..	..	..	..	..
Corn gluten meal, all analyses...	0.03	0.38	6.86	0.02	85	93	58	93	16
Corn gluten meal, 43% protein, or over......................	..	..	7.10	..	..	..	..	..	..
Corn gluten meal, below 43% protein.....................	..	..	6.69	..	..	..	..	..	..
Corn meal, degermed and bolted	0.01	0.32	1.41	0.31	..	..	..	..	..
Corn oil meal, old process.......	0.05	0.57	3.66	..	73	96	75	78	5
Corn oil meal, solvent process...	..	..	3.81	..	..	..	..	..	..
Corn-and-oat feed, good grade...	0.12	0.34	1.76	..	..	..	..	..	..
Corn-and-oat feed, low grade....	..	0.25	1.42	0.42	..	..	..	..	..
Cottonseed, whole.............	..	0.55	3.68	0.95	74	92	64	59	4
Cottonseed, whole, immature or bolly........................	..	..	3.28	..	..	..	..	..	..
Cottonseed, whole pressed, 28% protein, or over..............	..	..	4.56	..	81	96	48	72	4
Cottonseed, whole pressed, below 28% protein.............	0.17	0.64	4.30	1.24	..	..	..	..	..
Cottonseed kernel, without hull, Texas.....................	..	..	6.24	..	..	..	..	..	..

TABLE I. Average composition and digestible nutrients—*continued.*

Feeding stuff	Total dry matter	Dig. protein	Total dig. nutri- ents	Nutri- tive ratio	Average total composition					
					Protein	Fat	Fiber	N-free extract	Mineral matter	No. of anal.
	Per ct.	Per ct.	Per ct.	1:	Per ct.	Per ct.	Per ct.	Per ct.	Per c	
Concentrates—Cont.										
(Grains and other seeds and their by-products: miscella- neous concentrates.)										
Cottonseed kernel, without hull, other analyses*..............	93.3	27.2	118.7	3.4	32.8	34.6	3.1	17.5	5.3	8
Cottonseed meal, 45% protein and over...................	93.0	37.8	80.8	1.1	45.6	7.8	8.9	25.1	5.6	556
Cottonseed meal, 45% protein and over, not including Texas analyses...................	93.1	38.6	80.4	1.1	46.5	8.1	8.0	23.6	6.8	45
Cottonseed meal, 45% protein and over, Texas analyses.....	93.0	37.8	80.9	1.1	45.5	7.8	9.0	25.2	5.5	511
Cottonseed meal, 43% protein grade......................	93.5	35.0	75.5	1.2	43.2	7.2	10.6	27.0	5.5	10098
Cottonseed meal, 43% protein grade, not including Texas analyses...................	92.9	35.1	74.9	1.1	43.3	7.3	9.3	26.7	6.3	445
Cottonseed meal, 43% protein grade, Texas analyses........	93.5	35.0	75.5	1.2	43.2	7.2	10.7	27.0	5.4	9,653
Cottonseed meal, 41% protein grade*.....................	92.8	33.9	73.6	1.2	41.9	7.0	10.8	27.2	5.9	1,549
Cottonseed meal, 41% protein grade, not including Texas analyses*...................	93.0	33.9	73.5	1.2	41.8	7.0	9.9	27.8	6.5	677
Cottonseed feed, 41% protein grade, Texas analyses*.......	92.7	33.9	73.2	1.2	41.9	7.1	11.5	26.8	5.4	872
Cottonseed meal, 38.5—41% pro- tein........................	92.8	32.2	72.7	1.3	39.8	7.2	10.5	28.9	6.4	324
Cottonseed meal, 36—38.5% pro- tein*.......................	92.7	29.3	69.2	1.4	37.1	6.6	12.5	30.5	6.0	824
Cottonseed feed, below 36% pro- tein........................	92.4	26.6	65.9	1.5	34.6	6.3	14.1	31.5	5.9	145
Cottonseed feed, Texas 38.56% protein grade*..............	92.6	31.1	70.5	1.3	39.4	7.3	13.3	27.4	5.2	131
Cottonseed feed, Texas 36% pro- tein grade*.................	92.5	28.7	67.5	1.4	37.3	7.3	14.6	28.0	5.3	57
Cowpeas.....................	88.6	19.4	76.5	2.9	23.6	1.5	4.1	55.9	3.5	31
Crab meal*..................	92.0	25.6	33.8	12.2	36.5	2.9	5.7	7.4	39.5	2
Darso grain.................	89.9	7.7	82.4	9.7	10.6	3.3	2.8	71.7	1.5	10
Distillers' corn grains, dried.....	93.6	22.3	85.0	2.8	30.6	10.6	10.8	38.7	2.9	42
Distillers' rye grains, dried......	94.0	10.1	62.9	5.2	18.1	6.9	17.0	48.8	3.2	8
Distillers' grains, mixed, dried*..	93.8	15.0	75.6	4.0	23.1	9.0	12.2	47.6	1.9	5
Distillers' grains, wet*........	22.4	2.9	17.2	4.9	4.4	1.5	2.5	13.3	0.7	4
Distillery rye slop, dried*.......	88.0	16.8	51.3	2.1	30.0	3.0	8.0	38.0	9.0	1
Distillery slop, strained*........	4.2	0.9	3.7	3.1	1.4	0.8	0.2	1.5	0.3	9
Distillery slop, whole*..........	6.2	1.2	4.9	3.1	1.9	0.6	0.5	2.9	0.3	9
Durra grain*.................	89.8	6.9	77.7	10.3	10.3	3.5	1.6	72.4	2.0	7
Emmer grain (spelt)...........	91.2	9.6	74.7	6.8	12.0	1.9	9.8	63.8	3.7	41
Emmer, without hulls*.........	89.5	11.9	78.8	5.6	14.9	2.5	2.1	68.5	1.5	4
Feterita grain.................	89.6	10.1	79.7	6.9	13.0	2.9	2.2	69.8	1.7	60
Feterita head chops*..........	89.6	6.7	67.4	9.2	10.7	2.6	7.4	65.7	3.2	18
Fish meal, all analyses........	92.3	47.5	67.6	0.4	58.7	7.9	0.9	4.1	20.7	362
Fish meal, over 63% protein....	92.5	54.0	71.3	0.3	66.7	6.8	0.7	3.6	14.7	14
Fish meal, 58-63% protein......	92.2	48.8	67.7	0.4	60.2	7.5	0.8	3.9	19.8	203

TABLE I. Average composition and digestible nutrients—*continued.*

Feeding stuff	Mineral and fertilizing constituents				Digestion coefficients				
	Calcium	Phosphorus	Nitrogen	Potassium	Protein	Fat	Fiber	N-free extract	No. of trials
	Per ct.	Per ct.	Per ct.	Per ct.	Per ct.	Per ct.	Per ct.	Per ct.	
Concentrates—Cont. *(Grains and other seeds and their by-products; miscellaneous concentrates.)*									
Cottonseed kernel, without hull, other analyses	..	..	5.25	..	..	..	..	..	..
Cottonseed meal, 45% protein and over	0.24	1.14	7.30	..	83	97	69	79	2
Cottonseed meal, 45% protein and over, not including Texas analyses	..	..	7.44	..	..	..	..	..	..
Cottonseed meal, 45% protein and over, Texas analyses	..	..	7.28	..	..	..	..	..	..
Cottonseed meal, 43% protein grade	0.24	1.11	6.91	1.36	81	97	45	74	32
Cottonseed meal, 43% protein grade, not including Texas analyses	..	..	6.93	..	..	..	..	..	..
Cottonseed meal, 43% protein grade, Texas analyses	..	..	6.91	..	..	..	..	..	..
Cottonseed meal, 41% protein grade	0.20	1.19	6.70	1.48	..	..	..	..	..
Cottonseed meal, 41% protein grade, not including Texas analyses	..	..	6.69	..	..	..	..	..	..
Cottonseed feed, 41% protein grade, Texas analyses	..	..	6.70	..	..	..	..	..	..
Cottonseed meal, 38.5-41% protein	0.22	1.24	6.37	1.46	81	94	45	71	9
Cottonseed meal, 36-38.5% protein	..	..	5.94	..	..	..	..	..	..
Cottonseed feed, below 36% protein	0.26	0.83	5.54	1.22	77	85	32	72	8
Cottonseed feed, Texas 38.56% protein grade	..	..	6.30	..	..	..	..	..	..
Cottonseed feed, Texas 36% protein grade	..	..	5.97	..	..	..	..	..	..
Cowpeas	0.10	0.47	3.78	1.45	82	74	64	93	2
Crab meal	13.06	0.51	5.84	1.90	..	..	..	..	..
Darso grain	..	..	1.70	..	73	87	81	92	2
Distillers' corn grains, dried	0.05	0.31	4.90	0.13	73	97	83	79	23
Distillers' rye grains, dried	0.13	0.43	2.90	0.04	56	80	45	67	3
Distillers' grains, mixed, dried	..	..	3.70	..	..	..	..	..	..
Distillers' grains, wet	0.01	0.07	0.70	0.03	..	..	..	..	..
Distillery rye slop, dried	..	..	4.80	..	..	..	..	..	..
Distillery slop, strained	..	..	0.22	..	..	..	..	..	..
Distillery slop, whole	..	..	0.30	..	..	..	..	..	..
Durra grain	..	..	1.65	..	..	..	..	..	..
Emmer grain (spelt)	..	0.33	1.92	0.47	80	88	46	89	15
Emmer, without hulls	..	..	2.38	..	..	..	..	..	..
Feterita grain	..	..	2.08	..	78	75	50	91	6
Feterita head chops	..	..	1.71	..	..	..	..	..	..
Fish meal, all analyses	5.37	2.98	9.39	..	81	99	..	..	..
Fish meal, over 63% protein	4.24	3.06	10.67	..	..	..	..	..	..
Fish meal, 58-63% protein	..	..	9.63	..	..	..	..	..	..

TABLE I. Average composition and digestible nutrients—*continued*.

Feeding stuff	Total dry matter	Dig. protein	Total dig. nutri-ents	Nutri-tive ratio	Average total composition					
					Protein	Fat	Fiber	N-free extract	Mineral matter	No. of anal.
	Per ct.	Per ct.	Per ct.	1:	Per ct.	Per ct.	Per ct.	Per ct.	Per ct.	
Concentrates—Cont.										
(*Grains and other seeds and their by-products; miscellaneous concentrates.*)										
Fish meal, 53-58% protein......	92.5	45.4	67.7	0.5	56.1	8.8	1.0	4.6	22.0	113
Fish meal, below 53% protein...	91.8	40.9	62.9	0.5	50.5	9.3	0.4	2.3	29.3	9
Fish meal, menhaden..........	91.8	45.6	69.1	0.5	56.3	9.2	0.9	5.2	20.2	17
Fish meal, sardine.............	93.5	52.2	76.1	0.5	64.5	9.8	0.2	3.8	15.2	2
Fish meal, solvent process......	91.6	47.3	55.6	0.2	60.6	2.9	0.7	3.6	23.8	8
Fish meal, white..............	94.2	45.8	50.0	0.1	56.5	1.3	0.7	2.1	33.6	4
Flaxseed.....................	93.6	21.4	108.7	4.1	23.5	36.4	5.9	24.2	3.6	10
Flaxseed screenings*..........	91.3	11.5	65.6	4.7	16.4	9.6	12.6	45.6	7.1	45
Frijole (*Phaseolus vulgaris*)*.....	90.4	14.5	64.1	3.4	24.6	1.1	4.2	56.1	4.4	1
Garbage*.....................	39.3	2.2	34.6	14.7	6.0	7.2	1.1	22.2	2.8	3
Garbage, processed (high in fat)*.	95.9	6.3	85.5	12.6	17.5	23.7	20.0	21.8	12.9	4
Garbage, processed (low in fat)..	93.2	7.8	58.5	6.5	21.6	3.0	17.1	36.7	14.8	3
Grape fruit refuse, dried........	91.7	1.2	75.8	62.2	4.9	1.1	11.9	69.6	4.2	1
Grape seed oil meal*..........	91.0	0.5	17.2	33.4	12.8	6.7	37.1	31.9	2.5	1
Hegari grain*.................	90.0	7.9	81.2	9.3	9.7	2.5	2.3	73.7	1.8	12
Hemp seed oil meal...........	91.8	26.1	45.0	0.7	31.1	6.6	22.8	23.3	8.0	...
Hominy, pearled*.............	89.4	5.9	84.8	13.4	7.8	3.3	1.0	76.1	1.2	5
Hominy feed..................	90.9	7.8	85.2	9.9	11.0	6.9	4.8	65.5	2.7	1,270
Hominy feed, low in fat*.......	90.2	7.2	82.4	10.4	10.2	4.5	4.2	69.1	2.2	23
Horse beans*.................	87.5	21.3	76.1	2.6	25.7	1.4	8.2	48.8	3.4	5
Jackbeans....................	89.3	22.2	83.6	2.8	24.7	3.2	8.2	50.4	2.8	5
Kafir grain...................	88.6	9.1	80.1	7.8	11.2	3.0	2.3	70.3	1.7	230
Kafir head chops..............	89.1	7.6	76.9	9.1	10.0	2.7	6.9	66.4	3.1	49
Kaoliang grain*...............	89.9	8.5	82.5	8.7	10.5	4.1	1.6	71.8	1.9	16
Kelp, dried*..................	90.7	4.2	41.0	8.8	5.6	0.7	7.5	43.7	33.2	4
Lemon pulp, dried.............	92.8	2.9	72.7	24.1	6.4	1.2	15.0	65.2	5.0	1
Linseed meal, old process, all analyses.....................	91.3	30.6	78.2	1.6	35.2	6.3	8.0	36.3	5.5	1,142
Linseed meal, o. p., 37% protein or over.....................	91.2	33.5	77.8	1.3	38.5	5.6	7.5	34.5	5.1	151
Linseed meal, o. p., 33-37% protein........................	91.3	30.7	78.4	1.6	35.3	6.4	8.0	36.2	5.4	807
Linseed meal, o. p., 31-33% protein........................	91.2	27.9	77.9	1.8	32.1	6.7	8.4	38.0	6.0	162
Linseed meal, o. p., below 31% protein.....................	91.0	26.4	77.4	1.9	30.3	6.5	8.6	39.6	6.0	22
Linseed meal, solvent process...	90.4	31.0	72.3	1.3	36.9	2.9	8.7	36.3	5.6	182
Linseed meal and screenings oil feed, 33% protein and over*..	91.4	29.9	75.7	1.5	35.0	5.7	9.0	35.9	5.8	14
Linseed meal and screenings oil feed, 31-33% protein*........	91.4	27.4	75.4	1.8	32.1	6.0	9.3	37.7	6.3	18
Linseed meal and screenings oil feed, below 31% protein......	91.0	24.7	73.9	2.0	29.6	6.2	9.8	39.2	6.2	18
Malt sprouts.................	92.2	20.3	70.6	2.5	26.4	1.5	12.7	45.5	6.1	273
Manamar*....................	93.8	31.9	51.9	0.6	40.9	5.6	2.3	16.4	28.6	10
Meat scraps, or dry-rendered tankage, 55% protein grade*..	93.7	50.6	73.8	0.5	55.0	10.7	2.2	1.2	24.6	264
Meat and bone scraps, or dry-rendered tankage with bone, 50% protein grade*..........	93.8	46.7	71.2	0.5	50.8	11.1	2.1	2.0	27.8	989

TABLE I. Average composition and digestible nutrients—*continued.*

Feeding stuff	Mineral and fertilizing constituents				Digestion coefficients				
	Calcium	Phosphorus	Nitrogen	Potassium	Protein	Fat	Fiber	N-free extract	No. of trials
	Per ct.	Per ct.	Per ct.	Per ct.	Per ct.	Per ct.	Per ct.	Per ct.	
Concentrates—Cont.									
(Grains and other seeds and their by-products; miscellaneous concentrates.)									
Fish meal, 53-58% protein......	..	..	8.98	..	..	..	..	..	..
Fish meal, below 53% protein...	..	..	8.08	..	..	..	..	..	..
Fish meal, menhaden..........	..	..	9.01	..	..	..	..	..	..
Fish meal, sardine.............	..	..	10.32	..	..	..	..	..	..
Fish meal, solvent process......	..	..	9.70	..	..	..	..	..	..
Fish meal, white..............	..	..	9.04	..	..	..	..	..	..
Flaxseed......................	0.25	0.66	3.76	0.58	91	86	60	55	7
Flaxseed screenings............	..	0.23	2.62	1.05	..	..	..	..	..
Frijole (*Phaseolus vulgaris*)......	..	..	3.94	..	..	..	..	..	..
Garbage......................	..	..	0.96	..	..	..	..	..	..
Garbage, processed (high in fat)	..	0.33	2.16	0.62	36	82	88	82	3
Garbage, processed (low in fat).	..	..	3.46	..	..	..	..	..	..
Grape fruit refuse, dried........	..	..	0.78	..	25	79	72	92	4
Grape seed oil meal............	..	..	2.05	..	..	..	..	..	..
Hegari grain...................	..	..	1.55	..	..	..	..	..	..
Hemp seed oil meal............	..	..	4.98	..	84	85	12	15	6
Hominy, pearled...............	0.004	0.10	1.25	0.14	..	..	..	..	..
Hominy feed...................	0.03	0.57	1.76	0.60	71	92	86	90	11
Hominy feed, low in fat........	..	..	1.63	..	..	..	..	..	..
Horse beans...................	0.13	0.54	4.11	1.16	..	..	..	..	..
Jackbeans.....................	..	..	3.95	..	90	82	80	97	1
Kafir grain....................	0.04	0.30	1.79	0.34	81	76	55	92	2
Kafir head chops...............	..	..	1.60	..	..	..	..	..	2
Kaoliang grain.................	..	..	1.68	..	..	..	..	..	..
Kelp, dried...................	3.08	0.30	0.90	..	..	..	..	..	..
Lemon pulp, dried.............	..	..	1.02	..	46	27	60	92	4
Linseed meal, old process, all analyses....................	0.33	0.86	5.63	1.27	87	92	59	82	9
Linseed meal, o. p., 37% protein or over....................	0.38	0.80	6.16	1.10	..	..	..	..	..
Linseed meal, o. p., 33-37% protein.......................	0.36	0.74	5.65	1.13	..	..	..	..	..
Linseed meal, o. p., 31-33% protein.......................	..	..	5.14	..	..	..	..	..	..
Linseed meal, o. p., below 31% protein.....................	0.34	0.92	4.85	1.40	..	..	..	..	..
Linseed meal, solvent process...	..	..	5.90	..	84	89	74	80	12
Linseed meal and screenings oil feed, 33% protein and over...	..	..	5.60	..	..	..	..	..	..
Linseed meal and screenings oil feed, 31-33% protein.........	0.42	0.63	5.14	..	..	..	..	..	..
Linseed meal and screenings oil feed, below 31% protein......	..	..	4.74	..	..	..	..	..	..
Malt sprouts..................	0.24	0.71	4.22	1.52	77	85	87	80	5
Manamar.....................	7.73	0.58	6.54	..	..	..	..	..	..
Meat scraps, or dry-rendered tankage, 55% protein grade...	8.70	4.30	8.80	..	..	..	..	..	..
Meat and bone scraps, or dry-rendered tankage with bone, 50% protein grade...........	10.96	5.16	8.13	..	..	..	..	..	..

TABLE I. Average composition and digestible nutrients—*continued*.

Feeding stuff	Total dry matter	Dig. protein	Total dig. nutrients	Nutritive ratio	Average total composition					
					Protein	Fat	Fiber	N-free extract	Mineral matter	No. of anal.
	Per ct.	Per ct.	Per ct.	1:	Per ct.	Per ct.	Per ct.	Per ct.	Per ct.	
Concentrates—Cont.										
(Grains and other seeds and their by-products; miscellaneous concentrates.)										
Meat and bone scraps, or dry-rendered tankage with bone, 45% protein grade*..........	93.6	42.2	68.3	0.6	45.9	11.7	2.2	2.7	31.1	198
Mesquite beans and pods.......	94.0	11.7	71.6	5.1	13.0	2.8	26.3	47.4	4.5	8
Milk, cow's....................	12.8	3.3	16.2	3.9	3.5	3.7	...	4.9	0.7	...
Milk, ewe's*...................	19.2	6.1	26.0	3.3	6.5	6.9	...	4.9	0.9	...
Milk, goat's*..................	13.9	3.5	16.5	3.7	3.7	4.1	...	4.2	0.8	...
Milk, mare's*..................	9.4	1.9	10.1	4.3	2.0	1.1	...	5.9	0.4	72
Milk, sow's*...................	19.0	5.5	25.5	3.6	5.9	6.7	...	5.4	1.0	25
Milk albumin, dried*...........	93.7	43.2	86.3	1.0	45.5	11.0	...	19.5	17.7	2
Millet seed, foxtail.............	89.1	8.6	75.7	7.8	12.1	4.1	8.6	60.7	3.6	32
Millet seed, hog, or proso*......	90.7	8.3	77.1	8.3	11.7	3.3	8.1	64.2	3.4	61
Millet seed, Japanese*..........	89.8	7.6	72.4	8.5	10.7	4.7	16.0	52.8	5.6	3
Milo grain.....................	89.4	8.7	79.9	8.2	11.2	2.9	2.2	71.2	1.9	784
Milo head chops................	90.3	7.8	77.4	8.9	10.3	2.5	6.7	67.2	3.6	185
Molasses, beet.................	80.6	2.5	58.8	22.5	7.7	...	...	62.6	10.3	13
Molasses, beet, Steffen's process*.	80.2	4.8	59.9	11.5	9.3	...	...	60.5	10.4	2
Molasses, cane.................	74.1	0.9	56.6	61.9	2.8	...	...	61.9	9.4	13
Molasses, cane, high in sugar*...	79.7	0.4	67.8	168.5	1.3	...	...	74.9	3.5	1
Molasses, corn sugar, or hydrol*	80.5	0.1	70.1	700.0	0.2	...	...	77.8	2.5	1
Oats, not including Pacific Coast states.......................	91.1	9.4	71.5	6.6	12.0	4.7	10.6	60.2	3.6	960
Oats, light weight*.............	91.3	7.8	60.6	6.8	12.3	4.7	15.4	54.4	4.5	22
Oats, mill, or low grade*........	91.5	8.4	68.0	7.1	11.6	5.3	12.0	58.6	4.0	21
Oats, Pacific Coast states*......	91.2	7.0	72.2	9.3	9.0	5.4	11.0	62.1	3.7	117
Oats, winter, Pacific Coast states*	91.1	7.5	75.4	9.1	9.6	7.2	8.7	62.2	3.4	16
Oat flour*.....................	92.0	13.5	93.5	5.9	15.0	5.8	2.6	66.7	1.9	1
Oat clippings..................	92.2	3.5	51.0	13.6	8.8	2.3	25.3	44.9	10.9	5
Oat kernels, without hulls*......	91.7	14.6	93.9	5.4	16.2	6.4	1.9	65.3	1.9	133
Oat meal, feeding, or rolled oats..	91.5	14.7	92.5	5.3	16.3	5.9	2.8	64.1	2.4	71
Oat middlings..................	92.1	12.2	83.0	5.8	15.3	5.5	9.9	57.3	4.1	12
Oat mill feed, usual grade.......	93.7	4.0	42.6	9.7	5.5	2.1	27.6	52.3	6.2	130
Oat mill feed, high grade*......	92.6	9.4	62.1	5.6	12.3	4.3	17.1	52.5	6.4	15
Oat mill feed, poor grade*.......	93.8	0.9	38.6	41.9	4.2	1.6	31.5	49.9	6.6	13
Oat mill feed, with molasses*....	92.5	4.5	42.4	8.4	6.1	2.2	24.4	53.5	6.3	4
Olive pulp, dried, pits removed*.	95.1	7.0	81.3	10.6	14.0	27.4	19.3	31.0	3.4	1
Olive pulp, dried, with pits.....	92.0	0.0	36.5	0.0	5.9	15.6	36.5	31.5	2.5	1
Orange peel, dried.............	85.9	0.1	38.1	380.0	5.8	0.7	10.6	64.7	4.1	1
Orange pulp, dried.............	87.9	6.1	78.4	11.9	7.7	1.5	8.0	67.3	3.4	3
Orange pulp, wet*.............	20.0	1.3	18.0	12.8	1.7	0.8	1.6	15.2	0.7	...
Palm kernel oil meal, low in fiber*	87.7	14.4	71.7	4.0	19.0	7.4	11.1	45.9	4.3	2
Palm kernel oil meal, high in fiber	89.6	12.8	70.2	4.5	16.8	9.5	24.0	35.0	4.3	600
Palmo middlings*..............	94.1	13.3	85.4	5.4	16.0	9.6	6.7	56.5	5.3	31
Pea seed, field.................	90.5	20.2	79.6	2.9	23.8	1.2	6.2	56.2	3.1	11
Pea seed, field, cull*...........	90.3	21.0	79.4	2.8	24.7	2.2	7.6	52.4	3.4	3
Pea seed, garden*..............	89.2	21.0	78.4	2.7	25.3	1.7	5.7	53.6	2.9	12
Pea feed......................	90.4	14.3	78.5	4.5	17.4	1.4	24.6	43.7	3.3	3
Peanuts, with hulls............	94.1	20.2	103.5	4.1	24.9	36.2	17.5	12.6	2.9	68
Peanut kernels, without hulls*...	94.7	27.1	139.9	4.2	30.5	47.7	2.5	11.7	2.3	104
Peanut-oil-meal, o.p., all analyses	93.4	38.0	82.1	1.2	42.7	8.5	8.9	27.0	6.3	208
Peanut-oil-meal, o. p., 45% protein and over...............	94.0	41.3	83.5	1.0	46.4	8.6	9.2	24.3	5.5	63

Table I. Average composition and digestible nutrients—*continued*.

Feeding stuff	Mineral and fertilizing constituents				Digestion coefficients				
	Calcium	Phosphorus	Nitrogen	Potassium	Protein	Fat	Fiber	N-free extract	No. of trials
	Per ct.	Per ct.	Per ct.	Per ct.	Per ct.	Per ct.	Per ct.	Per ct.	
Concentrates—Cont. *(Grains and other seeds and their by-products; miscellaneous concentrates.)*									
Meat and bone scraps, or dry-rendered tankage with bone, 45% protein grade	..	..	7.34	..	..	..	..	..	..
Mesquite beans and pods	..	..	2.08	..	90	95	59	81	2
Milk, cow's	0.12	0.09	0.56	0.14	94	97	..	98	13
Milk, ewe's	0.21	0.12	1.04	0.19	..	..	..	..	..
Milk, goat's	0.13	0.10	..	0.15	..	..	..	..	..
Milk, mare's	0.08	0.05	0.32	0.08	..	..	..	..	..
Milk, sow's	..	..	0.94	..	..	..	..	..	..
Milk albumin, dried	..	..	7.28	..	..	..	..	..	..
Millet seed, foxtail	..	0.20	1.94	0.31	71	73	53	92	6
Millet seed, hog, or proso	0.01	0.32	1.87	0.43	..	..	..	..	..
Millet seed, Japanese	..	0.54	1.71	0.33	..	..	..	..	..
Milo grain	..	0.34	1.79	0.36	78	78	58	91	16
Milo head chops	..	..	1.65	..	76	87	52	91	4
Molasses, beet	0.05	0.02	1.23	4.77	52	..	..	91	4
Molasses, beet, Steffen's process	0.02	0.03	1.49	4.62	..	..	..	..	..
Molasses, cane	0.56	0.06	0.45	2.62	32	..	..	90	26
Molasses, cane, high in sugar	..	..	0.21	..	..	..	..	..	..
Molasses, corn sugar, or hydrol.	..	..	0.03	..	..	..	..	..	..
Oats, not including Pacific Coast states	0.09	0.33	1.92	0.40	78	88	38	81	19
Oats, light weight	..	0.36	1.97	0.47	..	..	..	..	..
Oats, mill, or low grade	..	0.26	1.86	0.52	..	..	..	..	..
Oats, Pacific Coast states	..	..	1.44	..	..	..	..	..	..
Oats, winter, Pacific Coast states	..	..	1.54	..	..	..	..	..	..
Oat flour	..	..	2.40	..	..	..	..	..	..
Oat clippings	..	..	1.41	..	40	71	63	62	6
Oat kernels, without hulls	0.09	0.44	2.59	0.39	..	..	..	..	..
Oat meal, feeding, or rolled oats	0.06	0.45	2.61	0.37	90	96	80	98	2
Oat middlings	..	0.56	2.45	0.57	80	93	49	95	2
Oat mill feed, usual grade	0.26	0.18	0.88	0.57	73	73	40	46	18
Oat mill feed, high grade	..	..	1.70	..	..	..	..	..	..
Oat mill feed, poor grade	..	..	0.67	..	..	..	..	..	..
Oat mill feed, with molasses	..	..	0.98	..	..	..	..	..	..
Olive pulp, dried, pits removed	..	..	2.24	..	..	..	..	..	..
Olive pulp, dried, with pits	..	..	0.94	..	0	86	0	20	5
Orange peel, dried	..	..	0.93	..	2	0	10	57	5
Orange pulp, dried	..	..	1.23	..	79	49	84	95	5
Orange pulp, wet	..	..	0.27	..	..	..	..	..	..
Palm kernel oil meal, low in fiber	..	..	3.04	..	..	..	..	..	..
Palm kernel oil meal, high in fiber	..	0.48	2.69	0.42	76	89	39	83	..
Palmo middlings	..	..	2.56	..	..	..	..	..	..
Pea seed, field	0.07	0.40	3.81	1.03	85	62	87	93	6
Pea seed, field, cull	..	..	3.95	..	..	..	..	..	..
Pea seed, garden	0.08	0.40	4.05	0.90	..	..	..	..	..
Pea feed	..	..	2.78	..	82	68	87	93	3
Peanuts, with hulls	..	0.33	3.98	0.53	81	93	34	13	4
Peanut kernels, without hulls	0.06	0.38	4.88	0.54	..	..	..	..	..
Peanut-oil-meal, o.p., all analyses	0.17	0.55	6.83	1.16	89	95	37	84	4
Peanut-oil, meal, o. p., 45% protein and over	..	..	7.42	..	..	..	..	..	..

TABLE I. Average composition and digestible nutrients—*continued*.

Feeding stuff	Total dry matter	Dig. protein	Total dig. nutri- ents	Nutri- tive ratio	Average total composition					No. of anal.
					Protein	Fat	Fiber	N-free extract	Mineral matter	
	Per ct.	Per ct.	Per ct.	1:	Per ct.	Per ct.	Per ct.	Per ct.	Per ct.	
Concentrates—Cont. *(Grains and other seeds and their by-products; miscella- neous concentrates.)*										
Peanut-oil-meal, o. p., 43-45% protein....................	93.5	38.6	80.9	1.1	43.4	8.2	10.0	25.0	6.9	40
Peanut-oil-meal, o. p., 36-43% protein....................	93.0	35.9	81.8	1.3	40.3	8.6	8.3	29.2	6.6	105
Peanut-oil-meal, solvent process*	91.6	45.8	73.8	0.6	51.5	1.4	5.7	27.2	5.8	2
Peanut oil feed, partly hulled*...	93.5	26.8	73.1	1.7	33.2	8.7	17.7	28.2	5.7	9
Peanut skins*..................	93.5	12.9	68.8	4.3	15.9	22.4	10.6	41.9	2.7	3
Peanuts, whole pressed*........	92.2	28.7	57.8	1.0	35.4	9.1	21.4	21.6	4.7	159
Perilla oil meal................	91.9	34.6	62.2	0.8	38.5	8.1	20.8	16.3	8.2	3
Pigeon-grass seed..............	89.3	10.1	57.5	4.7	14.4	5.4	17.2	45.7	6.6	3
Pineapple pulp, dried..........	90.2	0.9	64.9	71.1	4.2	0.8	15.2	66.7	3.3	2
Poppy seed oil cake*...........	88.0	27.4	68.7	1.5	36.0	10.2	11.8	19.7	10.3	...
Potato flakes, dried*...........	87.9	3.6	77.2	20.4	7.1	0.3	2.9	73.6	4.0	...
Potato flour*..................	89.4	1.4	77.6	54.4	2.7	0.8	2.2	81.3	2.4	2
Potato pomace, dried*..........	89.1	3.5	69.6	18.9	6.6	0.5	10.3	69.0	2.7	1
Pumpkin seed, not dried*.......	55.0	13.0	65.0	4.0	17.6	20.6	10.8	4.1	1.9	2
Raisins, cull*.................	84.8	1.3	61.8	46.5	3.4	0.9	4.4	73.1	3.0	3
Raisin pulp, dried.............	89.4	2.3	47.5	19.7	9.6	7.8	16.1	50.6	5.3	4
Rape seed oil meal.............	90.0	28.2	61.3	1.2	34.8	5.1	11.7	30.4	8.0	...
Rice grain, or rough rice........	88.6	6.3	69.1	10.0	8.3	1.8	8.8	64.7	5.0	12
Rice, brewers'*................	88.0	5.4	79.7	13.8	7.4	0.6	0.8	78.4	0.8	4
Rice, brown*..................	90.2	6.5	82.5	11.7	8.9	2.0	1.0	77.2	1.1	2
Rice, polished*................	87.8	5.4	79.9	13.8	7.4	0.4	0.4	79.1	0.5	39
Rice bran.....................	91.1	8.8	67.7	6.7	12.8	13.4	13.0	41.1	10.8	481
Rice bran, low grade*..........	90.1	5.3	45.2	7.5	10.0	7.9	20.2	36.8	15.2	44
Rice polish...................	90.5	9.3	85.7	8.2	12.7	11.5	3.0	57.2	6.1	214
Rubber seed oil meal...........	91.1	20.4	63.4	2.1	28.8	9.2	10.0	37.6	5.5	2
Rye grain....................	90.0	10.3	80.1	6.8	12.3	1.7	2.3	71.7	2.0	58
Rye feed.....................	90.4	12.8	77.4	5.0	16.0	3.3	4.6	62.8	3.7	148
Rye flour*....................	88.4	7.6	87.0	10.4	8.3	1.3	0.6	77.3	0.9	7
Rye flour middlings*...........	89.9	13.5	77.9	4.8	16.9	3.6	4.2	60.2	3.2	5
Rye middlings*................	90.2	13.2	77.1	4.8	16.5	3.4	5.0	61.5	3.8	76
Rye middlings and screenings*..	90.2	13.1	75.7	4.8	16.6	3.8	5.9	59.7	4.2	58
Schrock sorghum grain*........	89.1	8.3	80.4	8.7	10.2	3.0	3.4	70.8	1.7	3
Sesame oil meal................	93.5	36.0	76.6	1.1	39.6	12.6	6.1	23.2	12.0	5
*Sesbania macrocarpa**.........	90.8	25.7	68.8	1.7	31.7	4.3	13.5	38.0	3.3	1
Shallu grain*.................	89.8	10.9	81.6	6.5	13.4	3.7	1.9	68.9	1.9	19
Shrimp meal*.................	88.8	29.5	38.7	0.3	42.1	2.2	9.3	1.4	33.8	2
Skimmilk, centrifugal..........	9.6	3.5	8.6	1.5	3.7	0.1	...	5.0	0.8	...
Skimmilk, gravity.............	10.3	3.5	10.2	1.9	3.7	0.8	...	5.0	0.8	...
Skimmilk, dried*.............	93.8	33.1	84.1	1.5	34.8	0.9	...	50.1	8.0	101
Skimmilk, sour, dried*.........	92.2	32.1	83.5	1.6	33.8	1.4	...	49.3	7.6	15
Sorghum grain, sweet..........	88.8	5.6	74.3	12.3	9.8	3.3	2.3	71.6	1.8	21
Soybeans.....................	90.2	32.8	86.2	1.6	36.9	17.2	4.5	26.3	5.3	161
Soybean oil meal, hydraulic or expeller process, all anal......	91.7	37.7	82.2	1.2	44.3	5.7	5.6	30.3	5.7	92
Soybean oil meal, hyd. or exp. proc., 48% protein or over....	93.1	42.4	83.8	1.0	49.9	6.2	5.1	26.4	5.5	21
Soybean oil meal, hyd. or exp. proc., 43-48% protein........	91.9	37.6	82.8	1.2	44.2	5.6	5.2	31.5	5.5	38
Soybean oil meal, hyd. or exp. proc., below 43% protein.....	90.5	34.8	80.5	1.3	40.9	5.4	6.4	31.6	6.2	33

TABLE I. Average composition and digestible nutrients—*continued*.

Feeding stuff	Mineral and fertilizing constituents				Digestion coefficients				
	Calcium	Phosphorus	Nitrogen	Potassium	Protein	Fat	Fiber	N-free extract	No. of trials
	Per ct.	Per ct.	Per ct.	Per ct.	Per ct.	Per ct.	Per ct.	Per ct.	
Concentrates—Cont. *(Grains and other seeds and their by-products; miscellaneous concentrates.)*									
Peanut-oil-meal, o. p., 43-45% protein.................	..	..	6.94	..	..	..	..	..	..
Peanut-oil-meal, o. p., 36-43% protein.................	..	..	6.45	..	..	..	..	..	..
Peanut-oil-meal, solvent process.	..	..	8.24	..	..	..	..	..	..
Peanut oil feed, partly hulled...	..	..	5.31	..	..	..	..	..	..
Peanut skins..................	..	..	2.54	..	..	..	..	..	..
Peanuts, whole pressed.........	..	..	5.66	..	..	..	..	..	..
Perilla oil meal...............	..	..	6.16	..	90	94	22	36	9
Pigeon-grass seed.............	..	..	2.30	..	..	..	..	..	..
Pineapple pulp, dried..........	..	..	0.67	..	21	0	70	80	4
Poppy seed oil meal...........	..	..	5.76	..	..	..	..	..	..
Potato flakes, dried...........	0.04	0.21	1.14	1.87	..	..	..	..	..
Potato flour..................	..	..	0.43	..	..	..	..	..	..
Potato pomace, dried..........	..	..	1.06	..	..	..	24	84	3
Pumpkin seed, not dried.......	..	..	2.82	..	..	..	..	..	..
Raisins, cull.................	..	..	0.54	..	..	..	..	..	..
Raisin pulp, dried.............	..	..	1.54	..	24	90	19	52	5
Rape seed oil meal............	..	..	5.57	..	81	79	8	76	7
Rice grain, or rough rice........	..	0.21	1.33	0.22	76	76	10	91	6
Rice, brewers'.................	0.04	0.10	1.18	..	..	..	..	..	..
Rice, brown...................	..	..	1.42	..	..	..	..	..	..
Rice, polished.................	0.01	0.09	1.18	0.04	..	..	..	..	..
Rice bran.....................	0.08	1.36	2.05	1.08	69	83	26	74	12
Rice bran, low grade...........	..	..	1.60	..	..	..	..	..	..
Rice polish...................	0.04	1.10	2.03	1.18	73	86	33	93	8
Rubber seed oil meal...........	..	..	4.61	..	71	92	21	58	4
Rye grain.....................	0.04	0.37	1.97	0.54	84	64	..	92	2
Rye feed......................	0.08	0.69	2.56	0.83	80	90	..	88	3
Rye flour.....................	0.02	0.29	1.33	0.46	..	..	..	..	..
Rye flour middlings............	..	..	2.70	..	..	..	..	..	..
Rye middlings.................	..	0.44	2.64	0.63	..	..	..	..	..
Rye middlings and screenings...	..	..	2.66	..	..	..	..	..	..
Schrock sorghum grain.........	..	..	1.63	..	..	..	..	..	..
Sesame oil meal...............	2.02	1.61	6.34	1.35	91	82	48	62	7
Sesbania macrocarpa..........	..	..	5.07	..	..	..	..	..	..
Shallu grain...................	..	..	2.14	..	..	..	..	..	..
Shrimp meal..................	..	..	6.74	..	..	..	..	..	..
Skimmilk, centrifugal..........	0.14	0.12	0.59	0.14	95	98	..	98	3
Skimmilk, gravity.............	..	..	0.59	..	..	..	..	..	..
Skimmilk, dried...............	1.24	0.96	5.57	1.46	..	..	..	..	..
Skimmilk, sour, dried..........	..	..	5.41	..	..	..	..	..	..
Sorghum grain, sweet..........	..	0.36	1.57	0.37	57	56	100	87	2
Soybeans.....................	0.20	0.60	5.90	1.91	89	88	37	67	35
Soybean oil meal, hydraulic or expeller process, all anal......	0.28	0.66	7.09	2.20	85	86	68	98	29
Soybean oil meal, hyd. or exp. proc., 48% protein or over....	..	..	7.98	..	..	..	..	..	..
Soybean oil meal, hyd. or exp. proc., 43-48% protein........	..	..	7.07	..	..	..	..	..	..
Soybean oil meal, hyd. or exp. proc., below 43% protein.....	..	..	6.54	..	..	..	..	..	..

TABLE I. Average composition and digestible nutrients—*continued*.

Feeding stuff	Total dry matter	Dig. protein	Total dig. nutrients	Nutritive ratio	Average total composition					
					Protein	Fat	Fiber	N-free extract	Mineral matter	No. of anal.
	Per ct.	Per ct.	Per ct.	1:	Per ct.	Per ct.	Per ct.	Per ct.	Per ct.	
Concentrates—Cont. *(Grains and other seeds and their by-products: miscellaneous concentrates.)*										
Soybean oil meal, solvent process*	91.6	39.4	77.6	1.0	46.4	1.6	5.9	31.7	6.0	...
Soybean oil meal and minerals (Supersoy)*	91.9	33.0	80.2	1.4	38.8	7.0	5.2	30.8	10.1	4
Sunflower seed*	93.4	14.6	87.8	5.0	15.9	25.1	28.1	21.2	3.1	11
Sunflower seed, without hulls*	95.5	25.5	122.5	3.8	27.7	41.4	6.3	16.3	3.8	6
Sunflower seed oil cake, from hulled seed	90.0	32.0	87.4	1.7	34.8	18.3	10.9	21.8	4.2	1
Tankage, or meat meal (digester process), 60% protein grade*	92.2	56.4	78.0	0.4	61.3	8.8	1.4	1.5	19.2	830
Tankage, or meat meal (digester process), 55% protein grade*	92.7	51.5	74.2	0.4	56.0	10.1	2.0	2.6	22.0	107
Tankage with bone, or meat and bone meal (digester process), 50% protein grade*	92.2	46.3	71.5	0.5	50.3	11.3	2.0	2.7	25.9	75
Tankage with bone, or meat and bone meal (digester process), 45% protein grade*	94.0	42.8	66.3	0.5	46.5	10.6	2.0	2.2	32.7	48
Tankage with bone, or meat and bone meal or scraps, below 43% protein*	94.3	35.8	75.2	1.1	38.9	17.1	2.9	6.5	28.9	65
Tomato pomace, dried*	94.3	10.4	55.3	4.3	22.6	14.8	32.1	21.6	3.2	5
Vegetable ivory meal	89.4	0.8	79.0	97.8	4.7	0.9	7.2	75.5	1.1	4
Velvet beans and pods (velvet bean feed)	90.0	13.4	73.8	4.5	18.1	4.4	13.0	50.3	4.2	73
Velvet bean, seed only*	90.0	17.3	76.7	3.4	23.4	5.7	6.4	51.5	3.0	10
Velvet bean pods*	89.0	1.1	42.4	37.5	5.1	0.8	27.2	50.2	5.7	4
Vinegar grains	93.1	11.9	60.8	4.1	18.6	6.3	18.8	46.9	2.5	4
Wheat, recent analyses	89.8	11.3	83.6	6.4	13.1	1.7	3.0	70.0	2.0	26
Wheat, Minn., N. D., S. D., Nebr., Kan	89.6	11.6	84.0	6.2	13.5	2.1	2.4	69.8	1.8	190
Wheat, Rocky Mountain states	91.5	11.4	85.7	6.5	13.3	2.2	2.1	71.9	2.0	193
Wheat, Pacific Coast states	89.1	8.5	83.6	8.8	9.9	2.0	2.7	72.6	1.9	57
Wheat, shrunken*	91.4	10.2	82.9	7.1	11.9	2.6	4.6	70.2	2.1	9
Wheat chops, Texas	90.9	13.4	84.8	5.3	15.6	1.9	2.5	69.0	1.9	40
Wheat bran, all analyses	90.6	13.1	70.2	4.4	15.8	5.0	9.5	54.3	6.0	3,990
Wheat bran, chiefly hard spring wheat	90.9	13.2	70.9	4.4	15.9	5.5	9.6	53.9	6.0	1,344
Wheat bran, winter	90.9	13.0	69.5	4.3	15.7	4.2	9.1	55.1	6.4	103
Wheat bran and screenings, all analyses	90.8	13.2	69.5	4.3	16.1	4.9	9.6	54.2	6.0	1,750
Wheat bran and screenings, chiefly hard spring wheat*	91.2	12.7	70.7	4.6	15.6	5.6	9.8	54.5	5.7	771
Wheat brown shorts	90.1	15.1	76.3	4.1	17.8	4.7	6.2	57.0	4.4	178
Wheat brown shorts and screenings*	90.3	14.5	73.9	4.1	17.7	4.7	6.8	56.5	4.7	52
Wheat flour, graham*	88.2	12.7	86.0	5.8	13.8	2.1	1.9	68.9	1.5	12
Wheat flour, low grade	88.8	13.9	87.6	5.3	15.1	2.5	0.8	69.1	1.3	72
Wheat flour, white*	87.5	10.6	86.6	7.2	11.5	1.6	0.4	73.4	0.6	16
Wheat flour middlings	89.6	15.0	79.5	4.3	17.0	4.9	4.4	59.9	3.4	868
Wheat flour middlings and screenings*	89.5	14.4	75.7	4.3	17.1	5.0	5.3	58.4	3.7	528

TABLE I. Average composition and digestible nutrients—*continued*.

Feeding stuff	Mineral and fertilizing constituents				Digestion coefficients				
	Calcium	Phosphorus	Nitrogen	Potassium	Protein	Fat	Fiber	N-free extract	No. of trials
	Per ct.	Per ct.	Per ct.	Per ct.	Per ct.	Per ct.	Per ct.	Per ct.	
Concentrates—Cont.									
(*Grains and other seeds and their by-products; miscellaneous concentrates.*)									
Soybean oil meal, solvent process	..	..	7.57	..	..	..	..	..	..
Soybean oil meal and minerals (Supersoy)..................	..	..	6.21	..	..	..	..	..	..
Sunflower seed..............	..	0.55	2.54	0.66	..	..	..	..	..
Sunflower seed, without hulls....	..	..	4.43	..	..	..	..	..	..
Sunflower seed oil cake, from hulled seed..................	0.43	1.04	5.57	1.08	92	90	26	71	..
Tankage, or meat meal (digester process), 60% protein grade...	6.21	3.42	9.81	0.55	..	..	..	..	..
Tankage, or meat meal (digester process, 55% protein grade...	7.21	3.85	8.96	..	..	..	..	..	..
Tankage with bone, or meat and bone meal (digester process), 50% protein grade..........	..	..	8.05	..	..	..	..	..	..
Tankage with bone, or meat and bone meal (digester process), 45% protein grade..........	..	..	7.44	..	..	..	..	..	..
Tankage with bone, or meat and bone meal or scraps, below 43% protein.................	13.49	5.18	6.22	..	..	..	..	..	..
Tomato pomace, dried.........	..	..	3.62	..	..	..	..	..	..
Vegetable ivory meal..........	..	..	0.75	..	18	49	86	94	8
Velvet beans and pods (velvet bean feed)..................	0.24	0.38	2.90	1.20	74	80	67	87	24
Velvet bean, seed only........	..	..	3.74	..	..	..	..	..	..
Velvet bean pods..............	..	..	0.82	..	..	..	..	..	..
Vinegar grains...............	..	..	2.98	..	64	83	58	56	..
Wheat, recent analyses........	0.03	0.43	2.10	0.44	86	83	90	95	6
Wheat, Minn., N. D., S. D., Nebr., Kan..............	..	..	2.16	..	..	..	..	..	..
Wheat, Rocky Mountain states..	..	..	2.13	..	..	..	..	..	..
Wheat, Pacific Coast states.....	..	..	1.58	..	..	..	..	..	..
Wheat, shrunken.......	..	..	1.90	..	..	..	..	..	..
Wheat chops, Texas...........	..	..	2.50	..	..	..	..	..	..
Wheat bran, all analyses.......	0.12	1.32	2.53	1.24	83	81	53	79	5
Wheat bran, chiefly hard spring wheat.....................	0.13	1.35	2.54	..	..	..	..	..	..
Wheat bran, winter...........	..	..	2.51	..	..	..	..	..	..
Wheat bran and screenings, all analyses...................	0.14	1.21	2.58	..	..	..	..	..	..
Wheat bran and screenings, chiefly hard spring wheat.........	..	..	2.50	..	..	..	..	..	..
Wheat brown shorts...........	..	..	2.85	..	85	85	60	85	6
Wheat brown shorts and screenings.......................	..	..	2.83	..	..	..	..	..	..
Wheat flour, graham..........	0.04	0.36	2.21	0.46	..	..	..	..	..
Wheat flour, low grade.........	0.07	0.52	2.42	0.60	92	87	50	99	2
Wheat flour, white...........	0.03	0.13	1.84	0.12	..	..	..	..	..
Wheat flour middlings..........	0.09	0.72	2.72	0.89	88	86	54	88	4
Wheat flour middlings and screenings........................	0.14	0.68	2.74	..	..	..	..	..	..

TABLE I. Average composition and digestible nutrients—*continued*.

Feeding stuff	Total dry matter	Dig. protein	Total dig. nutrients	Nutritive ratio	Average total composition					
					Protein	Fat	Fiber	N-free extract	Mineral matter	No. of anal.
	Per ct.	Per ct.	Per ct.	1:	Per ct.	Per ct.	Per ct.	Per ct.	Per ct.	
Concentrates—Cont. *(Grains and other seeds and their by-products; miscellaneous concentrates.)*										
Wheat germ meal*	91.1	26.2	92.9	2.5	28.5	10.7	2.5	44.9	4.5	26
Wheat gray shorts	90.1	15.0	78.9	4.3	17.9	4.5	5.6	57.8	4.1	1,169
Wheat gray shorts and screenings*	90.1	14.6	77.5	4.3	17.7	4.5	5.9	57.7	4.3	827
Wheat mixed feed*	90.6	13.9	73.5	4.3	16.8	4.9	7.2	56.9	4.8	1,595
Wheat mixed feed and screenings*	90.1	13.4	71.1	4.3	16.6	4.7	7.9	55.9	5.0	204
Wheat red dog*	89.2	15.2	86.9	4.7	16.9	4.0	2.4	63.3	2.6	857
Wheat screenings	90.4	9.7	64.0	5.6	13.9	4.7	9.0	58.2	4.6	140
Wheat standard middlings, all analyses	90.0	14.4	78.4	4.4	17.4	5.5	6.8	56.1	4.2	959
Wheat standard middlings, chiefly hard spring wheat	89.8	14.6	78.7	4.4	17.6	5.6	6.2	56.4	4.0	362
Wheat standard middlings, and screenings*	90.0	13.7	75.6	4.5	17.1	5.6	7.4	55.4	4.5	668
Wheat standard middlings and screenings, chiefly hard spring wheat*	90.1	13.7	75.9	4.5	17.0	5.7	7.3	55.7	4.4	531
Wheat white shorts	89.7	14.5	86.4	5.0	16.1	3.1	2.9	65.1	2.5	202
Whey, from American cheese*	6.6	0.9	6.4	6.1	0.9	0.3	...	5.0	0.7	...
Whey, skimmed*	6.6	0.9	5.8	5.4	0.9	0.03	...	5.0	0.7	...
Whey, dried (milk-sugar feed)*	95.0	11.9	84.1	6.1	12.5	0.7	...	72.1	9.7	12
Yeast, dried*	92.0	35.6	74.6	1.1	45.0	3.0	1.0	36.0	7.0	...
Yeast, with added cereal*	89.5	9.7	81.4	7.4	12.3	4.0	2.7	68.4	2.1	8
Yeast grains, dried*	93.7	13.3	61.1	3.6	20.8	6.3	16.1	47.7	2.8	9

TABLE I. Average composition and digestible nutrients—*continued*.

Feeding stuff	Mineral and fertilizing constituents				Digestion coefficients				
	Calcium	Phosphorus	Nitrogen	Potassium	Protein	Fat	Fiber	N-free extract	No. of trials
	Per ct.	Per ct.	Per ct.	Per ct.	Per ct.	Per ct.	Per ct.	Per ct.	
Concentrates—Cont.									
(Grains and other seeds and their by-products; miscellaneous concentrates.)									
Wheat germ meal.............	0.07	1.05	4.56	0.30	..	..	..	..	..
Wheat gray shorts............	..	..	2.86	..	84	93	54	89	6
Wheat gray shorts and screenings	..	..	2.83	..	..	..	..	..	..
Wheat mixed feed.............	0.11	1.09	2.69	..	..	..	..	..	..
Wheat mixed feed and screenings	0.11	0.96	2.66	..	..	..	..	..	..
Wheat red dog................	0.07	0.52	2.70	0.60	..	..	..	..	..
Wheat screenings.............	0.44	0.39	2.22	..	70	80	17	76	6
Wheat standard middlings, all analyses...................	0.08	0.94	2.78	1.04	83	85	60	88	7
Wheat standard middlings, chiefly hard spring wheat........	0.08	0.82	2.82	..	..	..	..	..	..
Wheat standard middlings, and screenings..................	0.15	0.88	2.74	..	..	..	..	..	..
Wheat standard middlings and screenings, chiefly hard spring wheat.....................	0.15	0.88	2.72	..	..	..	..	..	..
Wheat white shorts...........	..	..	2.58	..	90	89	42	99	4
Whey, from American cheese....	0.05	0.04	0.14	0.18	..	..	..	..	..
Whey, skimmed...............	0.05	0.04	0.14	0.18	..	..	..	..	..
Whey, dried (milk-sugar feed)...	1.18	0.66	2.00	..	..	..	..	..	..
Yeast, dried..................	1.48	1.28	7.20	..	..	..	..	..	..
Yeast, with added cereal.......	0.06	0.40	1.97	..	..	..	..	..	..
Yeast grains, dried............	..	..	3.33	..	..	..	..	..	..

TABLE II. ESTIMATED NET ENERGY VALUES OF FEEDING STUFFS

It has been emphasized in Chapter III that net energy values, in spite of their limitations, are more accurate than total digestible nutrients as a basis for comparing the value of a roughage with that of a concentrate for productive purposes. (84-94) This is also true when it is desired to compare a high-grade concentrate, containing but little fiber, with a low-grade concentrate relatively high in fiber. Also, some persons prefer to use net energy values instead of total digestible nutrients in computing rations for livestock.

The following table of net energy values of the most important feeding stuffs has therefore been prepared by the author. These figures are presented as estimated net energy values which are based upon a study of all the available data that provide information concerning the relative values of these feeds for productive purposes. It should be distinctly understood that these data are not considered final values, but that they are merely estimated values, subject to revision and change, as additional data may become available. It is hoped that they will prove helpful in comparing the values of different feeds for productive purposes.

It will be noted that the first two columns of figures give the percentage of dry matter and the percentage of digestible protein in each feed. These values are the same as those given in Appendix Table I, and they are repeated here for ease in computing rations according to the net energy method, by the use of the feeding standards presented in Appendix Table III. The figures for digestible protein are the values for *digestible crude protein,* and not values for *digestible true protein.* (18)

These data indicate the relative net energy values of the various feeding stuffs when each feed is used in a complete, well-balanced ration, which provides adequate supplies of proteins, minerals, and vitamins. If any feed is improperly used or if it forms part of a ration that has nutritive deficiencies, its value may be much less than shown in this table. Also, when a protein-rich feed is fed in great excess of the amount necessary to balance the ration, it may have a considerably lower net energy value than here estimated.

Attention should be called to the fact that these estimated net energy values indicate merely the worth of the various feeds as sources of energy, and do not take into consideration the values of the feeds as sources of protein, minerals, and vitamins. Thus, the high-grade protein-rich concentrates have no higher net energy values than such feeds as corn and wheat, which are relatively low in protein.

It should also be borne in mind that net energy values do not indicate the relative efficiency of different feeds for maintaining farm animals. (88) In comparing the values of feeds for maintenance, the total digestible nutrient values given in Appendix Table I should be used.

These net energy values are primarily for cattle and sheep, but may also be employed in computing rations for horses and swine, when used with the net energy recommendations given in the last column of the Morrison feeding standards. (Appendix Table III.) The values are based chiefly upon the experiments with fattening cattle and sheep, for most of the net energy investigations have been with these classes of stock.

As has been shown in Chapter III, the various feeding stuffs have materially higher net energy values for milk production than for the fattening of animals. (90) However, the *relative* net energy values of most feeds for milk production and for fattening are probably not far different. Where it is believed that the relative net energy value of a particular feed for dairy cows differs materially from its value for fattening cattle or sheep, the estimated net energy value of the feed for dairy cows is shown separately. It seems probable that the relative net energy value, or productive value, of good-quality hay for dairy cows is somewhat higher in relation to the values of concentrates, than in the case of fattening cattle and sheep. However, there is not sufficient definite information on this question to warrant separate figures for the net energy value of such hay for dairy cows.

In the case of dry roughages these values are based upon the results secured when the roughages are fed in mangers or racks so as to prevent undue waste. The estimated value for each roughage takes into consideration the amount of the feed that is usually refused when it is thus fed. For such coarse roughage as dry corn fodder, dry corn stover, sorghum fodder, or sorghum stover, the estimates are for roughage that has been chopped or shredded to reduce the wastage. Likewise, the values for the various grains are based upon the grain being ground or crushed when such preparation is necessary to prevent poor utilization.

It has been shown previously that the net energy values have been actually determined for only a very few feeds by investigations with a respiration apparatus or a respiration calorimeter. Also, probably because of the complex nature of such investigations, there have been rather wide differences in the net energy values thus directly determined for these few feeds. In arriving at the net energy values given in this table, it has therefore been necessary to utilize all possible data bearing on the values of the various feeds for productive purposes.

Where the relative values of different feeds have been definitely determined by means of a sufficient number of suitable feeding experiments, the net energy values have been based primarily on these experiments. For other feeds the values have been computed from the content of total digestible nutrients given in Appendix Table I, by the use of factors based on the chemical composition of the particular feeding stuff and on all available information concerning its feeding value.

In the computation and estimation of these values, the "production coefficients" of Fraps have been utilized in certain instances. (94) Likewise, due attention has been given to the table of net energy values presented by Armsby in his book, "The Nutrition of Farm Animals." These net energy values were computed by him, with the permission of the author of this volume, from the tables of digestible nutrients for American feeding stuffs which were first published in 1915 in the fifteenth edition of Feeds and Feeding. These digestible nutrient values have now been superseded by the new values given in Appendix Table I of this edition of Feeds and Feeding. The starch values of Kellner and the Scandinavian feed unit values have also been considered in arriving at the net energy values of certain feeding stuffs. (95, 96)

TABLE II. Estimated net energy values of feeding stuffs

	Dry matter	Digestible protein	Net energy per 100 lbs.
Dry Roughages	Per ct.	Per ct.	Therms
Alfalfa hay, all analyses	90.4	10.6	41.5
Alfalfa hay, very leafy (less than 25% fiber)	90.0	12.4	44.3
Alfalfa hay, leafy (25-28% fiber)	90.4	12.0	42.2
Alfalfa hay, good (28-31% fiber)	90.4	10.3	41.5
Alfalfa hay, fair (31-34% fiber)	90.4	9.6	39.8
Alfalfa hay, stemmy (over 34% fiber)	90.4	8.2	35.6
Alfalfa meal, good	91.9	10.8	45.8
Alfalfa meal, stemmy	92.3	8.8	38.9
Barley hay	91.9	4.9	40.6
Barley straw	90.0	0.9	23.6
Bean straw, field	89.1	3.0	20.7
Bermuda hay	90.7	3.7	32.3
Brome grass hay	88.1	5.0	36.7
Carpet grass hay	92.1	3.1	37.5
Clover hay, alsike	89.0	7.7	41.6
Clover hay, crimson	89.4	9.7	39.0
Clover hay, red, all analyses	88.2	7.0	42.8

TABLE II. Estimated net energy values of feeding stuffs—*continued*

	Dry matter	Digest- ible protein	Net energy per 100 lbs.
Dry Roughages—Cont.	Per ct.	Per ct.	Therms
Clover hay, red, leafy (less than 25% fiber).....................	88.2	8.6	45.0
Clover hay, red, good quality (25 to 31% fiber)...............	88.8	6.8	44.5
Clover hay, red, stemmy (over 31% fiber).....................	88.2	6.0	39.2
Clover hay, sweet (first year)............................	93.3	14.6	42.8
Clover hay, sweet (second year)...........................	92.0	10.5	34.9
Clover and mixed grass hay, high in clover....................	89.7	5.2	41.4
Clover and mixed grass hay, second crop.....................	89.0	7.9	44.2
Clover and timothy hay, all analyses........................	88.0	4.4	38.4
Clover and timothy hay, 30 to 50% clover....................	91.9	4.8	41.6
Corn fodder, very dry.....................................	91.9	4.1	38.6
Corn fodder, medium in water..............................	82.5	3.5	35.5
Corn fodder, high in water.................................	60.7	2.5	26.1
Corn stover (ears removed), very dry........................	90.6	2.2	27.0
Corn stover, medium in water..............................	81.0	2.1	23.9
Corn stover, high in water.................................	59.0	1.4	17.5
Cottonseed hulls..	90.6	0.1	30.6
Cowpea hay..	90.4	12.6	40.8
Grass hay, mixed, eastern states, good quality.................	89.0	3.5	36.2
Grass hay, mixed, second cutting...........................	89.0	8.0	40.0
Johnson grass hay..	90.1	2.9	37.7
Kafir fodder, dry, including grain..........................	91.1	4.6	35.2
Kafir fodder, high in water................................	71.7	3.4	29.7
Kafir stover, medium in water..............................	83.7	1.7	25.4
Kafir stover, high in water.................................	72.7	1.3	22.0
Lespedeza hay, annual.....................................	89.1	9.2	43.1
Marsh or swamp hay, fair quality...........................	90.2	2.9	24.4
Millet hay, common, or Hungarian...........................	90.0	5.2	36.1
Millet hay, Japanese......................................	86.5	5.1	30.7
Milo fodder, dry, including grain...........................	88.9	4.3	34.5
Milo stover, dry..	91.0	1.1	24.4
Native hay, western mt. states, good quality..................	90.0	4.9	39.0
Native hay, western mt. states, mature and weathered..........	90.0	1.6	23.8
Oat hay...	88.0	4.5	34.7
Oat hulls..	93.5	0.8	20.2
Oat straw..	89.6	0.9	23.3
Orchard grass hay, early-cut...............................	88.6	4.6	35.2
Pasture grasses and clovers, mixed, from closely-grazed, fertile pasture, dried.....	90.0	13.1	53.4
Pea hay, field..	89.2	11.6	42.7
Peas and oats hay...	89.0	8.9	39.2
Peanut hay, without nuts or with few nuts....................	91.4	6.3	40.5
Peanut hulls...	92.3	3.2	− 9.0
Prairie hay, western, good quality..........................	90.4	2.6	36.9
Prairie hay, western, mature or weathered....................	90.4	0.6	28.3
Red top hay..	91.0	4.5	34.8
Rye straw...	92.9	0.7	11.5
Sorghum fodder, sweet, dry................................	89.2	3.6	34.3
Sorghum fodder, sweet, high in water........................	65.2	2.5	25.9
Soybean hay, all analyses..................................	90.8	11.1	38.5
Soybean hay, seed well developed...........................	90.8	11.9	40.3
Soybean straw..	88.0	0.9	14.6
Sudan grass hay..	89.2	4.3	34.0
Timothy hay, all analyses..................................	88.7	2.9	35.2
Timothy hay, before bloom.................................	88.7	5.6	40.2
Timothy hay, early bloom..................................	88.7	4.2	41.3

TABLE II. Estimated net energy values of feeding stuffs—*continued*

	Dry matter	Digest-ible protein	Net energy per 100 lbs.
Dry Roughages—Cont.	Per ct.	Per ct.	Therms
Timothy hay, full bloom................................	88.7	3.2	38.4
Timothy hay, in bloom, nitrogen-fertilized....................	88.7	4.8	41.4
Timothy hay, late bloom to early seed.....................	88.7	2.4	31.1
Timothy hay, late seed.................................	87.7	2.1	27.9
Vetch and oats hay, mostly vetch........................	90.0	9.1	42.0
Wheat hay..	89.0	3.2	32.6
Wheat straw....... :.................................	90.1	0.8	10.0
Green Roughages, Roots, Etc.			
Alfalfa, green..	25.4	3.4	12.8
Barley fodder..	22.6	2.3	12.2
Beet tops, sugar.....................................	11.4	1.9	6.3
Beets, common......................................	13.0	1.2	10.2
Beets, sugar...	16.4	1.2	13.8
Bluegrass, Kentucky, before heading.....................	24.8	4.4	15.4
Bluegrass, Kentucky, headed out......................	36.4	2.8	16.8
Brome grass, smooth.................................	33.8	2.9	15.8
Cabbage, entire.....................................	9.4	1.9	8.1
Carrots...	11.9	0.8	9.6
Clover, alsike.......................................	22.2	2.4	11.5
Clover, red...	25.0	2.6	13.4
Clover, sweet.......................................	22.0	3.0	11.9
Clover and mixed grasses.............................	27.3	1.9	14.9
Corn fodder, dent, all analyses........................	24.0	1.2	14.7
Corn fodder, dent, in milk............................	19.9	0.9	12.3
Corn fodder, dent, dough to glazing, well-eared.............	26.9	1.2	19.1
Corn fodder, dent, kernels ripe, well-eared................	37.7	1.7	26.0
Corn fodder, flint, all analyses........................	22.3	1.2	13.7
Cowpeas..	16.3	2.3	9.5
Johnson grass.......................................	29.1	1.1	14.0
Kafir fodder..	23.6	1.3	14.0
Lespedeza, annual...................................	36.6	5.0	18.2
Mangels, roots......................................	9.4	1.0	7.3
Millet, foxtail varieties...............................	29.9	1.9	15.3
Millet, Japanese.....................................	21.7	1.0	10.9
Milo fodder...	22.7	1.0	13.6
Oat fodder..	25.4	2.3	13.1
Orchard grass.......................................	29.1	1.7	13.6
Parsnips, roots......................................	16.6	1.3	14.3
Peas, field, Canada..................................	16.6	2.9	9.5
Peas and oats.......................................	22.1	2.4	12.3
Potatoes..	21.2	1.1	17.3
Rape...	16.4	2.6	11.3
Red top...	39.3	1.9	18.5
Rutabagas, roots....................................	11.1	1.0	9.3
Rye fodder..	22.3	2.3	13.0
Sorghum fodder, sweet...............................	24.9	0.8	14.7
Soybeans...	24.4	3.2	13.1
Sudan grass...	25.7	1.4	15.0
Sweet potatoes......................................	31.5	0.8	26.7
Timothy, all analyses.................................	31.3	1.8	15.4
Timothy, pasture stage...............................	22.8	3.7	13.6
Turnips...	9.5	1.3	8.5
Vetch, common......................................	20.4	2.7	10.6
Wheat fodder..	26.0	2.6	12.2

TABLE II. Estimated net energy values of feeding stuffs—*continued*

	Dry matter	Digest-ible protein	Net energy per 100 lbs.
Silages	Per ct.	Per ct.	Therms
Alfalfa, wilted before being ensiled........................	54.0	5.1	25.2
Alfalfa, high in water.....................................	23.9	1.9	11.0
Clover, red..	24.4	2.0	11.7
Corn, dent, well-matured, all anal......................	28.3	1.3	18.7
Corn, dent, well-matured, all anal., for *dairy cows*..............	28.3	1.3	14.3
Corn, dent, well-matured, well-eared.......................	29.2	1.5	21.4
Corn, dent, well-matured, well-eared, for *dairy cows*...........	29.2	1.5	15.8
Corn, dent, well-matured, fair in ears.....................	26.7	1.1	16.5
Corn, dent, well-matured, fair in ears, for *dairy cows*...........	26.7	1.1	13.3
Corn, dent, well-matured, few ears.........................	26.6	1.1	14.7
Corn, dent, well-matured, few ears, for *dairy cows*..............	26.6	1.1	12.5
Corn, dent, immature, before dough stage....................	20.4	1.0	11.3
Corn, dent, stover silage (ears removed)....................	22.6	0.8	8.8
Corn and soybeans, mostly corn............................	28.3	1.5	19.5
Corn and soybeans, mostly corn, for *dairy cows*................	28.3	1.5	15.0
Pea and oat...	30.0	2.7	16.7
Pea and oat, for *dairy cows*..............................	30.0	2.7	13.6
Sorghum, grain varieties..................................	31.3	1.1	16.0
Sorghum, grain varieties, for *dairy cows*.....................	31.3	1.1	13.6
Sorghum, sweet..	25.1	0.8	13.6
Sunflower..	22.2	1.1	11.0
Concentrates			
Barley, common, not including Pacific Coast states.............	90.4	9.3	70.5
Barley, common, for *dairy cows*...........................	90.4	9.3	79.2
Beet pulp, dried...	92.0	4.8	70.5
Beet pulp, wet...	11.6	0.8	9.2
Blood meal, or dried blood.................................	91.2	70.7	74.6
Brewers' grains, dried....................................	92.8	20.7	58.8
Brewers' grains, dried, for *dairy cows*......................	92.8	20.7	62.0
Brewers' grains, wet......................................	23.9	4.6	14.9
Brewers' grains, wet, for *dairy cows*.......................	23.9	4.6	15.8
Buckwheat, common......................................	90.4	8.9	58.4
Buckwheat feed, good grade................................	89.1	14.7	50.2
Buttermilk..	10.0	3.3	10.0
Coconut oil meal, old process..............................	90.7	18.7	72.4
Corn, dent, well dried....................................	88.5	7.4	82.3
Corn, dent, Grade No. 1..................................	87.2	7.3	81.1
Corn, dent, Grade No. 2..................................	85.2	7.1	79.2
Corn, dent, Grade No. 3..................................	83.5	7.0	77.7
Corn ears, including kernels and cobs (corn-and-cob meal)......	88.5	6.0	70.2
Corn gluten feed..	90.5	22.7	69.4
Corn gluten feed, for *dairy cows*..........................	90.5	22.7	76.1
Corn gluten meal..	91.5	36.5	80.4
Corn oil meal, old process.................................	91.8	16.7	70.5
Corn-and-oat feed, good grade.............................	89.7	8.4	76.2
Cottonseed, whole..	92.7	17.0	89.5
Cottonseed, whole pressed, 28% protein or over...............	94.7	23.1	56.8
Cottonseed meal, 43% protein grade........................	93.5	35.0	74.2
Cottonseed meal, 41% protein grade........................	92.8	33.9	72.3
Cottonseed meal, 38.5–41% protein.........................	92.8	32.2	71.5
Cottonseed meal, 36–38.5% protein.........................	92.7	29.3	68.0
Cottonseed feed, below 36% protein.........................	92.4	26.6	64.8
Cowpeas..	88.6	19.4	75.2
Darso grain...	89.9	7.7	75.2
Distillers' corn grains, dried...............................	93.6	22.3	83.6

TABLE II. Estimated net energy values of feeding stuffs—*continued*

	Dry matter	Digestible protein	Net energy per 100 lbs.
Concentrates—Cont.	Per ct.	Per ct.	Therms
Distillers' rye grains, dried	94.0	10.1	53.5
Emmer grain	91.2	9.6	67.8
Feterita grain	89.6	10.1	75.2
Fish meal	92.3	47.5	66.5
Flax seed	93.6	21.4	106.9
Hominy feed	90.9	7.8	83.8
Kafir grain	88.6	9.1	75.2
Kafir head chops	89.1	7.6	68.6
Linseed meal, old process, all analyses	91.3	30.6	76.9
Linseed meal, 33-37% protein	91.3	30.7	77.1
Linseed meal, 31-33% protein	91.2	27.9	76.6
Malt sprouts	92.2	20.3	60.0
Meat scraps, 55% protein grade	93.7	50.6	72.5
Meat scraps, 50% protein grade	93.8	46.7	70.0
Milo grain	89.4	8.7	75.2
Milo head chops	90.3	7.8	69.4
Molasses, beet	80.6	2.5	57.8
Molasses, cane	74.1	0.9	55.6
Molasses, cane for *dairy cows*	74.1	0.9	70.5
Oats, not including Pacific Coast states	91.1	9.4	64.9
Oats for *dairy cows*	91.1	9.4	71.3
Oats, light weight	91.3	7.8	54.5
Oat mill feed, usual grade	93.7	4.0	39.6
Oat mill feed, for *dairy cows*	93.7	4.0	44.7
Palm kernel oil meal	89.6	12.8	59.7
Palm kernel oil meal for *dairy cows*	89.6	12.8	66.7
Pea seed, field	90.5	20.2	78.2
Peanuts, with hulls	94.1	20.2	93.2
Peanut oil meal, old process	93.4	38.0	80.7
Peanut oil feed (unhulled)	93.5	26.8	58.5
Rice grain, or rough rice	88.6	6.3	62.7
Rice bran	91.1	8.8	60.0
Rice polish	90.5	9.3	84.2
Rye grain	90.0	10.3	72.1
Rye feed	90.4	12.8	69.7
Skimmilk, centrifugal	9.6	3.5	9.5
Skimmilk, dried	93.8	33.1	92.5
Soybeans	90.2	32.8	84.7
Soybean oil meal, hydraulic or expeller process	91.7	37.7	80.8
Tankage, or meat meal (digester process), 60% protein grade	92.2	56.4	76.7
Tankage, or meat meal (digester process), 55% protein grade	92.7	51.5	72.9
Wheat, recent analyses	89.8	11.3	84.7
Wheat for *fattening lambs*	89.8	11.3	70.5
Wheat bran	90.6	13.1	59.7
Wheat bran, for *dairy cows*	90.6	13.1	66.7
Wheat bran and screenings	90.8	13.2	59.1
Wheat bran and screenings, for *dairy cows*	90.8	13.2	66.0
Wheat brown shorts	90.1	15.1	68.7
Wheat flour middlings	89.6	15.0	75.5
Wheat gray shorts	90.1	15.0	75.0
Wheat mixed feed	90.6	13.9	63.2
Wheat mixed feed, for *dairy cows*	90.6	13.9	70.0
Wheat red dog	89.2	15.2	85.4
Wheat screenings	90.4	9.7	52.8
Wheat standard middlings	90.0	14.4	70.6

TABLE II.   Estimated net energy values of feeding stuffs—*continued*

	Dry matter	Digestible protein	Net energy per 100 lbs.
Concentrates—Cont.	Per ct.	Per ct.	Therms
Wheat standard middlings, for *dairy cows*	90.0	14.4	71.4
Wheat standard middlings and screenings	90.0	13.7	68.0
Wheat white shorts	89.7	14.5	84.9
Whey, from American cheese	6.6	0.9	7.0

TABLE III.   MORRISON FEEDING STANDARDS FOR FARM ANIMALS

The following feeding standards have been prepared by the author to serve as guides in the computation of balanced rations for the various classes of livestock. These recommendations are presented, not as final, arbitrary standards, but as approximate guides in practical stock feeding.

It has been emphasized in the various chapters of this volume that feeding stuffs of the same name may differ appreciably from the average composition. Individual animals of the same kind also differ to some extent in ability to digest and utilize feed. To serve as safe guides in stock feeding, the recommendations made in feeding standards should therefore not be statements of the theoretical nutrient requirements, but should provide a margin of safety to cover such differences.

Minimum and more liberal recommendations.—It will be noted that in all cases both minimum and more liberal recommendations are given for each class of stock. When protein-rich feeds are not unduly expensive in comparison with feeds low in protein, it is wise to supply enough digestible protein to bring the protein of the rations well up toward the higher figures in the standards. On the other hand, when protein-rich feeds are unusually expensive in comparison with farm grains or other feeds low in protein, it may be more economical to provide only enough digestible protein to meet the lower recommendations. (288)

Unless concentrates are very high in price in comparison with roughages, it is generally advisable to include a sufficient amount of concentrates in rations to provide as much total digestible nutrients (or net energy) as recommended in the higher figures of the standards. On the other hand, when grain and other concentrates are unusually high in price in comparison with roughage, it may be most economical to supply no more total digestible nutrients (or net energy) than recommended in the lower figures.

In general, when as much total digestible nutrients are furnished as recommended in the higher figures, there should be sufficient protein in the ration to approach the higher figures for digestible protein given in the standards.

Net energy recommendations.—For the convenience of those desiring to compute rations according to the net energy method, the last column of figures in the standards shows the amounts of net energy, expressed in therms, which are advised for various classes of stock. In computing rations by the net energy method, the net energy values of feeding stuffs given in Appendix Table II should be used, instead of the total digestible nutrient values given in Appendix Table I.

For the reason stated in Chapter III, total digestible nutrient values, instead of net energy values, should always be used in computing maintenance rations for wintering farm animals in sections where the winter climate is cold. (88) For this reason the net energy recommendations for wintering various classes of stock are given in parentheses.

Computing economical balanced rations.—Before attempting to work out economical balanced rations for any class of stock, it is important to study carefully the explanations and general hints given in Chapters IX and X. (252-264, 276-293)

It is impossible to compute satisfactory balanced rations if reliance is placed only on the mathematical recommendations of any feeding standard. As is explained in these chapters, several other factors are just as important in determining the efficiency of a ration as are the amounts of digestible protein and of total digestible nutrients (or net energy). Special attention must likewise be given to the quality of protein in the ration and to the content of vitamins and minerals, as well as to the general suitability of the feeds to the particular class of stock.

The special rules and hints on feeding the particular class of stock, which are given in the respective chapters of Part III, should be carefully consulted before proceeding to work out a balanced ration. For convenience the following references to important articles discussing balanced rations for the various farm animals are here given:

Dairy cows, **794-820, 905-913**
Dairy calves, **945-952**
Dairy heifers, **977-982**
Growing beef cattle, **990-991, 997-1001, 1116-1120**
Fattening cattle, **990-1006, 1123-1136, 1144**
Beef breeding cows, **1104-1109**
Work horses and mules, **696-706, 763-765**
Brood mares, **769**
Growing colts, **774-779**
Fattening lambs, **1160-1170, 1261-1266**
Breeding ewes, **1235-1240**
Growing and fattening pigs, **1279-1301**
Brood sows, **1405-1417**

Guides to proportions and amounts of concentrates and roughages.—In computing rations one should have in mind the approximate amounts of roughage and of concentrates required per 100 lbs. live weight by the various classes of animals. As has been shown in the experiments reviewed in Part III, the proportion of concentrates to roughages depends first of all on how much it is desired to force the animal: For example, when it is desired to fatten animals rapidly the allowance of concentrates must be considerably larger than when they are fattened more slowly and over a longer period. In a similar manner, the horse at hard work should be given more grain and less roughage than the horse working but little.

In general, the following will be helpful as guides in computing rations:

Dairy cows in milk will eat about 2 lbs. of good-quality dry roughage daily per 100 lbs. live weight. Silage may be substituted for dry roughage at the rate of 3 lbs. of silage for 1 lb. of dry roughage. A common rule is to feed 1 lb. of hay and 3 lbs. of silage daily per 100 lbs. live weight. Sufficient concentrates should be fed in addition to bring the nutrients up to the standard.

If the roughage is of especially good quality dairy cows will eat as much as 2.5 lbs. of hay equivalent daily per 100 lbs. live weight, and they then need correspondingly less concentrates. On the other hand, if the roughage is of poor quality, they may eat no more than 1.5 lbs. of hay equivalent daily per 100 lbs. live weight. Their concentrate allowance must then be increased over the amount needed with good roughage.

The amounts of concentrates required daily by cows producing different amounts of milk of the various fat percentages are shown in the grain feeding tables given in Appendix Table IX.

Fattening cattle should receive 2.1 lbs. or more of concentrates and dry roughage (or equivalent in silage) daily per 100 lbs. live weight, the allowance of concentrates ranging from less than 1 lb. to 1.7 lbs. or more daily per 100 lbs. live weight, depending on the rate of gain desired and the character of the roughage.

Beef breeding cows may be wintered satisfactorily on roughage of reasonably good quality, without any concentrates. If the roughage is of very poor quality,

1 lb. per head daily of protein supplement should be fed, and a small amount of grain may be needed in addition.

Beef calves and yearlings can be wintered satisfactorily on roughage alone, if it is of good quality. A small amount of protein supplement should be fed when needed to balance the ration.

Work horses and mules should be fed approximately the following amounts daily per 100 lbs. live weight of concentrates (including grain and other concentrates) and of hay:

At hard work, 1.00 to 1.40 lbs. of concentrates and about 1.00 lb. of hay.

At medium work, 0.75 to 1.00 lb. of concentrates and about 1.00 to 1.25 lbs. of hay.

At light work, 0.40 to 0.75 lb. of concentrates and 1.25 to 1.50 lbs. of hay.

Idle, chiefly or entirely on roughage, unless it is of poor quality, when some grain must be used.

Fattening lambs averaging 70 to 75 lbs. in weight will consume about 1.4 lbs. per head daily of hay or other dry roughage when fed all the grain they will eat. They will eat 2.3 lbs. or more of hay per head daily when the grain allowance is restricted. The amounts of feed eaten by smaller or larger lambs will be roughly proportional to their live weights.

Breeding ewes may be wintered satisfactorily on good roughage alone up to 4 to 6 weeks before lambing, if they are in good condition in the fall. During the 4 to 6 weeks before lambing, 0.5 lb. or slightly more of a suitable concentrate mixture should be fed per head daily. Ewes, not on pasture, that are nursing lambs need 1.0 lb. or more per head daily of concentrates in addition to good roughage.

Swine can make but very limited use of dry roughage, except in the case of brood sows not nursing litters. However, it is very important under most conditions that swine not on pasture be supplied with well-cured legume hay as insurance against any lack of vitamin A or vitamin D. **(1297-1298)**

Sources of recommendations in standards.—These standards are based chiefly upon extensive studies, made by and under the supervision of the author, of the results of feeding experiments and other investigations that supply information concerning the nutrient requirements of the various classes of stock.

The standards for dairy cows are based upon the extensive investigations discussed in some detail in Chapter XXIV. **(794-809)** The author wishes to acknowledge especially the aid of Dr. G. W. Salisbury in the preparation of these standards. The experiments upon which the recommendations for dairy calves and heifers are chiefly based are summarized in Chapter XXVII. **(945-948)**

The standards for beef cattle are based upon studies of the results of feeding experiments conducted at the American experiment stations, including recent experiments with fattening cattle conducted at the New York (Cornell) Station by Professor R. B. Hinman and the author. In the compilation and analysis of the data upon which these standards are based much assistance has been rendered by Mr. H. M. Briggs, Mr. J. I. Miller, and Dr. W. C. Stiles.

The standards for sheep and lambs are based upon studies of the results of feeding experiments at various experiment stations and especially upon data secured in recent trials with fattening lambs and breeding ewes conducted at the New York (Cornell) Station by Professor J. P. Willman and the author.

The standards for swine are similarly based on the results of feeding experiments at various stations, especially on investigations by the author, Professor J. M. Fargo, and Professor G. Bohstedt at the Wisconsin Station and experiments by the author and Professor J. P. Willman at the New York (Cornell) Station.

Standards for dairy cows.—The amount of dry matter to be fed daily per 1,000 lbs. live weight to dairy cows may range from 15.0 lbs. or even less for dry cows to 30.0 lbs. for cows yielding 2.0 lbs. of butter fat per head daily. Cows producing 1.0 lb. of fat per head daily should receive about 21.0 to 25.0 lbs. of dry matter daily per 1,000 lbs. live weight.

The amounts of nutrients required for a cow producing a given amount of milk which contains a certain percentage of fat are found as follows: Add together the maintenance requirements for a cow of the particular live weight, (shown in Division **1A** of the standards), and the requirements for producing the given amount of milk (computed from Division **1B**).

As an illustration, let us find the amount of protein advised in the column headed "Recommended for good cows under usual conditions for a 1,200 lb. cow producing 30 lbs. of 3.5 per cent milk daily." For the maintenance of a cow of this live weight, the standard recommends 0.762 lb. digestible protein. For producing each pound of 3.5 per cent milk, the allowance recommended is 0.046 lb. digestible protein. Therefore 30 times this amount, or 1.380 lbs. digestible protein, will be required for the production of 40 lbs. of milk. Adding together the maintenance requirement (0.762 lb.) and the production requirement (1.380 lb.), we have a total of 2.142 lbs. digestible protein, which is the amount advised for such a cow under usual conditions.

The nutritive ratio may readily be found by computation, after adding together the requirements for maintenance and for the production of the amount of milk yielded. For example, a 1,200-lb. cow yielding daily 30.0 lbs. of 3.5 per cent milk will require, if fed according to the recommendations "for good cows under usual conditions," 2.14 lbs. digestible protein and 18.29 lbs. total digestible nutrients. The nutritive ratio should hence be not wider than 1:7.5.

Standards for growing dairy cattle.—The standards for growing dairy cattle provide enough nutrients for normal growth. Young cattle consuming suitable rations that contain the amounts of nutrients shown in the standards should reach good size for their breed.

Standards for beef cattle.—The standards for growing beef cattle are intended for young cattle that are being grown rapidly throughout the entire period, and not for cattle that are "roughed through the winter," as is the common practice in most sections of the range area. Recommendations for wintering beef calves and yearlings according to this method are given later in the standards. The recommendations for fattening cattle are for animals that are to be fattened rapidly on a liberal amount of grain or other concentrates. Cattle fed a limited amount of concentrates will consume less total digestible nutrients (or net energy) than here shown and will not make maximum gains. (1004-1006)

The standards for calves being fattened for baby beef are intended for calves that are placed on feed when weighing 300 to 400 lbs. and are then fattened rapidly for marketing at a weight of not over 900 to 1000 lbs. The recommendations for fattening yearlings are for well-grown yearling cattle which weigh 600 to 750 lbs. when placed on feed and which are marketed at about 1100 lbs. in weight. The standards for fattening 2-year-old cattle are for cattle which weigh about 900 lbs. at the start and are marketed at about 1,200 lbs. During the period when fattening cattle are being gotten on feed, they will consume less nutrients than shown in these standards.

The standards for wintering beef calves and for wintering yearling cattle provide sufficient nutrients to produce approximately the rates of gain stated in the table.

The standards for wintering beef breeding cows provide sufficient nutrients to enable the cows to gain slightly in weight as pregnancy advances.

Standards for horses.—The standards for horses at hard work are for horses actually doing hard work at least 7 to 8 hours a day. Horses working hard for a shorter daily period should be classed as "at medium work" or "at light work" as the case may be. The amounts of nutrients advised for idle horses should keep them in thrifty condition and should prevent loss of weight.

Standards for lambs and sheep.—The standards for fattening lambs are intended for fattening thrifty lambs that weigh about 50 to 65 lbs. at the start and that are fed a sufficiently liberal amount of concentrates to make them fat at a weight of about 90 lbs. or less. (1264) While they are being started on feed, lambs will not consume as much nutrients as shown in the standards.

The amount of nutrients advised for breeding ewes should keep them in thrifty condition.

Standards for pigs.—The recommendations for pigs are intended for full-feeding and not for limited-feeding. (1303-1308) Pigs of excellent breeding that are unusually growthy may consume somewhat more nutrients than shown in the standards when self-fed an excellent ration.

TABLE III.   Morrison feeding standards

	Digestible protein		Total digestible nutrients		Net energy	
	Minimum allowance advised	Recommended for good cows under usual conditions	Minimum allowance advised	Recommended for good cows under usual conditions	Minimum allowance advised	Recommended for good cows under usual conditions
1. Dairy cows	Lbs.	Lbs.	Lbs.	Lbs.	Therms	Therms
A. For maintenance						
(Per head daily)						
700-lb. cow	0.440	0.476	5.13	5.81	4.10	4.65
750-lb. cow	0.467	0.506	5.45	6.18	4.36	4.94
800-lb. cow	0.494	0.536	5.77	6.53	4.62	5.22
850-lb. cow	0.521	0.564	6.08	6.88	4.86	5.50
900-lb. cow	0.547	0.593	6.38	7.23	5.10	5.78
950-lb. cow	0.574	0.621	6.69	7.58	5.35	6.06
1,000-lb. cow	0.600	0.650	7.00	7.93	5.60	6.34
1,050-lb. cow	0.626	0.678	7.30	8.27	5.84	6.62
1,100-lb. cow	0.652	0.706	7.60	8.61	6.08	6.89
1,150-lb. cow	0.677	0.734	7.90	8.95	6.32	7.16
1,200-lb. cow	0.703	0.762	8.20	9.29	6.56	7.43
1,250-lb. cow	0.730	0.790	8.51	9.64	6.81	7.71
1,300-lb. cow	0.754	0.817	8.80	9.97	7.04	7.98
1,350-lb. cow	0.779	0.844	9.09	10.29	7.27	8.23
1,400-lb. cow	0.805	0.872	9.39	10.63	7.51	8.50
1,450-lb. cow	0.829	0.898	9.67	10.96	7.74	8.77
1,500-lb. cow	0.854	0.925	9.96	11.28	7.97	9.02
1,550-lb. cow	0.878	0.952	10.25	11.61	8.20	9.29
1,600-lb. cow	0.904	0.979	10.54	11.94	8.43	9.55
1,650-lb. cow	0.928	1.005	10.82	12.26	8.66	9.81
1,700-lb. cow	0.952	1.032	11.11	12.58	8.89	10.06
1,750-lb. cow	0.976	1.058	11.39	12.90	9.11	10.32
1,800-lb. cow	1.001	1.084	11.68	13.23	9.34	10.58
B. For milk production per pound of milk.						
(To be added to allowance for maintenance)						
For 2.5% milk	0.034	0.040	.238	.251	.221	.233
For 3.0% milk	0.036	0.043	.261	.276	.243	.257
For 3.5% milk	0.038	0.046	.284	.300	.264	.279
For 4.0% milk	0.041	0.049	.307	.324	.286	.301
For 4.5% milk	0.044	0.052	.330	.349	.307	.325
For 5.0% milk	0.046	0.056	.353	.373	.328	.347
For 5.5% milk	0.049	0.059	.376	.397	.350	.369
For 6.0% milk	0.052	0.062	.399	.422	.371	.392
For 6.5% milk	0.054	0.065	.422	.446	.392	.415
For 7.0% milk	0.057	0.068	.445	.470	.414	.437

TABLE III. Morrison feeding standards—*continued*

	Requirements per head daily				
	Dry matter	Digestible protein	Total digestible nutrients	Nutritive ratio	Net energy
2. Growing dairy cattle	Lbs.	Lbs.	Lbs.	1:	Therms
Weight 100 lbs..........	1.4-2.4	0.24-0.40	1.2-2.0	3.9-4.5	1.2-2.0
Weight 150 lbs..........	3.0-4.0	0.41-0.52	2.3-3.0	4.4-5.1	2.3-2.9
Weight 200 lbs..........	4.6-5.6	0.52-0.62	3.3-4.0	5.0-5.5	3.2-3.8
Weight 250 lbs..........	5.9-6.9	0.61-0.71	4.1-4.8	5.7-6.2	3.9-4.5
Weight 300 lbs..........	7.2-8.0	0.67-0.78	4.9-5.5	6.3-6.8	4.5-5.1
Weight 400 lbs..........	9.0-10.0	0.80-0.90	6.1-6.6	6.5-7.0	5.5-5.9
Weight 500 lbs..........	10.6-11.8	0.87-0.98	6.9-7.7	6.9-7.4	6.1-6.8
Weight 600 lbs..........	12.0-13.6	0.94-1.06	7.7-8.7	7.2-7.7	6.8-7.7
Weight 700 lbs..........	13.4-15.5	1.00-1.13	8.4-9.7	7.4-7.9	7.3-8.4
Weight 800 lbs..........	14.8-17.4	1.06-1.20	9.1-10.7	7.6-8.1	7.9-9.3
Weight 900 lbs..........	16.1-19.2	1.11-1.27	9.8-11.7	7.8-8.3	8.5-10.1
Weight 1,000 lbs........	17.5-21.0	1.16-1.33	10.4-12.6	8.0-8.4	8.9-10.8
3. Growing beef cattle, fed liberally for rapid growth					
Weight 100 lbs..........	1.4-2.4	0.24-0.40	1.2-2.0	3.9-4.5	1.2-2.0
Weight 150 lbs..........	3.1-4.1	0.42-0.54	2.4-3.1	4.4-5.1	2.4-3.0
Weight 200 lbs..........	4.8-5.8	0.54-0.64	3.4-4.2	5.0-5.5	3.3-4.0
Weight 250 lbs..........	6.2-7.2	0.64-0.75	4.3-5.0	5.7-6.2	4.1-4.7
Weight 300 lbs..........	7.7-8.6	0.72-0.83	5.2-5.9	6.3-6.8	4.8-5.5
Weight 400 lbs..........	9.8-10.9	0.87-0.98	6.6-7.2	6.5-7.0	6.0-6.4
Weight 500 lbs..........	11.7-13.0	0.96-1.08	7.6-8.5	6.9-7.4	6.7-7.5
Weight 600 lbs..........	13.2-15.0	1.03-1.17	8.5-9.6	7.2-7.7	7.5-8.5
Weight 700 lbs..........	14.7-17.1	1.10-1.24	9.2-10.7	7.4-7.9	8.0-9.2
Weight 800 lbs..........	16.3-19.1	1.17-1.32	10.0-11.8	7.6-8.1	8.7-10.2
Weight 900 lbs..........	17.7-21.1	1.22-1.40	10.8-12.9	7.8-8.3	9.4-11.1
Weight 1,000 lbs........	19.3-23.1	1.28-1.46	11.4-13.9	8.0-8.9	9.8-11.9
4. Calves being fattened for baby beef					
Weight 400 lbs..........	9.6-12.7	0.98-1.23	7.4-9.8	6.5-7.0	6.7-8.9
Weight 500 lbs..........	11.4-14.5	1.19-1.43	9.0-11.4	6.6-7.1	8.2-10.4
Weight 600 lbs..........	13.3-16.1	1.39-1.60	10.6-12.9	6.6-7.1	9.8-11.9
Weight 700 lbs..........	14.8-17.5	1.55-1.75	12.0-14.2	6.7-7.2	11.2-13.2
Weight 800 lbs..........	16.1-18.7	1.69-1.89	13.1-15.2	6.7-7.2	12.3-14.3
Weight 900 lbs..........	17.0-19.4	1.75-1.95	13.8-15.8	6.8-7.3	13.0-14.9
5. Fattening yearling cattle					
Weight 600 lbs..........	13.2-16.3	1.20-1.41	10.3-12.7	7.0-8.0	9.3-11.5
Weight 700 lbs..........	15.2-18.3	1.41-1.60	12.0-14.4	7.0-8.0	11.0-13.2
Weight 800 lbs..........	17.0-20.3	1.59-1.79	13.5-16.1	7.0-8.0	12.6-15.0
Weight 900 lbs..........	18.5-21.8	1.74-1.94	14.8-17.4	7.0-8.0	13.9-16.4
Weight 1,000 lbs........	19.7-22.9	1.87-2.06	15.9-18.5	7.0-8.0	14.9-17.4
Weight 1,100 lbs........	20.8-24.0	1.99-2.17	16.9-19.5	7.0-8.0	15.9-18.3
6. Fattening 2-year-old cattle					
Weight 900 lbs..........	18.7-22.3	1.62-1.83	14.6-17.4	7.5-8.5	13.3-15.8
Weight 1,000 lbs........	20.0-23.5	1.78-1.98	16.0-18.8	7.5-8.5	14.9-17.5
Weight 1,100 lbs........	20.9-24.1	1.87-2.07	17.0-19.6	7.5-8.5	16.0-18.4
Weight 1,200 lbs........	21.8-24.7	1.95-2.12	17.7-20.1	7.5-8.5	16.6-18.9

TABLE III. Morrison feeding standards—*continued*

	Requirements per head daily				
	Dry matter	Digestible protein	Total digestible nutrients	Nutritive ratio	Net energy
	Lbs.	Lbs.	Lbs.	1:	Therms
7. Wintering beef calves to gain 0.75 to 1.00 lb. per head daily					
Weight 300 lbs...........	7.0-8.3	0.52-0.58	3.9-4.6	6.5-7.0	(3.2-3.8)
Weight 400 lbs...........	8.7-10.3	0.63-0.70	4.8-5.7	6.7-7.2	(4.0-4.8)
Weight 500 lbs...........	10.3-12.1	0.71-0.78	5.7-6.7	7.1-7.6	(4.7-5.6)
Weight 600 lbs...........	11.7-13.9	0.79-0.88	6.5-7.7	7.3-7.8	(5.3-6.2)
8. Wintering yearling beef cattle to gain 0.50 to 0.75 lb. per head daily					
Weight 600 lbs...........	11.6-13.3	0.67-0.75	6.3-7.2	8.1-8.6	(5.0-5.8)
Weight 700 lbs...........	12.9-14.8	0.76-0.83	7.0-8.0	8.2-8.7	(5.6-6.4)
Weight 800 lbs...........	14.2-16.3	0.83-0.90	7.7-8.8	8.3-8.8	(6.2-7.0)
9. Wintering pregnant beef cows					
Weight 900 lbs...........	13.1-18.4	0.56-0.65	6.9-9.7	10.0-15.0	(4.5-6.3)
Weight 1,000 lbs.........	14.2-20.0	0.60-0.70	7.5-10.5	10.0-15.0	(4.9-6.8)
Weight 1,100 lbs.........	15.2-21.5	0.64-0.75	8.0-11.3	10.0-15.0	(5.2-7.3)
Weight 1,200 lbs.........	16.3-22.8	0.69-0.80	8.6-12.0	10.0-15.0	(5.6-7.8)
10. Horses, idle					
Weight 1,000 lbs.........	13.0-18.0	0.6-0.8	7.0-9.0	10.0-12.0	(5.6-7.2)
Weight 1,100 lbs.........	13.9-19.3	0.6-0.9	7.5-9.7	10.0-12.0	(6.0-7.7)
Weight 1,200 lbs.........	14.8-20.6	0.7-0.9	8.0-10.3	10.0-12.0	(6.4-8.2)
Weight 1,300 lbs.........	15.7-21.8	0.7-1.0	8.5-10.9	10.0-12.0	(6.8-8.7)
Weight 1,400 lbs.........	16.6-23.0	0.8-1.0	8.9-11.5	10.0-12.0	(7.2-9.2)
Weight 1,500 lbs.........	17.5-24.2	0.8-1.1	9.4-12.1	10.0-12.0	(7.5-9.7)
Weight 1,600 lbs.........	18.3-25.4	0.8-1.1	9.9-12.7	10.0-12.0	(7.9-10.1)
Weight 1,700 lbs.........	19.1-26.5	0.9-1.2	10.3-13.3	10.0-12.0	(8.2-10.6)
Weight 1,800 lbs.........	20.0-27.6	0.9-1.2	10.8-13.8	10.0-12.0	(8.6-11.1)
11. Horses at light work					
Weight 1,000 lbs.........	15.0-20.0	0.8-1.0	9.0-11.0	9.0-11.0	7.5-9.1
Weight 1,100 lbs.........	16.2-21.6	0.9-1.1	9.7-11.9	9.0-11.0	8.1-9.8
Weight 1,200 lbs.........	17.4-23.1	0.9-1.2	10.4-12.7	9.0-11.0	8.7-10.5
Weight 1,300 lbs.........	18.5-24.7	1.0-1.2	11.1-13.6	9.0-11.0	9.3-11.2
Weight 1,400 lbs.........	19.6-26.2	1.0-1.3	11.8-14.4	9.0-11.0	9.8-11.9
Weight 1,500 lbs.........	20.8-27.7	1.1-1.4	12.5-15.2	9.0-11.0	10.4-12.6
Weight 1,600 lbs.........	21.9-29.2	1.2-1.5	13.1-16.0	9.0-11.0	10.9-13.3
Weight 1,700 lbs.........	23.0-30.6	1.2-1.5	13.8-16.8	9.0-11.0	11.5-13.9
Weight 1,800 lbs.........	24.0-32.0	1.3-1.6	14.4-17.6	9.0-11.0	12.0-14.6
12. Horses at medium work					
Weight 1,000 lbs.........	16.0-21.0	1.0-1.2	11.0-13.0	9.0-11.0	9.4-11.1
Weight 1,100 lbs.........	17.4-22.8	1.1-1.3	11.9-14.1	9.0-11.0	10.2-12.1
Weight 1,200 lbs.........	18.8-24.6	1.2-1.4	12.9-15.2	9.0-11.0	11.0-13.0
Weight 1,300 lbs.........	20.1-26.4	1.3-1.5	13.8-16.3	9.0-11.0	11.8-14.0
Weight 1,400 lbs.........	21.5-28.2	1.3-1.6	14.8-17.4	9.0-11.0	12.6-14.9
Weight 1,500 lbs.........	22.8-29.9	1.4-1.7	15.7-18.5	9.0-11.0	13.4-15.8
Weight 1,600 lbs.........	24.1-31.6	1.5-1.8	16.6-19.6	9.0-11.0	14.2-16.7
Weight 1,700 lbs.........	25.4-33.3	1.6-1.9	17.5-20.6	9.0-11.0	14.9-17.6
Weight 1,800 lbs.........	26.7-35.0	1.7-2.0	18.3-21.7	9.0-11.0	15.7-18.5

TABLE III.   Morrison feeding standards—*continued*

	Requirements per head daily				
	Dry matter	Digestible protein	Total digestible nutrients	Nutritive ratio	Net energy
13. Horses at hard work	Lbs.	Lbs.	Lbs.	1:	Therms
Weight 1,000 lbs........	18.0-22.0	1.2-1.4	13.0-16.0	9.0-11.0	11.3-13.9
Weight 1,100 lbs........	19.7-24.0	1.3-1.5	14.2-17.5	9.0-11.0	12.4-15.2
Weight 1,200 lbs........	21.3-26.1	1.4-1.7	15.4-19.0	9.0-11.0	13.4-16.5
Weight 1,300 lbs........	23.0-28.1	1.5-1.8	16.6-20.5	9.0-11.0	14.5-17.8
Weight 1,400 lbs........	24.7-30.2	1.6-1.9	17.8-21.9	9.0-11.0	15.5-19.1
Weight 1,500 lbs........	26.3-32.2	1.8-2.0	19.0-23.4	9.0-11.0	16.5-20.3
Weight 1,600 lbs........	28.0-34.2	1.9-2.2	20.2-24.8	9.0-11.0	17.5-21.6
Weight 1,700 lbs........	29.6-36.2	2.0-2.3	21.4-26.3	9.0-11.0	18.6-22.9
Weight 1,800 lbs........	31.2-38.1	2.1-2.4	22.5-27.7	9.0-11.0	19.6-24.1
14. Brood mares nursing foals, but not at work					
Weight 1,000 lbs........	15.0-22.0	1.2-1.5	9.0-12.0	6.5-7.5	7.6-10.0
Weight 1,100 lbs........	16.2-23.8	1.3-1.6	9.7-13.0	6.5-7.5	8.2-10.8
Weight 1,200 lbs........	17.4-25.5	1.4-1.7	10.4-13.9	6.5-7.5	8.8-11.6
Weight 1,300 lbs........	18.5-27.1	1.5-1.9	11.1-14.8	6.5-7.5	9.4-12.3
Weight 1,400 lbs........	19.6-28.8	1.6-2.0	11.8-15.7	6.5-7.5	10.0-13.1
Weight 1,500 lbs........	20.8-30.4	1.7-2.1	12.5-16.6	6.5-7.5	10.5-13.8
Weight 1,600 lbs........	21.9-32.1	1.7-2.2	13.1-17.5	6.5-7.5	11.1-14.6
Weight 1,700 lbs........	23.0-33.7	1.8-2.3	13.8-18.4	6.5-7.5	11.6-15.3
Weight 1,800 lbs........	24.0-35.2	1.9-2.4	14.4-19.2	6.5-7.5	12.2-16.0
15. Growing draft colts, after weaning					
Weight 400 lbs..........	9.2-11.3	0.8-0.9	5.6-7.2	6.5-7.0	4.9-6.3
Weight 500 lbs..........	10.9-13.3	0.9-1.0	6.6-8.4	6.6-7.1	5.7-7.3
Weight 600 lbs..........	12.4-15.2	1.0-1.2	7.6-9.6	6.7-7.2	6.5-8.3
Weight 700 lbs..........	13.9-17.0	1.1-1.3	8.5-10.8	6.8-7.3	7.3-9.3
Weight 800 lbs..........	15.3-18.7	1.2-1.4	9.4-11.9	6.9-7.4	8.0-10.1
Weight 900 lbs..........	16.7-20.4	1.3-1.5	10.2-13.0	7.0-8.0	8.7-11.0
Weight 1,000 lbs........	18.0-22.0	1.4-1.6	11.0-14.0	7.0-8.0	9.2-11.8
Weight 1,100 lbs........	19.3-23.6	1.5-1.6	11.8-15.0	7.2-8.2	9.9-12.6
Weight 1,200 lbs........	20.6-25.1	1.5-1.7	12.6-16.0	7.5-8.5	10.6-13.4
16. Pregnant ewes, up to 4 to 6 weeks before lambing					
Weight 100 lbs..........	2.0-2.3	0.16-0.18	1.5-1.8	7.5-8.5	(1.2-1.5)
Weight 110 lbs..........	2.2-2.4	0.17-0.20	1.6-1.9	7.5-8.5	(1.3-1.6)
Weight 120 lbs..........	2.3-2.6	0.18-0.21	1.7-2.0	7.5-8.5	(1.4-1.7)
Weight 130 lbs..........	2.4-2.8	0.19-0.22	1.8-2.1	7.5-8.5	(1.5-1.8)
Weight 140 lbs..........	2.6-2.9	0.20-0.23	1.9-2.2	7.5-8.5	(1.6-1.9)
Weight 150 lbs..........	2.7-3.1	0.21-0.24	2.0-2.4	7.5-8.5	(1.7-2.0)
17. Pregnant ewes, last 4 to 6 weeks before lambing					
Weight 100 lbs..........	2.5-2.8	0.21-0.23	1.9-2.2	7.2-8.2	(1.6-1.9)
Weight 110 lbs..........	2.7-2.9	0.22-0.25	2.0-2.3	7.2-8.2	(1.7-2.0)
Weight 120 lbs..........	2.8-3.1	0.23-0.26	2.1-2.4	7.2-8.2	(1.8-2.1)
Weight 130 lbs..........	2.9-3.3	0.24-0.27	2.2-2.5	7.2-8.2	(1.9-2.2)
Weight 140 lbs..........	3.1-3.4	0.25-0.28	2.3-2.6	7.2-8.2	(2.0-2.3)
Weight 150 lbs..........	3.2-3.6	0.26-0.29	2.4-2.8	7.2-8.2	(2.1-2.4)

TABLE III. Morrison feeding standards—*continued*

	Requirements per head daily				
	Dry matter	Digestible protein	Total digestible nutrients	Nutritive ratio	Net energy
	Lbs.	Lbs.	Lbs.	1:	Therms
18. Ewes nursing lambs					
Weight 100 lbs............	2.9-3.2	0.27-0.29	2.3-2.6	6.7-7.7	1.9-2.2
Weight 110 lbs............	3.1-3.3	0.28-0.31	2.4-2.7	6.7-7.7	2.0-2.3
Weight 120 lbs............	3.2-3.5	0.29-0.32	2.5-2.8	6.7-7.7	2.1-2.4
Weight 130 lbs............	3.3-3.7	0.30-0.33	2.6-2.9	6.7-7.7	2.2-2.5
Weight 140 lbs............	3.5-3.8	0.31-0.34	2.7-3.0	6.7-7.7	2.3-2.6
Weight 150 lbs............	3.6-4.0	0.32-0.35	2.8-3.2	6.7-7.7	2.4-2.7
19. Fattening lambs					
Weight 50 lbs............	1.9-2.3	0.16-0.19	1.2-1.5	6.5-7.0	1.0-1.3
Weight 60 lbs............	2.0-2.5	0.20-0.23	1.5-1.8	6.7-7.2	1.3-1.6
Weight 70 lbs............	2.2-2.7	0.21-0.24	1.7-2.0	6.9-7.4	1.5-1.8
Weight 80 lbs............	2.3-2.8	0.22-0.25	1.8-2.1	7.1-7.6	1.6-1.9
Weight 90 lbs............	2.4-2.9	0.23-0.26	1.9-2.2	7.3-7.8	1.8-2.1
Weight 100 lbs............	2.5-3.0	0.25-0.27	2.0-2.3	7.5-8.0	1.9-2.2
20. Growing and fattening pigs					
Weight 30 lbs............	1.3-1.9	0.25-0.32	1.2-1.7	4.0-4.5	1.1-1.6
Weight 50 lbs............	2.1-2.8	0.35-0.43	1.9-2.5	4.5-5.0	1.7-2.3
Weight 75 lbs............	2.9-3.9	0.43-0.52	2.6-3.5	5.3-5.8	2.4-3.2
Weight 100 lbs............	3.6-4.8	0.50-0.60	3.2-4.3	5.8-6.2	2.9-4.0
Weight 150 lbs............	4.8-6.2	0.65-0.75	4.3-5.6	6.2-6.5	4.0-5.2
Weight 200 lbs............	5.8-7.1	0.73-0.83	5.2-6.4	6.4-6.7	4.8-5.9
Weight 250 lbs............	6.5-7.8	0.80-0.90	5.9-7.0	6.5-6.8	5.4-6.4
Weight 300 lbs............	7.1-8.4	0.85-0.95	6.4-7.6	6.6-7.0	5.9-7.0
21. Wintering pregnant gilts					
Weight 200 lbs............	3.3-4.0	0.43-0.47	3.0-3.6	6.0-7.0	(2.7-3.3)
Weight 250 lbs............	3.9-4.7	0.50-0.55	3.5-4.2	6.0-7.0	(3.2-3.9)
Weight 300 lbs............	4.4-5.4	0.57-0.63	4.0-4.8	6.0-7.0	(3.6-4.4)
22. Wintering pregnant older sows					
Weight 300 lbs............	3.7-4.5	0.43-0.49	3.2-4.1	6.5-7.5	(2.9-3.7)
Weight 400 lbs............	4.6-5.6	0.53-0.60	4.0-5.0	6.5-7.5	(3.6-4.6)
Weight 500 lbs............	5.4-6.6	0.63-0.71	4.7-5.9	6.5-7.5	(4.2-5.4)
Weight 600 lbs............	6.2-7.6	0.72-0.81	5.4-6.8	6.5-7.5	(4.9-6.2)
23. Brood sows nursing litters					
Weight 300 lbs............	8.9-10.9	1.16-1.23	8.1-9.5	6.0-7.0	7.5-8.8
Weight 400 lbs............	9.4-11.5	1.22-1.29	8.5-10.0	6.0-7.0	7.9-9.3
Weight 500 lbs............	9.8-12.7	1.28-1.35	8.9-10.5	6.0-7.0	8.3-9.8
Weight 600 lbs............	11.2-13.8	1.34-1.42	9.4-11.0	6.0-7.0	8.7-10.2

TABLE IV. MINERAL MATTER IN TYPICAL FEEDING STUFFS AND IN
FARM ANIMALS

The data presented in this table concerning the amounts of mineral constituents in typical feeding stuffs and in the bodies of farm animals have been compiled chiefly from analyses reported by the experiment stations of this country. In addition, certain data from European sources have been included. The content of iodine in various feeds is not shown, since this is highly variable. Also, even in the case of feeds supplied with a normal amount of iodine the iodine content is so small that it is measured in parts per billion of the total weight, instead of in per cent. The percentages of calcium, phosphorus, and potassium in many other feeding stuffs are given in Appendix Table I.

The percentages of the various minerals given in this table are the percentages of the mineral elements, and not of the oxides, as calcium oxide (lime), potassium oxide (potash), etc. (673)

TABLE IV. Mineral matter in feeding stuffs and farm animals

Feeding stuff	Cal-cium	Phos-phorus	Potas-sium	Sodium	Magne-sium	Iron	Sulfur	Chlorine	Silicon
Dry Roughages	Per ct.	Per ct.	Per ct.	Per ct.	Per ct.	Per ct.	Per ct.	Per ct.	Per ct.
Alfalfa hay............	1.43	0.21	2.02	0.14	0.26	0.06	0.25	0.24	0.25
Barley straw..........	0.32	0.09	1.26	0.13	0.07	0.03	0.13	0.61	0.61
Bluegrass hay, Kentucky	0.30	0.22	1.26	0.13	0.22	....	0.31	0.22	....
Clover hay, red.......	1.21	0.18	1.58	0.08	0.28	0.10	0.14	0.08	0.15
Corn stover, medium in water..............	0.41	0.08	1.50	0.05	0.08	0.05	0.15	0.25	0.22
Cowpea hay..........	1.13	0.25	1.45	0.19	0.50	....	0.32	0.15	....
Lespedeza hay, annual.	0.99	0.19	0.84	....	0.25	0.03	....	....	0.44
Millet hay, common...	0.30	0.17	1.75	0.09	0.24	....	0.15	0.11	....
Oat hay..............	0.22	0.17	1.09	....	0.16	0.05	....	....	....
Oat straw............	0.36	0.13	1.66	0.17	0.08	0.03	0.10	0.77	0.69
Pea straw, field.......	1.58	0.10	1.08	0.19	0.20	0.04	0.15	0.70	0.08
Sorghum fodder, sweet, dry................	0.49	0.14	1.30	....	0.31	0.06	....	0.56	0.28
Soybean hay..........	0.96	0.25	0.82	....	0.50	0.11	0.12	....	....
Timothy hay..........	0.27	0.16	1.36	0.33	0.14	0.03	0.10	0.22	0.70
Wheat straw..........	0.22	0.07	0.80	0.22	0.06	0.03	0.15	0.20	1.33
Green Roughages, Roots, Etc.									
Alfalfa, green.........	0.40	0.06	0.57	0.04	0.07	0.02	0.07	0.07	0.07
Bluegrass, Kentucky, gr.	0.16	0.08	0.53	0.05	0.05	0.06	0.11	0.17	0.29
Carrots...............	0.06	0.06	0.40	0.12	0.02	....	0.02	0.09	0.01
Cabbage..............	0.06	0.03	0.24	0.003	0.02	....	0.08	0.02	....
Clover, red, green......	0.43	0.07	0.54	0.02	0.11	0.03	0.03	0.02	0.04
Mangels, roots........	0.01	0.03	0.36	0.07	0.03	0.001	0.02	0.13	0.01
Orchard grass, green...	0.12	0.09	0.77	0.10	0.04	0.04	0.06	0.27	0.37
Potatoes, tubers.......	0.01	0.05	0.45	0.03	0.05	0.003	0.02	0.045	0.004
Rape, green...........	0.34	0.07	0.37	0.01	0.02	....	0.04	0.09	....
Rutabagas............	0.07	0.05	0.41	0.08	0.02	....	0.08	0.06	....
Sudan grass..........	0.14	0.06	0.43	0.01	0.05	0.03	0.01	0.01	0.18
Sweet potatoes, tubers.	0.03	0.06	0.38	0.02	0.07	....	0.04	0.02	....
Timothy, green........	0.14	0.06	0.56	0.07	0.04	0.02	0.04	0.19	0.23
Silages									
Corn silage, dent, well-matured............	0.07	0.06	0.30	0.01	0.06	0.01	0.02	0.04	0.26
Sunflower silage.......	0.39	0.04	0.65	0.17	0.11	0.03	0.03	0.18	0.15

TABLE IV. Mineral matter in feeding stuffs and farm animals—*continued*

Feeding stuff	Cal-cium	Phos-phorus	Potas-sium	Sodium	Magne-sium	Iron	Sulfur	Chlorine	Silicon
Concentrates	Per ct.	Per ct.	Per ct.	Per ct.	Per ct.	Per ct.	Per ct.	Per ct.	Per ct.
Barley grain..........	0.05	0.38	0.52	0.05	0.12	0.004	0.02	0.11	0.15
Beans, field...........	0.14	0.45	1.16	0.07	0.18	0.007	0.06	0.07	0.01
Beet pulp, dried.......	0.68	0.07	0.18	0.13	0.26	0.08	0.20	0.04	0.13
Beet pulp, dried, molasses.................	0.52	0.07	1.60	....	0.13	....	0.38	....	....
Blood meal...........	0.33	0.26	0.09	0.32	0.22	0.02	0.28	0.14	....
Bone meal, steamed....	32.61	15.17	0.18	0.52	0.85	....	0.40	0.09	0.52
Brewers' grains, dried..	0.25	0.47	0.05	0.26	0.15	0.03	....	0.06	0.70
Buttermilk, dried......	1.36	0.74	0.71	0.95	0.81	0.43	0.08	0.36	....
Corn grain, dent.......	0.01	0.28	0.33	0.03	0.11	0.004	0.14	0.05	0.02
Corn gluten feed.......	0.14	0.55	0.54	0.70	0.30	....	0.45	0.16	....
Cottonseed meal, 41% protein grade........	0.20	1.19	1.48	0.05	0.65	0.06	0.46	0.03	0.04
Cowpeas	0.10	0.47	1.45	0.17	0.21	....	0.25	0.04	....
Distillers' corn grains, dried..............	0.05	0.31	0.13	0.10	0.09	....	0.47	0.05	0.21
Distillers' rye grains, dried..............	0.13	0.43	0.04	0.07	0.18	....	0.38	0.03	....
Flaxseed............	0.25	0.66	0.58	0.04	0.36	0.01	0.05	0.02	0.76
Hominy feed..........	0.03	0.57	0.60	....	0.24	....	0.02	....	....
Horsebeans..........	0.13	0.54	1.16	0.04	0.13	0.01	0.08	0.08	0.01
Kafir grain...........	0.04	0.30	0.34	0.06	0.15	....	0.16	0.10	....
Linseed meal, old process.............	0.33	0.86	1.27	0.11	0.53	0.10	0.38	0.05	0.18
Malt sprouts.........	0.24	0.71	1.52	0.11	0.18	0.08	0.80	0.36	0.76
Molasses, beet........	0.05	0.02	4.77	0.97	0.02	....	....	....	....
Oat grain............	0.09	0.33	0.40	0.14	0.12	0.01	0.03	0.05	0.43
Oat meal, feeding, or rolled oats..........	0.06	0.45	0.37	0.06	0.11	0.004	....	0.07	....
Pea seed, field........	0.07	0.40	1.03	0.06	0.13	0.004	0.10	0.08	0.01
Peanut oil meal.......	0.17	0.55	1.16	0.07	0.22	0.03	0.21	0.03	0.06
Rice polish...........	0.04	1.10	1.18	0.11	0.65	....	0.17	0.13	....
Rye grain............	0.04	0.37	0.54	0.05	0.10	0.004	0.06	0.02	0.03
Rye feed.............	0.08	0.69	0.83	....	0.23	....	0.04	....	....
Skimmilk, centrifugal..	0.14	0.12	0.14	0.08	0.10	0.004	0.04	0.05	....
Soybean seed.........	0.20	0.60	1.91	0.46	0.23	0.02	0.41	0.03	....
Soybean oil meal, hydraulic or expeller process.............	0.28	0.66	2.20	0.51	0.25	0.02	0.45	0.04	....
Wheat...............	0.03	0.43	0.44	0.04	0.11	0.005	0.18	0.06	0.02
Wheat bran..........	0.12	1.32	1.24	0.06	0.55	0.008	0.21	0.04	0.03
Wheat flour, white.....	0.03	0.13	0.12	0.06	0.02	0.001	0.18	0.07	....
Wheat middlings, flour.	0.09	0.72	0.89	0.07	0.32	....	0.20	0.04	0.03
Wheat middlings, standard................	0.08	0.94	1.04	0.17	0.36	0.01	0.21	0.03	....
Whey, from American cheese..............	0.05	0.04	0.18	0.03	0.01	....	0.01	0.12	....
Farm Animals *(not including contents of digestive tract)*									
Beef calf, at birth......	1.25	0.68	0.22	0.21	0.05	0.02	0.17	0.16	....
Beef calf, wt. 250 lbs...	1.36	0.80	0.24	0.20	0.04	0.02	0.16	0.13	....
Beef calf, wt. 450 lbs...	1.11	0.65	0.22	0.18	0.04	0.01	0.15	0.12	....
Beef steer, fat, wt. 1,110 lbs.................	1.47	0.79	0.20	0.16	0.04	0.02	0.14	0.11	....

TABLE IV. Mineral matter in feeding stuffs and farm animals—*continued*

Feeding stuff	Cal-cium	Phos-phorus	Potas-sium	Sodium	Magne-sium	Iron	Sulfur	Chlorine	Silicon
Farm Animals *(not including contents of digestive tract)*	Per ct.	Per ct.	Per ct.	Per ct.	Per ct.	Per ct.	Per ct.	Per ct.	Per ct.
Beef steer, very fat, wt. 1,850 lbs............	0.94	0.51	0.12	0.10	0.03	0.01	0.10	0.07	....
Lamb, fat.............	0.92	0.49	0.14	....	0.03	....	....	....	....
Sheep, before fattening.	0.94	0.52	0.14	....	0.03	....	....	....	....
Sheep, fat.............	0.85	0.45	0.12	....	0.03	....	....	....	....
Pig, before fattening...	0.77	0.46	0.16	....	0.03	....	....	....	....
Pig, fat...............	0.45	0.29	0.11	....	0.02	....	....	....	....
Wool									
Wool, unwashed.......	0.13	0.03	4.67	....	0.02	....	....	....	....

TABLE V. VITAMIN CONTENT OF FEEDING STUFFS

The data concerning the relative amounts of vitamins in various feeding stuffs are still very limited, since most of the investigations in this field have been conducted with human foods, rather than on feeds for livestock. The following table is presented to indicate approximately the relative values of representative feeding stuffs as sources of vitamins A, B, C, D, E, and G. Additional information on this subject is given in the discussions of the various vitamins in Chapter VI. (184-200)

It should be borne in mind that the amount of a particular vitamin in a certain kind of feed may vary widely, especially in the case of roughages. For example, the vitamin A content of hay varies greatly, depending on the stage of growth at which it was cut, and on the manner in which the hay was cured.

As has been explained in Chapter VI, in the case of feeds of plant origin it is probable that all or nearly all of the vitamin A value is due to the carotene the feeds contain, and that they have little or no actual vitamin A. (187) Since carotene can readily be converted into vitamin A in the bodies of animals, the terms "vitamin A value" or "vitamin A content" are commonly used to indicate the combined effect of the carotene plus any vitamin A the feed may contain. The vitamin A values of various feeds given in this table are estimated on this basis, and thus include both the content of carotene and any content of actual vitamin A.

The relative amounts of the different vitamins in each feed are indicated by the following symbols:

O indicates that the feed has none of the vitamin or only an insignificant amount.

+ indicates that the feed contains an appreciable amount of the vitamin.

+ + indicates that the feed is a good source of the vitamin.

+ + + indicates that the feed is an excellent source of the vitamin.

+ + + + indicates that the feed is exceptionally rich in the vitamin.

— indicates that information concerning the amount of the vitamin is lacking or is not conclusive.

These symbols indicate only very roughly the relative content of a given feed in the different vitamins, and where the same symbol is used to indicate the vitamin content of two feeds, one of the feeds may contain materially larger amounts than the other.

The data in this table have been compiled from a variety of sources, including the books and scientific articles to which references are given in Chapter VI. The author wishes particularly to acknowledge the use of data from the table showing the vitamin content of poultry feeds, prepared by Norris and Heuser of the Poultry Husbandry department of Cornell University.

TABLE V.   Vitamin content of feeding stuffs

Feeding Stuff	Vitamins					
	A	B	C	D	E	G
Dry Roughages						
Alfalfa hay, excellent quality (very leafy and green-colored)	+++	+	O	++	+++	++
Alfalfa hay, good quality (leafy and well-cured)	++	+	O	++	+++	++
Alfalfa hay, poor quality	O to +	+	O	—	—	+
Alfalfa hay, dehydrated	++++	+	—	O	+++	+++
Clover hay, good quality	++	+	O	++	+++	++
Corn fodder, well-cured	+	+	O	+	—	—
Cottonseed hulls	O	—	O	—	—	—
Legume hay in general, good quality	++	+	O	++	+++	++
Sorghum fodder	+	+	O	+	—	—
Straw from the small grains	O	—	O	—	—	—
Timothy hay and other grass hay, good quality	+ to ++	+	O	+	++	+
Timothy hay and other grass hay, poor quality	O to +	—	O	—	—	—
Green Roughages, Roots, Etc.						
Apples	O to +	+	+	O	—	—
Alfalfa, green	+++	+	+++	O	+++	++
Beets, common	O	O	+	O	—	—
Beets, sugar	O	O	+	O	—	—
Cabbage, green leaves	++	+	+++	O	—	+
Cabbage, white portion	O to +	+	+++	O	—	—
Carrots, yellow	+++	+	++	O	—	—
Clover, green	+++	+	+++	O	+++	++
Grasses, green, growing actively	+++	+	+++	O	+++	++
Kale, green	+++	+	+++	O	—	—
Mangels	O	O	O	O	—	—
Potatoes	O	+	++	O	—	—
Rutabagas	O to +	+	+++	O	—	—
Sweet potatoes, yellow	++	+	++	O	—	—
Tomatoes	++	+	+++	O	—	—
Silages						
Corn silage, good quality, from green corn forage at silage stage	+ to ++	+	O to +	O to +	+	—
Sorghum silage, good quality	+ to ++	+	O to +	O to +	+	—

Table V. Vitamin content of feeding stuffs—*continued*

Feeding stuff	Vitamins					
	A	B	C	D	E	G
Concentrates						
Barley	O to +	++	O	O	++	+
Beans	O	++	O	O	—	—
Beet pulp, dried	O	—	O	O	O	—
Buckwheat	O	++	O	O	—	+
Buttermilk	+	+	O to +	O	+	++
Buttermilk, dried	+	+	O to +	O	+	+++
Corn, white	O	+++	O	O	++	+
Corn, yellow	++	+++	O	O	++	+
Corn gluten feed (chiefly from yellow corn)	++	—	O	O	O	O
Corn gluten meal (chiefly from yellow corn)	+++	—	O	O	O	O
Cottonseed meal	O	—	O	O	—	—
Fish meal	O to +	O	O	O to +	—	O to ++
Hominy feed, yellow	++	+++	O	O	++	+
Hominy feed, white	O	+++	O	O	++	+
Linseed meal	O	—	O	O	+	—
Millet seed	O to +	++	O	O	—	—
Milk, whole	++	+	+	O to +	+	++
Molasses, cane	O	++	O	O	++	—
Oats	O	++	O	O	++	+
Peanuts	O	++	O	O	++	—
Peanut oil meal	O	++	O	O	++	—
Peas, green-colored	++	++	O	O	++	+
Rice, whole grain	O	++	O	O	++	—
Rye	O	++	O	O	++	+
Skimmilk	O	+	O to +	O	+	++
Skimmilk, dried	O	+	O to +	O	+	+++
Sorghum grain	O	++	O	O	++	—
Soybeans	O	++	O	O	—	+
Soybean oil meal	O	++	O	O	—	+
Tankage	O	O	O	O	—	+
Wheat	O	++	O	O	++	+
Wheat bran	O	++	O	O	++	+
Wheat germ	O	++++	O	O	++++	+
Wheat middlings, standard	O	+++	O	O	+++	+
Whey	O	+	O to +	O	+	++
Whey, dried	O	+	O to +	O	+	+++
Miscellaneous						
Butter	+++	O	O	+	+	—
Cod-liver oil	++++	O	O	++++	O	O
Eggs	++	+	O	++	++	+++
Liver, dried	++	+	+	+	—	+++
Yeast	O	++++	O	O	O	+++

TABLE VI. WEIGHT OF CONCENTRATES AND OTHER FEEDS

In computing rations for farm animals it is desirable to know the weight per quart, or the bulk, of the different concentrates. The following table, compiled chiefly from *Massachusetts Bulletin 136* by Smith and Perkins, *Louisiana Bulletin 114* by Halligan, and *Indiana Bulletin 141* by Jones, Haworth, Cutler, and Summers is therefore presented.

Feeding stuff	One quart weights	One pound measures	Feeding stuff	One quart weights	One pound measures
Concentrates	Lbs.	Qts.	**Concentrates—Cont.**	Lbs.	Qts.
Barley, whole............	1.5	0.7	Oats....................	1.0	1.0
Barley, ground...........	1.1	0.9	Oats, ground............	0.7	1.4
Beans, field.............	1.7	0.6	Oatmeal, without hulls....	1.7	0.6
Beet pulp, dried..........	0.6	1.7	Oat middlings............	1.5	0.7
Brewers' grains, dried......	0.6	1.7	Oat mill feed............	0.8	1.3
Buckwheat, whole.........	1.4	0.7	Peas, field..............	2.1	0.5
Buckwheat feed..........	0.6	1.7	Rice bran...............	0.8	1.3
Buckwheat flour..........	1.6	0.6	Rice polish..............	1.2	0.8
Buckwheat middlings.......	0.9	1.1	Rye, whole..............	1.7	0.6
Coconut oil meal..........	1.5	0.7	Rye, ground.............	1.5	0.7
Corn, dent, whole.........	1.7	0.6	Rye, bran...............	0.8	1.3
Corn, dent, ground........	1.5	0.7	Rye feed................	1.3	0.8
Corn-and-cob meal........	1.4	0.7	Rye middlings...........	1.6	0.6
Corn bran...............	0.5	2.0	Soybeans................	1.8	0.6
Corn germ meal...........	1.4	0.7	Sunflower seed...........	1.5	0.7
Corn gluten feed..........	1.3	0.8	Tankage.................	1.6	0.6
Corn gluten meal.........	1.7	0.6	Wheat, whole............	1.9	0.5
Cottonseed, whole........	0.8	1.3	Wheat, ground...........	1.7	0.6
Cottonseed meal..........	1.5	0.7	Wheat, bran.............	0.5	2.0
Cowpeas.................	1.7	0.6	Wheat mixed feed........	0.6	1.7
Distillers' corn grains, dried.	0.6	1.7	Wheat flour middlings......	1.2	0.8
Flaxseed.................	1.6	0.6	Wheat screenings..........	1.0	1.0
Flaxseed screenings........	1.1	0.9	Wheat standard middlings..	0.8	1.3
Hominy feed.............	1.1	0.9	**Roughages**		
Linseed meal, old process...	1.1	0.9	Alfalfa meal..............	0.6	1.7
Linseed meal, new process..	0.9	1.1	Buckwheat hulls..........	0.5	2.0
Malt sprouts.............	0.6	1.7	Cottonseed hulls..........	0.3	3.3
Millet seed, foxtail........	1.6	0.6	Oat hulls................	0.4	2.5
Molasses, cane...........	3.0	0.3			
Molasses feeds...........	0.8	1.3			

TABLE VII. EXAMPLE RATIONS FOR FARM ANIMALS

The following examples of balanced rations for the different classes of stock are presented as guides in the selection of efficient balanced rations adapted to various conditions. In using this table, one should not limit his choice of rations to the particular combinations of feeds here given. Instead, he should determine whether modifications cannot be made in these rations which will make them more economical under his local conditions. One can readily determine which of various available feeds are actually the cheapest by using the methods explained in Chapter X. (276-287)

The following will indicate the changes that can be made in these rations:

Ground corn can be replaced by hominy feed, corn feed meal, ground grain sorghum, barley, wheat. When barley or wheat is fed in place of corn, the amount of protein supplement may be reduced somewhat.

Ground oats can be replaced by ground barley, ground emmer, or ground spelt.

Ground rye and ground buckwheat may be used to replace part of the other grain in these rations.

Wheat bran can be replaced by wheat mixed feed. If the greater bulk of wheat bran is not needed in the ration, bran can also be replaced by wheat standard middlings.

Corn gluten feed can be replaced by a slightly larger proportion of coconut oil meal or brewers' dried grains, as these latter supplements contain somewhat less digestible protein.

Linseed meal can be replaced by ground soybeans or by a combination of one-half linseed meal and one-half soybeans, cottonseed meal, soybean oil meal, or corn gluten meal.

Cottonseed meal can be replaced by soybean oil meal, peanut oil meal, or ground soybeans.

One-half of the linseed meal, cottonseed meal or soybean oil meal can be replaced by corn gluten meal, if there is some legume forage in the ration.

Unless otherwise indicated, the amounts of feed shown in the tables are the amounts to be fed per head daily. For animals of different sizes than stated in the tables, the amounts of feed should be increased or decreased in accordance with the amounts of nutrients recommended in Appendix Table III for animals of the particular size.

DAIRY CATTLE

Concentrate or "grain" mixtures for dairy cows and heifers

A. Mixtures containing approximately 12 per cent protein

For cows in milk which are fed good alfalfa, soybean, or cowpea hay (at least 1 lb. daily per 100 lbs. live weight) with corn silage, sorghum silage, corn fodder, sorghum fodder, or roots. When alfalfa, soybean, or cowpea hay is fed as the only roughage, merely a mixture of farm grain supplies sufficient protein for all except unusually high-producing cows.

For cows in milk which are fed red clover hay as the only roughage.

For cows in milk which are on excellent pasture.

For dry cows, when at least one-third the roughage (on the dry basis) is legume.

For heifers over 6 months old, when one-half the roughage (on the dry basis) is alfalfa, soybean, or cowpea hay.

1.		
Ground corn	840	lbs.
Ground oats	840	lbs.
Wheat bran	200	lbs.
Linseed meal	100	lbs.
Salt	20	lbs.
Total	2,000	lbs.

Dig. protein, 9.8%
Total dig. nutr., 74.8%

2.		
Ground barley or wheat	950	lbs.
Ground oats	730	lbs.
Wheat bran	300	lbs.
Salt	20	lbs.
Total	2,000	lbs.

Dig. protein, 9.8%
Total dig. nutr., 74.0%

3. Ground corn ....1,000 lbs.
Ground oats .... 620 lbs.
Wheat bran .... 240 lbs.
Corn gluten feed.......... 70 lbs.
Soybean oil meal.......... 50 lbs.
Salt .... 20 lbs.

Total ....2,000 lbs.
Dig. protein, 9.8%
Total dig. nutr., 75.7%

4. Ground corn ....1,000 lbs.
Ground oats .... 630 lbs.
Wheat bran .... 240 lbs.
Corn distillers' grains....... 60 lbs.
Soybean oil meal.......... 50 lbs.
Salt .... 20 lbs.

Total ....2,000 lbs.
Dig. protein, 9.7%
Total dig. nutr., 75.8%

5. Ground corn .... 810 lbs.
Ground oats .... 600 lbs.
Cane molasses .... 200 lbs.
Wheat bran .... 200 lbs.
Cottonseed meal .... 60 lbs.
Corn gluten feed........... 70 lbs.
Soybean oil meal.......... 40 lbs.
Salt .... 20 lbs.

Total ....2,000 lbs.
Dig. protein, 9.7%
Total dig. nutr., 73.3%

6. Corn-and-cob meal ....1,330 lbs.
Wheat bran .... 500 lbs.
Cottonseed meal .... 80 lbs.
Linseed meal .... 70 lbs.
Salt .... 20 lbs.

Total ....2,000 lbs.
Dig. protein, 9.7%
Total dig. nutr., 73.7%

B. Mixtures containing approximately 14 per cent protein

For cows in milk which are fed red clover hay (at least 1 lb. daily per 100 lbs. live weight) and corn or sorghum silage or corn or sorghum fodder, when protein supplements are expensive.

For cows in milk which are on very good pasture.

For dry cows when only one-fourth of the roughage (on the dry basis) is legume.

For heifers over 6 months old, when one-half the roughage (on the dry basis) is clover hay.

1. Ground corn .... 740 lbs.
Ground oats .... 740 lbs.
Wheat bran .... 250 lbs.
Linseed meal .... 250 lbs.
Salt .... 20 lbs.

Total ....2,000 lbs.
Dig. protein, 11.6%
Total dig. nutr., 74.8%

2. Ground barley or wheat.... 880 lbs.
Ground oats .... 750 lbs.
Wheat bran .... 200 lbs.
Cottonseed meal .... 150 lbs.
Salt .... 20 lbs.

Total ....2,000 lbs.
Dig. protein, 11.5%
Total dig. nutr., 74.0%

3. Ground corn .... 860 lbs.
Ground oats .... 600 lbs.
Wheat bran .... 200 lbs.
Corn gluten feed........... 220 lbs.
Soybean oil meal.......... 100 lbs.
Salt .... 20 lbs.

Total ....2,000 lbs.
Dig. protein, 11.6%
Total dig. nutr., 75.8%

4. Ground corn .... 880 lbs.
Ground oats .... 600 lbs.
Wheat bran .... 200 lbs.
Corn distillers' grains ...... 220 lbs.
Soybean oil meal .... 80 lbs.
Salt .... 20 lbs.

Total ....2,000 lbs.
Dig. protein, 11.2%
Total dig. nutr., 76.6%

5. Ground corn .... 670 lbs.
   Ground oats .... 600 lbs.
   Cane molasses .... 200 lbs.
   Wheat bran .... 200 lbs.
   Cottonseed meal .... 100 lbs.
   Corn gluten feed .... 110 lbs.
   Soybean oil meal .... 100 lbs.
   Salt .... 20 lbs.
       Total ....2,000 lbs.
   Dig. protein, 11.4%
   Total dig. nutr., 73.2%

6. Corn-and-cob meal ....1,190 lbs.
   Wheat bran .... 500 lbs.
   Cottonseed meal .... 140 lbs.
   Linseed meal .... 150 lbs.
   Salt .... 20 lbs.
       Total ....2,000 lbs.
   Dig. protein, 11.5%
   Total dig. nutr., 73.7%

C. Mixtures containing approximately 16 per cent protein

For cows in milk which are fed good red clover or alsike clover hay (at least 1 lb. daily per 100 lbs. live weight) with corn silage, sorghum silage, corn fodder, sorghum fodder, or roots.

For cows in milk which are fed good mixed clover-and-grass hay (containing at least 30 per cent clover) and corn or sorghum silage or corn or sorghum fodder, when protein supplements are unusually expensive.

For cows in milk which are on good pasture.

For dry cows which are fed little or no legume roughage.

1. Ground corn .... 660 lbs.
   Ground oats .... 650 lbs.
   Wheat bran .... 250 lbs.
   Linseed meal .... 420 lbs.
   Salt .... 20 lbs.
       Total ....2,000 lbs.
   Dig. protein, 13.5%
   Total dig. nutr., 75.0%

2. Ground barley or wheat ... 750 lbs.
   Ground oats .... 750 lbs.
   Wheat bran .... 200 lbs.
   Cottonseed meal .... 280 lbs.
   Salt .... 20 lbs.
       Total ....2,000 lbs.
   Dig. protein, 13.1%
   Total dig. nutr., 73.6%

3. Ground corn .... 670 lbs.
   Ground oats .... 600 lbs.
   Wheat bran .... 200 lbs.
   Corn gluten feed .... 360 lbs.
   Soybean oil meal .... 150 lbs.
   Salt .... 20 lbs.
       Total ....2,000 lbs.
   Dig. protein, 13.4%
   Total dig. nutr., 75.6%

4. Ground corn .... 710 lbs.
   Ground oats .... 610 lbs.
   Wheat bran .... 200 lbs.
   Corn distillers' grains ...... 350 lbs.
   Soybean oil meal .... 110 lbs.
   Salt .... 20 lbs.
       Total ....2,000 lbs.
   Dig. protein, 12.7%
   Total dig. nutr., 76.8%

5. Ground corn .... 600 lbs.
   Ground oats .... 370 lbs.
   Cane molasses .... 200 lbs.
   Wheat bran .... 250 lbs.
   Cottonseed meal .... 120 lbs.
   Corn gluten feed .... 350 lbs.
   Soybean oil meal .... 90 lbs.
   Salt .... 20 lbs.
       Total ....2,000 lbs.
   Dig. protein, 13.3%
   Total dig. nutr. 73.5%

6. Corn-and-cob meal ....1,060 lbs.
   Wheat bran .... 500 lbs.
   Cottonseed meal .... 190 lbs.
   Linseed meal .... 230 lbs.
   Salt .... 20 lbs.
       Total ....2,000 lbs.
   Dig. protein, 13.2%
   Total dig. nutr., 73.8%

D. Mixtures containing approximately 18 per cent protein

For cows in milk which are fed mixed clover-and-timothy hay or other mixed clover-and-grass hay containing at least 30 per cent clover (at least 1 lb. of hay daily per 100 lbs. live weight), this hay being fed with corn or sorghum silage, corn or sorghum fodder, or roots.

For cows in milk which are on fair pasture.

For heifers over 6 months old, when only about one-fourth the roughage (on the dry basis) is legume.

1. Ground corn .... 580 lbs.
   Ground oats .... 580 lbs.
   Wheat bran .... 250 lbs.
   Linseed meal .... 570 lbs.
   Salt .... 20 lbs.

   Total ....2,000 lbs.

Dig. protein, 15.1%
Total dig. nutr., 75.2%

2. Ground barley or wheat ... 700 lbs.
   Ground oats .... 580 lbs.
   Wheat bran .... 300 lbs.
   Cottonseed meal .... 400 lbs.
   Salt .... 20 lbs.

   Total ....2,000 lbs.

Dig. protein, 14.7%
Total dig. nutr., 72.9%

3. Ground corn .... 630 lbs.
   Ground oats .... 400 lbs.
   Wheat bran .... 250 lbs.
   Corn gluten feed .... 500 lbs.
   Soybean oil meal .... 200 lbs.
   Salt .... 20 lbs.

   Total ....2,000 lbs.

Dig. protein, 15.2%
Total dig. nutr., 76.0%

4. Ground corn .... 690 lbs.
   Ground oats .... 400 lbs.
   Wheat bran .... 250 lbs.
   Corn distillers' grains ...... 500 lbs.
   Soybean oil meal .... 140 lbs.
   Salt .... 20 lbs.

   Total ....2,000 lbs.

Dig. protein, 14.2%
Total dig. nutr., 77.9%

5. Ground corn .... 470 lbs.
   Ground oats .... 380 lbs.
   Cane molasses .... 200 lbs.
   Wheat bran .... 250 lbs.
   Cottonseed meal .... 230 lbs.
   Corn gluten feed .... 350 lbs.
   Soybean oil meal .... 100 lbs.
   Salt .... 20 lbs.

   Total ....2,000 lbs.

Dig. protein, 14.9%
Total dig. nutr., 73.1%

6. Corn-and-cob meal .... 920 lbs.
   Wheat bran .... 500 lbs.
   Cottonseed meal .... 240 lbs.
   Linseed meal .... 320 lbs.
   Salt .... 20 lbs.

   Total ....2,000 lbs.

Dig. protein, 15.0%
Total dig. nutr., 70.6%

E. Mixtures containing approximately 20 per cent protein (Add 20 lbs. ground limestone per ton if roughage is grown on soil very deficient in calcium.)

For cows in milk which are fed mixed legume-and-grass hay containing less than 30 per cent legumes, this hay being fed with corn or sorghum silage, corn or sorghum fodder, or roots.

For cows in milk which are fed non-legume roughage of good quality and which are producing sufficient milk so that they require at least 8 to 10 lbs. of concentrate or grain mixture.

For cows in milk which are on poor pasture.

For heifers over 6 months old which are fed no legume roughage.

1. Ground corn .... 580 lbs.
   Ground oats .... 420 lbs.
   Wheat bran .... 220 lbs.
   Linseed meal .... 760 lbs.
   Salt .... 20 lbs.
   Total ....2,000 lbs.

Dig. protein, 17.1%
Total dig. nutr., 75.8%

2. Ground barley or wheat ... 610 lbs.
   Ground oats .... 500 lbs.
   Wheat bran .... 300 lbs.
   Cottonseed meal .... 400 lbs.
   Linseed meal .... 170 lbs.
   Salt .... 20 lbs.
   Total ....2,000 lbs.

Dig. protein, 16.5%
Total dig. nutr., 73.8%

3. Ground corn .... 560 lbs.
   Ground oats .... 300 lbs.
   Wheat bran .... 250 lbs.
   Corn gluten feed .... 600 lbs.
   Soybean oil meal .... 270 lbs.
   Salt .... 20 lbs.
   Total ....2,000 lbs.

Dig. protein, 16.9%
Total dig. nutr., 76.4%

4. Ground corn .... 600 lbs.
   Ground oats .... 330 lbs.
   Wheat bran .... 250 lbs.
   Corn distillers' grains ...... 600 lbs.
   Soybean oil meal .... 200 lbs.
   Salt .... 20 lbs.
   Total ....2,000 lbs.

Dig. protein, 15.8%
Total dig. nutr., 78.5%

5. Ground corn .... 370 lbs.
   Ground oats .... 300 lbs.
   Cane molasses .... 200 lbs.
   Wheat bran .... 250 lbs.
   Cottonseed meal .... 250 lbs.
   Corn gluten feed .... 460 lbs.
   Soybean oil meal .... 150 lbs.
   Salt .... 20 lbs.
   Total ....2,000 lbs.
   Dig. protein, 16.7%
   Total dig. nutr., 73.2%

6. Corn-and-cob meal .... 790 lbs.
   Wheat bran .... 500 lbs.
   Cottonseed meal .... 320 lbs.
   Linseed meal .... 370 lbs.
   Salt .... 20 lbs.
   Total ....2,000 lbs.
   Dig. protein, 16.7%
   Total dig. nutr., 73.8%

F. Mixtures containing approximately 24 per cent protein (Add 20 lbs. of ground limestone per ton if roughage is grown on soil very deficient in calcium.)

For cows in milk which are fed good-quality non-legume roughage and which are not producing sufficient milk to require so much as 8 lbs. of concentrate or grain mixture.

For cows in milk which are fed only non-legume roughage of fair to poor quality.

1. Ground corn .... 400 lbs.
   Ground oats .... 400 lbs.
   Wheat bran .... 230 lbs.
   Linseed meal .... 500 lbs.
   Cottonseed meal .... 450 lbs.
   Salt .... 20 lbs.
   Total ....2,000 lbs.
   Dig. protein, 20.1%
   Total dig. nutr., 74.6%

4. Ground corn .... 380 lbs.
   Ground oats .... 300 lbs.
   Wheat bran .... 250 lbs.
   Corn distillers' grains ...... 650 lbs.
   Soybean oil meal .... 400 lbs.
   Salt .... 20 lbs.
   Total ....2,000 lbs.
   Dig. protein, 19.2%
   Total dig. nutr., 78.9%

2. Ground barley or wheat .... 390 lbs.
   Ground oats .... 400 lbs.
   Wheat bran .... 300 lbs.
   Cottonseed meal .... 490 lbs.
   Linseed meal .... 400 lbs.
   Salt .... 20 lbs.
   Total ....2,000 lbs.
   Dig. protein, 20.1%
   Total dig. nutr., 73.8%

5. Ground corn .... 150 lbs.
   Ground oats .... 250 lbs.
   Cane molasses .... 200 lbs.
   Wheat bran .... 250 lbs.
   Cottonseed meal .... 300 lbs.
   Corn gluten feed.......... 530 lbs.
   Soybean oil meal .... 300 lbs.
   Salt .... 20 lbs.
   Total ....2,000 lbs.
   Dig. protein, 20.2%
   Total dig. nutr., 73.3%

3. Ground corn .... 300 lbs.
   Ground oats .... 300 lbs.
   Wheat bran .... 250 lbs.
   Corn gluten feed .... 650 lbs.
   Soybean oil meal .... 480 lbs.
   Salt .... 20 lbs.
   Total ....2,000 lbs.
   Dig. protein, 20.5%
   Total dig. nutr., 76.5%

6. Corn-and-cob meal......... 530 lbs.
   Wheat bran .... 500 lbs.
   Cottonseed meal .... 450 lbs.
   Linseed meal .... 500 lbs.
   Salt .... 20 lbs.
   Total ....2,000 lbs.
   Dig. protein, 20.1%
   Total dig. nutr., 73.8%

BEEF CATTLE

Calves being fattened for baby beef, average weight 600 lbs.

1. Corn or sorghum silage, 10 lbs.; alfalfa or other legume hay, 2 lbs.; corn or ground grain sorghum, 10 lbs.; linseed meal, cottonseed meal, or other high-protein supplement, 1.5 lbs.

2. Alfalfa, soybean, or cowpea hay, 4 to 5 lbs.; corn or grain sorghum, 11 lbs.; cottonseed meal, linseed meal, or other high-protein supplement, 0.50 to 0.75 lb.

3. Alfalfa, soybean, or cowpea hay, 4 to 5 lbs.; ground barley, wheat, or oats, 12 lbs.

4. Red clover hay, 4 to 5 lbs.; corn or ground grain sorghum, 11 lbs.; linseed meal, cottonseed meal, or other high-protein supplement, 1.0 lb.
5. Clover-and-timothy hay (containing 30 per cent or more clover), 4 to 5 lbs.; corn or ground grain sorghum, 11 lbs.; cottonseed meal, soybean oil meal, or other high-protein supplement, 1.5 lbs.
6. Corn or sorghum silage, 16 lbs.; corn or ground grain sorghum, 10 lbs.; cottonseed meal, linseed meal, or other high-protein supplement, 2 lbs.; ground limestone, 0.1 lb.
7. Cottonseed hulls, 4 lbs.; cowpea hay, 2 lbs.; corn or ground grain sorghum, 10 lbs.; cottonseed meal or other high-protein supplement, 1.5 lbs.

Fattening yearling cattle, average weight 900 lbs.

1. Corn or sorghum silage, 15 lbs.; alfalfa or other legume hay, 3 lbs.; corn or ground grain sorghum, 13 lbs.; linseed meal, cottonseed meal, or other high-protein supplement, 1 lb.
2. Alfalfa, soybean, or cowpea hay, 6 to 8 lbs.; corn or other grain, 14 lbs.
3. Red clover hay, 6 to 8 lbs.; corn or ground grain sorghum, 13.5 lbs.; cottonseed meal, soybean oil meal, or other high-protein supplement, 0.5 lb.
4. Red clover hay, 6 to 8 lbs.; ground barley, wheat, or oats, 14 lbs.
5. Clover-and-timothy hay (containing 30 per cent or more clover), 6 to 8 lbs.; corn or ground grain sorghum, 13 lbs.; linseed meal, cottonseed meal, or other high-protein supplement, 1 lb.
6. Corn or sorghum silage, 20 lbs.; corn or ground grain sorghum, 13 lbs.; soybean oil meal or other high-protein supplement, 1.5 lbs.; ground limestone, 0.1 lb.
7. Cottonseed hulls, 6 lbs.; cowpea hay, 2 lbs.; corn or ground grain sorghum, 13 lbs.; cottonseed meal or other high-protein supplement, 1.5 lbs.

Fattening 2-year-old cattle, weight 1,000 lbs.

1. Corn or sorghum silage, 25 lbs.; alfalfa, soybean, or cowpea hay, 4 lbs.; corn or ground grain sorghum, 14 lbs. Adding 0.5 lb. high-protein supplement will increase the rate of gain slightly and may be profitable. The supplement should be added if less legume hay is fed.
2. Corn or sorghum silage, 25 lbs.; red clover hay, 4 lbs.; corn or ground grain sorghum, 14 lbs.; linseed meal, cottonseed meal, or other high-protein supplement, 1.25 lbs.
3. Alfalfa, soybean, or cowpea hay, 10 lbs.; corn or other grain, 15 lbs.
4. Red clover hay, 10 lbs.; corn or ground grain sorghum, 14.5 lbs.; cottonseed meal, or other high-protein supplement, 0.5 lb.
5. Clover-and-timothy hay (containing 30 per cent or more clover), 10 lbs.; corn or ground grain sorghum, 14 lbs.; soybean oil meal or other high-protein supplement, 1.0 lb.
6. Corn or sorghum silage, 30 lbs.; corn or ground grain sorghum, 14 lbs.; linseed meal or other high-protein supplement, 1.5 lbs.; ground limestone, 0.1 lb.
7. Cottonseed hulls, 7 lbs.; cowpea hay, 2 lbs.; corn or ground grain sorghum, 14 lbs.; cottonseed meal or other high-protein supplement, 1.5 lbs.

Wintering beef calves to gain 0.75 to 1.00 lb. per head daily

1. Legume hay or mixed hay containing at least one-half legumes, 8 to 14 lbs.
2. Corn silage or sorghum silage, 25 to 35 lbs.; cottonseed meal, linseed meal, or other high-protein supplement, 1 lb.; ground limestone, 0.1 lb. unless silage is raised on soil well supplied with calcium.
3. Corn silage or sorghum silage, 20 to 25 lbs.; legume hay, 3 to 4 lbs.
4. Prairie hay, other grass hay, or corn or sorghum fodder, 7 to 14 lbs.; linseed meal cottonseed meal, or other high-protein supplement, 0.5 to 1.0 lb.; ground limestone, 0.1 lb. unless roughage is raised on soil well supplied with calcium.

5. Prairie hay or other grass hay, or corn or sorghum fodder, 7 to 14 lbs.; ground barley, ground oats, ground grain sorghum, or ground wheat, 2 lbs.; ground limestone, 0.1 lb. unless roughage is raised on soil well supplied with calcium.

Wintering beef yearlings

In general the same types of rations are satisfactory as have been suggested for wintering beef calves, except that greater amounts of feed are required and some of the roughage may consist of such cheap feeds as corn or sorghum stover, or cereal straw.

Wintering mature beef breeding cows in calf, weight 1,000 lbs.

1. Legume hay, 5 to 8 lbs.; cereal straw, 10 to 15 lbs.
2. Legume hay or mixed legume-and-grass hay of good quality, 16 to 20 lbs.
3. Corn silage or sorghum silage, 40 to 60 lbs.; cottonseed meal, linseed meal, or other high-protein supplement, 1 lb.
4. Corn silage or sorghum silage, 25 to 40 lbs.; legume hay, 5 to 7 lbs.
5. Cereal straw full-fed; linseed meal, cottonseed meal, or other high-protein supplement, 1 lb.; ground limestone, 0.1 lb.
6. Prairie hay or other grass hay, 16 to 20 lbs.; plus 0.5 lb. cottonseed meal, linseed meal, or other high-protein supplement unless hay is early-cut. It is advisable to add 0.1 lb. ground limestone if hay is grown on soil deficient in calcium.

HORSES AND MULES
Horses and mules at hard work, weight 1,200 lbs.

1. Grass hay, 12 lbs.; oats, 16 lbs.
2. Grass hay, 12 lbs.; corn, 13 lbs.; linseed meal or other high-protein supplement, 1 lb.
3. Legume hay, 12 lbs.; corn, 13.5 lbs.
4. Legume hay, 6 lbs.; grass hay, 6 lbs.; corn, 14 lbs.
5. Shredded corn fodder, 6 lbs.; legume hay, 6 lbs.; oats, 15 lbs.
6. Oats or barley straw, chopped, 4 lbs.; legume hay, 8 lbs.; oats, 16 lbs.

Horses and mules at medium work, weight 1,200 lbs.

1. Grass hay, 14 lbs.; oats, 11 lbs.
2. Grass hay, 14 lbs.; corn, 9 lbs.; linseed meal or other high-protein supplement, 0.75 lb.
3. Legume hay, 14 lbs.; corn, 9 lbs.
4. Legume hay, 7 lbs.; grass hay, 7 lbs.; corn, 9.5 lbs.
5. Shredded corn fodder, 7 lbs.; legume hay, 7 lbs.; oats, 10 lbs.
6. Oat or barley straw, chopped, 5 lbs.; legume hay, 9 lbs.; oats, 11 lbs.

Horses and mules at light work, weight 1,200 lbs.

1. Grass hay, 16 lbs.; oats, 6 lbs.
2. Grass hay, 16 lbs.; corn, 4.5 lbs.; linseed meal or other high-protein supplement, 0.5 lb.
3. Legume hay, 16 lbs.; corn, 4 lbs.
4. Legume hay, 8 lbs.; grass hay, 8 lbs.; corn, 4.5 lbs.
5. Shredded corn fodder, 8 lbs.; legume hay, 8 lbs.; oats, 5 lbs.
6. Oat or barley straw, chopped, 6 lbs.; legume hay, 10 lbs.; oats, 6 lbs.

Idle horses and mules, live weight 1,200 lbs.

1. Grass hay, 17.5 lbs.; linseed meal or other high-protein supplement, 0.75 lb.
2. Legume hay, 17 lbs.
3. Legume hay, 9 lbs.; grass hay, 9 lbs.
4. Corn or sorghum stover, 11 lbs.; legume hay, 8 lbs.
5. Corn or sorghum silage, 15 lbs.; oat or barley straw, 6 lbs.; legume hay, 7 lbs.
6. Oat or barley straw, 6 lbs.; legume hay, 12 lbs.

Brood mares nursing foals, but not at work, live weight 1,200 lbs.

1. Alfalfa, soybean, or cowpea hay, 16 lbs.; corn or other grain, 6 lbs.
2. Red clover hay, 16 lbs.; oats or ground barley 3 lbs.; corn, 3 lbs.
3. Mixed clover-and timothy hay (containing 30 per cent or more clover), 16 lbs.; oats, 6 lbs.
4. Timothy or other grass hay, 16 lbs.; oats, 3 lbs.; bran, 3 lbs.; linseed meal or other high-protein supplement, 1 lb.

SHEEP

Wintering pregnant ewes up to 4 to 6 weeks before lambing, weight 120 lbs.

1. Good-quality legume hay or mixed legume-and-grass hay containing 50 per cent legumes, 3.4 to 4.0 lbs.
2. Legume hay, 2.6 to 3.3 lbs.; corn or sorghum silage, 2.0 lbs.
3. Corn fodder, sorghum fodder, corn stover, sorghum stover, or cereal straw, 1.0 lb.; legume hay 2.0 lbs. It may be necessary to add 0.25 to 0.50 lb. grain to this ration to keep the ewes in the desired condition.
4. Roots, 2.0 to 3.0 lbs.; legume hay, 3.1 to 3.6 lbs.
5. Early-cut, well-cured grass hay, 1.7 to 2.0 lbs.; legume hay 1.7 to 2.0 lbs.
6. Early-cut grass hay, 2.3 to 3.0 lbs.; corn or sorghum silage, 2.0 lbs.; 0.25 lb. linseed meal or other high-protein supplement; 0.25 ounce ground limestone per head daily.

Wintering pregnant ewes during 4 to 6 weeks before lambing

To one of the preceding roughage allowances, add 0.5 lb. per head daily (or more if necessary) of one of the concentrate mixtures listed later.

Ewes not on pasture nursing lambs

To one of the preceding roughage allowances, add 1.0 lb. or slightly more of one of the following concentrate mixtures:

Concentrate or grain mixtures for ewes

These concentrate mixtures are suitable for ewes which are nursing lambs or for pregnant ewes.

A. For feeding when at least one-half the roughage (on the dry basis) is actually good legume roughage

1. Oats, 67 lbs.; wheat bran, 33 lbs.
2. Corn or other grain, 50 lbs.; oats, 20 lbs.; wheat bran, 20 lbs.; linseed meal, 10 lbs.
3. Corn 80 lbs.; linseed meal, 20 lbs.
4. Oats, 50 lbs.; corn, 50 lbs. This mixture is slightly too low in protein to use for ewes nursing lambs unless nearly all of the roughage is legume forage.
5. A good mixed dairy feed containing 12 to 14 per cent protein.

B. For feeding when only a small part or none of the roughage is legume

(When fed such roughage, ewes nursing lambs should receive 1.25 lbs. per head daily of concentrate mixture.)

1. Oats, 30 lbs.; corn or other grain, 20 lbs.; wheat bran, 30 lbs.; linseed meal or other high-protein supplement, 20 lbs.
2. Oats 60 lbs.; wheat bran, 25 lbs.; linseed meal or other high-protein supplement, 15 lbs.

Fattening lambs on full feed, weight 70 lbs.

1. Legume hay, 1.4 lbs.; corn or grain sorghum, 1.5 lbs. The addition of 0.1 lb. high-protein supplement will increase the gains a trifle, but will usually not be profitable.
2. Legume hay, 1.4 lbs.; barley, wheat, or oats, 1.5 lbs.
3. Corn or sorghum silage, 1.75 lbs.; legume hay, 0.75 lb.; corn or other grain, 1.5 lbs.; linseed meal, cottonseed meal, or other high-protein supplement, 0.10 lb. Lambs will make satisfactory gains without the supplement, if at least this much good legume hay is fed. However, unless supplements are unusually high in price, it will generally pay to add the supplement.

4. Corn or sorghum silage, 3.0 to 4.0 lbs.; corn or other grain, 1.5 lbs.; cottonseed meal, linseed meal, soybean oil meal, or other high-protein supplement, 0.20 lb.; ground limestone, 0.25 ounce.
5. Mixed clover-and-grass hay, 1.4 lbs.; corn, 1.5 lbs.; linseed meal, 0.10 to 0.15 lb.
6. Cottonseed hulls, 1.0 lb.; cowpea hay, 0.50 lb.; corn or other grain, 1.5 lbs.; cottonseed meal or other high-protein supplement, 0.10 to 0.15 lb.

SWINE

Except where indicated, the amounts of feed stated are the amounts in each 100 lbs. of concentrate mixture, and not the amounts eaten per head daily.

Self-feeding growing and fattening pigs not on pasture from weaning to market

1. Corn or grain sorghum, self-fed; trio mixture, self-fed, free-choice. (See Articles 1341-3 for explanation and discussion of trio mixtures.)
2. Corn or grain sorghum, self-fed; skimmilk or buttermilk, 6 lbs. per head daily; choice alfalfa hay fed in rack.
3. Barley or wheat, self-fed; skimmilk or buttermilk, 4 to 5 lbs. per head daily; choice alfalfa hay fed in rack.
4. Corn or grain sorghum, self-fed; tankage, meat scraps, or fish meal, self-fed, free-choice; choice alfalfa hay fed in rack.

Self-feeding growing and fattening pigs on good pasture from weaning to market

1. Corn or grain sorghum, self-fed; mixture self-fed, free-choice, of one-half tankage, meat scraps, or fishmeal and one-half linseed meal, cottonseed oil meal, or soybean oil meal.
2. Corn or grain sorghum, self-fed, skimmilk or buttermilk, 3 to 4 lbs. per head daily.
3. Barley or wheat, self-fed; skimmilk or buttermilk, 2 to 3 lbs. per head daily.
4. Corn or grain sorghum, self-fed; tankage, meat scraps, or fish meal, self-fed, free-choice.

Mixtures for self-feeding or hand-feeding to growing and fattening pigs of various live weights

The mixtures suggested for pigs on pasture are for pigs on good pasture, such as alfalfa, clover, or rape. For feeding in these mixtures the grain should be ground and the legume hay should be chopped or ground. Flour wheat middlings or wheat red dog are preferred to wheat standard middlings for young pigs up to 50 lbs. in weight.

	Weaning to 50 lbs.	Not on pasture 50–100 lbs.	Not on pasture, over 100 lbs.	On pasture, 50–100 lbs.	On pasture, over 100 lbs.
	Lbs.	Lbs.	Lbs.	Lbs.	Lbs.
1. Corn or grain sorghum	76	80	85	88	92
Tankage, meat scraps, or fish meal....	14	10	5	6	4
Linseed meal, soybean oil meal, or cottonseed meal	5	5	5	6	4
Legume hay	5	5	5	..	..
Total	100	100	100	100	100
2. Barley or wheat	80	84	89	94	98
Tankage, meat scraps, or fish meal....	10	6	3	3	2
Linseed meal, soybean oil meal, or cottonseed meal	5	5	3	3	..
Legume hay	5	5	5	..	..
Total	100	100	100	100	100

	Weaning to 50 lbs.	Not on pasture, 50–100 lbs.	Not on pasture, over 100 lbs.	On pasture, 50–100 lbs.	On pasture, over 100 lbs.
	Lbs.	Lbs.	Lbs.	Lbs.	Lbs.
3. Corn or grain sorghum	63	68	70	74	77
Wheat middlings	15	15	20	20	20
Tankage, meat scraps, or fish meal	12	7	5	6	3
Linseed meal, soybeans, or cottonseed meal	5	5	..	..	..
Legume hay	5	5	5	..	..
Total	100	100	100	100	100
4. Corn or grain sorghum	62	67	66	73	75
Oats	15	15	20	20	20
Tankage, meat scraps, or fish meal	13	8	5	7	5
Linseed meal, soybeans, or cottonseed meal	5	5	4	..	..
Legume hay	5	5	5	..	..
Total	100	100	100	100	100

Brood sows, gilts, and boars

An excellent ration for pregnant brood sows and gilts is merely sufficient corn or other grain, with choice legume hay fed in a rack, and either 0.25 to 0.35 lb. per head daily of tankage, meat scraps, or fish meal, or else 4 to 5 lbs. skimmilk or buttermilk per head daily.

The following mixtures are also excellent for brood sows, gilts, and boars. For sows not on pasture that are nursing litters it may be wise to reduce the amount of legume hay in the mixtures to 5 lbs. per 100 lbs. of mixture.

	Not on pasture	On pasture
	Lbs.	Lbs.
1. Corn or grain sorghum	82	92
Tankage, meat scraps, or fish meal	4	4
Linseed meal, soybean oil meal or cottonseed meal	4	4
Legume hay	10	..
Total	100	100
2. Barley or wheat	87	98
Tankage, meat scraps, or fish meal	3	2
Legume hay	10	..
Total	100	100
3. Corn or grain sorghum	67	72
Wheat standard middlings	20	25
Tankage, meat scraps, or fish meal	3	3
Legume hay	10	..
Total	100	100
4. Corn or grain sorghum	61	71
Oats	25	25
Tankage, meat scraps, or fish meal	4	4
Legume hay	10	..
Total	100	100

TABLE VIII. FACTORS AND CONSTANTS FOR VALUING FEEDS

In order to select economical rations for livestock, it is necessary to determine which of the available feeds that are otherwise satisfactory provide nutrients at least expense. It has been emphasized previously that the best guides to the relative values of various feeds for any class of stock are furnished by the results of actual feeding experiments with that particular class of stock. (67-69) Extensive summaries of such experiments have therefore been presented in Part III of this volume which show the results that have been secured with most of the important feeding stuffs when fed to the various classes of stock.

The relative values of the same two feeds for different classes of farm animals may vary to a considerable extent. Before deciding upon the feeds to use in a ration for any kind of stock one should therefore consult the chapter in Part III which discusses the values of the different available feeds for that class of stock. Where definite statements are there made, based on feeding experiments, concerning the relative values of two or more available feeds for the particular kind of animal, one should base his judgment on the specific facts presented, rather than on a comparison of the amounts of digestible nutrients these feeds furnish.

For example, it is shown that ground barley is about equal to ground corn per 100 lbs. for dairy cows, while barley is of distinctly lower value than corn for fattening cattle, for fattening lambs or sheep, or for swine.

The relative values of many feeding stuffs have not yet been determined accurately for the various classes of stock. In deciding which of such feeds are most economical, one must base his judgment on the amounts of digestible nutrients they furnish and on the general information that is available concerning the usefulness of the respective feeds for the particular class of stock.

When protein-rich feeds are more expensive than feeds low in protein, as is commonly the case in most districts of the United States, a method of comparison should be used that considers both the amount of digestible protein in a feed and also the amount of total digestible nutrients (or net energy) it supplies. The method of valuing feeds, developed by Petersen of the Minnesota Station, which has been explained in Chapter X, is a convenient method of making such comparisons[1]. (281) The first two columns of figures in the following table give the constants for valuing the most important feeds according to this method. These constants have been computed with dent corn of Federal grade No. 2 and cottonseed meal of 43 per cent protein grade (not including Texas analyses) as the base or standard feeds, taking for these feeds the composition shown in Appendix Table I.

In the case of most of the concentrates these constants have been computed from the percentages of digestible protein and of total digestible nutrients given in Table I. In the case of all the roughages and in the case of a few concentrates which are rather high in fiber or which have a relatively low energy value, the factors have been computed from the content of digestible protein and of net energy given in Appendix Table II. For these feeds there is an asterisk after the name of the feed in the table.

The net energy content has been used for these feeds instead of the percentage of digestible nutrients because net energy values are more accurate than total digestible nutrients as a basis for a direct comparison of a concentrate and of a roughage. (94) This is also true in a comparison of a high-grade concentrate, containing but little fiber, with a low-grade concentrate which is high in fiber.

The method of using these constants has been explained in Chapter X. (281, 283-286) To illustrate their use further, let us assume that dent corn (Grade No. 2) is $22.00 per ton and cottonseed meal (43 per cent protein grade) is $36.00 per ton. We wish to find the approximate value of brewers' dried grains, considering its content both of digestible protein and total digestible nutrients, in comparison with these base feeds at the prices stated.

First, multiply $22.00, the price of corn per ton, by 0.323, the figure given for brewers' dried grains in the first column of figures in the table, entitled "Constants for corn." This gives us $7.11. We next multiply $36.00, the price of cottonseed meal per ton, by 0.525, the "Constant for cottonseed meal," given in the second column of figures. This gives us $18.90. We then add these amounts together, and have $26.01 as the approximate value per ton of brewers' dried grains in comparison with corn and cottonseed meal at the prices assumed.

When there is a minus sign before either the "Constant for corn" or the "Constant for cottonseed meal," the product is to be subtracted, instead of being added. For example, in the case of fish meal the "Constant for corn" is —0.516 and the "Constant for cottonseed meal" is 1.458. Multiplying $22.00, the price of corn per ton, by the factor —0.516, we have as the result —$11.35. Multiplying $36.00, the price of cottonseed meal per ton, by 1.458, gives us $52.49. Subtracting $11.35 from $52.49, we have $41.14 as the approximate value per ton of fish meal.

When protein-rich feeds cost no more than protein-poor feeds, the factors given in the third column of figures should be used for determining the relative values of feeds, instead of the constants in the first two columns. These factors show the relative amount of total digestible nutrients furnished by each feed in comparison with dent corn of Federal grade No. 2 taken as 100 per cent. In the case of the feeds marked with an asterisk, these factors have been computed from the net energy values given in Appendix Table II, for the reason stated previously.

To illustrate the method of using these "Total digestible nutrient factors" in the last column, let us find the value as a source of total digestible nutrients of common barley (not including Pacific Coast states) in comparison with dent corn of Federal grade No. 2 at $22.00 per ton.

The factor for barley in the third column is 97.6 per cent, which means that barley has 97.6 per cent as much total digestible nutrients as No. 2 dent corn. Taking 97.6 per cent of $22.00, we find that the value of barley as a source of total digestible nutrients is $21.47, in comparison with corn at the price stated.

The author wishes to acknowledge the aid in the preparation of this table of Mr J. I. Miller of the Animal Husbandry Department of Cornell University, who has computed the constants and factors here presented.

As has been stated previously, Petersen has devised convenient graphs or charts from which the relative values of feeds can easily be read, with the base or standard feeds (corn and cottonseed meal) at any particular prices. (282) A method has been devised by Salisbury, Miller, and Hodson, working with the author, of making more comprehensive combination charts which can be used for three distinct purposes. First, the relative values of feeds can be read from the chart, according to the Petersen method. This method should be used when protein-rich feeds are more expensive than feeds low in protein. Second, the relative values of feeds based solely on their content of total digestible nutrients (or net energy) can be easily read from the chart. Third, for each feed on the chart, the cost of 100 lbs. of total digestible nutrients can be read with the feed at any particular price. Graphs for valuing the most important feeds by these methods, with directions for their use, may be obtained from the Animal Husbandry department, Cornell University, Ithaca, New York. There is a small charge to cover the cost of publication.

---

[1] Petersen, Jour. Dairy Sci., 15, 1932, pp. 293-297; Petersen, Minn. Exten. Pamphlet 33.

TABLE VIII. Constants and factors for valuing feeding stuffs

	Constants for corn	Constants for cottonseed meal	Total digestible nutrient factors (On net energy basis for certain feeds)
Concentrates			Per ct.
Barley, common, not including Pacific Coast states.....................................	0.899	0.083	97.6
Beet pulp, dried.........................	0.941	−0.053	89.1
Beet pulp, wet...........................	0.111	0.001	11.1
Blood meal, or dried blood...............	−1.146	2.246	94.2
Brewers' grains, dried....................	0.323	0.525	81.0
Brewers' grains, wet.....................	0.104	0.110	20.6
Buckwheat, common......................	0.694	0.113	79.9
Buckwheat feed, good grade*.............	0.302	0.358	63.4
Buckwheat middlings....................	0.316	0.671	93.9
Buttermilk.............................	0.031	0.088	11.3
Coconut oil meal, old process............	0.625	0.406	100.2
Corn, dent, Grade No. 1.................	1.023	0.000	102.4
Corn, dent, Grade No. 2.................	1.000	0.000	100.0
Corn, dent, Grade No. 3.................	0.979	0.000	98.0
Corn ears (corn- and cob-meal)...........	0.964	−0.024	94.2
Corn feed meal..........................	1.039	0.006	104.5
Corn gluten feed........................	0.443	0.557	96.0
Corn gluten meal	0.060	1.028	101.5
Corn oil meal, old process................	0.658	0.343	97.6
Corn-and-oat feed, good grade...........	0.941	0.049	98.6
Cottonseed, whole.......................	0.836	0.315	112.9
Cottonseed meal, 43% protein grade, all analyses.............................	0.012	0.995	93.7
Cottonseed meal, 43% protein grade, not inc. Texas analyses....................	0.000	1.000	92.9
Cottonseed meal, 43% protein grade, Texas analyses.............................	0.012	0.995	93.7
Cottonseed meal, 41% protein grade, all analyses.............................	0.019	0.962	91.3
Cottonseed feed, below 36% protein*......	0.140	0.730	81.8
Distillers' corn grains, dried..............	0.572	0.520	105.5
Distillers' rye grains, dried*..............	0.502	0.186	67.5
Fish meal..............................	−0.516	1.458	83.9
Flax seed..............................	0.963	0.415	134.9
Hominy feed............................	1.048	0.010	105.7
Kafir grain.............................	0.927	0.072	99.4
Kafir head chops........................	0.927	0.029	95.4
Linseed meal, old process, all analyses.....	0.197	0.832	97.0
Linseed meal, 37% protein or over........	0.097	0.935	96.5
Malt sprouts*...........................	0.270	0.524	75.7
Meat scraps, 55% protein grade..........	−0.522	1.547	91.6
Meat scraps, 50% protein grade..........	−0.435	1.418	88.3
Milo grain..............................	0.938	0.058	99.1
Molasses, beet..........................	0.817	−0.094	73.0
Molasses, cane..........................	0.836	−0.143	70.2
Oats, not including Pacific Coast states....	0.786	0.109	88.7
Oat mill feed, usual grade*...............	0.485	0.016	50.0
Peanut oil meal, old process, all analyses...	0.015	1.080	101.9
Rice bran..............................	0.748	0.100	84.0
Rice polish.............................	1.006	0.062	106.3
Rye grain..............................	0.888	0.114	99.4
Rye feed...............................	0.765	0.210	96.0
Skimmilk, centrifugal...................	0.017	0.096	10.7

Table VIII. Constants and factors for valuing feeding stuffs—*continued*

	Constants for corn	Constants for cottonseed meal	Total digestible nutrient factors (On net energy basis for certain feeds)
Concentrates—continued			Per ct.
Skimmilk, dried.........................	0.206	0.902	104.3
Sorghum grain, sweet....................	0.953	−0.033	92.2
Soybean seed...........................	0.248	0.885	106.9
Soybean oil meal, hydraulic or expeller process, all analyses.......................	0.027	1.069	102.0
Tankage, or meat meal (digester process), 60% protein grade.	−0.647	1.738	96.8
Tankage, or meat meal (digester process), 55% protein grade....................	−0.546	1.578	92.1
Wheat, recent analyses...................	0.909	0.138	103.7
Wheat bran, all analyses.................	0.646	0.243	87.1
Wheat brown shorts.....................	0.674	0.294	94.7
Wheat flour middlings...................	0.714	0.283	97.6
Wheat gray shorts......................	0.716	0.282	97.9
Wheat mixed feed.......................	0.670	0.261	91.2
Wheat red dog..........................	0.832	0.265	107.8
Wheat standard middlings, all analyses....	0.729	0.263	97.3
Wheat white shorts.....................	0.848	0.242	107.2
Whey, from American cheese.............	0.068	0.012	7.9
Dry Roughages			
Alfalfa hay, all anal.*...................	0.299	0.241	52.4
Alfalfa hay, very leafy (less than 25% fiber)*	0.285	0.296	56.0
Alfalfa hay, leafy (25-28% fiber)*.........	0.264	0.289	53.2
Alfalfa hay, good (28-31% fiber)*..........	0.309	0.231	52.3
Alfalfa hay, fair (31-34% fiber)*..........	0.306	0.212	50.2
Alfalfa hay, stemmy (over 34% fiber)*.....	0.286	0.176	44.9
Alfalfa meal, good*.....................	0.360	0.235	57.8
Barley straw*..........................	0.337	−0.043	29.8
Bermuda hay*..........................	0.382	0.028	40.8
Clover hay, red, all anal.*...............	0.436	0.111	54.0
Clover hay, red, leafy (less than 25% fiber)*	0.420	0.160	56.8
Clover hay, red, good quality (25-31% fiber)*	0.470	0.099	56.2
Clover hay, red, stemmy (over 31% fiber)*.	0.414	0.087	49.5
Clover and timothy hay, all anal.*.........	0.454	0.034	48.5
Clover and timothy hay, 30 to 50% clover*	0.490	0.038	52.5
Corn fodder, medium in water*..........	0.437	0.011	44.8
Corn stover, medium in water*..........	0.303	−0.001	30.1
Cottonseed hulls*......................	0.473	−0.093	38.6
Cowpea hay*...........................	0.223	0.314	51.5
Johnson grass hay*.....................	0.492	−0.017	47.6
Kafir fodder, dry, including grain*........	0.397	0.051	44.4
Kafir stover, medium in water*..........	0.339	−0.020	32.0
Lespedeza hay, annual*.................	0.369	0.187	54.3
Marsh or swamp hay, fair quality*........	0.285	0.025	30.8
Millet hay, common*...................	0.391	0.069	45.5
Milo stover, dry*.......................	0.343	−0.038	30.8
Native hay, western mt. states, good quality*	0.447	0.049	49.3
Native hay, western mt. states, mature and weathered*.........................	0.318	−0.019	30.0
Oat straw*.............................	0.333	−0.042	29.4
Prairie hay, western, good quality*........	0.488	−0.025	46.5
Prairie hay, western, mature or weathered*.	0.421	−0.068	35.7
Sorghum fodder, sweet, dry*.............	0.416	0.018	43.3

TABLE VIII.   Constants and factors for valuing feeding stuffs—*continued*

	Constants for corn	Constants for cottonseed meal	Total digestible nutrient factors (On net energy basis for certain feeds)
Dry Roughages—continued			Per ct.
Soybean hay, all anal.*..................	0.237	0.268	48.6
Sudan grass hay*......................	0.388	0.044	42.9
Timothy hay, all anal.*.................	0.453	−0.009	44.4
Timothy hay, early bloom*.............	0.505	0.018	52.1
Timothy hay, full bloom*..............	0.493	−0.009	48.5
Timothy hay, in bloom, nitrogen-fertilized*.	0.487	0.038	52.2
Timothy hay, late bloom to early seed*....	0.404	−0.013	39.2
Timothy hay, late seed*.................	0.366	−0.014	35.2
Wheat straw*.........................	0.128	−0.003	12.5
Green Roughages, Roots, Etc.			
Alfalfa, green*........................	0.088	0.079	16.1
Beets, roots, common*.................	0.120	0.010	12.9
Beets, roots, sugar*...................	0.175	−0.001	17.4
Clover, red*..........................	0.123	0.049	16.9
Corn fodder, dent, all anal.*...........	0.190	−0.004	18.6
Kafir fodder*.........................	0.175	0.002	17.6
Mangels, roots*.......................	0.081	0.012	9.2
Potatoes*............................	0.233	−0.016	21.8
Rutabagas, roots*.....................	0.113	0.006	11.8
Sorghum fodder, sweet*................	0.203	−0.018	18.6
Sudan grass*.........................	0.188	0.002	19.0
Sweet potatoes*......................	0.390	−0.056	33.7
Silages			
Alfalfa, high in water*.................	0.109	0.032	13.9
Corn, dent, well-matured, well-eared*......	0.284	−0.015	27.0
Corn, dent, well-matured, well-eared, for *dairy cows*.........................	0.197	0.003	20.0
Corn, dent, well-matured, fair in ears*.....	0.221	−0.013	20.8
Corn, dent, well-matured, fair in ears, for *dairy cows*.........................	0.171	−0.003	16.7
Corn, dent, well-matured, few ears*........	0.193	−0.008	18.6
Corn, dent, well-matured, few ears, for *dairy cows*.........................	0.158	−0.001	15.8
Corn, dent, immature, before dough stage*.	0.143	0.000	14.3
Sorghum, grain varieties*................	0.213	−0.012	20.2
Sorghum, grain varieties, for *dairy cows*...	0.175	−0.004	17.1
Sorghum, sweet*......................	0.185	−0.015	17.1

TABLE IX. GRAIN FEEDING TABLES FOR DAIRY COWS

It has been emphasized previously that the amount of concentrates, or "grain mixture," to be fed each cow in a herd should be adjusted to her actual production of milk and fat. Otherwise, some cows may be wastefully overfed and others seriously underfed. (787, 907) The common "thumb rules" often used for estimating the amount of grain mixture that should be fed to the various cows are not accurate guides to their real requirements. (908) The amount of grain required by any cow can be determined by computing a balanced ration according to the feeding standards, but to do this for the individual cows in a herd takes considerable time.

The following tables have therefore been prepared to indicate how many pounds of a good concentrate mixture, or so-called "grain mixture," are required by cows producing various amounts of milk of different fat percentages. The first of these tables, Table IXa, is for cows not on pasture, and the second one, Table IXb, is for cows which are on pasture. Sufficient amounts of grain mixture are advised to meet the recommendations for total digestible nutrients given in the Morrison feeding standards in the column entitled, "Recommended for good cows under ordinary conditions." (Appendix Table III.) When grain and other concentrates are very high in price in comparison with roughage, then it may be advisable to feed smaller amounts of grain mixture than shown in these tables.

The amounts of grain mixture advised are for mature cows during the chief part of the lactation period. As has been emphasized previously, the amount of grain mixture should be increased very gradually after a cow freshens. (926) Three weeks or more should be taken to get high producers on full feed. Even at that time and for a few weeks thereafter, high producers are often unable to consume safely as much grain as would be required to produce the amount of milk they are yielding. They therefore draw temporarily on the store of nutrients in their bodies.

The allowance of grain should be increased somewhat over the amounts shown in the tables in the case of excellent cows during the latter part of the lactation period, if they have run down in flesh during the height of milk production. Since heifers need additional feed for the growth of their own bodies, it is wise to feed them a trifle more liberally than shown in the tables.

Table IXa. Grain feeding table for cows not on pasture.—The amount of the grain mixture that it is necessary to feed daily to any particular cow will depend not only on the amount of milk she gives and on its richness in fat, but also on the amount and quality of the roughage she consumes. Also, it will depend to some extent on her live weight.

This table therefore gives recommendations for three different rates of roughage feeding, as shown by the first three columns. The second column, in bold-faced type, gives the figures for the most common rate of feeding roughage to dairy cows. This rate is to feed approximately 2 lbs. of good hay daily per 100 lbs. live weight, or the equivalent in other good roughage (for example, 1 lb. of good hay and 3 lbs. of silage).

When cows are fed *very liberally* on roughage of *excellent quality* and the allowance of grain is restricted to their needs, they will consume per 100 lbs. live weight about 2.5 lbs. of hay equivalent. The first column of figures is designed to fit these conditions.

The third column of figures is for use when cows are fed a scanty allowance of good roughage, or when they are fed as much poor roughage as they will consume without undue waste. This column is designed for use when cows consume only about the equivalent of 1.5 lbs. of good hay daily per 100 lbs. live weight.

In using the table, first estimate approximately the number of pounds of hay equivalent the cows are actually consuming daily per 100 lbs. live weight, after deducting the wastage. In making this estimate, use the following conversion factors for converting the amounts of other roughages actually consumed into the equivalent amounts of good hay. (Good-quality legume hay or well-cured, early-cut grass hay is taken as the standard.)

Fair-quality hay ....80 per cent
Poor-quality hay; cut or shredded corn
    or sorghum stover ....60 per cent
Good silage; potatoes ....33 per cent
Mangels; rutabagas; cabbage ....20 per cent
Oat straw; barley straw ....50 per cent

After estimating the pounds of good hay equivalent consumed per 100 lbs. live weight, then use the particular one of the first three columns that most nearly fits the rate of roughage feeding. Go down this column to the amount of milk given by the particular cow, and then follow the horizontal row of figures across the table to the right until the column is reached for milk having the percentage of fat nearest to that of the milk produced by the cow. The figure in this column shows the pounds of grain mixture to be fed daily to the cow.

To illustrate the use of the table, let us assume that a cow yielding 36 lbs. of milk containing 3.5 per cent fat is being fed approximately 2.0 lbs. of good hay equivalent per 100 lbs. live weight. We go down the second column, which is for this rate of roughage feeding, until we come to the figure 36. We then go horizontally to the right across the table until we reach the column for 3.5 per cent fat, where we find the figure 10.8. Therefore this cow should be fed 10.8 lbs. of a good grain mixture daily to meet her requirements.

Adjustment for difference in live weights.—The amounts of grain mixture required by different cows producing the same amount and richness of milk depend somewhat on their respective live weights. When fed roughage at the usual rate, for each additional 100 lbs. a cow weighs in comparison with a smaller cow, she will consume approximately 2 lbs. more hay equivalent. This furnishes about 1.0 lb. total digestible nutrients. However, for each 100 lbs. increase in body weight, she requires for maintenance only about 0.65 to 0.70 lb. more total digestible nutrients. Therefore, for each 100 lbs. of additional body weight, she will have available for milk production approximately 0.35 to 0.30 lb. of total digestible nutrients. This will save about 0.4 lb. of grain mixture.

This table and Table IXb have been computed for cows of the following average weights:

For 3.0, 3.5 and 4.0 per cent milk........1,200 lbs. live weight
For 4.5 and 5.0 per cent milk............1,000 lbs. live weight
For 5.5 and 6.0 per cent milk............ 850 lbs. live weight

There will be no important error in using the tables for cows of other weights, unless the difference in weight is too great. If greater accuracy is desired, 0.4 lb. should be deducted from the amount of grain mixture recommended in the table, for each 100 lbs. the weight of a given cow exceeds the standard weights shown above. If the weight of a cow is considerably less than these standard weights, 0.4 lb. should be added to the recommended amount of grain mixture for each 100 lbs. she weighs less than the standard used in the table for cows producing milk containing the given percentage of fat.

Table IXb. Grain feeding table for cows on pasture.—This table shows the approximate amounts of a good concentrate mixture, or "grain mixture," required per head daily by cows on excellent, good, and fair pasture. The method of using this table is similar to that for Table IXa.

The column of figures for excellent pasture is to be used for cows which are on pasture that provides an abundance of very palatable, nutritious forage. Such forage is furnished by usual grass pasture only during the flush of growth in late spring and early summer. Only pasture that is liberally fertilized and also well managed will generally furnish such pasturage later in the season.

The second column of figures, which is for good pasture, is for use when the cows have a plentiful supply of good pasturage, but when the pasture can hardly be called excellent. On such pasture the cows must be able to secure somewhat more feed from the pasture than they do from a full feed of good hay and average silage in winter.

The third column of figures is for use when the cows are on fair pasture, but not on pasture that is distinctly poor. On poor pasture cows will need fully as large an allowance of grain mixture as when fed roughage at the rate shown in the third column of Table IXa.

If a cow differs considerably in live weight from the weight used in computing this table, adjustments in the amount of grain mixture should be made, as previously stated in this explanation.

These tables have been adapted from tables prepared by Mr. J. W. Avery, formerly in charge of the Central Dairy Record Club Laboratory of the New York State College of Agriculture, and by Professor W. T. Crandall of the Department of Animal Husbandry of the New York State College of Agriculture, Cornell University.

TABLE IXa. Grain feeding table for cows not on pasture

Hay equivalent consumed per 100 lbs. of live weight daily			Total pounds of grain or concentrates to feed						
2½ lbs. Very liberal feeding of good roughage	2 lbs. Usual rate of feeding good hay or good hay and silage	1½ lbs. feeding scanty amount of good roughage or feeding poor roughage							
Milk produced daily, pounds			Percentage of fat in milk						
			3.0%	3.5%	4.0%	4.5%	5.0%	5.5%	6.0%
Lbs.	Lbs.	Lbs.	Lbs.	Lbs.	Lbs.	Lbs.	Lbs.	Lbs.	Lbs.
17	10	..	....	....	....	1.9	2.2	3.1	3.5
19	12	..	....	....	1.6	2.8	3.2	4.2	4.6
21	14	..	1.5	2.0	2.4	3.8	4.2	5.3	5.7
23	16	9	2.3	2.8	3.3	4.7	5.2	6.3	6.8
25	18	11	3.0	3.6	4.2	5.6	6.2	7.4	8.0
27	20	13	3.7	4.4	5.0	6.5	7.2	8.4	9.1
29	22	15	4.5	5.2	5.9	7.5	8.2	9.5	10.2
31	24	17	5.2	6.0	6.8	8.4	9.2	10.5	11.3
33	26	19	6.0	6.8	7.6	9.3	10.2	11.6	12.5
35	28	21	6.7	7.6	8.5	10.3	11.2	12.7	13.6
37	30	23	7.4	8.4	9.3	11.2	12.2	13.7	14.7
39	32	25	8.2	9.2	10.2	12.1	13.2	14.8	15.8
41	34	27	8.9	10.0	11.1	13.1	14.2	15.8	17.0
43	36	29	9.6	10.8	11.9	14.0	15.1	16.9	18.1
45	38	31	10.4	11.6	12.8	14.9	16.1	18.0	19.2
47	40	33	11.1	12.4	13.7	15.9	17.1	19.0	20.3
49	42	35	11.8	13.2	14.5	16.8	18.1	20.1	21.5
51	44	37	12.6	14.0	15.4	17.7	19.1	21.1	22.6
53	46	39	13.3	14.8	16.3	18.7	20.1	22.2	23.7
55	48	41	14.1	15.6	17.1	19.6	21.1	23.3	
57	50	43	14.8	16.4	18.0	20.5	22.1		
59	52	45	15.5	17.2	18.9	21.4	23.1		
61	54	47	16.3	18.0	19.7	22.4			
63	56	49	17.0	18.8	20.6	23.3			
65	58	51	17.7	19.6	21.4	24.2			
67	60	53	18.5	20.4	22.3		Regardless of the amount of grain theoretically required by a cow, she should not be fed more than she can safely handle.		
69	62	55	19.2	21.2	23.2				
71	64	57	19.9	22.0	24.0				
73	66	59	20.7	22.8	24.9				
75	68	61	21.4	23.6	25.8				

TABLE IXb. Grain feeding table for cows on pasture

Quality of pasture			Total pounds of grain or concentrates to feed						
Excellent	Good	Fair	Percentage of fat in milk						
Milk produced daily			3.0%	3.5%	4.0%	4.5%	5.0%	5.5%	6.0%
Lbs.	Lbs.	Lbs.	Lbs.	Lbs.	Lbs.	Lbs.	Lbs.	Lbs.	Lbs.
22	13	..	....	....	....	....	....	....	1.2
24	15	..	....	....	....	....	1.2	2.0	2.3
26	17	..	....	....	....	1.9	2.2	3.1	3.5
28	19	10	....	....	1.6	2.8	3.2	4.2	4.6
30	21	12	1.5	2.0	2.4	3.8	4.2	5.3	5.7
32	23	14	2.3	2.8	3.3	4.7	5.2	6.3	6.8
34	25	16	3.0	3.6	4.2	5.6	6.2	7.4	8.0
36	27	18	3.7	4.4	5.0	6.5	7.2	8.4	9.1
38	29	20	4.5	5.2	5.9	7.5	8.2	9.5	10.2
40	31	22	5.2	6.0	6.8	8.4	9.2	10.5	11.3
42	33	24	6.0	6.8	7.6	9.3	10.2	11.6	12.5
44	35	26	6.7	7.6	8.5	10.3	11.2	12.7	13.6
46	37	28	7.4	8.4	9.3	11.2	12.2	13.7	14.7
48	39	30	8.2	9.2	10.2	12.1	13.2	14.8	15.8
50	41	32	8.9	10.0	11.1	13.1	14.2	15.8	17.0
52	43	34	9.6	10.8	11.9	14.0	15.1	16.9	18.1
54	45	36	10.4	11.6	12.8	14.9	16.1	18.0	19.2
56	47	38	11.1	12.4	13.7	15.9	17.1	19.0	20.3
58	49	40	11.8	13.2	14.5	16.8	18.1	20.1	21.5
60	51	42	12.6	14.0	15.4	17.7	19.1	21.1	22.6
62	53	44	13.3	14.8	16.3	18.7	20.1	22.2	23.7
64	55	46	14.1	15.6	17.1	19.6	21.1	23.3	
66	57	48	14.8	16.4	18.0	20.5	22.1		Regard-less of the
68	59	50	15.5	17.2	18.9	21.4			amount of grain
70	61	52	16.3	18.0	19.7	22.4			theoretically required
72	63	54	17.0	18.8	20.6	23.3			by a cow, she should not
74	65	56	17.7	19.6	21.4				be fed more than she can safely handle.

TABLE X. ESTIMATING WEIGHTS OF DAIRY CATTLE FROM HEART GIRTHS

In computing balanced rations for dairy cows and other dairy cattle, it is necessary to know their approximate live weights. If one does not have suitable scales available for weighing the cattle, their weights can be estimated approximately from a measurement of the heart girth.

The following table shows the estimated live weights of dairy cattle having various heart girths, as determined in tests by Kendrick and Parker of the Bureau of Dairy Industry, United States Department of Agriculture.[1] In finding the heart girth, an accurate tape measure should be placed around the animal directly back of the front legs. The animal should stand squarely on all four legs.

Cattle that are fat will tend to weigh somewhat more than indicated in this table for the particular heart girth, and those that are thin, somewhat less. A similar table has recently been published by Ragsdale of the Missouri Station, in which the estimated live weights for a given heart girth are somewhat lower than here shown, especially for the animals of larger size.[2]

Heart girth	Estimated live weight	Heart girth	Estimated live weight	Heart girth	Estimated live weight
Inches	Lbs.	Inches	Lbs.	Inches	Lbs.
25	76*	48	354	71	1,027
26	80	49	374	72	1,069
27	84	50	394	73	1,111
28	89	51	414	74	1,153
29	95	52	434	75	1,197
30	101	53	456	76	1,241
31	108	54	478	77	1,285
32	118	55	501	78	1,331
33	128	56	526	79	1,377
34	138	57	552	80	1,423
35	148	58	579	81	1,469
36	158	59	607	82	1,515
37	168	60	637	83	1,561
38	180	61	668	84	1,607
39	192	62	700	85	1,653
40	208	63	732	86	1,699
41	224	64	766	87	1,745
42	240	65	800	88	1,791
43	257	66	835	89	1,837
44	275	67	871	90	1,883
45	294	68	908	91	1,929
46	314	69	947	92	1,975
47	334	70	987		

*Estimated. Not included in original table.

[1] Kendrick and Parker, U. S. Dept. of Agr., mimeo. rpt. and Dairy Herd-Improvement Assoc. Letter, Dec., 1934.
[2] Ragsdale, Mo. Bul. 354.

INDEX

The References are to Pages

WITHDRAWN

Date Due

Jan 3 '38	JUN 26 '7	SEP 9 '86	MAR 8 '90
Jan 18 '38		MAR 9 '87	JAN 10 '91
Apr 25 '39		MAR 7 '89	APR 15 '93
Feb 6 '40		APR 13 '90	SEP 28 '00
Feb 22 '40		APR 29 '92	
Feb 13 '41		FEB 23 '00	
Taylor	JUL 26 '78		
002650	APR 5 '79		
MAR 19 '73	MAY 3 '79		
MAR 28 '73	MAY 23 '79		
JUN 2 '75	MAY 31 '79		
Jun 26	JUL 3 '79		
JUL 8 '75	DEC 3 '79		
FEB 12 '77	MAR 4 '80		
FEB 23 '77	DEC 7 '81		
SEP 20 '77	MAR 17 '82		
OCT 12 '77	JAN 24 '83		
JUN 14 '78	JUL 15 '86		